MOLECULAR REARRANGEMENTS

PART ONE

MOLECULAR REARRANGEMENTS

edited by
PAUL DE MAYO

1

INTERSCIENCE PUBLISHERS
a division of John Wiley & Sons
New York · London

Contributing Authors:

G. M. Badger

Jerome A. Berson

Ronald Breslow

J. W. Clark-Lewis

L. A. Cohen

M. J. S. Dewar

J. F. King

R. U. Lemieux

P. B. D. de la Mare

Paul de Mayo

Y. Pocker

V. Prelog

Sara Jane Rhoads

Peter A. S. Smith

James G. Traynham

Cheves Walling

E. W. Warnhoff

N. L. Wendler

B. Witkop

H. E. Zimmerman

Every great advance in natural knowledge has involved the absolute rejection of authority, the cherishing of the keenest scepticism, the annihilation of the spirit of blind faith; and the most ardent votary of science holds his firmest convictions . . . because his experience teaches him that whenever he chooses to bring these convictions into contact with their primary source, nature—whenever he thinks fit to test them by appealing to experiment and to observation—nature will confirm them. . . .

T. Huxley

"There's no use trying," she said: *"one* ca'n't *believe impossible things."*
"I dare say you haven't had much practice," said *the Queen.*

L. Carroll

FOREWORD

It has been evident for some time that the solutions to at least some of the problems confronting organic chemists would have been facilitated if recourse could have been had, on occasion, to witchcraft. The need has been noticeably greater in those reactions wherein organic molecules undergo contortions of varying complexity and assume a new structure; that is, in molecular rearrangements.

These rearrangements have provided the stimuli to the creation of new concepts; a particularly notable example is that of bridged ions, evolved in the study of the camphane series of terpenoids. Investigators have reacted to these stimuli in a manner not necessarily restricted to chemists. First bewilderment, followed, then, by slow and grudging acceptance. Finally, when the phenomenon has been lived with long enough to be homely, there is the declaration, with the confidence of hindsight, that the whole business was eminently predictable. It is rather surprising, therefore, in view of the interest and instruction gained from such studies, that no recent volume entirely devoted to the topic has appeared. The present volume is an attempt to remedy this deficiency.

One of the immediate problems was the definition of what constituted a rearrangement. This has been solved in a practical and broad sense, if not a semantic one. Provided a change in atomic disposition in the molecule (with concomitant bond cleavage, σ or π, and re-formation) has occurred, it has been accepted as a rearrangement—so long as chemical interest justified it.

Accordingly, subjects such as epimerization (and the protonation of enols) and anomerization have been included because their discussion seemed especially timely, even though these subjects are not always covered by the term rearrangement. Conversely, a number of rearrangements have been omitted, except for brief mention, either because they have not reached a stage suitable for profitable discussion, or because such discussion is available elsewhere in the recent literature. In addition, instances of bond cleavage or of bond formation have been included because, although not perhaps constituting rearrangements in themselves, they so frequently form an integral part of such a change that their omission seemed artificial.

The treatment accorded their subjects by the authors has necessarily varied, but in no case was it intended that they should be merely encyclopedic in approach: to be so would have precluded the possibility of critical and

vii

constructive discussion, which is the only real justification for a text of this kind. Nevertheless, the literature has been widely covered and references frequently provided where discussion is eschewed.

Although the subject matter of molecular rearrangements could more logically have been divided entirely into sections on the basis of mechanistic concepts, it was felt that in certain cases a greater utility would be served by considering some classes of compounds separately, and this, especially, with certain naturally occurring substances. These, for the most part, have had little detailed quantitative treatment, and discussion of such transformations must frequently be more diffuse and more conjectural than in the more precise studies considered elsewhere in this volume. Their value is nevertheless considerable, since it is frequently at this stage that new concepts, stereochemical and electronic, are evolved (the imagination being variously considered unfettered or uncontrolled, depending on whether or not the concept is viewed with approval).

The present manuscripts were received between November 1960 and March 1961. Opportunity for limited additions and revisions was provided at the galley stage: that is, in the first half of 1962.

I should like to thank, here, the many friends who spared time to read the manuscripts and who made many constructive suggestions. I should also like to thank Dr. A. Stoessl for undertaking the demanding task of the preparation of the Index.

PAUL DE MAYO

The University of Western Ontario,
London, Canada, 1963

AUTHORS OF
PART ONE

G. M. Badger Department of Organic Chemistry, University of Adelaide, South Australia

Jerome A. Berson Department of Chemistry, University of Southern California, Los Angeles, California

Ronald Breslow Department of Chemistry, Columbia University, New York, New York

J. W. Clark-Lewis Department of Organic Chemistry, University of Adelaide, South Australia

M. J. S. Dewar Department of Chemistry, The University of Chicago, Chicago, Illinois

P. B. D. de la Mare Department of Chemistry, Bedford College, University of London, London, England

Y. Pocker Department of Chemistry, University of Washington, Seattle, Washington (formerly Department of Chemistry, University College, London, England)

V. Prelog Laboratorium für Organische Chemie, Eidgenössische Technische Hochschule, Zürich, Switzerland

Sara Jane Rhoads Department of Chemistry, University of Wyoming, Laramie, Wyoming

Peter A. S. Smith Department of Chemistry, University of Michigan, Ann Arbor, Michigan

James G. Traynham Department of Chemistry, Louisiana State University, Baton Rouge, Louisiana

Cheves Walling Department of Chemistry, Columbia University, New York, New York

H. E. Zimmerman Department of Chemistry, University of Wisconsin, Madison, Wisconsin

AUTHORS OF PART TWO

L. A. Cohen National Institute of Arthritis and Metabolic Diseases, National Institutes of Health, U.S. Public Health Service, Bethesda, Maryland

J. F. King Department of Chemistry, University of Western Ontario, London, Canada

R. U. Lemieux Department of Chemistry, University of Alberta, Edmonton, Canada

Paul de Mayo Department of Chemistry, University of Western Ontario, London, Canada

E. W. Warnhoff Department of Chemistry, University of Western Ontario, London, Canada

N. L. Wendler Merck Sharpe & Dohme Research Laboratories, Merck & Co., Inc., Rahway, New Jersey

B. Witkop National Institute of Arthritis and Metabolic Diseases, National Institutes of Health, U.S. Public Health Service, Bethesda, Maryland

CONTENTS

xi

Part Two

WAGNER-MEERWEIN AND PINACOLIC REARRANGEMENTS IN ACYCLIC AND CYCLIC SYSTEMS[1]

Y. POCKER

University of Washington, Seattle, Washington

CONTENTS

I. GENERAL INTRODUCTION

A. Classification of Reaction Mechanisms [2a, 2b]

In spite of their numerous kinds and complexities, the rearrangements of organic chemistry can be broken down into relatively simple steps involving most commonly only one or two molecular species. It is well recognized that the individual reaction steps fall into three broad classes:

[1] The preparation of this manuscript was carried out in the Department of Chemistry of Indiana University, Bloomington, Indiana, while the author was on leave from University College, London, England.

[2a] E. D. Hughes, *Trans. Faraday Soc.*, **37**, 603 (1941).

[2b] C. K. Ingold, *Structure and Mechanism in Organic Chemistry*, Cornell University Press, Ithaca, N.Y., 1953.

1

1. *Homolytic reactions.* In these bond breaking takes place in such a fashion that an odd electron remains with each of the fragments. Similarly when these fragments recombine each species donates a single electron (eq. 1).

$$R{-}X \underset{\text{Radical recombination}}{\overset{\text{Homolysis}}{\rightleftharpoons}} R\cdot + \cdot X \tag{1}$$

2. *Heterolytic reactions.* In these bond breaking takes place in such a fashion that the electron pair remains with one of the fragments. Similarly, when a bond is formed heterolytically, one species donates and the other accepts the necessary electron pair.

3. *Molecular reactions.*[3] These proceed without the intermediate formation of either ions or radicals.

The Wagner-Meerwein and pinacolic rearrangements involve the initial production, by heterolysis, of an electron-deficient center with a sextet of electrons. Whitmore[6] avoided calling this intermediate a carbonium ion, but his description of the electron-deficient system seems to be very similar to that of Meerwein's[7] carbonium ion.

B. Ionization and Dissociation

The ionization step of a *neutral* organic molecule, RR'R"CX, is envisaged as the heterolysis of the C—X bond. In heterolysis solvation forces are of prime importance;[8] i.e., many solvent molecules are concerned in every ionization.[9] The Hughes-Ingold definition of molecularity has therefore concentrated attention on the number of molecules *necessarily* undergoing covalence change in the rate-determining step and has deliberately excluded those solvent molecules which are involved in stabilizing the activated com-

---

[3] Such reactions appear to be in their simplest form four-center reactions like *cis* additions, *cis* eliminations (*Ei*), and intramolecular substitution reactions (*S*$_N$*i*) which proceed with complete retention of configuration. Some[4,5] restrict the name "molecular reactions" to processes in which two or more bonds are broken and two or more bonds are formed simultaneously and classify under this heading only the Claisen and Cope rearrangements, the Diels-Alder reaction, and the last stage in the Tschugaeff dehydration, i.e., reactions whose transition states have about the same polarity as their initial states.

[4] P. D. Bartlett in H. Gilman, ed., *Organic Chemistry*, Vol. III, Wiley, New York, 1953, p. 4.

[5] J. Hine, *Physical Organic Chemistry*, McGraw-Hill, New York, 1956, p. 453.

[6] F. C. Whitmore and G. H. Fleming, *J. Chem. Soc. (London)*, **1934**, 1269; F. C. Whitmore, E. L. Wittle, and A. H. Popkin, *J. Am. Chem. Soc.*, **61**, 1586 (1939).

[7] H. Meerwein and K. van Emster, *Ber.*, **53**, 1815 (1920), **55**, 2500 (1922).

[8] Ref. 2b, p. 315.

[9] Solvent effects are not negligible, even when appreciable bond cleavage occurs without charge separation; for even homolytic reactions are subject to solvent effects.

plex. The transition state representing the ionization of a netural molecule corresponds to a stage between a normal dipole and an ion pair, i.e., to a stretched (partial) bond and a partial charge transfer. In its simplest form we write equation 2. If the R—X bond heterolysis is rate determining we

$$RX \; \underset{}{\overset{}{\rightleftharpoons}} \; \left[\underset{\substack{\text{Transition} \\ \text{state}}}{\overset{\delta+ \quad \delta-}{[R \cdots X]}} \right] \xrightarrow{} \underset{\substack{\text{Inter-} \\ \text{mediate}}}{R^+ + X^-} \; \underset{-Y^-}{\overset{+Y^-}{\rightleftharpoons}} \; RY + X^- \tag{2}$$

have the familiar S_N1 (substitution, nucleophilic, unimolecular) mechanism; but, if the reaction of the carbonium ion, R^+, with the reagent Y is rate determining, we have the so-called $S_N2(C^+)$[10] (substitution, nucleophilic, bimolecular, with a rapidly formed carbonium ion).

Unimolecular reactions can still be observed in solvents of very low polarity but we have little or no evidence for the formation of free carbonium ions and the reactions proceed through an ionized but undissociated intermediate (eq. 3). It has become common to refer to this intermediate as an ion pair,

$$RX \; \underset{}{\overset{}{\rightleftharpoons}} \; \left[\underset{\substack{\text{Transition} \\ \text{state}}}{\overset{\delta+ \quad \delta-}{[R \cdots X]}} \right] \xrightarrow{} \underset{\substack{\text{Inter-} \\ \text{mediate}}}{R^+ X^-} \; \underset{-Y}{\overset{+Y}{\rightleftharpoons}} \; RY + X^- \tag{3}$$

but the properties ascribed to it are often not those defined by Bjerrum,[11] since the intermediate has a very short lifetime before it reacts or rearranges. Fuoss[12] has recently redefined an ion pair as two counterions in actual contact, indicating that Bjerrum has overlooked the effect of the discontinuous nature of the solvent.

In benzene solvent the dielectric constant is 2.25 at 25.0°C., and large electrostatic forces operate between oppositely charged ions; two univalent counterions at a separation less than 500A. attract each other with an energy larger than their mean kinetic energy. It has been suggested[13] that in this solvent the unimolecular generation of an ion pair from a neutral alkyl halide (e.g., Ph_3CCl) is followed by a very rapid association with the reagent ion pair or the reagent molecule to give a quadrupole followed by the rearrangement of the quadrupole as indicated in equation 4.

$$Ph_3CCl \rightleftharpoons Ph_3^+Cl^- \underset{-M^+X^-}{\overset{+M^+X^-}{\rightleftharpoons}} Ph_3C^+Cl^-M^+X^-$$

$$\rightleftharpoons Ph_3C^+X^-M^+Cl^- \underset{+M^+Cl^-}{\overset{-M^+Cl^-}{\rightleftharpoons}} Ph_3C^+X^- \rightleftharpoons Ph_3CX \tag{4}$$

In solvents of intermediate polarity the ionization scheme involves both

[10] E. Gelles, E. D. Hughes, and C. K. Ingold, *J. Chem. Soc. (London)*, **1954**, 2918.

[11] Bjerrum, *Kgl. Danske Videnskab. Selskab, Mat. fys.-Medd.*, **7**, No. 9 (1926).

[12] R. Fuoss, *J. Am. Chem. Soc.*, **80**, 5059 (1958).

[13] E. D. Hughes, C. K. Ingold, S. F. Mok, S. Patai, and Y. Pocker, *J. Chem. Soc. (London)*, **1957**, 1265, and accompanying papers.

ion pairs and free ions [14, 15] (eq. 5). Winstein [16, 17] and his associates have elaborated this scheme and developed the idea that the ionization of a

$$RX \xrightarrow[\text{ion-pair}]{\text{ionization}} R^+X^- \xrightarrow[\text{ion-pairing}]{\text{dissociation}} R^+ + X^- \tag{5}$$
$$\text{recombination}$$

neutral molecule, RX, should be dissected into three rather than two stages (eq. 6). The intermediate R^+X^- is an intimate ion pair and consists of a pair

$$RX \rightleftharpoons R^+X^- \rightleftharpoons R^+\|X^- \rightleftharpoons R^+ + X^- \tag{6}$$

of ions held in contact by coulomb attraction with no interposed solvent molecules. $R^+\|X^-$ is an external ion pair and consists of a pair of ions separated by one or at most a few solvent molecules and held together by coulombic attraction. R^+ and X^- are kinetically free ions. The intermediates R^+X^- and $R^+\|X^-$ are ionized but undissociated, while R^+ and X^- are both ionized and dissociated. Regeneration of RX from an ion pair is not aided by the addition of common anion, X^-, and has been called "internal return." Common anion, X^-, however, reduces the concentration of free carbonium ions, R^+, by a mass law effect and can in principle suppress entirely the concentration of free carbonium ions. By the principle of microscopic reversibility the recombination of two oppositely charged ions should also proceed in stages, and this has actually been found.[18]

C. Stereochemical Consequences

Ions in solution are stabilized by virtue of their interaction with solvent molecules. From the Hughes-Ingold [19,20] picture one would expect complete inversion of configuration if, very soon after ionization, the substituting agent were to form a covalent bond with the carbonium ion intermediate before the latter had completely freed itself of the departing group, as is the case with the less stable carbonium ions. This arises because the leaving group will tend to selectively shield one side of the carbonium ion thus favoring

[14] N. N. Lichtin and P. D. Bartlett, *J. Am. Chem. Soc.*, **73**, 5530 (1951).

[15] Y. Pocker, *Proc. Chem. Soc. (London)*, **1959**, 386.

[16] S. Winstein, E. Clippinger, A. H. Fainberg, and G. C. Robinson, *Chem. & Ind. (London)*, **1954**, 664; *J. Am. Chem. Soc.*, **76**, 2597 (1954).

[17] S. Winstein and G. C. Robinson, *J. Am. Chem. Soc.*, **80**, 169 (1958), and previous papers in the same series; S. Winstein and A. H. Fainberg, *J. Am. Chem. Soc.*, **80**, 459 (1958).

[18] M. Eigen, *Discussions Faraday Soc.*, **24**, 25 (1957).

[19] E. D. Hughes, C. K. Ingold, and A. D. Scott, *J. Chem. Soc. (London)*, **1937**, 1201; E. D. Hughes, C. K. Ingold, and S. Masterman, *J. Chem. Soc. (London)*, **1937**, 1196.

[20] C. K. Ingold, *Structure and Mechanism in Organic Chemistry*, Cornell University Press, Ithaca, N.Y., 1953, p. 381.

nucleophilic attack by external reagent to occur at the opposite side of the ion. However, a relatively stable carbonium ion might persist in its solvation shell long enough to free itself completely of the leaving anion and to become symmetrically solvated so that the front and back attacks on the ion would become equivalent. Accordingly, in the absence of special stabilizing features, a mixture of racemization and inversion is observed.

Doering and Zeiss [21] consider that there is a partly covalent attachment of two solvent molecules to a carbonium ion involving an overlap of both lobes of the vacant p orbital of the carbonium ion with the orbitals of the solvent molecules. Inversion is obtained when the leaving group occupies a solvation site on one side of the plane of the carbonium ion, but racemization is obtained when a solvent molecule replaces the leaving group during the lifetime of the ion, and thereby produces a symmetrical carbonium ion. It appears to the present author that the solvated long-lived carbonium ion, in contrast to the highly reactive short-lived ion, is not satisfactorily visualized as involving any type of *covalent* link between carbon and the solvent molecule, for this would deprive the ion of the special resonance which otherwise accounts for its stability and its color. Rather, such interaction is better visualized as an ion-dipole interaction of the carbonium ion and the highly polarized cluster of solvent molecules in the so-called solvation complex.

Grunwald, Heller, and Klein [22] have elaborated the Hughes-Ingold scheme and have suggested that the molecules of the solvation sheath occupy a definite number of sites around the carbonium ion. The departing group will occupy the site of one of the solvating molecules and thereby reduce asymmetrically the number of sites from which solvent attacks the carbonium ion.

With optically active compounds such as norbornyl derivatives which form bridge cations with a plane of symmetry the rate of racemization can be identified in the Winstein scheme with the ionization step $RX \rightarrow R^+X^-$. More recently it has been found that the racemization rates of 1-phenylethyl chloride and substituted benzhydryl chlorides [23] in nitromethane and liquid sulfur dioxide are faster than the respective unimolecular elimination (E_1) and radiochlorine exchange (S_N1) even though no bridged ions are involved. Similar results were obtained with substituted benzhydryl chloride in acetic acid and 80% aqueous acetone.[24] It is clear that in all these examples racemization precedes, and is lower in free energy than, any chemical reaction.

[21] W. von E. Doering, and H. H. Zeiss, *J. Am. Chem. Soc.*, **75**, 4733 (1953).

[22] E. Grunwald, A. Heller, and J. Klein, *J. Chem. Soc.*, **1957**, 2604; Y. Pocker, unpublished observations.

[23] Y. Pocker, *Trans. Faraday Soc.*, **55**, 1266 (1959); W. A. Mueller and Y. Pocker, unpublished results; W. A. Mueller, Ph.D. Thesis, London University (1959); cf. also B. Swedlund, Ph.D. thesis, London University (1957).

[24] S. Winstein, J. S. Gall, M. Hojo, and S. Smith, *J. Am. Chem. Soc.*, **82**, 1010 (1960); Y. Pocker, *Proc. Chem. Soc. (London)*, **1961**, 140 and unpublished results.

These racemizations could, in principle, proceed with or without the formation of an intermediate.[23] The latter can be visualized as an intramolecular tunneling whereby the hydrogen and the chlorine atoms remain partly bound to the asymmetric carbon atom but exchange their relative positions. Such a process would involve a partial but incomplete bond cleavage coupled with a partial but incomplete charge transfer and may therefore be assumed to parallel the solvent sensitivity of a true ionization process.

Racemization via an ionic intermediate can be visualized as occurring at an early stage of ionization, i.e., via a tightly held, but sufficiently long-lived, intermediate to allow rotation of one partner relative to the other within the solvent cage. In this representation racemization does not measure the entire rate of "intimate" ion pair production but only that fraction in which configurational changes have occurred. The relatively small deuterium isotope effects observed in these racemizations [23] argue against the tunneling and accord with the "intimate" ion pair mechanism.

2. WAGNER-MEERWEIN REARRANGEMENTS

The present section is concerned with the Wagner-Meerwein rearrangement in acyclic and cyclic systems, but excludes from the latter small ring systems and bridged compounds; these are treated in detail by Breslow[25] and Berson,[26] respectively.

A. Nature of First Capturable Intermediate; Timing of Covalence Change

Wagner[27] was the first to recognize that rearrangements in saturated systems occur in different bicyclic terpenes. Meerwein[28] generalized Wagner's deductions and established these rearrangements as a more general phenomenon of organic chemistry, indicating that they occur in various substitution, elimination, and addition reactions. He was also the first to recognize that these rearrangements occur via carbonium ion intermediates.

Whitmore[29] and his co-workers found that neopentyl alcohol and its halides undergo certain standard substitutions only with great reluctance and that those reactions which occur easily lead to rearranged products, i.e., to tert-amyl compounds and isoamylene. Dostrovsky and Hughes[30] showed kinetically that the very slow substitution reactions were generally $S_N 2$

[25] This volume, Section 4.

[26] This volume, Section 3.

[27] G. Wagner, J. Russ. Phys. Chem. Soc., **31**, 680 (1899); Ber., **32**, 2302 (1899).

[28] H. Meerwein, Ann., **405**, 129 (1914), **417**, 255 (1918).

[29] F. C. Whitmore, and H. S. Rothrock, J. Am. Chem. Soc., **55**, 1100 (1933), **54**, 3431 (1932); F. C. Whitmore, E. L. Wittle, and A. H. Popkin, J. Am. Chem. Soc., **61**, 1586 (1939).

[30] I. Dostovsky and E. D. Hughes, J. Chem. Soc. (London), **1946**, 166.

processes and that the products were unrearranged, exemplified by equation 7. They also showed that the ready nucleophilic substitutions or eliminations

$$(CH_3)_3CCH_2Br + C_2H_5O^- \longrightarrow \left[\begin{array}{c} H \\ \overset{\delta-}{C_2H_5O} \cdots \overset{|}{\underset{|}{C}} \cdots \overset{\delta-}{Br} \\ H \quad \diagdown C(CH_3)_3 \end{array} \right] \longrightarrow C_2H_5OCH_2C(CH_3)_3 + Br^- \quad (7)$$

(S$_N$2: One transition state separates reactants from products; synchronous bond forming-bond break-process; no intermediate formed)

were unimolecular processes of the S_N1 and E_1 type. Indeed, in wet formic acid, which is a good ionizing medium, the rate of hydrolysis of neopentyl bromide is not very different from that of ethyl bromide; yet, no detectable quantities of *unrearranged* solvolysis products accompany the rearranged product. If one assumes that the hydrolysis of ethyl bromide in wet formic acid is essentially an S_N1 process, then one is led to the conclusion that the migrating methyl in the neopentyl group does not assist the carbon halogen heterolysis. If the neopentyl ion is assumed to be the first ionic intermediate, then its reaction with a solvent molecule must be considerably slower than the intramolecular methyl migration which produces the *tert*-amyl cation. Another way in which this situation might arise is if the methyl migration occurs before the halogen has passed out of the shielding range, so that *tert*-amyl ion becomes the first capturable [31] intermediate.

[31] The question of whether protonated cyclopropanes can be transient storage configurations for the neopentyl ion has also aroused recent interest.[32] It has been shown by isotopic labeling that protonated cyclopropanes are not intermediates in the rearrangement of this ion. One compelling observation [33] is that the ion $(CH_3)_3CC^+D_2$ rearranges only to the $(CH_3)_2C^+CD_2CH_3$ ion and not to a mixture of $(CH_3)_2C^+CD_2CH_3$ and $(CH_3)_2C^+CH_2CD_2H$. Another compelling observation [34] is that neopentyl -1-C^{13} reacts with hydrogen bromide to give products derived from the classical *tert*-amyl cation

$$\begin{array}{cc} \underset{\underset{Br}{|}}{\overset{\overset{CH_3}{|}}{CH_3-C-^{13}CH_2CH_3}} & \overset{\overset{CH_3}{|}}{CH_3-C=C^{13}HCH_3} \end{array}$$

while if protonated cyclopropane were an intermediate the following pairs of bromides and olefins should have been produced, respectively:

$$(CH_3)_3C^{13}CH_2C \rightarrow (CH_3)_2C\underset{\diagdown}{\overset{\diagup}{}}\!\!\!\begin{array}{c}CH_2\\ {}^{13}CH_2\end{array} \overset{H}{\longrightarrow} \quad \underset{\underset{Br}{|}}{\overset{\overset{CH_3}{|}}{CH_3-C-^{13}CH_2CH_3}} + \underset{\underset{Br}{|}}{\overset{\overset{CH_3}{|}}{CH_3-C-CH_2{}^{13}CH_3}}$$
$$+ \qquad or \qquad +$$
$$(CH_3)_2C={}^{13}CHCH_3 \qquad (CH_3)_2C=CH^{13}CH_3$$

[32] P. S. Skell and I. Starer, *J. Am. Chem. Soc.*, **82**, 2971 (1960); M. S. Silver, *J. Am. Chem. Soc.*, **82**, 2971 (1960).

[33] P. S. Skell, I. Starer, and A. P. Krapcho, *J. Am. Chem. Soc.*, **82**, 5257 (1960).

[34] G. J. Karabatsos and J. D. Graham, *J. Am. Chem. Soc.*, **82**, 5250 (1960).

It has been suggested,[35] however, that the comparison with ethyl bromide is not valid and that in order to understand the rate of solvolysis of neopentyl and more ramified systems one has to invoke neighboring group assistance through methyl bridging, but this argument is only of a permissive kind. Indeed, in certain other instances *small* increases in rate have been attributed to neighboring group participation. Such explanations should be accepted with caution unless supported by other evidence, since the rate in the absence of participation for any given compound cannot be predicted to any high degree of accuracy. In any case, such considerations, even if correct, ascribe to the transition state for ionization some assistance from the migrating methyl, but we do not know if the first capturable intermediate is the bridged or the rearranged ion. Indeed, Roberts [36] and co-workers find both methyl and hydrogen migration in the deamination of *n*-propylamine, but in this and other systems could find no evidence for the intervention of either hydrogen or methyl-bridged carbonium ions. The latter have been frequently invoked, but so far no compelling evidence has been presented for their intervention as reaction intermediates in such systems.

On the other hand, 2,2,2-triphenylethyl chloride in wet formic acid yields exclusively triphenylethylene, and the reaction proceeds 6×10^4 times faster than the respective solvolysis of neopentyl chloride under the same conditions.[37] This higher velocity can be explained if one assumes that this heterolysis is assisted by the participating phenyl group in what might be regarded as an internal S_N2 process (eq. 8). Neighboring group participation tells us only

about the transition state and does not necessarily indicate the presence of a chemically capturable nonclassical bridged carbonium ion intermediate.

[35] S. Winstein and H. Marshall, *J. Am. Chem. Soc.*, **74**, 1120 (1952).

[36] (a) J. D. Roberts and J. A. Yancey, *J. Am. Chem. Soc.*, **74**, 5943 (1952). (b) J. D. Roberts and C. M. Regan, *J. Am. Chem. Soc.*, **75**, 2069 (1953). (c) J. D. Roberts and M. Halmann, *J. Am. Chem. Soc.*, **75**, 5759 (1953). (d) J. D. Roberts and J. A. Yancey, *J. Am. Chem. Soc.*, **77**, 5558 (1955). (e) The 1-propanol recovered from the deamination of 1-propylamine-1-C^{14} has the label only at C-1 and C-3 so that methyl does not migrate in this rearrangement: O. A. Reutov and T. N. Shatkina, *Dokl. Akad. Nauk S.S.S.R.*, **133**, 606 (1960); *Tetrahedron*, **18**, 237 (1962). (f) The formation of 1-propanol-3-C^{14} described in Ref. 36 (e) could, in principle, result from either a 1,3 hydride shift or from successive 1,2 shifts. By employing 1-propylamine 1,1,2,2-d_4 it has been recently demonstrated that the rearranged 1-propanol is mainly, if not exclusively, due to a 1,3 shift and that the 2-propanol produced in this deamination is due to an irreversible 1,2 shift: G. J. Karabatos and C. E. Orzech, Jr., *J. Am. Chem. Soc.*, **84**, 2838 (1962).

[37] J. C. Charlton, I. Dostovsky, and E. D. Hughes, *Nature*, **167**, 986 (1951).

Hughes and Ingold [38] have used the word "synarthesis" [39] to describe this type of phenomenon. The name is intended to suggest that a split single bond fastens together the locations of a split ionic charge. Winstein [40] has used the adjective "anchimeric" [39] to indicate an accelerated ionization caused by the neighboring group participation of carbon, hydrogen, and also functional groups (see also Section 3, footnote 126a).

The direct generation of a bridged ion in preference to the classical ion in any particular reaction can be understood if the nonclassical ion is the more stable. The stability ascribed to some bridged carbonium ions is, however, far from being fully understood. Whatever the cause of such stabilization, the transition state for the bridged ion formation should in principle also be stabilized by neighboring group participation. Abnormally high ionization rates are strongly indicative of bridged ion intermediates, but such an interpretation is only of a permissive rather than of a compelling kind, since account should be taken in particular of nonbonding neighboring group effects.

B. Stereochemical Consequences

Cram [41] and his co-workers have been able to rationalize the stereochemistry of solvolytic substitutions and elimination reactions of $R_1R_2R_3C_\beta R_4R_5C_\alpha X$ (eq. 9) in terms of the following criteria:

$$-\overset{|}{\underset{|}{C}}_\beta-\overset{|}{\underset{|}{C}}{}_\alpha^+(\equiv R_\alpha^+)$$

$$\begin{matrix} R_1 & R_4 \\ R_2-C_\beta-C_\alpha-X \\ R_3 & R_5 \end{matrix} \longrightarrow -C\overset{R}{\underset{}{\cdots}}\overset{+}{\cdots}C\quad(\equiv R_{cyclic}^+)$$

$$+\overset{+}{\underset{|}{C}}_\beta-\overset{|}{\underset{|}{C}}{}_\alpha-(\equiv R_\beta^+)$$

$$\qquad(9)$$

1. Inversion at both C_α and C_β is taken to mean that only a cyclic intermediate is involved.

2. A mixture of inversion and racemization at both C_α and C_β is taken to mean that two open carbonium ions R_α^+ and R_β^+ are intermediates and the cyclic system might be an intermediate or might only be a transition state.

3. (a) Retention or a mixture of retention and racemization at C_α but inversion at C_β is taken to mean that the R_β^+ is not an intermediate and that the first intermediate is the open carbonium R_α^+ with the bridged carbonium

[38] F. Brown, E. D. Hughes, C. K. Ingold, and J. F. Smith, *Nature*, **168**, 65 (1951).

[39] It is not clear to the present author whether synarthetic and anchimeric assistance are in every respect identical descriptions of the same phenomenon since the former has been defined in terms of σ electrons whilst the latter in terms of both σ and π electrons.

[40] S. Winstein, C. R. Lindegren, H. Marshall, and L. L. Ingraham, *J. Am. Chem. Soc.*, **75**, 147 (1953).

[41] D. J. Cram in M. S. Newman, ed., *Steric Effects in Organic Chemistry*, Wiley, New York, 1956, Ch. 5 and references given there.

ion as a possible second intermediate. (*b*) Inversion at C_α and retention, or a mixture of retention and inversion, at C_β is taken to mean that $R_\alpha{}^+$ is not an intermediate and that either the bridged carbonium ion is the first intermediate followed by $R_\beta{}^+$ or $R_\beta{}^+$ formed directly is the first and only intermediate.

The stability of phenyl-bridged carbonium ions ("phenonium ions") is certainly more understandable than that of alkyl-bridged carbonium ions, but this stability must be partly offset by the loss of normal benzene resonance. A simple molecular orbital treatment led Simonetta and Winstein to conclude that phenyl bridging causes a considerable overall increase in resonance energy. The question then arises: Can phenyl group participation occur without rate acceleration?

3-Phenylbutan-2-ol exists in *threo* and *erythro* forms, each of which is an enantiomeric pair. Cram [42] has established that acetolysis of optically active *erythro-p*-toluenesulfonate gave *erythro*-acetate of about 97% purity, whereas the *threo-p*-toluenesulfonate gave racemic *threo*-acetate. He suggested that the loss of optical activity in the *threo* compound is a consequence of the formation of phenonium ion (**1**) possessing a plane of symmetry and so attack at either carbon atom yields racemic product. In the case of the *erythro* compound the intermediate phenonium ion (**2**) is optically active, and ring opening at either C_α or C_β leads to the same optically active product which possesses the same configuration as the starting material. Cram has also

(1)   (2)

made an exhaustive study of the reactions of 3-phenyl-2-pentyl and 2-phenyl-3-pentyl *p*-toluenesulfonates in anhydrous acetic acid. Here no racemizations occur, since none of the bridged carbonium ions has a plane of symmetry.

C. Redistribution of Isotopic Label ; Classical and Nonclassical Carbonium Ions

The radiochemistry of the Wagner-Meerwein rearrangement during the solvolysis and deamination of several ^{14}C-labeled 1,2,2-triphenylethyl compounds has been subject to a detailed investigation by Bonner and Collins.[43] In these reactions neither phenyl nor the chain carbon labels achieve their

[42] D. J. Cram, *J. Am. Chem. Soc.*, **71**, 3863, 3871, 3875 3883; **74**, 2129, 2137, 2149, 2152, and subsequent papers in the same series. Cf. also S. Winstein and K. Schreiber, *J. Am. Chem. Soc.*, **74**, 2165, 2171 (1952).

[43] (a) W. A. Bonner and C. J. Collins, *J. Am. Chem. Soc.*, **75**, 5372 (1953), **77**, 99, 6725 (1955), **78**, 5587 (1956). (b) C. J. Collins and W. A. Bonner, *J. Am. Chem. Soc.*, **75**, 5379 (1953), **77**, 92 (1955). (c) C. J. Collins, W. A. Bonner, and C. T. Lester, *J. Am. Chem. Soc.*, **81**, 466 (1959).

statistical values. In the phenyl-labeled reactions (eq. 10) the mole fraction, N_1, of rearranged products was less than the statistical value of 2/3. Similarly,

$$Ph_2CHCH(X)Ph^* \rightarrow Ph_2CHCH(Y)Ph^* + Ph_2^*CHCH(Y)Ph \qquad (10)$$
$$\quad (I) \qquad\qquad (1-N_1) \qquad\qquad (N_1)$$

in the chain-labeled reactions (eq. 11) the mole fraction, N_2 of the rearranged products was less than the statistical 1/2. For any given reaction, however,

$$Ph_2CH^*CH(X)Ph \rightarrow Ph_2CH^*CH(Y)Ph + Ph_2^*CHCH(Y)Ph \qquad (11)$$
$$\quad (I) \qquad\qquad (1-N_2) \qquad\qquad (N_2)$$

$N_1 > N_2$ by an amount generally predictable on the basis of a mechanism involving equilibrating classical carbonium ions. The same general mechanism was used in explaining the acetoxyl exchange which actually leads to $N_1 = 2/3$ and $N_2 = 1/2$.

Open carbonium ions have also been demonstrated in the deamination of 3-phenyl-2-butylamine,[44] a system whose solvolytic reactions are best explained through the intervention of bridged ions (page 10). The general possibility that the stereochemistry of the products from open carbonium ions might, however, be controlled by restricted rotation about the central carbon-carbon bond had already been recognized by Winstein and Grunwald [45] in 1948.

Reactions which show stereospecificity need neither be necessarily concerted nor proceed via a bridged ion. Stereospecificity is indeed a requirement of concerted migrations and also of those reactions which involve bridged ion intermediates, but the converse is not true. Open (classical) carbonium ion intermediates, C_1^+, may show stereospecificity if the rate of rotation (R_θ) is not very fast compared with the rate of migration (R_m). The relative rates can be expressed in terms of differences in the free energy of activation for rotation, $\Delta F_\theta^\ddagger$, and for migration, $\Delta F_m^\ddagger$.

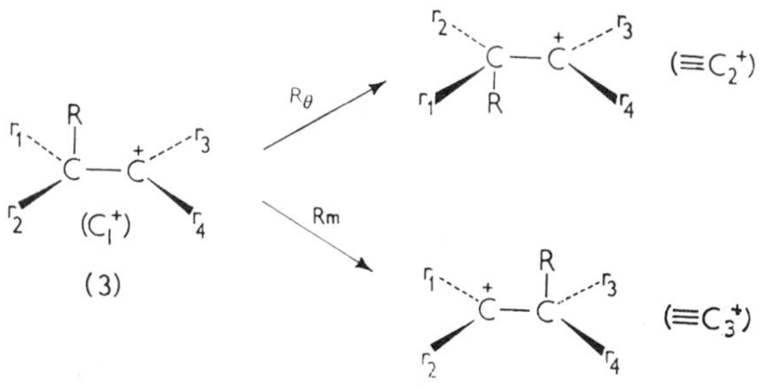

$$R_\theta/R_m = k_\theta[C_1^+]/k_m[C_1^+] = k_\theta/k_m = \exp\left[(-\Delta F_\theta^\ddagger + \Delta F_m^\ddagger)/RT\right]$$

[44] D. J. Cram and J. E. McCarty, *J. Am. Chem. Soc.*, **79**, 2866 (1957).

[45] S. Winstein and E. Grunwald, *J. Am. Chem. Soc.*, **70**, 835 (1948); S. Winstein and K. Morse, *J. Am. Chem. Soc.*, **74**, 1134 (1952); S. Winstein and L. I. Ingraham, *J. Am. Chem. Soc.*, **77**, 1739 (1955).

The rotational barrier for ethane [46],[47] has been calculated to be 2.8 kcal./mole, and in more complicated molecules it is assumed to be no less than 3.6 kcal./mole.[48] In nitromethane, in difluoromethyl borane, and in acetaldehyde, whose geometries probably approach that of an open carbonium ion, the rotational energy barriers are 0.006, 0.014, and 1.15 kcal./mole, respectively.[49] In most cases we do not know $\Delta F_m^{\ddagger}$, and we cannot predict a priori when $\Delta F_{\theta}^{\ddagger} > \Delta F_m^{\ddagger}$ and when $\Delta F_m^{\ddagger} > \Delta F_{\theta}^{\ddagger}$.

Stereochemical studies of the products of hydrolysis and acetolysis of 1,2,2-triphenylethyl p-toluenesulfonate and of deamination of 1,2,2-triphenylethylamine with nitrous acid indicate that a mixture of racemization and retention of configuration is obtained. Simultaneous radiochemical assay of the carbinol obtained in deamination indicates that there is more rearrangement of ^{14}C label in the carbinol of inverted configuration than there is in carbinol of retained configuration, so that retention of configuration in this particular system cannot [50],[50a] be due to bridged nonclassical ion intermediates. The results are compatible with classical ionic intermediates if it is assumed that the rate of rotation about the central carbon-carbon bond is not much faster than phenyl migration and if it is further assumed that a front attack by the entering group is preferred. The front attack can be made plausible on the grounds that an ortho hydrogen from one of the adjacent phenyls prevents back attack by sterically shielding the positively charged carbon atom.

A large number of similar systems have been stereochemically examined by Cram and his co-workers[42] with the general conclusion that both open and phenyl-bridged cations can be intermediates. Indeed, while the elegant work of Bonner and Collins[43] rules out the possibility that bridged ions are the cause of retention of configuration in the 1,2,2-triphenylethyl system, these data should not be taken as evidence against bridged ions in other systems. In view of the great stability of benzyl and benzyhdryl cations the classical structure of 1,2,2-triphenylethyl cation may be favored. Indeed, various

[46] K. S. Pitzer, *Chem. Revs.*, **27**, 39 (1940).

[47] W. G. Dauben and K. S. Pitzer in M. S. Newman, ed., *Steric Effects in Organic Chemistry*, Wiley, New York, 1956, ch. 1.

[48] A. Bondi, *J. Phys. Chem.*, **58**, 929 (1954).

[49] E. B. Wilson, *Proc. Natl. Acad. Sci. U. S.*, **43**, 816 (1957); in I. Prigogine, ed., *Advances in ChemicalPhysics*, Vol. II, Interscience, New York, 1959, pp. 367–393.

[50] This is only a permissive and not a compelling argument[50a] since retention can in principle be the consequence of double inversion; these deaminations were carried out in the presence of chloride ions, and the sequence might be $RN_2^+ \rightarrow RCl \rightarrow ROH$. The use of an excess of nitrite ions might also have caused some complication. In the solvolysis of the corresponding p-toluene sulfonate, the simultaneous study of polarimetric and exchange rates coupled with a radiochemical product assay in the presence of externally added isotopically labeled common anions has not been carried out.

[50a] After the submission of this manuscript important additional evidence of a more compelling type has been published: B. M. Benjamin, P. Wilder, Jr., and C. J. Collins, *J. Am. Chem. Soc.*, **83**, 3654 (1961); B. M. Benjamin and C. J. Collins, *J. Am. Chem. Soc.*, **83**, 3662 (1961); and C. J. Collins, J. B. Christie, and V. F. Raaen, *J. Am. Chem. Soc.*, **83**, 4267 (1961).

kinetic and stereochemical studies offer strong support in favor of a neighboring phenyl participation.

D. Hydrogen and Deuterium Migration

Linneman [51] has established that *tert*-butyl acetate and isobutene are formed in the reaction of isobutyl halides with silver acetate. Similar rearrangements involving hydrogen migration in the isobutyl group have been observed in deamination reactions and in *p*-toluene-sulfonate ester hydrolysis.[52] Roberts and Yancey [36a] have examined the distribution of ^{14}C in ethanol formed by deamination of $CH_3{}^{14}CH_2NH_2$. Only $\sim 2\%$ of $^{14}CH_3CH_2OH$ is formed so that the two ends of the molecule do not become equivalent at any stage during the reaction. The ratio of rearranged to unrearranged ethanol, $^{14}CH_3CH_2OH/CH_3{}^{14}CH_2OH$, is about $1:50$. If the reaction proceeds via carbonium ions, these cannot be bridged ions of type

$$\left[CH_2 \overset{\cdots H \cdots}{\underline{\quad\quad}} CH_2 \right]^+ .$$

The deamination of cyclodecylamine [53] isotopically labeled in the 1 position yields products with isotopic label not only in the 1 but also in the 5 and 6 positions. The results can be interpreted as a transannular hydrogen shift in the cyclodecyl cation.

In the acetolysis of *cis*-4-*tert*-butylcyclohexyl *p*-toluenesulfonate Winstein and Holness [54] observed that the acetates produced had the composition: 40% *trans*-4-*tert*-butyl cyclohexyl acetate (**4**), 30% *cis*-4-*tert*-butylcyclohexyl acetate (**5**) and 30% 3-*tert*-butylcyclohexyl acetate (**6**). In the last product hydrogen has migrated and the migration origin has retained its configuration. The authors assumed that the reaction proceeds via nonclassical hydrogen-bridged carbonium ion ("protonium ion") intermediates which undergo *trans* ring opening as indicated.

Cram and Tadanier [55] find that *erythro*-3-cyclohexyl-2-butyl-3-*d* *p*-toluenesulfonate reacts slower than the corresponding undeuterated compound, $k_H/k_D = 1.85$; while for the corresponding *threo* compounds $k_H/k_D = 1.72$. Isotope factors k_H/k_D of 1.85–2.26 were observed in the solvolysis of 3-methyl-2-butyl-3-*d* *p*-toluenesulfonate [56] and the undeuterated compound. In contrast, the $C_\beta(H)/C_\beta(D)$ effect in simple unassisted ionization is certainly not

[51] E. Linnemann, *Ann.*, **162**, 12 (1872).

[52] L. G. Cannel and R. W. Taft, Jr., *J. Am. Chem. Soc.*, **78**, 5812 (1956); Y. Pocker and G. F. W. Smith, unpublished observations; cf. also R. Huisgen and C. Ruchardt, *Ann.*, **601**, 1 (1956), and references quoted therein; R. M. Roberts, Y. W. Haus, C. H. Schmid, and D. A. Davis, *J. Am. Chem. Soc.*, **81**, 640 (1959), and references quoted therein.

[53] V. Prelog, *Experientia*, Suppl. No. 7, 261 (1957); *Bull. soc. chim. France*, **1960**, 1433; H. J. Urech and V. Prelog, *Helv. Chim. Acta*, **40**, 477 (1957); J. D. Dunitz and V. Prelog, *Angew Chem.*, **72**, 896 (1960). For related migrations, see also A. C. Cope, S. W. Fenton, and C. F. Spencer, *J. Am. Chem. Soc.*, **74**, 5884 (1952); and A. C. Cope and B. C. Anderson, *J. Am. Chem. Soc.*, **70**, 3892 (1957).

[54] S. Winstein and N. J. Holness, *J. Am. Chem. Soc.*, **77**, 5562 (1955).

[55] D. J. Cram and J. Tadanier, *J. Am. Chem. Soc.*, **81**, 2737 (1959).

[56] S. Winstein and J. Takahashi, *Tetrahedron*, **2**, 316 (1958).

much larger than $k_H/k_D = 1.3$.[57] Where the higher k_H/k_D ratios accord with an intramolecular hydrogen migration, they provide little information regarding the question of whether nonclassical hydrogen-bridged cations are intermediates in solvolysis. In the system 3-cyclohexyl-2-butyl p-toluenesulfonate

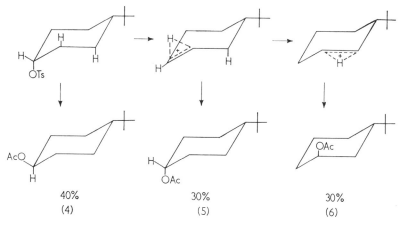

40%   30%   30%
(4)   (5)   (6)

both the migration origin and terminus are asymmetric, whereas in the solvolytic product the migration origin is asymmetric (eq. 12). In 20% water–80%

$$\underset{\underset{OTs}{\overset{C_6H_{11}}{\mid}}}{CH_3-\overset{\overset{H}{\mid}}{C}^*-\overset{\mid}{C}^*HCH_3} \xrightarrow{H_2O} CH_3-\underset{\underset{C_6H_{11}}{\mid}}{\overset{\overset{OH}{\mid}}{C}^*}-CH_2CH_3 \qquad (12)$$

dioxane 2-cyclohexyl-2-butanol is the major solvolytic product, and 3-cyclo-hexyl-2-butanol is the minor substitution product. The *threo-p*-toluene-sulfonate produced 2-cyclohexyl-2-butanol with 59% optical purity and the *erythro-p*-toluenesulfonate produced 2-cyclohexyl-2-butanol with 44% optical purity. It appears, therefore, that the solvent molecule reacts at the tertiary carbon atom predominantly from the side originally occupied by hydrogen. With all other migrating groups in 1,2 rearrangements the migration origin inverts or racemizes (page 9), but with hydrogen the migration origin appears to retain its configuration.

One possible explanation of this unique property of hydrogen is that the solvent "hydrogen-bonds" with the bridged ion and is well directed to attack carbon from the side of the bridge. Such a mechanism is in principle similar to that proposed for the so-called *"cis"* opening of ethylene oxide rings with acids.[58,59] This mechanism can account for the rearrangement of optically

[57] V. J. Shiner, Jr., *J. Am. Chem. Soc.*, **76**, 1603 (1954).

[58] J. H. Brewster, *J. Am. Chem. Soc.*, **78**, 4061 (1956).

[59] D. Y. Curtin, A. Bradley, and Y. G. Hendrickson, *J. Am. Chem. Soc.*, **78**, 4064 (1956).

active phenyl-*o*-tolylacetaldehyde [60] and also for the results of Winstein and Holness.[54] However, it is also possible to account for the observations of Cram and Tadanier in terms of open carbonium ions which partition between several products faster than they undergo conformational equilibration.

3. PINACOLIC REARRANGEMENTS

A. Introduction [61a,61b, 62]

The pinacolic rearrangement can be represented by the general scheme of equation 13, in which R_1, R_2, R_3, and R_4 represent either hydrogen atoms or alkyl, aralkyl, or aryl groups. The rearrangement is effected by acid. The reversal of the above arrows corresponds to a retropinacolic change.

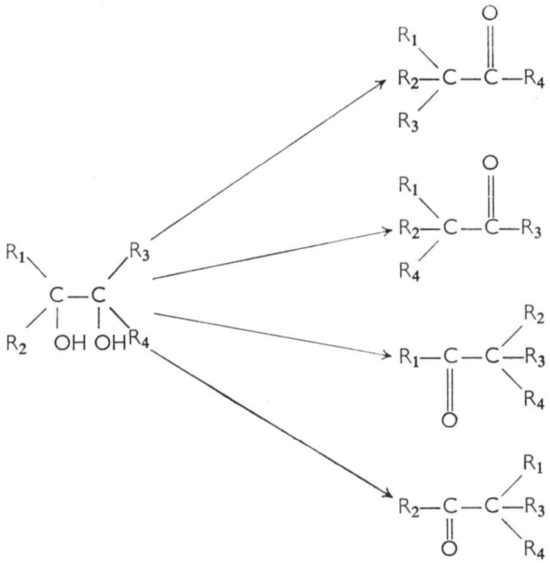

$$(13)$$

The pinacolic rearrangement derives its name from Fittig's [63] original observation that sulfuric acid transforms tetramethylethylene glycol (**7**, pinacol) into methyl *tert*-butyl ketone (**8**, pinacolone).

[60] K. Mislow, and M. Siegel, *J. Am. Chem. Soc.*, **74**, 1060 (1952).

[61a] C. K. Ingold, *Structure and Mechanism in Organic Chemistry*, Cornell University Press, Ithaca, N.Y., 1953, and references cited there.

[61b] G. W. Wheland, *Advanced Organic Chemistry*, 2nd ed., Wiley, New York, 1949, 494 and references cited there.

[62] Since the submission of this review, an excellent summary dealing with the pinacol rearrangement has appeared: C. J. Collins, *Quart. Revs.* (*London*), **14**, 357 (1960).

[63] R. Fittig, *Ann.*, **110**, 17 (1859); **114**, 54 (1860).

Actually, the name pinacol is strictly applied to a tetrasubstituted ethylene glycol, and in the older literature the transformation is described as pinacolic

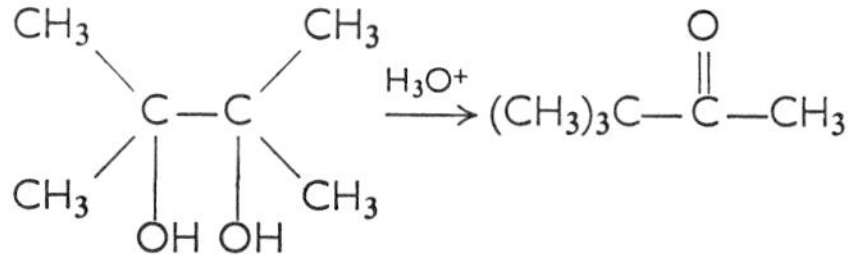

$$
\begin{array}{c}
CH_3 \quad\quad CH_3 \\
\underset{CH_3}{\overset{}{\diagdown}}\!C\!-\!C\!\underset{CH_3}{\overset{}{\diagup}} \xrightarrow{\; H_3O^+ \;} (CH_3)_3C\!-\!\overset{\displaystyle O}{\overset{\|}{C}}\!-\!CH_3 \\
\quad\; OH \; OH \\
(7) \quad\quad\quad\quad\quad\quad (8)
\end{array}
$$

when both hydroxyls are tertiary, i.e., when R_1, R_2, R_3, and R_4 are alkyl, aralkyl, or aryl groups. When $R_4 = H$ and the tertiary hydroxyl group is lost, the resulting transformation is described as semihydrobenzoinic, while when the secondary hydroxyl group is lost the transformation is described as semipinacolinic. As there is no fundamental difference between the various transformations, the wider definition given at the beginning of this section will be used in this article. Thus, ethylene glycol ($R_1 = R_2 = R_3 = R_4 = H$) gives acetaldehyde (and some decomposition products derived from acetaldehyde) when heated with strong acid, and this transformation is accordingly classified as a pinacolic rearrangement.

In addition to the pinacolic transformation proper there exist a number of closely related rearrangements which belong to the same class of chemical transformations. The dimethyl ether of pinacol and tetramethylethylene oxide both rearrange to pinacolone under acidic conditions. The rearrangement of ethylene oxides to carbonyl compounds under the influence of acids is quite general and can be represented by the general scheme of equation 14.

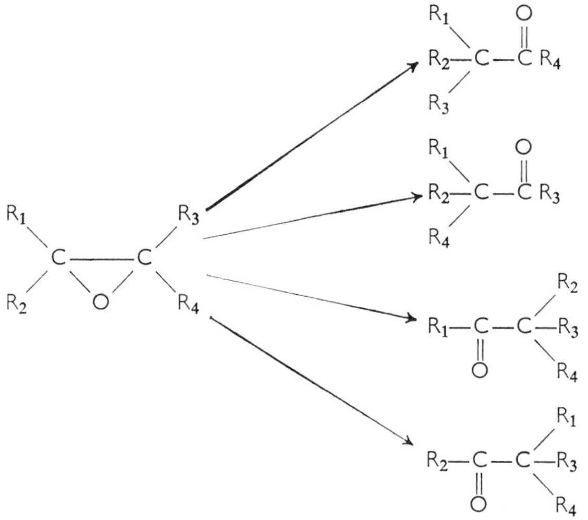

$$\text{(14)}$$

Closely analogous rearrangements accompany the action of nitrous acid on 2-amino alcohols (eqs. 15 and 16). If the deamination is carried out under mild acidic conditions, one normally finds that only the groups attached to the same carbon atom as the hydroxyl group do actually migrate, as indicated. These transformations are called pinacolic deaminations.

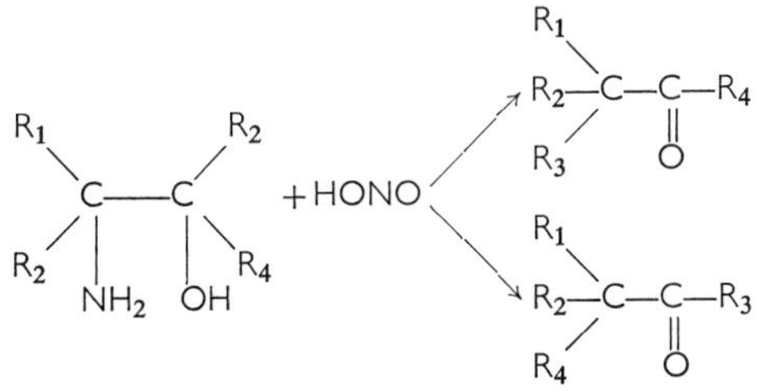

$$(15)$$

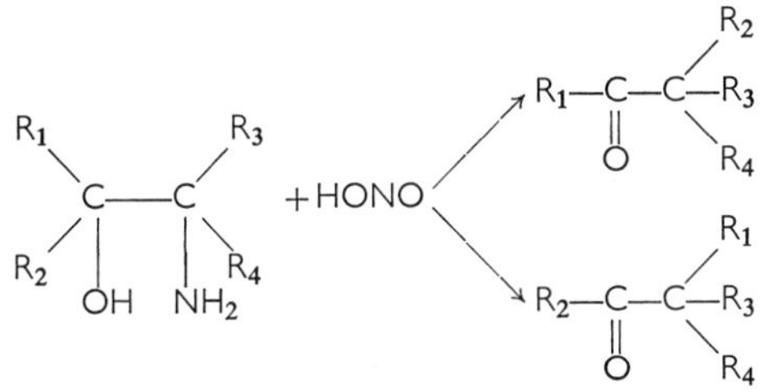

$$(16)$$

A similar transformation is the halohydrin rearrangement which occurs in good ionizing solvents with or without the electrophilic catalysis of silver and mercury salts (eqs. 17 and 18). Here, too, as in pinacolic deamination,

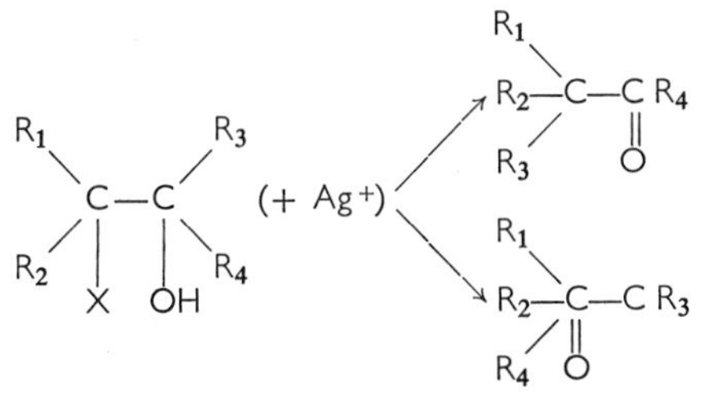

$$(17)$$

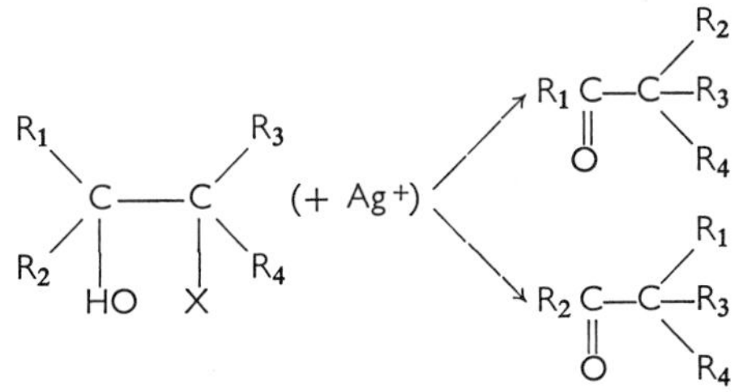

$$(18)$$

only the groups originally attached to the carbon atom carrying the hydroxyl group do actually migrate.

Another such related rearrangement is the acyloin transformation, which refers to the conversion, under the influence of acids, of α-hydroxy ketones or α-hydroxy aldehydes into isomeric α-hydroxy ketones (eq. 19).[63a]

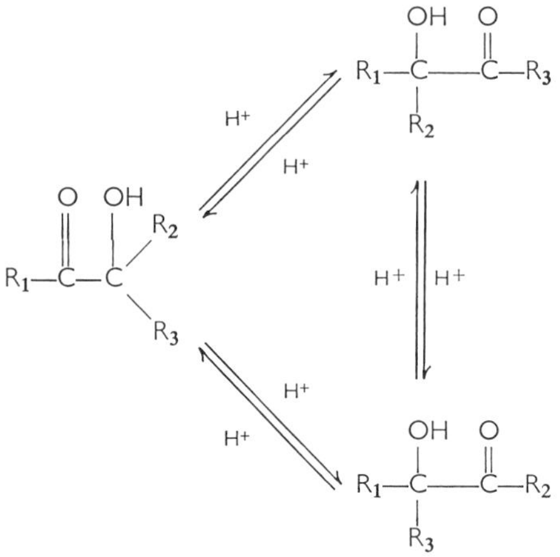

$$
\begin{array}{c}
\text{O} \quad \text{OH} \\
\| \quad | \quad R_2 \\
R_1\text{--C--C} \\
\quad \quad \quad \text{\textbackslash} R_3
\end{array}
\quad
\begin{array}{c}
H^+ \\
\rightleftharpoons \\
H^+
\end{array}
\quad
\begin{array}{c}
\text{OH} \quad \text{O} \\
| \quad \quad \| \\
R_1\text{--C----C--}R_3 \\
\quad | \\
\quad R_2
\end{array}
$$

$$H^+ \updownarrow H^+$$

$$
\begin{array}{c}
\text{OH} \quad \text{O} \\
| \quad \quad \| \\
R_1\text{--C----C--}R_2 \\
\quad | \\
\quad R_3
\end{array}
$$

(19)

Still another rearrangement is the conversion of aldehydes, under the influence of acid, to ketones (eq. 20).

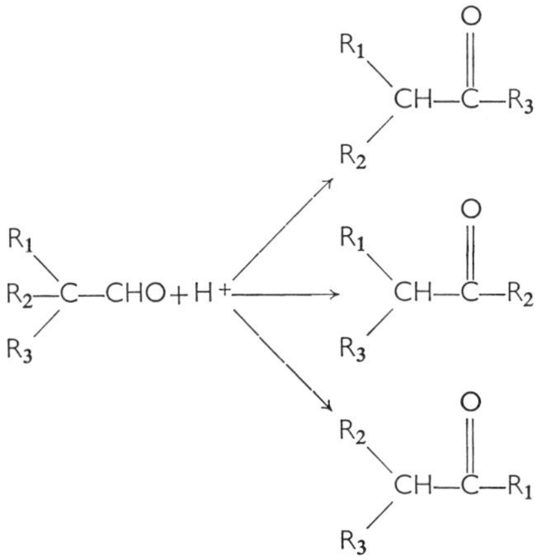

$$
\begin{array}{c}
R_1 \\
\quad \text{\textbackslash} \\
R_2\text{--C--CHO} + H^+ \longrightarrow \\
\quad / \\
R_3
\end{array}
$$

$$
\begin{array}{c}
R_1 \quad \text{O} \\
\quad \text{\textbackslash} \quad \| \\
\quad \text{CH--C--}R_3 \\
\quad / \\
R_2
\end{array}
$$

$$
\begin{array}{c}
R_1 \quad \text{O} \\
\quad \text{\textbackslash} \quad \| \\
\quad \text{CH--C--}R_2 \\
\quad / \\
R_3
\end{array}
$$

$$
\begin{array}{c}
R_2 \quad \text{O} \\
\quad \text{\textbackslash} \quad \| \\
\quad \text{CH--C--}R_1 \\
\quad / \\
R_3
\end{array}
$$

(20)

The accepted mechanism for pinacolic transformation involves the prior formation of a carbonium ion intermediate. Carbonium ion rearrangements were originally written as simply involving the shift of an alkyl group or hydrogen atom from an adjacent carbon atom to the electron-deficient carbon atom, the transition state for the rearrangement being formulated as **9**.

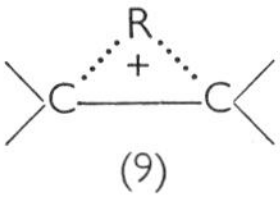

$$
\begin{array}{c}
\quad \overset{\cdots R \cdots}{} \\
{>}C\overset{+}{\cdots\cdots}C{<}
\end{array}
$$

(9)

[63a] This transformation may also be induced by base (see this volume, Section 6).

By analogy with Wagner-Meerwein rearrangements, this structure may also represent an intermediate. This nonclassical bridged intermediate would in principle be partitioned between substitution and rearrangement (eq. 21).

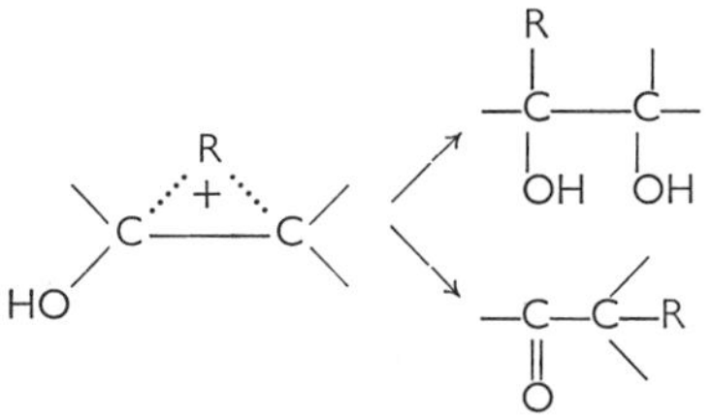

(21)

It is evident that if one considers the pinacolic rearrangement of the symmetrical glycol, $RR'C(OH)C(OH)RR'$, one has, neglecting conformational isomers, five possible carbonium ion intermediates. Structures **10**, **13**, and **14** represent open carbonium ions, while **11** and **12** represent bridged carbonium ions. In ion **10** the migrating group is still attached to the migration origin, while in **13** and **14** the migrating group is fully attached to the migration terminus. In the bridged ions the migrating group is partly attached to both the migration origin and the migration terminus.

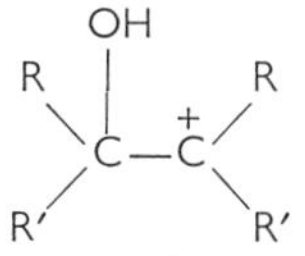

(10) 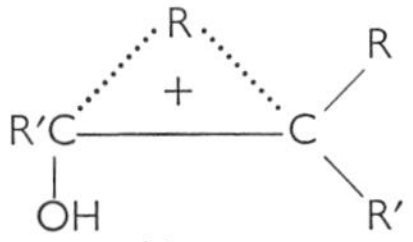   (11)

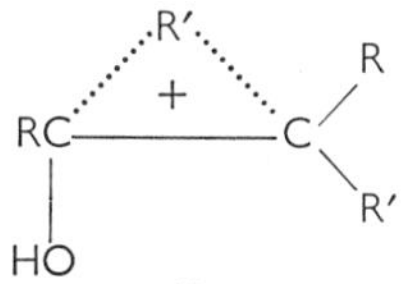

(12) 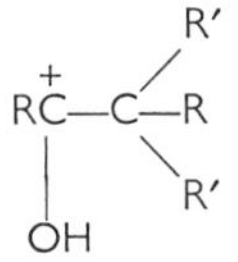   (13) 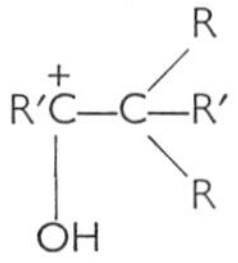   (14)

In the rearrangement of pinacol itself only three structurally different carbonium ions could in principle be involved (**15–17**), while in the rearrange-

$(CH_3)_2C(OH)\overset{+}{-}\overset{+}{C}(CH_3)_2$

(15)   (16) 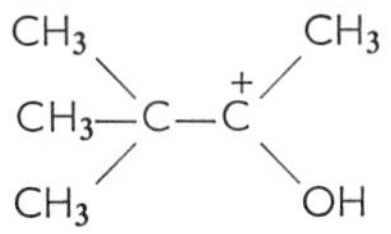   (17)

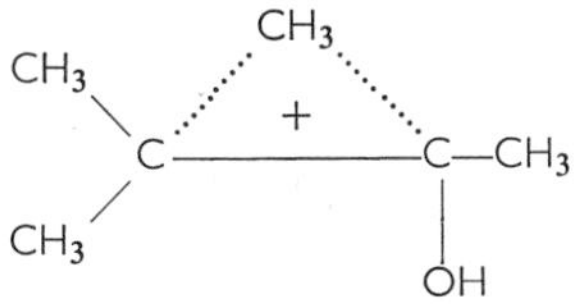

ment of an unsymmetrical pinacol, $R_2C(OH)-C(OH)R'_2$, six structurally different carbonium ions need be considered; three are derived from the conjugate acid $R_2C(\overset{+}{O}H_2)-C(OH)R'_2$, and three are derived from the second conjugate acid, $R_2C(OH)-C(\overset{+}{O}H_2)R'_2$.

B. Partitioning of Intermediates

Evidence for a carbonium ion intermediate in the rearrangement of pinacol comes from the oxygen exchange between pinacol and water during rearrangement.[64] The relative rates of rearrangement and oxygen exchange show that at low acidities 70–75% of the carbonium ions revert to pinacol and ~ 25–30% rearrange to pinacolone.

The carbonium ions produced in (a) the acid-catalyzed ring opening of tetramethylethylene oxide, (b) the solvolysis of tetramethylethylene chloro- and bromohydrins, (c) the silver-ion-catalyzed solvolysis of the above halohydrous, and (d) the deamination of 3-amino-2,3-dimethylbutan-2-ol partition under similar conditions to give pinacol and pinacolone in the same proportions.[65] All these reactions must proceed through a common intermediate since under the same competitive situation they give the same products in the same ratio. These reactions proceed at vastly different rates, yet, in each one of them, the departing group is sufficiently far removed from the carbonium ion not to affect the relative proportions of products.

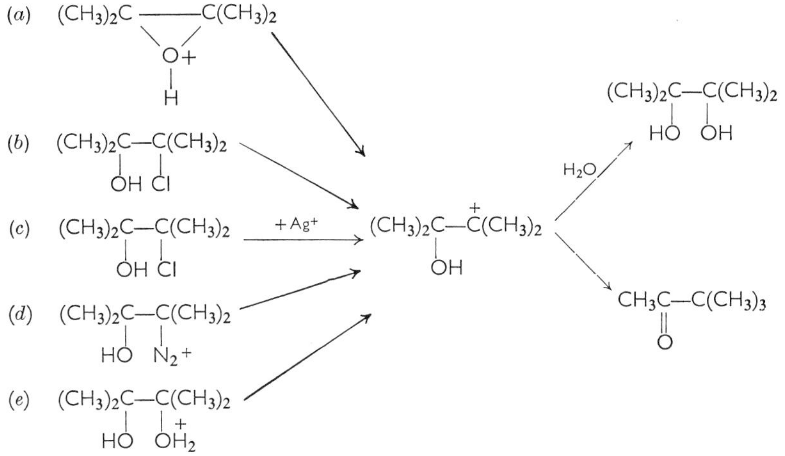

Evidence for the role of water in the partitioning of the intermediate comes from the dependence of the product composition on the activity of water. The partitioning is pictured as a competition between capture of the carbonium ion by water to produce pinacol and an intramolecular methyl migration not involving direct participation by water. The formation of pinacolone from the rearranged carbonium ion could involve two routes, one either a rapid proton loss, the other a hydration followed by dehydration, but the role

[64] C. A. Bunton, T. Hadwick, D. R. Llewellyn, and Y. Pocker, *Chem. & Ind. (London)*, **1956**, 547; *J. Chem. Soc. (London)*, **1958**, 403; T. S. Rothrock and A. Fry, *J. Am. Chem. Soc.*, **80**, 4349 (1958); cf. also N. C. Deno and D. J. Perizzolo, *J. Org. Chem.*, **22**, 836 (1957); and W. B. Smith, R. E. Bowman, and T. J. Kmet, *J. Am. Chem. Soc.*, **81**, 997 (1959).

[65] Y. Pocker, *Chem. & Ind. (London)*, **1959**, 332.

of water in these rapid processes is of no consequence since their transition states are much lower in energy than the transition state for the migration of the methyl. The relative proportions of the two products are therefore given by:

$$[\text{Pinacol}]/[\text{Pinacolone}] = k_s[\text{R}^+][\text{H}_2\text{O}]/k_\text{R}[\text{R}^+] = k_s^\circ a_{\text{H}_2\text{O}} f_\text{R}/k_\text{R}^\circ f_\text{S}.$$

It has indeed been found that the product ratio [Pinacol]/[Pinacolone] decreases linearly with decrease in the activity of water $a_{\text{H}_2\text{O}}$. Rate comparisons indicate that the production of the pinacolic carbonium ion is not detectably assisted by the migrating methyl or by the second hydroxyl group.

With less stable carbonium ions the product composition does depend on the source of the carbonium ion. Accordingly, Ley and Vernon [66] find that the hydrogen migration in the ion $(\text{CH}_3)_2\text{C}^+\text{CH}_2\text{OH}$ produces much more isobutyraldehyde when this ion is the intermediate in the acid-catalyzed rearrangement of isobutylene glycol than when it is formed in the acid-catalyzed decomposition of isobutylene oxide. One possible interpretation would be that the ion reacts with water before its initially more strained configuration has time to pass into the more stable (unstrained) configuration which might be the original form in which the ion is produced from isobutylene glycol. The deamination of 2-amino-1,1-diphenylpropan-1-ol proceeds via open carbonium ions which must undergo solvolysis faster than rotation about the C—C bond.[67]

On the other hand, isotopic labeling experiments might be taken to indicate that the deamination of 2-amino-3-phenylbutane-1-^{14}C (18) by nitrous acid proceeds via the symmetrical carbonium ion.[68]

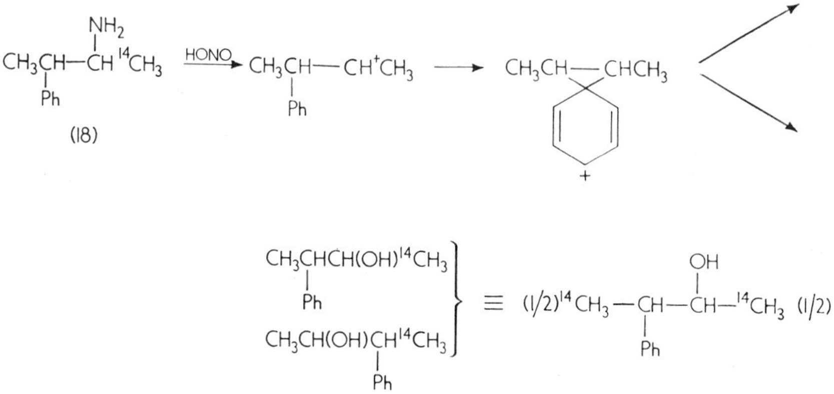

[66] B. J. Ley and C. A. Vernon, *Chem. & Ind. (London)*, **1956**, 146; *J. Chem. Soc. (London)*, **1957**, 2387, 3256.

[67] B. M. Benjamin, H. J. Shaeffer, and C. J. Collins, *J. Am. Chem. Soc.*, **79**, 6160 (1957).

[68] W. A. Bonner and D. D. Tanner, *J. Am. Chem. Soc.*, **80**, 1447 (1958).

C. Migratory Aptitude

By examining series of symmetrical glycols of the type $ArAr'C(OH)$-$C(OH)ArAr'$, W. E. Bachmann[69] and his co-workers were able to assign migratory aptitudes with a considerable degree of internal consistency. They found the order of decreasing migratory aptitude (relative to phenyl = 1) to be p-anisyl (500) > p-tolyl (15.7) > p-isopropylphenyl (9) > p-ethylphenyl (5) > m-anisyl (1.6) > phenyl (1.0) > p-chlorophenyl (0.7) > o-anisyl (0.3) > m-chlorophenyl (0.1). Since the two hydroxyls were strictly equivalent, only one conjugate acid was formed. Under such conditions, and in the absence of any steric factors, the substituent effects would be expected to show the same trend as the relative rates of electrophilic aromatic substitution of the corresponding monosubstituted benzenes. From the point of view of the migrating group, pinacolic rearrangements are essentially electrophilic substitutions with a difference, namely, that in the former an alkyl or aryl is normally being displaced whereas in the latter a hydrogen is being displaced. The migratory aptitudes of para-substituted phenyl groups are in accord with these considerations but not so the migratory aptitude of the o-anisyl group. The low migrating aptitude of the latter is usually ascribed to steric hindrance.[70,71]

A number of pinacolic deaminations are known in which the expected group does not migrate.[74] In the system $ArPhC(OH)CH(NH_2)Ph$ there are

[69] W. E. Bachmann and F. H. Moser, J. Am. Chem. Soc., 54, 1124 (1932). W. E. Bachmann and H. R. Sternberger, J. Am. Chem. Soc., 55, 3821 (1933), 56, 170 (1934); W. E. Bachmann and J. W. Ferguson, J. Am. Chem. Soc., 56, 2081 (1934). Bachmann and co-workers did not consider the question of whether the benzopinacols they used were dl or meso; however, it seems likely that such pinacols would arrange via long-lived carbonium ion intermediates in which the rate of interconversion of the different rotational isomers is rapid compared with the rate of aryl group migration.

[70] C. K. Ingold, Structure and Mechanism in Organic Chemistry, Cornell University Press, Ithaca, N.Y., 1953, p. 478.

[71] However, in view of the observations made by Winstein and Heck[72] relating to the interaction of the o-anisyl oxygen with a developing primary carbonium ion, it would be desirable, in the opinion of the present reviewer, to reinvestigate the pinacolic rearrangement of symmetrical 1,2-di-o--anisyldiphenyl glycol.

One does not know how far similar interactions would be significant in a case where the migration terminus is a tertiary carbonium ion; but, if they are, the o-tolyl group, in contrast to the o-anisyl group, should have a "normal" migratory aptitude. Indeed, R. F. Brown's observation[73] that ortho-substituted phenyls migrate as readily as the para in the corresponding cis- and trans-di-o(and p)-tolyl acenaphthenediols is in accord with this view. Also in agreement is the observation that when the life of the carbonium ions produced in pinacolic deaminations is long enough for various conformational isomers to equilibrate by rotation, the migratory aptitude is o-tolyl > phenyl.

[72] S. Winstein and R. Heck, quoted by S. Winstein, Experientia, Suppl. No. 2, 153 (1955).

[73] R. F. Brown, J. Am. Chem. Soc., 76, 1279 (1954).

[74] (a) P. I. Pollak and D. Y. Curtin, J. Am. Chem. Soc., 72, 961 (1950). (b) D. Y. Curtin and P. I. Pollak, J. Am. Chem. Soc., 73, 992 (1951). (c) D. Y. Curtin, E. E. Harris, and P. I. Pollak, J. Am. Chem. Soc., 73, 3453 (1951). (d) D. Y. Curtin and E. K. Meislich, J. Am. Chem. Soc., 74, 5898 (1952). (e) 5905 (1952). (f) D. Y. Curtin and M. C. Crew, J. Am. Chem. Soc., 76, 3719 (1954), (g) 77, 354 (1955).

two assymmetric centers and there exist two racemic diastereoisomeric amino alcohols which are prepared by Grignard reactions by interchanging groups between the ketone and the Grignard reagent.

By explaining such phenomena through the *cis* effect Curtin et al.[74] were able to establish the relative configurations of two asymmetric centers of the amino alcohols studied. This method has also been used by Collins *et al.* for determining *threo* and *erythro* configurations of triaryl-substituted glycols.

Curtin [74] *et al.* have demonstrated that when the amino alcohol formed by addition of a substituted-phenyl Grignard reagent to aminodeoxybenzoin (**19**)

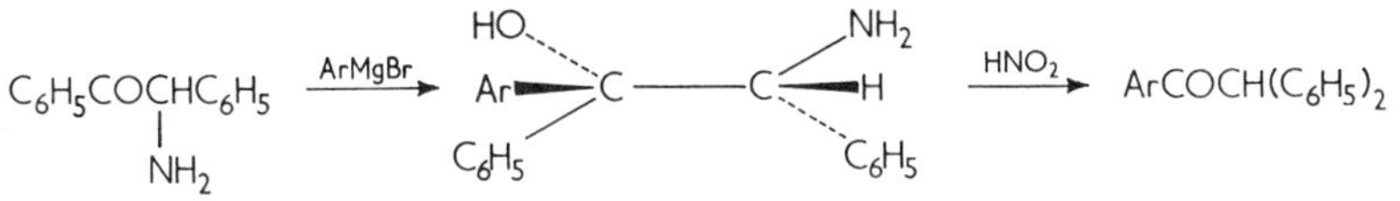

Erythro

(19)

was subjected to deamination, the predominant product was formed by migration of phenyl rather than substituted phenyl. When the mode of addition was reversed—i.e., when phenylmagnesium bromide was added to the appropriately substituted aminodeoxybenzoin (**20**) and the product subjected

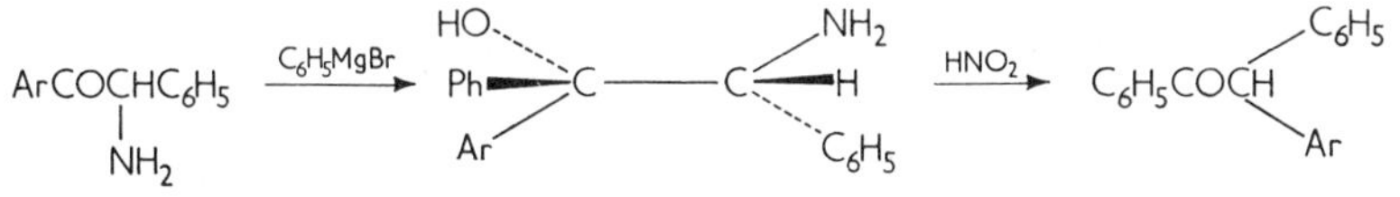

Threo

(20)

to deamination—then the predominant product was formed with migration of substituted phenyl rather than phenyl. Curtin has correlated a large number of such reactions in terms of the relative strain involved in eclipsing various groups in the transition states in question. More specifically the approaches to the transition states for migration of R_1 and R_2 involve different increments of steric strain. In the migration of R_1 (**21**), R_2 and R_4

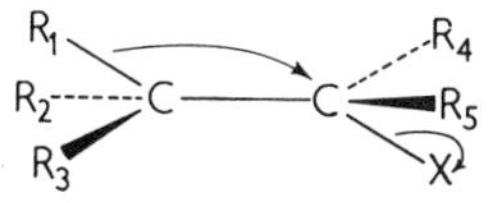

(21)

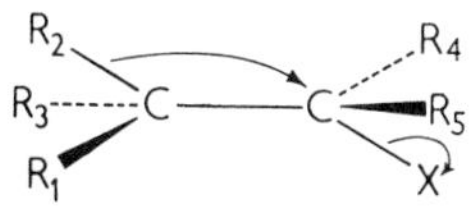

(22)

and R_3 and R_5 come into direct opposition, while in the migration of R_2 (**22**), R_1 and R_5 and R_3 and R_4 come into direct opposition. One reaction may therefore be more sterically hindered than the other.

The aryl/phenyl migration ratios in the rearrangement of 2-aryl-2-hydroxy-2-phenylethylamine and 2-aryl-2-phenylethylamine by nitrous acid are much less sensitive to the effects of substituents in Ar than are those of the acidic rearrangements of the pinacols, ArPhC(OH)—C(OH)PhAr, and the alcohols PhArCHCH$_2$OH. It follows that resonance structures of the type **23** rather than **24** make relatively large contributions to the transition states of deamination.

(23)   (24)

The tendencies of alkyl groups to migrate in pinacol rearrangements have been established [75] to be: *tert*-butyl/ethyl/methyl = > 4000 : 17 : 1.

In the rearrangement of triphenylethylene substituted glycols the ratio of phenyl to hydrogen migration varies from 7.3 to 0.04 depending on the catalyst used.[76] On the other hand, the k_H/k_D ratios as measured in undeuterated and deuterated triphenylethylene-^{2}H$_1$-glycols were about 3 and almost independent of the catalyst used. Primary isotope effects of about 3 are in the high range of isotope effects for reactions proceeding by intramolecular [77] hydride ion shifts; but otherwise they provide little or no information regarding the question of whether nonclassical hydrogen-bridged cations are intermediates in pinacolic rearrangements. Indeed, Collins and his co-workers[76] have shown that the acid-catalyzed rearrangements of 1,1,2-triphenylethylene glycol and of diphenyltolylethylene glycols are satisfactorily explained by a mechanism involving equilibration of classical carbonium ions in which no participation of neighboring substituents is required, followed by the migration of hydrogen or phenyl.

D. Steric Course

By its very nature the pinacolic transformation does not allow the stereochemistry of the carbon atom at the migration origin to be examined, and we are left with two fundamental problems: (1) What is the stereochemical consequence at the migrating group? (2) What is the stereochemical conse-

[75] M. Stiles and R. P. Mayer, *J. Am. Chem. Soc.*, **11**, 1497 (1959).

[76] C. J. Collins, *J. Am. Chem. Soc.*, **77**, 5517 (1955); B. M. Benjamin and C. J. Collins, *J. Am. Chem. Soc.*, **78**, 4329 (1956); V. F. Raaen and C. J. Collins, *J. Am. Chem. Soc.*, **80**, 1409 (1958); L. W. Kendrick, Jr., B. M. Benjamin, and C. J. Collins, *J. Am. Chem. Soc.*, **80**, 4057 (1958); C. J. Collins, W. T. Rainey, W. B. Smith, and I. A. Raye, *J. Am. Chem. Soc.*, **81**, 460 (1959); C. J. Collins and N. S. Bowman, *J. Am. Chem. Soc.*, **87**, 3614 (1959).

[77] The infrared and NMR spectra of the ketone fractions establish unambiguously the intramolecular nature of the deuterium (and hydrogen) migration.

quence at the migration terminus? The first question has not yet been answered for pinacolic transformations, but in related reactions where the migration process is likewise intramolecular, configuration is retained.[78] With respect to the second question, it has been established by Bernstein and Whitmore [82] that a net inversion of configuration occurred at the migration terminus in the pinacolic deamination of $(+)$- or of $(-)$-1,1-diphenyl-2-aminopropanol **(25)**.

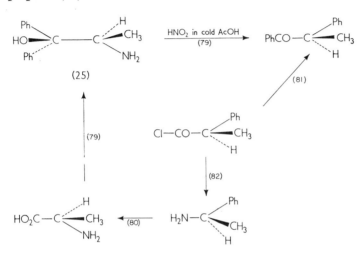

The demonstration that the migration terminus is inverted does not necessarily mean that phenyl participated in the dissociation of the diazonium ion.[67] A short-lived open carbonium ion produced by dissociation may be sterically oriented to attack the migrating phenyl group and give inversion. In deamination reaction [83] the difference in migratory aptitude of various para-substituted phenyls is relatively small compared to other carbonium-forming reactions, an observation which is consistent with the view that neighboring group participation is relatively unimportant in deamination.

[78] (a) E. S. Wallis in H. Gilman, ed., *Organic Chemistry, An Advanced Treatise*, Vol. I, Wiley, New York, 1943, ch. 12. (b) C. K. Ingold, *Structure and Mechanism in Organic Chemistry*, Cornell University Press, Ithaca, N.Y., 1953, pp. 500–3. (c) C. L. Arcus and J. Kenyon, *J. Chem. Soc. (London)*, **1939**, 916; A. Campbell and J. Kenyon, *J. Chem. Soc. (London)*, **1946**, 25. (d) J. F. Lane and E. S. Wallis, *J. Am. Chem. Soc.*, **63**, 1674 (1941); *J. Org. Chem.*, **6**, 443 (1941).

[79] A. McKenzie, R. Roger, and G. D. Wills, *J. Chem. Soc. (London)*, **1926**, 779.

[80] W. Leithe, *Ber.*, **64**, 2827 (1931).

[81] J. B. Conant and G. H. Carlson, *J. Am. Chem. Soc.*, **59**, 4048 (1932).

[82] H. I. Bernstein and F. C. Whitmore, *J. Am. Chem. Soc.*, **61**, 1324 (1939).

[83] J. G. Burr, Jr., and L. S. Ciereszko, *J. Am. Chem. Soc.*, **74**, 5426, 5431 (1952).

REARRANGEMENTS IN THE CHEMISTRY OF ALLYLIC COMPOUNDS

2

P. B. D. de la MARE
Bedford College, University of London,
London, England

CONTENTS

I. INTRODUCTION

A. Allylic Shifts

The chemistry of allylic compounds, which have the part structure **1**, has played an important part in the development of theoretical organic chemistry.

Rearrangements in these substances have been long known (cf. Ref. 1); a typical *isomeric rearrangement* is the conversion of a 1-phenylallyl ester into its 3-isomer:[2]

$$PhCH(OCOR)CH=CH_2 \rightarrow PhCH=CHCH_2OCOR \qquad (1)$$

$$\overset{|}{C}=\overset{|}{C}-\overset{|}{C}-X$$
$$(I)$$

It was first clearly recognized by Burton and Ingold[3] that such reactions may involve migration of a nucleophilic or anionic fragment from one potentially electrophilic center to another. Considered in this light, an allylic shift of the type illustrated is a *tautomeric change* involving *three-carbon anionotropy*. It should be remembered that, if we consider anionotropy to be one of the two main categories of tautomeric changes, many other types of anionotropy can be recognized;[4] some are mentioned later (Part 3).

Non-isomeric rearrangements are also common in the chemistry of these compounds. Thus, when allylic alcohols react with thionyl chloride, mixtures of isomeric chlorides are often produced; and when these chlorides are separately solvolyzed, they in turn often give mixtures of isomeric derivatives. Equation 2 gives an example;[5] the reaction involves *displacement accompanied by three-carbon anionotropic rearrangement*.

$$\underset{\overset{|}{Cl}}{Me_2CCH=CH_2} \xrightarrow[-HCl]{+MeOH} \begin{cases} Me_2C=CHCH_2OMe \\ Me_2CCH=CH_2 \\ \qquad\quad\overset{|}{OMe} \end{cases} \qquad (2)$$

The qualitative electronic theory of organic chemistry, in the form in which it is so useful today, had its origins in the literature of chemistry of the period 1920–30. The view that allylic shifts were anionotropic originated at much the same time and developed contemporaneously. It is now a commonplace that a plurality of mechanism is rather common in organic processes, and that heterolytic fission of bonds to carbon is often encountered. Allylic shifts were among the first reactions for which it was suggested specifically that *carbonium ions* may frequently play an essential role as transient intermediates. From this followed the realization that for this process, as for any process in which more than one bond is formed or broken, the timing and the sequence of the several stages may change with structure and with conditions.

[1] A. Gillet, *Bull. soc. chim., Belges*, **31**, 365 (1922).

[2] H. Burton, *J. Chem. Soc. (London)*, **1928**, 1650.

[3] H. Burton and C. K. Ingold, *J. Chem. Soc. (London)*, **1928**, 904.

[4] J. W. Baker, *Tautomerism*, Routledge, London, 1934.

[5] A. J. Ultée, *Rec. trav. chim.*, **68**, 352 (1949).

Ideas of this sort, now an accepted part of the fabric of organic chemistry, were the subject of much controversy until about 1940.[6]

A concept of even greater generality and importance is that of *mesomerism*, and in the development of this idea, three-carbon anionotropy was also concerned. A possible intermediate in an allylic transformation is an allylic cation; and for any such cation two structures (e.g., **2** and **3**) can be written.

$$CH_2\!\!=\!\!CH\overset{+}{C}H_2 \qquad \overset{+}{C}H_2CH\!\!=\!\!CH_2 \qquad [CH_2\text{----}CH\text{----}CH_2]^+$$

$$\text{(2)} \qquad\qquad\qquad \text{(3)} \qquad\qquad\qquad \text{(4)}$$

These (provided that no special geometric or electrostatic restrictions are placed on particular atoms of the system) differ only in the position of electrons. The result is electronic distribution **(4)** over the mesomeric system, and this is associated with an increase in stability as compared with that expected for either of the contributing individual structures. Many reviews of the history and theoretical justification in terms of quantum mechanics are available (see Ingold [7] and Wheland [8]).

Allylic cations are formed relatively easily, particularly under conditions conducive to ionization. The first part of this Section deals with allylic rearrangements, which can in principle (but do not necessarily) proceed as illustrated in equation 3. Some formally similar reactions are also mentioned.

$$CH_2\!\!=\!\!CHCHRX \xrightarrow[-X^-]{} [CH_2\text{----}CH\text{----}CHR]^+ \xrightarrow{+Y^-} YCH_2CH\!\!=\!\!CHR \qquad (3)$$

B. Addition to Olefinic Compounds

Allylic cations can be produced not only by heterolysis, but also by addition to dienes. Thus when hydrogen chloride reacts with butadiene to give a mixture of allylic isomers, it can be presumed that the route is that shown in equation 4.

$$CH_2\!\!=\!\!CHCH\!\!=\!\!CH_2 \xrightarrow{+H^+} [CH_3CH\text{----}CH\text{----}CH_2]^+ \xrightarrow{+Cl^-} \begin{cases} CH_3CHClCH\!\!=\!\!CH_2 \\ CH_3CH\!\!=\!\!CHCH_2Cl \end{cases} \qquad (4)$$

Burton and Ingold [3(cf. 7)] first drew attention to the interrelation between allylic rearrangements and addition of electrophilic reagents to dienes; and the latter reactions are also dealt with in this Section (page 94ff.). Discussion of these processes involves, however, some consideration of the detailed mechanism of addition reactions themselves. Some light is thrown on the nature of these processes by an important series of rearrangements which

[6] Cf. H. B. Watson, *Ann. Repts. on Progr. Chem.*, **35**, 210 (1938).

[7] C. K. Ingold, *Structure and Mechanism in Organic Chemistry*, G. Bell and Sons, London, 1953.

[8] G. W. Wheland, *Resonance in Organic Chemistry*, Wiley, New York, 1955.

may accompany substitution and addition reactions involving olefinic compounds in general, and allylic compounds in particular. Of the former type is the reaction of chlorine with isobutene to form 2-methylallyl chloride as the main product; this involves migration of the double bond (eq. 5), as has been shown by the method of isotopic labeling.[9] Of the second type is the reaction

$$Cl_2 + CH_2{=}C(CH_3)_2 \rightarrow Cl^- + ClCH_2CMe{=}CH_2 + H^+ \tag{5}$$

of hypochlorous acid with allyl bromide; this gives a considerable amount of 2-bromo-3-chloropropanol (eq. 6).[10] The opportunity has been taken,

$$ClOH + CH_2{=}CHCH_2Br \longrightarrow \begin{cases} ClCH_2CHBrCH_2OH \\ \text{Other chlorobromohydrins} \end{cases} \tag{6}$$

therefore, to review the reactions of hydrogen halides and of halogen carriers with olefinic compounds, particular attention being given to evidence for, and the rearrangements available as a consequence of, the participation of carbonium ionic intermediates in the reaction sequences.

2. ALLYLIC TRANSFORMATIONS

A. Mechanisms Available

Homolytic (S_H1). A number of mechanisms are available for allylic transformations, but not all of them have been investigated extensively. There seems little doubt that homolytic rearrangements are possible. They would be expected particularly for bromides and iodides, since the carbon-halogen bond is easily broken homolytically. Bromination of olefins by the use of N-bromosuccinimide sometimes gives a rearranged allylic bromide,[11] but this may be a reflection of the instability of the product initially formed. More pertinent is the observation[12] that the isomerization of 1-methylallyl bromide to 3-methylallyl bromide (eq. 7) can be catalyzed by peroxides; it has been suggested[13] that this is an example of the S_H mechanism. Further discussion of the scope of this mechanism is to be found in Section 7.

$$CH_2{=}CHCHMeBr \rightleftharpoons BrCH_2CH{=}CHMe \tag{7}$$

Intramolecular ($S_N i'$). Many apparently spontaneous isomeric rearrangements of allylic compounds are known (cf. eq. 1); and the possibility that they may occur intramolecularly, in a process analogous with the $S_N i$ mechanism

---

[9] W. Reeve, D. H. Chambers, and C. S. Prickett, *J. Am. Chem. Soc.*, **74**, 5369 (1952).

[10] P. B. D. de la Mare, P. G. Naylor, and D. L. H. Williams, *Chem. & Ind. (London)*, **1959**, 1020; *J. Chem. Soc. (London)*, **1962**, 443.

[11] C. Djerassi, *Chem. Revs.*, **43**, 271 (1948); H. J. Dauben, Jr., and L. L. McCoy, *J. Am. Chem. Soc.*, **81**, 5404 (1959).

[12] M. S. Kharasch, E. T. Margolis, and F. R. Mayo, *J. Org. Chem.*, **1**, 393 (1936).

[13] F. R. Mayo and C. Walling, *Chem. Revs.*, **27**, 399 (1940).

of replacement, has for many years been realized. It is often, however, experimentally difficult to obtain definite evidence for this mode of reaction. Cases will be discussed in the chemistry of halides, esters, and alcohols. The mechanism is, of course, most easily realizable when the geometry of the system will easily allow breaking of the old and formation of the new bond to proceed synchronously, and when the conditions are not particularly conducive to separation of the fragments obtained by heterolysis. These conditions do not, however, seem to be essential; a number of examples are now known in which it seems that the bond-breaking and bond-forming processes can occur successively, even in fairly ionizing solvents, although the fragments do not become kinetically free in the course of the reaction. Equation 8 formally describes such a case, of which an early example was given by Young, Winstein, and Goering.[14]

$$R—X \overset{(a)}{\rightleftharpoons} [R^+ \quad X^-] \to R'X \qquad (8)$$

The rate-determining stage (a) of such a process can have much of the character of an ionization. It is therefore facilitated by change in structure, and by change in solvent, in a manner similar to that observed for reactions which lead to fully separated fragments. It is useful, therefore, to categorize such intramolecular rearrangements as nucleophilic substitutions (S_Ni'), and to remember that the ionic character of the transition state may be subject to considerable variation.

Reactions which are appropriately considered as intramolecular allylic shifts include non-isomeric rearrangements also. Thus the conversion of alcohols to chlorides by the use of thionyl chloride can almost certainly involve an S_Ni' process, as shown in equation 9.[15,16] Processes of this sort,

$$\underset{\underset{OH}{|}}{RCHCH=CH_2} \xrightarrow[-HCl]{+SOCl_2} \underset{\underset{OSOCl}{|}}{RCHCH=CH_2} \xrightarrow[-SO_2]{} RCH=CHCH_2Cl \qquad (9)$$

in which the structure of the product is determined by the special structural features of a cyclic transition state, often provide the most convenient routes to the synthesis of the thermodynamically less stable allylic structures from derivatives of their more stable allylic isomers (cf. page 33).

Unimolecular (S_N1'). The unimolecular (S_N1) mechanism for nucleophilic replacement is now well documented for alkyl halides and related compounds; the importance of the analogous (S_N1') mode of allylic transformation was recognized at a very early stage; it has been discussed by Burton, Ingold, Hughes, and their co-workers,[2,3,7,16] and by many other writers. Equation 3 is a formulation of this mechanism in one of its simplest

[14] W. G. Young, S. Winstein, and H. L. Goering, *J. Am. Chem. Soc.*, **73**, 1958 (1951).

[15] J. D. Roberts, W. G. Young, and S. Winstein, *J. Am. Chem. Soc.*, **64**, 2157 (1942).

[16] A. G. Catchpole, E. D. Hughes, and C. K. Ingold, *J. Chem. Soc. (London)*, **1948**, 8.

forms, for the case of non-isomeric substitution with rearrangement. The more general description given in Scheme 1 includes the possibility that the

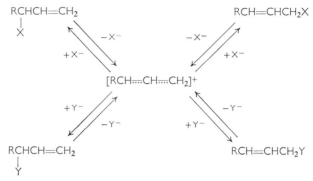

Scheme 1.   Unimolecular heterolysis of allylic compounds.

heterolysis is reversible, so that isomeric rearrangements may accompany the substitution reactions. It is clear that, even with only this one mechanism available, quite complicated experimental possibilities exist, depending on the degree of reversibility of the various ionizations.

Various lines of evidence have been adduced to support the view [14,17,18] that full description of the course of S_N1 reactions requires introduction of at least two more intermediate stages, particularly for reactions in poorly ionizing solvents. Scheme 2 shows one type of elaboration which originated

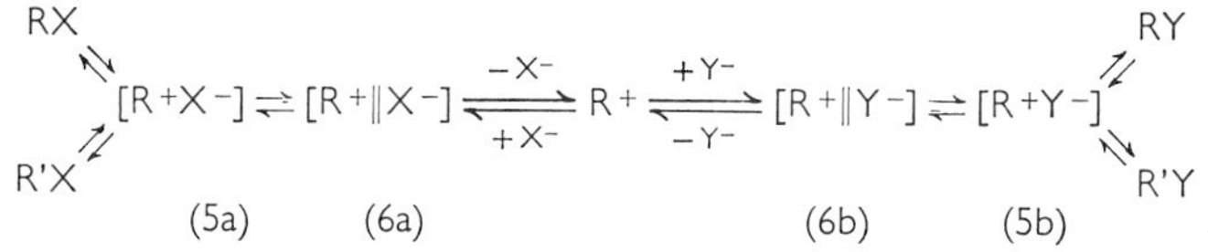

RX
R'X
$$[R^+X^-] \rightleftharpoons [R^+\|X^-] \underset{+X^-}{\overset{-X^-}{\rightleftharpoons}} R^+ \underset{-Y^-}{\overset{+Y^-}{\rightleftharpoons}} [R^+\|Y^-] \rightleftharpoons [R^+Y^-]$$
RY
R'Y
(5a)   (6a)   (6b)   (5b)

Scheme 2.   Possible details of reaction paths for unimolecular heterolysis
with subsequent substitution and rearrangement.

from work [14] on allylic shifts; it is clear that certain types of $S_N i'$ reactions are thereby included as one of the paths available for isomeric rearrangement accompanying unimolecular substitution with rearrangement. The intermediates 5 and 6 are, respectively, the "intimate" and "solvent-separated" ion pairs discussed in Section 1. Complicated reaction schemes of this sort allow description of a variety of kinetic phenomena in terms of the rate coefficients of individual steps; and they can be further expanded (e.g., by allowing the anions to react directly with the ion pairs or by including still more intermediates, such as isomeric ion pairs) to allow description of data of

[17] A. H. Fainberg and S. Winstein, *J. Am. Chem. Soc.*, **78**, 2763, 2767, 2780 (1956).

[18] E. D. Hughes, C. K. Ingold, S. F. Mok, S. Patai, and Y. Pocker, *J. Chem. Soc.* (*London*), **1957**, 1265.

any accessible complexity. It is more difficult to be certain that particular intermediates are identified uniquely by the data.

One important general feature of the reactions involving mesomeric carbonium ionic intermediates is the fact that the mixtures of isomeric products are often far removed from thermodynamic equilibrium, in the direction that they contain more than would be expected of the thermodynamically less stable isomer. Thus Meisenheimer and Link [19] showed that 3-phenylallyl chloride (cinnamyl chloride), the more thermodynamically stable member of a pair of anionotropic chlorides, on treatment with potassium acetate in acetic acid, gives a mixture of 1- and 3-phenylallyl acetates, even though after a considerably longer period in the same solvent 1-phenylallyl acetate isomerizes to the thermodynamically more stable 3-isomer. Catchpole, Hughes, and Ingold [16] have discussed the evidence that this particular case involves a unimolecular reaction and have suggested that such examples indicate a

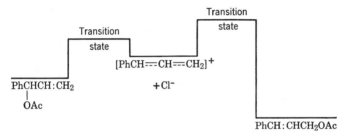

Figure 1.   Kinetic control of products in solvolysis of cinnamyl chloride in acetic acid.

situation where distinction is necessary between *kinetic control* and *thermodynamic control* in ion recombination. The type of energy diagram involved is indicated in Figure 1. Kinetic control of the isomer proportions is regulated by the top two levels, thermodynamic control by the bottom two. It seems very likely that this behavior is generally a property of the free ions themselves (and not only of ion pairs), because it persists under quite highly ionizing conditions.

Bimolecular (S_N2').   A fourth possible mechanism for three-carbon anionotropy is the analog of the S_N2 mechanism of nucleophilic replacement,

$$X^- \quad CH_2{=}CH{-}CHR{-}Y$$

(7)

namely, the process in which bond making, double-bond migration, and bond breaking are synchronous, or nearly so (7). There has been some controversy concerning priorities relating to this mechanism. The parallel between

[19] J. Meisenheimer and J. Link, *Ann.*, **479**, 221 (1930).

mechanisms S_N2 and S_N2', on the one hand, and of S_N1 and S_N1', on the other, seems to have been recognized independently at about the same time by E. D. Hughes,[20] and by S. Winstein, [21] both of whom have since been associated with prolonged [22,23] and ultimately successful efforts to obtain convincing evidence for its availability.

Inhibition of S_N2 attack, either by steric or by polar factors, seems to be desirable for the realization of non-isomeric S_N2' substitution, as in the reactions of $CH_2:CHCHBu^tCl$ and $CH_2:CHCHCl_2$, respectively.[24,25] A number of examples exist [26] where internal hydrogen bonding may assist the formation of an S_N2'-like transition state (e.g., 8).

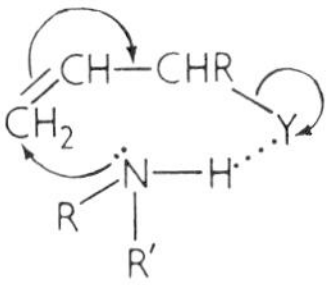

(8)

Allylic rearrangements are often also observed in bimolecular reactions involving the anions of pseudoacidic carbonyl compounds. It is often difficult,[27,28] however, to establish whether such reactions involve S_N2' attack by nucleophilic carbon or S_N2 attack by nucleophilic oxygen followed by rearrangement. The two possibilities are indicated in Scheme 3, which

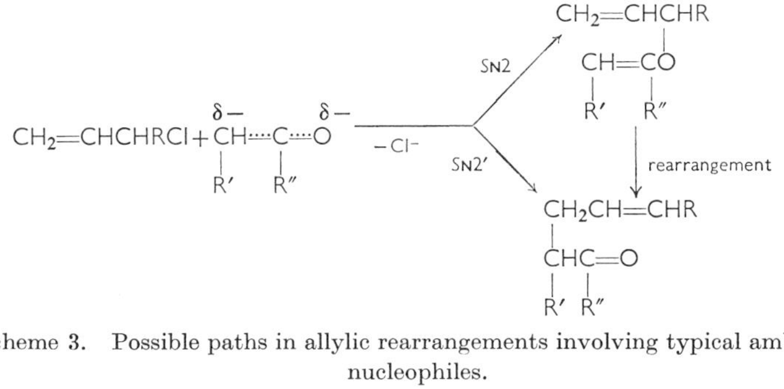

Scheme 3.   Possible paths in allylic rearrangements involving typical ambient nucleophiles.

[20] E. D. Hughes, *Trans. Faraday Soc.*, **34**, 185 (1938).

[21] S. Winstein, Dissertation, California Institute of Technology, 1938; through R. H. DeWolfe, and W. G. Young, *Chem. Revs.*, **56**, 753 (1956).

[22] B. D. England and E. D. Hughes, *Nature*, **168**, 1002 (1951).

[23] R. E. Kepner, S. Winstein, and W. G. Young, *J. Am. Chem. Soc.*, **71**, 115 (1949.)

[24] P. B. D. de la Mare, E. D. Hughes, P. C. Merriman, L. Pichat, and C. A. Vernon, *J. Chem. Soc. (London)*, **1958**, 2563.

[25] P. B. D. de la Mare and C. A. Vernon, *J. Chem. Soc. (London)*, **1952**, 3325.

[26] W. G. Young, I. D. Webb, and H. L. Goering, *J. Am. Chem. Soc.*, **73**, 1076 (1951).

[27] M. J. S. Dewar, *Bull. soc. chim. France*, **1951**, C43.

[28] S. Winstein, *Bull. soc. chim. France*, **1951**, C43.

can be applied, with appropriate modification, to attack by other ambident nucleophiles.

Other Possible Base-Catalyzed Modes of Anionotropic Rearrangement. A possible variant of the S_N2' mechanism is the non-synchronous process shown in equation 10.

$$CH_2{=}CHCHRX + Y^- \rightarrow [YCH_2CHCHRX]^- \xrightarrow[-X^-]{} YCH_2CH{=}CHR \qquad (10)$$

Yet another possibility is the addition-elimination sequence of equation 11.

$$CH_2{=}CHCHRX \xrightarrow{+Y^-} [YCH_2CHCHRX]^- \underset{-H^+}{\overset{+H^+}{\rightleftharpoons}} YCH_2CH_2CHRX \rightleftharpoons YCH_2CH{=}CHR + HX$$

$$(11)$$

Either of the base-catalyzed elimination-addition sequences given in equations 12 and 13 might also be responsible for the interconversion of

$$CH_2{=}CHCHRX \xrightarrow[-HY,\ -X^-]{+Y^-} CH_2{=}C{=}CHR \xrightarrow{+HY} YCH_2CH{=}CHR \qquad (12)$$

$$CH_2{=}CHCHRX \xrightarrow[-HY,\ -X^-]{+Y^-} CH_2{=}CHCR \xrightarrow{+HY} YCH_2CH{=}CHR \qquad (13)$$

allylic structures. Since they do not involve proton migration (only inter-mediate proton loss), and since ultimately the position of the nucleophilic fragment becomes changed, it seems more reasonable to categorize them as anionotropic than as prototropic changes.

Little is known concerning the possible scope of such sequences, although an example of a type which appears to be formally very similar to that of equation 13 and involves a methylene or carbene intermediate, is the conversion by bases of $CMe_2{:}C{:}CHCl$ to $YCMe_2C{:}CH$ (pages 88, 89). Considera-tion of these possibilities focuses attention on the conditions which, De Wolfe and Young[29] have stated, "must be met before a reaction can be classified as an example of the S_N2' mechanism," namely:

1. The rate of the reaction must be proportional to the concentration of both the substituting reagent and the compound being substituted.

2. The reaction must give isolable amounts of abnormal substitution product.

3. It must be demonstrated that neither the starting material nor the normal substitution product undergoes rearrangement under the conditions of the reaction.

Since any of the processes represented by equations 10 through 13 could fulfill all these conditions, it is clear that they are not in themselves sufficient for unambiguous classification. Nor are they all necessary (although they may sometimes be helpful). The first cannot be tested experimentally for solvolytic reactions, although one might feel impelled to include certain solvolyses in this class. The second is not entirely relevant; for one can envisage an example

[29] R. H. De Wolfe and W. G. Young, *Chem. Revs.*, **56**, 753 (1956).

in which a reaction should be classified as S_N2' because other mechanisms can be considered to be unattainable under the prevailing conditions. The third is likewise not relevant, for the fact that the normal substitution product undergoes rearrangement under the conditions of reaction has no bearing on whether or not it is ever formed in the reaction.

B. Equilibria in Allylic Systems

General Considerations. The equilibrium constant (K) between two allylic isomers depends on the free energy difference (ΔF) between the isomeric structures (eq. 14) expressed in equation 15. For qualitative and

$$\overset{|}{\underset{|}{C_1}}=\overset{|}{C_2}-\overset{|}{\underset{|}{C_3}}-X \rightleftarrows X-\overset{|}{\underset{|}{C_1}}-\overset{|}{C_2}=\overset{|}{\underset{|}{C_3}} \tag{14}$$

$$\Delta F = -RT \ln K \tag{15}$$

semiquantitative discussion, it is usually sufficiently accurate to identify ΔF with the change in heat content and to discuss the effects of substituents attached to the carbon atoms C_1, C_2, and C_3 in terms of what is known of the stabilization energies resulting from the presence of substituents adjacent to the C_1–C_2 double bond in the first isomer and to the C_2–C_3 double bond in the second isomer.

Some of the relevant facts are available from consideration of the heats of hydrogenation or of combustion of unsaturated compounds. Wheland [29a] has given a detailed account of the best values available in 1955; more recent data can be obtained from Turner's review.[30] Among the factors which will be relevant are stabilization energy resulting from conjugation, hyperconjugation, and changes in bond hybridization; energy of steric compression in sufficiently congested systems; and energy of ring strain.

Alkyl Groups. There is not much systematic experimental information concerning these equilibria. In general, substituents attached to the β position of the allylic system (C_2, eq. 14) have little effect, as would be expected, since they stabilize the double bond nearly equally in the two isomers. The equilibrium between 1-methylallyl bromide and 3-methylallyl bromide (eq. 16) was investigated in some detail by Winstein and Young.[31]. They

$$\text{MeCH(Br)CH=CH}_2 \rightleftarrows \text{MeCH=CHCH}_2\text{Br} \tag{16}$$

showed that the equilibrium proportions vary little with temperature. The free energy difference at $293°$K. is 1.1 kcal./mole, and this may be identified approximately with the increased stabilization of the double bond system by an extra alkyl group in 3-methylallyl bromide. The observed value is in

---

[29a] G. W. Wheland, *Resonance in Organic Chemistry*, Wiley, New York, 1955.

[30] R. B. Turner, "Theoretical Organic Chemistry," Butterworths, London, 1958, p. 67.

[31] S. Winstein and W. G. Young, *J. Am. Chem. Soc.*, **58**, 104 (1936).

reasonable accordance with estimates in the range 1–2 kcal./mole which would be deduced from heats of hydrogenation of simple olefins.[29a] Two alkyl groups are correspondingly more effective than one; in the system of equation 17 the amount of 1,1-dimethyl-substituted isomer at equilibrium is very small.[32]

$$Me_2CCR{=}CH_2 \rightleftharpoons Me_2C{=}CRCH_2X \tag{17}$$
$$\underset{X}{|}$$
$$\sim 100\% \text{ at equilibrium}$$
$$R = H, Me$$

Aryl Groups. Aryl groupings attached to the double bond system stabilize it by conjugation. In simple systems, the position of these equilibria indicate stabilization greater than would be estimated from the heats of hydrogenation of simple analogs. Thus the extra stabilization energy of styrene as compared with ethylbenzene [29a] is only 1.7 kcal./mole; yet the equilibrium between 1-phenylallyl and cinnamyl compounds appears to be almost entirely in the direction of the latter isomer [33,34,34a] (eq. 18);

$$PhCHCH{=}CH_2 \rightleftharpoons PhCH{=}CHCH_2X \tag{18}$$
$$\underset{X}{|}$$
$$\sim 100\% \text{ at equilibrium}$$

Spectroscopic data [34] indicate, for the system with phenyl and methyl in competition for stabilization of the double bond (eq. 19), that the equilibrium

$$PhCHCH{=}CHMe \rightleftharpoons PhCH{=}CHCHMe \tag{19}$$
$$\underset{OH}{|} \qquad\qquad \underset{OH}{|}$$
$$\sim 92\% \text{ at equilibrium (300°K)}$$

favors the phenyl group by a factor of at least 10:1. This implies a free energy difference in stabilizing power betweeen the phenyl and methyl groups of at least 1.6 kcal./mole, and hence a stabilization energy of ~ 2.7 kcal./mole provided by the phenyl substituent.

Substitution in, or change of, the aryl group does not have a very large effect on the position of equilibrium, although extension of the conjugated system does somewhat increase the stabilization energy. Thus for the system shown in equation 20 the listed values of the free energies of isomerization have been reported; [35,36] negative values imply greater stabilization by X than by Ph.

$$PhCHCH{=}CHX \rightleftharpoons PhCH{=}CHCHX \tag{20}$$
$$\underset{OH}{|} \qquad\qquad \underset{OH}{|}$$

X (eq. 20):	p-O$_2$N.C$_6$H$_4$	1–naphthyl	2-naphthyl
$-\Delta F$ (kcal./mole):	−0.12	−0.20	−0.04

[32] J. Claisen, *J. prakt. Chem.*, **105**, 65 (1922).

[33] Y. Pocker, *J. Chem. Soc. (London)*, **1958**, 4318.

[34] E. A. Braude, E. R. H. Jones, and E. S. Stern, *J. Chem. Soc. (London)*, **1946**, 396.

[34a] A. G. Catchpole, E. D. Hughes, and C. K. Ingold, *J. Chem. Soc. (London)*, **1948**, 8.

[35] E. A. Braude and E. S. Waight, *J. Chem. Soc. (London)*, **1953**, 419.

[36] E. A. Braude and P. H. Gore, *J. Chem. Soc. (London)*, **1959**, 41.

A nitro group, introduced into a position where it is conjugated through the phenyl group with the allylic double bond, provides a little additional stabilization. Both 1- and 2-naphthyl substituents are more effective than a phenyl group. The difference in this respect between the two positions of attachment is in the direction theoretically anticipated; but Braude and Gore [36] have pointed out that greater stabilization, particularly by the 1-naphthyl group, might have been expected. These authors have discussed special structural effects which might affect the influence of conjugation on the equilibrium constant. In principle at least three such special effects might be predicted.

1. The substituent X will modify [37] the hyperconjugative influence of the group CHX(OH).

2. Steric interference (illustrated in structure **9** for a naphthyl substituent) may in certain cases reduce the conjugation between an aryl group and the double bond.

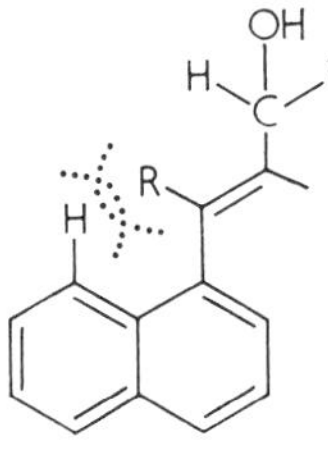

(9)

3. Steric congestion in the group to which the allylic hydroxyl substituent is attached may in some cases specifically destablize one isomer.

Little evidence helpful in the disentangling of these effects is available; the last seems to give a plausible interpretation of the abnormally great stability of the cinnamyl system (eqs. 18 and 19).

Vinyl, Ethynyl, and Carbonyl Groups. Not much is known quantitatively concerning the position of these equilibria. It is clear that double bonds tend under influence of catalysts to move into conjugation with either double or triple bonds, as is shown by the fact that the equilibria shown in equations 21 and 22 lie almost entirely to the right.[38]

[37] J. W. Baker, J. A. L. Brieux, and D. G. Saunders, *J. Chem. Soc. (London)*, **1956**, 404; cf. J. W. Baker, *Conference on Hyperconjugation*, Pergamon, London, 1959, p. 135; *Tetrahedron*, **5**, 135 (1959).

[38] E. A. Braude and E. R. H. Jones, *J. Chem. Soc. (London)*, **1944**, 436, **1946**, 122, 128; E. A. Braude, *J. Chem. Soc. (London)*, **1944**, 443, **1948**, 794; E. A. Braude and E. S. Stern, *J. Chem. Soc. (London)*, **1947**, 1096, **1948**, 1982. For a recent examination of details of this reaction, see J. M. Shackelford and L. H. Schwartzman, *J. Org. Chem.*, **27**, 1047 (1962).

The carbonyl group also supplies sufficient energy of stabilization to move a double bond from hyperconjugation with two methyl groups,[39] as is shown

$$MeCH{=}CHCHCH{=}CH_2 \underset{}{\overset{H^+}{\rightleftharpoons}} MeCHCH{=}CHCH{=}CH_2 \qquad (21)$$
$$\underset{OH}{|} \qquad\qquad\qquad \underset{OH}{|}$$

~100% at equilibrium

$$MeCH{=}CHCHC{\equiv}CH \underset{}{\overset{H^+}{\rightleftharpoons}} MeCHCH{=}CHC{\equiv}CH \qquad (22)$$
$$\underset{OH}{|} \qquad\qquad\qquad \underset{OH}{|}$$

~98% at equilibrium

by equation 23. Quantitative measurements of changes in energy have not, however, been recorded, and in the case under discussion determination of the position of equilibrium was complicated by cyclization of the product.

$$Me_2C{=}CHC(Me)COMe \rightleftharpoons HOC(Me_2)CH{=}C(Me)COMe \qquad (23)$$
$$\underset{OH}{|}$$

Alicyclic Ring Systems. In alicyclic systems the structural principles already discussed are subject to modification by consideration of ring strain and conformational preference. Normally, however, conjugation is still a dominant structural influence, and there are many examples of three-carbon anionotropy in the literature of organic synthesis. Thus the tertiary carbinol **10** was considered[40] to rearrange to the conjugated secondary carbinol **11**

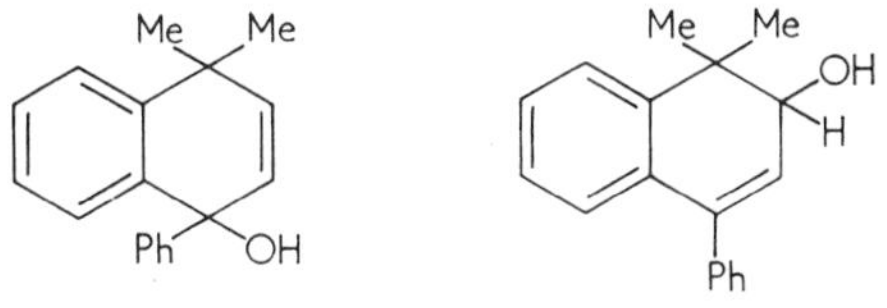

(10)   (11)

under very mild conditions, as is by no means unexpected in view of the considerable activation of the tertiary center in **10** by the three attached unsaturated groupings.

Similarly, in the cyclopentenylcarbinol **12**, and the cyclohexenyl homologs, investigated by Braude and Forbes,[41] the reactions proceeded to give substantially the conjugated isomers indicated.

[39] E. A. Braude and C. J. Timmons, *J. Chem. Soc. (London)*, **1950**, 2000, 2007, **1953**, 3131, 3138; cf. M. Julia, *Bull. soc. chim. France*, 1951, C13.

[40] N. H. Cromwell, H. H. Eby, and D. B. Capps, *J. Am. Chem. Soc.*, **73**, 1224 (1951).

[41] E. A. Braude and J. F. Coles, *J. Chem. Soc. (London)*, **1950**, 2014; E. A. Braude and W. F. Forbes, *J. Chem. Soc. (London)*, **1951**, 1755; E. A. Braude, W. F. Forbes, B. F. Gofton, R. P. Houghton, and E. S. Waight, *J. Chem. Soc. (London)*, **1957**, 4711.

Goering and co-workers [42] have investigated the equilibrium between the *cis* and *trans* isomers of 5-methylcyclohex-2-enyl hydrogen phthalate

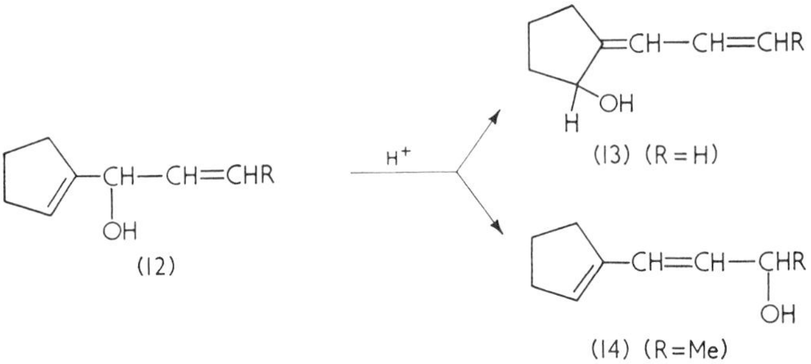

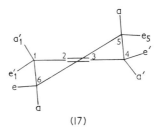

(12)

H^+

CH—CH=CHR
OH
H
(13) (R = H)

CH=CH—CHR
OH
(14) (R = Me)

(**15** and **16**). In 1,3-disubstituted cyclohexanes the *cis* isomer is generally the more stable,[43] because the bulky substituents can both lie satisfactorily in

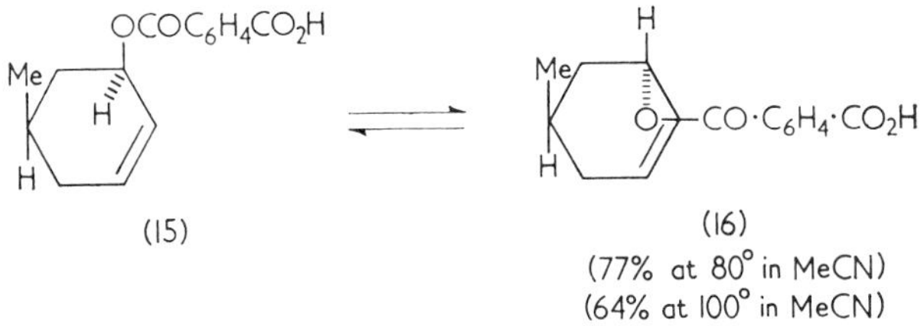

$OCOC_6H_4CO_2H$

Me
H
H
(15)

Me
O—$CO \cdot C_6H_4 \cdot CO_2H$
H
H
(16)
(77% at 80° in MeCN)
(64% at 100° in MeCN)

the strain-minimizing diequatorial conformation. In the cyclohexene system, however, it has been pointed out by Turner, Meador, and Winkler [44] that distortion of the molecule necessitated by the planar arrangement of carbon atoms 1–4 (**17**) forces the substituents on C_1 and C_4 into partial eclipse with

a
a'_1
e_5
e'
e'_1
e
a'
a
(17)

those on C_6 and C_5, respectively. It seems possible, therefore, that although the 5-methyl group may in both isomers (**15** and **16**) adopt the truly equatorial

[42] H. L. Goering, J. P. Blanchard, and E. F. Silversmith, *J. Am. Chem. Soc.*, **76**, 5409 (1954).

[43] D. H. R. Barton, *J. Chem. Soc.* (*London*), **1953**, 1027.

[44] R. B. Turner, W. E. Meador, and R. E. Winkler, *J. Am. Chem. Soc.*, **79**, 4122 (1957).

conformation, the *trans*-1-hydrogen phthalate substituent finds advantage in adopting the quasi-equatorial (e′) position, with the result that isomer **16** (in **17**, $a_1' = OCOC_6H_4CO_2H$, $e_5 = Me$) is slightly more stable than isomer **15** (in **17**, $e_1' = OCOC_6H_4CO_2H$, $e_5 = Me$). In other words, the balance between 1,2 and 1,3 interactions has been altered by making part of the system rigid.

There have been several recent discussions of the relative stability of anionotropically related compounds in which rearrangement involves migration of an endocyclic double bond to an exocyclic position or vice versa. Brown, Brewster, and Schechter [45] suggested on general grounds, and from correlations of existing experimental data over a wide field, that reactions will proceed in such a manner as to avoid the formation or retention of an *exo* double bond in a six-membered ring system. This principle appears to be soundly based, both theoretically and experimentally.[46] It undoubtedly is important in determining the position of some anionotropic equilibria, as has been pointed out by Baddeley.[47] Thus Grob and Rumpf [48] have shown that the alcohol **18** is more thermodynamically stable than **19**; the former does not rearrange, even under forcing conditions, to give a preponderating proportion of the latter, despite the fact that **18** is structurally analogous with 1,1-dimethylallyl alcohol and **19** with the 3,3 isomer. Again, Wheeler [49] has

suggested that the acid stability of perillyl alcohol [50] (**20**) is to be associated with its endocyclic double bond, whereas the lability of pulegol [51] (**21**) results

from its potential anionotropic rearrangement, which is diverted toward irreversible dehydration through the carbonium ion, as is indicated.

[45] H. C. Brown, J. H. Brewster, and H. Schechter, *J. Am. Chem. Soc.*, **76**, 467 (1954).

[46] R. B. Turner and R. H. Garner, *J. Am. Chem. Soc.*, **80**, 1424 (1958); A. C. Cope, D. Ambros, E. Ciganek, C. F. Howell, and Z. Jacura, *J. Am. Chem. Soc.*, **82**, 1750 (1960).

[47] G. Baddeley, *Ann. Repts. on Progr. Chem.*, **51**, 171 (1954).

[48] C. A. Grob and J. A. Rumpf, *Helv. Chim. Acta*, **37**, 1479 (1954).

[49] O. H. Wheeler, *Chem. & Ind.* (*London*), **1954**, 900.

[50] Y. R. Naves, *Helv. Chim. Acta*, **28**, 1220 (1945).

[51] W. J. Grubb and J. Read, *J. Chem. Soc.* (*London*), **1934**, 242; A. G. Short and J. H. Read, *J. Chem. Soc.* (*London*), **1939**, 1306.

It originally seems to have been thought that the converse relationships might apply in the five-membered ring systems,[45,49] and hence [49] that cyclopentenylmethanol (22) might rearrange to an equilibrium mixture containing a preponderance of 2-methylenecyclopentanol (23). Evidence from heats of

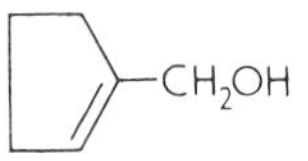

(22) 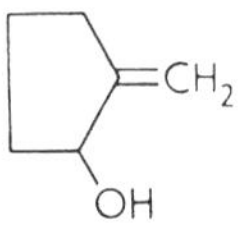   (23)

hydrogenation, however, suggests [46] that the *exo* isomer will generally be the less stable even in five-membered ring systems. There seems to be little experimental evidence relating to anionotropic pairs of this type.

The situation with rings containing more than six atoms is probably similar and, other things being equal, favors the *endo* location of the double bond.[46] Thus even the presence of the phenyl substituent is not sufficient to make the equilibrium between 24 and 25 favor the *exo* isomer exclusively.[41]

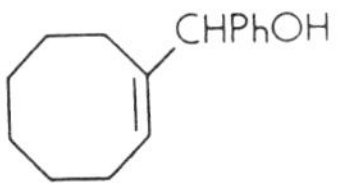

(24) 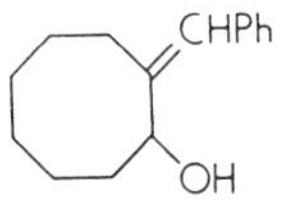   (25)

C. Allylic Halides

Unimolecular Reactions: Over-all Reactivities. The allyl cation, $[CH_2 \cdots CH \cdots CH_2]^+$, is mesomeric. Its resonance energy should be reflected in the rate of a displacement reaction on an allyl derivative to the extent to which the carbonium character is developed in the transition state. In a unimolecular (S_N1) reaction, therefore, it might be expected that allylic compounds would be considerably more reactive than the corresponding saturated compounds.

Comparison of allyl and *n*-propyl chlorides for unimolecular solvolysis in formic acid shows [52] that the former is more reactive, but only by a factor of about 25, which corresponds with a difference in free energy of activation of about 2.4 kcal./mole. The adjacent double bond system would have reduced the reactivity by its inductive effect, the quantitative influence of which is difficult to estimate. It seems likely, however, that the mesomeric influence of the allylic system in the allyl cation does not reduce the energy of activation for unimolecular solvolysis of an allylic halide by more than a few kcal./mole. It is interesting that, although theoretical calculations indicate

[52] C. A. Vernon, *J. Chem. Soc.* (*London*), **1954**, 423.

the resonance energy of the allyl cation to be about 18 kcal./mole, measurements by electron impact of the appearance potential of this ion from allyl chloride suggest that the true value may be much smaller.[53]

3-Substituents. The reactivities, under unimolecular conditions, of a number of substituted allylic halides have been surveyed by Vernon.[52] Estimates of relative reactivities, supplemented by data tabulated by De Wolfe and Young,[53a] are given in Table I. Comparison was not possible for

TABLE I

Relative Reactivities of Substituted Allylic Halides

Compound	Relative rate (k_R/k_H) of solvolysis (S_N1)	$\log_{10} k_R/k_H$	$\sum \sigma^+$
CH_2:$CHCH_2Cl$	1.0	0.0	0.00
trans-$ClCH$:$CHCH_2Cl$	3.1	0.49	0.11
cis-$ClCH$:$CHCH_2Cl$	~ 2.1	0.32	0.11
trans[a]-Bu^tCH:$CHCH_2Cl$	2.3×10^3	3.36	-0.25
trans-$MeCH$:$CHCH_2Cl$	3.6×10^3	3.56	-0.31
trans[a]-$PhCH$:$CHCH_2Cl$	$\sim 5 \times 10^5$	5.70	-0.18
Me_2C:$CHCH_2Cl$	$\sim 1.5 \times 10^7$	7.18	-0.62
$\begin{smallmatrix}Me \\ \diagdown \\ \diagup \\ Et\end{smallmatrix} C$:$CHCH_2Cl$	$\sim 1.2 \times 10^7$	7.08	-0.60
CH_2:$C(Me)CH_2Cl$	~ 0.5	—	—
CH_2:$CHCHCl_2$	65.4	—	—
CH_2:$CHCHBu^tCl$	2.5×10^3	—	—
CH_2:$CHCHMeCl$	5.7×10^3	—	—
CH_2:$CHCMe_2Cl$	$\sim 8 \times 10^7$	—	—
$MeCH$:$CHCHMeCl$	$\sim 1.5 \times 10^8$	—	—
$PhCH$:$CHCHCl_2$	$\sim 2.2 \times 10^8$	—	—

[a] The geometric configurations were not rigorously established, but almost certainly are as shown.

all compounds at the same temperature or in the same solvent, but it was considered that this does not greatly affect the situation.

Linear free energy relationships of the Hammett type[54] are used extensively nowadays to correlate structural effects in aromatic systems. Some interest[55,56] attaches to extension of such correlations to the analogous

[53] J. L. Franklin and H. E. Lumpkin, *J. Chem. Phys.*, **19**, 1073 (1951).

[53a] R. H. De Wolfe and W. G. Young, *Chem. Revs.*, **56**, 753 (1956).

[54] L. P. Hammett, *Trans. Faraday Soc.*, **34**, 156 (1938).

[55] M. Charton and H. Meislich, *J. Am. Chem. Soc.*, **80**, 5940 (1958); W. L. Orr and N. Kharasch, *J. Am. Chem. Soc.*, **78**, 1201 (1956).

[56] P. B. D. de la Mare, *J. Chem. Soc. (London)*, **1960**, 3823.

olefinic structures. In Figure 2 the logarithms of the relative reactivities of 3-substituted allyl halides are plotted against the substituent constants, σ^+ (or $\sum \sigma^+$, when two γ substituents are present). These substituent constants correlate with fair success [57] the effects of substituents on the rates of solvolysis of aryldimethylcarbinyl chlorides with those on other related reactions and on some aromatic substitutions.

Despite the considerable formal similarity between the benzyl and allyl systems, the σ^+ constants do not well predict the effects of substituents on

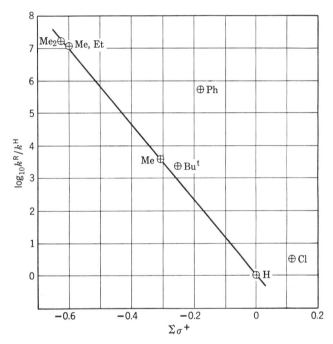

Figure 2. Hammett-type plot for $S_N 1$ solvolyses of γ-substituted allyl halides, $RR'C:CHCH_2Cl$.

rates of unimolecular solvolysis of allylic halides. A straight line can be drawn to include the alkyl-substituted compounds, and this has a very high slope ($\rho = -12$), indicating the great importance of electron release in determining reactivity. Other reactions having similarly high slopes are known; they are those (e.g., molecular chlorination and molecular bromination of aromatic compounds) in which conjugative electron release to the reaction center is of prime importance. So it is not surprising that the phenyl group is particularly effective from the 3 position in allyl chloride. The point representing its behavior lies some three logarithmic units above the line defined by the alkyl

[57] H. C. Brown and Y. Okomoto, J. Am. Chem. Soc., **80**, 4979 (1958).

substituents; a phenyl group is therefore more effective than a methyl group in facilitating reaction.

The graph shows also that this reaction is one of the few in which chlorine is electron releasing relative to hydrogen. The alkyl groups fall in the hyperconjugation order, $Me > Et > Bu^t > H$; and it is reasonable [52] to believe that a large portion of the enhanced reactivity of 3-t-butylallyl chloride is to be associated with electron release by carbon-carbon hyperconjugation.

2-Substituents. Not much systematic work has been done on unimolecular reactions of 2-substituted halides, but the effects of substituents at this position appear normally to be small. This would be expected, because such groups are not conjugated or hyperconjugated with the reaction center. Thus 2-methylallyl chloride is, in formic acid, slightly less reactive than allyl chloride, whereas methyl groups in either the 1- or the 3-position markedly accelerate the solvolysis.

1-Substituents. Generally, conjugating or hyperconjugating substituents increase the rate of unimolecular solvolysis to an extent which is rather greater in the 1- than in the 3-position. This is to be expected, for two reasons. First, the substituent is nearer to the reaction center, and so conjugation cannot be diminished in transmission through the unsaturated system. Second, the 1-substituted compounds are generally thermodynamically rather less stable; and, to the extent to which the transition state for ionization resembles the mesomeric ion (**26**) derivable from either structure, this difference in thermodynamic stability should be reflected in the rate of ionization. Rate comparisons supporting this generalization are given in Table I.

$$RCH{=}CHCH_2Cl \rightarrow [RCH\cdots CH\cdots CH_2]^+ \leftarrow RCHCH{=}CH_2$$
$$\qquad\qquad\qquad\qquad\qquad\qquad\qquad\qquad\overset{|}{Cl}$$

(26)

Cyclic Halides. The rates of unimolecular solvolysis of several analogs of 1,3-dimethylallyl chloride (**27–31**) have been compared by Goering, Nevitt, and Silversmith.[58] The open-chain compound, 1,3-dimethylallyl chloride (**30**), is only slightly more reactive than cyclohexenyl chloride (**29**) and other analogs (**27** and **28**) with six-membered rings. Cyclopentenyl chloride (**31**), on

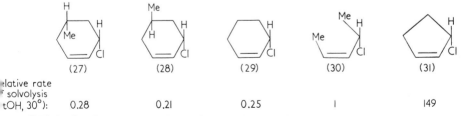

	(27)	(28)	(29)	(30)	(31)
Relative rate of solvolysis (tOH, 30°):	0.28	0.21	0.25	1	149

[58] H. L. Goering, T. D. Nevitt, and E. F. Silversmith, *J. Am. Chem. Soc.*, **77**, 5026 (1955).

the other hand, is very reactive indeed. Similar effects in saturated systems have been attributed [59] to release of initial-state nonbonding repulsions in forming the transition state.

Solvent Effects. In unimolecular reactions of halides much ionic character is developed in the transition state. So these reactions are greatly facilitated by increase in the ionizing power of the medium. In Table II are given approximate estimates [52,60,60a] of the reactivity of 3,3-dimethylallyl chloride in some common solvents.

TABLE II

Unimolecular Solvolysis of 3,3-Dimethylallyl Chloride at 25°

Solvent	Relative rate of solvolysis (r)	$Log_{10}r$	$2 + Y$
CH_3CO_2H	0.5	-0.3	0.4
EtOH	1	0	0
75% EtOH	177	2.2	2.3
50% EtOH	5100	3.7	3.6
HCO_2H	~ 8000[a]	3.9	4.1

[a] Estimated from values for 1-methylallyl chloride.

It can be seen that the logarithms of the relative rates have numerical trends similar to that shown by the function Y, which is a measure [61] of the effect of solvent on the logarithm of the rate of unimolecular solvolysis of *tert*-butyl chloride. Solvent effects on the allylic system are therefore very similar to those found for typical unimolecular solvolyses of saturated halides. The correlation is not, however, perfect: *tert*-butyl chloride is more readily solvolyzed in acetic acid than in ethanol, whereas the reverse relationship applies to 3,3-dimethylallyl chloride.

Effects of Catalysts. It is generally conceded that catalysts can promote the unimolecular reactions of aliphatic halides. Thus Oae and van der Werf [62] have recorded the relative reactivities of a number of allylic chlorides under catalysis by silver nitrate in ethanol; and Hatch and his co-workers [63] have

[59] H. C. Brown, R. S. Fletcher, and R. B. Johannesen, *J. Am. Chem. Soc.*, **73**, 212 (1951).

[60] P. B. D. de la Mare and C. A. Vernon, *J. Chem. Soc. (London)*, **1954**, 2504.

[60a] W. G. Young, S. Winstein, and H. L. Goering, *J. Am. Chem. Soc.*, **73**, 1958 (1951).

[61] E. Grunwald and S. Winstein, *J. Am. Chem. Soc.*, **70**, 846 (1948); cf. L. Wilputte-Steinert and P. J. C. Fierens, *Bull. soc. chim. Belges*, **64**, 308 (1955).

[62] S. Oae and C. A. van der Werf, *J. Am. Chem. Soc.*, **75**, 2724 (1953).

[63] L. F. Hatch, A. N. Brown, and H. P. Bailey, *J. Am. Chem. Soc.*, **72**, 3198 (1950); L. F. Hatch, L. O. Morgan, and V. L. Tweedie, *J. Am. Chem. Soc.*, **74**, 1826 (1952).

recorded a number of examples of catalysis by cuprous chloride of solvolyses in aqueous solution. The detailed mechanisms of these processes are, however, not clear. It seems likely that the metal acts as an electrophile in assisting the heterolysis of the carbon-halogen bond; but it is by no means certain to what extent the nucleophile participates covalently in the over-all transformation, which may have some characteristics of both unimolecular and bimolecular processes.

Products of Unimolecular Reactions: Product Spread.   If a free allylic cation were produced in a reaction, and if it lasted long enough to reach its equilibrium configuration before undergoing further change, both of the anionotropic isomers giving that cation should give the same ratio of products.

It is quite clear that ionizing conditions promote the formation of a mixture of rearranged and unrearranged products from allylic halides; but it is characteristic also that it is difficult to find conditions under which an anionotropically related pair of halides give exactly the same ratio of products. This phenomenon has been described by De Wolfe and Young [63a] as involving a "product spread," and many examples are tabulated in their valuable review.

It is often difficult to be certain what interpretation is to be put on such an observation. The difference is generally in the direction that one, or both, of the isomers must be supposed to give more unrearranged material than would be expected if both reactions involved the same intermediate. This would be explained if part of the reaction of one or of both isomers were a bimolecular displacement without rearrangement. Furthermore, it is necessary to be certain that the products are not allowed to rearrange under catalysis by the acid liberated. Scheme 4 illustrates a case in which these difficul-

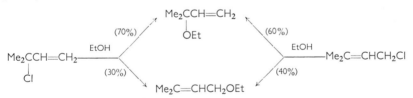

Scheme 4.   Product spread in the solvolyses of dimethylallyl chlorides.

ties have been minimized. The solvolyses of 3,3- and 1,1-dimethylallyl chlorides appear to give the same ratio of products under neutral conditions in water.[64] In the somewhat less ionizing solvent, ethanol, the solution being kept neutral during the reaction by titration with sodium ethoxide, results shown in Scheme 4 were obtained;[60] it was considered that the difference in product ratio was greater than the experimental uncertainty.

[63a] R. H. De Wolfe and W. G. Young, *Chem. Revs.*, **56**, 753 (1956).
[64] W. G. Young, unpublished experiments, through ref. 29.

A second example [65] involves the dichloropropenes (Scheme 5). Here again, evidence was presented that both the allylic isomers reacted unimolecularly

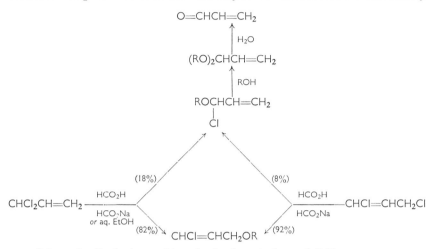

Scheme 5.   Product spread in unimolecular solvolyses of dichloropropenes.

and that the products did not rearrange under the chosen conditions. As well as illustrating "product spread" in a unimolecular reaction, these experiments describe the general behavior of allylic *gem*-dihalides, where attachment of a nucleophile at one of the possible carbonium ionic centers leads to further reaction.

The energetic differences which determine product spreads of this sort are small, but the interpretation is quite clear. Under the most ionizing conditions, with compounds which give relatively stable carbonium ions (e.g., the dimethylallyl chlorides in water), these ions reach their geometric and electronic arrangement of lowest energy before they have time to react; so the same mixture of products is found for both isomers. In less ionizing solvents (e.g., in ethanol), or when less stable carbonium ions are produced (e.g., for the dichloropropenes), the reaction with solvent follows so rapidly on the passage over the transition state that the leaving anion is near to the allylic system when reaction occurs with the solvent. Reaction then gives more of the unrearranged product than would be expected if the departing group were completely removed, for the developing charge is partly maintained electrostatically on the carbon atom which previously held the nucleophile (cf. **32**).

This phenomenon is closely related to the "shielding effect" which accounts for the incompleteness of racemization when optically active halides are

[65] P. B. D. de la Mare and C. A. Vernon, *J. Chem. Soc. (London)*, **1954**, 3679; *Research (London)*, **6**, 56S (1953).

solvolyzed by the unimolecular mechanism.[66] It should be recognized that although structure **32** represents a stage in the reaction process intermediate

$$\overset{\delta+}{R}CHCH=CH_2$$
$$\vdots$$
$$\underset{\delta-}{Cl}$$

(32)

between reactants and products (necessarily, in the case we are discussing, one which is reached after the energy maximum in the reaction coordinate has been traversed), it does not necessarily represent a reaction intermediate in the proper sense of an energy minimum in the reaction coordinate. All that is required by the experimental observations is that the further reaction can occur before what would be the final configuration of the carbonium ion has been reached. Encounter of the activated molecule with the solvent while the activated molecule is still losing energy in the reaction coordinate may allow such reaction; further evidence is required if it is desired to establish that a point of minimum energy in this coordinate has been reached when reaction occurs, and hence that two different intermediates are concerned in the reactions of the isomers.

Stereochemistry: Asymmetric centers in acyclic systems. The stereochemistry of solvolyses of optically active allylic halides has been studied by Arcus, Kenyon, and their co-workers.[67] (+) 3-Methyl-1-ethylallyl alcohol (**33**) was

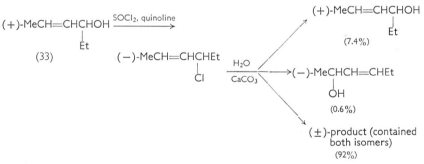

Scheme 6.   Racemization accompanying allylic transformations.

converted into its chloride, and this was hydrolyzed in the presence of calcium carbonate. The products were extensively racemized, but the un-isomerized alcohol was considered to have been formed from the chloride by

[66] E. D. Hughes, C. K. Ingold, R. J. L. Martin, and D. F. Meigh, *Nature*, **166**, 679 (1950).

[67] C. L. Arcus and J. Kenyon, *J. Chem. Soc. (London)*, **1938**, 1912; C. L. Arcus and J. W. Smith, *J. Chem. Soc. (London)*, **1939**, 1748; R. S. Airs, M. P. Balfe, and J. Kenyon, *J. Chem. Soc. (London)*, **1942**, 18.

inversion of configuration, a result which parallels that found for simple tertiary halides.[66] The small amount of activity in the rearranged alcohol was thought to be of doubtful significance.

Scheme 6 is consistent with the picture that the reaction involves the formation of a relatively stable carbonium ion which does not quite reach its equilibrium arrangement before reaction with the solvent. A "shielding effect" gives partial inversion at the center from which the anion leaves, and rearrangement is extensive, with little stereochemical preference for any particular orientation in attachment of the nucleophile at the formerly olefinic carbon atom in formation of the rearranged product.

Geometrical isomerism. The problem of geometrical isomerization accompanying unimolecular displacement reactions of acyclic chlorides is of some theoretical interest.[68] Two aspects of the situation require separate consideration. The first concerns the maintenance, or loss, of geometrical isomerism in the double bond when substitution occurs without rearrangement. Consider, for example, the hydrolysis of *cis*-3-methylallyl chloride (34; eq. 25). It would be expected, if the cation did not last long in solution,

that the product of substitution without rearrangement would, to a considerable degree, retain the geometrical configuration of the starting material. If, on the other hand, the cation had considerable life, rotation about the original double bond might become possible, and could proceed if the geometrically isomerized product were the more stable thermodynamically.

This system has recently been investigated by Young, Sharman, and Winstein.[69] They examined the products from the hydrolysis of *cis*- and *trans*-3-methylallyl chlorides and 1-methylallyl chloride with aqueous silver nitrate. The results are given in Table III. The geometric isomers of 3-methylallyl chloride both give to a good approximation the same ratio of anionotropically rearranged to nonrearranged product; and most of the 3-methylallyl product from the reaction of the *cis* isomer was not geometrically rearranged either. It was considered that most of the 8.4% of *trans* product from the *cis* chloride was formed by concomitant intramolecular rearrangement of the starting material, and that the displacement reaction had proceeded with at least 99% of retention of geometric configuration. This result accords, therefore, with the view that simple allylic carbonium ions react with nucleophiles very soon after they are formed (cf. page 49).

[68] S. Winstein, *Bull. soc. chim. France*, 1951, C43.

[69] W. G. Young, S. H. Sharman, and S. Winstein, *J. Am. Chem. Soc.*, **82**, 1376 (1960).

The second aspect concerns cases where rearrangement accompanies substitution, and two geometrically isomeric, allylically rearranged products are possible. This is the situation in the hydrolysis of α-substituted allyl

TABLE III

Products of Reactions of 3- and 1-Methylallyl Chlorides with Aqueous Silver Nitrate

	Product, %		
Starting material	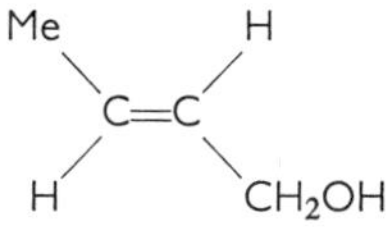 Me, H / C=C / H, CH₂OH	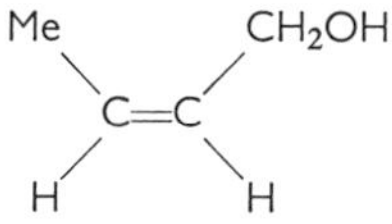 Me, CH₂OH / C=C / H, H	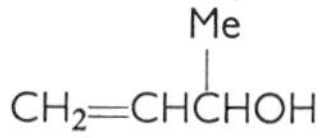 Me / CH₂=CHCHOH
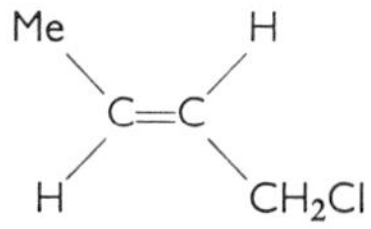 Me, H / C=C / H, CH₂Cl	48.6		51.4
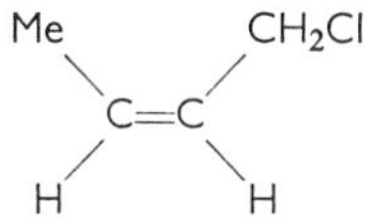 Me, CH₂Cl / C=C / H, H	8.4	42.2	49.4
CH₂=CHCHMeCl	36.0		64.0

halides. In such a case as 1-methylallyl chloride (**35** and **36**, R = Me), stereo-electronic requirements determine that the ionization will occur in either conformation **35** or **36**;[69] and it appears that conformation **36**, which keeps

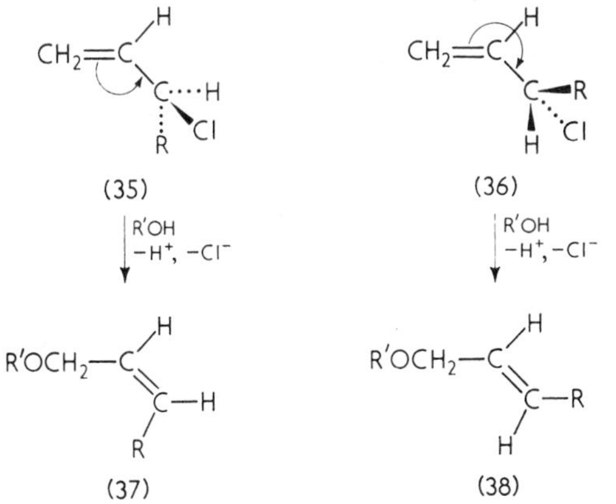

Scheme 7.   Formation of geometrical isomers accompanying allylic shifts.

the two largest substituents as far apart as possible, is, in this case, the more important. For it has been shown [69] that, in the solvolysis catalyzed by silver nitrate of 1-methylallyl chloride, *trans*-3-methylallyl alcohol preponderates in the product. Even if the cation had a long life, this conformation might still be maintained to the point that the product formed in larger amount would be the thermodynamically favored *trans* isomer, (**38**). It should be remembered, however, that the energetic differences between such *cis* and *trans* isomers are small (e.g., for *cis*- and *trans*-but-2-enes, 1.0 kcal./mole)[69a] and they may be even less in the appropriate transition states; it is likely that generally both geometrical isomers will be formed in such reactions.

Isomeric Rearrangements: Rearrangements in the Absence of Solvent. The spontaneous isomeric rearrangement of allylic halides has long been recognized preparatively. It poses a problem particularly in the experimental preparation of allylic bromides; England, for example,[70] has given an account of the difficulties associated with the preparation and storage of 1-methylallyl bromide, which rapidly rearranges to the isomer on standing (eq. 16, page 36). It seems likely that several mechanisms of rearrangement are available, one of them involving acid catalysis, for the most stable samples were those to which a little dry ammonia gas had been admitted.

The use of inorganic halides as catalysts for the rearrangement of 3-chlorobut-1-ene to 1-chlorobut-2-ene was described by Kharasch and coworkers[71] and has been applied more recently for the conversion of 3,3,3-trichloropropene and its analogs into the isomeric structures (eq. 26, R = H, Me).[72] In cases of this sort, the spontaneous or catalyzed rearrangement

$$Cl_3CCR{=}CH_2 \xrightarrow{\text{PCl}_5,\ \text{SOCl}_2,\ \text{etc.}} Cl_2C{=}CRCH_2Cl \qquad (26)$$

sometimes allows the preparative isolation of more than the equilibrium amount of the isomer of lower boiling point, since rearrangement can occur in the still-pot. That this type of reaction can result in geometric isomerization is exemplified by the demonstration [73] that the 1,3-dichlorobut-2-enes can become interconverted during fractional distillation (eq. 27).

$$(27)$$

[69a] G. W. Wheland, *Resonance in Organic Chemistry*, Wiley, New York, 1955.

[70] B. D. England, *J. Chem. Soc. (London)*, **1955**, 1615.

[71] M. S. Kharasch, J. Kritchevsky, and F. R. Mayo, *J. Org. Chem.*, **2**, 489 (1937).

[72] A. Kirrmann and R. Jacob, *Bull. soc. chim. France, Mem.*, [5], **7**, 586 (1940); D. G. Kundiger and H. N. Haney, *J. Am. Chem. Soc.*, **76**, 615 (1954); C. H. Shuford, Jr., D. L. West, and H. W. Davis, *J. Am. Chem. Soc.*, **76**, 5803 (1954).

[73] L. F. Hatch and S. S. Ballin, *J. Am. Chem. Soc.*, **71**, 1039 (1949).

Valkanas and Waight [74] have investigated in some detail the rearrangement of the rather unstable 1-phenylallyl chloride (eq. 28). The reaction in aprotic

$$CH_2=CHCHPhCl \rightleftharpoons ClCH_2CH=CHPh \qquad (28)$$

solvents (e.g., chlorobenzene) was found to be catalyzed by hydrogen chloride, as well as by carboxylic acids, the rate being approximately proportional to the strength of the acid. The possibility was discussed that a halonium ion, $CH_2:\overset{+}{CHCHPhClH}$, is formed;[cf. 75] it seems more likely that the catalysis involves hydrogen bonding between the chlorine substituent and the H—X molecules. The effect of solvent on the spontaneous rearrangement was such that the rate was more rapid the more ionizing the solvent, as is shown by Table IV. The rate bore no simple relation to the ionizing power

TABLE IV

Solvent Effect in the Isomerization of 1-Phenylallyl Chloride

Solvent	Relative rate
Chlorobenzene	~ 0.28
2-Nitropropane	0.28
Dimethylformamide	3.4
Ethanol	632
Dioxane–Water	740
Methanol	~ 3800

of the solvent as judged by Kosower's criterion,[76] namely, the energy of charge-transfer complex formation for 1-ethyl-4-methoxycarbonylpyridinium iodide; so the authors suggested the possibility that two mechanisms may be contributing differently in the different solvents. It seems more likely that the solvent effects on formation of charge-transfer complexes are not a perfect measure of the power of the solvent to assist the partial heterolysis required for attaining the transition state for rearrangement.

Rearrangements Accompanying Solvolysis: The Dimethylallyl Halides. The first demonstration of rearrangement accompanying solvolysis of an allylic chloride was made by Young, Winstein, and Goering.[76a] They examined the acetolysis of 1,1-dimethylallyl chloride and showed that the kinetics of liberation of hydrogen chloride could be interpreted only on the hypothesis that 3,3-dimethylallyl chloride was in part formed in the reaction without

[74] G. Valkanas and E. S. Waight, *Proc. Chem. Soc. (London)*, **1959**, 8; *J. Chem. Soc. (London)*, **1959**, 2720.

[75] E. A. Braude, *Quart. Revs. Chem. Soc.*, **4**, 404 (1950).

[76] E. M. Kosower, *J. Am. Chem. Soc.*, **80**, 3253 (1958).

[76a] W. G. Young, S. Winstein, and H. L. Goering, *J. Am. Chem. Soc.*, **73**, 1958 (1951).

kinetic participation of added halide ion. The transition state for such a rearrangement must be represented approximately as in structure **39**. They

showed that this rearrangement does not compete with the solvolysis as extensively in ethanol as in acetic acid, and so reached the important conclusion that the effect of solvent on the rate of rearrangement can be just as profound as its effect on the rate of solvolysis. So, contrary to some trends of thought at the time, a reaction which formally is of the $S_N i$ variety can involve development of considerable polarity in the transition state.

Many analogs for such a situation are now known. Reactions involving heterolysis or ionization in benzene[77] and other poorly ionizing solvents,[78] or even in the gas phase,[79] are well recognized. Some further observations on the dimethylallyl chlorides were made by de la Mare and Vernon.[79a] They found that, although solvolysis of 1,1-dimethylallyl chloride in ethanol is not accompanied by much formation of its allylic isomer, the corresponding reaction in aqueous (75%) ethanol is accompanied by substantial rearrangement. This reaction is somewhat catalyzed by chloride ion, and in the presence of chloride ion is accompanied by a little, but not complete, incorporation of chloride ion into the unrearranged and into the rearranged organic chloride.

Clearly, part of the reaction can be described in terms of the simple ($S_N 1$, $S_N 1'$) picture of the reaction (cf. Scheme 1, page 32) and part in terms *either* of a simple intramolecular rearrangement involving much ionic character in the transition state (e.g., **39**) *or* of an expanded scheme for unimolecular solvolysis as outlined in Scheme 2 (page 32). The latter formulation involves the postulation of discrete intermediates.

Whichever hypothesis is favored, the effect of solvent on the relative rates of solvolysis and rearrangement (Table V[76a,79a]) is puzzling. The relative rates of solvolysis are qualitatively not in accordance with the sequence of ionizing power, as measured by values of Y, which are determined by the rate of a typical unimolecular reaction, the solvolysis of *tert*-butyl chloride. In competing with the solvolysis, the intramolecular reaction is relatively

[77] E. D. Hughes, C. K. Ingold, S. F. Mok, S. Patai, and Y. Pocker, *J. Chem. Soc. (London)*, **1957**, 1220.

[78] C. G. Swain, C. B. Scott, and K. H. Lohmann, *J. Am. Chem. Soc.*, **75**, 136 (1953).

[79] A. Maccoll and P. J. Thomas, *Nature*, **176**, 392 (1955).

[79a] P. B. D. de la Mare and C. A. Vernon, *J. Chem. Soc. (London)*, **1954**, 2504.

very ineffective in ethanol and relatively very effective in acetic acid. Streitwieser [80] has proposed that this is a manifestation of the relative nucleophilicities of ethanol and acetic acid for the carbonium ion; ethanol is more

TABLE V

Rates of Solvolysis (k_T) and Rearrangement (k_i) of 1,1-Dimethylallyl Chloride at 25° in Solvents of Different Ionizing Power

Solvent	Ionizing power $(2+Y)$	$10^5 k_T$, sec.$^{-1}$	$10^5 k_i$, sec.$^{-1}$
EtOH	0	1.8	~ 0
CH_3CO_2H	0.4	1.5	4.0
75% EtOH	2.3	380	180

nucleophilic, and therefore, in this solvent, solvolysis more satisfactorily competes with rearrangement. It is difficult, however, to obtain an independent measure of the relative nucleophilicities of different solvents for carbonium ions in a way which is independent of other solvent properties. Furthermore, when applied to the comparison of ethanol and 75% ethanol, this argument implies that water is less nucleophilic than ethanol as judged by its power to compete with other processes in attacking a carbonium ion. Water and ethanol can be compared in other ways, however—for example, in terms of ability to compete for the *tert*-butyl carbonium ion, results [81] of which are given in Table VI.

TABLE VI

Product Composition in the Solvolysis of *tert*-Butyl Bromide

Solvent, mole % EtOH	Bu^tOEt, % $(100[Bu^tOEt]/[Bu^tOEt]+[Bu^tOH])$
73.6	53
55.3	33
31.7	18

Less of the ethyl ether is produced than would be expected from the molar proportion of ethanol in the solvent, and this suggests that in the same solvent water is more (not less) effective than ethanol. In the writer's opinion, therefore, the results given in Table V are not explicable in the simple terms

[80] A. Streitwieser, Jr., *Chem. Revs.*, **56**, 571 (1956).
[81] L. C. Bateman, E. D. Hughes, and C. K. Ingold, *J. Chem. Soc.* (*London*), **1938**, 881; M. L. Bird, E. D. Hughes, and C. K. Ingold, *J. Chem. Soc.* (*London*), **1943**, 255.

proposed by Streitwieser,[80] and so do not differentiate between the mechanistic possibilities already mentioned.

The 5-Methylcyclohex-2-enyl Chlorides.   Examination of the kinetics and stereochemistry of rearrangements in cyclic systems can have some special advantages, in that the more rigid geometry permits examination of the degree of movement available to the migrating nucleophile.

Four isomers (two racemic modifications) of 5-methylcyclohex-2-enyl chloride are possible: the enantiomorphic forms (**40** and **42**) of the *cis*, and those (**41** and **43**) of the *trans*, isomer. Because of the symmetry of the system, if the migrating group remains on the same side of the ring, the only structural change accompanying anionotropic rearrangement is the conversion of one enantiomorph into the other (**40** ⇌ **42** or **41** ⇌ **43**). If, on the

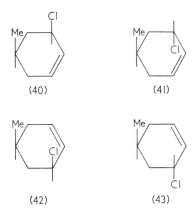

(40)   (41)

(42)   (43)

other hand, the migrating group becomes free enough to recombine with the opposite side of the ring, geometric isomerization (e.g., **40** → **41** and **43**) will be associated with the anionotropic rearrangement.

The reaction was studied [81a] in ethanol and in acetic acid. In both solvents, the rate of disappearance of optical activity was somewhat greater than that of the total solvolysis as measured titrimetrically. The solvolysis was shown to be of the S_N1 type, and the greater polarimetric rate was attributable to "internal return," i.e., to the S_Ni' reaction in the sense in which that term is used in this article. Ethanolysis of the isomeric chlorides gave mixtures of *cis*- and *trans*-5-methylcyclohex-2-enyl ethyl ethers of the same composition, and acetolysis of the isomeric chlorides gave mixtures of the corresponding acetates of the same composition. The authors interpreted the results in terms of Scheme 8.

[81a] H. L. Goering, T. B. Nevitt, and E. F. Silversmith, *J. Am. Chem. Soc.*, **77**, 5026 (1955).

Since in each solvent the products are stable under the conditions of the reaction, it seems that a common intermediate (e.g., **46**) is concerned and that

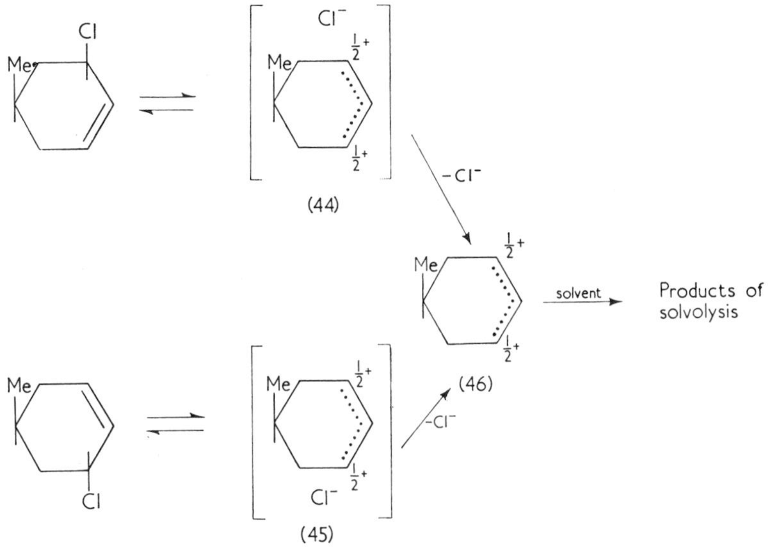

Scheme 8.   Solvolysis of 5-methyl-2-cyclohexenyl chlorides.

the formation of this intermediate is effectively irreversible, since much of the solvolysis product, but none of the starting material, was geometrically isomerized during the reaction. As in the case of 1,1-dimethylallyl chloride, the solvent effect on the proportion of internal return to solvolysis did not admit of simple interpretation. Although it is intuitively reasonable to propose that ion-pair intermediates (e.g., **44** and **45**) concerned in the rearrangement are also stages on the way to the solvolysis intermediate (**46**), it does not seem to the writer that there is compelling evidence for this view.

Bimolecular (S_N2') *Rearrangements.*   Bimolecular isomeric rearrangements involve attack on the allylic halide by an anion of the same nature as that already present in the molecule. Only one such case has been investigated thoroughly, namely, that of equation 29; [70,81b] but this study provided funda-

$$CH_2\!=\!CHCHMeBr + Br^- \rightleftharpoons BrCH_2CH\!=\!CHMe + Br^- \tag{29}$$

mental information which facilitated search for examples of bimolecular non-isomeric rearrangements.

Table VII gives rate coefficients and Arrhenius parameters for S_N2 and S_N2' reactions of 1- and 3-methylallyl bromides with bromide ion in acetone. The S_N2 substitution of 1-methylallyl bromide is 60 times faster than the

[81b] B. D. England and E. D. Hughes, *Nature*, **168**, 1002 (1951).

corresponding S_N2' rearrangement at 25°, and this difference arises largely from the difference of 3 kcal./mole in activation energy. Such a difference is large enough to make it difficult to detect products of rearrangement in non-isomeric nucleophilic substitutions; for isomeric rearrangements, however, the S_N2 process regenerates starting material, so the rearrangement is accessible for study. The corresponding ratio of rates in 3-methylallyl bromide is much greater, since the S_N2, but not the S_N2', process is facilitated by the hyperconjugating methyl groups.

TABLE VII

Rates (k_2) and Arrhenius Parameters (E, $\log_{10} A$) for Exchange and Rearrangement of 1- and 3-Methylallyl Bromides with Bromide Ion in Acetone

Compound	Mechanism	$10^6 \, k_2(25°)$, liter mole^{-1} sec.$^{-1}$	E, kcal. mole^{-1}	$\log_{10} A$, liter mole^{-1} sec.$^{-1}$
1-Methylallyl bromide	S_N2	879	16.5	9.06
1-Methylallyl bromide	S_N2'	14.9	19.4	9.40
3-Methylallyl bromide	S_N2	141,000	14.7	9.93
3-Methylallyl bromide	S_N2'	5	~ 19	~ 9

Catalysis by chloride ions in the rearrangement of 1-phenylallyl chloride has been established,[74] and may be of the S_N2' type. It is possible that some of the rearrangements discussed in the previous section, involving catalysis of the rearrangement of chlorides by inorganic chlorides or by hydrogen chloride, also proceed by this mechanism.

Bimolecular Reactions: Over-all Reactivities.   Many workers have studied aspects of the effect of structure on the rates of bimolecular displacement reactions on allylic halides. Conant and his co-workers[82] noted that allyl chloride is more reactive than n-propyl or n-butyl chloride in the Finkelstein reaction (eq. 30). Others, including Hatch and his co-workers,[83] have extended

$$RCl + KI \xrightarrow{\text{acetone}} RI + KCl \qquad (30)$$

this conclusion to reactions with other anions and have studied a wide variety of allylic halides.

With many simple allylic halides (indeed, with most allylic halides containing no 1-substituent), bimolecular displacement proceeds essentially without rearrangement.[83a,83b] It may be noted also that no more than traces of products of bimolecular elimination, be they 1,2- or 1,3-dienes, are found

[82] J. B. Conant, W. R. Kirner, and R. E. Hussey, *J. Am. Chem. Soc.*, **47**, 488 (1925).

[83] L. F. Hatch and P. R. Noyes, *J. Am. Chem. Soc.*, **79**, 345 (1957), and earlier papers in this series.

[83a] J. D. Roberts, W. G. Young, and S. Winstein, *J. Am. Chem. Soc.*, **64**, 2157 (1942).

[83b] A. G. Catchpole, E. D. Hughes, and C. K. Ingold, *J. Chem. Soc. (London)*, **1948**, 8.

when these reactions are carried out in the temperature range at which they can conveniently be studied kinetically (e.g., 25–100°C.).[84]

TABLE VIII

Relative Rates of Bimolecular Substitutions of Allyl and Alkyl Halides with Ethoxide Ions at 44.6°

Compound	Relative rate	Compound	Relative rate
CH_2:$CHCH_2Cl$	1.00	$CH_3CH_2CH_2Cl$	0.027
CH_2:$C(Me)CH_2Cl$	0.89	$CH_3CHMeCH_2Cl$	0.0024
$ClCH$:$CHCH_2Cl$	2.60	$MeCH_2CH_2CH_2Cl$	0.0265
$MeCH$:$CHCH_2Cl$	2.62	$MeCH_2CHMeCl$	0.0019
Bu^tCH:$CHCH_2Cl$	1.96	CH_2:$CHCHMeCl$	~ 0.049
$PhCH$:$CHCH_2Cl$	6.83		
Me_2C:$CHCH_2Cl$	15.0		

Table VIII gives some illustrative rate comparisons.[84,84a]

3-Substituents. The most striking feature of Table VIII is the demonstration that substituents in the 3-position have an effect on reactivity which,

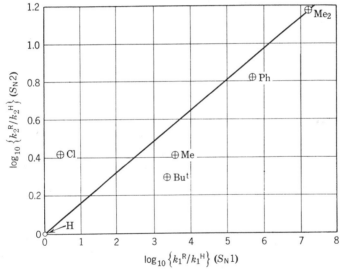

Figure 3. Relation between structural effects for uni- and bimolecular reactions of γ-substituted allyl halides, RR′C:$CHCH_2Cl$.

though not as large as is observed in the corresponding unimolecular solvolyses, is qualitatively in close accordance. Quantitative comparison is given in Figure 3; the logarithms of the relative rates for the two reactions show

[84] C. A. Vernon, *J. Chem. Soc.* (*London*), **1954**, 4462.

[84a] P. B. D. de la Mare and C. A. Vernon, *J. Chem. Soc.* (*London*), **1954**, 3679; *Research* (*London*), **6**, 56S (1953).

only a poor approximation to a linear plot. However, it is noteworthy that the chlorine substituent has a small accelerative effect on both reactions, that in both cases the alkyl groups fall in the hyperconjugation order $Me > Bu^t > H$, and that in both cases a phenyl group is notably more effective than a single alkyl group. Since conjugative effects are important in contributing to the reactivity by the unimolecular process, they must be playing a major role also in determining the relative reactivity with nucleophiles. This result can be rationalized [84,84a] by pointing out that the transition state for the bimolecular reaction of an allylic halide can be represented as a hybrid structure in which one contributing form is **47**. Another structure, for which no important

(47)   (48)   (49)

analog is available in saturated systems, is **48**; its contribution no doubt determines in part that allyl chloride is more reactive than n-propyl chloride. Yet another is **49**, and its importance determines that conjugating or hyperconjugating substituents in the γ position have an accelerative effect on the reaction.

This theory emphasizes the point made particularly by Hughes [85] and by Ingold [85a] that such bimolecular reactions have opposed electronic requirements; the bond-forming process is facilitated by electron withdrawal, and the bond-breaking process is facilitated by electron release. Different systems will be expected to vary in the relative contributions of these factors; in allylic compounds the bond-breaking process is dominant.

2-Substituents. Much of the work on 2-substituted allylic halides has been done by Hatch and his co-workers.[85] Thus Hatch and Patton [86] examined the reactions of $CH_2 : C(Y)CH_2Cl$ with potassium iodide and acetone, and with sodium ethoxide in ethanol. The maximum rate factor was no more than 2.5, and the observed sequence was $Y = Ph > Me > H > Br > Cl$. Some not very large anomalies were observed in reactions of β-substituted polyhalides; the data have been summarized by De Wolfe and Young [86a] and are not discussed further here, since it is not quite clear that in all cases the only reaction under observation was of the S_N2 type.

[85] E. D. Hughes, *Trans. Faraday Soc.*, **37**, 603 (1941).

[85a] C. K. Ingold, *Structure and Mechanism in Organic Chemistry*, G. Bell and Sons, London, 1953.

[86] L. F. Hatch and T. L. Patton, *J. Am. Chem. Soc.*, **76**, 2705 (1954).

[86a] R. H. De Wolfe and W. G. Young, *Chem. Revs.*, **56**, 753 (1956).

1-Substituents. By contrast with unimolecular reactions, where 1- and 3-alkyl substituents have much the same accelerating effect on reactivity, bimolecular processes are much retarded by 1-alkyl groups (cf. Table VIII). The steric effects of these substituents are clearly just as important in allyl systems as in the corresponding saturated ones, and this has the result that it is relatively easier to achieve purely unimolecular substitutions in 1- than in 3-substituted allylic halides.

A similar retardation is found for 1-chlorine substituents, as is consistent with the fact [cf. 87] that *gem*-dihalides are much more reluctant to undergo bimolecular substitution than are the corresponding monohalides.

Solvent Effects. Bimolecular reactions between alkyl halides and negative ions are slightly retarded in rate by an increase in the polarity of the solvent. Allylic chlorides, however, frequently behave differently; for example, change of solvent from ethanol to 50% ethanol slightly increases the bimolecular reactivity of allyl and 2-methylallyl chloride. Exceptions to this are known, e.g., for *trans* (but not for *cis*)-1,3-dichloropropene. But it seems that, as compared with alkyl halides, polar structures (e.g., **49**) are generally more important in the transition states for bimolecular reactions of alkyl halides and that the increase in rate with increase in ionizing power of the solvent is to be associated with an important contribution of solvation to the stability of the transition state.[84a]

Variation of the Displaced Group and of the Nucleophile. In these respects, the reactivities of allylic halides qualitatively parallel those of the corresponding saturated compounds. Thus for symmetrical exchanges,[88-92] as well as for reactions with other nucleophiles,[88,93] the sequence of reactivity of RX, viz., $X = Cl < Br < I$, seems well established both for allylic and nonallylic structures. Some detailed comparisons are given in Table IX (page 64).

Work on variation of the nucleophile is rather desultory as applied to allylic compounds, but it seems that the situation for the S_N2 reactions of

[87] P. B. D. de la Mare and E. D. Hughes, *J. Chem. Soc. (London)*, **1956**, 845.

[88] B. D. England and E. D. Hughes, unpublished work; cf. refs. 22 and 70; P. B. D. de la Mare, L. Fowden, E. D. Hughes, C. K. Ingold, and J. D. H. Mackie, *J. Chem. Soc. (London)*, **1955**, 3200.

[89] V. B. Miller, M. B. Neiman, and Y. M. Shapovalov, *Doklady Akad. Nauk S.S.S.R.*, **75**, 419 (1950); M. B. Neiman, and Y. M. Shapovalov, *Doklady Akad. Nauk S.S.S.R.*, **77**, 423 (1951); M. B. Neiman, G. V. Maksimova, and Y. M. Shapovalov, *Doklady Akad. Nauk S.S.S.R.*, **85**, 1289 (1952).

[90] S. May, P. Daudel, J. Schottey, M. Sarraf, and A. Vobaure, *J. chim. phys.*, **49**, 64 (1952).

[91] H. Seelig and D. E. Hull, *J. Am. Chem. Soc.*, **64**, 940 (1942).

[92] A. Juvala, *Ber.*, **63**, 1989 (1930).

[93] F. G. Bordwell, R. Ross, and J. Weinstock, *J. Am. Chem. Soc.*, **82**, 2878 (1960); F. G. Bordwell, P. E. Sokol, and J. D. Spainhour, *J. Am. Chem. Soc.*, **82**, 2881 (1960).

saturated halides is paralleled for the corresponding reactions of their allylic analogs. Thus in ethanol and aqueous ethanol OH^-, OEt^-, and OPh^- react at rather similar rates with representative allylic halides, whereas the SPh^- ion reacts very much more rapidly (by a factor of more than 10^2).[84,94,95,95a] It is interesting also to note the considerable nucleophilic power of the diethyl malonate ion, $\overline{C}H(CO_2Et)_2$; Kepner, Winstein, and Young[95b] showed that the rate of the S_N2 reaction of this ion with 1-ethylallyl chloride at $50°$ in ethanol was $ca.$ 9×10^{-5} liter mole^{-1} sec.$^{-1}$; with ethoxide ions under the same conditions, 1-methylallyl chloride reacts about five times more slowly,[84] despite the smaller degree of steric congestion in the transition state for the latter reaction.

Products of Bimolecular Reactions: Structures Favorable for S_N2' Reactions. The commonest bimolecular reactions in allylic systems contrast with the corresponding unimolecular processes in that they usually give one single product, that of substitution without rearrangement (S_N2). The main developments which led to appreciation of the range of validity of the corresponding rearrangement (S_N2') followed England and Hughes' experiments[70,81b] (summarized in Table VII). These showed that in 3-methylallyl bromide the S_N2 process was favored as compared with the reaction involving rearrangement by at least four powers of ten, whereas in 1-methylallyl bromide the direct substitution was favored by a factor of only about fifty.

As a result, it became clear that 3- and 2-substituted allylic primary halides would be unlikely to reveal S_N2' processes through the products of their reactions with anions. De Wolfe and Young's review[86a] gives documentation of this for a number of systems of the type $RR'C\!:\!CR''CH_2Cl$. The substituents R, R', and R'' can be alkyl, aryl, or halogeno groups, and it is also known[96] that 3-carbethoxyallyl halides react with nucleophiles without initial anionotropic rearrangement (although prototropic changes here often follow the replacement of halide ion).

Substituents in the 1-position can, however, profoundly modify the reactivity of the 1-chlorine atom; it might be supposed that they would not so greatly influence the ease of attack by a nucleophile on the more remote C_3 atom. Groups having steric effects substantially greater than that of hydrogen would be expected to behave in this way, and this is borne out by

[94] P. B. D. de la Mare and C. A. Vernon, *J. Chem. Soc.* (*London*), **1952**, 3331.

[95] O. R. Quayle and E. E. Royals, *J. Am. Chem. Soc.*, **64**, 226 (1942).

[95a] P. B. D. de la Mare and C. A. Vernon, *J. Chem. Soc.* (*London*), **1952**, 3325.

[95b] R. E. Kepner, S. Winstein, and W. G. Young, *J. Am. Chem. Soc.*, **71**, 115 (1949).

[96] L. Canonica, A. Fiecchi, and M. Adobbati, *Rend. ist. lombardo sci.*, *Pt. I*, **87**, 257 (1954); through *Chem. Abstr.*, **50**, 6376 (1956); V. P. Mamaev, N. N. Suvorov, and V. I. Gunar, *Zhur. Obshchei Khim.*, **23**, 1206 (1953); V. P. Mamaev and N. N. Suvorov, *Zhur. Obshchei Khim.*, **26**, 538 (1956); L. Birkofer and I. Hartung, *Chem. Ber.*, **87**, 1189 (1954).

experiment. It has been shown that 1-*tert*-butylallyl chloride [96a] and 1,1-dimethylallyl chloride [97] can both be made to undergo bimolecular substitution to give substantially entirely the rearranged product (eqs. 31 and 32). In both cases the steric effects would be predicted by theory [88] to inhibit sufficiently the formation of the product of direct substitution.

$$CH_2{=}CHCHBu^tCl \xrightarrow[-Cl^-]{+EtO^-} EtOCH_2CH{=}CHBu^t \tag{31}$$

$$CH_2{=}CHCMe_2Cl \xrightarrow[-Cl^-]{+PhS^-} PhSCH_2CH{=}CMe_2 \tag{32}$$

Polar effects can be combined with steric effects to produce qualitatively the same result. Thus 3,3-dichloropropene (eq. 33) gives, with either sodium

$$CH_2{=}CHCHCl_2 \underset{EtOH}{\overset{EtO^-}{\xrightarrow{\hspace{1cm}}}} \begin{cases} EtOCH_2CH{=}CHCl \\ CH_2{=}CHCH(OEt)_2 \end{cases} \tag{33}$$

ethoxide or sodium thiophenoxide, roughly equal amounts of S_N2 and S_N2' products.[95a] Likewise, 3,3,3-trichloro-2-methylpropene with sodium thiophenoxide gives mainly the product of substitution with rearrangement (eq. 34).[98] Similarly, a number of polyfluorochlorides have been shown preparatively to react with halide ions with rearrangement (cf. eq. 35).[99]

$$CH_2{=}C(Me)CCl_3 \xrightarrow[-Cl^-]{+PhS^-} PhSCH_2C(Me){=}CCl_2 \tag{34}$$

$$CF_2{=}CHCFCl_2 \xrightarrow[-Cl^-]{+F^-} CF_3CH{=}CFCl \tag{35}$$

For such reactions as have been studied in ethanol, using ethoxide or thiophenoxide ion as the nucleophile, estimates can be made of the reactivity of different structures by the S_N2' path. They fall in the sequence $CH_2:CHCMe_2Cl > CH_2:CMeCCl_3 > CH_2:CHCHCl_2 > CH_2:CHCHBu^tCl$. The first three compounds have been compared for reaction with SPh^-; the last two only for reaction with OEt^-. Two opposing polar effects of substituents can be seen in these reactions, just as they can be seen in the reactivities for bimolecular substitution without rearrangement (cf. page 60). The relatively greater reactivity of 1,1-dimethylallyl chloride shows that the electron-releasing effect of alkyl groups can facilitate the bond-breaking process

[96a] P. B. D. de la Mare, E. D. Hughes, P. C. Merriman, L. Pichat, and C. A. Vernon, *J. Chem. Soc.* (*London*)), **1958**, 2563.

[97] P. B. D. de la Mare and C. A. Vernon, *J. Chem. Soc.* (*London*), **1953**, 3555.

[98] P. B. D. de la Mare and C. A. Vernon, *J. Chem. Soc.* (*London*), **1952**, 3628; D. G. Kundiger and G. F. Morris, *J. Am. Chem. Soc.*, **80**, 5988 (1958).

[99] J. H. Fried and W. T. Miller, Jr., *J. Am. Chem. Soc.*, **81**, 2078 (1959); W. T. Miller, Jr., J. H. Fried and H. Goldwhite, *J. Am. Chem. Soc.*, **82**, 3091 (1960).

sufficiently to increase the reactivity. The relatively small reactivity of 1-*tert*-butylallyl chloride relative to that of 3,3-dichloropropene suggests that when the C—Cl bond is not intrinsically very reactive, an electron-withdrawing effect is favorable, and an electron-releasing effect inhibitory, to reaction at the olefinic carbon atom. This accords with the idea [100] that inductive electron withdrawal may polarize the unsaturation electrons so as to make more easy the attachment of a nucleophile at the more remote carbon atom.

Bordwell and his co-workers [93] have recently used this theory to interpret the relative rates of bimolecular substitutions activated by the sulfone group. Compounds of type **50** (X = Cl, Br, I) react with thiophenoxide ion by S_N2 processes without rearrangement, but the related structures (**51**) undergo

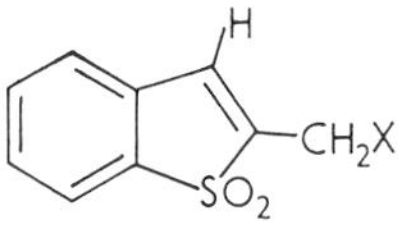

(50)   (5l)

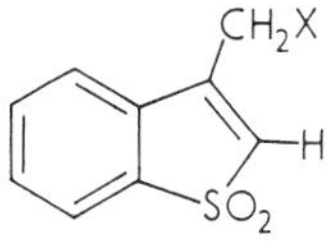

displacement with rearrangement. These cases are among the very few known of S_N2' reactions at a substituted olefinic center, and it was suggested [93] that the sulfone group by its electron-withdrawing effect makes more easy the attack by the nucleophile at the unsaturated carbon atom.

Relative rates are given in Table IX. The spread of reactivities with change in the displaced group is similar for all three types of compound, namely,

TABLE IX

Relative Rates of Bimolecular Displacements with Sodium Thiophenoxide in Ethanol

Compound	Reaction Mechanism	Relative rate (25°), X = Br	Relative rate (X = Cl taken as 1)		
			X = Cl	X = Br	X = I
MeCH$_2$CH$_2$X	S_N2	1	1	128	556
CH$_2$:CHCH$_2$X	S_N2	137	1	62	183
PhSO$_2$CH:CHCH$_2$X	S_N2	507	1	82	312
50	S_N2	295	1	28	75
51	S_N2'	790	1	79	230

saturated halides, allylic halides undergoing direct displacement, and allylic halides undergoing displacement with rearrangement. It was suggested [93] that this provides evidence that the S_N2' process is synchronous in character (cf. page 35), or at least as nearly synchronous as is the S_N2 reaction. A more critical test would have involved inclusion of allylic fluorides in the comparison.

[100] E. D. Hughes and C. K. Ingold, *J. chim. phys.*, **45**, 241 (1948).

Effect of Change in the Nucleophile. Various reports in the early litera-ture [cf. 86a] suggested that neutral nucleophiles might participate in S_N2' reactions more readily than anionic nucleophiles. Young, Clement, and Shih [101] showed that 1-methylallyl chloride reacts with trimethylamine in acetone, by a second-order process, to give as stable products a mixture of the unrearranged ($k_2 = 0.0092$ liter mole^{-1} sec.$^{-1}$ at 40.1° in acetone) and re-arranged ($k_2 = 0.0196$ liter mole^{-1} sec.$^{-1}$) materials (eq. 36). This reaction

$$CH_2{=}CHCHMeCl \xrightarrow{\,+NMe_3\,} \begin{array}{l} CH_2{=}CHCH(Me)NMe_3{}^+Cl^- \\ \text{(32\%)} \\[6pt] Me_3N^+CH_2CH{=}CHMe\ Cl^- \\ \text{(trans, 62\%)} \\ \text{(cis, 6\%)} \end{array} \qquad (36)$$

is much more rapid than the corresponding reaction with chloride ion ($k_2 = 1.8 \times 10^{-6}$ liter mole^{-1} sec.$^{-1}$ at 44.6°).[84,88] Since in the latter case the S_N2' process is probably some fifty times less rapid, the change from halide ion to trimethylamine as a nucleophile has here given the S_N2' process an advantage in rate relative to the S_N2 reaction by a factor of the order of 10^2.

Secondary amines with 1-methylallyl chloride give still more of the re-arranged product (eq. 37). It was suggested [81b,85a,95b,101a] that here the

$$CH_2{=}CHCHMeCl \xrightarrow[{-Cl^-}]{+Et_2NH} Et_2NCH_2CH{=}CHMe \qquad (37)$$
$$\text{(82\%)}$$

S_N2' process is assisted by hydrogen bonding between the amine and the chloride atom of the halide (52). Since it has been shown [102] that this process

(52)

is not changed in rate by using N-deuteroamines instead of their proto analogs, the N—H bond cannot be much stretched in the transition state. Bell, Madroñero, and Whiting [103] have described a rearrangement (eq. 38)

$$trans\text{-}MeCH(Cl)CH{=}CHC{\equiv}CH \xrightarrow[{-HCl}]{+Et_2NH} MeCH{=}CHCHC{\equiv}CH \qquad (38)$$
$$\underset{\textstyle NEt_2}{|}$$

which they consider also to be of the S_N2' type; the ratio of the competing processes was found to be very dependent on the nucleophile and on the

[101] W. G. Young, R. A. Clement, and C. H. Shih, *J. Am. Chem. Soc.*, **77**, 3061 (1955).
[101a] W. G. Young, I. D. Webb, and H. L. Goering, *J. Am. Chem. Soc.*, **73**, 1076 (1951).
[102] D. C. Dittmer and A. F. Marcantonio, *Chem. & Ind. (London)*, **1960**, 1237.
[103] I. Bell, R. Madroñero, and M. C. Whiting, *J. Chem. Soc. (London)*, **1958**, 3195.

solvent. Other neutral nucleophiles which can in appropriate circumstances give primarily the product of bimolecular substitution with rearrangement include thiourea.[104]

Definite establishment of S_N2' reactions involving the anions of pseudoacids (e.g., the anion, $MeCOCH^-CO_2Et$, of acetoacetic ester) is complicated by the facts that these materials have two or more potentially nucleophilic centers and that the product of normal attack by oxygen on the allylic halide might undergo a Claisen-type rearrangement to give the abnormal product. A number of such cases have been discussed at various times.[81b,85,85a,86a,95b,104a,104b] The most important are the second-order reactions of 1-methyl and 1-ethylallyl chlorides with the anion, $\overline{C}H(CO_2Et)_2$, of diethyl malonate in ethanol. These give 10 and 23%, respectively, of the product (e.g., **54**) of abnormal bimolecular displacement, together with that of normal substitution. It seems likely that the abnormal product comes from S_N2' processes, and that these are here more important than in related reactions involving ethoxide and similar ions because the large anion of diethyl malonate is diverted sterically from the 1 to the 3 position. Even in this case, however, the alternative route via the ketene acetal (**53**) does not seem to the writer [cf. 105] yet to have been completely excluded. Despite opinions to the contrary,[86a,104b] there seems no reason to believe that this ketene acetal would add ethanol under the basic conditions of the displacement reaction, since the structural analog, $EtO_2CCH:C(OEt)_2$, can be prepared and seems to be sufficiently stable in solution in ethanol.[106,107] The proposed rearrangement (**53 → 54**) has well-authenticated analogies

$$CH_2=CHCHEt$$

$$EtO_2CCH=C\underset{OEt}{\overset{O}{<}} \longrightarrow \begin{array}{c} CH_2CH=CHEt \\ | \\ EtO_2C\dot{C}HCO_2Et \end{array} \qquad (39)$$

$$(53) \qquad\qquad\qquad (54)$$

$$\begin{array}{c} CH_2=CHCH_2 \\ CH_2=C \end{array}\overset{O}{<}_{OCH_2CH=CH_2} \longrightarrow \begin{array}{c} CH_2CH=CH_2 \\ | \\ CH_2 \quad O \\ \quad\quad C \\ \quad OCH_2CH=CH_2 \end{array} \qquad (40)$$

$$(55) \qquad\qquad\qquad (56)$$

[104] J. M. Rule, I. J. Wilk, T. I. Wrigley, and W. G. Young, *J. Am. Chem. Soc.*, **79**, 6529 (1957).

[104a] M. J. S. Dewar, *Bull. soc. chim. France*, C43 (1951).

[104b] S. Winstein, *Bull. soc. chim. France*, C43 (1951).

[105] P. B. D. de la Mare and W. A. Waters, *Ann. Repts. on Progr. Chem.*, **50**, 139 (1953).

[106] S. M. McElvain, *Chem. Revs.*, **45**, 453 (1949); S. M. McElvain, H. I. Anthes, and S. H. Shapiro, *J. Am. Chem. Soc.*, **64**, 2525 (1942).

[107] H. Reitter and A. Weindel, *Ber.*, **40**, 3358 (1907).

(e.g., **55** → **56**, eq. 40) which seem to proceed under quite mild conditions (e.g., below 80° in *tert*-butanol).[106]

Stereochemistry. It is generally considered [85a,95b,101,101a] that, essentially for reasons analogous to those which determine that bimolecular substitutions at a saturated carbon atom give inversion of configuration, bimolecular substitutions with rearrangement will have essentially the stereoelectronically determined stereochemistry indicated in structure **57**. Here the entering and

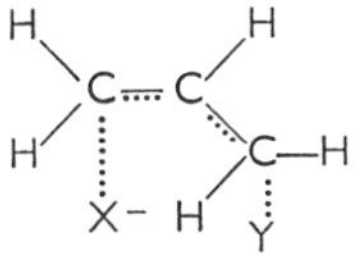

(57)

leaving groups are *cis* to each other; (i.e., on the same side of the plane containing the displaced and forming double bonds). We can think of the reaction as involving a displacement by X^- of the double bond electrons from the side of the double bond system remote from X, together with a displacement of the bonding electrons of Y from the side of the CH_2 group remote from the electrons displaced from the double bond.

Evidence that this course can be taken in the S_N2' reaction of halides has been given by Stork and Clarke,[108] who describe S_N2' replacements by piperidine on the α- and β-chlorocodides involving entry of the substituent *cis* to the displaced chloride (e.g., **58** → **59**). Further evidence has been provided in less complex ester systems and is mentioned on page 76.

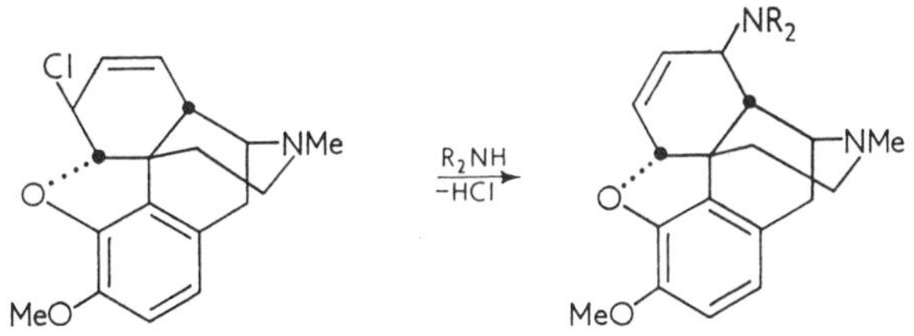

(58)   (59)

The stereochemistry about the formed double bond presents a separate problem. Bimolecular attack on 1-methylallyl chloride or any analogous system can accord with the stereoelectronic requirements (which define the geometrical relationships of the double bond system and the displaced group) either in conformation **60** (which gives the *cis*-crotyl derivative **62**), or in conformation **61** (which gives the *trans*-crotyl derivative **63**). As in the unimolecular reactions discussed on pages 51–52, one might expect the

[108] G. Stork and F. H. Clarke, *J. Am. Chem. Soc.*, **78**, 4619 (1956).

difference in thermodynamic stability between the two possible products to be reflected in part in relative internal strain in the transition states. So it would be predicted—and it is found [102]—that, although both isomers are produced, the *trans* isomer is formed in amount larger than that of the *cis* isomer by a small factor (cf. eq. 36).

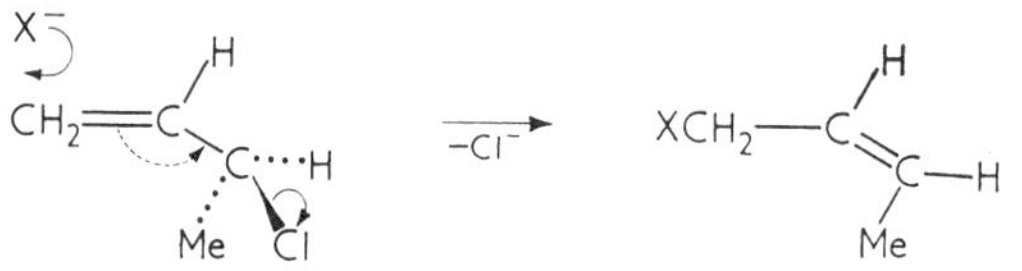

(60)   (62)

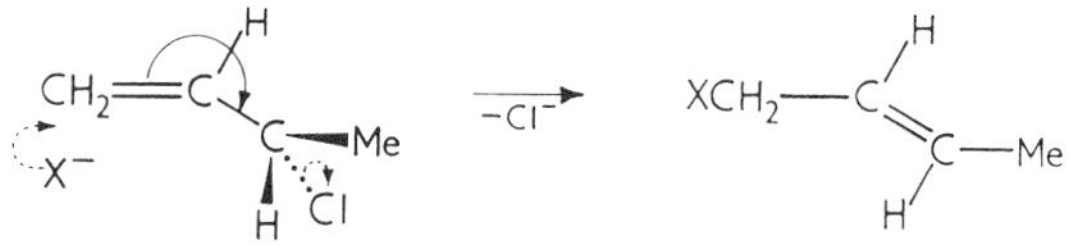

(61)   (63)

This aspect of the stereochemistry of allylic rearrangement is, therefore, determined not by the degree of involvement of the nucleophile with the double bond in the transition state, but by stereoelectronically determined steric factors within the allylic system. E. R. H. Jones, M. C. Whiting, and their co-workers [108a] are currently developing this principle in regard to the acid-catalyzed rearrangements of allylic alcohols, particularly in the hexa-dienol series (cf. page 78).

D. Allylic Esters

Allylic carboxylic esters, $R \cdot O \cdot CO \cdot Z$ (where R is an allyl or substituted allyl group), can undergo heterolysis as indicated in structure **64**. So they

$$R \overset{\curvearrowright}{\vdots} O \cdot CO \cdot Z$$

(64)

have available in principle all the types of reaction undergone by allyl halides, and all the observed phenomena should have their parallels in the chemistry already discussed. An additional complexity arises, however, because esters have a second site, the carbonyl carbon atom, available for attack by a nucleophile, and a second type of bond fission is possible.[109,110,110a]

[108a] Personal communication from M. C. Whiting, 1960.

[109] J. N. E. Day and C. K. Ingold, *Trans. Faraday Soc.*, **37**, 686 (1941).

[110] A. G. Davies and J. Kenyon, *Quart. Revs. (London)*, **9**, 203 (1955).

[110a] C. K. Ingold, *Structure and Mechanism in Organic Chemistry*, G. Bell and Sons, London, 1953.

If the nucleophile attacks the carbonyl carbon atom, with consequent acyl-oxygen fission in the ester, the allylic system is unchanged in the reaction and no rearrangement occurs.

The most certain way of ensuring that allylic esters undergo reactions by acyl-oxygen fission is to use a strong base. Under these circumstances, such esters as 1-methylallyl acetate,[111] 1,3-dimethylallyl hydrogen phthalate,[112] and 3-methyl-1-phenylallyl hydrogen phthalate [113] undergo bimolecular base-catalyzed hydrolysis or alcoholysis with acyl-oxygen fission (e.g., eq. 41), and consequent preservation of the allylic skeleton.

$$
CH_2{=}CHCHOC(O)Me \xrightarrow{+OH^-} CH_2{=}CHCHO\overset{\overset{O^-}{|}}{C}Me \rightarrow CH_2{=}CHCHO^-{+}\overset{\overset{O}{\|}}{C}Me \rightarrow
$$

with Me below first; Me OH below second; Me OH below third.

$$
CH_2{=}CHCHOH{+}\overset{\overset{O}{\|}}{C}Me
$$

(41)

with Me and O⁻ below.

Acid-catalyzed hydrolysis or transesterification can also occur with acyl-oxygen fission; and this is observed for 1- and 3-methylallyl acetates (eq. 42).[111,114] This mode of hydrolysis is, however, often less practically satis-

$$
CH_2{=}CHCHOCOCH_3{+}H^+ \rightleftharpoons CH_2{=}CHCH\overset{+}{O}COCH_3 \xrightarrow{H_2O}
$$

with Me below first; Me H below second.

$$
CH_2{=}CHCHOH + CH_3COOH + H^+ \quad (42)
$$

with Me below.

factory for ensuring the isolation of unrearranged products, for under acidic conditions the alcohol will often itself rearrange anionotropically.

Other types of ester (e.g., sulfonates, $ROSO_2Z$; sulfates, $(RO)_2SO_2$; sulfites $(RO)_2SO$; nitrates, $RONO_2$; nitrites, $RONO$) have similar complexities of reaction path available, and each case will involve consideration of the ease of achieving appropriate bond fission (64) under the accessible experimental conditions. In this section we deal with those allylic ester systems which have been chosen for experimental study to illustrate specific chemical points and elucidate particular modes of reaction.

1- and 3-Phenylallyl Benzoate and Its Analogs: The Uncatalyzed Rearrangement. In the historical development of the theory of anionotropy, study of

[111] E. H. Ingold and C. K. Ingold, *J. Chem. Soc. (London)*, **1932**, 756; C. Prévost, *Ann. Chim.*, **10**, 147 (1928).

[112] H. W. J. Hills, J. Kenyon, and H. Phillips, *J. Chem. Soc. (London)*, **1936**, 576.

[113] J. Kenyon, S. M. Partridge, and H. Phillips, *J. Chem. Soc. (London)*, **1936**, 85, **1937**, 207; M. P. Balfe and J. Kenyon, *Trans. Faraday Soc.*, **37**, 721 (1941).

[114] S. C. Datta, J. N. E. Day, and C. K. Ingold, *J. Chem. Soc. (London)*, **1939**, 838.

the esters of 1- and 3-phenylallyl alcohol played an important part. Burton and Ingold [114a,114b,115] considered that the rearrangement of 1- to 3-phenylallyl p-nitrobenzoate involved separation of the mobile group as an anion (cf. Scheme 9). Their reasons were that the ease of rearrangement was (a) correlated in a general way with the tendency of X to separate as an anion, (b) known to be facilitated by electron-donating substituents in the allyl residue, (c) facilitated by increase in the ionizing power of the solvent; and that (d) the isomeric rearrangement could be diverted by added anions toward substitution with accompanying partial rearrangement.

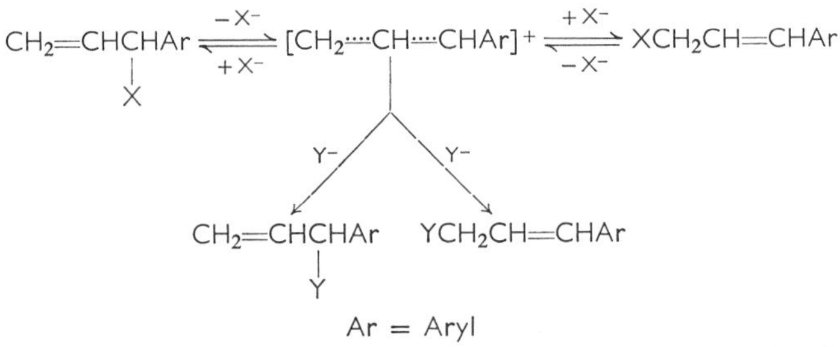

$$CH_2{=}CHCHAr \underset{+X^-}{\overset{-X^-}{\rightleftharpoons}} [CH_2 \cdots CH \cdots CHAr]^+ \underset{-X^-}{\overset{+X^-}{\rightleftharpoons}} XCH_2CH{=}CHAr$$
$$\underset{X}{|}$$

$$Y^- \swarrow \qquad \searrow Y^-$$

$$CH_2{=}CHCHAr \qquad YCH_2CH{=}CHAr$$
$$\underset{Y}{|}$$

Ar = Aryl

Scheme 9. Rearrangement and substitution in allylic esters.[114a,114b]

Meisenheimer and his co-workers,[116,116a] who examined some of these reactions kinetically, showed that they were of the first order and were to a small extent catalyzed by added salts in the relatively nonionizing solvents acetic acid and chlorobenzene. Catchpole, Hughes, and Ingold [116b,116c] reassessed and summarized the general conclusions, arising from the earlier work and from their own experiments, and made it probable that the catalytic effects of added salts were essentially environmental effects and did not represent any substantial incursion of the S_N2' reaction.

Of more recent years evidence has been adduced, as is discussed above and elsewhere (page 32; Section 1), that the S_N1 mechanism should be elaborated, especially to describe the course of reaction in aprotic solvents and those of low dielectric constant. As a consequence, the status of intramolecular isomerization has become altered; it now seems that a considerable degree of heterolysis of a C—X bond can be tolerated without causing X to become kinetically free. With these considerations in mind, Pocker [117] and Braude,

[114a] H. Burton, J. Chem. Soc. (London), 1928, 1650.

[114b] H. Burton and C. K. Ingold, J. Chem. Soc. (London), 1928, 904

[115] H. Burton, J. Chem. Soc. (London), 1934, 1268.

[116] J. Meisenheimer, W. Schmidt, and G. Schäfer, Ann., 501, 131 (1933); J. Meisenheimer and G. Beutter, Ann., 508, 58 (1934).

[116a] J. Meisenheimer and J. Link, Ann., 479, 221 (1930).

[116b] A. G. Catchpole, E. D. Hughes, and C. K. Ingold, J. Chem. Soc. (London), 1948, 8.

[116c] E. D. Hughes, Trans. Faraday Soc., 37, 603 (1941).

[117] Y. Pocker, J. Chem. Soc. (London), 1958, 4318, 4323.

Turner, and Waight[118] have re-examined the thermal isomerization and the accompanying exchange reactions of 1-phenylallyl benzoate and p-nitrobenzoate in chlorobenzene, in the presence of added anions. In the absence of added acids the reactions follow a unimolecular course. They are catalyzed only slightly by added neutral salts. Tracer experiments showed that added common anions were incorporated after partial reaction both into the unrearranged starting material and into the product and that the acyl oxygen atom of the starting material largely became the alkyl oxygen atom in the rearranged product. For this reason, and because rearrangement was more rapid than exchange into the 3 position, it was considered that a scheme of rearrangement of the S_N1 type involving ion pairs (Scheme 10) best explained the results.[117]

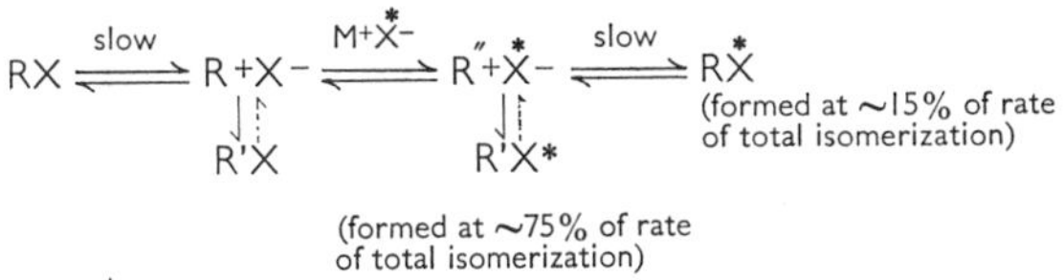

(R = CH$_2$=CHCHPh; R' = CH$_2$CH=CHPh; the structure of R″ was not explicitly considered; $\overset{*}{X}$ = labeled benzoate ion)

Scheme 10.   Exchange and isomerization of allylic esters.

It is interesting that under these particular experimental conditions (in chlorobenzene at 155°) the ion pair R″$^+$X$^-$ partitions to give a greater amount of the thermodynamically more stable, rearranged product R′X* than of the nonrearranged product RX*. This result contrasts with the general experience that mesomeric cations usually give the thermodynamically less stable product (cf. page 33) and specifically with the observation that the 1-phenylallyl cation, when produced at lower temperatures in other solvents, gives more of that substitution product which is derived from the unrearranged structure.[119,119a,120] It is possible that the difference is merely a reflection of the change in temperature, since reaction to give the thermodynamically more stable structure would be considered to have the higher activation energy (see Fig. 1, page 33).

Formally, these rearrangements can be classified as of the $S_N i'$ type; but, as for the halides, the effect of change of solvent on the rate suggests that the transition states have considerable ionic character. This also is confirmed by

118 E. A. Braude, D. W. Turner, and E. S. Waight, *J. Chem. Soc.* (*London*), **1958**, 2396.
119 C. A. Bunton, Y. Pocker, and H. Dahn, *Chem. & Ind.* (*London*), **1958**, 1516.
119a G. Valkanas and E. S. Waight, *Proc. Chem. Soc.* (*London*), **1959**, 9; *J. Chem. Soc.* (*London*), **1959**, 2720.
120 Y. Pocker, *Chem. & Ind.* (*London*), **1959**, 195; Y. Pocker, *Proc. Chem. Soc.* (*London*), **1959**, 226.

the observation that the reactivities are in the sequence expected for separation of the mobile group as an anion, namely,[114a,114b,118] OH [120a] $< OAc <$ $OBz < O \cdot C_6H_4 \cdot NO_2\text{-}(p) \ll Cl$.

The isomeric rearrangement, which was shown to be intramolecular, accompanying solvolysis of *trans*-1,3-dimethylallyl *p*-nitrobenzoate has been examined by Goering and his co-workers.[122, cf.123] This rearrangement, if, as was postulated, it occurs in such a conformation as **65**, gives the enantiomorphic product (**66**) of the same geometrical configuration. The relative positions of the oxygen atoms in the reactant and product were determined by using pure dextrorotatory ester labeled at the carbonyl oxygen. The rate

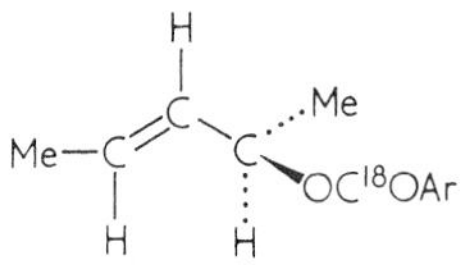

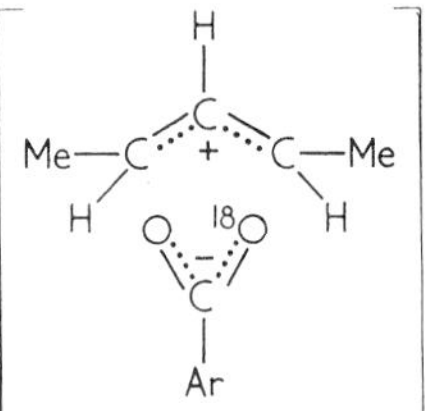

of equilibration of [18]O between the two possible positions is about a third that of the racemization; there appears to be about one chance in three that the oxygen atoms become equivalent on passing through the intermediate. Apparently the ion pair cannot have such a rigid structure as would be implied by either of the intermediates **67** and **68**.

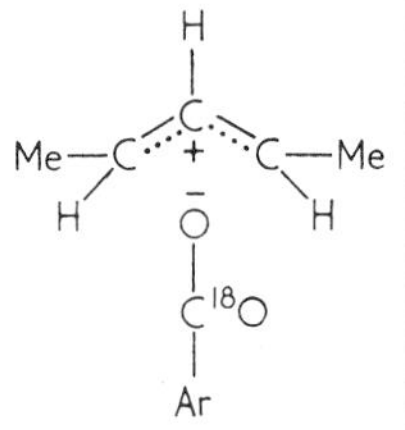

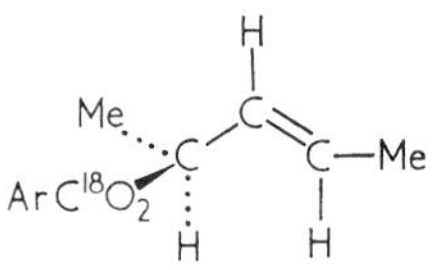

Acid Catalysis. These recent reinvestigations [117,118] of the rearrangements of allylic esters have amply confirmed the early view [110a,114a,114b,116b] that acid catalysis is not essential for these processes. There is no doubt, however,

[120a] Under acid catalysis, alcohols and esters may rearrange at similar rates,[121] but this is because alcohols are more basic than esters, so that the concentration of the conjugate acid is greater for the former class of compound.

[121] E. A. Braude, *J. Chem. Soc. (London)*, **1948**, 794.

[122] H. L. Goering and R. W. Greiner, *J. Am. Chem. Soc.*, **79**, 3464 (1957); H. L. Goering and M. M. Pombo, *J. Am. Chem. Soc.*, **82**, 2515 (1960).

[123] R. A. Sneen, *J. Am. Chem. Soc.*, **82**, 4261 (1960); R. A. Sneen and A. M. Rosenberg, *J. Am. Chem. Soc.*, **83**, 895 (1961).

that acids can act as catalysts. Such a result would be expected from the general chemistry of esters; the heterolysis of the OCOZ group from ROCOZ must be facilitated by attachment of a proton (eq. 44).

$$ROCOZ + H^+ \rightleftharpoons R\overset{+}{\underset{H}{O}}COZ \rightarrow R^+ + \underset{H}{O}COZ \qquad (44)$$

Thus the rearrangement of 1-phenylallyl p-nitrobenzoate in chlorobenzene is catalyzed by p-nitrobenzoic acid.[117,118] The details of the function of the acid in facilitating reaction through a path analogous to that of Scheme 10 is especially complicated in a solvent of low dielectric constant; it is interesting that the catalysis is linear in added molecular p-nitrobenzoic acid over the range 0.0004–0.05M.

Perhaps even more significant is the report [120] that the rearrangement of $(-)$-1-phenylallyl-^{14}C acetate in isotopically normal acetic acid involves concurrent exchange, racemization, and rearrangement. Perchloric acid was found to be a powerful catalyst for all three processes, and the rates were proportional to h_0, the acidity function which measures the tendency of the environment to protonate a neutral base; the slope of $\log_{10} k_1$ against H_0 was 1.1. These results were taken to indicate an ionization mechanism. The rate of dilution of tracer in the ester mixture was equal to the rate of racemization, but was $\sim 50\%$ higher than the rate of rearrangement. The 3-phenylallyl acetate recovered after complete rearrangement was free from tracer, although its directly measured rate of exchange was slower than the rearrangement of its isomer; and the 1-phenylallyl-^{14}C acetate recovered after partial reaction had partially exchanged its acetate group with the solvent.

It seems, therefore, that in this more ionizing solvent, with perchloric acid as catalyst, there is virtually no intramolecular rearrangement; all the rearranged product is derived by reaction with solvent. The simplest interpretation of the results is that both racemization and symmetrical exchange proceed through an intermediate, which could be a free carbonium ion, and reacts with an acetic acid molecule at either of the two available positions to give unrearranged, but racemized, 1-phenylallyl acetate, and 3-phenylallyl acetate of practically normal abundance. Although 1-phenylallyl chloride has not been examined under these experimental conditions, it will be remembered that even in solvents of relatively high dielectric constant considerable intramolecular rearrangement was observed for this compound.[119a] It seems that, as would be expected, a developing carbonium ionic center more easily captures internally an incipiently heterolyzing anion than a neutral fragment (cf. **69–71**).

Acid-catalyzed rearrangements can accompany hydrolyses of esters even in substantially aqueous solvents. Braude[121] studied the acid-catalyzed

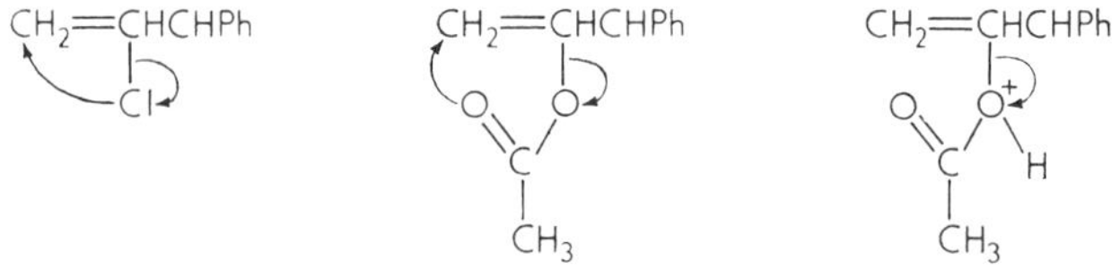

(69)   (70)   (71)

rearrangement and accompanying hydrolysis of propenylethynylcarbinyl acetate (**72**) in aqueous dioxane (Scheme 11). The rearrangement had an

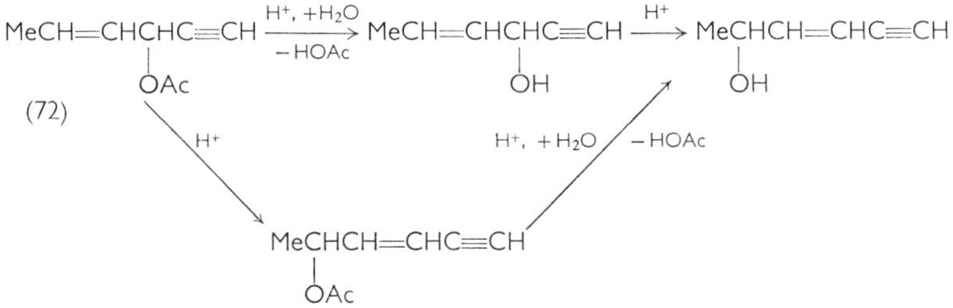

Scheme 11.   Rearrangement and hydrolysis of propenylethynylcarbinyl acetate.

energy of activation higher than that of the hydrolysis; the general kinetic features of the two reactions were very similar. It was considered (although not rigidly proved) that the hydrolysis proceeded with acyl-oxygen fission. The rearrangement is almost certainly in part intramolecular, in which case it seems that for this structure the heterolyzing neutral fragment can at least in part be trapped by the developing carbonium center before it becomes free.

Hydrogen Phthalates.   The chemistry of the allylic hydrogen phthalates was studied extensively by Kenyon and his co-workers.[112,113,123a] They showed that optically active 1-methyl-3-phenylallyl hydrogen phthalate (**73**) and 1,3-dimethylallyl hydrogen phthalate on hydrolysis in very weakly

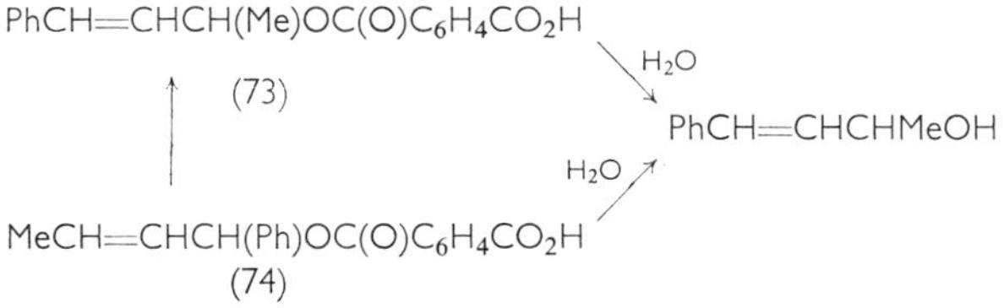

$$PhCH{=}CHCH(Me)OC(O)C_6H_4CO_2H$$

(73)

$$PhCH{=}CHCHMeOH \qquad (45)$$

$$MeCH{=}CHCH(Ph)OC(O)C_6H_4CO_2H$$
(74)

alkaline solution gave the corresponding completely racemized alcohols and that 1-phenyl-3-methylallyl hydrogen phthalate (**74**) gave in large part the

[123a] C. L. Arcus and J. Kenyon, *J. Chem. Soc.* (*London*), **1938**, 1912; C. L. Arcus and J. W. Smith, *J. Chem. Soc.* (*London*), **1939**, 1748; R. S. Airs, M. P. Balfe, and J. Kenyon, *J. Chem. Soc.* (*London*), **1942**, 18.

rearranged alcohol (eq. 45). These results indicated the accessibility of unimolecular ester hydrolysis with alkyl-oxygen fission in these systems. It was
discovered also that a rearrangement, accompanied by retention of optical
activity, could be realized; optically active **74** gave optically active **73**. The
latter results led to some discussion [110a,113,116b,116c] as to the best mode of
representation of the isomeric rearrangement; in retrospect, the results
perhaps provide the first definite indication of the phenomena which are now
generally interpreted in terms of ion pair intermediates.

Goering and his co-workers [124,124a] have examined the hydrogen phthalates
of *cis*- and *trans*-5-methylcyclohex-2-enyl hydrogen phthalates (e.g., **75**) in

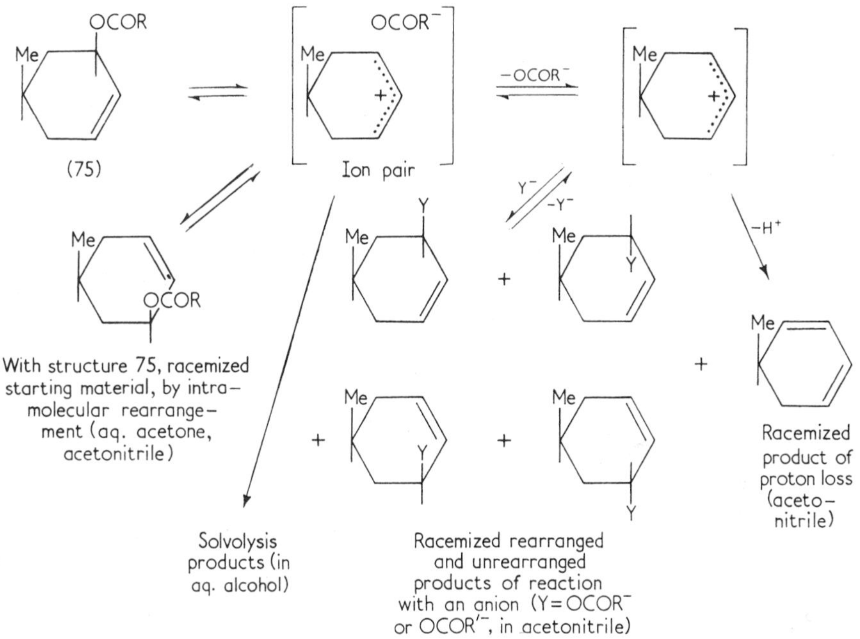

Scheme 12.   Rearrangement and replacement reactions of 5-methyl-2-cyclohexenyl
hydrogen phthalates.

acetonitrile and in aqueous acetone as solvents. The general chemistry is as
already described for the halides. Intramolecular anionotropic rearrangement
(which for this system racemizes the optically active starting material) was
observed in both solvents. In acetonitrile, geometrical isomerization, diversion of the reaction by a foreign anion, and proton loss to give 5-methyl-1,3-
cyclohexadiene (indications of the formation of a free carbonium ionic

[124] H. L. Goering and E. F. Silversmith, *J. Am. Chem. Soc.*, **77**, 1129 (1955).

[124a] H. L. Goering, J. P. Blanchard, and E. F. Silversmith, *J. Am. Chem. Soc.*, **76**,
5409 (1954).

intermediate) were observed. In aqueous acetone the geometrical rearrangement was completely diverted to the formation of products of solvolysis. Measurements of the rates of the various processes at different temperatures were held to suggest that all the reaction products were determined by a reaction path which started with a heterolysis (Scheme 12).

Stereochemistry: The S_N2' Reaction. Stork and White [125] have used an ester system to illustrate the stereochemistry of the S_N2' reaction. They studied the products and kinetics of the reactions of *trans*-6-alkylcyclohex-2-en-1-yl 2,6-dichlorobenzoates (**76**) with piperidine. The reactions were kinetically of the second order and proceeded with allylic rearrangement. The entering group was shown to take up the position *cis* to that formerly occupied by the displaced group, in agreement with the theory discussed above and such experimental data as are available by study of allylic halides (cf. page 67). The results are indicated in Scheme 13. Displacement by the diethyl malonate ion proceeded similarly; for the 6-methyl compound (**76**, R = Me), the S_N2 process accompanied the S_N2' reaction with this nucleophile, but it was inhibited by bulkier alkyl groups.

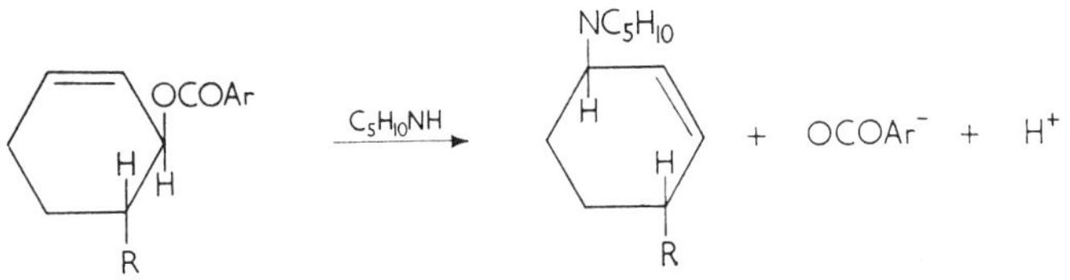

(Ar = 2,6-dichlorophenyl; R = Me, Pr^i, Bu^t)

Scheme 13.   Stereochemistry of the S_N2' reaction.

S_N2' displacements on 1-trifluoromethylallyl *p*-bromobenzene sulphonate have been discussed by Pegolotti and Young.[125a]

E. Allylic Alcohols

The reactions which it is convenient to consider under this heading fall into two general classes. In the first, we have processes which involve nucleophilic replacement of —OH or of —OH$_2^+$ by a nucleophile, with or without allylic rearrangement. These are analogous to replacements which we have considered in dealing with halides and with esters, and most of them are isomeric (the so-called "oxotropic") rearrangements.

In the second class are reactions in which the replacement occurs in a derivative, first formed by replacement of active hydrogen, of the alcohol.

[125] G. Stork and W. N. White, *J. Am. Chem. Soc.*, **78**, 4609 (1956).

[125a] J. A. Pegolotti and W. G. Young, *J. Am. Chem. Soc.*, **83**, 3251 (1961).

An example is the reaction of an allylic alcohol with thionyl chloride, which often gives a mixture of rearranged and unrearranged chlorides (cf. eq. 46).

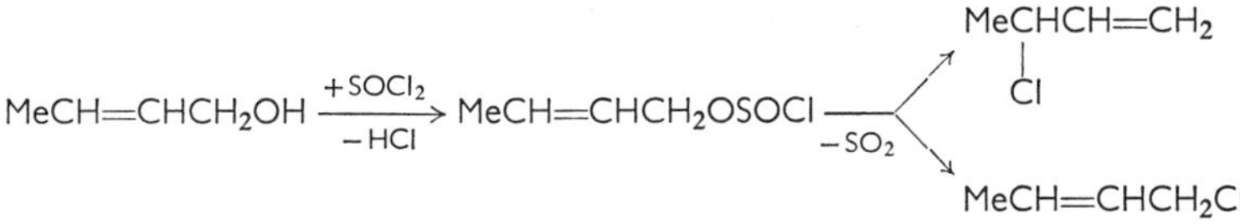

$$MeCH{=}CHCH_2OH \xrightarrow[-HCl]{+SOCl_2} MeCH{=}CHCH_2OSOCl \underset{-SO_2}{\overset{\nearrow}{\underset{\searrow}{\qquad}}} \begin{array}{l} MeCHCH{=}CH_2 \\ \quad | \\ \quad Cl \\[4pt] MeCH{=}CHCH_2Cl \end{array} \qquad (46)$$

Isomeric Rearrangements. A simple example of this type is the acid-catalyzed rearrangement of 1- to 3-phenylallyl alcohol [126,126a,126b] (eq. 47),

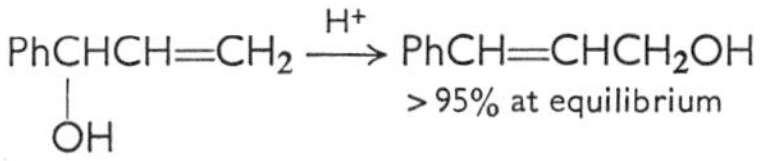

$$\underset{\underset{OH}{|}}{PhCHCH{=}CH_2} \xrightarrow{H^+} PhCH{=}CHCH_2OH \qquad (47)$$
$$\text{> 95\% at equilibrium}$$

which proceeds at least to 95% conversion. The rate of this rearrangement has been shown to follow Hammett's acidity function, h_0, in a solvent in which h_0 and $[H^+]$ can be distinguished. This suggests that a water molecule is not concerned in the rate-determining step of the rearrangement. It has been shown also that (a) 1-phenylallyl alcohol recovered after interrupting the rearrangement has partially exchanged its oxygen atoms with the solvent water, (b) 3-phenylallyl alcohol recovered after complete rearrangement has the ^{18}O abundance of the enriched solvent, and (c) oxygen exchange between 3-phenylallyl alcohol and water is considerably slower than the rates both of oxygen exchange and of rearrangement of 1-phenylallyl alcohol.

There is, therefore, no indication from these experiments that either intramolecular or S_N2' processes participate in this rearrangement; the pattern of results is most simply interpreted in terms of a carbonium ionic intermediate (Scheme 14).[126,126b]

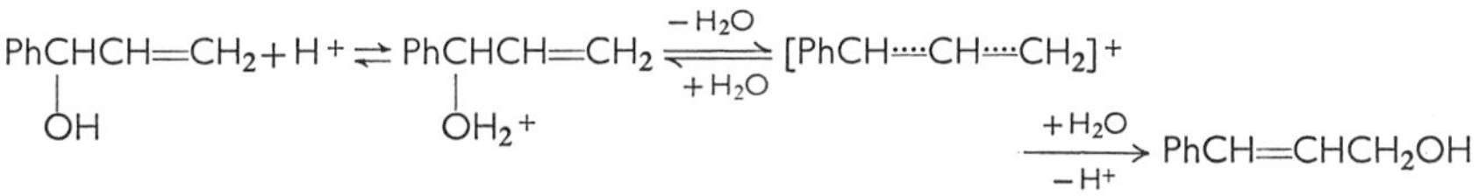

$$\underset{\underset{OH}{|}}{PhCHCH{=}CH_2} + H^+ \rightleftharpoons \underset{\underset{OH_2{}^+}{|}}{PhCHCH{=}CH_2} \underset{+H_2O}{\overset{-H_2O}{\rightleftharpoons}} [PhCH{\cdots}CH{\cdots}CH_2]^+$$
$$\xrightarrow[-H^+]{+H_2O} PhCH{=}CHCH_2OH$$

Scheme 14.   Acid-catalyzed rearrangement of 1-phenylallyl alcohol.

It seems, therefore, that this carbonium ion acquires substantial freedom from the departing group before reaction with the nucleophile. The stereochemistry about the forming double bond should be determined by the structural features discussed for the halides (pages 51, 52). Bell, Jones, and Whiting,[127] correcting an earlier report by Braude and Coles,[128] have shown

[126] H. L. Goering and R. E. Dilgren, J. Am. Chem. Soc., 81, 2556 (1959).

[126a] E. A. Braude, E. R. H. Jones, and E. S. Stern, J. Chem. Soc. (London), 1946, 396.

[126b] C. A. Bunton, Y. Pocker, and H. Dahn, Chem. & Ind. (London), 1958, 1516.

[127] I. Bell, E. R. H. Jones, and M. C. Whiting, J. Chem. Soc. (London), 1957, 2597.

[128] E. A. Braude and J. A. Coles, J. Chem. Soc. (London), 1951, 2085.

in agreement with this, that *trans*-propenylethynylcarbinol (**77**) rearranges to give a kinetically controlled mixture of *trans* and *cis* isomers (**78** and **79**,

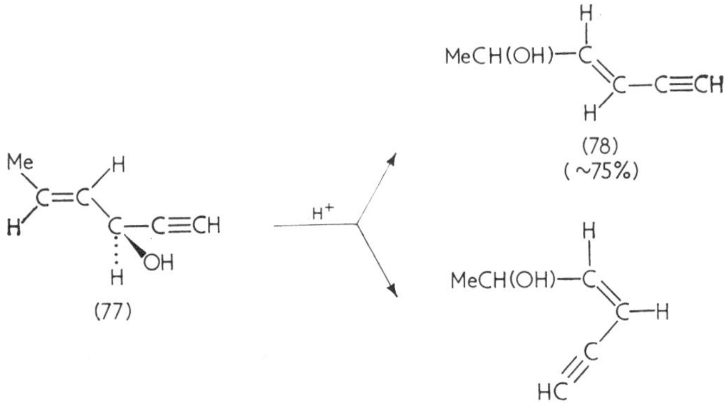

respectively), with the *trans* isomer in preponderating amount. These authors drew attention to the significant fact that in the analogous rearrangement of 3-methylpent-1-en-4-yn-3-ol, in which there would be little conformational preference for either of the conformational isomers (**80** and **81**), the *cis* and *trans* products are formed in similar amount,[129] the *cis* isomer actually predominating. Similar conclusions have been reached from studies in the analogous hexadienol systems.[130]

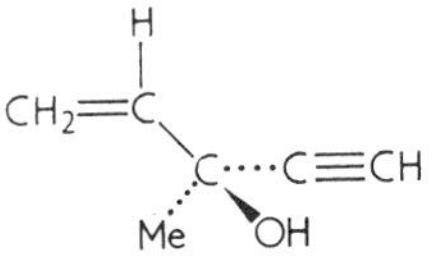

The mechanism involving free carbonium ions is, however, probably not the only one available to allylic alcohols. Goering and Silversmith[131] have examined the acid-catalyzed rearrangement of *cis*- and *trans*-5-methyl-cyclohex-2-en-1-ols in aqueous acetone. The rate of loss of optical activity for both isomers was greater than the rate of geometrical rearrangement. They interpreted the results as suggesting that the geometrical rearrangement

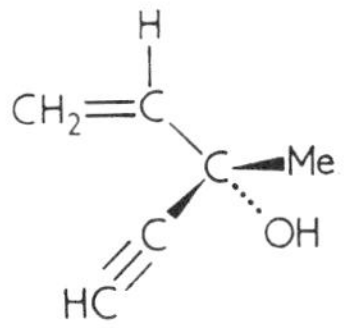

[129] W. Oroshnik, *J. Am. Chem. Soc.*, **78**, 2651 (1956).

[130] E. R. H. Jones and M. C. Whiting, personal communication, 1960.

[131] H. L. Goering and E. F. Silversmith, *J. Am. Chem. Soc.*, **79**, 348 (1957)

proceeded through the carbonium ion (82), whereas the racemization either was intramolecular or involved an S_N2' reaction (Scheme 15).

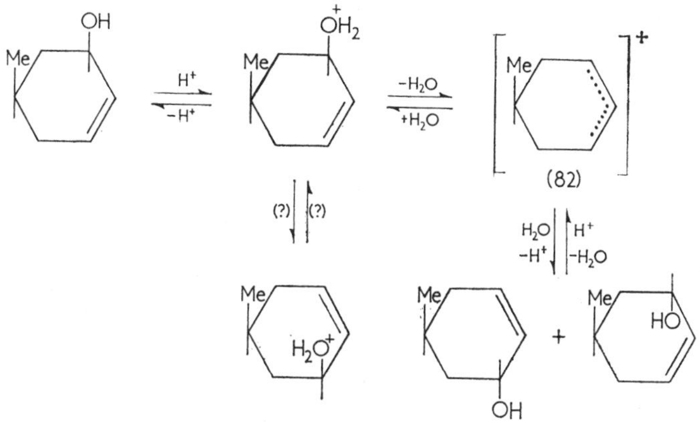

Scheme 15.   Acid-catalyzed rearrangement and racemization of 5-methylcyclohex-2-en-1-ol.

These papers refute the view that S_N2' processes are common in rearrangements of this sort. Structural effects in the anionotropic mobility of allylic alcohols have been studied extensively by Jones, Braude, and their co-workers.[128,131a–131i,132] For a carbonium ion reaction of the type shown in Scheme 14, both the pre-equilibrium protonation and the heterolysis should be facilitated by electron release. The comparisons summarized in Table X illustrate the magnitude of the observed effect of change in structure on the rate of anionotropic change. The pattern is analogous to that established for halides; conjugative effects are obviously of prime importance, but are subject to modification by the inductive effects of substituents. For detailed

[131a] E. A. Braude, E. R. H. Jones, and E. S. Stern, *J. Chem. Soc. (London)*, **1946**, 396.

[131b] E. A. Braude and E. S. Waight, *J. Chem. Soc. (London)*, **1953**, 419.

[131c] E. A. Braude and P. H. Gore, *J. Chem. Soc. (London)*, **1959**, 41.

[131d] E. A. Braude and E. R. H. Jones, *J. Chem. Soc. (London)*, **1944**, 436, **1946**, 122, 128; E. A. Braude, *J. Chem. Soc. (London)*, **1944**, 443, **1948**, 794; E. A. Braude and E. S. Stern, *J. Chem. Soc. (London)*, **1947**, 1096, **1948**, 1982.

[131e] E. A. Braude and C. J. Timmons, *J. Chem. Soc. (London)*, **1950**, 2000, 2007, **1953**, 3131, 3138; cf. M. Julia, *Bull. soc. chim. France*, C13 (1951).

[131f] E. A. Braude and J. F. Coles, *J. Chem. Soc. (London)*, **1950**, 2014; E. A. Baude and W. F. Forbes, *J. Chem. Soc. (London)*, **1951**, 1755; E. A. Braude, W. F. Forbes, B. F. Gofton, R. P. Houghton, and E. S. Waight, *J. Chem. Soc. (London)*, **1957**, 4711.

[131g] E. A. Braude, *Quart. Revs. (London)*, 4, 404 (1950).

[131h] E. A. Braude, D. W. Turner, and E. S. Waight, *J. Chem. Soc. (London)*, **1958**, 2396.

[131i] E. A. Braude, *J. Chem. Soc. (London)*, **1948**, 794.

[132] E. A. Braude, *Ann. Repts. on Progr. Chem.*, 46, 114 (1949).

discussions, the original papers should be consulted.[cf. 131a, 132] Recently, the acid-catalyzed isomeric rearrangement of *cis*- and *trans*-5-methyl-2-cyclo-hexenol-O^{18} has been studied by Goering and Josephson.[132a] Interesting differences between the behavior of the isomers were observed.

TABLE X

Structural Effects in Acid-Catalyzed Rearrangements of Alcohols [131a]

A. Rearrangement of $CH_2=CHCH(R)OH$

R	Relative rate[a]
C≡CH	0.00015
CH=CH$_2$	1.8
Ph	4.3

B. Rearrangement of $RC_6H_4CH(OH)CH=CHMe$

R	Relative rate[a]
p-OMe	189
p-Me	16
o-Me	3.6
m-Me	2.1
H	1.8
p-F	1.5
p-Cl	0.4
p-Br	0.3

C. Rearrangement of $R_1R_1'C=CR_2CR_3(OH)C≡CR_5$

Substituents and position	Relative rate (unsubstituted compound $= 1$)
$R_1,R_1' =$ Me	9×10^5
$R_1 =$ Me	3.9×10^3
$R_3 =$ Me	6×10^2
$R_5 =$ Me	3.6×10^2
$R_2 =$ Me	7.3

[a] In aqueous ethanol, with $0.1M$ HCl at 30°.

The *cis* isomer, in part, was shown to react by an intramolecular route which, for a reaction of this charge type, cannot involve an ion-pair intermediate.

Conversion of Allylic Alcohols to Allylic Halides: Reactions with Hydrogen Halides.[cf. 132b] Allylic alcohols with hydrogen halides readily form the

132a H. L. Goering and R. R. Josephson, *J. Am. Chem. Soc.*, **83**, 2588 (1961).

132b R. H. De Wolfe and W. G. Young, *Chem. Revs.*, **56**, 753 (1956).

corresponding halides. For obvious reasons, experimental conditions are generally chosen in which not too much water is present at the end of the reaction. Sulfuric acid is sometimes added as a catalyst, but generally is not necessary. Although these reactions have not been extensively studied from a mechanistic viewpoint, it seems clear that they generally involve the oxonium ion (e.g., $[CH_2:CHCH(R)OH_2]^+$ from a 1-substituted allyl alcohol). The less ionizing the conditions of reaction, the greater the divergence of the product ratio from the equilibrium proportions of isomers, but this divergence does not seem to be very large. It is by no means clear under what circumstances S_N1, S_N2, or S_N2' processes are involved, nor to what extent rearrangement follows or precedes the replacement.[132c]

Reactions with Halides of Phosphorus.[132b] The first products of reactions of phosphorus trihalides with alcohols are alkyl esters of phosphorous acid. A type of reaction sequence which can be involved in the replacement of hydroxyl by halogen using this reagent is represented in equation 48. The

$$ROH + PX_3 \xrightarrow{\text{(a)}} ROPX_2 + HX \xrightarrow{\text{(b)}} RX + HOPX_2 \qquad (48)$$

second stage of the reaction would be expected to be catalyzed by acids and could in principle be unimolecular, bimolecular, or intramolecular. In the case of an allylic alcohol, rearrangement could accompany any of these modes of reaction.

Primary allylic alcohols usually react with phosphorus trichloride to give mostly the primary chloride.[133] With the same reagent, resolved asymmetric alcohols usually give optically active chlorides with inversion of configuration and some racemization;[134] and *cis*-3-substituted alcohols usually give the corresponding *cis*-chlorides.[133,135] These reactions all could be S_N2 displacements of the type indicated in equation 48, but this is not the only mechanistic possibility.[132a] Unsymmetrically substituted secondary and tertiary allylic alcohols give mixtures containing less than the equilibrium amount of the isomeric allylic chloride, and the corresponding result is found in the reaction with phosphorus tribromide.[136]

Phosphorus pentahalides have also been used for the conversion of allylic alcohols to allylic halides.[cf. 137] No doubt these also are two-stage processes, but their details have not been elucidated.

[132c] De Wolfe and Young's statement [132b] that the reactions of 1- and 3-methylallyl alcohols with hydrogen chloride "have been postulated to involve the formation of an intermediate allylic carbonium ion" may be true, but is not documented by the reference which they cite.

[133] L. F. Hatch and S. S. Nesbitt, *J. Am. Chem. Soc.*, **72**, 727 (1950).

[134] E. R. Alexander and R. W. Kluiber, *J. Am. Chem. Soc.*, **73**, 4304 (1951).

[135] K. Mislow and H. M. Hellmann, *J. Am. Chem. Soc.*, **73**, 244 (1951).

[136] W. G. Young and J. F. Lane, *J. Am. Chem. Soc.*, **59**, 2051 (1937); **60**, 847 (1938).

[137] C. D. Hurd and M. P. Puterbaugh, *J. Org. Chem.*, **2**, 381 (1937).

Reactions with Thionyl Halides.[cf. 132b] The first product of the reaction of an alcohol with thionyl chloride is generally the chlorosulfite (eq. 49). Three

$$ROH + SOCl_2 \rightarrow ROS(O)Cl + HCl \qquad (49)$$

general mechanisms are available for conversion of chlorosulfites to chlorides; these are shown in their simplest forms in equations 50, 51, and 52.[138,139,139a]

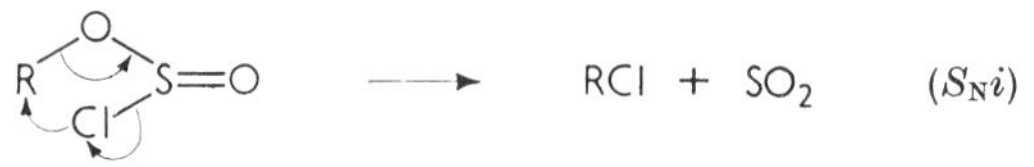

$$RCl + SO_2 \quad (S_N i) \qquad (50)$$

$$ROS(O)Cl + Cl^- \rightarrow ClR + SO_2 + Cl^- \quad (S_N 2) \qquad (51)$$

$$ROS(O)Cl \xrightarrow[-SO_2]{} R^+ + Cl^- \rightarrow RCl \quad (S_N 1) \qquad (52)$$

For allylic halides, the intramolecular process could involve replacement with or without rearrangement (eq. 53). In fact, it appears that when these

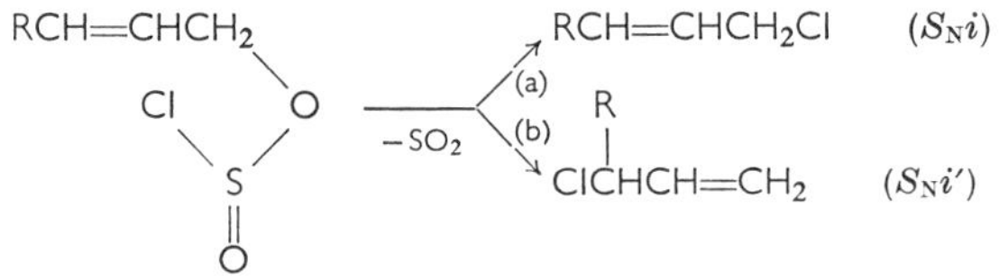

$$ (53) $$

two processes only are in competition, the rearrangement (which involves a six-center transition state (eq. 53b)) predominates over the replacement (which involves a four-center transition state (eq. 53a)) by a very large factor. This led to the development by Young and his co-workers [140] of a very valuable procedure for obtaining rearranged chlorides from primary alcohols, even when the products are thermodynamically unstable and quite labile. The reaction is performed at low concentration in ether solution, and in favorable cases either isomer can be obtained from the appropriate starting material in nearly 100% yield.

An interesting stereochemical feature of the rearrangement is that optically active 1,3-dimethylallyl alcohol under these conditions gives the rearranged chloride with maintained optical activity and inversion of absolute configuration.[140] This result implies that the chlorosulfite reacts mainly in conformation **83**, and not at all in conformation **84**. One would not expect the transition states for the conversion of these conformational isomers to the

[138] W. A. Cowdrey, E. D. Hughes, C. K. Ingold, S. Masterman, and A. D. Scott, *J. Chem. Soc. (London)*, **1937**, 1252.

[139] C. E. Boozer and E. S. Lewis, *J. Am. Chem. Soc.*, **75**, 3182 (1953).

[139a] J. A. Pegolotti and W. G. Young, *J. Am. Chem. Soc.*, **83**, 3251 (1961).

[140] F. F. Caserio, G. E. Dennis, R. H. DeWolfe, and W. G. Young, *J. Am. Chem. Soc.*, **77**, 4182 (1955).

rearranged halides (**85** and **86**), to differ energetically by much more than is found for the corresponding cases of the uni- and bimolecular reactions of 1-methylallyl derivatives discussed on pages 51 and 52. Although it has been claimed [140] that the reaction is highly stereospecific, the writer feels that more careful examination would reveal that a small amount (perhaps up to 5%, by analogy with the results for 1-methylallyl derivatives) of the reaction involves the conformer **84**, reaction through which is permitted stereoelectronically and gives the geometrically isomeric chloride, **86** (Scheme 16).

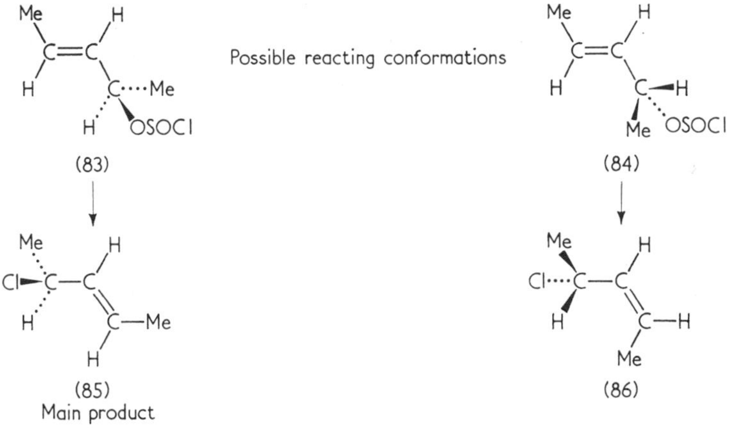

Scheme 16.   Intramolecular rearrangement of 1,3-dimethylallyl chlorosulfite.

The view has generally been taken that these rearrangements, though formally to be included in the class of $S_N i'$ reactions, involve considerable ionic character in the transition state. Study of solvent effects in the rearrangement of allyl chlorosulfite-1-^{14}C, which proceeds with quantitative allylic rearrangement in n-decane but with varying degrees of preservation of structure in other solvents, supports this hypothesis in a general way, although it suggests that specific solvent effects are also important in determining the rate and the ratio of allylic shift to total chlorination.[141]

An alternative mode of decomposition of an allylic chlorosulfite involves bimolecular attack by halide ion (eq. 51). This mode of reaction seems to become predominant when the reaction involving an alcohol and thionyl chloride is carried out in the presence of a base, so that the hydrogen chloride is kept in solution as a partly ionized hydrochloride. For most structures, a mixture of rearranged and unrearranged products are then formed, although, of course, when the S_N2 process is difficult or impossible, reaction with

[141] S. H. Sharman, F. F. Caserio, R. F. Nystrom, J. C. Leak, and W. G. Young, *J. Am. Chem. Soc.*, **80**, 5965 (1958).

rearrangement is maintained in the presence of a base, as in certain steroidal alcohols.[142]

It seems that unimolecular decompositions of allylic chlorosulfites can sometimes also take part in these reactions, but under many conditions it is difficult to assess the relative importance of the various mechanisms.

Rearrangements of Chloroformates. A reaction formally similar to the conversion of chlorosulfites to chlorides occurs when a chloroformate is heated. Olivier and Young [143] have investigated the rearrangement of 1-methylallyl chloroformate (which follows Scheme 17), and some of its analogs. Evidence

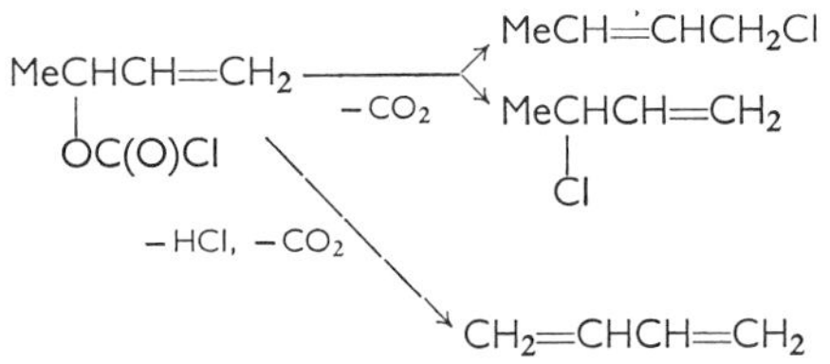

Scheme 17. Pyrolysis of 1-methylallyl chloroformate.

was presented that $S_N i'$ and $S_N 2$ reactions were much less important in this case than for the chlorosulfites; it was considered that ion pairs are intermediates in the rearrangement.

F. Allylic Amines

Although allylic rearrangements accompanying the deamination of unsaturated amines have been recognized for many years, the most important contribution in this field comes from the work of W. G. Young and his co-workers.[144] They studied under similar conditions not only the acetolyses, catalyzed by silver ion, of 1- and 3-methylallyl chlorides and of 1,1- and 3,3-dimethylallyl chlorides, but also the deaminations of the corresponding amines. The acetolyses gave no "product spread," so were considered to involve common carbonium ion intermediates from isomeric allylic structures. From the product ratios in the deamination, they were then able to estimate what percentage of the reaction involved some other path (termed "unusual" in Table XI, which summarizes the results).

No deuterium was incorporated into the amine when the reaction was performed in deuterium oxide, so reaction did not involve such an intermediate as $CH_2 : CHC(Me) : N : N$. No change in product composition was observed when sodium acetate was added. Optically active 1-methylallylamine gave predominant inversion and much racemization.

[142] R. E. Ireland, T. I. Wrigley, and W. G. Young, *J. Am. Chem. Soc.*, **80**, 4604 (1958), **81**, 2818 (1959).

[143] K. L. Olivier and W. G. Young, *J. Am. Chem. Soc.*, **81**, 5811 (1959).

[144] D. Semenov, C. H. Shih, and W. G. Young, *J. Am. Chem. Soc.*, **80**, 5472 (1958).

It was considered that the reaction involves a sequence of the type indicated in equation 54. The intermediate "hot carbonium ion" was thought to

$$RNH_2 \xrightarrow{HNO_2} R-\overset{+}{N}\equiv N \xrightarrow{-N_2} \text{"Hot carbonium ion"} \rightarrow \text{Products} \qquad (54)$$

be formed in a state which differs from that in which the ion R^+ is obtained in other reactions and to react before it had time to reach equilibrium with its environment. Evidence of a not completely compelling character was adduced against the view [cf. 145] that bimolecular reaction with the solvent on the diazonium cation $[RN\equiv N]^+$ might in part account for the unusual product ratio. In water, however, it seems [145a] that less of the reaction goes through this unusual path.

TABLE XI

Product Ratios in the Deamination of Allylic Amines

Amine	Product, %		
	Primary acetate	Secondary or tertiary acetate	Reaction by "unusual" path, %
MeCH:CHCH₂NH₂	80	20	52
MeCHCH:CH₂ | NH₂	33	67	43
Me₂C:CHCH₂NH₂	78	22	52
Me₂CCH:CH₂ | NH₂	60	40	—

G. Allylic Grignard Reagents

Allylic shifts often accompany reactions of Grignard reagents with allylic olefins. Typical equations are:

$$RCH{=}CHCH(X)R' \xrightarrow[-MgX_2]{R''MgX} \begin{cases} RCH{=}CHCHR'R'' \\ RR''CHCH{=}CHR' \end{cases} \qquad (55)$$

$$MeCH{=}CHCH_2MgX \xrightarrow[-MgXY]{HY} \begin{cases} MeCH_2CH{=}CH_2 \quad (57\%) \\ MeCH{=}CHCH_3 \quad (43\%) \end{cases} \qquad (56)$$

[145] A. Streitwieser, Jr. and W. D. Schaeffer, J. Am. Chem. Soc., 79, 2888 (1957); A. Streitwieser, Jr., J. Org. Chem., 22, 861 (1957).

$$PhCH{=}CHCH_2MgX \xrightarrow[-MgXY]{HY} \begin{array}{l} PhCH_2CH{=}CH_2 \\ (73\%) \\[1em] PhCH{=}CHCH_3 \\ (27\%) \end{array} \tag{57}$$

$$RCH{=}CHCH_2MgX + R'C(O)R'' \rightarrow \underset{\underset{CR'R''OH}{|}}{RCHCH{=}CH_2} \tag{58}$$

These reactions have been reviewed by De Wolfe and Young.[145a, cf. 146] Here we shall refer only to a recent important discovery by Nordlander and Roberts.[147] The proton magnetic resonance spectrum of allyl magnesium bromide in ether indicates that the equilibrium (eq. 59) is very rapidly established.

$$BrMg\overset{*}{C}H_2CH{=}CH_2 \rightleftharpoons \overset{*}{C}H_2{=}CHCH_2MgBr \tag{59}$$

H. Miscellaneous Allylic Rearrangements

Among the interesting allylic rearrangements that have been investigated since De Wolfe and Young's review [145a] are those of thiocyanates [148] and of hydroperoxides.[149,149a] Allylic thiocyanates rearrange to give the corresponding isothiocyanates (eq. 60). The rate of reaction is not very sensitive

$$MeCH{=}CHCH_2SCN \rightarrow \underset{\underset{NCS}{|}}{MeCHCH{=}CH_2} \tag{60}$$

to the solvent, but is increased by electron release, the relative reactivities of compounds RSCN being R = allyl < 3-methylallyl < 3,3-dimethylallyl. The reaction clearly can be intramolecular, but it is not thoroughly established to what extent the SCN group can become free during the reaction.

With regard to hydroperoxides, it has been shown that **87** rearranges in

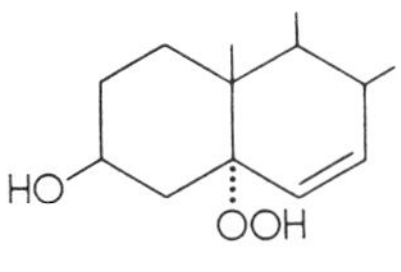

(87) 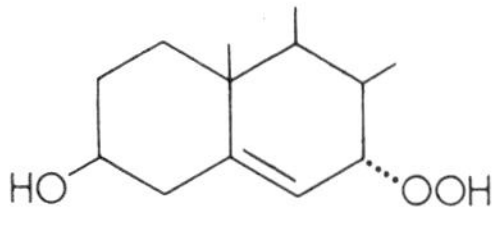   (88)

chloroform at room temperature to 7α-hydroperoxycholesterol (**88**). There are indications [149] that the reaction may be homolytic in nature.

[145a] R. H. De Wolfe and W. G. Young, *Chem. Revs.*, **56**, 753 (1956).

[146] W. G. Young and W. P. Norris, *J. Am. Chem. Soc.*, **81**, 490 (1959).

[147] J. E. Nordlander and J. D. Roberts, *J. Am. Chem. Soc.*, **81**, 1769 (1959).

[148] A. Iliceto, A. Fava, and U. Mazzucato, *Tetrahedron Letters*, No. **11**, 27 (1960); P. A. S. Smith and D. W. Emerson, *J. Am. Chem. Soc.*, **82**, 3076 (1960).

[149] G. O. Schenck, O. Neumüller, and W. Eisfeld, *Ann.*, **618**, 202 (1958).

[149a] B. Lythgoe and S. Trippett, *J. Chem. Soc. (London)*, **1959**, 471.

3. RELATED ANIONOTROPIC PROCESSES

Many types of anionotropic rearrangement are known, and can be related both formally and mechanistically to the three-carbon anionotropic rearrangements which we have considered in the previous sections.

A. Vinylogs of Three-Carbon Systems

Anionotropy involving higher vinylogs of three-carbon allylic systems (i.e., unsaturated systems of $(2n+1)$ carbon atoms, where n is an integer greater than one) is well known, although few such systems have been investigated mechanistically. The rearrangement of the carbinol 89 (eq. 61) involves a five-carbon allylic shift and has the same mechanistic characteristics as the related three-carbon process.[149b]

$$Me_2CCH=CHCH=CHR \rightarrow Me_2C=CHCH=CHCHR \qquad (61)$$
$$\underset{OH}{|} \qquad\qquad\qquad\qquad \underset{OH}{|}$$
$$(R = H, Me)$$
$$(89) \qquad\qquad\qquad (90)$$

Of course, the special steric relationships which favor three-carbon S_Ni' rearrangement will generally be absent in the higher vinylogs.

B. Acetylene-Allene Rearrangements

The propargyl cation, $HC\!:\!CCH_2^+$, like the allyl cation, is mesomeric. The second canonical form, $H\overset{+}{C}\!:\!C\!:\!CH_2$, is not expected to be the major contributor to the resonance hybrid,[cf. 150] since its formally allenic system is considerably strained. Nevertheless, the chemistry of substituted propargylic compounds includes examples of many of the processes made familiar through their allylic analogs.

Unimolecular acid-catalyzed rearrangements of alcohols in this series are exemplified by the reaction studied by Meyer and Schuster,[151,cf. 152] in which an acetylenic carbinol rearranges to an α,β-unsaturated aldehyde or ketone (eqs. 62 and 63). The probable course taken by such reactions [152] is indicated

$$PhCHC\equiv CH \xrightarrow{\ H^+\ } PhCH=CHCHO \qquad (62)$$
$$\underset{OH}{|}$$

$$Ph_2CC\equiv CPh \xrightarrow{\ H^+\ } Ph_2C=CHCOPh \qquad (63)$$
$$\underset{OH}{|}$$

[149b] E. A. Braude and C. J. Timmons, *J. Chem. Soc.* (*London*), **1950**, 2000, 2007, **1953**, 3131, 3138; cf. M. Julia, *Bull. soc. chim. France*, C13 (1951).

[150] J. Collin and F. P. Lossing, *J. Am. Chem. Soc.*, **79**, 5848 (1957).

[151] K. H. Meyer and K. Schuster, *Ber.*, **55**, 819 (1922).

[152] W. S. MacGregor, *J. Am. Chem. Soc.*, **70**, 3953 (1948); G. F. Hennion, R. B. Davis, and D. E. Maloney, *J. Am. Chem. Soc.*, **71**, 2813 (1949).

in Scheme 18; the indicated elimination-addition sequence (the Rupe rearrangement) can compete in appropriately substituted systems.[152,153]

These reactions take the indicated courses because they are driven forward by the irreversible processes involved in formation of the carbonyl compounds. The preferred first kinetically controlled product from substituted propargyl carbonium ions generally seems to be the corresponding propargyl derivative, as is shown by the fact that the solvolysis of 1,1-dimethylpropargyl chloride under neutral conditions[154] gives the corresponding alcohol (eq. 64).

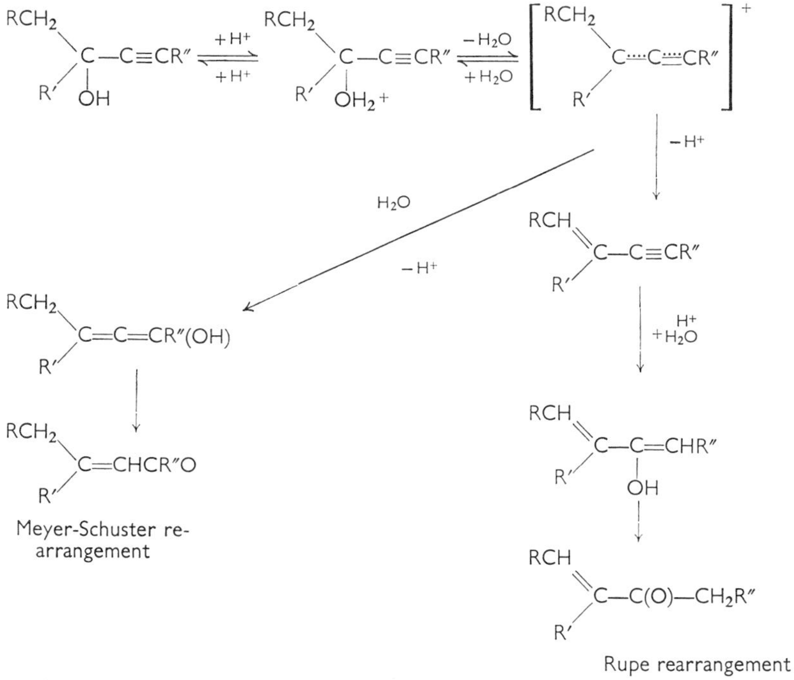

Scheme 18. Probable courses of the Meyer-Schuster and Rupe rearrangements.

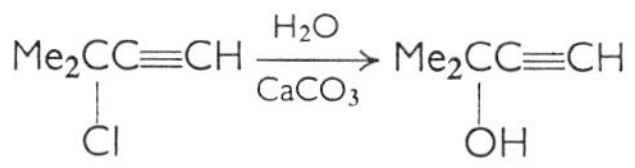

$$Me_2CC\equiv CH \xrightarrow[CaCO_3]{H_2O} Me_2CC\equiv CH \qquad (64)$$
$$\overset{|}{Cl} \qquad\qquad \overset{|}{OH}$$

Hennion and his co-workers[155] have examined the products and kinetics of solvolysis of such compounds in aqueous solvents. The reactions are slower than the corresponding reactions of tertiary alkyl chlorides, a fact which reveals the electron-withdrawing inductive effect of the ethynyl substituent (cf. page 80). Electron-releasing substituents increase the rate.

[153] H. Rupe and E. Kambli, *Helv. Chim. Acta*, **9**, 672 (1926).

[154] T. A. Favorskaya, *J. Gen. Chem. (U.S.S.R.)*, **9**, 386 (1939); through *Chem. Abstr.*, **33**, 9281 (1939).

These workers have also examined the rates of the analogous base-catalyzed reactions. These are kinetically of the second order, and the same product is obtained from both the propargylic and the allenic chlorides. The reaction sequences [155] suggested are indicated in Scheme 19. Proof that proton loss is

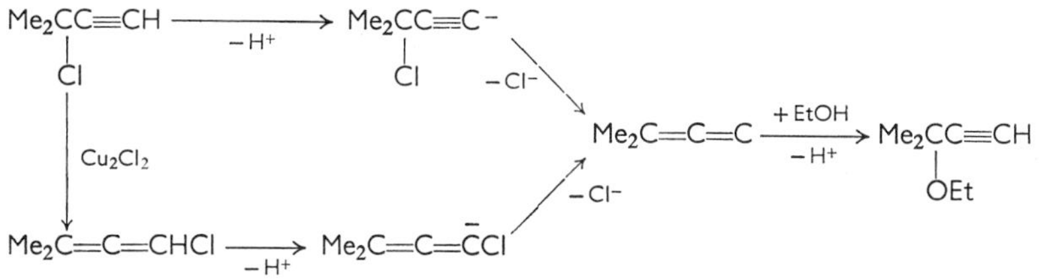

$$Me_2CC{\equiv}CH \xrightarrow{-H^+} Me_2CC{\equiv}C^-$$

(with CI substituents, Cu_2Cl_2, $-Cl^-$, $+EtOH$, $-H^+$ branches)

$$Me_2C{=}C{=}C \xrightarrow[-H^+]{+EtOH} Me_2CC{\equiv}CH$$

$$Me_2C{=}C{=}CHCl \xrightarrow{-H^+} Me_2C{=}C{=}\bar{C}Cl$$

Scheme 19. Interconversion and base-catalyzed reactions of propargylic and allenic halides.

concerned in the reaction of the propargylic isomer is provided by the fact that the bimolecular reaction of $Me_2C(Cl)C{:}CMe$ is much slower [155,156] than that of $Me_2CClC{:}CH$. It would be valuable to obtain formal proof relating to the allenic isomer, in view of the ambiguities discussed on page 35.

Direct rearrangements of acetylenic to allenic chlorides in this system have also been effected,[154,155] although the precise function of the catalyst, cuprous chloride, is not known. Intramolecular rearrangements involving cyclic transition states have been established by Landor and his co-workers for tertiary acetylenic carbinols.[157] Thus the optically active alcohol, 3,4-4-trimethylpent-1-yn-3-ol (91), with thionyl chloride in dioxane gave the optically active allenic chloride (92) (eq. 65).

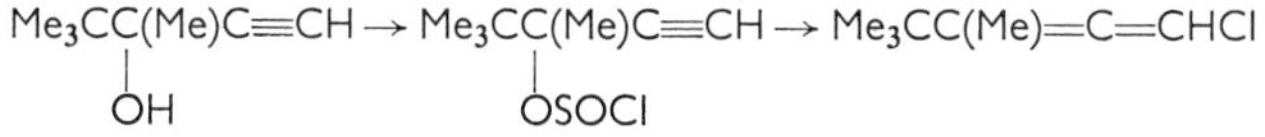

$$Me_3CC(Me)C{\equiv}CH \rightarrow Me_3CC(Me)C{\equiv}CH \rightarrow Me_3CC(Me){=}C{=}CHCl \quad (65)$$

with OH (91) and $OSOCl$ (92) substituents

Bimolecular reactions of propargylic halides with ambident anions which may involve S_N2' processes have also been described.[158]

C. Ring-Chain Anionotropy

If we consider double bonds and rings to be analogous in a formal sense, we can by the same analogy associate three-carbon anionotropy with ring-chain anionotropy. Many of these processes are considered in detail elsewhere

[155] G. F. Hennion, J. J. Sheehan, and D. E. Maloney, J. Am. Chem. Soc., 72, 3542 (1950); G. F. Hennion and D. E. Maloney, J. Am. Chem. Soc., 73, 4735 (1951); G. F. Hennion and E. G. Teach, J. Am. Chem. Soc., 75, 1653 (1953); G. F. Hennion and K. W. Nelson, J. Am. Chem. Soc., 79, 2142 (1957); cf. more recently V. J. Shiner, Jr., and J. W. Wilson, J. Am. Chem. Soc., 84, 2402 (1962).

[156] A. Burawoy and E. Spinner, J. Chem. Soc. (London), 1954, 3752.

[157] Y. R. Bhatia, P. D. Landor, and S. R. Landor, J. Chem. Soc. (London), 1959, 24; S. R. Landor and R. Taylor-Smith, Proc. Chem. Soc. (London), 1959, 154.

[158] L. Crombie and K. Mackenzie, J. Chem. Soc. (London), 1958, 4417.

in this volume (e.g., Sections 4 and 11). Here we shall merely mention some examples.

The so-called isosteroid rearrangement, illustrated by the work of Winstein and Kosower [159] in the case of 3,5-cyclocholestan-6-yl derivatives, has its simpler analogs; for example, the acid-catalyzed rearrangement of 1-cyclopropylethylmethyl ether (93) to pent-3-en-1-yl methyl ether (94).[160]

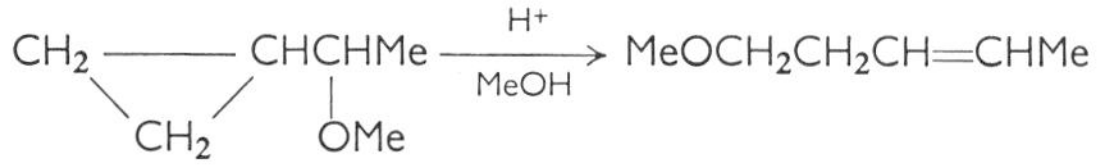

$$
\underset{(93)}{CH_2 \diagup \overset{\displaystyle CH_2}{\diagup} CHCHMe \overset{\displaystyle |}{\underset{\displaystyle OMe}{}}} \xrightarrow[MeOH]{H^+} \underset{(94)}{MeOCH_2CH_2CH{=}CHMe} \qquad (66)
$$

No doubt S_N1' and S_Ni' processes are both available in such systems. Roberts and his co-workers have considered in detail the carbonium ionic intermediates concerned in the interconversion by anionotropic processes of cyclopropylcarbinyl (95), cyclobutyl (96), and allylcarbinyl (97) derivatives and

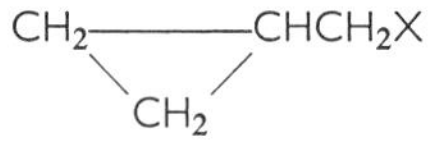

$$
\underset{(95)}{CH_2 \diagup \overset{\displaystyle CH_2}{\diagdown} CHCH_2X} \qquad \underset{(96)}{\overset{\displaystyle CH_2 - CHX}{\underset{\displaystyle CH_2 - CH_2}{|\qquad|}}} \qquad \underset{(97)}{CH_2{=}CH-CH_2-CH_2X}
$$

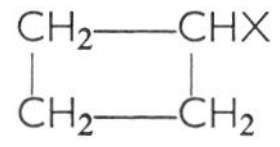

have regarded the results as best interpreted in terms of several isomeric non-classical unsymmetrical "bicyclobutonium ion" intermediates.[161] An interesting analogous ring expansion (eq. 67) has been described by Parham and his

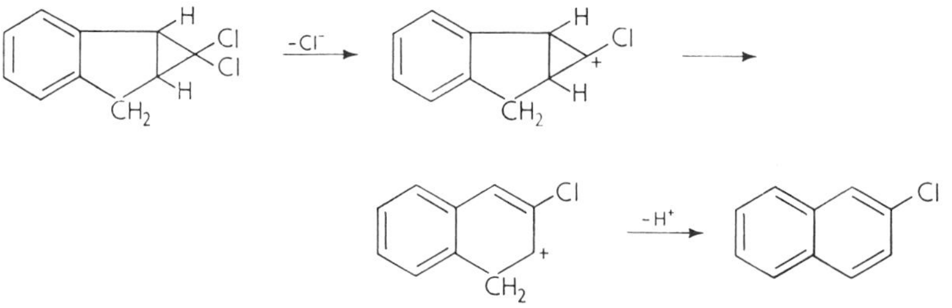

$$ (67) $$

co-workers.[162] Many examples [cf. 163,164] of related carbonium ion rearrangements are now known in the chemistry of compounds containing the so-called "medium rings."

[159] S. Winstein and E. M. Kosower, J. Am. Chem. Soc., 81, 4399 (1959).

[160] R. G. Pearson and S. H. Langer, J. Am. Chem. Soc., 75, 1065 (1953).

[161] R. H. Mazur, W. N. White, D. A. Semenov, C. C. Lee, M. S. Silver, and J. D. Roberts, J. Am. Chem. Soc., 81, 4390 (1959).

[162] W. E. Parham, H. E. Reiff, and P. Swartzentruber, J. Am. Chem. Soc., 78, 1437 (1956).

[163] H. L. Goering, H. M. Espy, and W. D. Closson, J. Am. Chem. Soc., 81, 329 (1959).

[164] A. C. Cope and P. E. Peterson, J. Am. Chem. Soc., 81, 1643 (1959).

4. ALLYLIC CARBONIUM IONS IN ADDITION REACTIONS

The initial product of attack by an electrophile on a diene can be an allylic cation, as was illustrated in equation 4 (page 29). So the chemistry encountered in anionotropic rearrangement involving carbonium ions may be paralleled in the chemistry of addition to dienes. This was recognized by Burton and Ingold,[164a] whose discussion was later [164b,165] put in more modern terms.

Few of these reactions have been investigated mechanistically. In part, this is because they are very rapid, or because the conditions convenient for isolation of the required products involve aprotic media. The products often delineate the general nature of the processes, but it must be recognized that the detailed paths have not been completely elucidated.

A. Heterolytic Addition of Hydrogen Halides

These reactions are generally considered to be initiated by electrophilic hydrogen, as is shown by their kinetic forms and by the effects of structure on the rates of reaction.[166,167] It is reasonable to believe that carbonium ions are intermediates. In aprotic solvents, the reactions are of high kinetic order in hydrogen halide,[166,167] but it is by no means clear how long the carbonium ions survive. The fact that some olefins react by *trans* addition has led to the view that attachment of the nucleophilic and electrophilic fragment may often be nearly synchronous, or alternatively that the nature of the intermediate is such as to hold the geometrical configuration about the double bond.[168,cf. 169]

Addition of hydrogen chloride to 1,3-dienes always seems to be initiated at the end of the conjugated system, where polarizability makes electrons most readily available. With butadiene and with isoprene, the initial products contain more than the equilibrium amount of the thermodynamically less stable isomer, formed by 1,2 addition.[170] It is interesting and important

[164a] H. Burton and C. K. Ingold, *J. Chem. Soc. (London)*, **1928**, 904.

[164b] C. K. Ingold, *Structure and Mechanism in Organic Chemistry*, G. Bell and Sons, London, 1953.

[165] P. B. D. de la Mare, E. D. Hughes, and C. K. Ingold, *J. Chem. Soc. (London)*, **1948**, 17.

[166] F. R. Mayo and J. J. Katz, *J. Am. Chem. Soc.*, **69**, 1339 (1947).

[167] Y. Pocker, *J. Chem. Soc. (London)*, **1960**, 1292.

[168] G. S. Hammond and J. Warkentin, *J. Am. Chem. Soc.*, **83**, 2554 (1961).

[169] G. S. Hammond and T. D. Nevitt, *J. Am. Chem. Soc.*, **76**, 4121 (1954); G. S. Hammond and C. H. Collins, *J. Am. Chem. Soc.*, **82**, 4323 (1960).

[170] A. J. Ultée, *J. Chem. Soc. (London)*, **1948**, 530; A. L. Henne, H. Chanan, and A. Turk, *J. Am. Chem. Soc.*, **63**, 3474 (1941).

that vinylacetylene gives a predominance of the allenic chloride [171] (eq. 69). In this case 1,4 addition has predominated, to give again the thermodynamically less stable isomer.

$$CH_2{=}C(Me)CH{=}CH_2 \xrightarrow[-Cl^-]{+HCl} [CH_3C(Me){\cdots}CH{\cdots}CH_2]^+ \xrightarrow{+Cl^-}$$

$$\begin{array}{l} CH_3C(Me)CH{=}CH_2 \\ \qquad | \\ \qquad Cl \\ \text{Major product} \end{array} \qquad (68)$$

$$CH_3C(Me){=}CHCH_2Cl$$
Minor product

$$CH_2{=}CHC{\equiv}CH \xrightarrow{HCl} ClCH_2CH{=}C{=}CH_2 \qquad (69)$$

With hydrogen bromide, it is generally difficult to effect addition under conditions in which the products do not rearrange; so generally the equilibrium mixture of isomers is obtained.[165]

The pattern of results can be treated in terms of initial reaction to give the thermodynamically less stable isomer, followed by rearrangement when the conditions allow it (cf. pages 32, 33). One case has, however, been examined in which the products of 1,2 and 1,4 addition are chemically the same (isotope effects being neglected) and therefore thermodynamically equivalent.[168] This is the addition of deuterium bromide to 1,3-cyclohexadiene (98) in pentane. The orientation and stereochemistry were determined. On the basis of plausible assumptions, it was suggested that the primary reaction gives 20% trans-1,2 (99) and 80% cis-1,4 (100) addition, and that the latter material in part underwent rearrangement to the cis-1,2 adduct (101). Under these

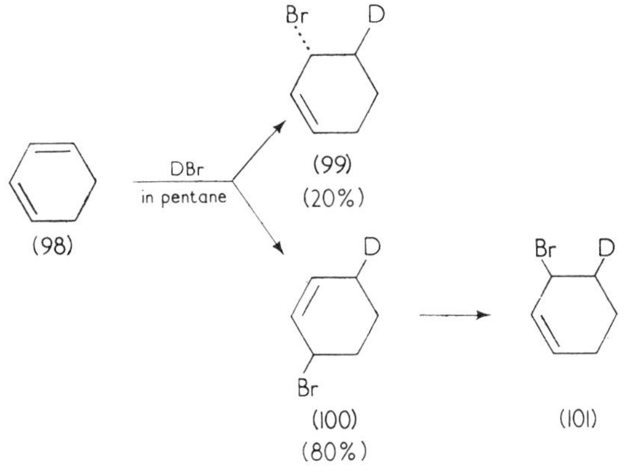

Scheme 20.   Addition of deuterium bromide to cyclohexadiene in pentane.

circumstances the cis-1,4 adduct must be formed through an intermediate which is not identical with that concerned in the rearrangement.

[171] W. H. Carothers, G. J. Berchet, and A. M. Collins, J. Am. Chem. Soc., 54, 4066 (1932).

B. *Addition of Chlorine*

Addition of chlorine to olefins is an electrophilic process, powerfully favored by electron accession to the double bond. The kinetics of the reaction have been examined mainly in acetic acid as solvent, where the kinetic form is

$$-d[Cl_2]/dt = k_2[\text{Olefin}][Cl_2]$$

and the rate is accelerated by added electrolytes, including lithium chloride, but only to the extent expected for a salt effect.[cf. 172]

It is well known that in hydroxylic solvents the formation of the dihalide is accompanied by products of reaction of the solvent or of added anions with the carbonium ion.[173] It is not clear for any single case, however, to what extent the product composition is determined in the rate-controlling process.

The stereochemistry of addition is known for certain compounds, but only under conditions which have not been examined kinetically. It has been considered generally that *trans* addition of chlorine to but-2-ene [174] indicates interaction between chlorine and the carbonium ion center in a "chloronium intermediate" (**102**), similar to that considered [174a] to be involved in the inter-

$$\text{MeCH} \overline{\qquad\qquad} \text{CHMe}$$
$$\underset{\overset{+}{Cl}}{\diagdown \diagup}$$

(102)

conversions of compounds of the type RCHClCHXR'. There is no evidence relating to the extent to which *cis* accompanies *trans* addition under conditions

[172] P. B. D. de la Mare, *Quart. Revs. (London)*, **3**, 126 (1949).

[173] G. Williams, *Trans. Faraday Soc.*, **37**, 749 (1941).

[174] H. J. Lucas and C. W. Gould, Jr., *J. Am. Chem. Soc.*, **63**, 2541 (1941).

[174a] The history of the status of chloronium intermediates, as it appears to the writer, is as follows. Roberts and Kimball [175] first proposed the bromonium intermediate to account for *trans*- addition of bromine to olefinic compounds. Lucas and Winstein,[176] having provided stereochemical evidence for such intermediates in replacement reactions, first mentioned that there may be analogous chloronium intermediates. Lucas and Gould [174] provided the related stereochemical evidence both for additions of chlorine and for replacement reactions involving neighboring chlorine. This evidence has been accepted explicitly by Winstein.[177] It should be remembered also that the chlorine substituent has been ascribed zero "driving force" for neighboring group participation in solvolysis,[178] and competes poorly with other substituents in this process.[cf. 179]

[175] I. Roberts and G. E. Kimball, *J. Am. Chem. Soc.*, **59**, 947 (1937).

[176] S. Winstein and H. J. Lucas, *J. Am. Chem. Soc.*, **61**, 2845 (1939).

[177] S. Winstein, *J. Am. Chem. Soc.*, **64**, 2791 (1942); *Bull. Soc. chim. France*, C55 (1951).

[178] S. Winstein, E. Grunwald, and L. L. Ingraham, *J. Am. Chem. Soc.*, **70**, 821 (1948).

[179] S. Winstein and D. Seymour, *J. Am. Chem. Soc.*, **68**, 119 (1946).

of known mechanism, though recent data concerning addition to acenaphthylene [180] and to phenanthrene [181] suggest that *cis* addition of chlorine may be more common than has generally been realized. Nor is there any evidence concerning whether the products are determined before or after the Cl—Cl bond is broken in the course of reaction; the intermediate in which neighboring group participation predominates could just as well be of the form [olefin·ClX] as of the form [olefin·Cl⁺] (cf. **103–106**).[173] Nor is there any

(103)   (104)   (105)   (106)

conclusive evidence whether in the configuration-controlling intermediate the electrophile is attached symmetrically (**103** and **105**) or unsymmetrically (**104** and **106**) to the double bond, although arguments which favor the latter view have been presented [182,183] and will be mentioned later.

These uncertainties of mechanistic detail being borne in mind, certain facts are clear in relation to the addition of chlorine to dienes. With chlorine and butadiene, the isomer formed in largest amount is the thermodynamically less stable 1,2 adduct.[184] The 1,4 adduct, which forms about a third of the monochloride present, is exclusively the *trans* isomer (**107**),[184a] so addition does not proceed through intermediates (e.g., **108** and **109**) involving the

(107)   (108)   (109)

s-cis conformation of butadiene. The 1,4 adduct must therefore be formed either in a stepwise or in a termolecular process, in which the entering chlorine interacts with only one of the double bonds.

There are a number of reports of addition of chlorine to other conjugated dienes. 1-Phenylbutadiene [185] and 1-vinylacrylic acid [186] both gave the

[180] S. J. Cristol, F. R. Stermitz, and P. S. Ramey, *J. Am. Chem. Soc.*, **78**, 4939 (1956).

[181] P. B. D. de la Mare and N. V. Klassen, *Chem. & Ind.* (*London*), **1960**, 498.

[182] P. B. D. de la Mare and J. G. Pritchard, *J. Chem. Soc.* (*London*), **1954**, 3910, 3990.

[183] E. S. Gould, *Mechanism and Structure in Organic Chemistry*. Holt, New York, 1959.

[184] I. E. Muskat and H. E. Northrop, *J. Am. Chem. Soc.*, **52**, 4043 (1930).

[184a] K. Mislow and H. M. Hellman, *J. Am. Chem. Soc.*, **73**, 244 (1951).

[185] I. E. Muskat and K. A. Huggins, *J. Am. Chem. Soc.*, **51**, 2496 (1929).

[186] I. E. Muskat and B. C. Becker, *J. Am. Chem. Soc.*, **52**, 812 (1930).

products of 3,4 addition, thermodynamically more stable because the conjugation with the substituent is preserved (eqs. 70 and 71). 2-Methylbutadiene [187,188] and 2-chlorobutadiene [189] are both reported as giving mainly the

$$PhCH{=}CHCH{=}CH_2 + Cl_2 \rightarrow PhCH{=}CHCHClCH_2Cl \qquad (70)$$

$$HO_2CCH{=}CHCH{=}CH_2 + Cl_2 \rightarrow HO_2CCH{=}CHCHClCH_2Cl \qquad (71)$$

thermodynamically more stable products of 1,4 addition (eqs. 72 and 73), together with some of the isomeric materials and other products. Although

$$CH_2{=}CH(Me)CH{=}CH_2 + Cl_2 \rightarrow ClCH_2C(Me){=}CHCH_2Cl \qquad (72)$$

$$CH_2{=}C(Cl)CH{=}CH_2 + Cl_2 \rightarrow ClCH_2C(Cl){=}CHCH_2Cl \qquad (73)$$

all these results can be interpreted in terms of prior addition to give the thermodynamically less stable adduct followed by rearrangement, it is not clear that the conditions were severe enough to ensure thermodynamic control in all cases, and reinvestigation of some of these systems would be valuable.

Interesting anionotropic systems can be concerned in the addition of chlorine to aromatic compounds. These additions often accompany substitutions, particularly in aprotic solvents. Few, if any, have been investigated from a mechanistic viewpoint. The addition of chlorine to naphthalene, for example, can give a dichlorodihydronaphthalene,[190] presumably either 1,2-dichloro-1,2-dihydronaphthalene (**110**) or 1,4-dichloro-1,4-dihydronaphthalene (**111**).

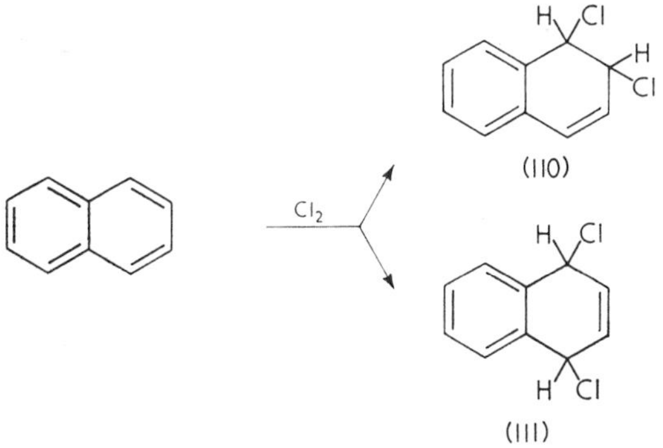

Both could exist in *cis* or *trans* forms, and the former would be the thermodynamically more stable product. The structure of the adduct does not seem to have been elucidated.[cf. 191]

[187] W. G. Jones and H. G. Williams, *J. Chem. Soc. (London),* **1934**, 829; D. V. Tishchenko, *J. Gen. Chem. U.S.S.R.,* **6**, 1131 (1936).

[188] A. J. Ultée, *Rec. trav. chim.,* **68**, 125 (1949).

[189] W. H. Carothers and G. J. Berchet, *J. Am. Chem. Soc.,* **55**, 1628 (1933); A. A. Petrov, *J. Gen. Chem. (U.S.S.R.),* **13**, 102 (1943).

[190] E. Fischer, *Ber.,* **11**, 735 (1878).

[191] F. Radt, ed., *Elsevier's Encyclopaedia of Organic Chemistry,* Vol. 12b, Elsevier, New York, 1948, p. 315.

C. Addition of Bromine

The mechanistic complexities in the field of chlorine addition are multiplied with the higher halogens because of the existence of kinetic forms of higher order than one in halogen. This kinetic behavior has been taken[192] as evidence that intermediates analogous to structure **105** are of greater importance than in chlorination.

Bromine is, of course, anionotropically much more labile than chlorine, so in addition reactions involving bromine the thermodynamically stable product is often obtained. Elsewhere,[165] reference has been made to a number of situations which may be of this type: other examples include the 1,4 addition of bromine to 2,3-dimethyl-1,3-butadiene[193] and the 1,6 addition of bromine to 2,4,6-hexatriene.[194]

Certain bromine additions to dienes have been examined under conditions where the product is known to be formed in a kinetically controlled step. Thus Hatch and his co-workers[195] have shown that addition of bromine to butadiene in a variety of solvents gives *trans*-1,4-dibromobut-2-ene and 3,4-dibromobut-1-ene in almost equal amounts, with a slight preponderance of the latter. So 3,4 addition, giving the thermodynamically less stable product, is preferred. The initial attack by bromine, as for chlorine,[184a] must involve attachment of the electrophile to one, and not both, of the double bonds, for the *cis*-1,4 adduct is not found in the product.

The addition of bromine to vinylacetylene also seems to give the thermodynamically less stable isomer (in this case the 1,4 adduct) as the major product (cf. eq. 69). It is not established whether the 1,4 adduct is obtained through initiation of reaction at the acetylenic or olefinic carbon atom. The former would be expected by analogy with the addition of hydrogen chloride, but products of 1,2 addition both to the double and to the triple bond were detected as minor components of the reaction mixture (eq. 74).[196]

$$CH_2=CHC\equiv CH \xrightarrow[CHCl_3]{Br_2} \begin{cases} BrCH_2CH=C=CHBr \\ CH_2=CHC(Br)=CHBr \\ BrCH_2CH(Br)C\equiv CH \end{cases} \qquad (74)$$

Young, Hall, and Winstein[197] have recently re-examined the addition of bromine to cyclopentadiene. In contrast with the reaction with butadiene,

[192] P. W. Robertson, *J. Chem. Soc. (London)*, **1954**, 1267.

[193] O. J. Sweeting and J. R. Johnson, *J. Am. Chem. Soc.*, **68**, 1057 (1946).

[194] C. Prévost, *Compt. rend.*, **183**, 1292 (1926); **184**, 458 (1927); R. Kuhn and A. Winterstein, *Helv. Chim. Acta*, **11**, 123 (1928).

[195] L. F. Hatch, P. D. Gardner, and R. E. Gilbert, *J. Am. Chem. Soc.*, **81**, 5943 (1959).

[196] A. A. Petrov, G. I. Semenov, and N. P. Sopov, *Zhur. Obshchei Khim.*, **27**, 928 (1957); A. A. Petrov and Y. I. Porfireva, *Zhur. Obshchei Khim.*, **27**, 1805 (1957).

[197] W. G. Young, H. K. Hall, Jr., and S. Winstein, *J. Am. Chem. Soc.*, **78**, 4338 (1956).

much of the product (113) of *cis*-1,4 addition was found. The mechanism of the reaction was discussed in terms of the possible formation either of an ion pair (112) as an intermediate or of 113 from bromine and cyclopentadiene directly.

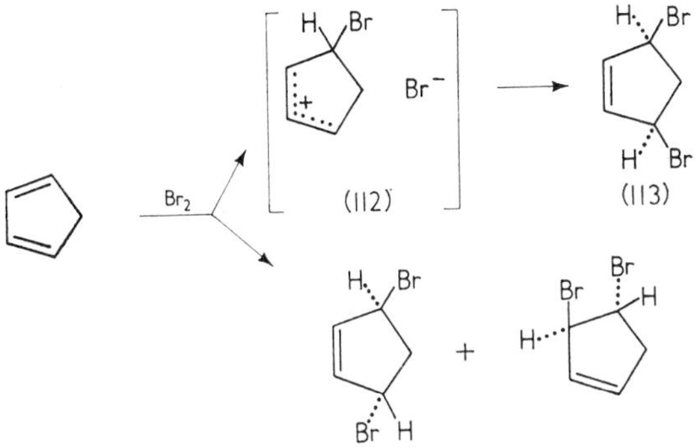

Scheme 21.   Addition of bromine to cyclopentadiene.

D. Addition of Hypohalous Acids

Hypohalous acids add to olefinic substances to form halogenohydrins (eq. 75). The reactions are electrophilic additions, being generally acid-

$$Me_2C{=}CH_2 + ClOH \rightarrow Me_2CCH_2Cl \qquad (75)$$
$$\underset{OH}{|}$$

catalyzed, [cf. 198] and facilitated by electron-releasing substituents in the olefin. [cf. 182,199] The chemistry of the reaction is such as to suggest that electrophilic chlorine, rather than electrophilic oxygen, is generally concerned in initiating attack on the unsaturated compound. Thus the orientation of addition is in the direction expected if chlorine were the electrophilic atom (eq. 75); [cf. 199,200] and diversion of the reaction by added nucleophiles, Y^-, gives [201,202] compounds of the type $>$CCl—CY$<$ rather than of the type $>$C(OH)—CY$<$.

Preparatively, the hypohalite can be supplied as aqueous hypochlorous acid, [cf. 199] as the halogen and water, [cf. 201] as an *N*-haloamine or amide, [cf. 202] or as an organic hypohalite. [203] If the reaction is carried out in a hydroxylic

[198] P. B. D. de la Mare, E. D. Hughes, and C. A. Vernon, *Research*, **3**, 242 (1950).

[199] P. Ballinger and P. B. D. de la Mare, *J. Chem. Soc.*, 1481 (1957).

[200] P. B. D. de la Mare and A. Salama, *J. Chem. Soc.*, 1956, 3337.

[201] E. M. Terry and L. Eichelberger, *J. Am. Chem. Soc.*, **47**, 1067 (1925); A. W. Francis, *J. Am. Chem. Soc.*, **47**, 2340 (1925).

[202] A. A. Petrov, *J. Gen. Chem. U.S.S.R.*, **9**, 2236 (1939); see also numerous other papers in this series.

[203] R. M. Evans and L. N. Owen, *J. Chem. Soc. (London)*, **1949**, 239.

solvent with such compounds as *tert*-butyl hypochlorite or *N*-chloroacetamide, ethers or esters are obtained (eq. 76).[203,204]

$$
RCH{=}CH_2
\begin{array}{l}
\text{Bu}^t\text{OCl, R'OH} \\
\nearrow \quad -\text{Bu}^t\text{OH} \quad \searrow RCHCH_2Cl \\
\searrow \quad \text{ClNHR'', R'OH} \quad \nearrow \overset{|}{O}R' \\
\quad -\text{R''NH}_2
\end{array}
\tag{76}
$$

(R' = alkyl, acyl)

Kinetically, all these reactions can become very complex. In water, at very low concentrations of hypochlorous acid, in the presence of silver ions, a kinetic term of the form

$$-d[\text{ClOH}]/dt = k[\text{olefin}][\text{ClOH}][\text{H}^+]$$

can be identified,[182,198,199] indicating reaction through Cl^+ or $ClOH_2^+$. Added anions catalyze the reaction, probably by forming new chlorinating agents (eqs. 77, 78, and 79).[199,205,206] As far as is known, all these modes of addition

$$ClOH_2{}^+ + Cl^- \rightarrow Cl_2 + H_2O \tag{77}$$

$$ClOH_2{}^+ + OAc^- \rightarrow ClOAc + H_2O \tag{78}$$

$$ClOH_2{}^+ + ClO^- \rightarrow Cl_2O + H_2O \tag{79}$$

give similar product ratios when two chlorohydrins are possible.[182] They are all clearly two stage in character and probably involve a major component of *trans* addition. [207,208]

Details of the mechanisms of addition of this type of reagent to conjugated dienes have not been elucidated. There is no doubt, however, that they follow the general pattern observed for halogens. Thus butadiene reacts with hypochlorous acid and with organic hypochlorites to give mixtures of 1,2 and 1,4 adducts.[203,204,209] A similar result has been established for addition of iodine chloride.[210] Phenyl- and chlorine-substituted 1,3-dienes with these reagents give behavior analogous to that found with halogens.[202,211]

[204] B. A. Arbuzov and V. M. Zoroastrova, *Compt. rend. acad. sci. U.R.S.S.*, **53**, 41 (1946).

[205] E. A. Shilov, G. V. Kupinskaya, and A. A. Yasnikov, *Doklady Akad. Nauk. S.S.S.R.*, **81**, 435 (1951).

[206] G. C. Israel, J. K. Martin, and F. G. Soper, *J. Chem. Soc. (London)*, **1950**, 1282; K. D. Reeve and G. C. Israel, *J. Chem. Soc. (London)*, **1952**, 2327.

[207] D. Atherton and T. P. Hilditch, *J. Chem. Soc. (London)*, **1943**, 204; W. G. Gensler and H. N. Schlein, *J. Am. Chem. Soc.*, **78**, 169 (1956).

[208] P. D. Bartlett, *J. Am. Chem. Soc.*, **57**, 224 (1935).

[209] R. D. Kadesch, *J. Am. Chem. Soc.*, **68**, 44 (1946).

[210] C. K. Ingold and H. G. Smith, *J. Chem. Soc. (London)*, **1931**, 2752.

[211] T. E. Muskat and L. B. Grimsley, *J. Am. Chem. Soc.*, **52**, 1574 (1930); O. Grummitt and R. M. Vance, *J. Am. Chem. Soc.*, **72**, 2669 (1950).

All these results indicate that under polar conditions addition is initiated terminally at the most polarizable unsaturated carbon atom. The reactions are probably kinetically controlled, for anionotropic chloro-alcohols are likely to be much less labile than the corresponding halides. A clear example of kinetic control is the reaction of *tert*-butyl hypochlorite with isoprene in acetic acid (Scheme 22).[212] The 1,2 adduct, which with its anionotropic

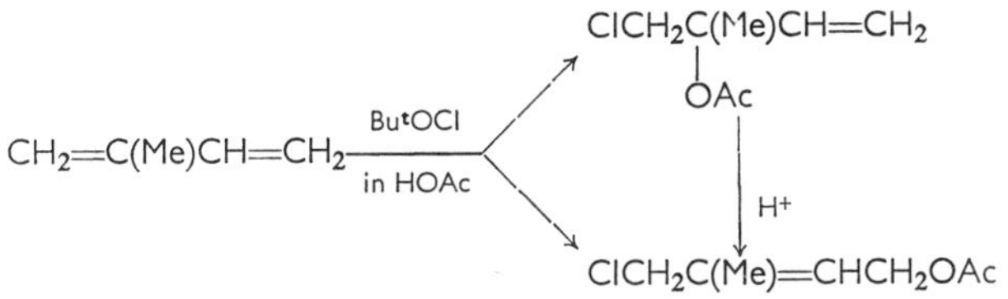

$$CH_2=C(Me)CH=CH_2 \xrightarrow[\text{in HOAc}]{Bu^tOCl} \begin{array}{c} ClCH_2C(Me)CH=CH_2 \\ | \\ OAc \end{array} \Big\downarrow H^+$$
$$ClCH_2C(Me)=CHCH_2OAc$$

Scheme 22.   Addition of chlorine acetate to isoprene.

isomer formed a substantial part of the product of addition, was stable under the reaction conditions, but isomerized under acid catalysis to the 1,4 adduct. Here again we have an example of 1,2 addition under kinetic control to give the thermodynamically less stable isomer.

The normal addition presumably involves a mesomeric intermediate, perhaps of the type **114**. Addition in *tert*-butanol, however, must involve

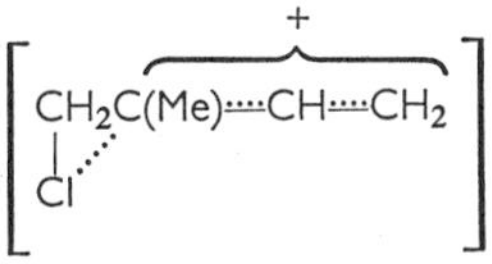

$$\left[\begin{array}{c} \overset{+}{\overbrace{CH_2C(Me)\cdots CH\cdots CH_2}} \\ | \\ Cl \end{array} \right]$$

(114)

another mechanism,[212] for it gives the reverse orientation, i.e., 1,4 addition (eq. 80). The nature of this reaction has not been elucidated; it is interesting that it involves the *s-trans* and not the *s-cis* conformation of the diene, since the product could be converted into tiglyl alcohol (eq. 80).

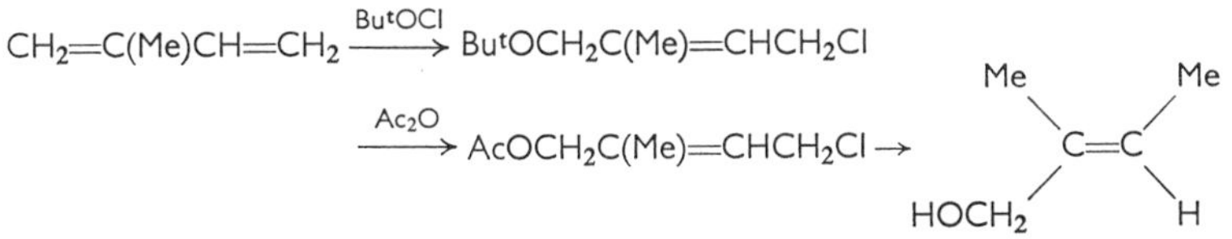

$$CH_2=C(Me)CH=CH_2 \xrightarrow{Bu^tOCl} Bu^tOCH_2C(Me)=CHCH_2Cl$$
$$\xrightarrow{Ac_2O} AcOCH_2C(Me)=CHCH_2Cl \rightarrow \begin{array}{c} \overset{Me}{\diagdown} \quad \overset{Me}{\diagup} \\ C=C \\ \overset{\diagup}{HOCH_2} \quad \overset{\diagdown}{H} \end{array} \quad (80)$$

5. NEIGHBORING-GROUP PARTICIPATION; SUBSTITUTION ACCOMPANYING ADDITION

As we have already noted, halogens do not always add in the *trans* sense to olefins, but *trans* addition is sufficiently general to make it reasonable to

[212] W. Oroshnik, *J. Am. Chem. Soc.*, **67**, 1627 (1945); W. Oroshnik and R. A. Mallory, *J. Am. Chem. Soc.*, **72**, 4608 (1950).

consider whether neighboring group participation has any other general consequences in the chemistry of allylic systems.

A. 1,2 Addition

One set of facts which have already been discussed could possibly be such a consequence, namely, the formation of products of 1,2 addition in amounts greater than would be expected under thermodynamic control (pages 92, 93). Since 1,4 interactions with entering electrophiles are excluded by the stereochemistry of 1,4 addition [195,212a] it seems certain that the entering halogen is initially attached only to one, and not to both, of the double bonds of the diene. Electrostatic or covalent interaction of the type illustrated in structure **115** must favor the contribution of this form over **116** to the reso-

$$\delta+ \ CH_2-\overset{+}{C}H-CH=CH_2 \qquad\qquad \delta+ \ CH_2-CH=CH-\overset{+}{C}H_2$$
$$\delta- \ \overset{|}{Cl} \qquad\qquad\qquad\qquad\qquad \delta- \ \overset{|}{Cl}$$
$$\text{(115)} \qquad\qquad\qquad\qquad\qquad \text{(116)}$$

nance hybrid. The partial localization of the carbonium center on C_2 should then ensure the preponderance of 1,2 addition.

The results for vinylacetylene (**117**),[196,212b] which gives predominantly 1,4 addition, forming the thermodynamically less stable adduct, then require separate interpretation. Here attack is known to be initiated at the acetylenic carbon atom; [212b] and of the two structures (**118** and **119**) which formally

$$\text{(117)} \qquad\qquad\qquad \text{(118)} \qquad\qquad\qquad \text{(119)}$$

contribute to the resonance hybrid, the geometry of **119** can better accord with the probability that the reagent will approach at right angles to the plane of the unsaturated system.   The resulting form (not shown) of the structure (**118**) is highly strained relative to its equilibrium conformation. So the ion may be formed to give a conformation to which the allenic carbonium structure (**119**) makes the major energetic contribution to the hybrid, and further reaction to give the 1,4 adduct may occur before the perturbed molecule distorts to allow the butadiene-like canonical form (**118**) to exert its full contribution. A consequence of this view, then, is that neighboring group interaction is of less importance in addition to vinylacetylene than to butadiene.

[212a] K. Mislow and H. M. Hellman, *J. Am. Chem. Soc.*, **73**, 244 (1951).

[212b] W. H. Carothers, G. J. Berchet, and A. M. Collins, *J. Am. Chem. Soc.*, **54**, 4066 (1932).

B. *Orientation of Proton Loss*

Yet another aspect of these interactions, it has been suggested, is the double bond rearrangement which occurs in the substitution reactions accompanying addition to allylic systems. An example is to be found in the chlorination of isoprene. Here, together with the products of 1,2 and 1,4 addition, there is formed a substantial quantity of the product of substitution, as shown in equation 81.[187,188]

$$CH_2=\overset{\underset{\displaystyle CH_3}{|}}{C}CH=CH_2 \xrightarrow[-HCl]{+Cl_2} CH_2=\overset{\underset{\displaystyle CH_2Cl}{|}}{C}CH=CH_2 \qquad (81)$$

Three explanations [200,213,214] have been given of this type of substitution; they have been formulated for the simpler case of chlorination of isobutene. This reaction proceeds in a liquid film of the products and gives predominantly the allylic, rather than the vinylic, substitution product, as is shown in Scheme 23.

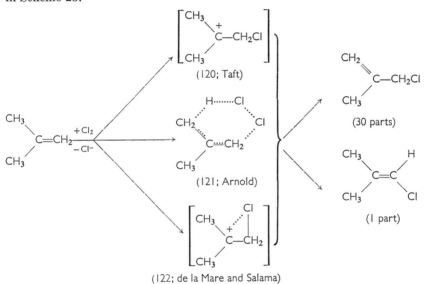

Scheme 23.   Substitutions accompanying addition to isobutene; possible intermediates or transition states.

The first is Taft's theory [213] that the carbonium ion (**120**) is formed, and that the inductive effect of chlorine would make proton loss more ready from methyl than from the chloromethyl group. This seems contrary to general chemical experience.

[213] R. W. Taft, Jr., *J. Am. Chem. Soc.*, **70**, 3364 (1948).

[214] R. T. Arnold and W. W. Lee, *J. Am. Chem. Soc.*, **75**, 5396 (1953).

The second theory, due to Arnold and his co-workers,[214] is that reaction involves a cyclic intermediate (121),[cf. 215] in which the proton is removed from the methyl group by the developing halide ion as it departs from the [olefin·Cl$_2$] complex. This theory gives the nucleophilic fragment from the electrophile a special role in determining the orientation.

More recently, de la Mare and his co-workers [200,216] have shown that hypochlorous acid reacts with isobutylene in water containing perchloric acid, and gives the two olefinic products in ratio very nearly the same as that found for the chlorination of isobutylene by chlorine. It seems probable that the change from an intermediate involving hydrogen bonding to chlorine (121) to one involving hydrogen bonding to a protonated hydroxyl group (123) would give a change in the orientation greater than is found. So a third

(123)

theory was suggested,[200,216] namely, that neighboring group interaction gives a geometric configuration (122) of the intermediate unfavorable for proton loss from the attacked carbon atom.

C. Group Migration in Addition

The development of neighboring group interaction between an entering reagent and a carbonium ionic center carries with it the consequence that, if fully developed, it may lead to movement of the entering reagent to the other olefinic carbon atom. Well-authenticated examples exist in which the chemistry of addition is best interpreted in terms of this behavior. Thus addition of bromine and of bromine chloride to cholesterol and its derivatives [217] (124; R = alkyl, acyl) can be called "anti-Markownikov" in character.[218] For since hydrogen chloride adds to give the 6-hydro-5-chloride (125),[219] bromine chloride would be expected—neighboring group interaction being neglected—to give the 6-bromo-5-chloride. The fact that it gives the 5α-bromo-6β-chloride (127) is most reasonably interpreted by saying that the electrophilic

[215] F. G. Bordwell and C. E. Osborne, *J. Am. Chem. Soc.*, **81**, 1995 (1959).

[216] P. Ballinger and P. B. D. de la Mare, *Chem. & Ind.* (*London*), **1957**, 1545; P. Ballinger, P. B. D. de la Mare, and D. L. H. Williams, *J. Chem. Soc.* (*London*), **1960**, 2467.

[217] J. B. Ziegler and A. C. Shabica, *J. Am. Chem. Soc.*, **74**, 4891 (1952).

[218] D. H. R. Barton, E. Miller, and H. T. Young, *J. Chem. Soc.* (*London*), **1951**, 2598.

[219] C. Kawasaki and J. Yamamura, *J. Pharm. Soc. Japan*, **57**, 155 (1937); through *Chem. Zentralblatt*, II, 82 (1938); cf. J. D. Bernal, D. Crowfoot, and I. Fankuchen, *Phil. Trans. Roy. Soc. London*, **A239**, 135, 142 (1940).

bromine initially attaches itself axially to C_6, but that neighboring group interaction is so well developed in the intermediate (126), and steric factors are so unfavorable for attack by the nucleophile at the 5-position, that reaction is completed by attack at the 6-position.[218,220]

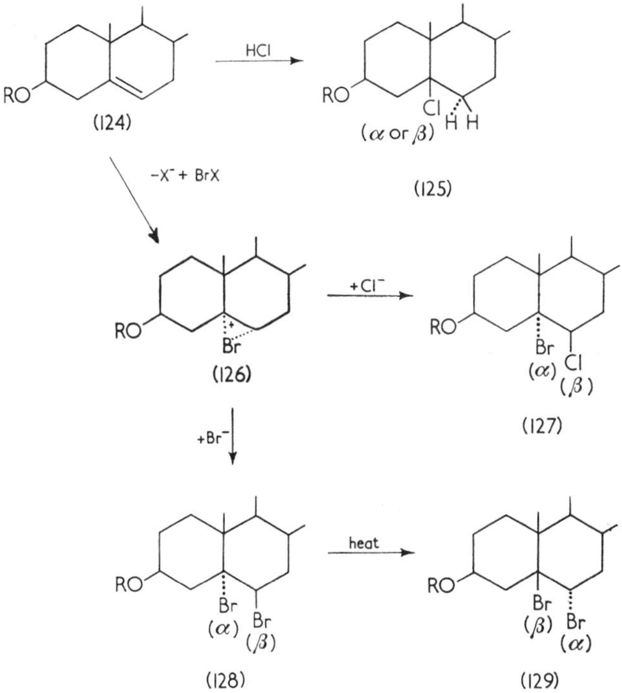

Scheme 24.   Addition to derivatives of cholesterol.

Newman and Puterbaugh[221] have interpreted similarly the reaction of *tert*-butylethylene with bromine in methanol to give nearly equal amounts of the dibromide and of 2-bromo-1-methoxy-3,3-dimethylbutane (eq. 82).

$$\text{Bu}^t\text{CH}=\text{CH}_2 + \text{Br}_2 \begin{array}{l} \xrightarrow[]{+\text{MeOH}} \text{Bu}^t\text{CH(Br)CH}_2\text{OMe} \\[2pt] -\text{HBr} \\[6pt] \searrow \text{Bu}^t\text{CH(Br)CH}_2\text{Br} \end{array}$$

(82)

The corresponding addition of chlorine to *trans*-1,2-di-*tert*-butyl-ethylene, where nucleophilic completion of the addition is very hindered, gives skeletally rearranged products.[221]

[220] P. B. D. de la Mare in W. Klyne, ed., *Progress in Stereochemistry*, Butterworths, London, 1953, pp. 118–20.

[221] W. H. Puterbaugh and M. S. Newman, *J. Am. Chem. Soc.*, **79**, 3469 (1957); **81**, 1611 (1959).

It is of interest that, if we formulate addition to olefins in this sort of way, we envisage a transition state for completion of the addition of the electrophile, EY, having the composition [olefin $\cdot$ E$^+$ $\cdot$ Y$^-$]. For example, in addition of bromine to cholesterol, the transition state for formation of the 5α,6β-dibromide (**128**) from bromine and cholesterol in chloroform, through the intermediate **126**, has the composition [olefin $\cdot$ Br$^+$ $\cdot$ Br$^-$]. It must then be recognized that the transition state for intramolecular rearrangement of the 5α,6β-dibromide (**128**) to the 5β,6α isomer (**129**) also has the composition [olefin, Br$^+$, Br$^-$], and has the two components of the adduct on opposite sides of the plane of the double bond, but must have a different structure and geometry.[cf. 220] This type of rearrangement (the diaxial-diequatorial rearrangement)[222] is discussed elsewhere in this volume (Section 16).

The intimate structure of the intermediate, formed by electrophilic attack by halogen on olefins, and involved in *trans* addition, has been considered by various authors in its relation to the direction of ring opening of epoxides.[220,222a,222b,222c] Compounds of the type CH₂—CH—R generally react

with hydrogen chloride by the route shown in equation 83. This orientation

$$\text{CH}_2\text{—CHMe} \xrightarrow{+\text{H}^+} \text{CH}_2\text{—CHMe} \xrightarrow{+\text{Cl}^-} \text{ClCH}_2\text{CHMe} \tag{83}$$

(130)

of ring opening, with nucleophilic attack at the primary carbon atom, usually persists in ring opening involving neutral nucleophiles (eq 84).[223]

$$\text{CH}_2\text{—CHMe} \xrightarrow{+\text{H}^+} \text{CH}_2\text{—CHMe} \xrightarrow[-\text{H}^+]{+\text{R}'\text{OH}} \text{CH}_2\text{—CHMe} \tag{84}$$

Cases in which this orientation is not observed (e.g., the acid-catalyzed alcoholysis of butadiene monoxide) have been interpreted[223a] as examples in which the ring opening occurs unimolecularly, as shown in Scheme 25. This interpretation was supported by demonstration that some of the product of allylic rearrangement accompanied the ordinary product of ring opening,

[222] D. H. R. Barton and J. F. King, *J. Chem. Soc. (London)*, **1958**, 4398.

[222a] P. B. D. de la Mare and J. G. Pritchard, *J. Chem. Soc. (London)*, **1954**, 3910, 3990.

[222b] E. S. Gould, *Mechanism and Structure in Organic Chemistry*, Holt, New York, 1959.

[222c] P. Ballinger and P. B. D. de la Mare, *J. Chem. Soc.*, 1481 (1957).

[223] S. Winstein and R. B. Henderson in R. C. Elderfield, ed., *Heterocyclic Compounds*, Vol. I, Wiley, New York, 1950, p. 1.

[223a] R. D. Kadesch, *J. Am. Chem. Soc.*, **68**, 44 (1946).

and the fact that the amount was small can be then taken as indicating that neighboring group interaction between the formed hydroxyl group and the

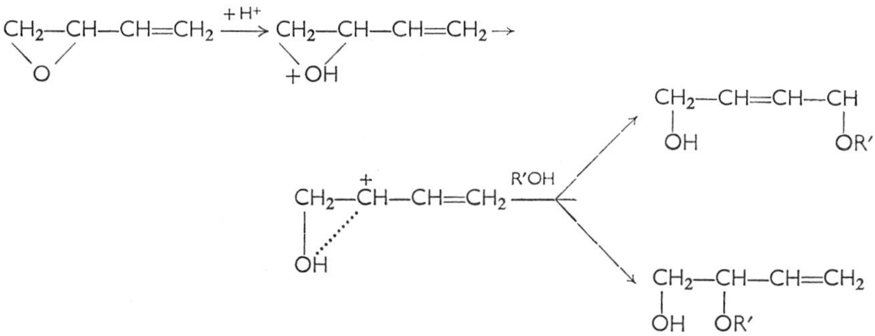

$$CH_2\!-\!CH\!-\!CH\!=\!CH_2 \xrightarrow{+H^+} CH_2\!-\!CH\!-\!CH\!=\!CH_2 \rightarrow$$
$$\underset{O}{\diagdown\diagup} \qquad\qquad \underset{+OH}{\diagdown\diagup}$$

$$CH_2\!-\!\overset{+}{C}H\!-\!CH\!=\!CH_2 \xrightarrow{R'OH}$$
$$\underset{OH}{\overset{|}{}}$$

$$\nearrow\; CH_2\!-\!CH\!=\!CH\!-\!CH$$
$$\qquad\underset{OH}{\overset{|}{}}\qquad\quad \underset{OR'}{\overset{|}{}}$$

$$\searrow\; CH_2\!-\!CH\!-\!CH\!=\!CH_2$$
$$\qquad\underset{OH}{\overset{|}{}}\;\; \underset{OR'}{\overset{|}{}}$$

Scheme 25.   Acid-catalyzed alcoholysis of butadiene monoxide.

carbonium center is maintained in the intermediate at least sufficiently long for the main product of reaction to be determined as the terminally unsaturated product.

Reaction of propylene with a carrier of positive chlorine gives the product in which the nucleophilic fragment has attacked the secondary carbon. This argues against formulation of the primary product of electrophilic attack as the chloronium cation (131). Such an ion, by analogy with the corresponding oxonium ion (130), should give the other chlorohydrin. Dewar, in arguing from these facts, formulated the intermediate addition as a π complex.[225]

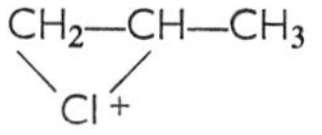

$$CH_2\!-\!CH\!-\!CH_3 \qquad \delta+\;CH_2\!-\!\overset{+}{C}H\!-\!CH_3 \xrightarrow{H_2O} CH_2\!-\!CH\!-\!CH_3$$
$$\underset{Cl\,+}{\diagdown\diagup} \qquad\qquad\quad \underset{\delta-\;Cl}{\overset{|}{}} \qquad\qquad \underset{Cl}{\overset{|}{}}\;\; \underset{OH}{\overset{|}{}}$$

(131) 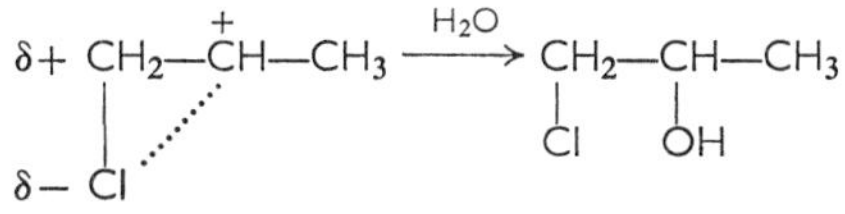   (132)

An alternative, perhaps better, interpretation [222a,222b,222c,225a] is that implied by structure 132, in which the residual neighboring group interaction is considered to be largely electrostatic in origin. It is very likely that the corresponding bromonium and iodonium structures are relatively more important.[225b,226]

[224] L. Smith and S. Skyle, Acta Chem. Scand., 4, 39, (1950).

[225] M. J. S. Dewar, Discussions Faraday Soc., 2, 50, 75 (1947); Bull. Soc. chim. France, C71 (1951).

[225a] P. B. D. de la Mare and A. Salama, J. Chem. Soc., 3337 (1956).

[225b] S. Winstein, J. Am. Chem. Soc., 64, 2791 (1942); Bull. soc. chim. France, 18, C55 (1951).

[226] P. B. D. de la Mare and S. Galandauer, J. Chem. Soc. (London), 1958, 36.

D. Competition with Other Neighboring Groups

Competition by neighboring groups elsewhere in the molecule for a carbonium ionic center produced in an addition is a well-recognized phenomenon which can have a variety of consequences.

One of these involves displacement by the neighboring group of the partial bond involved in the participation of the entering halogen. Such behavior may result in ring closure, and examples are known of the isolation of intermediates with three, four, and five-membered rings,[227–229] as illustrated in equations 85, 86, and 87.

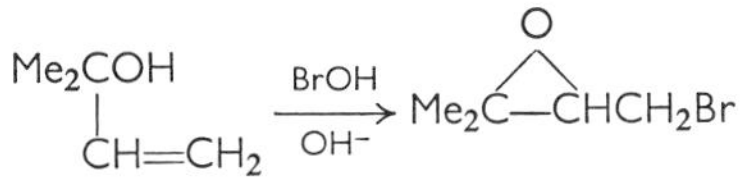

$$\underset{\overset{|}{CH=CH_2}}{Me_2COH} \xrightarrow[OH^-]{BrOH} Me_2\overset{\displaystyle O}{\overset{\displaystyle \triangle}{C-CH}}CH_2Br \tag{85}$$

$$\underset{\overset{\parallel}{MeCCO_2H}}{MeCCO_2H} \xrightarrow[NaOH]{Br_2} \underset{\overset{|}{\underset{CO_2H}{MeC\text{——}O}}}{MeCBr\text{—}CO} \tag{86}$$

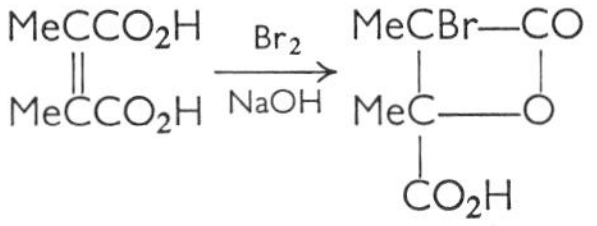

$$\underset{\overset{|}{CH_2CH=CH_2}}{Ph_2CCO_2H} \xrightarrow{Br_2} \underset{\overset{|}{CH_2\text{——}CHCH_2Br}}{Ph_2C\overset{\displaystyle CO}{\diagup \quad \diagdown}O} \tag{87}$$

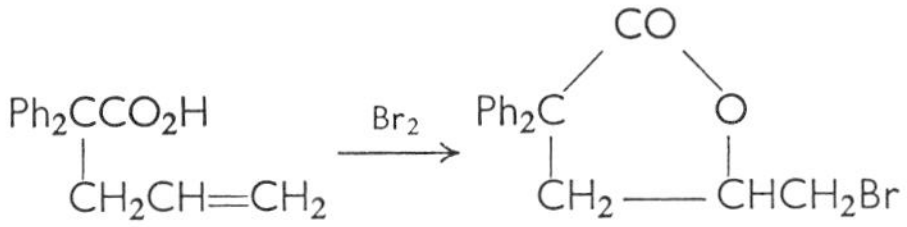

Examples involving other complex neighboring groups are well known.[230,231] The power of groups to exert this type of behavior is, of course, related to their power to contribute driving force to solvolyses in which the appropriate carbonium intermediates are formed.[231] The stereochemical consequences are also of importance;[231] thus salts of maleic acid

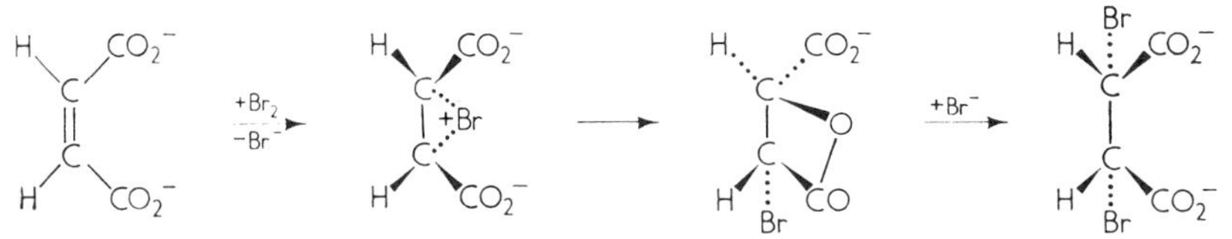

Scheme 26. Possible path in the addition of bromine to sodium maleate.

give *cis* addition of bromine and of chlorine in water,[231a] presumably because the neighboring group interaction of bromine becomes displaced by that of

227 S. Winstein and L. Goodman, *J. Am. Chem. Soc.*, **76**, 4368, 4373 (1954).

228 D. S. Tarbell and P. D. Bartlett, *J. Am. Chem. Soc.*, **59**, 407 (1937).

229 P. N. Craig and I. H. Witt, *J. Am. Chem. Soc.*, **72**, 4925 (1950).

230 R. T. Arnold, M. de M. Campos, and K. L. Lindsay, *J. Am. Chem. Soc.*, **75**, 1044 (1953); R. T. Arnold and K. L. Lindsay, *J. Am. Chem. Soc.*, **75**, 1048 (1953).

231 L. Goodman, S. Winstein, and R. Boschen, *J. Am. Chem. Soc.*, **72**, 2311 (1950); **80**, 4312 (1958); L. Goodman and S. Winstein, *J. Am. Chem. Soc.*, **79**, 4788 (1957).

231a E. M. Terry and L. Eichelberger, *J. Am. Chem. Soc.*, **47**, 1067 (1925); A. W. Francis, *J. Am. Chem. Soc.*, **47**, 2340 (1925).

the carboxylate ion group (Scheme 26). The detailed structure and charge distribution in the intermediate have not been elucidated.

Group migration, with the formation of rearranged products, is another possible consequence of this type of interaction. It has been demonstrated in the formation of rearranged halohydrins from allyl halides and hypohalous acids (e.g., eq. 88).[222a,231b] This type of reaction is not determined only by

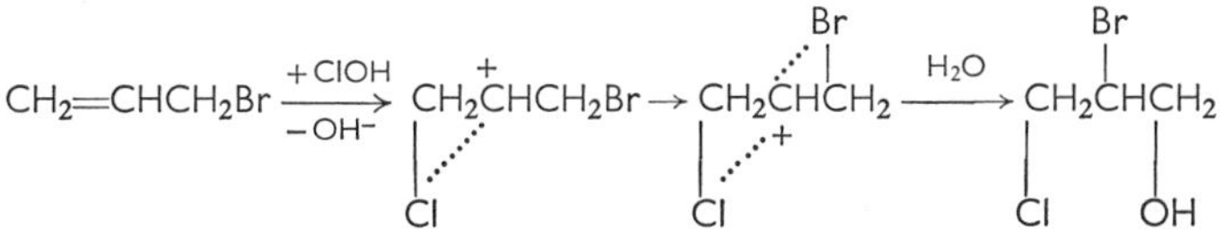

CH₂=CHCH₂Br
+ClOH
−OH⁻
CH₂CHCH₂Br
Cl
CH₂CHCH₂
Br
H₂O
CH₂CHCH₂
Br
Cl
OH
(88)

the energetics of neighboring group participation; the ease of heterolysis of the bond joining the neighboring groups to the carbon skeleton is also concerned. Thus the OH group is a better neighboring group than chlorine, but it migrates less readily.[222a,227] Factors concerned in these processes have been discussed by various workers.[222a,227,231,232]

These types of competition between neighboring groups for carbonium centers have not been investigated in substituted diene systems, but they should have interesting consequences here. Examples of possible additions involving rearrangement of the double bond skeleton associated with group migration or ring closure are given in equations 89 through 92 (R = alkyl, aryl; X = Cl, Br, I), and await investigation as analogs of established reaction paths (eqs. 85 through 88).

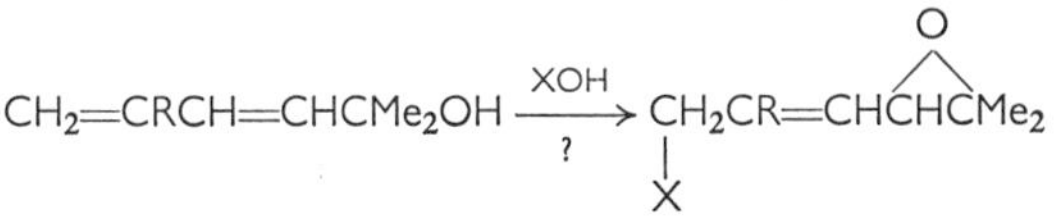

CH₂=CRCH=CHCMe₂OH
XOH
?
CH₂CR=CHCHCMe₂
O
X
(89)

CO₂H
CH₂=CHCH=CCR=CH₂
XOH
?
O—CO
CH₂
C=CRCH₂X
CH=CH
(90)

CO₂H
CH₂=CCR=CH₂
XOH
?
O—CO
CH₂—C=CRCH₂X
(91)

CH₂=CRCH=CHCH₂Br
XOH
?
CH₂CR=CHCHCH₂OH
X
Br
(92)

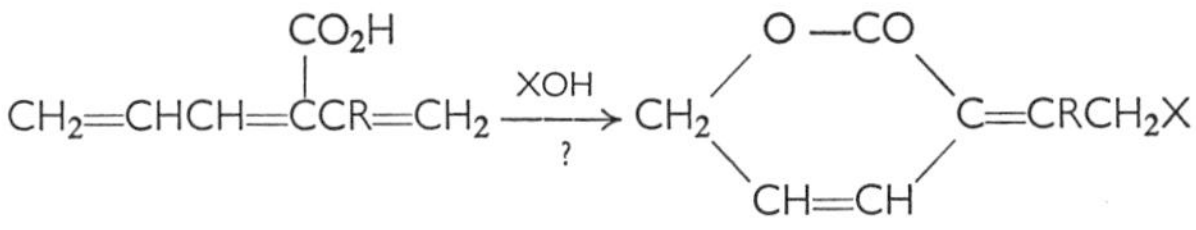

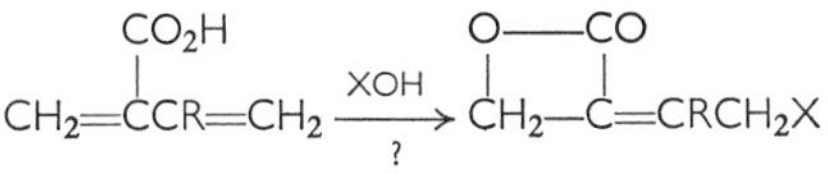

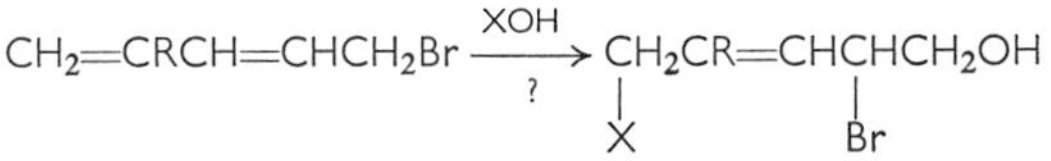

231b P. B. D. de la Mare, P. G. Naylor, and D. L. H. Williams, *Chem. & Ind.* (*London*), **1959**, 1020; *J. Chem. Soc.* (*London*), **1962**, 443.

232 J. H. C. Nayler, *J. Chem. Soc.* (*London*), **1959**, 189.

6. PROTOTROPIC SHIFTS IN ALLYLIC SYSTEMS

Anionotropic rearrangements of allylic compounds are favored by groups which can release electrons to the allylic center, particularly by effects of polarizability. This is illustrated in Figure 2 (page 44) for halides and in Table X (page 80), for alcohols. Many of the groups concerned in anionotropic rearrangements are, however, intrinsically electron withdrawing in character by virtue of their inductive effects. This is shown by the values of σ_m, given in Table XII, taken from McDaniel and Brown's compilation.[233] Positive values

TABLE XII

Substituent Constants (σ_m) for Inductively
Electron-Withdrawing Substituents

Substituent	σ_m
Ph	0.06
OMe	0.11
OH	0.12
SMe	0.15
OPh	0.25
F	0.34
Cl	0.37
CO$_2$Et	0.37
Br	0.39
OAc	0.39
CN	0.56
SO$_2$Me	0.60
NO$_2$	0.71

imply that the substituent (R) is electron withdrawing relative to hydrogen as measured by its effect on the dissociation constant (K_R) when introduced into the meta position of benzoic acid ($\sigma_m = \log_{10} K_{m\cdot R}/K_H$), where K_R is the dissociation constant of $R \cdot C_6H_4 \cdot CO_2H$. Other unsaturated groups are also inductively electron withdrawing, as shown, for example, by the fact that vinylacetic acid ($10^5 K_a = 4.6$) is stronger than acetic acid ($10^5 K_a = 1.7$).[234]

Such substituents will facilitate prototropic mobility through an inductive effect, even when they facilitate anionotropic mobility through a conjugative effect. Their influence on prototropic mobility will be even greater when, as in equation 93 (R = Ph, CH : CH$_2$, etc.) they are potentially conjugated with the developing carbanionic center.

In reactions of substituted allylic systems, therefore, prototropic shifts may often in principle accompany anionotropic rearrangements. A number

233 D. H. McDaniel and H. C. Brown, *J. Org. Chem.*, **23**, 420 (1958).
234 J. F. J. Dippy, *Chem. Rev.*, **25**, 157 (1939).

of examples of systems in which the two processes occur together have been described by Baker.[234a] Here we draw attention to two cases. It has been

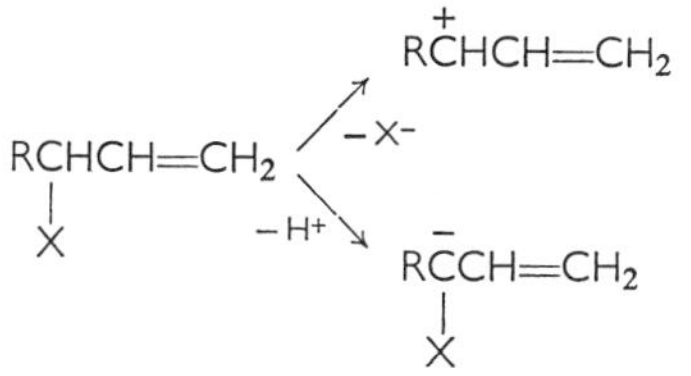

$$RCHCH=CH_2 \underset{-H^+}{\overset{-X^-}{\longrightarrow}}
\begin{cases}
\overset{+}{R}CHCH=CH_2 \\[2mm]
R\overset{-}{C}CH=CH_2 \\ \quad\mid \\ \quad X
\end{cases}$$

(with $RCHCH=CH_2$ bearing an X substituent at left)

(93)

shown that the reaction of 3-bromocrotonic ester with aryl oxide ions gives as the first product the corresponding ester, which on hydrolysis gives the prototropically rearranged acid (eq. 94). Here the combined influence of the

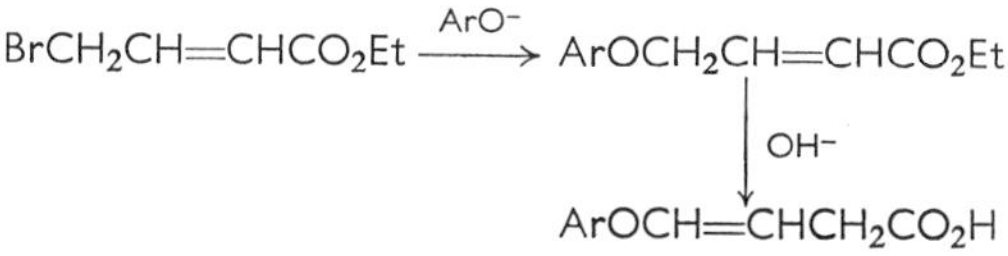

$$BrCH_2CH=CHCO_2Et \xrightarrow{ArO^-} ArOCH_2CH=CHCO_2Et$$
$$\downarrow OH^-$$
$$ArOCH=CHCH_2CO_2H$$

(94)

ArO— and —CH : CHCO$_2$Et groups is sufficient to render the system prototropically mobile under alkaline conditions, but the initial direct nucleophilic displacement can occur before prototropic rearrangement activated by —Br and —CH : CHCO$_2$Et has time to supervene.[234b] It may be noted in this connection that 3,3-dichloropropene does not significantly rearrange to 1,1-dichloropropene during its S_N2 and S_N2' reactions with ethoxide ion;[234c] so even in this system, which is not particularly activated for anionotropic and nucleophilic displacements, base-catalyzed prototropy is difficult to realize.

Prototropic shifts in allylic alcohols under acidic conditions have been recorded by many workers. Thus Heilbron, Jones, Smith, and Weedon [235] have drawn attention to the fact that anionotropic and prototropic changes often together determine the ultimate products of such reactions, especially in systems containing groups, such as COMe or CO$_2$H, which are deactivating

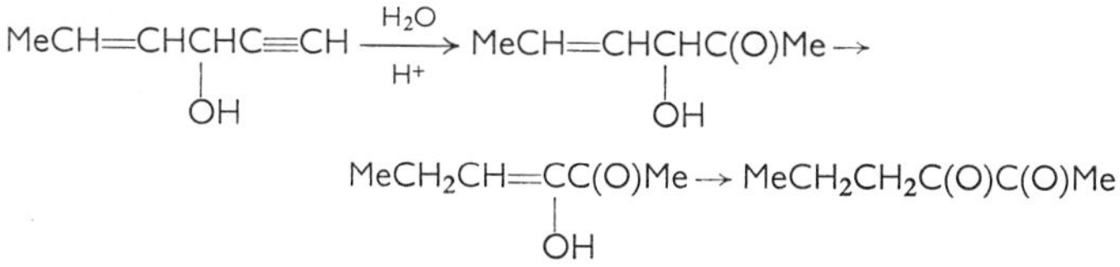

$$MeCH=CHCHC\equiv CH \xrightarrow[H^+]{H_2O} MeCH=CHCHC(O)Me \rightarrow$$
$$\quad\mid \qquad\qquad\qquad\qquad\qquad \mid$$
$$\quad OH \qquad\qquad\qquad\qquad\qquad OH$$

$$MeCH_2CH=CC(O)Me \rightarrow MeCH_2CH_2C(O)C(O)Me$$
$$\qquad\qquad\mid$$
$$\qquad\qquad OH$$

(95)

[234a] J. W. Baker, *Tautomerism*, Routledge, London, 1934.

[234b] P. B. D. de la Mare and C. A. Vernon, *J. Chem. Soc. (London)*, **1953**, 3555.

[234c] P. B. D. de la Mare and C. A. Vernon, *J. Chem. Soc. (London)*, **1952**, 3325.

[235] I. M. Heilbron, E. R. H. Jones, P. Smith, and B. C. L. Weedon, *J. Chem. Soc. (London)*, **1946**, 54.

for anionotropy. The reactions shown in equations 95 and 96 have been given the interpretations indicated.[235,235a]

$$MeCH{=}CHCHCO_2H \xrightarrow[aq]{HCl} MeCHCH{=}CHCO_2H \rightarrow$$
$$\qquad\quad \underset{OH}{|} \qquad\qquad\qquad \underset{OH}{|}$$

$$MeC{=}CHCH_2CO_2H \rightarrow MeC(O)CH_2CH_2CO_2H \qquad (96)$$
$$\underset{OH}{|}$$

It is not clear, however, to what extent thermodynamic, rather than kinetic factors are concerned in such cases in determining the directions taken in the reactions.

[235a] E. A. Braude and C. J. Timmons, *J. Chem. Soc.* (*London*), **1950**, 2000, 2007, **1953**, 3131, 3138; cf. M. Julia, *Bull. soc. chim. France*, C13 (1951).

3

CARBONIUM ION REARRANGEMENTS IN BRIDGED BICYCLIC SYSTEMS[1]

JEROME A. BERSON
University of Southern California, Los Angeles, California

CONTENTS

[1] Most of this chapter was written during the tenure of a Senior Post-Doctoral Fellowship for which I am indebted to the National Science Foundation. I am also grateful to the Departments of Chemistry of Harvard University and the California Institute of Technology for their hospitality during that period, to Professors R. B. Woodward and J. D. Roberts, who acted as official hosts, and to several faculty members and students of both institutions for informative discussions. Information pertinent to the topics discussed here was kindly supplied in advance of publication by Professors P. D. Bartlett, H. L. Goering, J. D. Roberts, P. R. Schleyer, H. M. Walborsky, and S. Winstein.

I. INTRODUCTION

Meerwein's demonstration[1a,2] that cationic carbon intermediates were
involved in the camphene hydrochloride–isobornyl chloride change was the
first modern attack on the theoretical problems of the 1,2 rearrangement.[3]
Meerwein's ideas had immediate pragmatic value; the structural aspects of
the baffling rearrangements of bridged bicyclic monoterpenes discovered by
Wagner,[4] which had rudely shocked an earlier generation of chemists, were

[1a] H. Meerwein and K. van Emster, *Ber.*, **53**, 1815 (1920).

[2] H. Meerwein and K. van Emster, *Ber.*, **55**, 2500 (1922).

[3] For reviews, see (a) P. D. Bartlett in H. Gilman, ed., *Organic Chemistry, An Advanced
Treatise*, Vol. III, Wiley, New York, 1953, p. 66; (b) C. K. Ingold, *Structure and Mechanism in Organic Chemistry*, Cornell University Press, Ithaca, N. Y., 1953, p. 482.

[4] For a historical review, see J. Simonsen and L. N. Owen, *The Terpenes*, Vol. II,
Cambridge University Press, 1949.

now reduced to order and clarity. From the theoretical point of view, attempts to define the subtler details of mechanism in these and related rearrangements have continued with increasing pace to the present. This section reviews and evaluates recent developments in the field.

A Note on Nomenclature. The term "Wagner-Meerwein rearrangement" originally referred to 1,2 migration of a ring member in a bridged bicyclic substance. Recently, its connotation has expanded to include all 1,2 migrations of alkyl or aryl groups from carbon to carbon. Since it is useful for our purposes to distinguish ring member migrations from other rearrangements which, although intimately related in mechanism, are structurally discrete, we revert in this chapter to the original meaning, without attempting to justify the general validity or desirability of the usage. The term "Nametkin rearrangement" has come to refer to 1,2 migrations of methyl groups in bridged bicyclic monoterpenoids and related substances. The early literature sometimes refers to these processes as "camphene rearrangements of the second kind," and there is some validity in the contention that the names of Houben and Bredt should also be associated with the transformation, at least as it applies to racemization phenomena in the camphane series (see heading 5A, page 155). Nevertheless, in this chapter, we use "Nametkin rearrangement" in its currently accepted sense, at the risk of doing an injustice. This usage is intended merely to prevent the elaboration of nomenclature.

2. EVIDENCE FOR IONIC INTERMEDIATES IN WAGNER-MEERWEIN REARRANGEMENTS

The skeletal rearrangement of bridged bicyclic systems to which the name Wagner-Meerwein rearrangement is applied involves, in a formal sense, breaking of a bond between the migrating carbon and the carbon atom representing the origin of migration and formation of a bond between the migrating group and a carbon atom (the terminus of migration) directly attached to the origin of migration. The change can be initiated in a number of ways: reaction of an olefin, alcohol, ester, or ether with mineral acid; solvolysis of a halide or sulfonate in hydroxylic solvent; deamination of a primary amine with nitrous acid; treatment of a halide with a Lewis acid catalyst in inert solvent; or, sometimes, simple dissolution of a halide in a nonhydroxylic solvent.

A. The Camphene Hydrochloride-Isobornyl Chloride-Bornyl Chloride System

A classic case is the rearrangement of camphene hydrochloride to isobornyl chloride. With the advantage of hindsight, it is easy to see that the major outlines of mechanism in bicyclic rearrangements could have been established by prior examination of other less complicated examples. This is not the first time, however, that entry into a garden of understanding has been effected by the side gate.

Camphene hydrochloride (2), a very reactive tertiary halide, is the product of the addition of gaseous hydrogen chloride to camphene (1a) at low temperature. The crystalline chloride is apparently a single stereoisomer, and it is assumed that the chlorine has the *exo* configuration. In solution in hydroxylic solvent, equilibrium with the olefin and hydrogen chloride is so rapidly established that titrimetric analysis for 2 is possible.[1a,2] Hydrogen chloride itself, however, can be titrated independently of 2 in the presence of ether, which suppresses the dissociation of 2.[2] In inert solvent, 2 rearranges to isobornyl chloride (3). It has long been assumed [5,6] that isobornyl chloride is

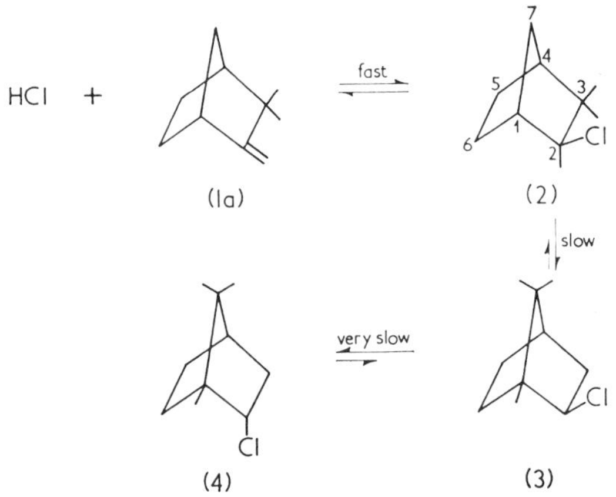

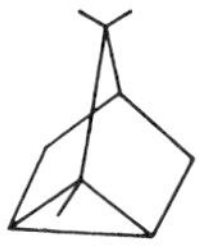

configurationally related to isoborneol (3, OH instead of Cl), which is a product of the hydration of camphene and which unequivocally has its hydroxyl group in the *exo* configuration.[7] This assumption has received experimental support.[8]

5 (a) P. D. Bartlett and I. Pöckel, *J. Am. Chem. Soc.*, **60**, 1585 (1938), (b) **59**, 820 (1937). (c) P. D. Bartlett and J. D. Gill, *J. Am. Chem. Soc.*, **63**, 1273 (1941). (d) P. D. Bartlett and H. J. Dauben, *J. Am. Chem. Soc.*, **62**, 1339 (1940).

6 T. P. Nevell, E. de Salas, and C. L. Wilson, *J. Chem. Soc.* (*London*), **1939**, 1188.

7 (a) Y. Asahina, M. Ishidate, and T. Sano, *Ber.*, **69**, 343 (1936); Y. Asahina, and M. Ishidate, *Ber.*, **68**, 555 (1935). (b) N. J. Toivonen, P. Hirsjarvi, A. Melaja, A. Kainulainen, A. Halonen, and E. Pulkinnen, *Acta. Chem. Scand.*, **3**, 991 (1949).

8 H. Kwart and G. Null, *J. Am. Chem. Soc.*, **78**, 5943 (1956).

The position of the $2 \rightleftharpoons 3$ equilibrium favors **3**, with equilibrium constants, $K = [3]/[2]$, ranging from about 7 to about 170, depending upon the solvent and temperature.[2] In the presence of a strong Lewis acid such as stannic chloride, **3** is slowly converted to its epimer, bornyl chloride (**4**). Although the equilibrium position for the $3 \rightleftharpoons 4$ reaction is not accurately measurable under these conditions because of side reactions, bornyl chloride (**4**) is the more stable epimer at ordinary temperature. The $4 \rightarrow 3$ reaction is detectable, however, and there is therefore not a large difference in stability.[2]

The rearrangement of camphene hydrochloride (**2**) to isobornyl chloride (**3**) clearly passes over some kind of cationic species; it is catalyzed by hydrogen chloride and by Lewis acids, and its rate is strongly dependent on the ionizing power of the solvent.[2] Tricyclene (**1b**), which is converted by hydrogen chloride to isobornyl chloride (**3**), is nevertheless not an intermediate in the $2 \rightarrow 3$ rearrangement: [1a] optically active isobornyl chloride (**3**) can be produced from optically active **1a**, and if tricyclene, an optically inactive molecule, were an intermediate, the isobornyl chloride would be racemic.

The "spontaneous" rearrangement in the absence of deliberately added Lewis acid catalyst, originally thought to be a simple first-order process,[2] is actually more complex; hydrogen chloride, which is always present in solutions of camphene hydrochloride, is a catalyst for the rearrangement.[1a] In nitrobenzene solution, under conditions where neither the substrate **2** nor hydrogen chloride is in great excess, the rate law is accurately expressed[5] by equation 1:

$$\text{Rate} = k'[2]^{3/2} \tag{1}$$

This is consistent with a mechanism in which the concentration of catalyst, [HCl], is controlled by a rapid equilibrium between camphene hydrochloride (**2**), camphene (**1a**), and hydrogen chloride, with equilibrium constant K, followed by a slow rearrangement of **2** to **3** catalyzed by hydrogen chloride, with rate constant k.

$$2 \underset{}{\overset{K}{\rightleftharpoons}} 1a + HCl \tag{2}$$

$$2 \underset{}{\overset{k}{\rightleftharpoons}} 3 \tag{3}$$

In this scheme $[HCl] = [1a] = (K[2])^{1/2}$; if the rate of the rearrangement step is proportional to the concentrations of hydrogen chloride and camphene hydrochloride, equation 1 results, with $k' = kK^{1/2}$.

These kinetics, requiring the presence of the elements of **2** and hydrogen chloride in the rate-determining transition state, are consistent with three conceivable mechanisms.

The first of these (mechanism *1*) involves rate-determining attack by hydrogen chloride on **2**, the chloride end of a hydrogen chloride molecule displacing C_6 from C_1 with Walden inversion, and concertedly, C_6 displacing chloride ion from C_2 with Walden inversion. The strongest evidence against this mechanism is the observation that added chloride ion, a much stronger

Mechanism 1

nucleophile than hydrogen chloride, is without effect on the rate of re-arrangement.[5a] It could be argued that molecular hydrogen chloride might be expected to be especially effective because a *single molecule* of it might perform two functions simultaneously: it could hydrogen-bond the leaving chloride, and it could also supply the nucleophilic chloride. The powerful catalytic effect of phenols on the rearrangement (*o*-cresol, for example, is about one-third as effective a catalyst as hydrogen chloride[5a]), however, is difficult to explain on this basis; under phenol catalysis, the catalyst and the nucleophile must be supplied by *different* molecules, since the phenol is not consumed. Further, the catalytic efficiencies of various phenols parallel their hydrogen-bonding abilities as measured[5d] by their enhancement of the acid strength of hydrogen chloride in dioxane. It seems reasonable to assume, as Bartlett has done,[5c] that the role of hydrogen chloride is to help remove the leaving chloride by hydrogen bonding, not to function as a nucleophile toward camphene hydrochloride.

If the concerted "push-pull" mechanism is rejected, the kinetics must be fitted on a mechanistic framework that includes ionic intermediates. In equation 4, it is assumed[6] that a single species of cation, or its kinetic equiva-lent, a rapidly interconverted pair of cations, intervene between camphene hydrochloride (**2**) and isobornyl chloride (**3**). Equation 4 represents the cation in ion pair association with HCl_2^-. The kinetic derivation is unchanged if the ions are assumed to be free as long as the ionization of **2** is assumed to be bimolecular with HCl, an assumption consistent with the form of the rate law established by Bartlett.

$$\mathbf{2} + \text{HCL} \underset{k_{-1}}{\overset{k_1}{\rightleftharpoons}} (\text{cation}^+ + \text{HCl}_2^-) \underset{k_2}{\overset{k_{-2}}{\rightleftharpoons}} \mathbf{3} + \text{HCl} \tag{4}$$

Since the reverse reaction ($\mathbf{3} \rightarrow \mathbf{2}$) is slow[1a] compared to the forward reaction, the term $k_2[\mathbf{3}]$ is small at the outset, and the rate law reduces to equation 5.[6]

$$d[\mathbf{3}]/dt = k_1 k_{-2}[\mathbf{2}][\text{HCl}]/(k_{-1} + k_{-2}) \tag{5}$$

The two remaining conceivable mechanisms are derivable as limiting cases from this scheme (eq. 4). The rate constant for rearrangement is the composite coefficient of equation 5. If $k_{-2} \gg k_{-1}$ (mechanism **2**), the partitioning of the intermediate ion is predominantly in favor of isobornyl chloride (**3**). The rate is then determined by k_1, the rate constant for bimolecular ionization of **2**. Nevell, de Salas, and Wilson [6] have disposed of this possibility by showing that camphene hydrochloride exchanges its chloride for radioactive chloride in chloroform at a rate about fifteen times the rate of rearrangement. Under the same conditions, chloride exchange with isobornyl chloride is negligibly slow. A mechanism for the exchange that does not involve the reaction of HCl_2^- with the same ion postulated in equation 4 is difficult to imagine. In terms of this scheme (eq. 4), the results demonstrate that $k_{-1} > k_{-2}$; thus, the rate constant for rearrangement, $k_1 k_{-2}/(k_{-1}+k_{-2})$, is smaller than the rate constant for ionization, k_1. Therefore, the only remaining mechanism (**3**) involves a rate-determining step in which the cation of equation 4 reacts with HCl_2^-. For the reverse rearrangement (**3** → **2**), microscopic reversibility requires that bimolecular ionization of **3** be rate determining.

The simplest mechanism for the dissociation of camphene hydrochloride to camphene and hydrogen chloride involves loss of a proton from the cation. Since the equilibrium position strongly favors camphene hydrochloride, it is reasonable to assume (*a*) that the rate of deuterium exchange in the presence of DCl would be equal to the rate of dissociation and (*b*) that the rate of chloride exchange in the presence of radiochloride would be greater than the rate of deuterium exchange.

With regard to point *a*, Nevell, de Salas, and Wilson [6] calculate "rate constants" for deuterium exchange and for dissociation, assuming second-order kinetics for the former and first-order kinetics for the latter. The deuterium exchange rate constant obtained in this way is about twenty times larger than necessary to give a rate identical with the rate of dissociation under the conditions ($0.1M$ camphene hydrochloride) of the exchange experiment. These observations are baffling until it is recognized [9a] that the calculated "rate constant" for deuterium exchange is derived without a knowledge of the extent of exchange at infinite time. If the assumption [6] that only one hydrogen of camphene hydrochloride exchanges is discarded [9a] in favor of the more reasonable one that three hydrogens (of the lone methyl group) exchange, a plot of "% unreacted" against time, without assumptions about reaction order, shows [9a] that points derived from deuterium exchange and dissociation data [6] fall on a single curve. There is, therefore, a strong suspicion that deuterium exchange and dissociation are in fact the same process.

A later study [9b] of this system in nitrobenzene solvent provides a

[9] (a) P. D. Bartlett and C. E. Dills, unpublished. Cf. C. E. Dills, Thesis, Harvard University, 1955. (b) Y. Pocker, *Proc. Chem. Soc. (London)*, **1960**, 216. (c) Cf. K. S. Pitzer and C. W. Beckett, *J. Am. Chem. Soc.*, **69**, 977 (1947); C. W. Beckett, K. S. Pitzer, and R. Spitzer, *J. Am. Chem. Soc.*, **69**, 2488 (1947).

substantial clarification. Both dissociation and deuterium exchange of camphene hydrochloride are strongly catalyzed by HCl (or DCl). The initial rate of dissociation to camphene and HCl is expressible as

$$\text{rate} = d[\text{H}^+]/dt = k_1^E[\mathbf{2}] + k_2^E[\mathbf{2}][\text{HCl}]$$

Deuterium exchange, measured in the presence of free DCl under conditions where the addition to give **2** predominates, is expressible by an equation of the same form:

$$\text{rate} = k_1^D[\mathbf{2}] + k_2^D[\mathbf{2}][\text{DCl}]$$

Further, the rate constants controlling the catalyzed and uncatalyzed contributions to the dissociation rate are about equal to the corresponding rate constants for deuterium exchange ($k_1^E \approx k_1^D$ and $k_2^E \approx k_2^D$). This is convincing evidence that dissociation and deuterium exchange proceed by the same mechanism, the exchange being a consequence of dissociation and recombination.

Isotopic dilution experiments [9b] show that the intermediate camphene-hydroisobornyl cation is partitioned to give **2** and **3** in the ratio of about 40 : 1. This is in good agreement with the ratio of rate constants ($k_2^*/k_R = 42$) derived from the rate laws for exchange of **2** with hydrogen radiochloride (rate $= k_1^*[\mathbf{2}] + k_2^*[\mathbf{2}][\text{HCl}]$) and rearrangement to **3** (rate $= k_R[\mathbf{2}][\text{HCl}]$).

The HCl-catalyzed components of the above reactions, in which the transition state has the stoichiometry (**2**·HCl), are interpreted [9b] as reactions of the (camphenehydro$^+$HCl$_2^-$) ion pair; the uncatalyzed reactions, with transition state stoichiometry (**2**), involve the (camphenehydro$^+$Cl$^-$) ion pair.[9b]

B. The Need for a "Special" Interpretation

The kinetics alone give no information on the structure of the cationic intermediate (or intermediates). The two cations **5** and **6**, formally derived

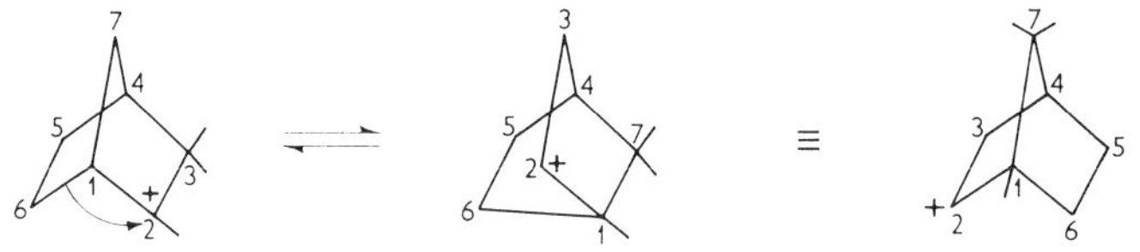

(5)   (6)

from **2** and **3**, are related by Wagner-Meerwein shift of a single bond (C$_1$—C$_6$). It is unlikely, however, that cation **6** occurs as a discrete species in the rearrangement,[5,6] since it is assumed that its reaction with HCl$_2^-$ would produce at least a large proportion of the *endo* isomer, bornyl chloride (**4**), whereas the virtually exclusive product is the *exo* isomer, isobornyl chloride (**3**). This assumption seems valid. Bornyl chloride is thermodynamically more stable than isobornyl chloride under the reaction conditions. Therefore, bornyl chloride cannot be formed first and then isomerize to isobornyl chloride. The instability of isobornyl chloride relative to bornyl chloride is largely attributable to nonbonded interactions between the 7-*syn*-methyl group and the *exo*-chlorine, a kind of repulsion that is analogous to, but possibly less severe than, the *axial-axial-cis*-1,3 repulsion in "chair" cyclohexanes.[9c] Since some of this repulsion would be present in the transition state for formation of **3**, it is to be expected that bornyl chloride (**4**) would be the kinetically favored product of the reaction of the "classical" cation (**6**) with HCl_2^-. Experimental support for this idea is available by analogy to another reaction involving irreversible addition of a nucleophile to sp^2-hybridized C_2 of the camphane system: the lithium aluminum hydride reduction of camphor (**7**) produces[10] predominantly isoborneol (**3**, OH instead of Cl), resulting from attachment of hydride ion to the *endo* side of C_2. Thus, the stereospecificity of the camphene hydrochloride rearrangement seems to require a special explanation. This is provided by the concept of Nevell, de Salas, and Wilson,[6] who formulate the immediate precursor of isobornyl chloride as the cation **8**. This species is a representative of a class of hypothetical inter-

(7)

(8)

mediates which have since been called by a variety of names: "mesomeric," "nonclassical," "bridged," "synartetic," and "complex." In function and operational meaning, Cram's "phenonium" ions[11] also belong to this class. In broader terms, these carbon-bridged ions are related to the cations responsible for neighboring group phenomena.[12]

C_6 of cation **8** is assumed to be partially bonded to both C_1 and C_2 and to occupy a position somewhere between these two atoms, i.e., the C_6—C_1 and C_6—C_2 bond lengths are different from those that would be characteristic of the "open," "classical" ions **5** and **6**. The bonding in the "nonclassical" cation may be represented in resonance hybrid terms as in **9** which, to the extent that structure **9d** makes a nonvanishing contribution, requires modification of the dotted-line notation from **8** to **9a**. Because of the partial covalency between C_6, C_1, and C_2, bimolecular nucleophilic attack at C_1 or C_2 is expected

[10] (a) L. W. Trevoy and W. G. Brown, *J. Am. Chem. Soc.*, **71**, 1675 (1949). (b) D. S. Noyce and D. B. Denney, *J. Am. Chem. Soc.*, **72**, 5743 (1950).

[11] See this volume, Section 1.

[12] S. Winstein, *Bull. soc. chim. France*, **18C**, 55 (1951).

to occur with Walden inversion, the observed stereospecificity thus being analogous to that observed [12] in nucleophilic attack on conventional bridged ions in which the bridging function is performed by a neighboring atom other than carbon (as in bromonium ions). It will be noted that mesomerism involving delocalization of the C_1–C_7 electrons would give an ion (**9e**) that would be attacked by external nucleophiles with Walden inversion to give *endo* products, epimeric with those of the camphene hydrochloride series. The absence of such derivatives in the products of carbonium ion reactions of bornyl, isobornyl, or camphenehydro systems is evidence against the presence of **9e** as an intermediate. Cation **9e** is, however, probably involved in reactions of the pinyl system (**9f**). The failure of 2-substituted bicyclo[2.2.1]heptanes

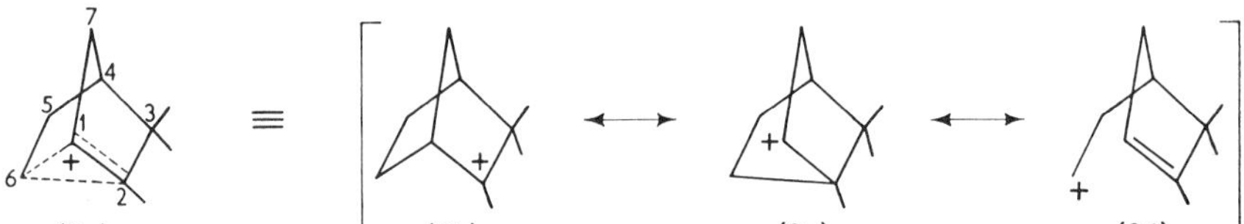

(9a)   (9b)   (9c)   (9d)

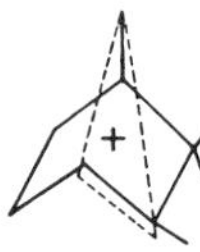

(9e) 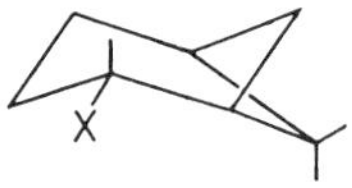   (9f)

to form mesomeric cations of type **9e** presumably signifies that the electronic stabilization that would be achieved in this way is insufficient to overcome the increased ring strain (see heading 7B, page 183).

In the mesomeric ions, of which **9a** is a prototype, a carbon atom (C_6) is bonded to two other carbon atoms (C_1 and C_2) by a single electron pair. No detailed quantum mechanical descriptions of such bonding have appeared. The difficulties may be appreciated by reference to the protracted controversy surrounding the detailed descriptions of other electron-deficient species—in particular, the boron hydrides[13]—which have points of analogy[14] with bridged ions. Qualitatively, the carbon-bridged species is a resonance hybrid[6,14-16] (**8** or **9a**). A more pictorial representation[15] proposes that the

---

[13] Cf. C. A. Coulson, *Valence*, Oxford University Press, 1952, p. 322.

[14] F. Brown, E. D. Hughes, C. K. Ingold, and J. F. Smith, *Nature*, **168**, 65 (1951).

[15] A. Streitwieser, Jr., *Chem. Revs.*, **56**, 571 (1956).

[16] (a) S. Winstein and D. Trifan, *J. Am. Chem. Soc.*, **71**, 2953 (1949), (b) **74**, 1147, 1154 (1952). (c) S. Winstein, B. K. Morse, E. Grunwald, H. W. Jones, J. Corse, D. Trifan, and H. Marshall, *J. Am. Chem. Soc.*, **74**, 1127 (1952).

electron-deficient bond contains two electrons in a three-center molecular orbital derived by overlap of a C_6 sp^3 orbital with p orbitals at C_1 and C_2. This picture is essentially the same as that used [17] to describe the transition state of a 1,2 rearrangement. Both the orbital and dotted-line notations impute some double bond character to the C_1—C_2 bond; as a corollary, the groups attached to C_1 (H and C_7) and C_2 (CH_3 and C_3) must assume a more nearly planar arrangement than in the "classical" ion. Presumably, this flattening relieves some angle strain in the five-membered ring of which the C_1—C_2 bond is a part, although it does not necessarily follow that the total angle strain in the bridged cation is less than that in the "classical" cation. Bridged bicyclic systems have an important advantage over open chain systems in forming mesomeric cations; whereas the open chain system usually must sustain a large entropy loss when the chain aligns itself for proper three-center interaction of a neighboring carbon with the termini of the bridge, this penalty is not exacted from the bicyclic cases, in which, the neighboring carbon (C_6) is already rigidly fixed in the proper position.[16c]

Much of the recent effort in the area of bicycloheptane chemistry has been directed toward determining whether or not mesomeric cation intermediates occur generally in reactions of these substances. In the discussion that follows, the facts are presented in what, to the writer, appears to be a logical sequence. This frequently is not the chronological sequence; no attempt is made to assign priority for specific ideas, although this is usually evident from the context.

3. STEREOCHEMISTRY AND STRUCTURE OF PRODUCTS FROM MESOMERIC BICYCLIC CATIONS

A. Some Necessary but Insufficient Evidence Supporting the Mesomeric Cation Hypothesis

A plausible extension of the idea that a mesomeric cation is an intermediate in the camphene hydrochloride–isobornyl chloride isomerization in an inert medium suggests that solvolytic reactions of these chlorides in hydroxylic media also generate the same cation. If this is correct and if both chlorides ionize directly to the bridged cation (an idea that is supported by kinetic evidence to be detailed), the solvolysis product from either chloride will be formed by reaction of the mesomeric cation with the solvent. Therefore, both chlorides should give the same product (or mixture of products) under conditions where the products are not subject to further reaction. This expectation is qualitatively confirmed: hydrolysis of either camphene hydrochloride (2a) or isobornyl chloride (3a) under weakly alkaline conditions (calcium hydroxide or dilute alkali hydroxide) gives camphene hydrate (2b). The added

[17] M. J. S. Dewar, *J. Chem. Soc. (London)*, **1953**, 2885.

alkali is without effect on the hydrolysis rate, an observation that argues against a bimolecular process in which OH^- attacks C_1 in concert with migration of C_6 and displacement of Cl^- from C_2. That the products are kinetically

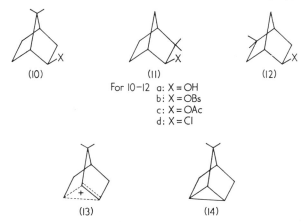

(2)
(3) 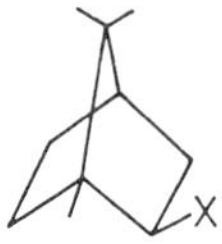

(2a, 3a: X = Cl)
(2b, 3b: X = OH)
(2c, 3c: X = OCH₃)

controlled is evident from the nature of the medium and from the formation of the thermodynamically unstable camphene hydrate (2b), which is converted[18] to isoborneol (3b) in acid. Comparable results are observed in the methanolysis of camphene hydrochloride: in the presence of potassium carbonate, the tertiary methyl ether (2c) is formed; this isomerizes to isobornyl methyl ether (3c) in acid.[19]

Only a few cases where quantitatively identical product mixtures have been obtained from either member of a Wagner-Meerwein related pair of starting materials have been worked out under conditions that insure kinetic control. Winstein has used this product-distribution criterion as evidence for a common mesomeric cation, 13, in the acetolyses of aposantenyl p-bromo-benzenesulfonate (10b) and exo-camphenilyl p-bromobenzenesulfonate (11b), which give a mixture of the acetates 10c and 11c and the product of 6,2 hydrogen shift, 12c (see heading 4) in identical distribution[20] (50% 10c, 1% 11c,

(10)
(11)
(12)

For 10-12   a: X = OH
            b: X = OBs
            c: X = OAc
            d: X = Cl

(13)
(14)

[18] (a) O. Aschan, Ber., 41, 1092 (1908); Ann., 383, 1 (1911), 410, 222 (1915). (b) G. Wagner, S. Moycho, and F. Zienkowski, Ber., 37, 1032 (1904).

[19] H. Meerwein and L. Gérard, Ann., 435, 174 (1924).

49% **12c**) from either starting material. In aqueous dioxane, the product distribution is[20] 70% **10a**, 12% **11a**, and 18% **12a**. These figures are comparable to those observed[21] in the hydrolysis (aqueous calcium hydroxide) of the chloride(s) obtained by treatment of apotricyclene (**14**) with hydrogen chloride: 80% **10a** and 20% **12a**. It is therefore reasonable to assume that the chloride hydrolysis uses the same intermediates as the *p*-bromobenzenesulfonate hydrolysis. With thionyl chloride, both alcohols **10a** and **11a** give aposantenyl chloride **10d**.[20]

Acetolysis of optically active *exo*-norbornyl *p*-bromobenzenesulfonate (**15a**) produces completely racemic *exo*-norbornyl acetate (**15b**).[16a,16b] This is to be expected if the mesomeric cation **16** is an intermediate, since **16** contains a plane of symmetry. Although some racemization of the starting arenesulfonate **15a** accompanies the solvolysis, and therefore part of the product acetate **15b** is formed from racemic **15a**, the part of the acetate that is formed from optically active **15a** is also racemic.[16a,16b] Although olefin

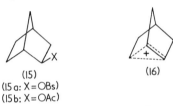

(15)
(15 a: X = OBs)
(15 b: X = OAc)

(16)

(norbornylene) and nortricyclene are imaginable optically inactive intermediates and have not been eliminated by direct control experiments, the observation[16a,16b] that racemic product is formed even when the acetolysis is conducted in the presence of a stoichiometric excess of potassium acetate permits the conclusion that these substances are not involved in the mechanism. The racemization, therefore, is an intrinsic feature of the solvolysis itself.

The observed apportionments of products alone, of course, do not uniquely require that mesomeric cations be intermediates in these reactions, since rapid interconversion of the Wagner-Meerwein pair of "classical" carbonium ions suffices as an explanation. The pattern of stereochemistry of the products, however, foreshadowed in the camphenehydro-isobornyl system and observed in a variety of other reactions of bicycloheptane derivatives (see page 130) has no rational explanation in terms of "classical" carbonium ion precursors.

B. Stereochemistry of Bicyclic Derivatives

Chemical Proofs of Stereochemistry.   By analogy with the ion from camphene hydrochloride, other bicycloheptyl mesomeric ions are expected to give

[20] S. Winstein, XIVth International Congress of Pure and Applied Chemistry, Zürich, *Experientia, Suppl.* No. **2**, 137 (1955).

[21] G. Komppa and G. A. Nyman, *Ber.*, **69**, 1813 (1936); G. Komppa and T. Hasselstrom, *Ann.*, **497**, 116 (1932).

rise to products of Walden inversion at the bridged positions. Thus, under kinetic control, any cation in which C_1 and C_2 are bridged by C_6 should give *exo* product by reaction with a nucleophile, regardless of whether C_1 or C_2 is attacked and regardless of whether or not the *exo* derivative is thermodynamically more stable than the corresponding *endo* isomer.[21a]

The following discussion develops a rational basis for stereochemical assignments in the bicycloheptanol series. The argument is independent of any assumption of the validity of the mesomeric cation hypothesis; consequently, the results will be useful in a test of the hypothesis that avoids circular reasoning. An account of the early (and inconclusive) debates on this topic is available [22a] and will not be repeated here.[22b]

The logical framework of stereochemical assignments in the bicycloheptane series rests on the unambiguous formulation of three pairs of stereoisomers: borneol (**17**)–isoborneol (**18**), 2-methyl-*endo*-norborneol (**19**)–2-methyl-*exo*-norborneol (**20**), and the norborneols (**27** and **28**). (See Table I.)

Sodium and alcohol reduction of the acid **21** gives a mixture of a lactone (**22**) and a hydroxy acid (**23**); the latter is converted to borneol via the indi-

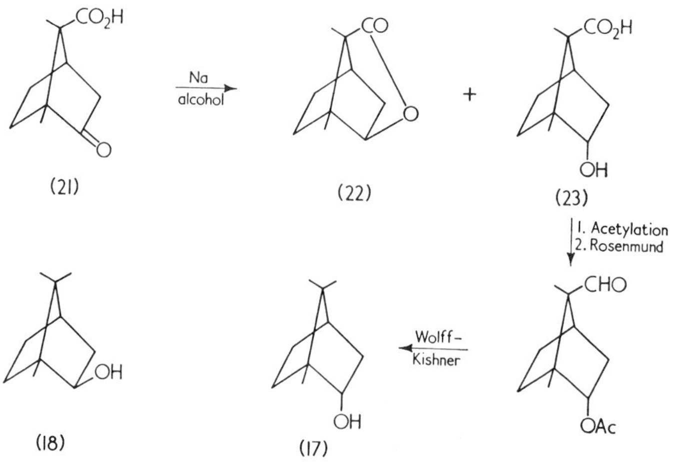

[21a] It is conceivable that steric hindrance could be made so severe that *exo* attack would be precluded; although no such examples are known in the reactions of carbon-bridged cations, severe steric shielding apparently does force *cis* addition of bromine to certain partially hydrogenated di- and tricyclopentadienes, despite the normal stereoelectronic preference for *trans* addition.[21b]

[21b] H. L. Donle, *Z. physik. Chem.*, **18B**, 146 (1932).

[22] (a) J. Simonsen and L. N. Owen, *The Terpenes*, Vol. II, Cambridge University Press, 1949, pp. 355 ff. (b) A more recent review, which contains many interesting correlations of physical and chemical properties, is given by P. von R. Schleyer, Thesis, Harvard University, 1956.

cated stages.[22c] The only step of this sequence that might conceivably jeopardize the configuration at C_2 is the Wolff-Kishner reduction; this possibility is eliminated by a control experiment[22c] in which isoborneol survives the reduction conditions. The series of transformations is therefore convincing evidence for the *endo*-hydroxyl configuration of borneol, since this hydroxyl corresponds to that in the epimer of the **22–23** pair that does not form a lactone.

An independent confirmation of this assignment[22d] takes advantage of the remarkable oxidations of bornyl acetate, isobornyl acetate, and camphor with chromic acid. This reagent introduces oxygen at C_5 and/or C_6 of these substrates.[23] One of the products, a 6-acetoxycamphorquinone (**24**) from the oxidation of bornyl acetate, gives with hydrogen peroxide an anhydride **25**.

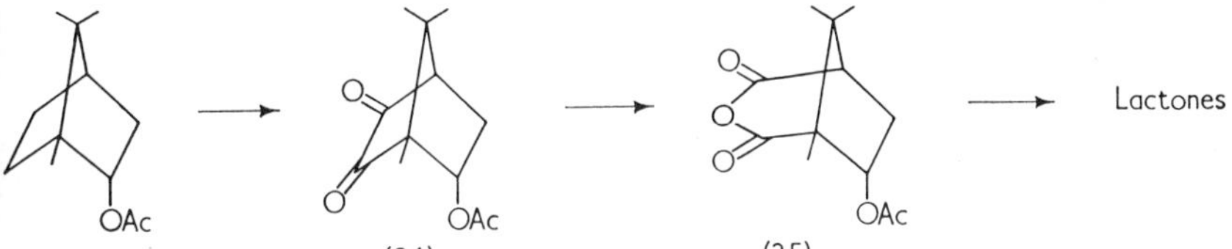

The *cis* relationship of the acetoxy and anhydride functions of **25** is established by saponification and lactone formation.[22d] In the stereoisomeric isoborneol series, the same set of transformations leads to an anhydride (**26**) that resists lactonization, giving instead a polymeric ester by intermolecular reaction.[22d]

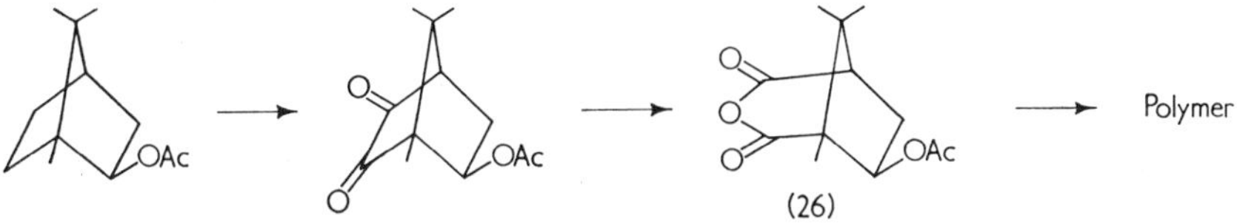

Norbornanone reacts with methyl Grignard reagent to give 2-methyl-*endo*-norborneol (**19**), which can also be prepared by hydrogenation of 2-methyl-*endo*-5-norbornen-2-ol (**29a**). Permanganate oxidation of **29a** gives a hydroxy dibasic acid which forms a β-lactone (**29c**)[24a] upon heating. The lactone regenerates the hydroxy acid upon saponification and loses carbon dioxide

[22c] Y. Asahina, M. Ishidate, and T. Sano, *Ber.*, **69**, 343 (1936); Y. Asahina, and M. Ishidate, *Ber.*, **68**, 555 (1935).

[22d] N. J. Toivonen, P. Hirsjarvi, A. Melaja, A. Kainulainen, A. Halonen, and E. Pulkinnen, *Acta. Chem. Scand.*, **3**, 991 (1949).

[23] (a) H. Schrötter, *Monatsh.*, **2**, 224 (1881). (b) J. Bredt and A. Goeb, *J. prakt. Chem.*, **2**, 101, 273 (1920). (c) Y. Asahina, M. Ishidate, and T. Tukamoto, *Ber.*, **69**, 349 (1936). (d) J. Bredt, *J. prakt. Chem.*, **2**, 106, 336 (1923). (e) K. Miyake, *Proc. Imp. Acad.* (*Tokyo*), **11**, 106 (1935), through *Chem. Abstr.*, **29**, 6226 (1935).

upon pyrolysis to give an olefinic acid. These observations establish the configuration of **19**. The isomer, 2-methyl-*exo*-norborneol, **20** is formed when

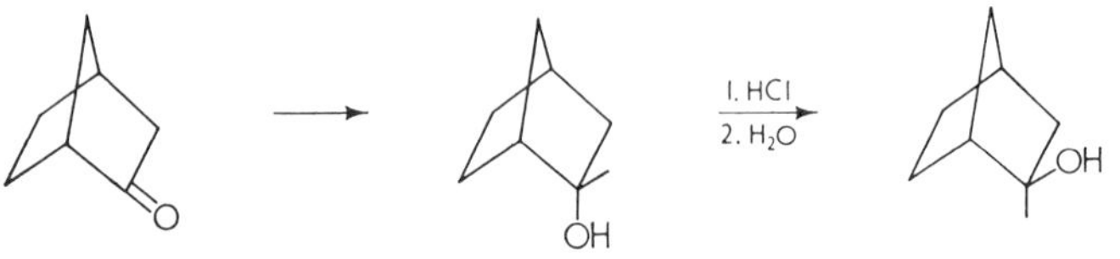

19 is treated with hydrogen chloride and the resulting chloride is hydrolyzed in basic solution.[24]

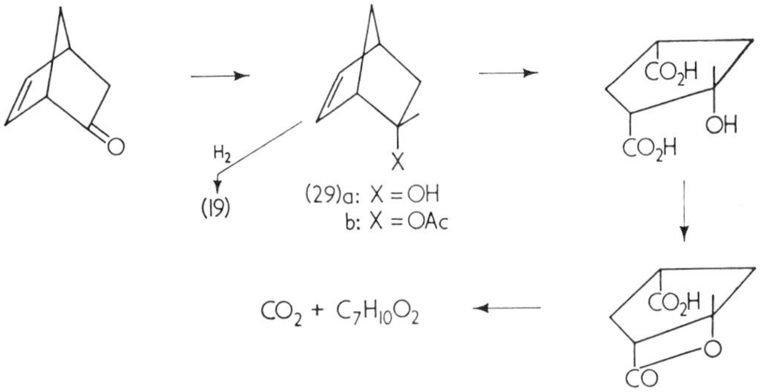

The predominant product of the Diels-Alder addition of cyclopentadiene and vinyl acetate [25] has generally been assumed to be *endo*-norbornenyl acetate. Although it is becoming increasingly obvious that stereochemical assignments based on the rule [26a] that *endo* products usually predominate are insecure,[26b–26f] there is ample independent evidence that, in this case, the assignment is correct. Hydrogenation and saponification of the major adduct give an epimer of the alcohol that is obtained in the lithium aluminum hydride

[24] N. J. Toivonen, XIVth International Congress of Pure and Applied Chemistry, Zürich, July, 1955, *Abstracts*, p. 45.

[24a] This substance is now formulated as a γ lactone: N. J. Toivonen, *Nord. Kemiker-møde*, **9**, *Aarhus*, Plenumsforedrag, **1956**, 117, as quoted by N. J. Toivonen and P. Mälkonen, *Suomen Kemistilehti*, **32B**, 277 (1959).

[25] K. Alder and H. F. Rickert, *Ann.*, **543**, 15 (1940).

[26] (a) For a review, see K. Alder in *Newer Methods of Preparative Organic Chemistry*, Interscience, New York, 1948, p. 381. (b) J. S. Meek and W. B. Trapp, *J. Am. Chem. Soc.*, **79**, 3909 (1957). (c) J. A. Berson, A. Remanick, and W. Mueller, *J. Am. Chem. Soc.*, **82**, 5501 (1960). (d) K. Alder, R. Hartmann, and W. Roth, *Ann.*, **613**, 6 (1958); *Chem. Ber.*, **93**, 2271 (1960). (e) J. A. Berson and W. A. Mueller, *Tetrahedron Letters*, No. 4, 131 (1961). (f) J. A. Berson, Z. Hamlet and W. A. Mueller, *J. Am. Chem. Soc.*, **84**, 297 (1962).

reduction [27] of *exo*-2,3-epoxy-norbornane. The latter epoxide is the product of peroxidation of norbornene,[27] and by analogy to many other additions to norbornene,[28] must have the *exo* configuration. The major adduct of the cyclopentadiene–vinyl acetate reaction must therefore be *endo*-norbornenyl acetate. Further, the derived alcohol, *endo*-norbornenol, can be epoxidized to a hydroxy epoxide (30) which is converted by potassium *tert*-butoxide to a hydroxytrimethylene oxide (31).[29] This reaction provides unequivocal confirmation of the assignments.

(30)   (31)

Physical Methods. Studies of intermolecular association of bicyclic alcohols in benzene provide a valuable guide to additional stereochemical assignments. The application [30,31] of this technique assumes that the degree of association is qualitatively inversely dependent on the severity of steric hindrance around the hydroxyl function. In the following discussion, the "degree of association" is given as the per cent elevation of the molecular weight for a solution of the alcohol at a standard concentration (0.6 molal) in benzene (see Table I). For the borneol-isoborneol pair, the more hindered environment of the isoborneol hydroxyl group (18), suggested by the lower thermodynamic stability [29b] and by the slower rates of formation and saponification of the esters,[29a] is confirmed by the weaker association:[30] isoborneol 24%, borneol 44%.

Sodium-alcohol reduction of camphor gives predominantly the less hindered alcohol, borneol.[32] The assumption that bicycloheptanones by

[27] (a) H. M. Walborsky and D. F. Loncrini, *J. Am. Chem. Soc.*, **76**, 5396 (1954). (b) S. B. Soloway and S. J. Cristol, *J. Org. Chem.*, **25**, 327 (1960).

[28] K. Alder, G. Stein, and S. Schneider, *Ann.*, **515**, 185 (1935), and many other papers by Alder and co-workers.

[29] H. B. Henbest and B. Nicholls, *J. Chem. Soc. (London)*, **1959**, 221.

[29a] G. Vavon and P. Peignier, *Bull. soc. chim. France*, [4] **35**, 925 (1924), [4] **39**, 924 (1926); G. Vavon, *Bull. soc. chim. France*, [4] **49**, 937 (1931). (b) G. Wagner and W. Brykner, *J. Russ. Phys. Chem. Soc.*, **35**, 537 (1903); through E. Josephy and F. Radt, eds., *Elsevier's Encyclopaedia of Organic Chemistry*, Vol. 12A, Elsevier, New York, 1948, p. 657.

[30] G. Komppa and S. Beckmann, *Ann.*, **522**, 137 (1936).

[31] (a) S. Beckmann and R. Mezger, *Chem. Ber.*, **90**, 1564 (1957). (b) S. Beckmann, and A. Dürkop, *Ann.*, **594**, 205 (1955). (c) See also W. Hückel, W. Doll, S. Eskola, F. Neumann, and I. Schneider, *Ann.*, **549**, 186 (1941), and references cited therein.

[32] C. J. Jackson and A. E. Menke, *Am. Chem. J.*, **5**, 270 (1883).

TABLE I

Elevation of Molecular Weight of a 0.6 Molal Solution in Benzene[30,31a,31b,35]

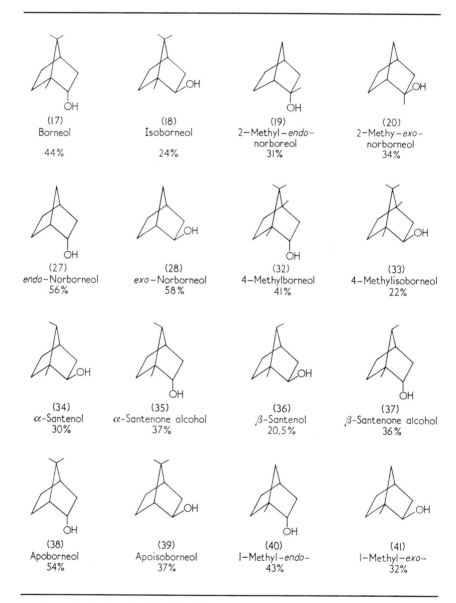

(17)
Borneol
44%

(18)
Isoborneol
24%

(19)
2−Methyl−*endo*-
norboreol
31%

(20)
2−Methy−*exo*-
norborneol
34%

(27)
endo−Norborneol
56%

(28)
exo−Norborneol
58%

(32)
4−Methylborneol
41%

(33)
4−Methylisoborneol
22%

(34)
α−Santenol
30%

(35)
α−Santenone alcohol
37%

(36)
β−Santenol
20.5%

(37)
β−Santenone alcohol
36%

(38)
Apoborneol
54%

(39)
Apoisoborneol
37%

(40)
1−Methyl−*endo*-
43%

(41)
1−Methyl−*exo*-
32%

[33] O. Wallach, *Ann.*, **300**, 294 (1898).

[34] S. Nametkin, *Ann.*, **432**, 207 (1923).

"alkaline reduction" (sodium-alcohol or sodium-water-ether) usually give predominantly the less hindered epimer of the corresponding pair of alcohols is well supported by cryoscopic measurements, at least in cases where the difference in hindrance for *endo* versus *exo* is clearly large. Sodium-water-ether reduction [33] of apocamphor gives a high yield of apoborneol (38), which is more highly associated than its epimer apoisoborneol (39). Because of the hindrance provided by the *syn*-7-methyl group, the *exo* isomer would be expected to be less associated. β-Santenone gives [31b] predominantly β-santenone alcohol (37). The degrees of association for this alcohol and its epimer, β-santenol (36), are very similar to those of the corresponding similarly hindered borneol-isoborneol pair. 4-Methylcamphor is quantitatively converted to 4-methylborneol (32) by sodium and alcohol.[34] The extra 4-methyl group is expected to be too remote from the hydroxyl function to affect the steric environment, and the association measurements for the epimeric pair confirm this; the values agree well with those for the 17–18 and 36–37 pairs (see Table I).

When the steric difference between the members of an *exo-endo* pair is not large, "alkaline reduction" frequently gives mixtures.[34a,34b] Lithium aluminum hydride reduction, however, is highly stereospecific in all cases.[35a] Camphor gives isoborneol (18) in high yield,[36] norbornanone gives *endo*-norborneol [35a] (27) in 94% yield, and apofenchocamphorone gives apoisoborneol (39) in 91% yield.[35a] The norborneol isomers 27 and 28 are of about equal stability,[35b] and it is significant that although the association measurements of Table I reveal a much smaller difference in hindrance between the members of this pair than that between the members of pairs 17–18, 36–37, or 38–39, the hydride reductions in all these cases proceed with the same high stereospecificity. The alcohol produced in each case is that resulting from addition of hydrogen to what is clearly the less hindered side of the carbonyl group. It does not necessarily follow that the alcohol produced will always be the more hindered one. In fact, α-santenone gives [31b] a 90% yield of the more highly associated member, α-santenone alcohol (35), of the 34–35 pair. Similarly, lithium aluminum hydride reduction of 1-methylnorbornanone gives [35a] 93% of the more highly associated member of the 40–41 epimeric pair (see

---

[34a] For a review see K. Alder, G. Stein, and H. F. Rickert, *Ann.*, **525**, 221 (1936).

[34b] For further studies of the stereochemistry of reductions of bicyclic ketones by dissolving metals, see G. Ourisson and A. Rassat, *Tetrahedron Letters*, No. **21**, 16 (1960).

[35] (a) S. Beckmann and R. Mezger, *Chem. Ber.*, **89**, 2738 (1956). (b) For further examples of hydride reductions of bicyclic ketones, see (b) C. H. DePuy and P. R. Story, *J. Am. Chem. Soc.*, **82**, 627, (1960).

[36] L. W. Trevoy and W. G. Brown, *J. Am. Chem. Soc.*, **71**, 1675 (1949); D. S. Noyce and D. B. Denney, *J. Am. Chem. Soc.*, **72**, 5743 (1950).

Table I). *Endo* configurations are nevertheless assigned [35a] to the two reduction products **35** and **40**. If the idea of preferred addition of hydride from the less hindered side is to be maintained, it is necessary to assume that what is (to, the hydrogen being added) the less hindered side of the molecule, is (to the hydroxyl in the product alcohol) the more hindered side. The anomaly disappears when it is recognized [30,31a,31b,35a,37] that a 1 substituent offers more hindrance to a 2-*exo* substituent than to a 2-*endo* substituent. This factor apparently does not control the direction of approach of the reducing agent, but comes into play only after the carbon-hydrogen bond is formed. The normal preference [28,35] for *exo* addition (when *syn*-7 substituents are absent) is therefore maintained.

In analogy to the hydride reductions, the addition of methyl Grignard reagents to norbornanone gives [38] exclusively 2-methyl-*endo*-norborneol (**19**), the configuration of which is rigorously established.[24]

The Pattern of Stereochemistry of the Products in Carbonium Ion Reactions. In the above discussion, eight epimeric pairs of alcohols are assigned configurations without recourse to assumptions about mesomeric cation intermediates in carbonium ion reactions of bicyclic systems. In such reactions, however, it is always the member of a pair assigned the *exo* configuration (or a derivative, e.g., ester or ether) that is formed: mineral-acid-catalyzed addition of alcohols, water, or carboxylic acids to camphene produces derivatives of isoborneol (**18**),[39] and solvolyses of either *endo*- or *exo*-norbornyl arenesulfonates or chlorides produce *exo*-norbornyl derivatives.[16a,16b,41] In Table II are collected a number of such reactions that lead to alcohols (or derivatives thereof) for which configurations are deduced above. (Table II does not list hydrocarbon products which accompany some of the alcohol products.)

Some additional results can now be fitted into the pattern. As is shown above, the stereochemistry of Grignard addition to norbornanone parallels hydride addition; the entering reagent approaches from the less hindered side of the carbonyl group to give *endo* alcohol. By analogy, the product of the reaction of apocamphor with methyl Grignard reagent is expected to have an *exo*-hydroxyl since hydride reduction of apocamphor gives the *exo* alcohol, apoisoborneol (**39**). From similar analogies, a list can be made [22b] of secondary and tertiary alcohols of presumed configuration derived by

[37] See also J. A. Berson and R. Swidler, *J. Am. Chem. Soc.*, **75**, 1721 (1953), fn. 22.

[38] N. J. Toivonen, E. Siltanen, and K. Ojala, *Ann. Acad. Sci. Fennicae, Ser. A*, **II**, No. 64 (1955); through *Chem. Abstr.*, **51**, 7329 (1957).

[39] J. Simonsen and L. N. Owen, *The Terpenoids*, Vol. II, Cambridge University Press, 1949, p. 315.

[40] S. Beckman, R. Schaber, and R. Bamberger, *Chem. Ber.*, **87**, 997 (1954).

[41] (a) J. D. Roberts, W. Bennett, and R. Armstrong, *J. Am. Chem. Soc.*, **72**, 3329 (1950). (b) L. Schmerling, *J. Am. Chem. Soc.*, **68**, 195 (1946).

TABLE II.—Formation of ... Products in Carbonium Ion Reactions of Bicyclic Derivatives

Starting material	Reaction conditions	Product (alcohol or alcohol derivative)	Ref.
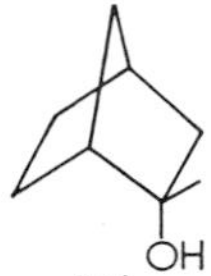 (19) or 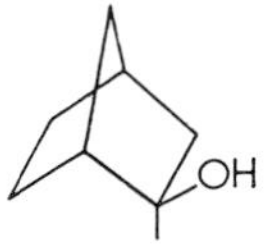 (20) or 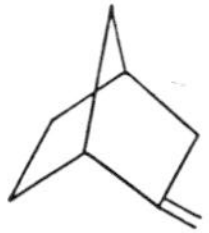 [structures]	HOAc–H$_2$SO$_4$	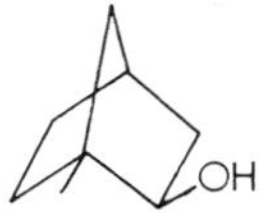 (41)	40,38,51
Chloride from 19 and conc. HCl	Aq. alkali	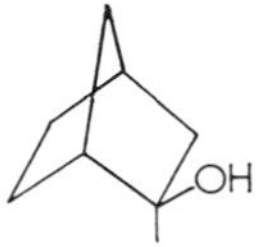 (20)	38
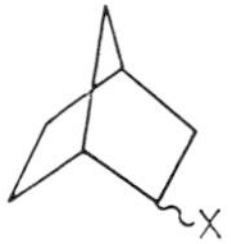 (X = OBs, OTs, Cl, or Br, endo or exo) (42)	HCO$_2$H, HOAc, or aq. acetone	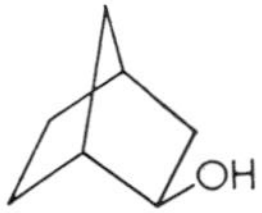 (28) and (34) and (36)	16a,16b,41
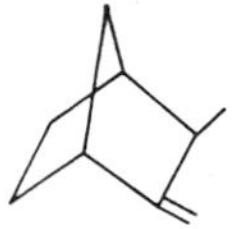  (43) or 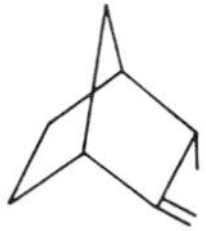 (44)	H$_2$SO$_4$–HOAc	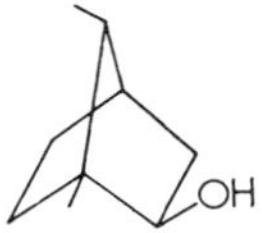 (34) and 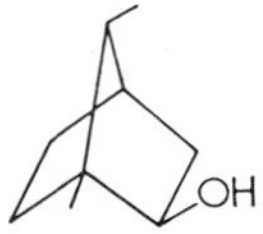 (36)	31b,47
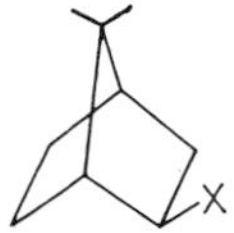 (10a or b)	HOAc or aq. dioxane on ROBs, or HCO$_2$H on ROH or aq. OH$^-$ on chloride	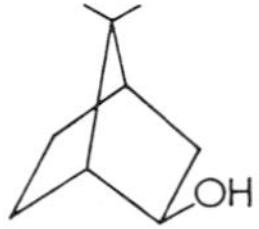 (39) and  (11) and 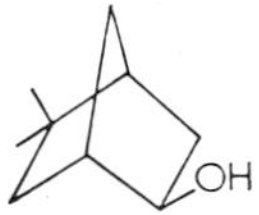 (12)	20,21,43
 (46)	HCO$_2$H on acid phthalate	 (41) and  (45)	43

(continued)

TABLE II—*continued*

Starting material	Reaction conditions	Product (alcohol or alcohol derivative)	Ref.
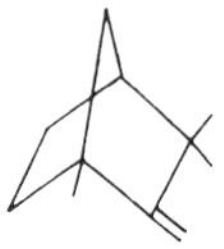 or 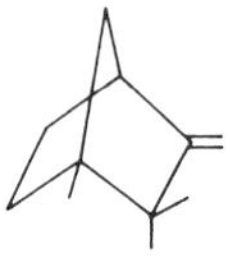	$H_2SO_4-H_2O$	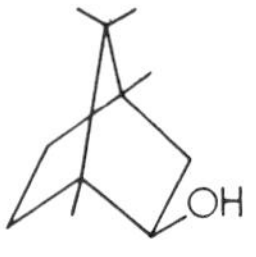 (33)	42
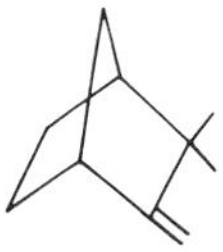	$RCO_2H + H^+$ or $H_2O + H^+$ or $ROH + H^+$	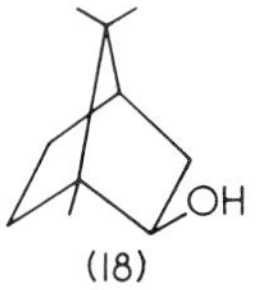 (18)	39

hydride reduction and Grignard addition, respectively, from the correspond-ing ketones (Table III). These can then be compared with products of car-bonium ion reactions. The results given in Table III show that when the product of hydride or Grignard addition is assigned the *exo* configuration by the above analogies, it is identical with the product obtained in the carbonium ion reaction; when the product of hydride or Grignard addition is assigned the *endo* configuration by the above analogies, however, it is epimeric with the product obtained in the carbonium ion reaction. This pattern is the same as that observed in Table II with the original set of eight pairs of alcohols, which are assigned configurations on other grounds.

The formation of *exo* products and the absence of *endo* products in car-bonium ion reactions of bicyclo[2.2.1]heptyl derivatives are thus a charac-teristic, self-consistent, and invariant pattern of behavior. It is critically important to examine interpretations other than the mesomeric cation hypothesis for consistency with these observations. In particular, one such

[42] S. Nametkin and L. Brüssoff, *Ann.*, **459**, 144 (1927); *J. prakt. Chem.*, **2**, 135, 155 (1932).

[43] S. Beckmann and G. Eder, *Chem. Ber.*, **91**, 2878 (1958).

[44] (a) G. Komppa and R. H. Roschier, *Ann. Acad. Sci. Fennicae*, **A10**, No. 3 (1917), (b) No. 15 (1917).

[45] G. Komppa and S. Beckmann, *Ann.*, **508**, 205 (1934).

[46] G. Komppa and G. A. Nyman, *Ann.*, **543**, 111 (1940).

[47] S. Beckmann and R. Bamberger, *Ann.*, **574**, 76 (1951).

[48] (a) G. Komppa and S. Beckmann, *Ann.*, **503**, 130 (1933), (b) **509**, 51 (1934).

[49] G. Komppa, *Ann.*, **472**, 179 (1929).

[50] G. Komppa and G. A. Nyman, *Ann.*, **523**, 87 (1936).

[51] S. Beckmann and R. Schaber, *Ann.*, **585**, 154 (1954).

alternative ascribes the absence of *endo* products to an especially unfavorable set of steric hindrance factors. It is true that an inspection of models of the parent norbornane skeleton suggests that approach to C_2 from the *endo* side is somewhat more hindered than from the *exo* side; further, there is experimental evidence, summarized in the *exo* addition rule of Alder [52] and exemplified in reductions of *syn-7-unsubstituted* 2-norbornanones described in this section, that *exo* addition is frequently favored. These generalizations, however, do not apply to *syn-7-substituted* substances. In these cases (e.g., camphor, apofenchocamphorone) *endo* addition is favored in hydride reductions of 2-ketones. Further, other additions to analogous systems give substantial or predominant amounts of *endo* addition product. The catalytic hydrogenations of camphor and camphoroxime give largely isobornyl products, resulting from *endo* addition; [29a] catalytic hydrogenation of camphene gives a mixture of *endo-* and *exo*-isocamphanes, [53] and the hydrogen abstraction reactions of the isocamphyl radical give mixtures of both isomers of isocamphane.[53a] Thus, it is difficult to support the idea that approach to the *endo* side of C_2 is prohibitively unfavorable. On the contrary, the evidence supports the idea that although *exo* approach is favored sterically when *syn*-C_7 bears only hydrogen, *endo* approach is favored when *syn*-C_7 bears alkyl. Yet carbonium ion reactions of bicyclo[2.2.1]heptyl derivatives (Tables II and III) give *exo* products exclusively,[57d] *regardless of whether or not a syn-7-alkyl group is present.* No reasonable grounds exist for ascribing this effect to steric hindrance. The postulation of configuration-maintaining product-determining intermediates (mesomeric cations) suffices to explain the stereochemical pattern. Whether such an interpretation is also a *necessary* one is a question that is essentially meaningless unless a reasonable alternative is offered.

C. Product Distributions

A second important pattern emerges [57a,57b] from the data on carbonium ion reactions. For all the cases in which a secondary alcohol and a tertiary

---

[52] K. Alder and G. Stein, *Ann.*, **515**, 185 (1935), **525**, 183 (1936).

[53] (a) J. A. Berson, C. J. Olsen, and J. S. Walia, *J. Am. Chem. Soc.*, **82**, 5000 (1960); C. J. Olsen and J. S. Walia, Ph.D. dissertations, University of Southern California, 1962 and 1960, respectively. (b) Cf. A. Lipp, *Ann.*, **382**, 265 (1911).

[54] P. D. Bartlett, E. R. Webster, C. E. Dills, and H. G. Richey, *Ann.*, **623**, 217 (1959).

[55] W. Hückel and F. Nerdel, *Ann.*, **528**, 57 (1937).

[56] W. Hückel, *Ann.*, **549**, 95 (1941).

[57] (a) P. Beltrame, C. A. Bunton, and D. Whittaker, *Chem. & Ind. (London)*, **1960**, 557. (b) J. A. Berson, *Tetrahedron Letters*, No. **16**, 17 (1960). (c) R. H. de Wolfe and W. G. Young, *Chem. Revs.*, **56**, 753 (1956). (d) It must be noted that the argument presented here does not depend on high analytical accuracy in the detection of *endo* product. Even a predominant amount of *exo* product in the *syn*-7-alkyl cases cannot be attributable to a steric effect, and seems to require that at least a major portion of the product comes from a mesomeric cation.

TABLE III

Comparison of Alcohol Products Derived by Hydride or Grignard Addition with Those of Carbonium Ion Reactions

| Ketone | Addition | | Carbonium ion reaction | | |
	Reagent[a]	Analogically assigned stereochemistry of hydroxyl group in product	Starting material[a]	Reaction conditions	Identical or epimeric with ketone adduct?	Ref.
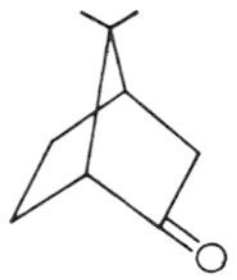 Apocamphor	A	exo	C	Aq. OH⁻	Identical	44a, 45, 46
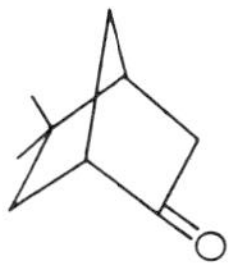	A	endo	C	Aq. OH⁻	Epimeric	44b, 48
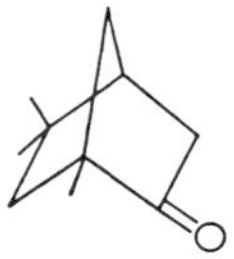	A	endo	C	Aq. OH⁻	Epimeric	49, 50

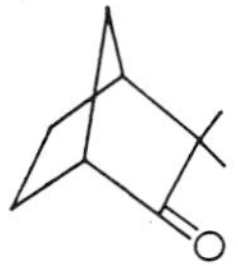	A	endo	C	Aq. OH⁻	Epimeric	55, 31c, 56, 18
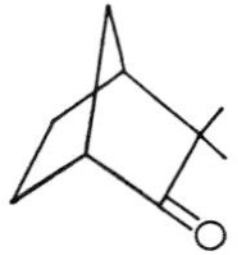	B	endo	D	HOAc or Aq. dioxane	Epimeric	35, 20
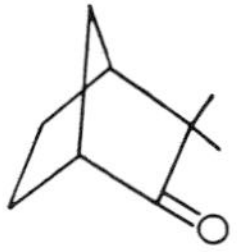	E	endo	F	H_2SO_4 then H_2O	Epimeric	54
			C	1 equiv. CO_3^{2-}, H_2O	Epimeric	54
				0.5 equiv. CO_3^{2-}, H_2O	Identical	

a A = methyl Grignard reagent; B = LiAlH₄; C = chloride from HCl and olefin or alcohol; D = arenesulfonate of **39** or **12** (see Table II); E = p-methoxyphenyl Grignard reagent; and F = either epimeric alcohol.

alcohol are alternative products by virtue of a Wagner-Meerwein relationship —for example, camphene hydrate and isoborneol—the thermodynamically unstable tertiary product predominates under conditions (usually basic) that insure kinetic control. This generalization has long been recognized in terpene chemistry and has served as a guide in preparative work. Its theoretical basis is not entirely clear, but the tendency of unsymmetrically substituted bicyclic mesomeric cations to give the more highly substituted product resembles the behavior of allylically mesomeric cations. In kinetically controlled reactions, the latter species give high or even predominant proportions of products resulting from attack of a nucleophile at the more highly substituted carbon of the allylic system, despite the pronounced thermodynamic preference for the allylically isomeric product, which has the more highly substituted double bond.[57c] Further, the unsymmetrically substituted phenonium ions derived from the solvolyses of 1-phenyl-2-propyl-p-toluenesulfonate and 1-p-anisyl-2-propyl-p-toluenesulfonate are attacked with high selectivity at the more highly substituted carbon.[58] In most of the bicyclic cases, the degree of selectivity is unknown, since usually only the tertiary product is isolated. A selectivity factor of about fifteen in favor of the tertiary position is observed [58a] in the chloride exchange versus rearrangement experiments in the camphene-hydroisobornyl system in chloroform. This factor rises to about forty in nitrobenzene.[58b] If a factor about this large applies to the other cases discussed, the amount of secondary product would be small enough to escape detection in an ordinary preparative operation.

The selectivity favoring nucleophilic attack at the more highly substituted carbon of the bridged cations is formally analogous to Markownikoff behavior of unsymmetrical olefins and cyclopropanes. It may signify [57b] either (a) that the carbonium ion intermediates are unsymmetrically bridged, with the more highly substituted center bearing a greater burden of charge or (b) that the electrical effects of the attached alkyl groups come into play in the transition states for conversion of the bridged intermediate to products; these effects would be expected to favor localization of charge at the more highly substituted carbon. Further observations that appear to be at least in part attributable to this kind of effect include the reactions of halogen- or oxygen-substituted norbornyl and norbornenyl cations, which give only nonvicinally disubstituted products (see heading 5B).[58c]

[58] S. Winstein, M. Brown, K. C. Schreiber, and A. H. Schlesinger, *J. Am. Chem. Soc.*, **74**, 1141 (1952).

[58a] T. P. Nevell, E. de Salas, and C. L. Wilson, *J. Chem. Soc. (London)*, **1939**, 1188.

[58b] Y. Pocker, *Proc. Chem. Soc. (London)*, **1960**, 216.

[58c] For a related interpretation of the behavior of cations derived from substituted allylcarbinyl-cyclopropylcarbinyl-cyclobutyl systems, see J. D. Roberts, Abstracts of Papers, ACS 16th National Organic Chemistry Symposium, Seattle, Washington, June, 1959, *Abstracts*; M. S. Silver, M. C. Caserio, H. E. Rice, and J. D. Roberts, *J. Am. Chem. Soc.*, **83**, 3671 (1961).

As a practical consequence of these generalizations, the occurrence or non-occurrence of skeletal rearrangement in a reaction of a bicyclic substance is, *per se*, not a criterion for the presence or absence of mesomeric cation intermediates. If due attention is paid to the above pattern, however, rearrangement or retention of skeletal structure can be predicted.

Although the migrating carbon itself presumably bears some positive charge in the mesomeric cation, products resulting from attack at this position usually are not observed. In the isobornyl mesomeric cation, attack on the migrating carbon by X^- would lead to monocyclic olefin. The absence

of such products may be taken as support for the general pattern outlined above, since in this case and virtually all others for which data are available, the migrating carbon is less highly substituted than the origin or terminus of migration. A reaction that may be of this type, in a case where the migrating carbon is *tertiary*, is described in the section on the pinyl system (see page 185).

Those experimental conditions which produce *exo* secondary product when a Wagner-Meerwein-related tertiary alternative is available, therefore, do not lead to truly kinetically controlled reactions. Thus, although the alkaline solvolysis of camphene hydrochloride or isobornyl chloride gives camphene hydrate, the Bertram-Walbaum hydration (sulfuric acid and a carboxylic acid) of camphene gives an isobornyl ester (Table II), and the acetolyses of bornyl chloride or isobornyl chloride give isobornyl acetate.[39,59] The instability of tertiary materials relative to their secondary Wagner-Meerwein isomers under acidic conditions is further exemplified by the conversion of either 2-methyl-*endo*-norborneol (19) or 2-methyl-*exo*-norborneol (20) to esters of 1-methyl-*exo*-norborneol (41) in formic acid or under Bertram-Walbaum conditions.[38,40] The acid conditions suffice to reform the mesomeric cation from the proximate product, the tertiary derivative; a slower reaction of the bridged cation then leads to *exo* secondary material. If the conditions are sufficiently drastic and if the *endo* secondary derivative is more stable than the *exo* epimer, *endo* secondary product may also be formed. The hydration of camphene ordinarily leads predominantly to isobornyl derivatives, but bornyl derivatives are also found in small yield,[59] and isobornyl chloride is slowly converted to bornyl chloride at 100° in the presence of stannic chloride.[60] The formation of *endo* product is usually very slow, however, even under reversible conditions. The 2-*p*-anisylcamphenilol *endo-exo* isomers (tertiary), which in acid solution instantaneously form a particularly stable

[59] O. Aschan, *Ber.*, **49**, 4918 (1907).
[60] H. Meerwein and K. van Emster, *Ber.*, **53**, 1815 (1920).

mesomeric cation (**47**), illustrate an exception; although formation of the *exo* alcohol is rapid and can be observed by quenching the solution of the carbonium ion (formed from the Wagner-Meerwein-related chloride) with an

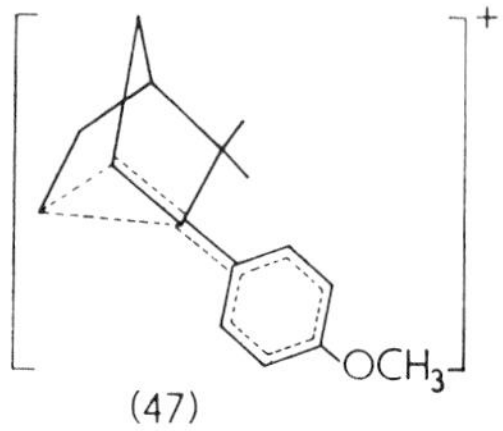

(47)

equivalent of aqueous carbonate, reversion of the *exo* product to the carbonium ion is so rapid in acid that quenching with a stoichiometric deficiency of carbonate gives the *endo* isomer (*exo-p*-anisyl group), which is presumably less strained.[54]

D.　2-Bicyclo[2.2.1]heptyl Mesomeric Cations by Ring Closure

The norbornyl mesomeric cation appears to be formed in solvolyses of 2-(Δ^3-cyclopentenylethyl) derivatives.[60a,60b] For example, acetolyses of the derivatives **47a** (X = OBs, or X = OTs, or X = p-NO$_2$C$_6$H$_4$SO$_3$) give *exo*-norbornyl acetate **47b** and little or no *endo* acetate or uncyclized acetate.

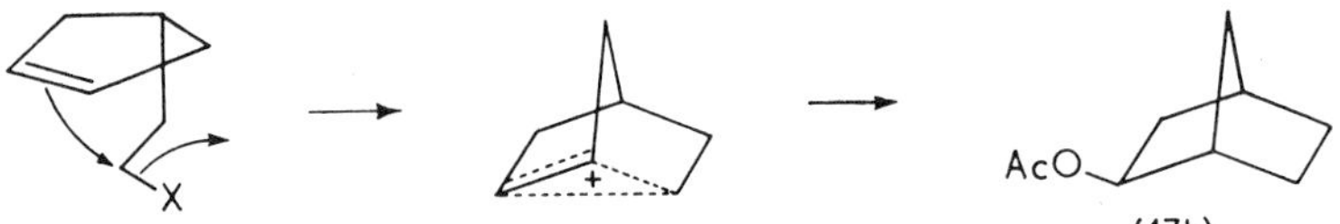

(47a)　　　　　　　　　　　　　　　　　　　　　AcO　(47b)

· (47c)　　　　　　　　　　　(47d)

The rates of solvolysis exceed those of the corresponding derivatives of the saturated analog, 2-cyclopentylethanol, by factors that range from about 6 to about 1900, depending on the solvent. The enhancement of solvolytic reactivity and the almost exclusive formation of *exo* products suggest that most of the reaction proceeds by way of anchimerically assisted (see headings 7 and 8) formation of a mesomeric cation.[60a,60b] Examples of analogous ring

[60a] R. G. Lawton, *J. Am. Chem. Soc.*, **83**, 2399 (1961).

[60b] P. D. Bartlett and S. Bank, *J. Am. Chem. Soc.*, **83**, 2591 (1961).

closures are given in heading 10. These results are to be contrasted with those observed [60c] in the case of Δ^3-cyclohexenylcarbinyl p-bromobenzenesulfonate **47c**, acetolysis of which occurs at a rate virtually identical with that of the saturated analog and gives only uncyclized acetate **47d**.

4. INTRAMOLECULAR 6,2 AND 3,2 HYDROGEN SHIFTS

A. Introduction

Reactions involving carbonium ions generated from optically active camphene, pinene, camphenehydro, bornyl, or isobornyl derivatives frequently give partially racemized products. For example, the Lewis-acid-catalyzed conversion of isobornyl chloride to bornyl chloride is accompanied by some racemization,[61] and the hydration of pinene to bornyl derivatives (**47e** → **48**) gives largely racemic product.[62] Meerwein and Montfort[61] propose two explanations of these phenomena.

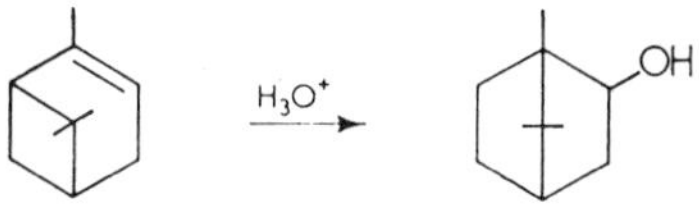

(47e)   (48)

The first suggests that the intermediate bornyl cation racemizes by assuming a planar molecular configuration, **49b**; that is, one enantiomer of the cation is converted to the other by inversions of C_1 and C_4. Although this would require enormous activation energy and is therefore improbable, a variant of the hypothesis, namely, the reversible formation of the optically inactive

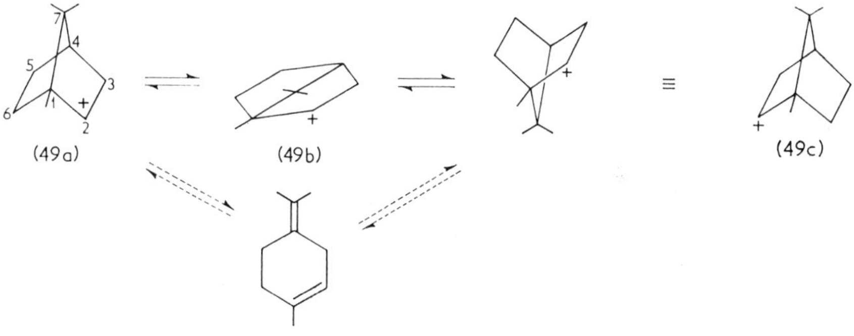

(49a)   (49b)   (49c)

(50)

60c G. LeNy, *Compt. rend.*, **251**, 1526 (1960).
61 H. Meerwein and F. Montfort, *Ann.*, **435**, 207 (1924).
62 For a review, see J. Simonsen and L. N. Owen, The Terpenes, Vol. II, Cambridge University Press, 1949, p. 163.

hydrocarbon terpinolene (**50**), is worth considering. The strongest argument against this is the apparent failure of terpinolene to recyclize to bornyl or camphenehydro derivatives; the literature records many reactions of terpinolene with acids, none of which give products of the requisite type.

Meerwein's second hypothesis proposes interconversion of the enantiomeric bornyl cations by a shift of hydrogen (hydride ion or the equivalent) from C_6 to C_2. The history of this 6,2 shift hypothesis provides a good example of the viability of chemical ideas. Apparently lifeless after the realization that the Nametkin rearrangement (see heading 5A) provided alternative explanations for the observations upon which it was based, the 6,2 shift hypothesis was in fact only dormant; it was revived in 1951 as a result of two independent and virtually simultaneous experiments. These demonstrated intramolecular 6,2 hydrogen shifts in the fenchyl and norbornyl systems.

B.   Proof of 6,2 Shifts by Isotope-Position Labeling Experiments

O-Deuterofenchol (**51**) is dehydrated by deuterated potassium bisulfate to a mixture of α-, β-, and γ-fenchenes (**52**, **53**, and **54**) and cyclofenchene (**55**).

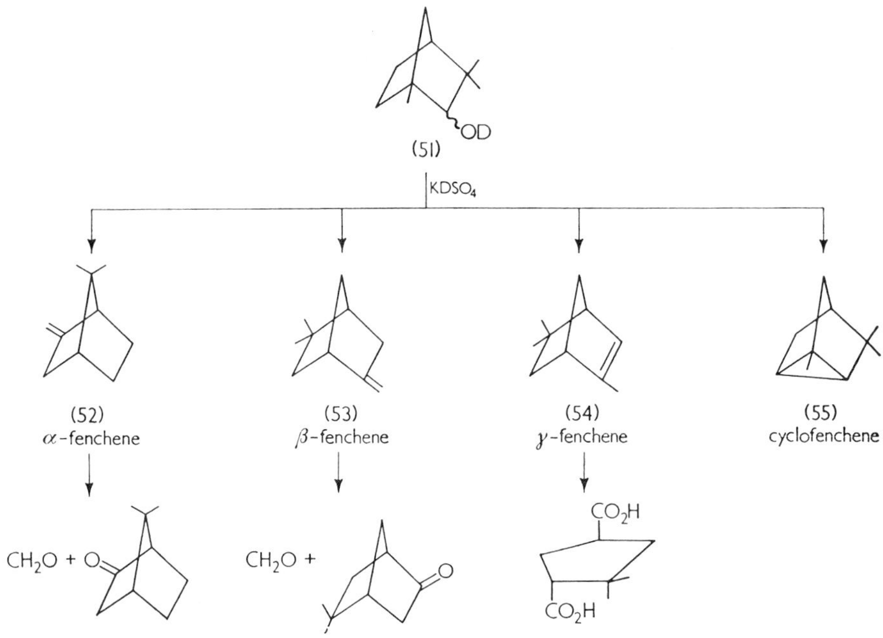

Analyses of these products for total deuterium content and for deuterium distribution indicate that deuterium is bound almost exclusively to the double bond carbons and the carbons adjacent to double bonds.[63a] α-Fenchene (**52**) is a product of normal Wagner-Meerwein rearrangement, but β- and γ-fenchenes (**53** and **54**) are products of formal 6,2 hydrogen shift and Wagner-Meerwein rearrangement and cannot be derived from fenchol by any reasonable combination of 1,2 carbon and hydrogen shifts. Although cyclofenchene (**55**) is converted by potassium bisulfate to a mixture of **53** and **54**,[63b]

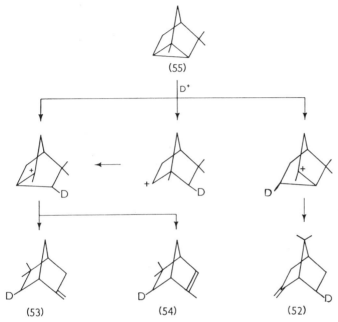

the deuterium distribution indicates that it cannot be an important intermediate in the formation of **53** and **54** under the conditions used by Doering and Wolf[63a] (minimum contact time of the reactant and products with the acid catalyst). Any ring opening of cyclofenchene to give a carbonium ion precursor of α-, β-, or γ-fenchene would introduce deuterium into a position remote from the double bond. The formation of β- and γ-fenchenes is therefore attributable to a genuine intramolecular 6,2 hydrogen shift.

Formally, the observation that the solvolysis of optically active *exo*-norbornyl *p*-bromobenzenesulfonate (**15a**) produces racemic *exo*-norbornyl acetate (**15b**)[64a,64b] does not require that the mesomeric cation (**16**) associated

[63] (a) A. P. Wolf, Dissertation, Columbia University, 1952; W. von E. Doering, and A. P. Wolf, XIIth International Congress of Pure and Applied Chemistry, New York, 1951, *Abstracts*, p. 437; *Perfumery Essent. Oil Record*, **42**, 414 (1951); *Chem. Abstr.*, **46**, 7080 (1952). (b) G. Komppa and G. A. Nyman, *Ann.*, **535**, 252 (1938).

[64] (a) S. Winstein and D. Trifan, *J. Am. Chem. Soc.*, **71**, 2953 (1949), (b) **74**, 1147, 1154 (1952).

with Wagner-Meerwein rearrangement be the only product-forming intermediate; in fact, there is no direct evidence, from this result, that a Wagner-Meerwein rearrangement has occurred at all. Of the other conceivable optically inactive intermediates, norbornylene (56) and nortricyclene (57) can

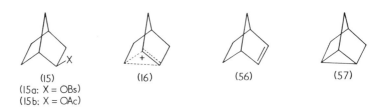

(15)   (16)   (56)   (57)
(15a: X = OBs)
(15b: X = OAc)

be dismissed on the grounds already given (heading 3A). There are, however, no simple grounds for rejecting in advance such racemizing processes as 58 and 59.[64] Reaction 58 is the prototype of 6,2 hydrogen shift; reaction 59 is the hydrogen analog of the Nametkin rearrangement (see heading 5A).

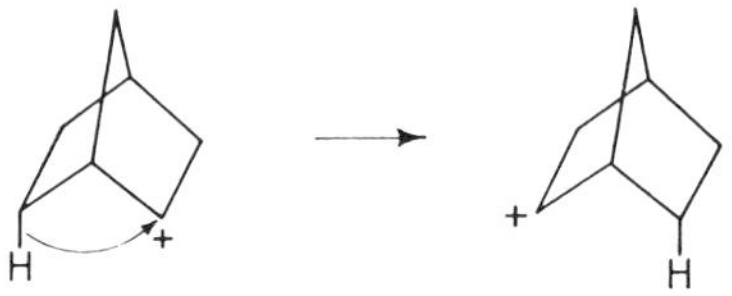

(58)

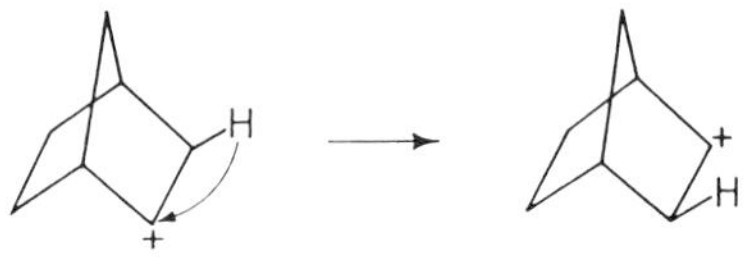

(59)

Information on how many of these processes are involved in carbonium ion reactions of norbornane derivatives is available from the study by Roberts and co-workers[65] of the ^{14}C distribution in the solvolysis of *exo-* and *endo-*norbornyl-2,3-^{14}C-*p*-bromo-benzene sulfonate (60). The per cent rearrangement, defined as 100 (activity of 62/activity of 61) in the indicated degradation scheme, is a gross measure of the fraction of the ^{14}C that has migrated from its original positions at C_2 and C_3. The difference (activity of 61–activity of 62) represents the activity at C_2 and C_3; the difference (activity of 62–activity of 63) represents the activity at C_7; the difference (activity of 63–activity of 64) represents the activity at C_1 and C_4, and the activity of 64 represents the activity of C_5 and C_6. Table IV lists the percent rearrangement

[65] J. D. Roberts, C. C. Lee, and W. H. Saunders, Jr., *J. Am. Chem. Soc.*, **76**, 4501 (1954); J. D. Roberts and C. C. Lee, *J. Am. Chem. Soc.*, **73**, 5009 (1951).

and isotopic distribution (as per cent of the activity of **61** expected for each of the racemization mechanisms mentioned above).

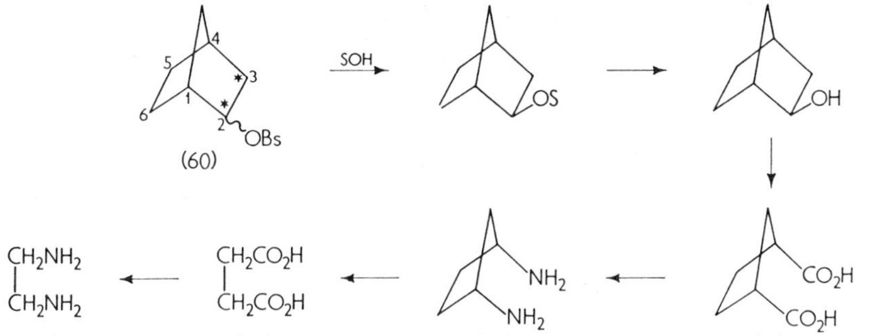

Neither the cation **16** nor the hypothetical processes **58** or **59** can account, by itself, for more than 50% rearrangement. Further, the only pairwise combination that is consistent with more than 50% rearrangement is that of **16** (carbon-bridged mesomeric cation) and **58** (6,2 shift); the isotopic position rearrangement results may therefore be taken as direct evidence for the formal equivalent of both Wagner-Meerwein and 6,2 hydrogen shifts in this system. The occurrence of 6,2 hydrogen shift is directly indicated by the activity found in the degradation product **64**.[65a]

TABLE IV

Calculated[a] Per Cent Rearrangements and Isotopic Distributions for Product from Various Processes in the Solvolysis of **60**

Racemization mechanisms	Rearrange-ment, %	Activity, %			
		At $C_2 + C_3$	At $C_1 + C_4$	At C_7	At $C_5 + C_6$
Carbon-bridged cation (**16**)	50	50	25	25	0
6,2 Shift (**58**)	50	50	0	0	50
3,2 Shift (**59**)	0	100	0	0	0

[a] Some experimental values are given in Table V.

Rearrangement of isotope position, barely observable when labeled nor-bornyl acetate is subjected to the acetolysis conditions, is more pronounced

[65a] With respect to the original numbering of the intact norbornane skeleton, the equivalence of C_1 and C_2 produced by carbon bridging makes 6,2 and 6,1 shifts in the cation **16** equally probable.

when norbornyl formate is subjected to the formolysis conditions. These extra rearrangements of the product esters are too slow, however, to account for the rearrangement in excess of 50% observed in the solvolysis of the p-bromobenzenesulfonate; the solvolysis itself, therefore, is associated with more than 50% rearrangement.[65]

Whether a true intermediate (65) with three-fold symmetry is formed in the hydrogen shift reaction or 65 is merely a transition state for interconversions of the structurally identical ions 66–68 is not known.[65]

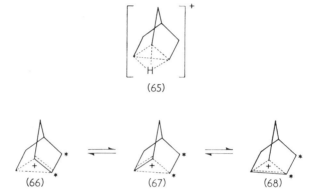

The isotopic distribution results (Table V) in the acetolysis of *exo*-60 are best fitted [65] by assuming that 55% of the product comes from the two-fold symmetrical carbon-bridged mesomeric cation 66 and 45% from the three-

TABLE V

Experimental Values [65] of Isotope Distribution in Solvolyses of **60**

Reactant	Conditions	Rearrangement, %	Activity, %			
			At $C_2 + C_3$	At $C_1 + C_4$	At C_7	At $C_5 + C_6$
exo-60	75% acetone, reflux	54.5	—	—	—	—
exo-60	HOAc–KOAc, 45°	60.6	40	23	22	15
exo-endo-60	HCO$_2$H–NaHCO$_2$, reflux	69.6	31.3	22.1	18.5	28.1
endo-60	75% acetone, reflux	44.5	—	—	—	—
endo-60	HOAc–KOAc, reflux	56.1	—	—	—	—

fold symmetrical hydrogen-bridged mesomeric cation 65 (or its equivalent in isotope distribution, a 1:1:1 mixture of 66, 67, and 68). As is shown by the smaller per cent rearrangement, the contribution of 65 is less in aqueous acetone. This is interpreted [65] as indicating sequential formation of ions 66 and 65, with the formation of 65 following that of 66; the more nucleophilic aqueous solvent is believed to capture the two-fold symmetrical ion 66 sooner than does acetic acid (for further discussion of this point, see heading 4D).

C. 3,2 Hydrogen Shifts

3,2 Hydrogen shift (59) appears to be the slowest of the three rearrangement processes. In combination with carbon bridging and 6,2 shift it would lead to the appearance of activity at C_4 in the product and eventually to spreading of the activity equally over all the carbon atoms of the norbornane skeleton.[65] This statistical distribution of activity would then require that any carbon atom have half the activity of any two of the other atoms. Cations 65 and 66 in any combination, however, could never lead to statistical distribution of the isotope in the product. In particular, the activity at C_7 would always remain equal to the sum of the activities of C_1 and C_4.[65] The data for the acetolysis of exo-60 meet this condition; here, the 3,2 shift is undetectable. In formic acid, however, the isotopic distribution drifts in a direction that seems to indicate the onset of the 3,2 shift; the C_7 activity is slightly less than the sum of the C_1 and C_4 activities (see Table V). Further, ions 65 and 66, separately or in combination, require that the sum of the activities of C_1, C_4 and C_7 be equal to the sum of the activities of C_2 and C_3.[66] Experimentally, this is not the case in formic acid; the sum of the C_1, C_4 and C_7 activities is considerably greater than that of C_2 and C_3.[66a]

The results can be fitted quantitatively [66] by a distribution derived from 52% of 16, 32% of 58, and 16% of 3,2 (and 7,1) hydride shift. Because of experimental error, the fit is rather loose, and some departure from this distribution could be tolerated, but at least the occurrence of the 3,2 shift seems established.

D. The Timing of Wagner-Meerwein, 6,2 and 3,2 Shifts; Sequential or Competitive Formation of Carbon-Bridged and Hydrogen-Bridged Cations?

Table V (heading 4B) shows that 6,2 hydrogen shift in the solvolysis of exo-norbornyl p-bromobenzenesulfonate decreases in importance as the solvent

[66] C. E. Dills, Thesis, Harvard University, 1955.

[66a] That this discrepancy is well outside experimental error is clear from an evaluation of the statistical probable error. From the reported [65] standard deviation of 3% in the activity measurements and the reported [65] activities, the sum of the C_7, C_1, and C_4 activities can be expressed as 2330 ± 120 dis./min./mg. corrected for background, self-absorption, and dilution by non-radioactive carbons and that of C_2 and C_3 as 1800 ± 140 on the same basis.

is changed from acetic acid to aqueous acetone.[65] Similar results are observed in the solvolysis of aposantenyl or *exo*-camphenilyl *p*-bromobenzenesulfonates (**69** and **70**); the amount of β-fenchoisocamphoryl product (**72**), resulting from

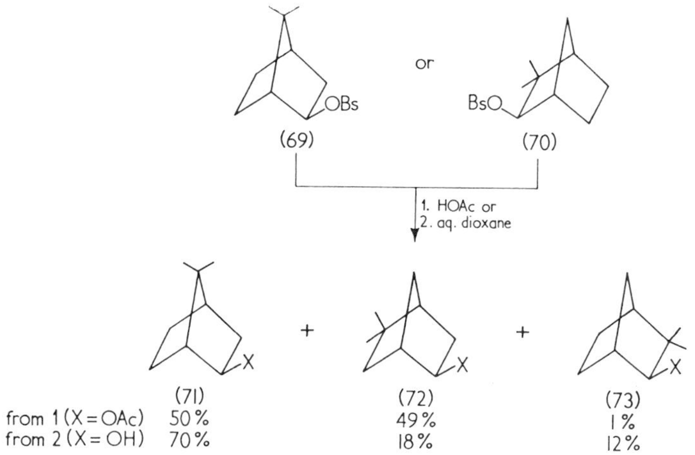

	(71)	(72)	(73)
from 1 (X = OAc)	50%	49%	1%
from 2 (X = OH)	70%	18%	12%

6,2 shift, is less in aqueous solvent than in acetic acid.[67] The results are interpreted[67] as confirming the idea[65] that 6,2 shift occurs *after* carbon bridging. In terms of the attached scheme, the hypothesis means that the steady-state concentration of the hydrogen-bridged intermediate **74**, formed *sequentially* from the carbon-bridged cation **75** (path A), is smaller in water than in acetic acid—in other words, that $(k_3 + k_4)/k_1$, the ratio that measures partitioning of **75** between reaction with solvent and isomerization to **74**, is larger in the more nucleophilic solvent, water. While it certainly must be true that $(k_3 + k_4)_{H_2O} > (k_3 + k_4)_{HOAc}$, it does not necesssarily follow that

$$[(k_3 + k_4)/k_1]_{H_2O} > [(k_3 + k_4)/k_1]_{HOAc}.$$

Therefore, the hypothesis, while plausible, is not uniquely required by the data. There are at least two alternative interpretations; one of these derives from path A (sequential formation of **75** and **74**) and the other from path B (competing formation of **75** and **74**).

1. Alternative derived from path A. The hypothesis given above contains the implicit assumption that the *relative* magnitudes of the rate constants k_3, k_4, k_5, k_6, and k_7, which measure the rates of capture of the cations **75** and **74** by solvent, do not change much when the system is transferred from one solvent to another. This assumption is reasonable, but it has no real experi-

[67] (a) S. Winstein, XIVth International Congress of Pure and Applied Chemistry, Zurich, *Experientia, Suppl.* No. **2**, 137 (1955). (S. Winstein, A. Colter, and N. J. Holness, unpublished.)

mental support. If it is abandoned, the ratio $(k_3 + k_4)/k_1$ could be the same in both solvents, or even larger in acetic acid than in water, but the smaller proportion of 6,2-shifted product (72) in water could be a consequence of a smaller value of k_7 relative to k_5 and k_6.

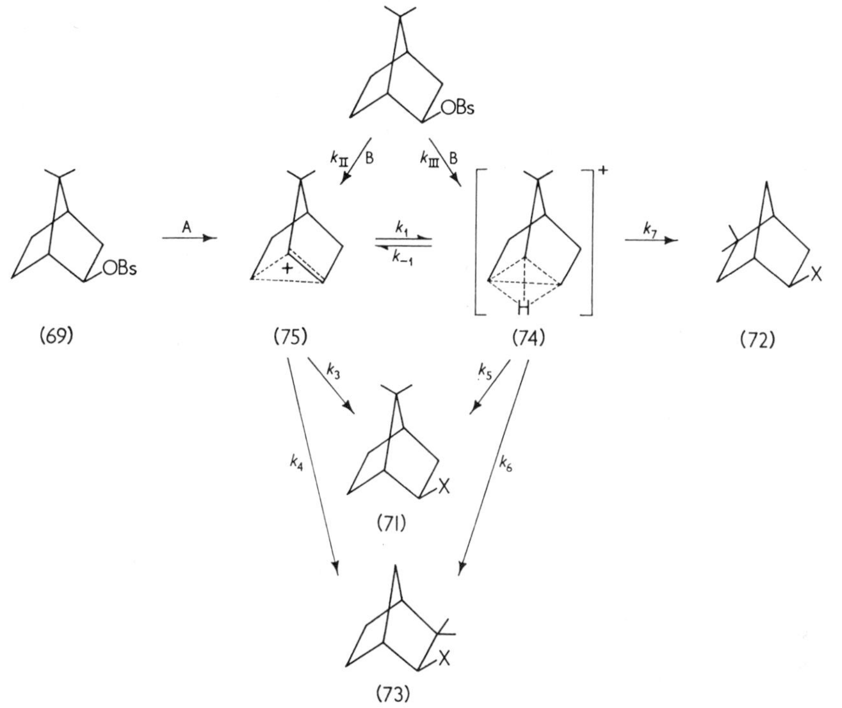

2. *Alternative derived from path B.* If **75** and **74** are formed in *competing* processes (path B), the solvent effect could be the result of a change in the rate constant ratio: $(k_{III}/k_{II})_{AcOH} > (k_{III}/k_{II})_{H_2O}$.

Clearly, there is no reason to assume that *both* paths, A and B, could not occur.

In the case of the norbornyl-2,3-^{14}C system, no alternative corresponding to (1) above exists, for if the isotopic difference is disregarded, the proportions of products derived from the hydrogen-bridged cation **65** must remain constant at $1:1:1$ by symmetry, regardless of solvent. Alternative (2), however, does have a direct analog in the norbornyl case.

There is no obvious way of predicting the direction of solvent effects on the ratios $k_7/(k_5 + k_6)$ or $[(k_{III}/k_{II})_{AcOH}]/[(k_{III}/k_{II})_{H_2O}]$. Aside from its greater simplicity, the principal advantage of the original hypothesis over the two alternatives presented is thus its *requirement* that the effect of a change in the solvent be the one observed; the alternatives, while compatible with the effect, do not require it.

The results allow still other interpretations when the possibility of 6,2 shift accompanying ion pair return is recognized (see heading 6).

An example of what appears to be an effect similar to the solvent effects noted in the norbornyl and camphenilyl systems is provided by additions to 4-chlorocamphene (**76**). This substance is converted by trichloroacetic acid to 4-chloroisobornyltrichloroacetate (**77**) with 69% retention of optical purity,

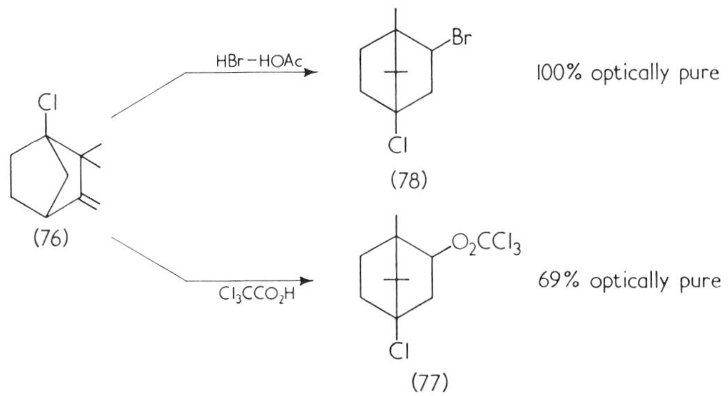

the partial racemization presumably being attributable to 6,2 shift. (Note that racemization by the Nametkin rearrangement, a process to be discussed in heading 5A, is impossible in this case.) With hydrogen bromide in acetic acid, presumably a more nucleophilic system, conversion to 4-chloroisobornyl bromide (**78**) occurs with complete retention of optical purity.[68]

The low proportion of camphenilyl derivative observed in the reaction with solvent of the ion **74** ($k_7 > k_6$) apparently is attributable to steric hindrance. A thermodynamic example of this kind of hindrance is provided by the equilibrium **79** $\rightleftharpoons$ **80**.[69]

The 6,2 hydrogen shift hypothesis bears a superficial resemblance to the

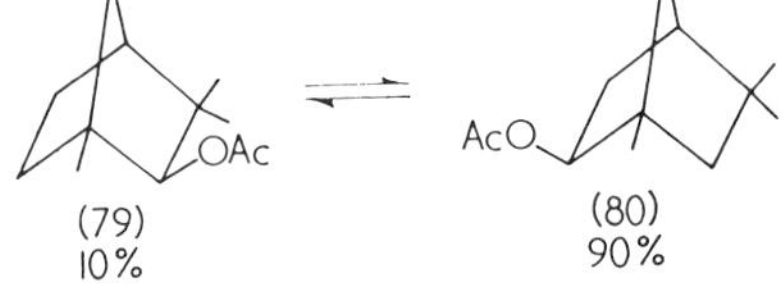

[68] J. Houben and E. Pfankuch, *Ann.*, **507**, 37 (1933).
[69] N. J. Toivonen, *Suomen Kemistilehti*, **24B**, 62 (1951).

once strongly held [70] idea that tricyclenic substances are intermediates in rearrangements of bicycloheptanes. The tricyclene hypothesis was conclusively discredited in the case of the camphene hydrochloride–isobornyl chloride rearrangement; [71] consequently, it seemed logical to limit to Wagner-Meerwein possibilities the assignment of structures to rearrangement products and to reject summarily structures apparently derivable only from tricyclenic intermediates. This procedure is no longer safe, since those non-Wagner-Meerwein structures derivable from tricyclenic intermediates are also formally derivable by combinations of 6,2 hydrogen shift and Wagner-Meerwein change. The hydration of dicyclopentadiene (81) serves as an example. The structure (82) or a double bond isomer originally assigned [72] is formally a product of ring opening of the tricyclene (83). It was therefore considered [73]

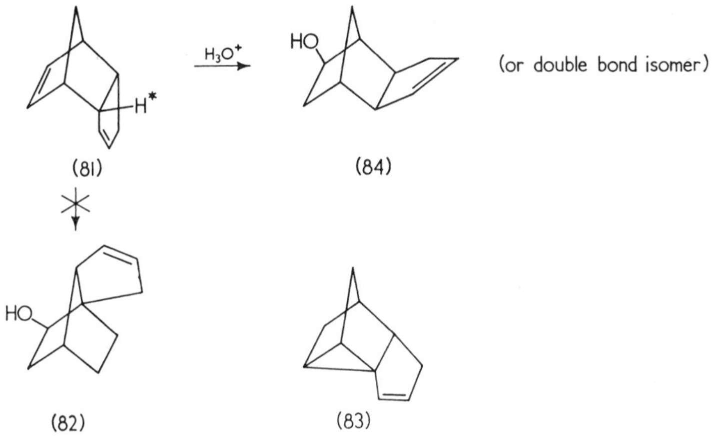

(81)   (84)   (or double bond isomer)

(82)   (83)

to be incorrect *a priori*, and experimental verification [73] of the Wagner-Meerwein structure **84** confirmed this conclusion. Structure **82**, however, is also formally a product of a 6,2 shift and a Wagner-Meerwein rearrangement. That it is not formed in the hydration probably is a consequence of the angle strain required to bridge C_7 and C_1 of the norbornane skeleton by an unsaturated three-atom chain. The geometry of the hydrogen (H* of **81**) that would have to shift may also be unfavorable.

E. Further Examples of 6,2 and 3,2 Shifts

Deamination by diazotization in aqueous acetic acid of a mixture of *endo*- and *exo*-camphenilylamines (85) gives [74] qualitatively the same kinds of

[70] L. Ruzicka, *Helv. Chim. Acta*, **1**, 110 (1918).
[71] H. Meerwein and K. van Emster, *Ber.*, **53**, 1815 (1920).
[72] H. Bruson and T. W. Riener, *J. Am. Chem. Soc.*, **67**, 723, 1178 (1945).
[73] P. D. Bartlett and A. Schneider, *J. Am. Chem. Soc.*, **68**, 6 (1946).
[74] S. Beckmann and R. Bamberger, *Ann.*, **574**, 65 (1951).

products obtained in the solvolyses [67,74,75] of camphenilyl or apoisobornyl derivatives and in the additions of water or formic acid [74,75] to apotricyclene (**86**) (see heading 4D), namely, the Wagner-Meerwein-related pair of products

(85)   (86)

(camphenilol (**73**) and aposantenol (**71**)) and the 6,2-shifted product, β-fen-choisocamphorol (**72**). The β-fenchoisocamphorol is formed in very small yield in the deamination (for a comparison of the results of deamination and solvolysis, see heading 9). Thus, although apocyclene (**86**) is recovered in high yield after being subjected to the deamination conditions, it cannot be rigorously excluded as an intermediate in the formation of the 6,2-shifted product.[74] A true intramolecular 6,2 shift is, however, the more likely mechanism.

Solvolyses of *syn*- and *anti*-7-chloro-*exo*-norbornyl *p*-toluenesulfonates (**87a** and **87b**, X = OTs) produce virtually identical mixtures (**87a** and **87b**,

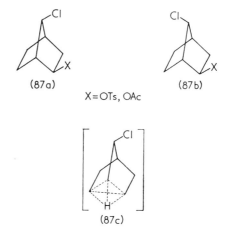

(87a)   (87b)

X = OTs, OAc

(87c)

X = OAc) of products. Further, interconversion of the *p*-toluenesulfonates themselves is observed in interrupted solvolyses. A simple interpretation involves the hydrogen-bridged cation **87c** as an intermediate. The absence of 3-chloro-*exo*-norbornyl derivatives in the products of these solvolyses is

75 G. Komppa and G. A. Nyman, *Ber.*, **69**, 1813 (1936).

attributable to the presence of the unfavorable carbon-chlorine dipole at C_7.[76] This opposes the concentration of positive charge in the transition state for formation of the 3-chloro isomer and appears to be a manifestation of the same kind of influence that favors tertiary over secondary product in the collapse of mesomeric cations (see heading 3c).

Formal 6,2 hydrogen shifts appear to be involved in the conversions **88** → **89**,[77,78] **90a** or **90b** → **91**,[79] and **92a** or **92b** → **93**.[80]

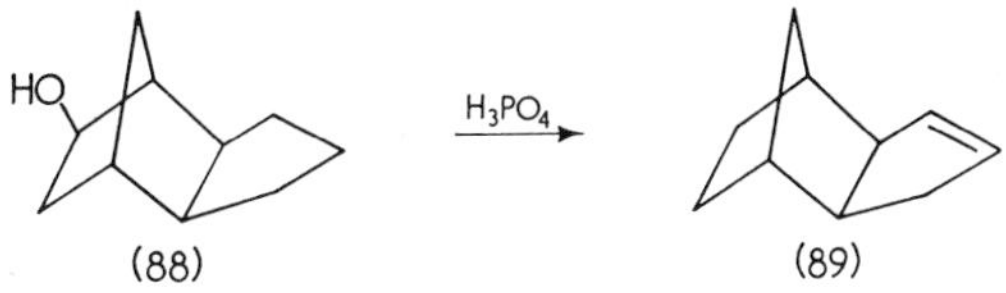

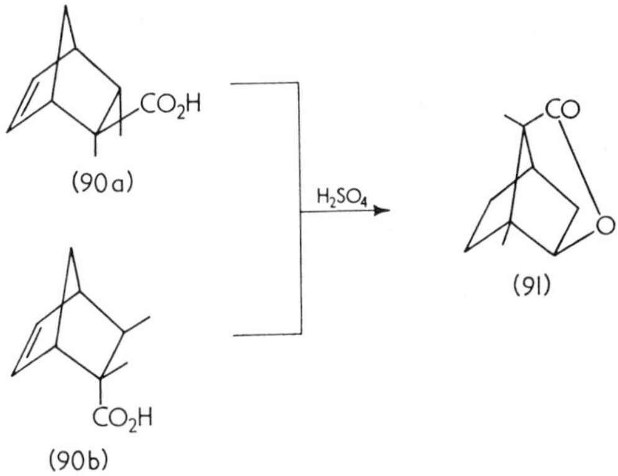

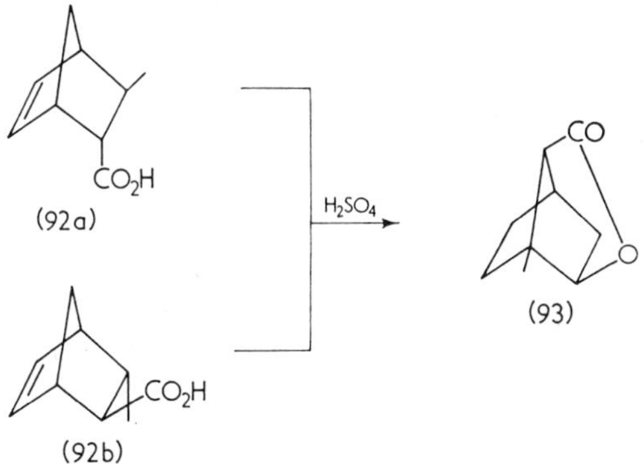

[76] W. G. Woods, R. A. Carboni, and J. D. Roberts, *J. Am. Chem. Soc.*, **78**, 5653 (1956).

[77] P. von R. Schleyer, *J. Am. Chem. Soc.*, **78**, 5702 (1956).

[78] P. Wilder and G. T. Youngblood, *J. Am. Chem. Soc.*, **78**, 5706 (1956).

[79] S. Beckmann and H. Geiger, *Chem. Ber.*, **92**, 2411 (1959).

[80] S. Beckmann, H. Geiger, and M. Schaber-Kiechle, *Chem. Ber.*, **92**, 2419 (1959).

The remarkable rearrangements of *endo*-tetrahydrodicyclopentadiene **93a** or its *exo* isomer to adamantane **93b**,[80a,80b] and of methyl derivatives of the tetrahydrodicyclopentadienes to methyl derivatives of adamantane,[80c] catalyzed by aluminum halides, have no simple explanation in analogies to known carbonium ion processes. A tentatively proposed mechanism[80b] invokes a 2,6-alkyl group shift (**93c** → **93d**).

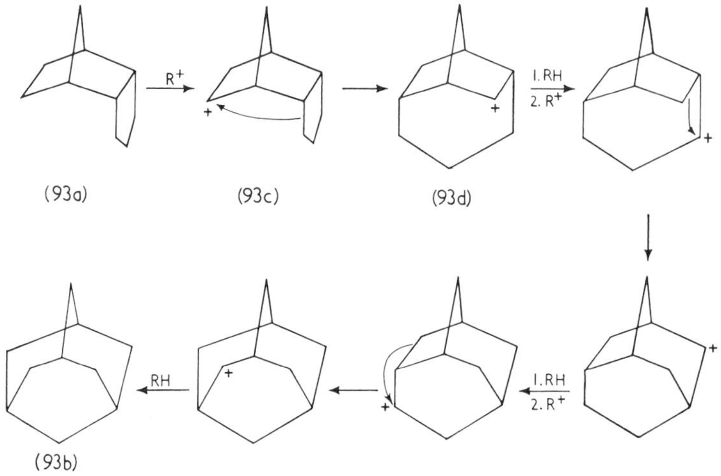

The competition among Wagner-Meerwein, 6,2 (i.e., transannular), and 3,2 (i.e., vicinal) shifts as a function of structure is clearly illustrated in the formolysis of *syn*-7-methyl-2-*exo*-norbornyl acid phthalate[81] (**94a**), which gives 1-methyl-2-*exo*-norbornyl formate (**95**) and 5-*exo*-methyl-2-*exo*-norbornyl formate (**96**) in a ratio of 60:40. The conditions probably suffice to re-form carbonium ions from the formates; e.g., *exo*-norbornyl formate-2,3-^{14}C suffers some isotope position rearrangement in formic acid (see Part 4B). Thus, slow processes leading to stable products may compete with those that normally predominate under irreversible conditions, and the results do not give a direct measure of the relative rates. Nevertheless, the occurrence of hydrogen shift is clear, the formation of both compounds **95** and **96** requiring this. Significantly, products of retained structure (**94b**) or Wagner-Meerwein rearrangement (**97**) are not observed. These are both more strained sterically than the observed products and would be expected to be present in only minor amounts at equilibrium. Unfortunately, is it not clear whether these products are formed but fail to survive under conditions of reversible

[80a] P. von R. Schleyer, *J. Am. Chem. Soc.*, **79**, 3292 (1957).

[80b] P. von R. Schleyer and M. M. Donaldson, *J. Am. Chem. Soc.*, **82**, 4645 (1960).

[80c] P. von R. Schleyer and R. D. Nicholas, *Tetrahedron Letters*, No. 9, 305 (1961).

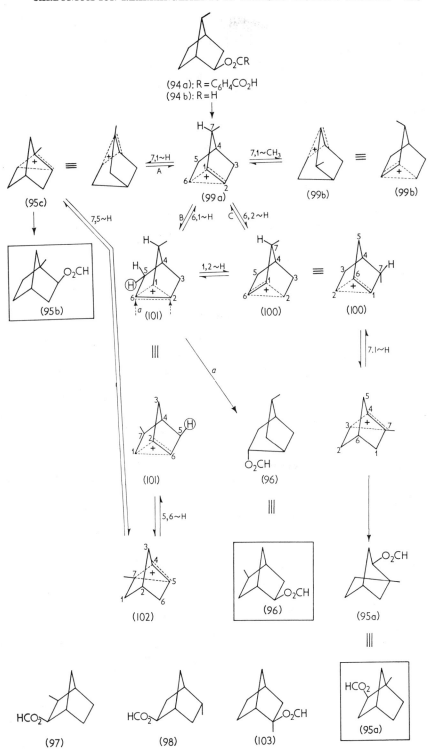

carbonium ion formation, or whether their absence represents a partition ratio for the cation **99a** that favors hydrogen shifts to the exclusion of direct reaction with formic acid.

1-Methyl-2-*exo*-norbornyl formate (**95**) is postulated [81] to arise from a 7,1 hydrogen shift (path A) in the first-formed cation (**99a**). This is the *shortest* path for generating **95c**, the precursor of **95**, but an argument can be made that it also is mechanistically the least likely path. The fundamental assumption upon which the argument is based is that only *exo* hydrogens (*trans* to the mesomeric bridge) can be involved in vicinal shifts. There is some evidence (see heading 5A) that this stereospecificity is required for vicinal alkyl or aryl shift (Nametkin rearrangement), and an extension to vicinal hydrogen shifts seems reasonable. The carbon-bridged cation **99a** has the potential migrating group, the 7-hydrogen, in the *endo* configuration, *cis* to the mesomeric bridge, and, by analogy, is not expected to suffer 7,1 hydrogen shift. There are two alternative paths to **95** that do not violate the assumed interdiction: path B, preliminary 6,1 hydrogen shift in **99a**, leading to **101**, followed by 5,6 and 7,5 shifts, and path C, preliminary 6,2 shift in **99a**, leading to **100**, followed by 7,1 shift. Although both paths C and B are stereoelectronically plausible, path C is more direct and therefore might be expected, on admittedly intuitive grounds, to be favored. If this analysis is correct, the order of probability of the three alternative paths is $C > B > A$. Provided that Nametkin shift of the 7-methyl group or vicinal shift of the 3-hydrogen of **99a** (which are stereoelectronically favorable and which convert **99a** to its mirror image, **99b**) are not fast enough to obliterate the trace of the mechanism, path C is distinguishable in principle from paths A and B. From a given enantiomer of the starting material **94a**, it gives a product (**95a**) that is the optical antipode of that (**95b**) given by paths A and B.

The absence of tertiary product **103** is readily understood,[81] since this is known [82] to be unstable with respect to the secondary Wagner-Meerwein isomer **95** under the reaction conditions. When pure **96** is resubmitted to formolysis, it is converted to **95** in good yield.[81] Apparently, **95** is favored over **96** at equilibrium; this is unanticipated, since **96**, in which repulsions between the substituents seem less, might be expected to be the more stable isomer. The reasons for the apparent absence of **98** (derivable by reaction of **101** at C_2) from the mixture of products are not evident. This substance has no more obvious reasons for instability under the reaction conditions than does **96** which is found in substantial quantities. An explanation based on kinetic control of the **96/98** product ratio would require reaction of solvent with **101** to be much faster at C_6 than at C_2; again, there are no obvious

[81] S. Beckmann and G. Eder, *Chem. Ber.*, **91**, 2878 (1958).

[82] S. Beckmann, R. Schaber, and R. Bamberger, *Chem. Ber.*, **87**, 997 (1954).

grounds for anticipating this. (Note that the 7-methyl group of **101**, although closer to C_2 than to C_6, is not in a position to block the stereospecific attack at C_2 indicated by the dashed arrow.)

The transformations brought to light by the experiments of Beckmann and co-workers in this series constitute one of the most complex systems of rearrangements yet studied. Further scrutiny doubtless would be fruitful.

Treatment of 2-*exo*-methyl-2-*endo*-norbornanol **95d** with acetic acid-sulfuric acid gives 1-methyl-2-*exo*-norbornyl acetate **95e**.[82a,82b] The Wagner-Meerwein rearrangement probably is accompanied or succeeded by 6,2-hydride shift, since loss of about 55% of optical purity is observed when optically active **95d** is used as starting material.[82c] Moreover, reexposure of the product acetate **95e** to the acidic reaction conditions causes racemization.[82c,82d]

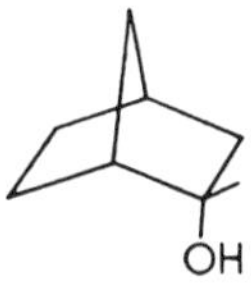

(95d) 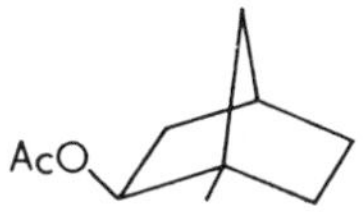   (95e) 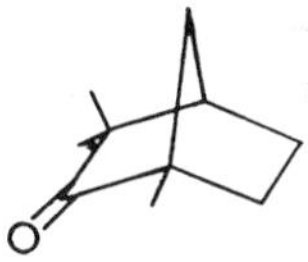   (95f)

5. NAMETKIN REARRANGEMENTS AND OTHER VICINAL INTERACTIONS. THE QUESTION OF MULTIPLE BRIDGES

A. *Nametkin Rearrangements*

Closely allied to the vicinal hydrogen shifts are the vicinal alkyl group shifts now known as the Nametkin rearrangements. Structural examples of this process include the conversion of α-methylcamphene (**104a**) to 4-methylisoborneol (**104b**),[83] shown here without specification of the electronic distribution in the intermediates. The combination of Nametkin and Wagner-Meerwein shifts leads to an amusing result in a sequence worked out by Houben and Pfankuch.[84] Conversion of one enantiomer of camphor to 2,2-

---

[82a] N. J. Toivonen, E. Siltanen, and K. Ojala, *Ann. Acad. Sci. Fennicae*, Ser. A II, No. 64 (1955), through *Chem. Abstr.*, **51**, 7329 (1957); (b) S. Beckmann, R. Schaber, and R. Bamberger, *Chem. Ber.*, **87**, 997 (1954); S. Beckmann and R. Schaber, *Ann.*, **585**, 154 (1954); (c) J. A. Berson, J. S. Walia, A. Remanick, S. Suzuki, P. Reynolds-Warnhoff, and D. Willner, *J. Am. Chem. Soc.*, **83**, 3986 (1961); (d) The optical activity that survives the original rearrangement conditions is useful because it permits the establishment of the configurational relationships among norbornanone (from which **95d** is prepared), 1-methyl-2-*exo*-norborneol, and fenchone (**95f**).[82c]

[83] S. Nametkin and L. Brüssoff, *Ann.*, **459**, 144 (1927); *J. prakt. Chem.*, [2] **135**, 155 (1932).

[84] J. Houben and E. Pfankuch, *Ann.*, **489**, 193 (1931).

dichlorocamphane and dehydrohalogenation (with Wagner-Meerwein rearrangement) of the latter give 4-chlorocamphene (**105**). Treatment of **105**

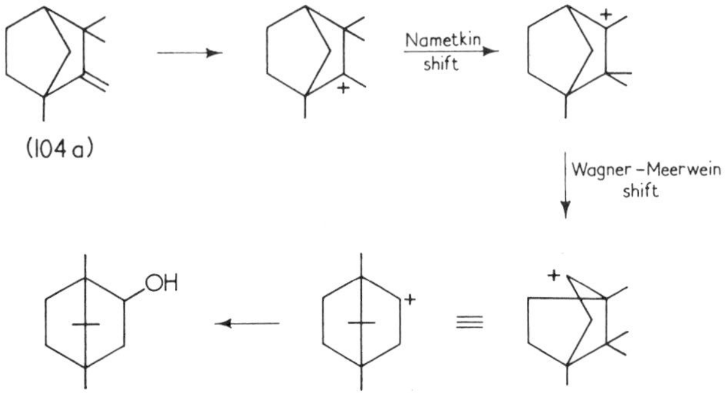

(104 a)

(104 b)

with trichloroacetic acid gives, via Wagner-Meerwein and Nametkin rearrangements, 4-chloroisobornyl trichloroacetate, which can be saponified,
reductively dehalogenated, and oxidized to the optical antipode of the camphor used as starting material.

Bredt[85] and Houben and Pfankuch[84] were the first to recognize that a methyl
shift of the type **106** → **107** in the case of the unsubstituted camphenehydro

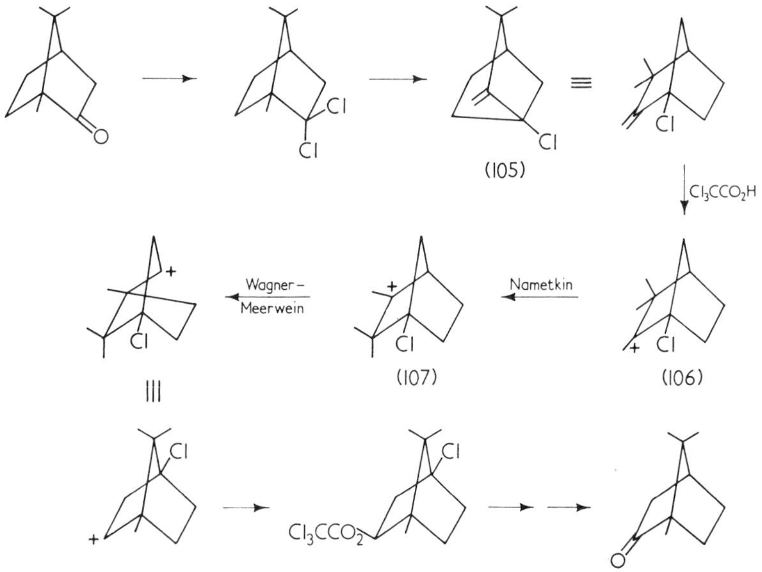

(105)

III   (107)   (106)

cation **108** (p. 158) would produce the mirror image. This appeared to provide
an alternative explanation for the racemization of camphene and of isobornyl

[85] J. Bredt, *J. prakt. Chem.*, [2] **131**, 144 (1931).

chloride, which Meerwein and Montfort (see heading 4A) had interpreted as 6,2 hydrogen shift. Although these observations brought the validity of the 6,2 shift interpretation of the racemization into serious question, the conclusion [84] that it was thereby necessarily excluded was not justified. In fact, as was subsequently recognized,[86] the equivalent of 6,2 shift is required to account for the partial racemization observed [84] in the sequence interconverting the camphor enantiomers.[86a]

That both Nametkin rearrangement and 6,2 shift are involved in the racemization of camphene is now established by ^{14}C tracer studies.[88,89] There are three formal mechanisms (without regard to the details of electronic distribution) by which the racemization of the camphenehydro cation (108) labeled with ^{14}C in the lone methyl group might occur: (1) a stereospecific migration of only one of the geminal methyls; (2) a nonstereospecific migration of either of the geminal methyls; or (3) a 2,6 hydride shift and Wagner rearrangement. Mechanism 2 predicts that at equilibrium, ^{14}C will be distributed equally among the three methyl groups; i.e., oxidation of the racemized camphene will produce formaldehyde and a C_9 fragment with one-third and two-thirds, respectively, of the activity of the starting camphene (66.7% rearrangement). Mechanism 1 predicts 50% rearrangement, and mechanism 3 predicts 0% rearrangement. The finding [88] that the equilibrium value is 66.3% rearrangement is direct evidence for methyl migration. This observation, however, does not rule out a mixed mechanism involving both 1 and 3, since occurrence of 3 converts an endo-methyl group into exo and vice versa; consequently, the equilibrium value will still be 66.7% rearrangement. The presence of hydride shift is revealed [89] by an examination of the ^{14}C distrib-

[86] J. Houben and E. Pfankuch, Ann., **507**, 37 (1933).

[86a] It is not difficult to understand how convincing the evidence against the 6,2 shift hypothesis must have seemed at the time. Meerwein and Wortmann [87] had observed a rearrangement of 2,2-dichlorocamphane (109) to an isomeric dichloride which they believed to be 2,6-dichlorocamphane (110), and Meerwein and Montfort [61] had used this

supposed rearrangement in support of the 6,2 shift hypothesis. When Houben and Pfankuch [84] showed that the alleged 2,6-dichlorocamphane was actually 2,4-dichlorocamphane (111) (derived by a Nametkin rearrangement), the case against the 6,2 shift idea must have appeared to be overwhelming.

[87] H. Meerwein and R. Wortmann, Ann., **435**, 190 (1923).

[88] W. R. Vaughan and R. Perry, Jr., J. Am. Chem. Soc., **75**, 3168 (1953).

[89] J. D. Roberts and J. A. Yancey, J. Am. Chem. Soc., **75**, 3165 (1953).

ution in partially racemized material. If only methyl shifts accounted for
the racemization (mechanisms *1* and/or *2*), the racemic portion of the product

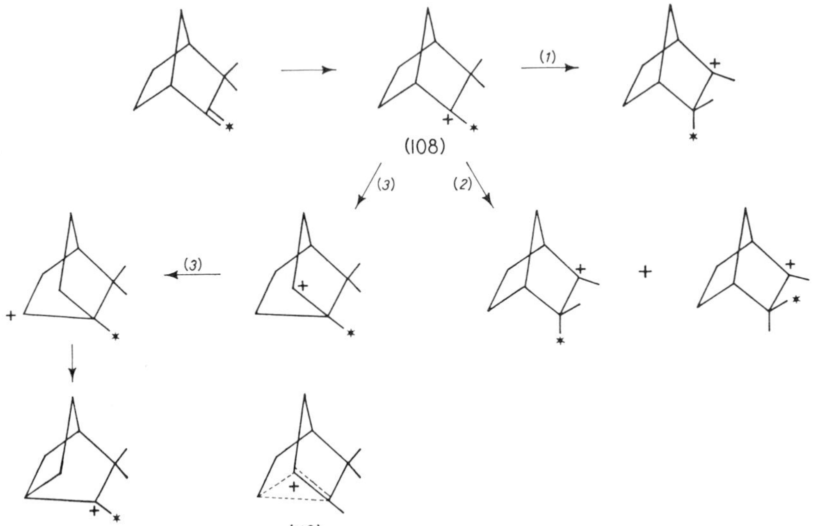

could not have a ^{14}C distribution representing less than 50% rearrangement.
Thus, a sample 77% racemized, for example, could not show less than 38.5%
rearrangement. In fact, however, the ^{14}C distribution of partially racemized
samples always shows a per cent rearrangement less than half the per cent
racemization. Clearly, some racemizing process in addition to methyl shift is
involved; this can only be the equivalent of mechanism *3*.

Although no direct evidence is available on the stereospecificity of the
methyl shifts, it is entirely probable (see below) that only the *exo*-methyl is
involved in any given cation, since the first-formed cation presumably has
the bridged structure **112** and the partial bonding would shield the *endo* side
from attack.

The dehydration of *p*-anisylcamphenilol [90] (**113**) provides a striking
example of this effect. The olefin (**116**) formed from optically active (**113**) in
formic acid is optically active. It presumably arises from the cation (**115**)
which is the product of a Nametkin rearrangement (methyl shift) in the
p-anisylcamphenilyl cation (**114**). Although the degree of retention of optical
purity is unknown, the product olefin has a substantial activity, and since a
shift of the *p*-anisyl group would convert cation **115** to its mirror image, little,
if any, of the cation is diverted in this direction. This is despite the fact that a

[90] P. D. Bartlett, E. R. Webster, C. E. Dills, and H. G. Richey, *Ann.*, **623**, 217 (1959);
P. D. Bartlett, C. E. Dills, and H. G. Richey, *J. Am. Chem. Soc.*, **82**, 5414 (1960).

p-anisyl group is generally far superior to a methyl group in ability to stabilize positive charge at a β carbon; the multiple bridge cation **117** clearly is not

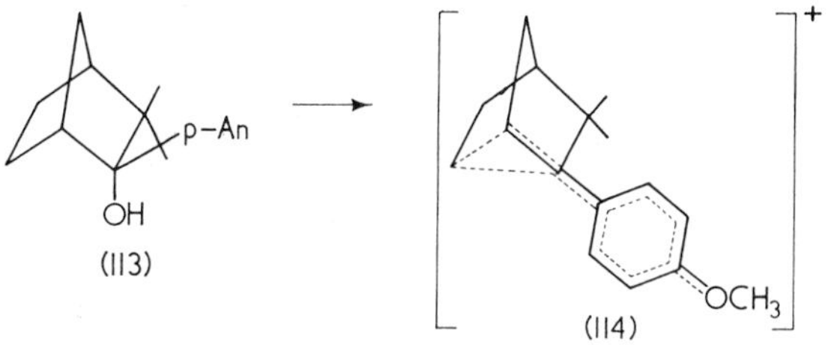

(113)

(114)

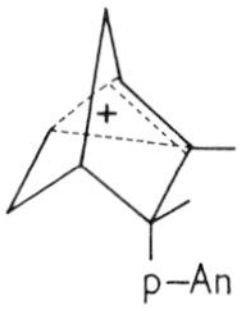

(115)

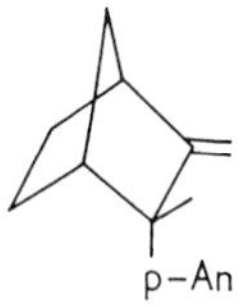

(116)

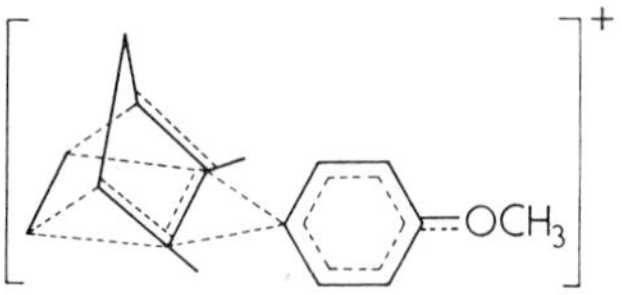

(117)

involved. The results are explicable if it is assumed that the *exo* configuration is specifically required of migrating groups in the Nametkin rearrangement. Such a requirement would lead to the configuration shown (*exo*-methyl, *endo*-p-anisyl) in the cation **115** which is the product of the first Nametkin change in **114**. A second rearrangement, this time of the *endo*-p-anisyl group, is excluded by the requirement; the only possible Nametkin rearrangement in **115** is methyl shift, the reverse of that leading to its formation. It seems highly probable that if *endo*-p-anisyl is prohibited from migrating in this case, then *endo*-methyl in the camphene racemization is also prohibited from migrating.

Vicinal methyl group shifts are common in dehydrations of appropriately substituted bicycloheptanols with potassium bisulfate. Among the examples are the conversions [91] of α-fenchocamphorol (apoborneol, **119**), β-fenchocamphorol (**120**), and camphenilol (**118**), to santene (**121**),[91] and of 4-methyl-

---

[91] L. Ruzicka and F. Liebl, *Helv. Chim. Acta*, **6**, 267 (1923); H. Meerwein, *Ann.*, **405**, 134 (1914); G. Komppa and S. V. Hintikka, *Bull. soc. chim.*, [4] **21**, 13 (1917).

camphenilol (**122**) to 1-methylsantene (**123**).[92] Note that the behavior of the camphenilyl, apobornyl, and β-fenchocamphoryl systems under these drastic

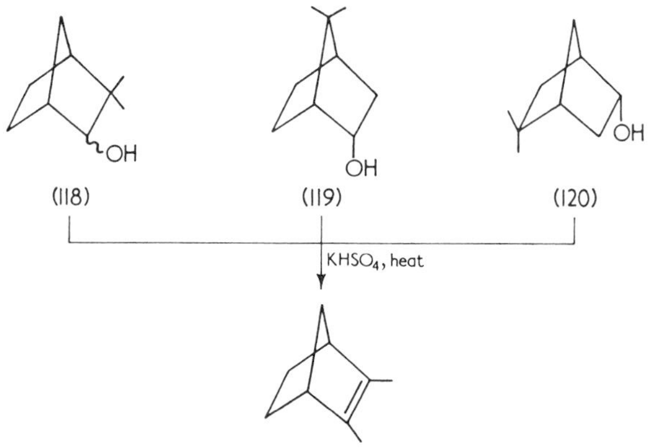

(118)   (119)   (120)

KHSO$_4$, heat

(121)

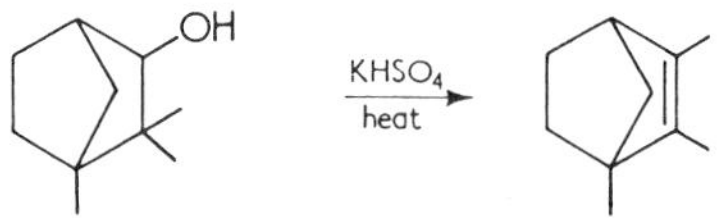

(122)   KHSO$_4$ heat   (123)

conditions is entirely different from that observed in solvolytic and deaminative reactions (see headings 4D and 9). The rearrangements in sulfuric acid of camphor and fenchone to 3,4-dimethylacetophenone[93] and of camphenilone to 4-methylacetophenone[94] also require vicinal methyl shifts.

B. Rearrangements of Functionally Substituted Bicycloheptanes and Additions of Functional Reagents to Bicycloheptenes

The presence in a bicyclic system of an atom or group (B) that is capable of acting as a neighboring group or of migrating to the next adjacent position raises the possibility that the electronic delocalization in such a system may be altered from that which is characteristic of mesomeric cations lacking the

[92] G. Komppa and G. A. Nyman, *Ber.*, **69**, 334 (1936).

[93] (a) H. E. Armstrong and F. S. Kipping, *J. Chem. Soc. (London)*, **63**, 75 (1893); J. E. Marsh, *J. Chem. Soc. (London)*, **75**, 1058 (1899). (b) R. P. Lutz and J. D. Roberts, *J. Am. Chem. Soc.*, **84**, 3715 (1962). R. P. Lutz dissertation, California Institute of Technology, 1961. These workers demonstrate that the rearrangement of fenchone (1,3,3-trimethyl-2-norbornanone), labeled with ^{14}C in the geminal methyls, gives 3,4-dimethylacetophenone with 48% of the label in the acetyl methyl group, 51% in the 4-methyl group, and 1% in the 3-methyl group. This requires that one step of the rearrangement involve a vicinal migration of a methyl group from C$_3$ to C$_2$ of the fenchone skeleton.

[94] D. S. Noyce, *J. Am. Chem. Soc.*, **72**, 924 (1950).

B group. A structure such as **124** may be an inadequate representation, and a more satisfactory description of the cationic intermediates may be provided by **125**, or by a mixture of **124** and **125**, or by **126**. The question of which of

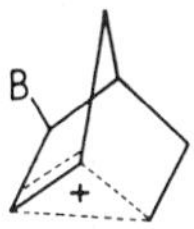

(124) 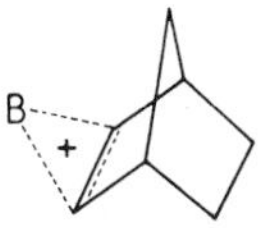   (125) 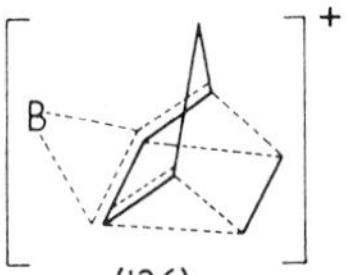   (126)

these intermediates require explicit mention in any given case is an extremely subtle one. At present, no general answer is possible, but a number of observations bearing on the problem are available.

Additions of sulfenyl halides (RSX) to norbornene or norbornadiene lead to "normal" *trans* addition products (**127**); no Wagner-Meerwein rearrangement is observed.[95,96]

When R = 2,4-dinitrophenyl, the *trans* addition product **127** is accompanied by some nortricyclyl thioether (**128**); the proportion of the latter increases with increasing polarity of the solvent.[95] *Trans* addition product **127** presumably arises from the cyclic sulfonium ion **129**,[95,96] as is the case in additions of sulfenyl halides to simple olefins.[97]

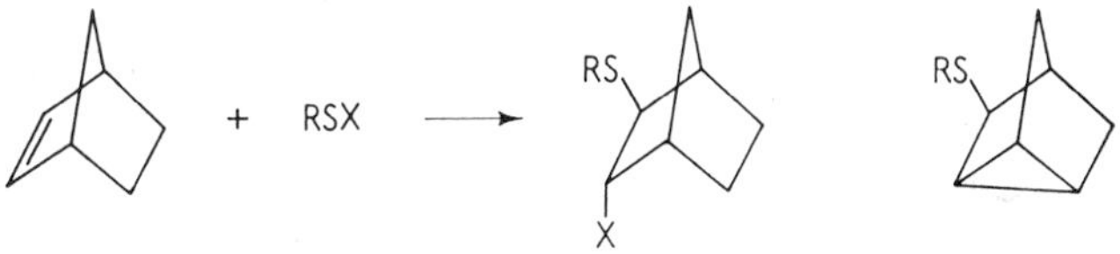

(127)   (128)

(129) 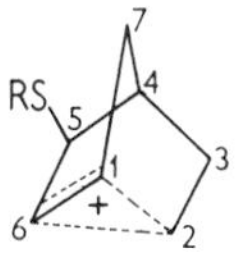   (130)

Nortricyclyl product could arise by loss of a proton from the bridged cation **130**[95] (although there is no direct evidence for **130** as an intermediate), or conceivably from **129**. For the case R = 2,4-dinitrophenyl, the equilibrium **129** ⇌ **130** is postulated,[95] the failure of **130** to give rearrangement product

[95] H. Kwart and R. K. Miller, *J. Am. Chem. Soc.*, **78**, 5678 (1956).

[96] S. J. Cristol, R. P. Arganbright, G. D. Brindell, and R. M. Heitz, *J. Am. Chem. Soc.*, **79**, 6035 (1957).

[97] W. I. Orr and N. Kharasch, *J. Am. Chem. Soc.*, **78**, 1201 (1956), and references cited therein.

by attack of chloride ion at C_1 being attributed to steric hindrance by the bulky SR group.

An alternative explanation,[96] without specifically proposing the equilibrium $129 \rightleftharpoons 130$, suggests that the choice of which mesomeric cation is the product-controlling intermediate depends on the relative stabilities of the cations. The relative efficiencies of β carbon and β sulfur in performing the neighboring group function, as judged by their abilities to enhance solvolysis rates, are used as a guide to the stabilities of mesomeric cations: a β sulfur atom produces a rate enhancement of about 10^7 in solvolyses of β-chlorosulfides, which proceed through cyclic sulfonium salt intermediates, whereas neighboring carbon, as in the exo-norbornyl derivatives, enhances solvolysis rate by a factor of only 10^2–10^3. Cation 129 is therefore expected, in the general case, to be more stable than 130, and the formation of trans product (127) is a consequence of a reaction path that proceeds through 129 rather than through 130. When R is 2,4-dinitrophenyl, a powerful electron-withdrawing group, the stability of 129 relative to 130 would decrease. The nortricyclyl product 128 is assumed[96] to arise from the carbon-bridged cation 130; the formation of some 128 when R = 2,4-dinitrophenyl[95] is then attributed[96] to the effect of this R group in making 129 and 130 more nearly comparable in energy.

Addition of bromine to norbornene produces both trans-2,3-dibromonorbornane (131) and syn-2,7-dibromonorbornane (132a).[99] The latter is essentially completely converted to the trans-2,3 isomer by stannic bromide or by hydrogen bromide via a mechanism believed[99] to involve the bromonium ion (133). The reaction is to be contrasted with the behavior of the chloronor-

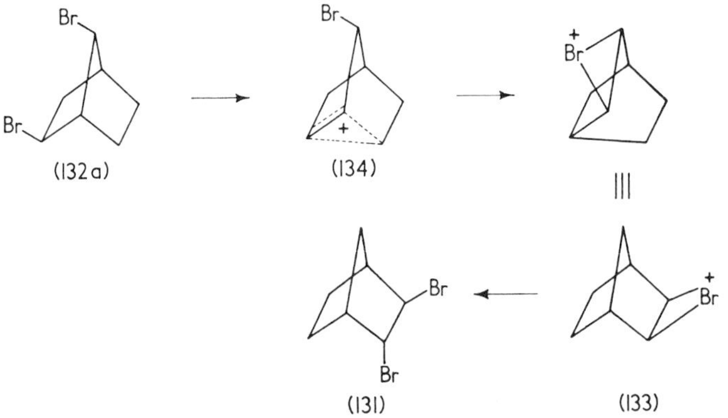

(132a)   (134)

|||

(131)   (133)

bornyl cation (see heading 4E), which produces no vicinal products. This pattern is consistent with the kind of analysis[96] discussed above in connection with

[98] S. Winstein and E. Grunwald, J. Am. Chem. Soc., 70, 828 (1948).
[99] H. Kwart and L. Kaplan, J. Am. Chem. Soc., 76, 4072 (1954).

sulfur-substituted cations: bromo is far more effective than chloro as a neighboring group,[98] and the more facile conversion of the carbon-bridged cation to the halogen-bridged cation is to be expected.

The possibility of alternative explanations, however, should not be overlooked. In particular, a 6,2 shift in the carbon-bridged cation **135**, exactly analogous to that observed[100] in the corresponding chlorine-substituted cation (see heading 4E) would convert **135** to **136**. Reaction of the latter could, in principle, occur either at C_2 to give anti-2,7-dibromonorbornane (**132b**) or at C_1 to give trans-2,3-dibromonorbornane (**131**). Reaction in the latter sense

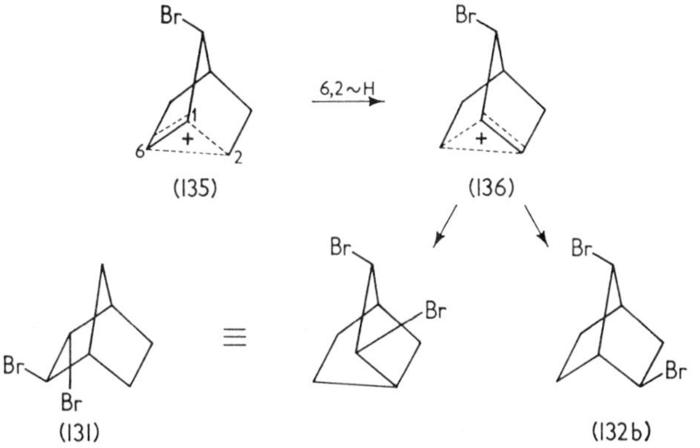

would have to overcome the unfavorable influence of the C_7-halogen dipole, which apparently prevents the formation of vicinal product from the 7-chloronorbornyl cation.

The trans-2,3 isomer (**131**) is the more stable of the **131**–**132a** pair,[99] and although the stability relationship of the anti-2,7 isomer (**132b**) to **131** and **132a** is unknown, the conditions used to effect the isomerization probably suffice to re-form the cationic intermediates repeatedly. In the solvolysis reactions of the chloronorbornyl cation, the products are formed essentially irreversibly. Thus, the difference in behavior between the bromo and chloro cations might be caused simply by an equilibrium favoring the trans-2,3 isomer (**131**) in the bromo case. At present, there is no definite evidence favoring either the bromonium ion or 6,2 shift hypotheses, but a straightforward solution is available in principle if the cationic intermediates can be generated from optically active starting materials: the bromonium ion **133** has a plane of symmetry and would produce racemic product, whereas the 6,2 shift mechanism would produce optically active product.

A number of other examples of the behavior of norbornyl cations illustrate

[100]   W. G. Woods, R. A. Carboni, and J. D. Roberts, J. Am. Chem. Soc., **78**, 5653 (1956).

the competitive relationship between carbon bridging and hydrogen or heteroatom bridging (conventional neighboring group effect). Hydrogen bromide converts *endo*-dicyclopentadiene (**137**) to a bromodihydrodicyclopentadiene which is largely but not entirely the rearranged compound (**138**).[101,102] The hydrogen-bridged intermediate (**140b**), analogous to that

(137)   or double bond isomer
                                              (138)

(139)   (140a)   (140b)

which controls the stereochemistry of hydrogen bromide additions to some simple olefins,[103] would produce simple *trans* addition product (**139**). Apparently, **140b**, if formed at all, reacts so slowly with bromide ion (perhaps because of steric hindrance to approach from the *endo* side) that conversion to the carbon-bridged cation **140a** and subsequent reaction of the latter is the important product-forming path. The presence of some *endo*-tetrahydrodicyclopentadiene in the product of hydrogenation and hydrogenolysis of the hydrogen bromide adduct [102a] demonstrates that the Wagner-Meerwein rearrangement is incomplete. Whether this is to be attributed to attack of bromide ion on the hydrogen-bridged cation **140b** or on the carbon-bridged cation **140a** is uncertain. An experimental test would involve a determination of the stereochemistry of the bromine in the minor product of the hydrogen

[101] G. T. Youngblood and P. Wilder, *J. Org. Chem.*, **21**, 1436 (1956).

[102] (a) S. J. Cristol, W. K. Seifert, and S. B. Soloway, *J. Am. Chem. Soc.*, **82**, 2351 (1960). (b) L. Kaplan, H. Kwart, and P. von R. Schleyer, *J. Am. Chem. Soc.*, **82**, 2341 (1960). (c) R. S. Barnes and P. von R. Schleyer, Theses, Harvard University, 1950 and 1956; P. D. Bartlett, ACS 12th National Organic Chemistry Symposium, Denver, Colo., 1951, *Abstracts*, pp. 4–7. (d) K. Alder and G. Stein, *Chem. Ber.*, **67**, 613 (1934); P. von R. Schleyer and M. M. Donaldson, unpublished observations, as cited in reference 102b.

[103] (a) G. S. Hammond and T. D. Nevitt, *J. Am. Chem. Soc.*, **76**, 4121 (1954). (b) For a discussion of hydrogen-bridged ions versus open carbonium ions as product-determining intermediates in the stereochemistry of additions of proton acid to olefins, see C. H. Collins and G. S. Hammond, *J. Org. Chem.*, **25**, 911 (1960).

bromide addition; the hydrogen-bridged cation would give an *endo*-bromo-*endo*-dihydrocyclopentadiene, whereas the carbon-bridged cation would give an *exo*-bromo isomer.

Hydrolysis of *exo*-2,3-epoxynorbornane and peroxide hydroxylation of norbornene both produce the rearranged glycol **141**.[104,105] Some of the

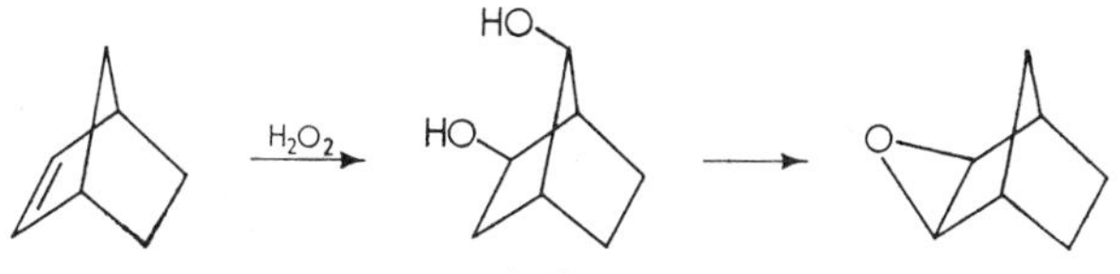

(141)

product of 6,2-hydride shift, *anti*-7-*exo*-2-norbornanediol [105a,105b] and a small amount of 3,5-nortricyclanol [105a] are also found in the products. Similarly, performic acid hydroxylation of *endo*-dicyclopentadiene produces only rearranged glycol,[106] and additions of hypochlorous acid and of chlorine to norbornene [107a] produce rearranged (*syn*-2,7) chlorohydrin and dichloride, respectively. On the other hand, oxymercuration gives the *cis*-*exo*-2,3 adduct.[107b]

Despite the stability of *exo*-trimethylenenorbornanes with respect to their *endo* isomers [102d] and the retardation of the rate of solvolysis of 2-*exo*-norbornyl derivatives produced [102c] by introduction of an *exo*-trimethylene substituent, rearrangements of *exo*- to *endo*-trimethylenenorbornanes do occur: *exo*-trimethylenenorbornene gives rearranged bromohydrin acetate (**142a**) with *N*-bromosuccinimide in acetic acid [102a] and rearranged glycol (**142b**) with performic acid.[102b] Addition of bromine gives essentially exclusively *trans*-dibromide in carbon tetrachloride solvent, but in pyridine, small

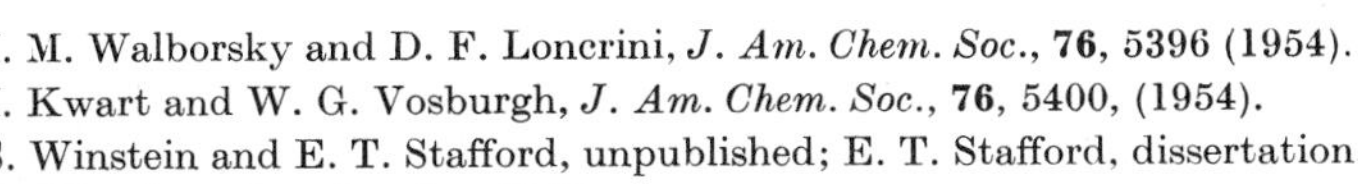

(142a)   (142b)

[104] H. M. Walborsky and D. F. Loncrini, *J. Am. Chem. Soc.*, **76**, 5396 (1954).

[105] H. Kwart and W. G. Vosburgh, *J. Am. Chem. Soc.*, **76**, 5400, (1954).

[105a] S. Winstein and E. T. Stafford, unpublished; E. T. Stafford, dissertation, University of California at Los Angeles, 1958.

[105b] H. Krieger, *Suomen Kemistilehti*, **31B**, 340 (1958).

[106] M. Gates and S. P. Malchik, *J. Am. Chem. Soc.*, **76**, 1378 (1954).

[107] (a) J. D. Roberts, F. O. Johnson and R. A. Carboni, *J. Am. Chem. Soc.*, **76**, 5692 (1954). (b) T. G. Traylor and A. W. Baker, *Tetrahedron Letters*, **19**, 14 (1959); cf. D. D. K. Chiu and G. F. Wright, *Can. J. Chem.*, **37**, 1425 (1959).

amounts of rearranged dibromide (as well as bromonortricyclene) are found.[102b]

These results show that the dipole-dipole repulsion effect (see heading 4E), which may contribute to determining the position of attack on a heteroatom-substituted carbon-bridged cation, is not the exclusive controlling factor. Specific structural features of the addends, as well as solvent effects, can play a major role. Further, in the *exo*-trimethylenenorbornene series, anchimeric assistance by carbon bridging may be much demoted in importance.[102b,102c] The detailed balance of these factors remains to be worked out.

The facility with which carbon bridging occurs is expected to decrease when the bridging carbon bears an electron-withdrawing substituent (X) because of the decreased contribution of structure **143** to the resonance

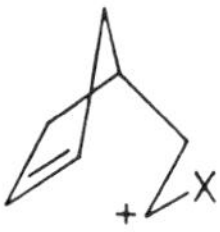

(143)

hybrid representing the mesomeric species.[108] A few scattered observations are at least qualitatively consistent with this view. The polar addition of bromine to **144** produces essentially exclusively the *trans*-dibromide **145**,[109,110] a

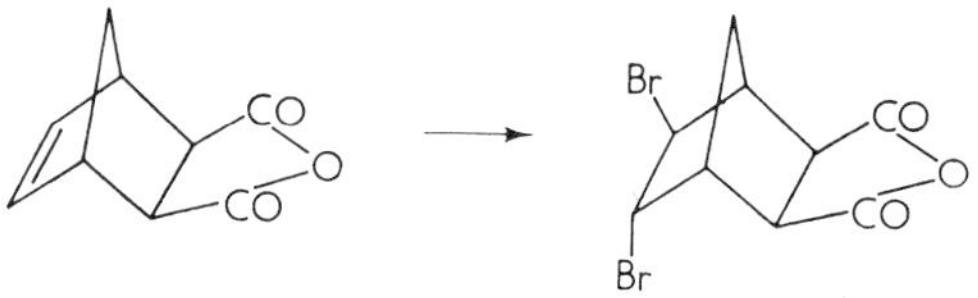

(144)   (145)

product to be expected from a conventional bromonium ion, but not from a carbon-bridged ion, which would give rearranged (i.e., 2,7-) dibromide and/or *cis*-2,3-dibromide. Despite the theoretically less favorable circumstances for electronic delocalization leading to mesomeric intermediates in systems of this type, rearrangements appear to be facile. Addition of bromine to **146** in

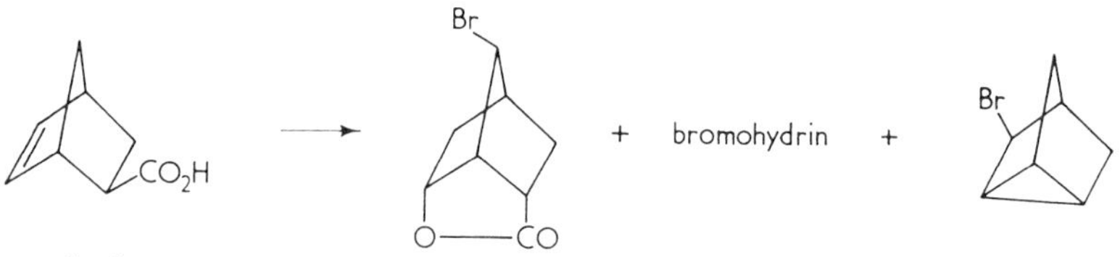

(146)   (147)

[108] J. A. Berson and R. Swidler, *J. Am. Chem. Soc.*, **76**, 4057 (1954).
[109] J. A. Berson, *J. Am. Chem. Soc.*, **76**, 5748 (1954).
[110] D. Craig, *J. Am. Chem. Soc.*, **73**, 4889 (1951).

bicarbonate solution gives, in addition to some (presumably vicinal) bromo-hydrin, the rearranged bromolactone **147**; under similar conditions, the analog **148** gives dibromide, bromohydrin, and rearranged bromolactonic acid **149**.[111] Peracid oxidation of **150** gives **151**.[112] Addition of bromine to the

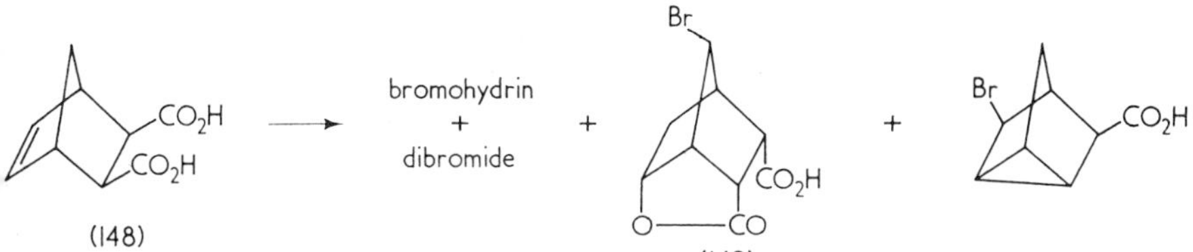

acid **152** in acid conditions produces a mixture of *trans*-dibromide **153** and rearranged bromolactone **154**; basic conditions suppress the formation of dibromide and increase the proportion of rearranged product.[113,114,115]

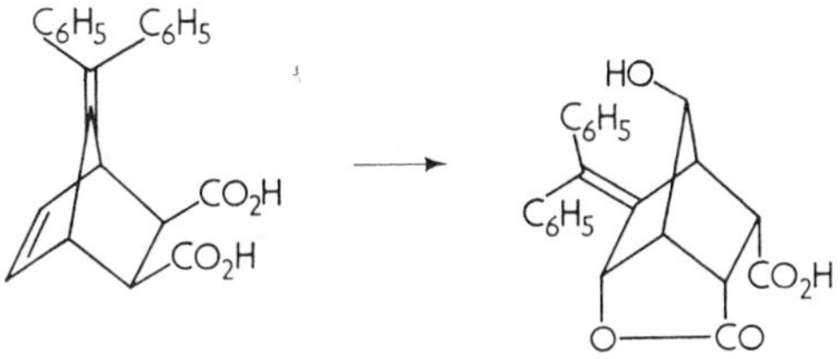

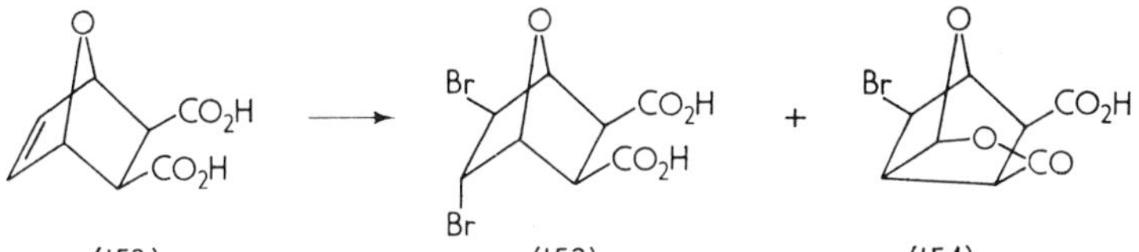

The hydration of **155** in aqueous sulfuric acid produces unrearranged *exo* alcohol **156**;[116,117] more vigorous conditions are required to convert **156** to the rearrangement product **157**. It is not clear whether these results are to be attributed to (*a*) formation of a bridged carbon intermediate which is in

[111] C. D. ver Nooy and C. S. Rondestvedt, *J. Am. Chem. Soc.*, **77**, 3583 (1955).

[112] K. Alder, F. W. Chambers, and W. T. Trimborn, *Ann.*, **566**, 36 (1950).

[113] J. A. Berson and R. Swidler, *J. Am. Chem. Soc.*, **75**, 1721 (1953).

[114] R. B. Woodward and H. Baer, *J. Am. Chem. Soc.*, **66**, 645 (1944).

[115] J. A. Berson and R. Swidler, *J. Am. Chem. Soc.*, **76**, 4060 (1954).

[116] K. Alder, G. Stein, F. v Buddenbrock, W. Eckardt, W. Frercks, and S. Schneider, *Ann.*, **514**, 1 (1934).

[117] J. A. Berson and S. Suzuki, *J. Am. Chem. Soc.*, **80**, 4341 (1958).

relatively rapid reversible equilibrium with the alcohol **156** and is only slowly drained off irreversibly to lactone **157**, or (*b*) formation of an open, "classical"

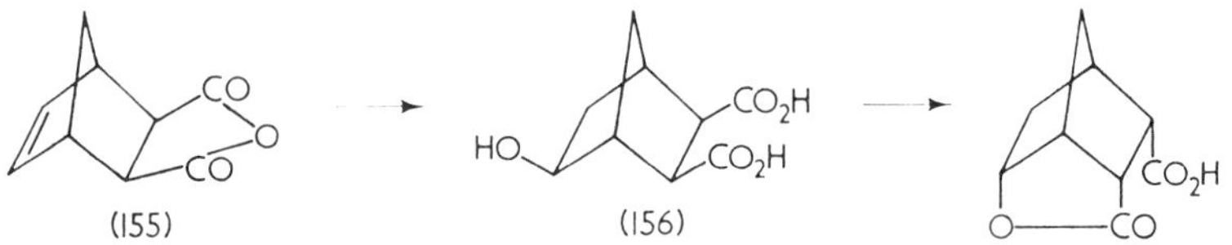

carbonium ion, which in accord with the usual preference for *exo* additions to norbornenes,[118] can collapse to alcohol **156**. If (*b*) is correct, carbon skeletal rearrangement in this case is a process requiring activation energy, and the bridged cation represents a transition state rather than a true intermediate.[118a]

6. INTERNAL RETURN IN SOLVOLYTIC REACTIONS OF BICYCLIC SUBSTANCES

A. Salt Effects on Titrimetric and Polarimetric Rates; Ion Pairs

The first-order rate constant, k_t, for solvolysis of *exo*-norbornyl *p*-bromobenzenesulfonate (**158**), as measured by titrimetric determination of *p*-bromobenzenesulfonic acid, is smaller than the first-order rate constant, k_α, for racemization of a solution of optically active **158** under the same conditions.[119a] In acetic acid, k_α/k_t is about 3.5. This kinetic disturbance appears to be less important in highly nucleophilic solvents, k_α/k_t falling to 2.94 in ethanol and to 1.40 in aqueous acetone. With *exo*-norbornyl bromide, the discrepancy between titrimetric and polarimetric rates is more pronounced, k_α/k_t being 24 in acetic acid and 4.9 in 75% acetone.[119b] In solvolyses of *endo*-norbornyl derivatives, k_α and k_t are identical within experimental error.

The discrepancy in the rate constants in solvolyses of *exo*-norbornyl *p*-bromobenzenesulfonate **158** is essentially insensitive to added *p*-bromobenzenesulfonate ion; consequently, any explanation involving recombination from the dissociated state to racemic **158** of the internally compensated mesomeric cation **159** and *p*-bromobenzenesulfonate ion is invalid. In other

[118] K. Alder and G. Stein, *Ann.*, **515**, 185 (1935); **525**, 183 (1936).

[118a] Examples of hydrations of norbornene carboxylic acids that involve hydride shifts are reported by S. Beckmann and H. Geiger, *Chem. Ber.*, **94**, 48 (1961).

[119] (a) S. Winstein and D. Trifan, *J. Am. Chem. Soc.*, **71**, 2953 (1949), **74**, 1147, 1154 (1952). (b) S. Winstein and E. Clippinger, unpublished work, quoted by S. Winstein, J. S. Gall, M. Hojo, and S. Smith, *J. Am. Chem. Soc.*, **82**, 1011 (1960).

words, solvolysis competes with an *internal* racemization of the starting material. The results imply an ion pair intermediate.[119,120] These observations and the recognition of their significance constitute one of the most important discoveries of recent years in the study of carbonium ion reactions. An extensive study [121] of ion pair phenomena in solvolyses of **158** and of other systems in solvents of low dielectric strength reveals that in general at least two kinds of ion pairs intervene between reactant and completely dissociated ion in solvolysis. The concepts are summarized in the scheme of equation 6.

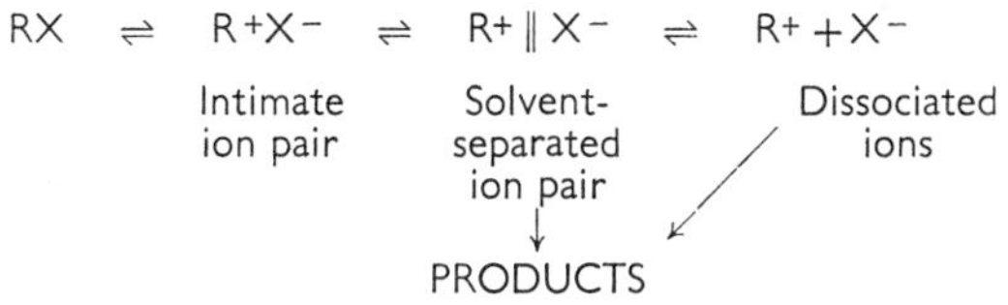

$$RX \rightleftharpoons R^+X^- \rightleftharpoons R^+ \| X^- \rightleftharpoons R^+ + X^-$$

Intimate   Solvent-   Dissociated
ion pair   separated   ions
     ion pair

PRODUCTS

(6)

In principle, return to the covalent condition (RX) can occur from any of the three ionic species. In some systems, notably cholesteryl, 3-*p*-anisyl-2-butyl (**160**), and β-(2,4-dimethoxyphenylethyl), there is extensive return from

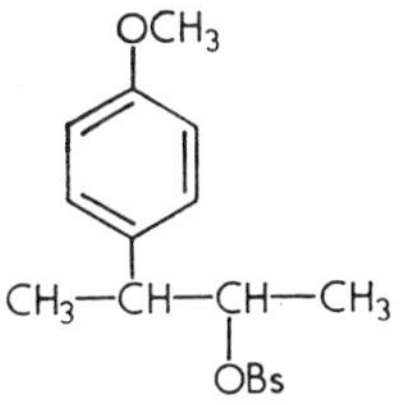

(160)

the solvent-separated ion pair. This is revealed by the "special" salt effect, the steep rise in solvolysis rate produced by added low concentrations of lithium perchlorate. The solvolysis rate for **158**, as measured by k_t, shows only a "normal" salt effect; therefore, return to **158** occurs only from the intimate ion pair stage. The racemization rates, k_α, for **158** and for the 3-*p*-anisyl-2-butyl system (**160**) show only "normal" salt effects. Racemization is thus a process that is independent of the trapping of the solvent-separated ion pair that produces the "special" salt effect; it must occur at the intimate ion pair stage. The relationships are shown schematically in Figures 1 and 2.

Added lithium perchlorate can prevent return from the solvent-separated ion pair stage but not from the intimate ion pair stage. The "special" salt effect, which represents suppression of the former kind of return, presumably

[120] S. Winstein and K. C. Schreiber, *J. Am. Chem. Soc.*, **74**, 2165 (1952).

[121] (a) For a summarizing article, see S. Winstein and G. C. Robinson, *J. Am. Chem. Soc.*, **80**, 169 (1958). (b) See also Section 1.

operates by converting ion pairs $R^+\|X^-$ to $R^+\|ClO_4^-$ metathetically. The gap that persists between k_α and k_t, even after the full "special" salt effect has

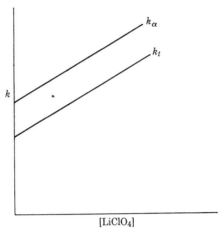

Figure 1.   Effect of LiClO$_4$ (schematic) on titrimetric (k_t) and polarimetric (k_α) rate constants for solvolysis of systems (e.g., *exo*-norbornyl *p*-bromobenzenesulfonate) that show return only from the intimate ion pair; both k_α and k_t show "normal" salt effect.

been expended (see Fig. 2), represents return from the intimate ion pair. In the solvolysis of **158**, which shows no "special" salt effect, the entire gap is

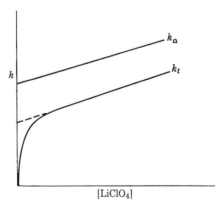

Figure 2.   Effect of LiClO$_4$ (schematic) on k_α and k_t for solvolysis of systems that (e.g., 3-*p*-anisyl-2-butyl *p*-bromobenzenesulfonate) show return from both the intimate ion pair and the solvent-separated ion pair; k_α shows "normal" salt effect, but k_t shows "special" salt effect.

due to return from the intimate ion pair. Consequently, in any detailed mechanism of solvolysis of **158** it may be assumed that reactions *with solvent* beyond the intimate ion pair stage are irreversible.

B. *Internal Return and Solvolysis: One Transition State or Two?*

Winstein and Schreiber [120] derive some relationships among the observable rate constants, k_α and k_t, and various theoretical rate constants on the basis of a mechanism in which the intimate ion pair is assumed to be related structurally to the carbon-bridged cation **159**. (This assumption predates the discovery of 6,2 hydrogen shift in this system, see heading 4B.) It seems entirely possible, however, that electronic delocalization at the intimate ion pair stage may proceed further and, therefore, that a place in the scheme should be assigned to the three-fold symmetrical ion **162**. The expanded scheme is shown in Scheme 1.

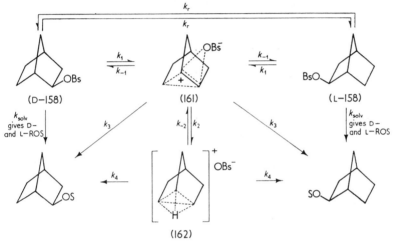

Scheme 1.

For the scheme with *both* two-fold and three-fold symmetrical ionic inter-mediates, $k_t = 2(k_3 + k_4)$ and $k_\alpha = k_1$. Assumption of a steady state in **161** and **162** gives the rate expression

$$-d([\text{D}]+[\text{L}])/dt = \{([\text{D}]+[\text{L}])k_\alpha[k_3(k_{-2}+2k_4)+k_2k_4]\}/\{k_{-1}(k_{-2}+2k_4)$$
$$+k_4(k_2+2k_3)+k_3k_{-2}\} \quad (7)$$

where [D] and [L] represent concentrations of **D-158** and **L-158**. The experi-mental value, k_t, is given by

$$k_t t = \ln([\text{D}]_0+[\text{L}]_0)/([\text{D}]+[\text{L}]) \quad (8)$$

Integration of equation 7 and substitution from equation 8 gives

$$(k_\alpha/k_t)-1 = [k_{-1}(k_{-2}+2k_4)]/[k_{-2}k_3+k_4(k_2+2k_3)] \quad (9)$$

The original scheme of Winstein and Schreiber,[120] which assigned no role to 6,2 hydrogen shift (economically indicated by **162**), assumes that the processes characterized in Scheme 1 by k_2, k_{-2}, and k_4 are absent; expression 9 then is replaced by equation 10, the one derived by Winstein and Schreiber.

$$(k_\alpha/k_t) - 1 = k_{-1}/k_3 \qquad (10)$$

In other words, the parameter $(k_\alpha/k_t) - 1$ measures the competition between return and solvolysis of the ion pair **161**. Actually, the significance of this parameter is more complicated when the three-fold symmetrical ion pair intermediate **162** is inserted into the scheme. If **162** can return to **161** ($k_{-2} \neq 0$), equation 9 applies; if **162** cannot return to **161** ($k_{-2} = 0$), equation 11 applies.

$$(k_\alpha/k_t) - 1 = 2k_{-1}/(k_2 + 2k_3) \qquad (11)$$

In the latter case, $(k_\alpha/k_t) - 1$ expresses the competition between return and total forward reaction of **161**. An experimental decision on whether equation 9 or 11 applies to the solvolysis scheme could be reached by studying the ^{14}C distribution in the p-bromobenzenesulfonate recovered from a partial solvolysis of **158**-2,3-[14]C. If $k_{-2} \neq 0$, this material should have ^{14}C at C_5 and C_6.

Direct evidence that 6,2 shift can accompany internal return is available from studies in other systems. Incomplete acetolyses and formolyses of apoisobornyl and exo-camphenilyl p-bromobenzenesulfonates (**163** and **164**) are accompanied not only by internal return of each member of the pair to the Wagner-Meerwein relative, but also by return to the isomeric β-fenchoiso-camphoryl p-bromobenzenesulfonate (**165**);[122a] incomplete acetolysis of syn-7-chloro-2-exo-norbornyl p-toluenesulfonate (**166**) leaves an unsolvolyzed sulfonate mixture of the starting material and the isomeric sulfonate **167**, the

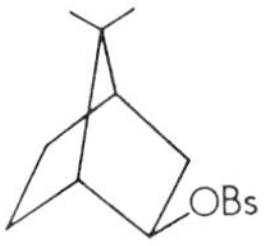

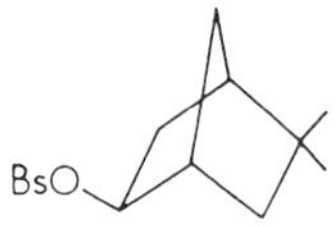

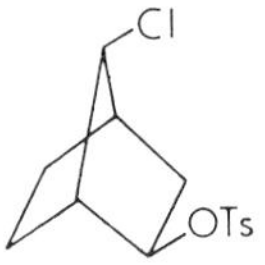

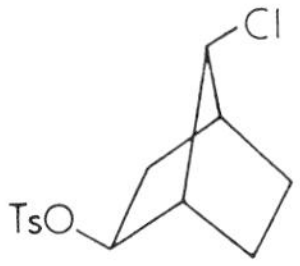

latter presumably resulting from 6,2 shift within an ion pair intermediate.[122b]

The internal racemization which accompanies the solvolysis of exo-norbornyl p-bromobenzenesulfonate (**158**) is most simply interpreted in terms of the same transition state as the solvolysis.[120,121] An alternative hypothesis proposes that interconversion of the enantiomers of **158** (arbitrarily designated D and L in Scheme 1) is a cyclic, nonionic rearrangement (rate constant k_r in Scheme 1) with a transition state different from that of the solvolysis. On this basis, the solvolysis is a competing process, with rate constant k_{solv}, which passes through unspecified intermediates to racemic products. In this mechanism, the experimental k_t is identical with k_{solv}. The relationship between k_r and experimental quantities can be derived readily [120] and is given by

$$k_r = (k_\alpha - k_t)/2 \tag{12}$$

The strongest argument [121a] against the hypothesis of a racemization independent of solvolysis is the variation with solvent of k_r, the rate constant derived from equation 12 for the alleged cyclic rearrangement. Thus, k_r is about as sensitive to changes in solvent as is k_t, the solvolysis rate constant; k_t can be made to vary over several powers of ten by appropriate choice of solvent, and this variation is faithfully mimicked by k_r. Also, for the system

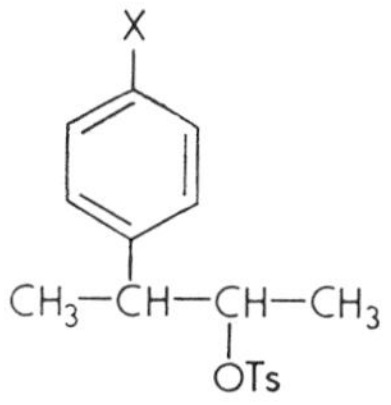

(168)

168, a change in structure produces almost the same change in k_r that it does in k_t; i.e.,

$$k_r(X = \text{ H})/k_r(X = \text{OCH}_3) \approx k_t(X = \text{H})/k_t(X = \text{OCH}_3)$$

It is hard to imagine a racemizing rearrangement process that shows nearly the same sensitivity to solvent and structure as does the solvolysis and yet proceeds through a different transition state.

One alternative remains. The ion pair **161** of Scheme 1 might represent a *transition state* between the enantiomers of **158**. Products of solvolysis might then be derived, for example, from a solvent-separated ion pair *intermediate* (or from dissociated ions) which would intervene between **161** and final products in the scheme of Scheme 1. Although intimate ion pairs such as **161** are treated as intermediates in the kinetic scheme of ion pair processes,[121] the subtle distinction between this concept and that which pictures intimate ion pairs as transition states has not been made experimentally.

The first-order rate constant for solvolysis of isobornyl chloride in 80%

ethanol[122] shows no tendency to increase during a kinetic run. Since the mesomeric cation in this system is known (see heading 2) to react with chloride ion to give camphene hydrochloride many times as fast as to give isobornyl chloride, a significant amount of isomerization to camphene hydrochloride would have accompanied the solvolysis of isobornyl chloride if the ion pair intermediate could return to covalent alkyl chloride. Since camphene hydrochloride is more reactive than isobornyl chloride in solvolysis, accumulation of camphene hydrochloride by isomerization would have caused the solvolysis rate constant to drift upward during a kinetic run. If, however, the rate of solvolysis of camphene hydrochloride were sufficiently fast to render the isomerization step rate determining, camphene hydrochloride would not accumulate, and steady kinetic behavior would have been observed. Quantitative data on the relative rates of isomerization versus solvolysis of the two isomeric chlorides in this solvent system are presently insufficient to allow a definite decision on whether the observed[122] steady rate constant signifies that ion pair return is insignificant or merely that the rate of solvolysis of the tertiary chloride is so large that the presence of ion pair return, if any, is obscured.[123] Camphene hydrochloride, however, is so reactive that it is doubtful that ion pair return could be observed.

The reported[123a] isomerization of *exo*-fenchyl *p*-toluenesulfonate to the *endo* isomer during ethanolysis has no parallel in solvolyses of other bicyclo-[2.2.1]heptyl derivatives. Since *exo* derivatives are more reactive in solvolysis than the corresponding *endo* isomers by factors of hundreds or thousands (see heading 7), *exo* → *endo* isomerizations of substrates during solvolysis should manifest themselves in rate "constants" that decrease during a kinetic run. That these disturbances generally are not observed may be taken as strong evidence against such isomerizations. Although anomalous kinetic behavior seems to be observed in the solvolyses of the fenchyl *p*-toluenesulfonates,[123a] no details of the kinetic runs are reported. The presence of *endo-p*-toluenesulfonate in the partially solvolyzed reaction mixture obtained by ethanolysis of *exo-p*-toluenesulfonate is inferred[123a] from the optical rotation of the crude preparation. Further investigation of such phenomena appears to be desirable. Acetolyses of the fenchyl *p*-bromobenzene sulfonates (*exo/endo*

[122] (a) S. Winstein and A. Colter, unpublished; see A. Colter, Dissertation, University of California at Los Angeles, 1956; see S. Winstein, ACS 15th National Organic Chemistry Symposium, Rochester, N. Y., June, 1957, *Abstracts*. (b) W. G. Woods, R. A. Carboni, and J. D. Roberts, *J. Am. Chem. Soc.*, **78**, 5653 (1956). (c) S. Winstein, B. K. Morse, E. Grunwald, H. W. Jones, J. Corse, D. Trifan, and H. Marshall, *J. Am. Chem. Soc.*, **74**, 1127 (1952).

[123] For discussions of related kinetic systems, see S. Winstein and K. C. Schreiber, *J. Am. Chem. Soc.*, **74**, 2171 (1952); W. Young, S. Winstein and H. Goering, *J. Am. Chem. Soc.*, **73**, 1958 (1951).

[123a] W. Hückel and H. D. Sauerland, *Ann.*, **592**, 190 (1955).

rate ratio $= 8100$ at $25°$) show steady first-order kinetic behavior.[123b] There is thus no indication of *exo* → *endo* isomerization in this case.

C. Detailed Structure of the Ion-Pairs

The detailed structure of the intimate ion pair is obscure at present. The nature of the bonding between cation and anion may be similar to that in charge transfer complexes [124] or may be partially electrostatic and partially covalent.[121a] The structure of the solvent-separated ion pair, which in the norbornyl case collapses to product and dissociated ions without return to the intimate stage, is also obscure. Some information is available, however, on what the structure *is not*. Winstein and Robinson [121a] visualize for the species a single solvent molecule sandwiched between cation and anion. Since the nature of the bonding forces and the relative geometry of the three fragments are unknown, the structure in acetic acid may be represented by **169** (R = norbornyl, X = OBs). In the perbenzoic acid oxidation of *exo*-2-acetylnorbornane, RCOCH₃ (R = norbornyl), the intermediate or transition state that gives the product, *exo*-norbornyl acetate, has the structure **170**

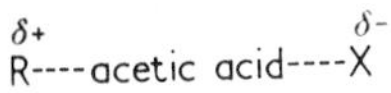

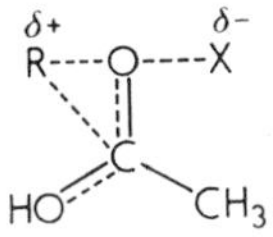

(R = norbornyl, X = benzoate ion or benzoic acid).[125] Although there is a superficial similarity between **169** and **170** as represented on paper, the two species are entirely different, since **169**, generated from optically active ROBs, collapses entirely to racemic *exo*-norbornyl acetate,[119] but **170**, generated from optically active RCOCH₃, collapses to *exo*-norbornyl acetate without loss of optical purity.[125]

7. RATES OF SOLVOLYSIS OF BRIDGED BICYCLIC SUBSTANCES AND RELATED COMPOUNDS

A. Bicyclo[2.2.1]heptanes

Mesomerism stabilizes a bridged cationic intermediate relative to the corresponding "classical" carbonium ion. If the bridged cation can be formed

[123b] S. Winstein, private communication.
[124] E. Kosower, *J. Am. Chem. Soc.*, **78**, 5700 (1956).
[125] J. A. Berson and S. Suzuki, *J. Am. Chem. Soc.*, **81**, 4088 (1959).

in concert with heterolysis, the transition state leading to it benefits energetically from similar mesomerism; it is therefore expected that a solvolysis in
which bridging and heterolysis occur simultaneously will be accelerated
relative to some standard solvolysis lacking such a feature.

Rate enhancements ascribable to concerted participation of neighboring
groups in solvolyses are readily discerned in reactions of 1,2-disubstituted
cyclohexanes,[126] where the geometry of the *trans* member of a *cis-trans* pair is
particularly favorable for simultaneous bridging and heterolysis. The kinetic
assistance ("driving force") provided by participation of the neighboring
group in these cases can be estimated[126,126a] by assuming that the rate of
solvolysis of the *cis* member of a *cis-trans* pair is not enhanced by participation and that it therefore is a rough model for what the rate of solvolysis of
the *trans* isomer would be in the absence of participation. Although the existence of conformational equilibria, differing dipole-dipole interactions, and
unequal ground state energies may require attention in a more detailed
analysis, the procedure is valid as a crude guide.

In bicyclo[2.2.1]heptyl systems, the geometry of the *exo* member of an
exo-endo pair is favorable for participation of C_6 in the heterolysis of a C_2
leaving group.[127,128] The onset of heterolysis projects a lobe of a developing
p orbital on the *endo* side of the molecule; interaction of this potential p lobe
with the C_6—C_1 bonding σ electrons must occur well before the transition
state is reached if a rate enhancement is to be observed. In fact, *exo* halides
or sulfonates solvolyze at greater rates than the corresponding *endo* isomers;[127] this is interpreted[127,128] as support for the idea of concerted
heterolysis and carbon migration ("synartetic acceleration," "anchimeric
assistance"). The amount of rate enhancement is strongly dependent on
structure, as is shown in Tables VI and VII.

[126] S. Winstein and E. Grunwald, *J. Am. Chem. Soc.*, **70**, 828 (1948), and references
cited therein.

[126a] The literature in the field of enhancements of solvolysis rates by neighboring group
participation suffers from a minor but curious malady which is characterized by hyper-
trophy of the nomenclature and sporadic outbreaks of classical erudition. The term
"synartetic acceleration" as originally introduced[128] refers to participation by the electrons binding the β substituent; in the mesomeric intermediate and the transition state
preceding it, "a split single bond fastens together the locations of a split ionic charge."
The term "anchimeric assistance" applies[134] "to neighboring carbon, hydrogen, and
functional groups, whether the participation involves electrons besides the β-bonding
electron-pair (e.g., Br, vinyl, phenyl) or not (e.g., H,R.)." Synartetic acceleration is thus
a special case of anchimeric assistance (see also Section 1, page 8).

[127] (a) S. Winstein and D. Trifan, *J. Am. Chem. Soc.*, **71**, 2953 (1949). (b) *J. Am. Chem.
Soc.*, **74**, 1147, 1154 (1952). (c) S. Winstein, B. K. Morse, E. Grunwald, H. W. Jones,
J. Corse, D. Trifan, and H. Marshall, *J. Am. Chem. Soc.*, **74**, 1127 (1952).

[128] F. Brown, E. D. Hughes, C. K. Ingold, and J. F. Smith, *Nature*, **168**, 65 (1951).

TABLE VI

Relative Titrimetric Acetolysis Rates at 25° of p-Bromobenzenesulfonates

ample no.	Substrate and relative k_t			exo/endo ratio	Ref.
1	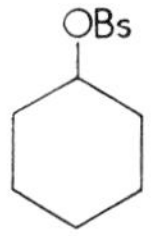 OBs (cyclohexyl)	1.0		—	127c
2	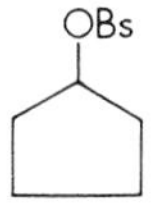 OBs (cyclopentyl)	32		—	127c
3	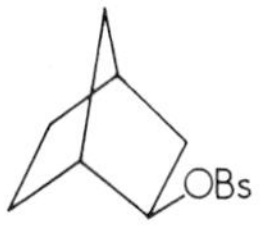 OBs	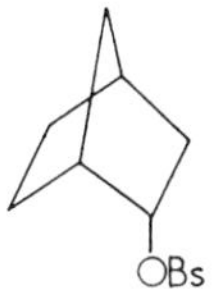 517	OBs 1.47	350	127
4	 OBs	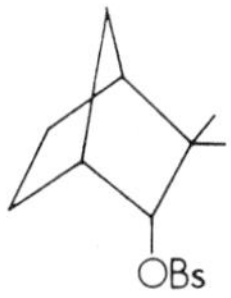 193	OBs 0.16	1230	129a
5	 OBs	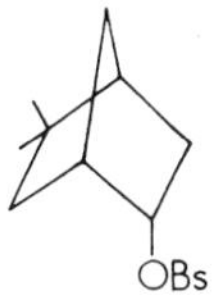 153	OBs 1.05	145	129a
6	 OBs	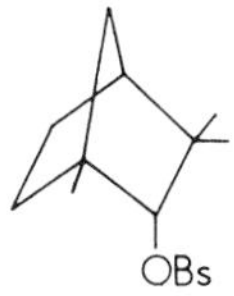 1840	OBs 0.22	8100	129a
7	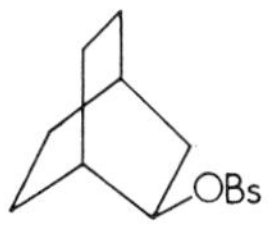 OBs	53	———	—	129b
8	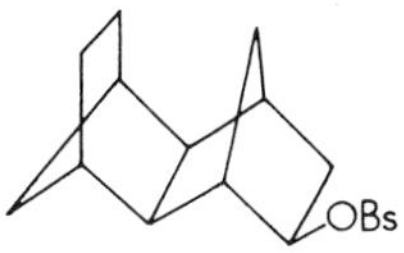 OBs	4.46[a]	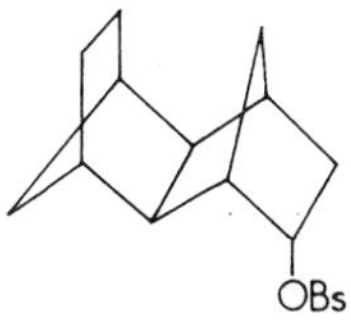 OBs 0.29[a]	15[a]	130

[a] At 75° relative to cyclohexyl OBs at 75°.

How much of the observed increase in rate of solvolysis of an *exo* derivative over that of its *endo* isomer is attributable to electronic delocalization (anchimeric assistance, synartetic acceleration) and how much to such other factors as steric retardation or acceleration and differences in ground state energies? There is no simple answer to this question. In the parent norbornane

TABLE VII

Relative Solvolysis Rates in Various Solvents
of Miscellaneous Bicyclic Substrates

Example no.	Substrate	Conditions	*exo/endo* Ratio	Ref.
9	Norbornyl chlorides	80% EtOH; 85°	~70	131
10	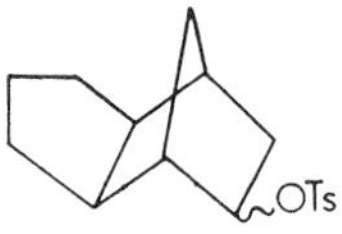	AcOH; 68.6°	13	130, 132
11	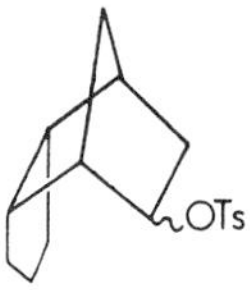	AcOH; 68.6°	40	130, 132
12	Bornyl OTs vs. isobornyl Cl	AcOH; 25°	2.5×10^5	127b
	bornyl Cl vs. isobornyl Cl	80% EtOH; 80°	10^5	128
13		EtOH; 30° EtOH; 50°	715 610	133 133

[129] (a) S. Winstein, A. Colter and N. J. Holness, ACS 15th National Organic Chemistry Symposium, Rochester, N. Y., June, 1957, *Abstracts*; A. Colter, Dissertation, University of California at Los Angeles, 1956. (b) H. M. Walborsky, M. E. Baum, and A. A. Youssef, *J. Am. Chem. Soc.*, **83**, 988 (1961). For acetolysis of the corresponding substrate 7, OBs = OTs, see page 215.

[130] P. D. Bartlett and R. S. Barnes, ACS 12th National Organic Chemistry Symposium, Denver, Colo., June, 1951, *Abstracts*; R. S. Barnes, Thesis, Harvard University, 1950.

[131] J. D. Roberts and W. Bennett, *J. Am. Chem. Soc.*, **76**, 4623 (1954).

[132] P. von R. Schleyer, Thesis, Harvard University, 1956.

[133] W. Hückel and H. D. Sauerland, *Ann.*, **592**, 190 (1955).

system (example 3 of Table VI), there is probably very little difference in ground state energies of the isomers. The *endo* isomer is not strictly comparable to either the cyclohexyl or the cyclopentyl system. Solvolysis of a cyclohexyl derivative introduces eclipsing strain between the substitutent at C_α and those at C_β; solvolysis of a cyclopentyl derivative relieves this strain, but introduces angle strain associated with incorporation of an sp^2 carbon in an already strained five-membered ring.[135] The angle strain introduced into the rigid norbornyl system in the transition state for formation of the "classical" carbonium ion is presumably greater than that in cyclopentyl.[127b] It is therefore not surprising that *endo* norbornyl solvolyses should be slower than those of cyclopentyl, although the close correspondence to cyclohexyl would not have been predicted. Steric retardation of the solvolysis of the *endo* norbornyl derivative may be a consequence of interference of the C_6 *endo* hydrogen with the departing sulfonate group, but it is doubtful that this would be sufficiently large to account for all of the factor of 350 between the solvolysis rates of *endo* and *exo*.

A serious obstacle to the development of a theory of rate enhancements arises from the internal return phenomenon. Ideally, one would like to be able to compare the rates of *ionization* of substances; this is the process for which one attempts to evaluate the relative importances of anchimeric assistance, steric strains, and the like. Unfortunately, it is uncertain what experimentally observed rate corresponds to the ionization rate. Winstein [120,121a,135a] has equated k_α, the polarimetric rate constant, with the rate constant for ionization in those cases (*exo*-norbornyl, 3-phenyl-2-butyl, 3-*p*-anisyl-2-butyl) where internal racemization of the starting material accompanies solvolysis. In the norbornyl case, for example, the *exo/endo* rate ratio as measured by k_α is 1225, compared to 350 as measured by k_t. No experimental test has been devised, however, that provides assurance that the first-formed ion in solvolysis of these materials is optically inactive. In other words, it is conceivable that an ion pair species that can return to the starting enantiomer intervenes between the starting material and the internally compensated ion pair. The observed k_α is, therefore, a *minimum* measure of the ionization rate. For *endo*-norbornyl, in the solvolysis of which k_α and k_t are experimentally identical,[119] there is no *detectable* internal return. This is not surprising, since formation of the mesomeric norbornyl cation would require the returning sulfonate group to attack from the *exo* side, and migration of this group from the *endo* to the *exo* side would be expected to compete

[134] S. Winstein, C. R. Lindegren, H. Marshall, and L. L. Ingraham, *J. Am. Chem. Soc.*, **75**, 147 (1953).

[135] H. C. Brown, R. S. Fletcher, and R. B. Johannesen, *J. Am. Chem. Soc.*, **73**, 212 (1951).

[135a] S. Winstein, J. S. Gall, M. Hojo, and S. Smith, *J. Am. Chem. Soc.*, **82**, 1010 (1960).

poorly with the formation of solvolysis products. Return from the endo side in an *endo* ion pair in which the cation is "classical," however, is conceivable; the observed solvolysis rate, therefore, is again a minimum value for the ionization rate.

The possibility of ion pair return makes it necessary to treat with reserve any conclusions regarding anchimeric assistance that are based on comparisons of solvolysis rates alone. For example, the *exo/endo* rate ratio for the norbornyl chlorides is only 70 in aqueous ethanolysis (Table VI) as compared to 350 for acetolysis of the *p*-bromobenzenesulfonates. This discrepancy becomes much smaller, however, when the greater importance of internal return with the halides [119b] is taken into account.

In Scheme 2, the significance of k_α for the *exo*-norbornyl solvolysis can be expressed in terms of rate constants for individual steps. The reaction of **D-171** to give optically inactive ion **173** directly requires that k_2, the ionization rate constant, be equal to the experimental k_α, as in the Winstein scheme. Intercession of an optically active ion (**172**) requires that k_i, the ionization rate constant for the alternative path (see Scheme 2) be smaller than k_α. For this path, the steady state approximation and the proportional relationship

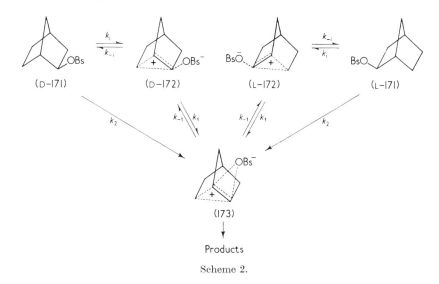

(D-171)   (D-172)   (L-172)   (L-171)

(173)

Products

Scheme 2.

of α to the difference in concentrations of **D-171** and **L-171** give equation 13.

$$k_\alpha = [k_i - k_{-i}k_i/(k_1 + k_{-i})]t \tag{13}$$

Only if conversion of the optically active ion **172** to **173** is much faster than return of **172** to starting material ($k_1 \gg k_{-i}$) does $k_\alpha \approx k_i$.

The acetolysis of optically active *endo*-norbornyl *p*-bromobenzene-sulfonate[119] gives *exo*-norbornyl acetate, which retains only a small fraction[125,136,136a] of the original optical purity. Since ionization of the *endo*-sulfonate directly to the internally compensated ion is unfavorable on stereoelectronic grounds, the solvolysis requires the formation of **174** or **175** (or both) as a preliminary stage.[136a] Collapse of **174** or **175** to optically active product competes poorly with conversion to the optically inactive ion;

(174)   (175)

despite the fact that the rate-determining step of the solvolysis is not anchimerically assisted, most of the product is formed from the mesomeric ion. Similarly, bornyl derivatives solvolyze much more slowly than iso-bornyl (see Tables VI and VII), yet solvolysis in aqueous calcium hydroxide gives camphene hydrate, the characteristic product from the mesomeric cation.[137, 137a]

[136] J. A. Berson and D. A. Ben-Efraim, *J. Am. Chem. Soc.*, **81**, 4094 (1959).

[136a] (a) S. Winstein and D. Trifan, *J. Am. Chem. Soc.*, **71**, 2953 (1949), **74**, 1147, 1154, 1952, (b) S. Winstein and E. Clippinger, unpublished work, quoted by S. Winstein, J. S. Gall, M. Hojo, and S. Smith, *J. Am. Chem. Soc.*, **82**, 1011 (1960).

[137] O. Aschan, *Ber.*, **41**, 1092 (1908); G. Wagner, S. Moycho, and F. Zienkowski, *Ber.*, **37**, 1032 (1904).

[137a] The intermediates that give rise to the *racemic* portion of the solvolysis product in the acetolysis of *endo*-norbornyl *p*-bromobenzenesulfonate appear to be identical with those that produce completely racemic material in the acetolysis of the *exo* isomer. This can be deduced by combining the stereochemical result in the former reaction with the isotope-position rearrangement data. Thus, using corrected[137b,137c] values for the maximum rotations of *endo*- and *exo*-norbornyl derivatives, the data[119a,137c] on the acetolysis of the *endo*-*p*-bromobenzenesulfonate can be expressed as $6.5 \pm 0.5\%$ retention of optical purity and 100% inversion of epimeric configuration. (The earlier conclusion[119a] that *exo*-acetate is formed to the exclusion of *endo*-acetate is now confirmed[137c] by capillary gas chromatography.) The over-all value of $56.1 \pm 0.2\%$ rearrangement of isotope position in the solvolysis of the *endo* derivative (see Part 4B) can now be corrected by the factor [100/(93.5] to give the extent of isotope-position rearrangement in the racemic portion. The derived value, $60.0 \pm 0.5\%$, is essentially identical with that found ($60.6 \pm 0.6\%$, Part 4B) in the acetolysis of the *exo* derivative, suggesting that the partitioning of the intermediates between carbon-bridged and hydrogen-bridged species is identical in the two systems.

This result is exactly that expected if the interpretation of carbon bridging and hydrogen bridging as sequential rather than competitive processes is correct (see Part 4D). Although it does not decisively exclude the competitive interpretation, a coincidence

The rate of aqueous ethanolysis of camphene hydrochloride (**176**) is 6000

(176)

times that of *tert*-butyl chloride.[128] It is difficult to fit this result into the pattern of Table VI, since an *endo-exo* comparison is not available. Neverthe-

TABLE VIIA

Acetolytic Reactivities at 25° of Norbornyl *p*-Toluenesulfonates Substituted with R at C_1

R^a	$k_{25}°C.$	$\Delta H^{\ddagger}$, kcal./mole	$\Delta S^{\ddagger}$, e.u.	Rate relative to *endo*-nor-OTs	Rate relative to *exo*-nor-OTs
			exo series		
H	2.44×10^{-5}	21.7	-6.9	295	1.00
CH_3	125×10^{-5}	—	—	14,100	51.2
C_2H_5	190×10^{-5}	—	—	22,900	77.8
p-O_2N	0.780×10^{-5}	23.7	-2.6	94.2	0.320
p-Cl	3.81×10^{-5}	23.0	-1.5	460	1.56
	9.55×10^{-5}	22.8	-0.33	1150	3.91
m-OCH_3	9.65×10^{-5}	22.9	-2.8	1170	3.95
p-CH_3	15.8×10^{-5}	22.3	-1.1	1910	6.47
p-OCH_3	18.8×10^{-5}	22.1	-1.6	2270	7.71
o-OCH_3	48.1×10^{-5}	21.7	-4.2	5810	19.7
			endo series		
H	8.28×10^{-8}	25.8	-4.4	1.00	
CH_3	9.32×10^{-8}	25.8	-4.1	1.13	
C_2H_5	9.33×10^{-8}	27.2	$+0.37$	1.13	
p-O_2N	0.418×10^{-8}	26.9	-6.6	0.0505	
p-Cl	1.89×10^{-8}	25.6	-7.9	0.228	
m-OCH_3	4.89×10^{-8}	25.5	-6.5	0.591	
p-CH_3	5.11×10^{-8}	25.9	-5.2	0.617	
	5.66×10^{-8}	25.1	-7.7	0.684	
p-OCH_3	6.23×10^{-8}	25.5	-6.1	0.752	
o-OCH_3	76.1×10^{-8}	25.3	-1.6	9.19	

[a] R is aryl with indicated substituent when position index (*o*, *m*, *p*) is shown.

is required in order to preserve the latter hypothesis: the competition ratio for carbon versus hydrogen bridging in the intermediates **174** and/or **175** derived from *endo* starting material would have to be exactly the same as in the *concerted* bridging-heterolysis processes in the *exo* case. The analysis, however, is subject to some question, since it ignores the possibility of 6,2 shift in the ion-pair derived from the *exo* system.

[137b] J. A. Berson and S. Suzuki, *J. Am. Chem. Soc.*, **81**, 4088 (1959).

[137c] J. A. Berson and A. Remanick, unpublished observations.

less, the rate is believed [128] to be much faster than would be expected for a tertiary chloride, even if the effect of the acceleration of solvolysis by release of steric strain is taken into account. In open chain systems, anchimeric assistance by neighboring alkyl or phenyl is less important in tertiary than in secondary derivatives.[138] In this connection, a comparison of the rate enhancement for **176** versus its (unknown) *endo* isomer with that for the analogously constituted secondary *endo-exo* pair of the camphenilyl system (example 4 of Table VI), would be valuable.[138a]

B. Systems Containing Four-Membered Rings

Nopinyl Derivatives.   Solvolyses of the stereoisomeric nopinyl *p*-bromobenzenesulfonates provide an exception to the pattern of Table VI; although in both the α (**177**) and β (**178**) isomers the geometry is favorable for partici-

(177)(α)   (178)(β)

pation of a ring member, and both isomers lead to product mixtures of completely rearranged skeleton, substantial enhancements of solvolysis rate over that expected for an unassisted secondary derivative are not observed.[139] Although there is some question [139] about what rate to expect if anchimeric assistance were absent, the solvolysis rate clearly does not receive the large driving force from expansion of the four-membered ring that is observed in the case of the monocyclic model, **179**, which solvolyzes 3900 times as fast as **177**.

Acetolysis or hydrolysis (aqueous acetone, calcium carbonate) give no nopinyl derivatives; thus, if the "classical" nopinyl cation is the first stage of

[138] S. Winstein, B. K. Morse, E. Grunwald, K. C. Schreiber, and J. Corse, *J. Am. Chem. Soc.*, **74**, 1113 (1952).

[138a] Rates of acetolysis have been reported [138b] for a series of 1-substituted-norbornyl *p*-toluenesulfonates. Some of the results are given in Table XVIII. The rate data for the 1-aryl-2-*exo-p*-toluenesulfonates are well correlated by the Hammett σ-ρ treatment, using σ values with $\rho = -1.36$. The correlation is less satisfactory with σ^+ values. This suggests that only a relatively small part of the cationic charge developing in the transition state is transmitted to C_1. Also, the relatively modest rate enhancement produced by the 1-aryl substituents is in accord with this idea. Nevertheless, 1-alkyl substitution produces a substantial rate enhancement in the *exo* series. For the *endo* series, a satisfactory correlation with σ values is observed, with $\rho = -1.06$.

[138b] P. von R. Schleyer and D. C. Kleinfelter, 138th Meeting, ACS, New York, September, 1960, *Abstracts*, p. 43P.

[139] S. Winstein and N. J. Holness, *J. Am. Chem. Soc.*, **77**, 3054 (1955).

solvolysis, it does not lead directly to product (contrast the *endo*-norbornyl solvolysis). Further, the bridged ions **180** and **181**, hypothetically derived by

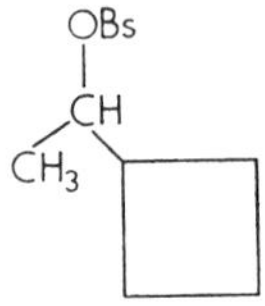

(179)

ordinary participation in the rate-determining ionization, do not lead to products either; **180** would give apoborneol (**182**), and **181** would give *endo*-

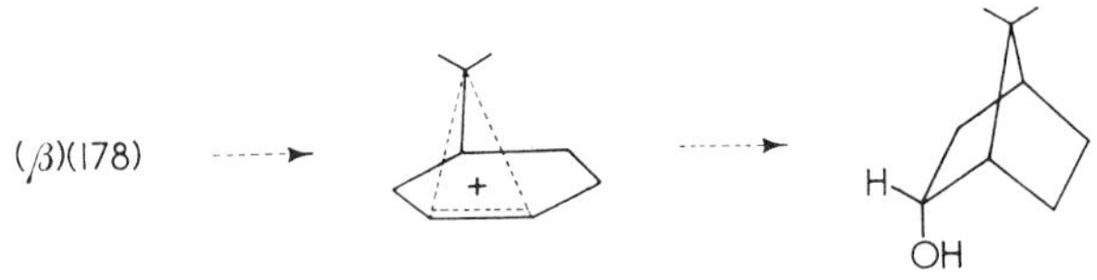

(β)(178) $\quad$ ------► $\quad$ (180) $\quad$ ------► $\quad$ (182)

camphenilol (**183**), neither of which is found. Thus, if ionization is assisted at all, **180** and **181** must represent transition states rather than true intermediates; that is, whatever rate enhancement occurs is a result of the reaction **184**, with no intermediate. Solvolysis of either the α or β isomer gives a mixture of apoisoborneol (**185**), β-fenchoisocamphorol (**186**) and *exo*-cam-

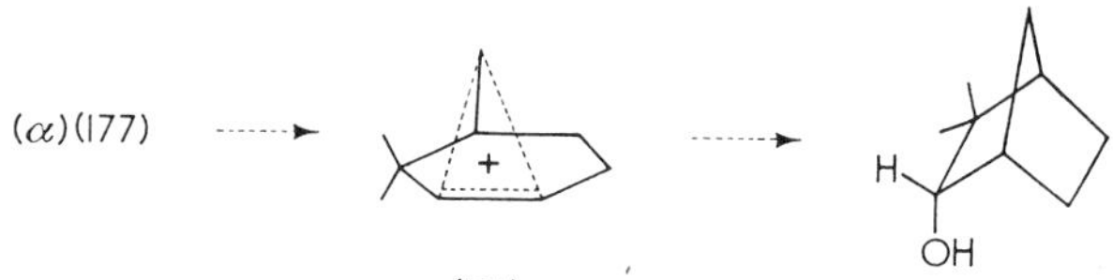

(α)(177) $\quad$ ------► $\quad$ (181) $\quad$ ------► $\quad$ (183)

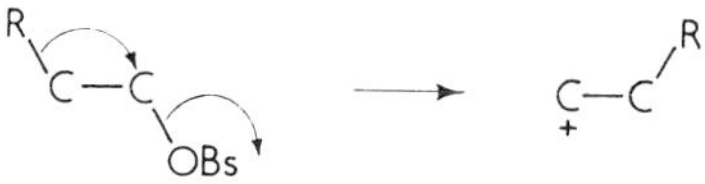

(184)

phenilol (**187**) in roughly the same proportions as those obtained in hydrolyses [140] of sulfonates of **185** or **187**. The apoisoborneol (**185**) obtained from optically active **177** is partially racemized, presumably because of 6,2 hydride shift. This observation and the formation of **186** establish hydride shifts as

[140] S. Winstein, XIVth International Congress of Pure and Applied Chemistry, Zürich, *Experientia, Suppl.* No. 2 137 (1955).

reaction paths competing with direct collapse to product for both enantiomeric ions **189** and **190**. Since the optical rotation of enantiomerically pure

(185)	(186)	(187)

185 is unknown, the optical purity of the product **185**, which would provide
an accurate measure of the relative rates of 6,2 shift and collapse for the ion
189, is unfortunately unavailable.

In contrast to most conventional Wagner-Meerwein and allied processes,
the formation of *exo* products (*exo*-camphenilol (**187**) and apoisoborneol (**185**))
in these reactions constitutes formal *retention* of configuration at the migration
origin.

Pinyl Derivatives.   Mere substitution of a methyl group for hydrogen at
the position adjacent to the bridgehead of the nopinyl system, giving pinyl
derivatives, produces a striking change in behavior. While the nopinyl system
passes through cations **189** and **190** and their variants resulting from 6,2

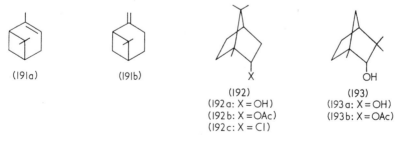

shift, and gives exclusively *exo* products, the pinyl system gives at least
largely *endo* products; clearly, methyl-substituted cations analogous to **189**
and **190** cannot be involved in the product-determining steps. Examples
include the conversion of α- or β-pinene (**191a** or **191b**) to mixtures of borneol
(**192a**) and α-fenchol (**193a**) or to esters thereof [141,142] and the rearrangement

(191a)	(191b)	(192)	(193)
		X	OH
		(192a: X = OH)	(193a: X = OH)
		(192b: X = OAc)	(193b: X = OAc)
		(192c: X = Cl)	

[141] M. Délépine and A. Adida, *Bull. soc. chim. France*, **4**, 39, 782 (1926); M. Délépine,
Compt. rend., **178**, 2088 (1924), **179**, 175 (1924).
[142] M. S. Kharasch and W. B. Reynolds, *J. Org. Chem.*, **9**, 148 (1944).

of pinene hydrochloride (**194**) to bornyl chloride (**192c**).[143,144] The formation of *endo-endo*-2,6-dichlorocamphane (**195**) by addition of chlorine to α-pinene[146] and the stereospecific rearrangements of the isomeric methylnopinols—**196** to bornyl acetate (**192b**) and **197** to α-fenchyl acetate (**193b**) [145]—fall into the same pattern. Cations derived from the pinyl system thus exhibit the stereochemical behavior expected of mesomeric intermediates of the type **198** and **199**; in the nopinyl system, the analogous cations, **180** and **181**, if formed at all, are rapidly converted to **189** and **190**. The reasons for the differences in behavior of the two systems remain to be elucidated.

There seem to be no reports in the literature of the formation of a tertiary bicyclic alcohol ("pinene hydrate") or derivative thereof by solvolysis of pinene hydrochloride; the substances corresponding to this structure (the methylnopinols (**196** and **197**)) are made by alternate means.[145,147,148] It will be recalled that other mesomeric cations (e.g., that involved in the camphene hydroisobornyl system) give tertiary products under kinetically controlled conditions of solvolysis (see heading 3C). A conceivable explanation,[148a] for which no independent experimental support is available, suggests that the normal partition ratio favoring tertiary product is qualitatively inverted by the strain involved in recontracting cation **198** or **199** to a bicyclo[3.1.1]hep-

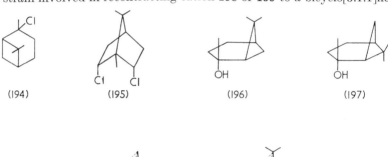

(194)   (195)   (196)   (197)

(198)   (199)

tane. If this is correct, an experiment analogous to the radiochloride exchange versus rearrangement study carried out with camphene hydrochloride (see heading 2) should reveal that the rate of exchange of pinene hydrochloride with radiochloride is slower than the rate of rearrangement to bornyl chloride.

[143] H. Meerwein and K. van Emster, *Ber.*, **55**, 2500 (1922).

[144] H. Meerwein and J. Vorster, *J. prakt. Chem.*, [2] **147**, 83 (1936).

[145] W. D. Burrows and R. H. Eastman, *J. Am. Chem. Soc.*, **81**, 245 (1959).

[146] H. Kwart and G. Null, *J. Am. Chem. Soc.*, **78**, 5943 (1956).

[147] A. Lipp, *Ber.*, **56**, 2098 (1923).

[148] O. Wallach, *Ann.*, **356**, 239 (1907).

[148a] J. A. Berson, *Tetrahedron Letters*, No. **16**, 17 (1960).

Numerical values for rates of solvolysis of pinene hydrochloride have not been published, although the substance is reported [149] to be extremely reactive.

Cleavage reactions in the pinyl system are particularly facile; for example, formic acid converts α-pinene to terpinyl formate (**200**) and limonene (**201**),

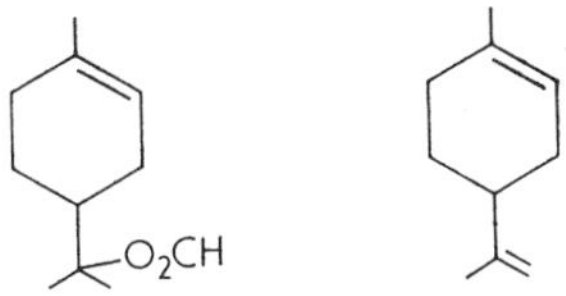

(200)   (201)

among other products.[150] At least part of the driving force for the cleavage undoubtedly is derived from relief of ring strain. Also, the structure of the cation **199**, which is presumably formed in the reaction, is electronically favorable to ring opening. The migrating group is fully substituted, and cleavage generates a tertiary carbonium ion.

The conversion of α-pinene oxide (**202**) to campholenic aldehyde (**203**) [151] is

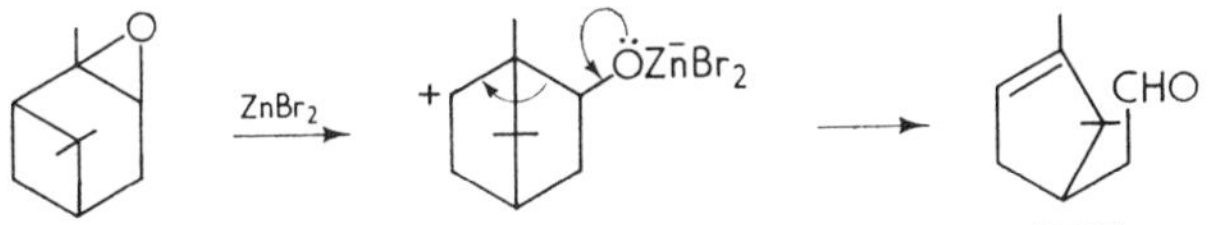

(202)   (203)

one of a relatively small group of reactions involving formal cleavage of a bicyclo[2.2.1]heptane. Other examples include the sulfuric-acid-induced conversions of camphor and fenchone to 3,4-dimethylacetophenone and of camphenilone to 4-methylacetophenone (heading 5A), and the nitrous acid deaminations of bornylamine and fenchylamine to α-terpineol (heading 9).

Among the few examples of rearrangements in which a contraction of a cyclopentane to a cyclobutane derivative is involved (for others, see Parts 7B and 8) is the transformation of camphorquinone **203a** to isocamphorquinone **203b**,[151a] induced by cold fuming sulfuric acid. The rearrangement is formulated as passing through the ring-contracted intermediate **203d**,[151a] the change **203c** → **203d** corresponding to conversion of a camphenehydro derivative to a pinyl derivative.

149 E. D. Hughes, *Bull. soc. chim. France*, C38 (1951); *Quart Revs.*, **5**, 245 (1951).

150 J. Reisman, *Bull. soc. chim. France*, [4] **41**, 94 (1927).

151 B. Arbusov, *Ber.*, **68**, 1430 (1935).

151a S. G. Levine, *J. Am. Chem. Soc.*, **82**, 2556 (1960).

An analogous conversion apparently is involved in the sulfuric acid-induced rearrangement of fenchone to camphor.[151b]

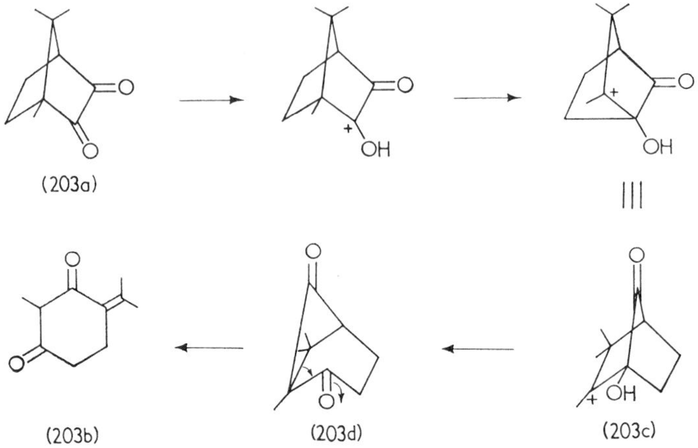
O
OH
+
(203a)
(203b)
(203d)
(203c)

Bicyclo[3.2.0]heptanes. Expansion of the four-membered ring appears to provide anchimeric assistance to the acetolysis of **204**[152] (see Scheme 3).

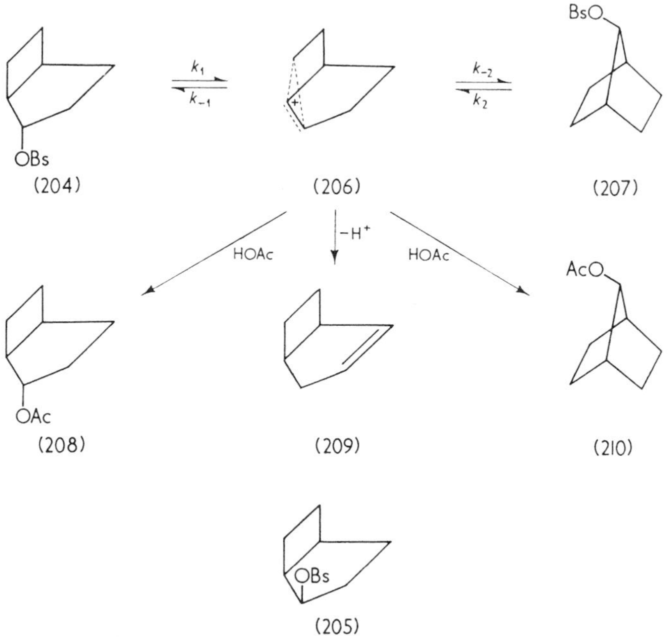
BsO
k_1
k_{-1}
k_{-2}
k_2
OBs
(204)
(206)
(207)
$-H^+$
HOAc
HOAc
AcO
OAc
(208)
(209)
(210)
OBs
(205)

Scheme 3.

[151b] R. P. Lutz and J. D. Roberts, *J. Am. Chem. Soc.*, **84**, 3715 (1962).

[152] S Winstein, F. Gadient, E. T. Stafford, and P. E. Klinedinst, Jr., *J. Am. Chem. Soc.*, **80**, 5895 (1958).

The rate is about 100 times that observed with the *cis* isomer (**205**). This factor is at the low end of the range of *exo/endo* rate ratios of Table VI. It is difficult to estimate how much anchimeric assistance contributes to the **204/205** rate ratio. In an unassisted solvolysis, the leaving group of **205** would encounter hindering hydrogens on the four-membered ring; its rate would be retarded relative to that of **204** by this effect. On the other hand, back-side participation by solvent is easier in **205** than in **204**.

The products are clearly formed from the bridged cation **206**, however. The bicyclo[3.2.0]heptyl acetate (**208**) is formed with total retention of configuration; no *cis*-acetate is found. A substantial amount of the ion **206** (present as an ion pair) is converted to the very unreactive 7-norbornyl *p*-bromobenzenesulfonate (**207**) under the solvolysis conditions. Results at several temperatures are given in Table VIII.

TABLE VIII

Product Distribution from Acetolyses of **204** or **207**

Starting material	Temp., °C.	Per cent of total product		Proportion of 208 + 209 + 210 mixture		
		207	208 + 209 + 210	208	209	210
204	25	86	17			
204	50	83	17	5	1	94
204	100	79	21			
207	205	0	100	7	2	91

The product ratio **207**/(**208** + **209** + **210**) represents the ratio (specific rate of ion pair return to **207**)/(collapse to solvolysis product), i.e., k_{-2}/k_{HOAc}, where k_{HOAc} is the sum of the rate constants for formation of solvolysis products. The difference in Arrhenius activation energies for the two processes can be calculated from the temperature dependence data of Table VIII. Ion pair return to **207** requires 1.3 kcal./mole less activation energy than does collapse to solvolysis product.[152]

C. Oxygen-Bridged Systems

In oxygen-bridged bicyclic systems, the possibility of involvement of the heteroatom in solvolytic processes must be considered. An investigation[153a] of solvolyses of the oxygen-bridged isomeric chlorides **211** and **212** shows that either starting material on hydrolysis in aqueous ethanol or dioxane

[153] (a) J. C. Martin and P. D. Bartlett, *J. Am. Chem. Soc.*, **79**, 2533 (1957). (b) J. C. Martin, Thesis, Harvard University, 1956.

gives the same hydroxy aldehyde product (**213**); the hemiacetal (**214**), related to the starting materials by Wagner-Meerwein change, is presumably the

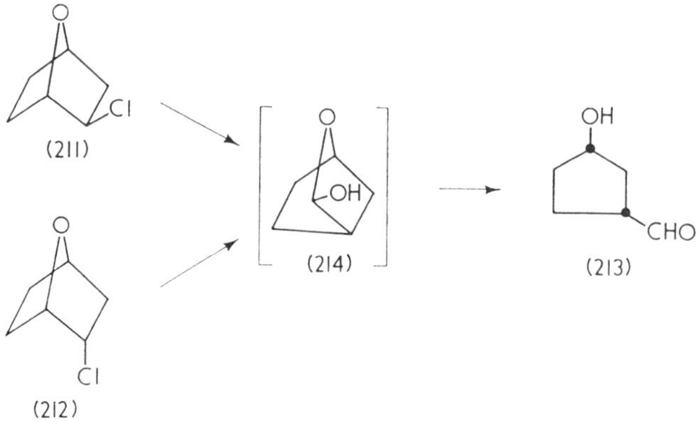

precursor of **213**. The ratio of solvolysis rates (*exo/endo*) for the chlorides is 318 at 25°, which is very close to the factor of 350 observed [136a] for the norbornyl *p*-bromobenzenesulfonate acetolysis at the same temperature. Table IX gives some further comparisons with norbornyl systems.

TABLE IX

Solvolytic Reactivities

Substrate	Solvent	Temp., °C.	k_{exo}/k_{endo}	k_{endo} sec.$^{-1}$	Ref.
Norbornyl Cl	80% EtOH	85	70	5.6×10^{-7}	131
Norbornyl OBs	HOAc	25	350	2.5×10^{-7}	127
Norbornyl OBs	HOAc	85	275	4.7×10^{-4}	127
	50% dioxane	140	163	3.5×10^{-7}	153
Endoxonorbornyl Cl		85	211	8.9×10^{-10}	153
		25	318	1.2×10^{-13}	153

It is argued [153a] that the correspondence of the *exo/endo* rate ratio for the oxygen-bridged system to that of the norbornyl system signifies that the oxygen bridge does not contribute a driving force to ionization, i.e., the transition state leading to the first cation in the solvolysis of *exo*-chloride (**211**) is not stabilized by electronic delocalization involving the oxygen bridge (as in **215**). Homoallylic interaction (**216**), which might enhance the rate of solvolysis of the *endo*-chloride and thereby fortuitously balance the enhancement by **215** of the *exo* solvolysis, is ruled out [153] on the grounds that both isomers should then show solvolysis rates faster than are actually observed. Using the rough factor of 10^2 for polar retardation of solvolysis by a β-alkoxy group,[154a,154b] one would expect a ratio of roughly this magnitude for the *endo*-norbornyl/**212** comparison. Although data for solvolyses of the two

(215)   (216)   (217)

chlorides under comparable conditions are not available from experiment, an estimate of such a comparison can be made [153b] and gives a reactivity factor of 6×10^3. Since this factor is much greater than would be anticipated by analogy to other β-alkoxy systems, it is concluded [153] that the oxide bridge is uniquely effective in retarding solvolysis.[155]

The interpretation [153] of the correspondence in *exo/endo* rate ratios for the methylene-bridged and oxygen-bridged systems needs further discussion. If

154 (a) S. Winstein, E. Grunwald, and L. L. Ingraham, *J. Am. Chem. Soc.*, **70**, 821 (1948). (b) S. Winstein and E. Grunwald, *J. Am. Chem. Soc.*, **70**, 828 (1948). (c) E. Grunwald and S. Winstein, *J. Am. Chem. Soc.*, **70**, 846 (1948). (d) S. Winstein, E. Grunwald, and H. W. Jones, *J. Am. Chem. Soc.*, **73**, 2700 (1951). (e) A. H. Fainberg and S. Winstein, *J. Am. Chem. Soc.*, **78**, 2770 (1956). (f) S. Winstein and A. H. Fainberg, *J. Am. Chem. Soc.*, **79**, 5937 (1957).

155 The basis for the above numerical estimate, which is not explicitly given in the paper,[153a] but is available in the less readily accessible thesis,[153b] may be of sufficient general interest to justify reproduction here. *endo*-Norbornyl chloride solvolyzes [131] in 80% ethanol (by volume) with $k = 5.6 \times 10^{-7}$/sec. The rate constant for solvolysis of *exo*-2-bromoendoxocyclohexane is decreased [153] by a factor of 9.6 when the solvent is changed from 50% dioxane to 80% ethanol (by volume). Assuming that a parallel change would apply to the *endo*-chloro compound (**212**), the rate constant for the latter in 80% ethanol (by volume) at 85° would be 9.3×10^{-11}. This gives [153] a reactivity ratio (*endo*-norbornyl/**212**) of 6×10^3. Alternatively, one might adjust the rate of solvolysis of *endo*-norbornyl chloride to one that would be observed in 50%-dioxane, the solvent used [153] for solvolysis of **212**. The Winstein-Grunwald correlation scheme,[154c –154f] which may be expressed as

$$\log k = m\mathbf{Y} + \log k_0$$

supplies a basis for a rough estimate of this rate. The term k_0 is the rate in 80% ethanol, $\mathbf{Y}$ is a measure of the ionizing power of the solvent (50% dioxane), and m is a correlation slope. If $\mathbf{Y}$ is considered to be temperature invariant,[154f] the value [154e] for 50% dioxane is 1.36; m may be estimated to be about 0.5, by analogy to a simple secondary system (for isopropyl bromide, $m = 0.544$, and for isopropyl *p*-bromobenzenesulfonate, $m = 0.408$ [154d]). The rate of solvolysis of *endo*-norbornyl chloride in 50% dioxane (k) should then be about 2.7×10^{-6}/sec., and the ratio of solvolysis rates (*endo*-norbornyl/**212**) under comparable conditions now becomes 3×10^3. The two methods of comparison, based on independent but similar assumptions, give reactivity ratios differing only by a factor of 2. The results suggest that the procedures are reliable for the order-of-magnitude estimates required here.

the oxygen bridge were ineffective in stabilizing the transition state for solvolysis of the *exo* isomer (**211**), the transition state would resemble **217** and not **215**. The carbon-oxygen dipole would then oppose the distribution of partial positive charge to C_1, and since this kind of opposition would be absent in the transition state for (unassisted) solvolysis of the *endo* isomer (**212**), the *exo/endo* rate ratio should be *smaller* for the **211/212** comparison than for the norbornyl comparison. Further, the significance of the correspondence in rate ratios is open to question, since at least the rate of solvolysis of *exo*-norbornyl *p*-bromobenzenesulfonate must be corrected for internal return (see Part 6). This changes the *exo/endo* rate ratio for the norbornyl series from 350 to 1225 in acetic acid. If it is assumed (*a*) that the latter figure represents the ratio of *ionization* rates, (*b*) that the ratio for the **211/212** series (determined in aqueous solvent) requires no correction for internal return, and (*c*) that the special retardation by the bridge oxygen observed with the *endo*-chloride (**212**) is also present in the solvolysis of the *exo*-chloride (**211**), then the blame for the discrepancy between 1225 and 318 might conceivably be assigned to the selective destabilization by charge-dipole opposition in the solvolysis of the oxygen-bridged *exo*-chloride (**211**). There is no simple way of estimating whether the factor of 4 is a reasonable one to attribute to this kind of influence.

8. HOMOALLYLIC AND HOMOBENZYLIC BICYCLO[2.2.1]HEPTENES

A. Evidence for Homoallylic Effects

From Rates and Products of Solvolysis.   The factor of about 7900 favoring *exo*- versus *endo*-5-norbornenyl *p*-bromobenzenesulfonate in acetolysis [155a,156] (see Figure 3) has been attributed [155a,156] to homoallylic interaction similar to that proposed [160,161] to account for the solvolysis products and reactivities of cholesteryl as against cholestanyl and epicholesteryl derivatives. Homoallylic electronic delocalization of the kind symbolized by **218** depends upon σ

(2|8)

[155a] S. Winstein, H. M. Walborsky, and K. C. Schreiber, *J. Am. Chem. Soc.*, **72**, 5795 (1950).

[156] (a) S. Winstein, M. Shatavsky, C. J. Norton, and R. B. Woodward, *J. Am. Chem. Soc.*, **77**, 4183 (1955). (b) W. G. Woods, R. A. Carboni, and J. D. Roberts, *J. Am. Chem. Soc.*, **78**, 5653 (1956).

[157] S. Winstein and E. T. Stafford, *J. Am. Chem. Soc.*, **79**, 505 (1957).

[158] S. Winstein and D. Trifan, *J. Am. Chem. Soc.*, **74**, 1147, 1154 (1952).

interaction of the relevant orbitals, in contrast to ordinary allylic delocalization, which typically involves π interaction.[162] The geometry of the *exo*-nor-

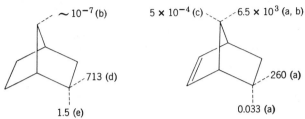

Figure 3.   Acetolytic reactivities (at 25°, relative to cyclohexyl *p*-bromobenzenesulfonate) of 5- and 7-norbornenyl and of 7- and 2-norbornyl *p*-bromobenzenesulfonates. Key to references: *a*, Refs. 155 and 156; *b*, Ref. 156; *c*, Ref. 157; *d*, Ref. 158; and *e*, Ref. 159a. For hydrolytic reactivities of anti-7-norbornenyl and *exo*-norbornyl chlorides (80% ethanol), see Ref. 159b.

bornenyl system is superior to that of the *endo* isomer for homoallylic delocalization, since departure of the leaving group from the *exo* side projects a *p* orbital lobe in a favorable direction for σ interaction with the transannular double bond. The maximum of quantum mechanical orbital overlap in the homoallylic ion is achieved at the expense of angle strain, the best compromise [162] giving a net stabilization over the corresponding "classical" ion of 4.2 kcal./mole.

The major products of the solvolysis of *exo*- or *endo*-5-norbornenyl or nortricyclyl halides or sulfonates and of the nitrous acid deaminations of the 5-norbornenylamines are nortricyclyl derivatives (**219**); [155a,163,164] *exo*-

(219)

norbornenyl derivatives are formed in small yield. The preferential formation of nortricyclyl derivatives probably is associated with the stability of the nortricyclene ring system with respect to the norbornene ring system. The direct equilibration of the parent hydrocarbons, norbornene and nortricyclene,

[159a] S. Winstein, B. K. Morse, E. Grunwald, H. W. Jones, J. Corse, D. Trifan, and H. Marshall, *J. Am. Chem. Soc.*, **74**, 1127 (1952).

[159b] W. G. Woods, R. A. Carboni, and J. D. Roberts, *J. Am. Chem. Soc.*, **78**, 5653 (1956).

[160] C. W. Shoppee, *J. Chem. Soc.* (*London*), **1946**, 1138.

[161] S. Winstein and R. Adams, *J. Am. Chem. Soc.*, **70**, 838 (1948).

[162] M. Simonetta and S. Winstein, *J. Am. Chem. Soc.*, **76**, 18 (1954).

[163] J. D. Roberts, W. Bennett, and R. Armstrong, *J. Am. Chem. Soc.*, **72**, 3329 (1950).

[164] J. D. Roberts, C. C. Lee, and W. H. Saunders, Jr., *J. Am. Chem. Soc.*, **77**, 3034 (1955).

favors the tricyclic isomer by a factor of about three at reflux temperature;[165] part of the energy difference is presumably reflected in the activation energies for partitioning the cationic intermediates into bicyclic and tricyclic solvolysis products.[165a]

Solvolyses of norbornenyl-$2,3$-^{14}C p-bromobenzenesulfonates and deaminations of norbornenyl-3-^{14}C-amines[164] followed by hydrogenation of the norbornenyl product give mixtures of norbornyl and nortricyclyl derivatives. The norbornyl product can be selectively degraded[164] according to the scheme used in the norbornyl series (see page 143). Carbon skeletal rearrangements are observed; "per cent rearrangement" varies from 30 to 50% depending upon the structure of the starting material and the reaction conditions. These results indicate that only a minor fraction (0–40%) of the norbornenyl portion of the product arises from ion **218a**, which permits reaction with a nucleophile to give norbornenyl derivative only at C_2; the major fraction of the norbornenyl product is derived from intermediates in which C_2 and C_1 of the original norbornenyl skeleton are equivalent. Such an intermediate might be the carbon-bridged ion **220** or its equivalent in terms of isotopic labeling, the enantiomeric pair of ions **218a** and **218b**. The product distributions and

(218a)   (218b)   (220)

rate phenomena in the norbornenyl system allow two interpretations. Either (a) the solvolysis is accelerated by homoallylic participation alone, but the initially produced ion **218a** is partitioned between collapse to products and conversion to the carbon-bridged ion **220** (ions **218a** and **220** formed consecutively), or (b) the solvolysis is accelerated by both homoallylic and carbon participation, ions **218a** and **220** being formed competitively from starting material.

Solvolysis of nortricyclyl p-bromobenzenesulfonate produces a lower proportion of olefinic product than does solvolysis of the homoallylically isomeric norbornenyl p-bromobenzenesulfonate.[166] This indicates that

[165] P. von R. Schleyer, *J. Am. Chem. Soc.*, **80**, 1700 (1958).

[165a] Actually, the observed equilibrium constant of 3 for the parent hydrocarbons is a deceptively small measure of the purely "chemical" energy difference. If the ratio of the symmetry numbers (3:1) is taken into account, the "chemical" equilibrium constant[165b] becomes 9.

[165b] For a discussion of symmetry corrections of rate and equilibrium constants, see S. W. Benson, *J. Am. Chem. Soc.*, **80**, 515 (1958).

[166] H. Schmid, unpublished work, quoted by S. Winstein and E. Kosower, *J. Am. Chem. Soc.*, **81**, 4399 (1959).

solvolysis products from the two starting materials do not arise from a single common intermediate. One interpretation [166] suggests that the norbornenyl isomer ionizes first to the unsymmetrical cation **218a** only, and the nortricyclyl isomer ionizes first to the symmetrical cation **220** only. (Microscopic reversibility then requires that **218a** react with bromobenzenesulfonate ion to give only the norbornenyl structure and that **220** give only the nortricyclyl structure.) This interpretation is equivalent to adding to scheme (a) above a step in which **220** is generated from nortricyclyl starting material. Alternatives derived from (b) above are easily imagined.

The related matter of solvolyses of allylcarbinyl, cyclopropylcarbinyl, and cyclobutyl derivatives, is discussed in Section 4.

The rate of solvolysis of endo-norbornenyl bromobenzenesulfonate is diminished relative to that of endo-norbornyl p-bromobenzenesulfonate by the polar effect of the transannular double bond.[155a] A rough estimate [155a,159a] of the retarding effect of a β-unsaturated group on solvolysis is obtained on the assumption that the increase in dissociation constants of phenylacetic acid (pK$_a$ 4.31) and vinylacetic acid (pK$_a$ 4.35) over that of acetic acid (pK$_a$ 4.77) would be paralleled by polar retardation of solvolysis. A chloro substituent β to the site of dissociation is about four times as effective logarithmically in enhancing acidity as is a β-phenyl substituent (pK$_a$ for chloroacetic acid, 2.85). The polar retarding effect of β-chloro on solvolysis rate is estimated from the comparison of solvolytic reactivities of cyclohexyl and cis-2-chlorocyclohexyl p-toluenesulfonates, the chloro derivative being less reactive by a factor of $\sim 10^4$. The assumption of proportionality affords the following relationship, where the K's are dissociation constants and the k's are solvolysis rate constants.

$$\log (K_\phi/K_H)/\log (K_{Cl}/K_H) \approx \log (k_\phi/k_H)/\log (k_{Cl}/k_H)$$

The ratio k_ϕ/k_H calculated from this is about 10. The theoretical basis for the assumptions involved is not precise, and the factor of 10 for the polar retarding effect of a β-phenyl or β-vinyl group is at best a rough guide.

Homoallylic acceleration of solvolysis is particularly pronounced in the 7-anti-norbornenyl system. The rate is 25 times that of the very reactive exo-5-norbornenyl system, but the full extent of the acceleration can be appreciated only by comparison with the saturated 7-norbornyl system. The latter is exceptionally unreactive (see Fig. 3); presumably because of (a) Bredt's rule interdictions of hydrogen hyperconjugation, (b) increase in steric strain at C$_7$ during the change in hybridization from sp^3 to sp^2, and (c) steric hindrance to solvation,[156,167] the development of positive charge at C$_7$ of the norbornyl system is resisted much more than is the case in ordinary secondary

[167] W. G. Woods, R. A. Carboni, and J. D. Roberts, J. Am. Chem. Soc., **78**, 5653 (1956).

alkyl systems. The mere introduction of a double bond enhances the solvolysis rate by a factor of 10^{11}. Although the geometry of the 7-norbornenyl system is, by inspection, not obviously especially favorable to σ interaction of the double bond orbitals and the C_7 p orbital, this is deceptive, for the kinetic results indicate that some particularly happy compromise is struck between angle strain and σ overlap, and estimates of the net stabilization (balance between angle strain and simple molecular orbital delocalization energy) indicate that the 7-norbornenyl homallylic cation is more stable than the corresponding classical cation by 10.5 kcal./mole.[167]

The sole product of the acetolysis of *anti*-7-norbornenyl *p*-toluenesulfonate is the *anti*-7-acetate;[156,168] hydrolysis of the dibromide (**221**) gives[169] at least predominantly the bromohydrin (**222**). In both cases, homoallylic

(221)   (222)

interaction in the intermediate cation protects one side of the site of solvolysis, and products are formed with over-all retention of configuration.

In *syn*-7-norbornenyl derivatives, the geometry is unfavorable to homoallylic participation in the rate step of the solvolysis. Nevertheless, the acetolysis rate of *syn*-7-norbornenyl *p*-toluenesulfonate (**223**) is greater than that of 7-norbornyl *p*-toluenesulfonate by a factor of about 10^4 (see Fig. 3). The origin of the rate enhancement is ascribed to methylene participation in the formation of the allylic cation **224**. The product of hydrolysis of **223** is 2-bicyclo[3.2.0]heptenol-4 (**225**) (configuration unknown). It is postulated[157]

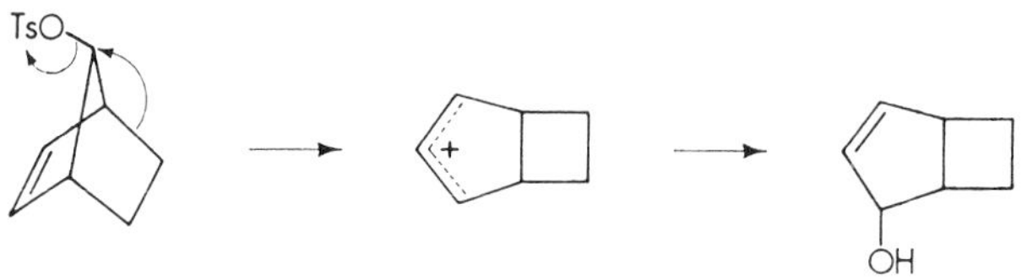

(223)   (224)   (225)

that allylic resonance in the transition state for formation of **224** outweighs the angle strain associated with ring contraction. Clearly, however, this strain is not very formidable, since acetolysis of even the saturated 7-norbornyl

[168] C. J. Norton, Thesis, Harvard University, 1955.

[169] S. Winstein and M. Shatavsky, *J. Am. Chem. Soc.*, **78**, 592 (1956).

p-bromobenzenesulfonate produces a detectable amount of bicyclo[3.2.0]-heptyl acetate.[152]

The rates of acetolysis of *endo*-7-isopropylidenedehydronorbornyl *p*-toluene-sulfonate **(226a)** and *endo*-7-isopropylidenenorbornyl *p*-toluenesulfonate **(227a)** are enhanced, these substances being more reactive than the analogs lacking the 7-isopropylidene group by $\sim 10^4$.[170a] The products are the un-rearranged *endo*-acetates. The rate enhancements and retentions of stereo-chemistry are in accord with homoallylic participation of the isopropylidene double bond.[170a] The *exo* derivatives, **226b** and **227b**, give only rearranged acetates in acetolysis **(227c** and dihydro-**227c**, respectively). Clearly, the

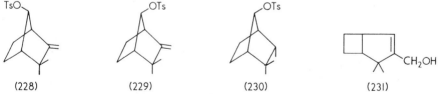

(226*a*)	(226*b*)	(227*a*)	(227*b*)	(227*c*)

solvolysis of *endo* materials in these systems involves intermediates that are entirely distinct from those in the *exo* series.[170b] Surprisingly, however, acetolysis rates for *anti*-7-camphenyl, *syn*-7-camphenyl, and *syn*-7-iso-camphanyl *p*-toluenesulfonates **(228, 229,** and **230,** respectively)[171] show only minor differences, the largest factor **(230/228)** being about three. All of these substances acetolyze slowly; the most reactive compound of the group, **230,** is only 18 times as reactive as the exceedingly sluggish 7-norbornyl *p*-toluene-sulfonate. The origin of these effects is not clear. Despite the lack of kinetic evidence for significant homoallylic participation in the rate-determining heterolysis, the acetolysis product from **228** is at least largely of retained structure and configuration and presumably arises from a homoallylic cation. Further, the hydrolysis product from **229** is probably[171] the ring-contracted allylic alcohol **231,** analogous to the 2-bicyclo[3.2.0]heptenol-4 **(225)** derived[157] from hydrolysis of *syn*-7-norbornenyl *p*-toluenesulfonate.

(228)	(229)	(230)	(231)

[170] (a) C. H. de Puy, P. R. Story, and I. A. Ogawa, 136th Meeting, ACS, Atlantic City, N. J., September, 1959, *Abstracts*, p. 30P. (b) C. H. de Puy, I. A. Ogawa, and J. C. McDaniels, *J. Am. Chem. Soc.*, **82,** 2397 (1960).

[171] E. E. van Tamelen and C. I. Judd, *J. Am. Chem. Soc.*, **80,** 6305 (1958).

The 7-norbornadienyl system (**232**) is enormously reactive, the chloride being about 10^3 times as reactive as *anti*-7-norbornenyl chloride and 10^{14}

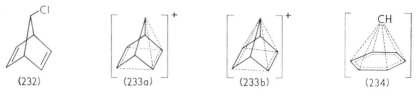

(232)   (233a)   (233b)   (234)

times as reactive as 7-norbornyl chloride.[172] The sole product of hydrolysis (80% aqueous acetone) is the unrearranged alcohol. The reactivity of the system clearly indicates an exceptional degree of stabilization in the transition state of the solvolysis.[172,173]

From Electrophilic Additions. Electrophilic additions to norbornadiene (**235**) are interpreted in terms of homoallylic intermediates.[173b,174a] Addition of bromine in methylene chloride solvent produces **236**, **237**, and **238**. Hypothetically, **236** represents one of the two possible modes of reaction of the

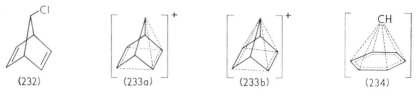

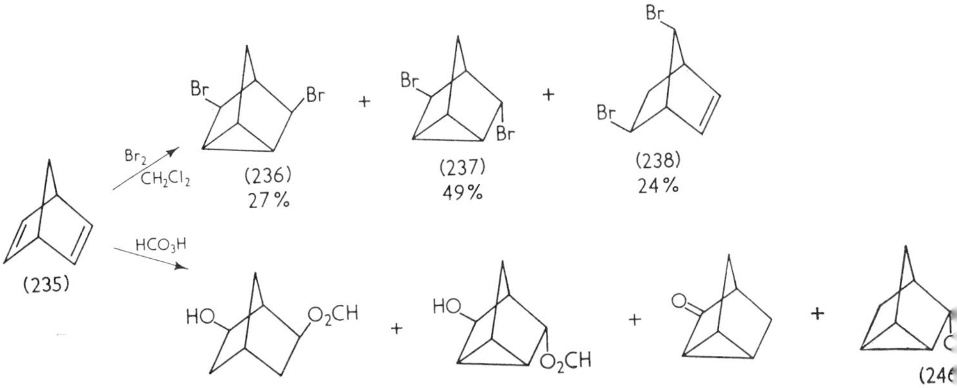

(236)   (237)   (238)
27%   49%   24%

(235)

(240)

[172] (a) S. Winstein and C. Ordronneau, *J. Am. Chem. Soc.*, **82**, 2084 (1960). (b) S. Winstein and L. DeVries, ACS 15th National Organic Chemistry Symposium, Rochester, N. Y., June, 1957, *Abstracts*.

[173] The 7-norbornadienyl cation is obtained in relatively stable form by treating the chloride in sulfur dioxide solution at $-80°$ with silver tetrafluoroborate.[173a] The proton magnetic resonance spectrum of the resulting solution, measured at $-10°$, shows four distinct peaks in the ratio $2:2:2:1$, a result that eliminates the symmetrical structures **233b** and **234** and is consistent with **233a**.[173a]

[173a] P. R. Story and M. Saunders, *J. Am. Chem. Soc.*, **82**, 6199 (1960).

[173b] S. Winstein and M. Shatavsky, *Chem. & Ind.* (*London*), **1956**, 56.

[174] (a) L. Schmerling, 128th Meeting, ACS, Minneapolis, Minn., September, 1955, *Abstracts*, p. 1Q; L. Schmerling, J. P. Luvisi, and R. W. Welch, *J. Am. Chem. Soc.*, **78**, 2819 (1956). (b) J. P. Schaefer, *J. Am. Chem. Soc.*, **82**, 4091 (1960).

homoallylic cation **239**, derived by *exo* addition to the diene **235**; the other possible dibromide, **240**, is not found, its absence being attributed,[173b] at least in part, to steric blocking (by the *exo* bromine in **239**) of *exo* attack by bromide ion at the adjacent carbon (see headings 3C and 5B for a discussion of polar effects that operate in the same direction). Dibromides **237** and **238** represent two of the four possible modes of reaction of the carbon-bridged cation **241** (the other two lead to **240** and **236**). Significantly, no *trans*-5,6-dibromide is formed; this is evidence against the occurrence of the bromonium ion (**242**) as an intermediate.

(239) 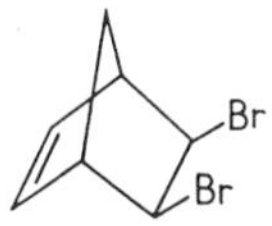   (240) 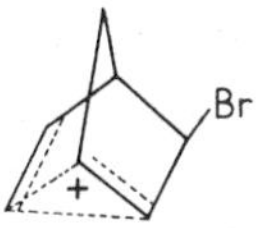   (241) 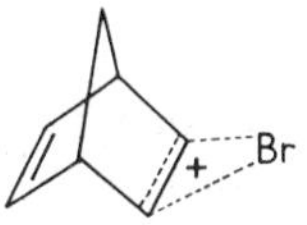   (242)

Performic acid converts **235** to a mixture of products, the principal ones being the nortricyclene diol monoformates corresponding to **236** and **237**. Small amounts of nortricyclenone and the monoformate of its hydrate (**246**)[174b] also are observed. The latter products may result from transannular hydrogen shift.

Additions of formic acid or aqueous hydrochloric acid to 5-methylene-2-norbornene (**243**) give the corresponding 1-methyl-3-nortricyclyl derivative (**244**), although addition of ethereal hydrogen chloride produces the tertiary olefinic chloride **245**.[175]

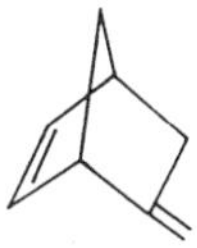

(243) 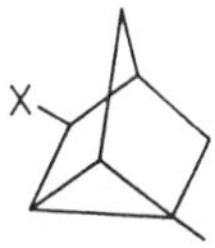   (244)   (245)
                      X = Cl or HCO$_2$

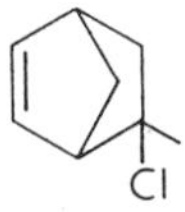

1,4-Cyclohexadiene shows no evidence of transannular interaction in electrophilic additions; the products are *trans*-4,5-disubstituted cyclohexene derivatives.[176]

From Other Reactions and from Spectra.   The full scope of transannular homoallylic interactions in the norbornane and analogous systems remains to be explored. Some scattered chemical results and a more complete set of spectroscopic results are instructive.

[175] P. von R. Schleyer and R. E. O'Connor, 134th Meeting, ACS, Chicago, Ill., September, 1958, *Abstracts*, p. 39P.

[176] E. E. van Tamelen, *J. Am. Chem. Soc.*, **77**, 1704 (1955).

Norbornenone reacts with Grignard reagents to give *exo*-2-alkyl-*endo*-2-norbornanols (**247**) and with hydrogen bromide to give *exo*-5-bromonorbornanone (**248**).[177] The homoconjugate adducts (**248**, Br = alkyl) are not found among the products of the Grignard reaction.

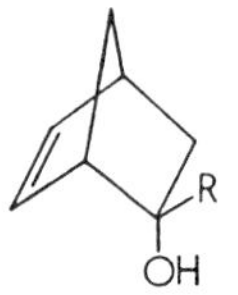

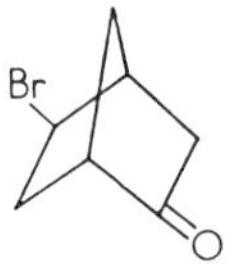

An example of what appears to be homoconjugate nucleophilic addition is provided by the conversion of photo-γ-tropolone methyl ether (**250**) to γ-tropolone methyl ether (**251**),[178,178a] via the enolate **249**.

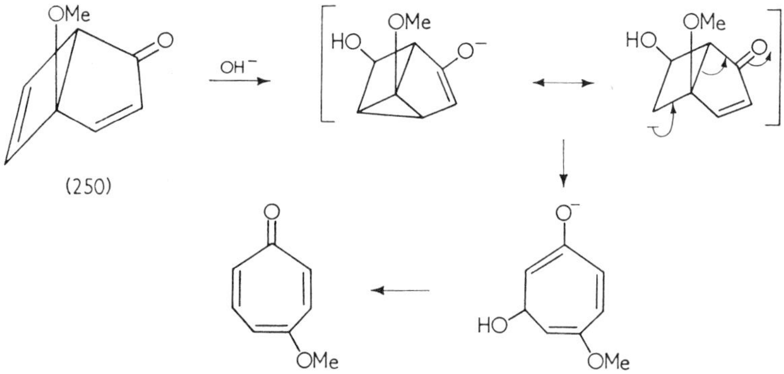

Other examples of transannular interaction include the photochemical isomerization of norbornadienedicarboxylic acid (**252**) to the tetracyclic acid (**253**),[179] and of norbornadiene to the corresponding tetracyclic hydrocarbon

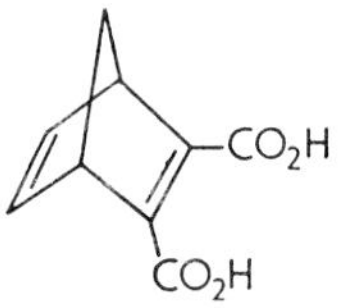

[177] S. J. Cristol and P. K. Freeman, *J. Am. Chem. Soc.*, **83**, 4427 (1961).

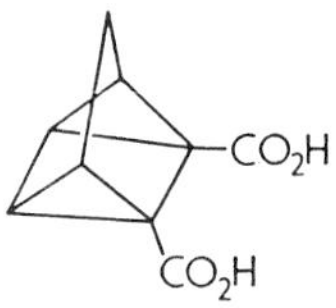

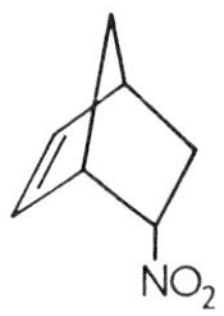

[178] O. L. Chapman and D. J. Pasto, *J. Am. Chem. Soc.*, **81**, 5510 (1959).

[178a] For a related example with tropolone methyl ether, see E. J. Forbes and R. A. Ripley, *Chem. & Ind. (London)*, **1960**, 589.

[179] S. J. Cristol and R. L. Snell, *J. Am. Chem. Soc.*, **80**, 1950 (1958).

quadricyclene.[179a] The failure of 2-nitro-5-norbornenes (e.g., **254**) to undergo the Nef reaction [180] is attributed [180c] to transannular electronic interaction. Ultraviolet spectra provide some evidence for transannular interaction of chromophores (see Table X). The spectra of bridged bicyclic systems must be interpreted with caution, however.[181] Ring strain apparently can produce anomalous effects even when the possibility of transannular electronic interaction is absent. Thus, absorption maxima in the spectra of 3-substituted 2-norbornene-2-carboxylic acids, in which a transannular homoallylic system is absent, occur at appreciably longer wavelengths than those of acyclic and monocyclic models (Table X).[195]

B. Homobenzylic Systems

The stereochemical results of solvolyses of benzonorbornenyl derivatives qualitatively parallel those in the analogous norbornenyl systems. Acetolysis of either *exo-* or *endo*benzonorbornenyl *p*-bromobenzenesulfonate (**255a** and

[179a] W. G. Dauben and R. L. Cargill, *Tetrahedron*, **15**, 197 (1961); G. S. Hammond, N. J. Turro, and A. Fischer, *J. Am. Chem. Soc.*, **83**, 4674 (1961).

[180] (a) W. C. Wildman and R. B. Wildman, *J. Org. Chem.*, **17**, 581 (1952). (b) W. C. Wildman and C. H. Hemminger, *J. Org. Chem.*, **17**, 1641 (1952). (c) W. C. Wildman and D. Saunders, *J. Org. Chem.*, **19**, 381 (1954). (d) W. E. Parham, W. T. Hunter, and R. Hanson, *J. Am. Chem. Soc.*, **73**, 5068 (1951). (e) E. E. van Tamelen and R. J. Thiede, *J. Am. Chem. Soc.*, **74**, 2615 (1952).

[181] S. J. Cristol, and R. T. LaLonde, *J. Am. Chem. Soc.*, **81**, 5417 (1959).

[182] E. R. H. Jones, G. H. Mansfield, and M. C. Whiting, *J. Chem. Soc.* (*London*), **1956**, 4073.

[183] S. J. Cristol and R. L. Snell, unpublished results, quotation in ref. 101d.

[184] W. E. Parham, W. N. Moulton, and A. Zuckerbraun, *J. Org. Chem.*, **21**, 72 (1956).

[185] R. Adams and B. L. Van Duuren, *J. Am. Chem. Soc.*, **75**, 4631 (1953).

[186] E. A. Braude and E. A. Evans, *J. Chem. Soc.* (*London*), **1955**, 3331.

[187] H. Ley and F. Rinke, *Ber.*, **56**, 771 (1923) (possibly the *trans* isomer, see ref. 181, fn. 24).

[188] A. T. Nielsen, *J. Org. Chem.*, **22**, 1539 (1957).

[189] J. L. H. Allen, E. R. H. Jones, and M. C. Whiting, *J. Chem. Soc.* (*London*), **1955**, 1862.

[190] (a) A. Wassermann and A. Smakula, *Z. physik. Chem.*, **A155**, 366 (1931). (b) H. E. Zimmerman and R. M. Paufler, *J. Am. Chem. Soc.*, **82**, 1514 (1960). (c) C. G. Krespan, B. C. McKusick, and T. L. Cairns, *J. Am. Chem. Soc.*, **82**, 1515 (1960).

[191] S. Stokes and L. W. Pickett, *J. Chem. Phys.*, **13**, 258 (1955).

[192] K. Bowden and E. R. H. Jones, *J. Chem. Soc.* (*London*), **1946**, 52.

[193] R. C. Cookson and N. S. Wariyar, *J. Chem. Soc.*, (*London*), **1956**, 2302.

[194] M. Saunders, Thesis, Harvard University, 1956.

[195] For further spectroscopic data on homoallylically conjugated systems, see J. Meinwald, S. L. Emerman, N. C. Yang, and G. Büchi, *J. Am. Chem. Soc.*, **77**, 4401 (1955); J. Meinwald and G. A. Wiley, *J. Am. Chem. Soc.*, **79**, 2569 (1957); E. R. H. Jones, G. H. Mansfield, and M. C. Whiting, *J. Chem. Soc.* (*London*), **1956**, 4073; K. W. Bentley, J. Dominguez, and J. P. Ringe, *J. Org. Chem.*, **22**, 418 (1957); P. G. Farrell and S. F. Mason,

TABLE X

Ultraviolet Spectra of Bridged Bicyclic Derivatives and Their Acyclic and Monocyclic Analogs

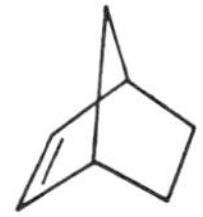

		$R = H$	$R = CH_3$	$R = CO_2H$	$R = C_6H_5$
	$\lambda max^{(m\mu)}$ log ε ref.	195.6 4.0 191			
	$\lambda max^{(m\mu)}$ log ε ref.	217 4.01 182	225 3.96 182	— —	245 3.87 184
	$\lambda max^{(m\mu)}$ log ε ref.	216 3.95 185	221 3.99 186	— —	shoulder at ~245 ~3.6 187
	$\lambda max^{(m\mu)}$ log ε ref.	<210 — 188	206 4.11 189	207 4.11 190a	264 4.00 184
	$\lambda max^{(m\mu)}$ log ε ref.	— 	234 3.91 182	247 (254) 3.95 183 (194)	—
	$\lambda max^{(m\mu)}$ log ε ref.	229 3.57 182	231 3.58 182	247 3.71 182	292 3.83 181

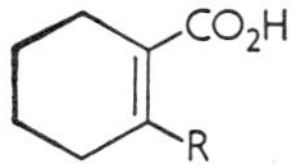

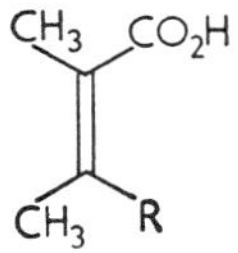

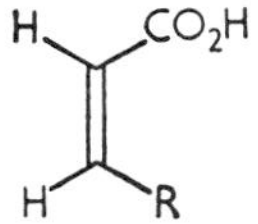

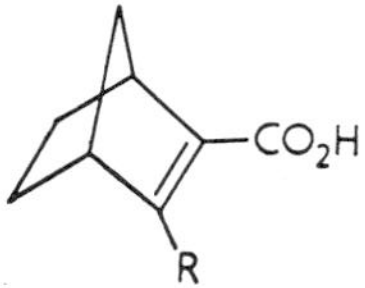

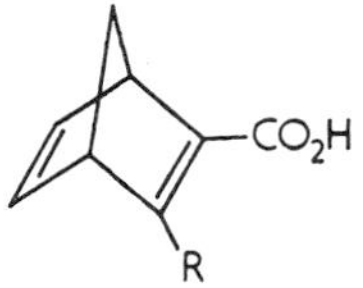

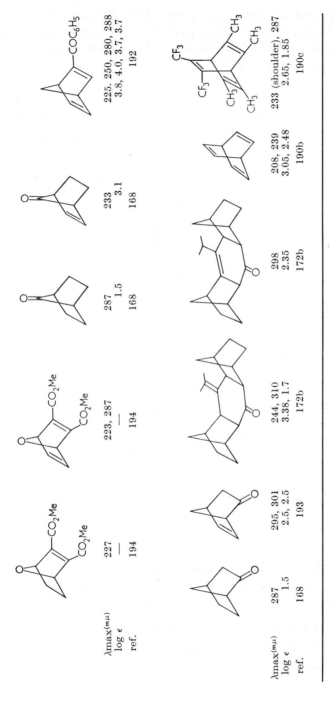

λmax$(m\mu)$	227	223, 287	287	233
log ϵ	—	—	1.5	3.1
ref.	194	194	168	168

					225, 250, 280, 288
					3.8, 4.0, 3.7, 3.7
					192

λmax$(m\mu)$	287	295, 301	244, 310	298	208, 239
log ϵ	1.5	2.5, 2.5	3.38, 1.7	2.35	3.05, 2.48
ref.	168	193	172b	172b	190b

233 (shoulder), 287	
2.65, 1.85	
190c	

256) gives *exo*-benzonorbornenyl acetate (**255b**); [196a] *anti*-7-benzonorbornenyl *p*-bromobenzenesulfonate (**257a**) gives the *anti*-7-acetate (**257b**), and *anti*-7-benzonorbornadienyl *p*-bromobenzenesulfonate (**258a**) gives the corresponding *anti*-7-acetate (**258b**).[196a]

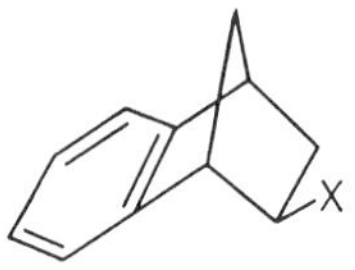

(255)
(255a: X = OBs)
(255b: X = OAc)

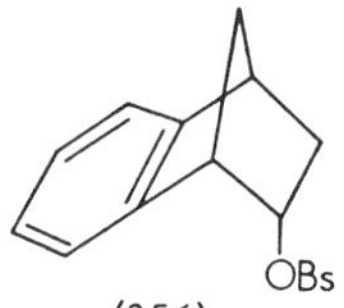

(256)

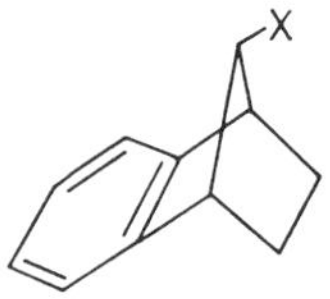

(257)
(257a: X = OBs)
(257b: X = OAc)

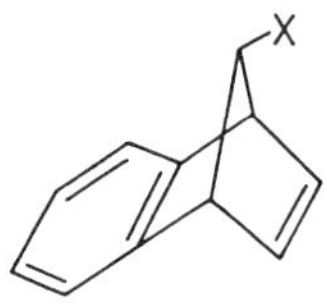

(258)
(258a: X = OBs)
(258b: X = OAc)

Acetolytic reactivities [196a] for this series of substances are given in Table XI. The ratio of rate constants, *exo/endo*, is 7200, almost identical with the corresponding ratio in the 2-norbornenyl analogs. Apparently, the benzene

TABLE XI

Relative Acetolysis Rate Constants (25°) for Benzonorbornenyl and Benzonorbornadienyl
p-Bromobenzenesulfonates [196a]

	Rate constant relative to		
Compound	Cyclohexyl	Norbornyl analog	Norbornenyl analog
255a	43	0.06	0.16
256	0.006	0.004	0.18
257a	0.06	5×10^5	10^{-5}
258	7.0	6×10^7	—

Proc. Chem. Soc. (*London*), **1961**, 256; R. C. Cookson, R. R. Hill, and J. Hudec, *Chem. & Ind.* (*London*), **1961**, 589; S. Winstein, L. de Vries, and R. Orloski, *J. Am. Chem. Soc.*, **83**, 2020 (1961).

[196] (a) P. D. Barlett and W. P. Giddings, *J. Am. Chem. Soc.*, **82**, 1240 (1960). (b) J. Meinwald, H. Nozaki, and G. A. Wiley, *J. Am. Chem. Soc.*, **79**, 5579 (1957), J. Meinwald and G. A. Wiley, *J. Am. Chem. Soc.*, **80**, 3667 (1958). (c) G. A. Wiley, 137th Meeting, ACS, Cleveland, Ohio, April, 1960, *Abstracts*, p. 280.

ring is about as effective in accelerating the solvolysis of the *exo* isomer as is the 5,6 double bond. When the benzene ring does not participate, as is the case in the *endo* isomer, the usual polar retardation is observed, the rate for the *endo*-benzonorbornenyl *p*-bromobenzenesulfonate being about 250 times slower than that of *endo*-2-norbornyl *p*-bromobenzenesulfonate. There appears to be appreciable homobenzylic assistance to solvolysis of the *anti*-7 isomer **257a**; its rate is faster than that of 7-norbornyl *p*-bromobenzenesulfonate by 5×10^5, but the acceleration is much less than that (a factor of 10^{11}) provided by the simple double bond. The cause of the additional factor of 100 provided by the extra double bond of **258a** is not certain, but may be connected with spreading of the C_1—C_7—C_4 angle.[196a] All of the comparisons are subject to the reservations associated with internal return mentioned above.

Basic hydrolysis converts the epoxide **259a** to the rearranged diol **259b**, presumably by transannular formation of a tetracyclic dienone,[196b] and lithium aluminum hydride reductions of the dimethyl ether of **259a** [196c] and of 2,3-epoxybenzonorbornene [196a] produce the rearranged anti-7-hydroxy-benzonorbornenes.

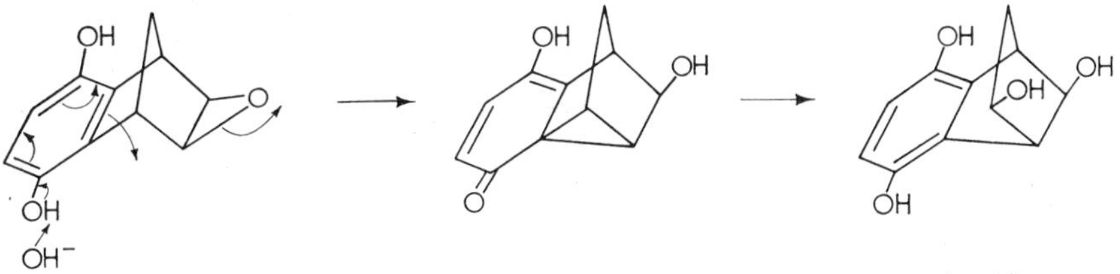

(259a)   (259b)

9. REACTIONS OF BRIDGED BICYCLIC PRIMARY AMINES WITH NITROUS ACID

Carbon skeletal rearrangements frequently can be initiated by nitrous acid deaminations of primary amines. The early stages of the mechanism of the amine–nitrous acid reactions, which involve formation of a diazonium cation (RN_2^+), do not presently appear to be in dispute,[197] but the fate of the diazonium cation in the reactions that follow its formation is a subject much studied, contentiously debated, and yet to be understood. A review of the mass of information dealing with the general problem of the reactions of aliphatic diazonium cations is not part of our duty,[198] but a comparison of

---

[197] For a review, see C. K. Ingold, *Structure and Mechanism in Organic Chemistry*, Cornell University Press, Ithaca, N. Y., 1953, p. 395.

[198] (a) For a review, see A. Streitwieser, *J. Org. Chem.*, **22**, 861 (1957). (b) See also A. Streitwieser and W. D. Schaeffer, *J. Am. Chem. Soc.*, **79**, 2893 (1957).

bicyclic rearrangements initiated by deaminations with those otherwise initiated is appropriate here.

Although there is a formal similarity between solvolytic reactions of halides or sulfonates on one hand and of diazonium cations on the other (in the sense that molecular nitrogen departing from RN_2^+ plays the same structural role that halide or sulfonate ions play departing from RX or $ROSO_2Ar$), anticipation of identity or even similarity of mechanism is naive. The leaving group, N_2, differs fundamentally from halide or sulfonate leaving groups in two ways: (a) it bears no charge, and, therefore, charge-charge interactions in the transition state(s) for its departure are small or absent; and (b) molecular nitrogen is an exceptionally stable entity, and, therefore, the driving force for its formation is exceptionally high. The simplest and most striking observable difference between conventional solvolytic reactions and diazonium salt decompositions is in the activation energies; solvolyses of halides or sulfonates typically require activation energies of 20 kcal./mole or more, while those of diazonium cations are so small that the rates are usually "immeasurably" fast. The mechanistic differences frequently produce qualitative differences in products or quantitative differences in product distributions. The exceptional behavior of diazonium salt decompositions is rationalized on either of two bases:[198]

1. Departure of N_2 leaves an exceptionally reactive, "hot" carbonium ion, which, since it requires less energy of activation for reaction than an ordinary, "cool," solvolytically produced carbonium ion, is much less selective in its reactions. Solvolysis, rearrangement, and elimination products derive from the "hot" ion, which thus represents a distribution point or railhead for the mechanism.

2. The distribution point is located earlier in the mechanism;[198,199] products are derived not from "hot" carbonium ions but rather from diazonium cations. These require but little activation energy for reaction, are relatively unselective, and distribute themselves to several reaction paths, among these paths being the formation of normal, "cool" carbonium ions.

The two hypotheses imply in common the idea that the compression of normal activation energy differences for competing processes into a narrow range permits the occurrence of reactions that are not observed in normal solvolyses.[200] They differ in the identification of the product-determining

[199] R. Huisgen and C. Rüchardt, *Ann.*, **601**, 1 (1956).

[200] A rule of thumb, frequently invoked in mechanistic discussions, states that of two reacting systems, each of which can be partitioned to a number of product-forming paths, the more reactive system will be the less selective one. In terms of transition state theory, this is equivalent to the statement that if reactant A can be partitioned between transition states A_1 and A_2 and reactant B between transition states B_1 and B_2, and if the

species. What is known of the behavior of bridged bicyclic diazonium salts does not allow the construction of a compelling case in favor of either of these hypotheses over the other.[200]

Nitrous acid deaminations of either exo- or endo-norbornylamines in acetic acid or in aqueous solvents produce at least predominantly exo-acetate or alcohol.[201-203] The amount of skeletal rearrangement, as determined by ^{14}C distribution in the products from 3-^{14}C-labeled amine, is substantially less than in solvolytic reactions of the corresponding sulfonates. Qualitatively the same pattern of extent of rearrangement and of stereochemistry of the product is observed in the comparison of deaminations of endo- and exo-norborneny-lamines and solvolyses of the corresponding sulfonates. Table XII gives a comparison of the ^{14}C distribution in deaminations and solvolyses under several sets of conditions. The "per cent rearrangement" has the same significance as in the discussion in heading 4B.

Although the experimental conditions are not strictly comparable, Table XII establishes a pattern of greater retention of structural integrity in deaminations than in solvolyses of the corresponding p-bromobenzenesulfonates. These results are consistent with (but do not require) the idea that part of the product in the deaminations arises from a "hot" carbonium ion.[203] In the case of exo-norbornylamine, for example, this would imply that either some of the diazonium cations lose nitrogen without carbon participation, to give a "hot," nonmesomeric cation, or that, although the loss of nitrogen occurs with carbon participation to give a mesomeric cation, this species is unsymmetrically bridged. An alternative interpretation, which avoids the "hot" ion idea, would propose either rear- or front-side displacement of N_2 by a solvent molecule or lyate ion. Rear-side displacement would require that some of the product have the endo configuration. The proportion of endo product to be expected, e.g., for the deamination in acetic acid, can be calculated by

---

activation energies for achieving A_1 and A_2 are small relative to those for achieving B_1 and B_2, then the *difference* in activation energies for the A system ($\Delta F^{\ddagger}_{A_1} - \Delta F^{\ddagger}_{A_2}$) will also be small relative to the difference in activation energies for the B system ($\Delta F^{\ddagger}_{B_1} - \Delta F^{\ddagger}_{B_2}$). The compressed energy scale of the A system then leads to lower selectivity. It should be made clear that this is a chemical conclusion, not a mathematical one, for there is nothing to prevent the difference between two small numbers from being as large as or larger than the difference between two large ones. The justification for the conclusion, aside from its pragmatic value in correlating experimental data, is largely intuitive; it is equivalent to the assumption that the slope of a plot of log rate constant against a parameter denoting structure for the more sluggish system B will be greater than that for the more reactive system A.

[201] G. Komppa and S. Beckmann, *Ann.*, **512**, 172 (1934).

[202] K. Alder, G. Stein, E. Rolland, and G. Schulze, *Ann.*, **512**, 211 (1934).

[203] J. D. Roberts, C. C. Lee, and W. H. Saunders, Jr., *J. Am. Chem. Soc.*, **76**, 4501 (1954).

assuming that the total product arises by a mixture of two mechanisms, one giving entirely *exo* product with a ^{14}C distribution identical with that obtained in the acetolysis (at a slightly higher temperature, 45°) of the *p*-bromobenzene-sulfonate, and the other giving *endo* product with a ^{14}C distribution identical with that of the starting material. The observed 48% rearrangement figure can be fitted by a mixture of 79% of *exo* product with 60.6% rearrangement (identical with that found [203] in the acetolysis of the *exo p*-bromobenzene-sulfonate) and 21% of *endo* product with 0% rearrangement.

TABLE XII

Skeletal Rearrangement in Reactions of Norbornyl and Norbornenyl Derivatives [203, 204]

Starting system and stereochemistry	Group replaced	Solvent or other conditions	Temperature, °C.	Rearrange-ment, %
exo-Norbornyl	OBs	75% acetone	45°	54.5
	NH$_2$	HBF$_4$–H$_2$O, HNO$_2$	Room	52.1
	OBs	HOAc	45°	60.6
	NH$_2$	HOAc, HNO$_2$	Room	48.0
endo-Norbornyl	OBs	75% acetone	Reflux	44.5
	NH$_2$	HBF$_4$–H$_2$O, HNO$_2$	Room	46.2
	OBs	HOAc	Reflux	56.1
	NH$_2$	HOAc, HNO$_2$	Room	41.6, 44.9
endo-Norbornenyl	OBs	HOAc	Reflux	30.1
	NH$_2$	HOAc, HNO$_2$	Room	38.5
	NH$_2$	HBF$_4$–H$_2$O, HNO$_2$	Room	35.0

While *endo*-acetate has now [206] been observed in the deamination of *exo*-norbornylamine, it constitutes only 3% of the total acetate product. Therefore, the discrepancy between the over-all isotopic labeling results of the solvolysis and deamination cannot be attributed entirely to rearside displacement. The mechanistic origin of the *endo*-acetate in the deamination is not yet clear, but it is significant that *endo* product is also observed [205] in the deamination of camphenilylamine.

With only the criteria of epimeric stereochemistry and of ^{14}C distribution, frontside displacement (*exo*-amine → *exo*-acetate) without racemization, regardless of mechanism, cannot be detected. The process is, however, disclosed when the deamination is carried out with optically active *exo*-amine. This experiment [206] shows that the deamination gives *exo*-acetate, retaining about 10% of the optical purity of the starting material. The total retention of skeletal integrity is, thus, 10% + 3% = 10%.

[204] J. D. Roberts, C. C. Lee, and W. H. Saunders, Jr., *J. Am. Chem. Soc.*, **77**, 3034 (1955).

[205] S. Beckmann and R. Bamberger, *Ann.*, **574**, 76 (1951).

[206] J. A. Berson and A. Remanick, unpublished observations.

In the case of *endo*-norbornylamine, gas liquid chromatography of the derived alcohols on a capillary column has revealed [206] the presence of 5% of *endo* material in the product acetate, an amount too small to detect by earlier [201-203,207] techniques. On the assumption that the *endo* product in the deamination of optically active *endo*-norbornylamine [206] retains 100% of the optical purity of the starting material, the *exo*-acetate is formed with 19% retention.[206] Thus, the total retention of skeletal integrity, 24%, is the same as that given earlier [207] on the assumption of 0% *endo* product. (The correspondence is, of course, attributable to the circumstance that the *endo*- and *exo*-acetates happen to have the same sign and about the same magnitude of rotation.)

The isotope-position rearrangement data (Table XII) can now be combined with the above stereochemical results in the manner already described in footnote 137a, heading 7A (page 181); this affords a comparison of the extent of isotope-position rearrangement in the portions of the deaminations of *endo* and *exo* amines that lead to *racemic* product. For the case of *exo* amine, only a single value (Table XII) for the over-all per-cent rearrangement is available. Assuming a 1% error in this value (48%) and in the value for the per-cent retention of skeletal integrity (13%), the extent of isotope-position rearrangement in the *racemic* portion of the acetate from the *exo* amine may be expressed as $55.2 \pm 2\%$. Similary, for *endo* amine, the observed $43.2 \pm 1.7\%$ over-all rearrangement figure can now be corrected for the 24% retention of skeletal integrity to give the value $56.7 \pm 4\%$ rearrangement in the racemic acetate. As is the case with the corresponding *p*-bromobenzenesulfonates (heading 7A), the extent of isotope-position rearrangement *in the racemic portion* of the product acetate seems to be essentially independent of whether the cationic intermediates are generated from *endo* or *exo* starting material. A comparison of the extent of isotope-position rearrangement for amine-derived racemic product (55.2 to 56.7%) with that for bromobenzenesulfonate-derived racemic product (60.6 to 60.9%) suggests that there is more hydrogen shift in the latter cases. Note that although the comparison is based on data taken from experiments at different temperatures, the apparent discrepancy does not seem to be interpretable as a temperature effect, since the per-cent rearrangement is essentially insensitive to temperature, at least in the only case that has been examined [203] (deamination of *endo* amine at 25° and at 90 to 100°). The over-all experimental error in the per-cent rearrangements, however, is large enough to suggest treating with reserve the conclusion that there is a real difference between the ^{14}C distributions in the solvolytically and deaminatively produced *racemic* acetate.

The literature contains few other examples upon which to base com-

[207] J. A. Berson and D. A. Ben-Efraim, *J. Am. Chem. Soc.*, **81**, 4094 (1959).

parisons of deaminations and solvolyses of bicyclic substrates. The comparison given in Table XIII seems to indicate only minor differences in behavior.

TABLE XIII

Comparison of Deamination and Solvolysis in the Camphenilyl System[208]

Starting material	Conditions	Product as per cent of alcohol mixture			Ref.
NH₂	dil. HOAc + NaNO₂; 100°	11–15	83–84	1.5–5	208a
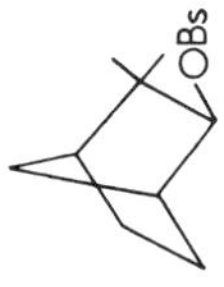 OBs	aq. dioxane; ?°	12	70	18	208b
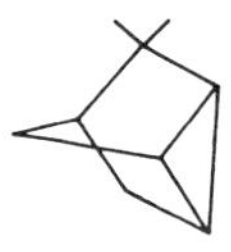	HCl, then aq. Ca(OH)₂; 60–70°	—	80	20	208c

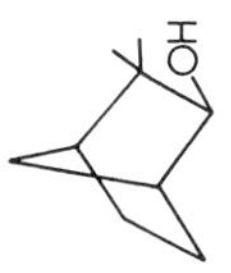

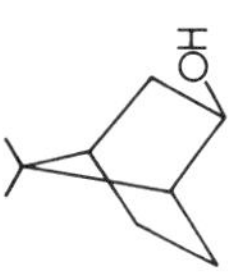

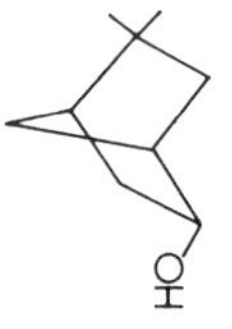

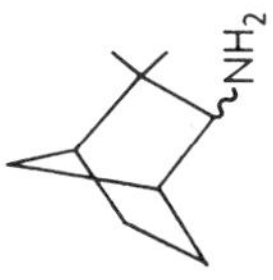

^a endo-exo Amine mixture from sodium-alcohol reduction of camphenolone oxime.

[208] (a) S. Beckmann and R. Bamberger, *Ann.*, **574**, 65 (1951). (b) S. Winstein, XIVth International Congress of Pure and Applied Chemistry, Zürich, *Experientia*, *Suppl.*, No. **2**, 137 (1955). (c) G. Komppa and G. A. Nyman, *Ber.*, **69**, 1813 (1936).

Striking differences, however, are observed in the bornyl system. Solvolyses of bornyl chloride or bornyl arenesulfonates give largely camphenehydro derivatives (or isobornyl derivatives) (see heading 3C), but deamination of bornylamine gives[209] a substantial quantity of α-terpineol (**260**), as well as camphene and camphene hydrate; isobornylamine gives camphene and camphene hydrate. In contrast to the camphenilylamine deamination (see Table XIII), there is no evidence for 6,2 shift in the deaminations of bornylamine and isobornylamine, the camphene being essentially optically pure. It is doubtful, however, that the occurrence of a small amount of 6,2 shift, comparable to that observed in the camphenilylamine case, could be detected in this way. The formation of α-terpineol (**260**) from bornylamine is particu-

(260)

larly interesting. This product may be formed by direct cleavage of the C_6—C_7 bond of the corresponding diazonium salt,[198] which is stereoelectronically favorable, or by collapse of the mesomeric cation (**261**), which is probably involved in reactions of the pinyl system, and which does produce α-terpinyl derivatives (see page 187.) Since, however, cation **261** gives bornyl derivatives as major products, the absence of borneol in the product is an argument against the latter interpretation.

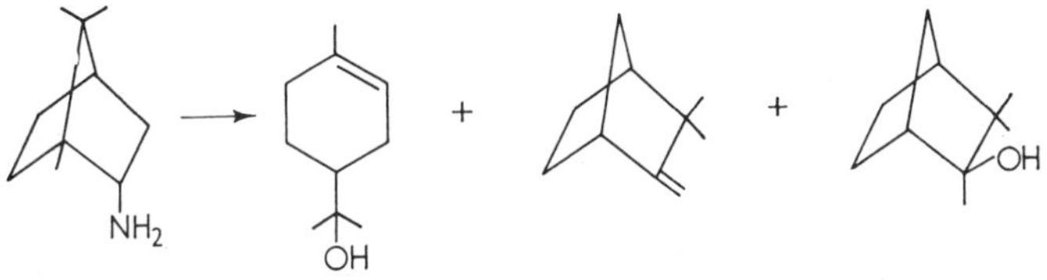

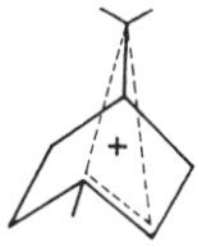

(261)

The results of the deaminations of the fenchylamines,[210] given in Table XIV, are puzzling. Although deamination of *exo*-fenchylamine produces no α-terpineol, and only traces of fenchols, the major hydroxylic product being the tertiary alcohol fenchene hydrate, deamination of *endo*-fenchylamine gives some *endo*-fenchol and α-terpineol. While the formation of *endo*-fenchol may imply either front-side displacement or the intervention of the meso-

[209] W. Hückel and F. Nerdel, *Ann.*, **528**, 57 (1937).

[210] W. Hückel and U. Ströle, *Ann.*, **585**, 182 (1954); W. Hückel and H. Wolowski, *Chem. Ber.*, **80**, 39 (1947).

TABLE XIV

Products of Nitrous Acid Deamination of the Fenchylamines [210]

Starting material	Solvent	Products (% yield)						
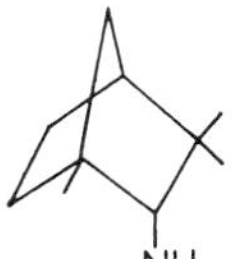 (structure, NH_2)	Amine hydrochloride in HOAc + NaNO$_2$	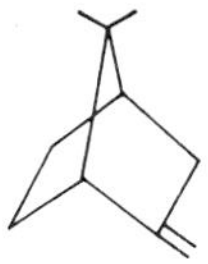 70	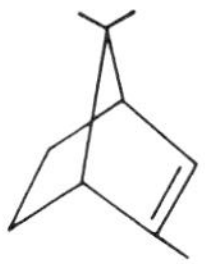 Some	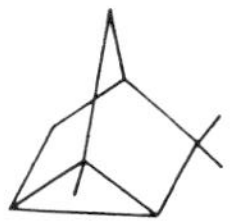 Little (+ a trace of limonene)	 Yes	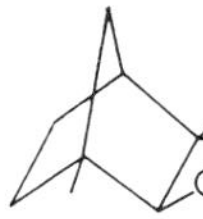 Yes	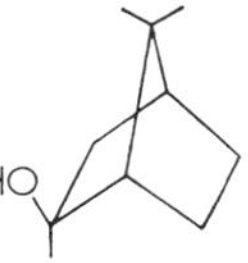 Yes	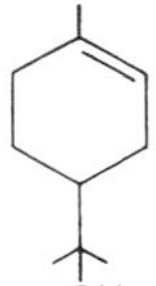 Yes
 (structure, NH_2)	Amine hydrochloride in HOAc + NaNO$_2$	80	At most a trace	15–20	Trace	Yes	Yes	No

meric cation **262**, or a "hot" carbonium ion, the formation of α-terpineol appears to require that either cation **263** [211] or the bridged variant **262** be a precursor.

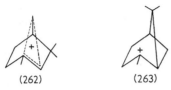

(262)   (263)

10. REARRANGEMENTS OF BRIDGED BICYCLOOCTANES AND RELATED SUBSTANCES

Bicyclo[2.2.2]-2-octyl derivatives (**264**) are related in the Wagner-Meerwein sense to two epimeric sets of bicyclo[3.2.1]-2-octyl derivatives (**265a** and **265b**).

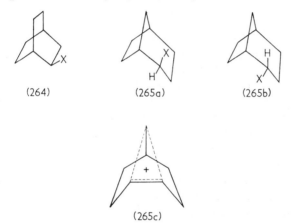

(264)   (265a)   (265b)

(265c)

Carbonium ion reactions of the bicyclo[2.2.2]-2-octyl series lead to mixtures of products which are very difficult to separate into the pure components by conventional techniques, and it is only with the advent of gas chromatography that an amplification [215–217] of earlier results [212–214] has been achieved.

[211] D. S. Noyce, *J. Am. Chem. Soc.*, **72**, 924 (1950).

[212] (a) W. von E. Doering and M. Farber, *J. Am. Chem. Soc.*, **71**, 1514 (1949). (b) M. Farber, Dissertation, Columbia University, 1949.

[213] (a) H. M. Walborsky, *Experientia*, **9**, 209 (1953). (b) M. S. Newman and Y. T. Yu, *J. Am. Chem. Soc.*, **74**, 507 (1952).

[214] (a) W. C. Wildman and D. R. Saunders, *J. Am. Chem. Soc.*, **76**, 946 (1954). (b) C. A. Grob, H. Kny, and A. Gagneux, *Helv. Chim. Acta.*, **40**, 130 (1957). (c) The acetate of alcohol **269c** is also reported to result from acetolysis of a mixture of *p*-toluenesulfonates derived from a mixture of *endo*- and *exo*-2-hydroxymethylnorbornanes by R. R. Sauers, *Tetrahedron Letters*, No. 4, 146 (1961).

Deaminations of the amine (**264**, X = NH₂) in acetic acid or in water give[216] both unrearranged (**264**, X = oAC or OH) and *exo*(axial)-rearranged (**265a**) products; hydrolysis of the *p*-toluenesulfonate [229] (**264**, X = OTs) and acetolysis of the *p*-bromobenzenesulfonate[215] (**264**, X = OBs) give the same products, although the proportions are slightly different from those observed in deamination of the amine. Significantly, none of the *endo*(equatorial) product is observed in these reactions. The stereospecificity suggests the intervention of the bridged cation **266**. Clear evidence that at least some of the reaction proceeds through the optically active bridged ion **266** rather than through the inactive classical ion **267** is provided by a study [215] of the acetolysis of optically active *p*-bromo-

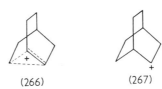

(266)   (267)

benzenesulfonate (**264**, X = OBs). This material gives optically active **264** (X = OAc) with 82 ± 15% retention of optical purity and configuration; the rearranged product **265a** (X = OAc) is also optically active. The per-cent retention of optical purity in **264** is subject to some uncertainty, since the *p*-bromobenzenesulfonate, used in the solvolysis, was *recrystallized* after having been prepared [215] from a sample of the corresponding alcohol that was later shown [218] to be optically impure.

Under conditions that repeatedly form the carbonium ion intermediates, the epimeric stereospecificity of the rearrangement is lost, Bertram-Walbaum addition of acetic acid to bicyclo[2.2.2]octene giving some *endo*(equatorial)-acetate **265b** (X = OAc) in addition to *exo*(axial)-acetate **265a** (X = OAc) and unrearranged acetate **264** (X = OAc).[216] The same mixture of products is obtained [216] when **264** (X = OH or OAc) is treated with acetic acid–sulfuric acid. Solvolysis of the *endo*(equatorial)-*p*-toluenesulfonate **265b** (X = OTs) under irreversible conditions gives pure *endo*(equatorial)-acetate **265b** (X = OAc), suggesting the symmetrical cation **265c** as an intermediate.[216] The latter ion may also be involved in the deaminative ring expansion of *endo*-2-aminomethylnorbornane (**294**) (*vide infra*).

An assessment of the importance of anchimeric assistance in the solvolysis of the *p*-toluenesulfonate (**264**, X = OTs) is difficult because the starting

[215] H. M. Walborsky, M. E. Baum, and A. A. Youssef, *J. Am. Chem. Soc.*, **83**, 988 (1961).

[216] H. L. Goering and M. F. Sloan, *J. Am. Chem. Soc.*, **83**, 1397 (1961).

[217] H. L. Goering, R. W. Greiner, and M. F. Sloan, *J. Am. Chem. Soc.*, **83**, 1391 (1961).

[218] J. A. Berson and D. Willner, *J. Am. Chem. Soc.*, **84**, 675 (1962).

material is rapidly isomerized to the Wagner-Meerwein related p-toluene-sulfonate (**265a**, X = OTs) by internal return.[219,219a]

Deamination of the unsaturated amine **268** gives an allylic alcohol to which the structure **269a** is assigned.[214a] This implies that the saturated carbon atom C_7 migrates in preference to the olefinic C_6. The specificity is reasonable, since the configuration of the amino function of **268** is *endo*,[214b] and C_7 of the derived diazonium salt is in an excellent position for concerted migration and displacement of N_2. The alcohol **269a** can be hydrogenated[214a,217] to *exo*-(axial)-bicyclo[3.2.1]octanol-2 (**265a**, X = OH); the unsaturated deamination product **269a** is therefore assigned[217] the *exo* stereochemistry **269c** rather

(268)	(269a)	(269b)	(269c)

than the *endo* **269b**. Compound **269c** is the expected product if the product-forming intermediate has the bridged structure **271**, although the possibility that ions **270a** or **270b** may be involved cannot be discounted.[219]

(270a)	(270b)	(271)

[219] H. L. Goering and M. F. Sloan, *J. Am. Chem. Soc.*, **83**, 1992 (1961).

[219a] A detailed analysis of the kinetics of the solvolyses of bicyclo[2.2.2]-2-octyl p-toluenesulfonate (**264b**) and *exo* (axial)-bicyclo[3.2.1]-2-octyl p-toluenesulfonate (**265a** X = OTs) is now available.[219] Ion pair return (presumably internal, since no special salt effect is observed) interconverts the two isomeric arenesulfonates during acetolysis or ethanolysis. In agreement with results found in the norbornyl series (see Part 6A), the relative importance of the internal isomerization is greater in the less nucleophilic solvent, acetic acid.

The total rates of ionization to the mesomeric cation **266** can be derived[219] from a knowledge of the isomerization and solvolysis rates. Although there is some question[219] about what system should be used as a standard of comparison, it is concluded[219] that the acetolysis of both **264** and **265a** (X = OTs) are anchimerically assisted, both substances being more reactive than the *endo*-norbornyl or cyclohexyl analogs by factors of the order of several hundreds.

Acetolysis of **265b** (X = OTs) occurs at only about 3 times the rate of the cyclohexyl analog. Anchimeric assistance either is not very important here or else is largely obscured by exceptionally efficient ion pair return.

Like deamination of the unsaturated amine **268**, acetolysis of the corresponding

The preference for migration by C_7 is further illustrated by the case of the *trans*-2,3-dibromide (272),[220] in which the *endo* bromine is sufficiently more reactive than the *exo* bromine to allow selective solvolysis in aqueous acetone. The product is the bromohydrin (273), which can be hydrogenated and

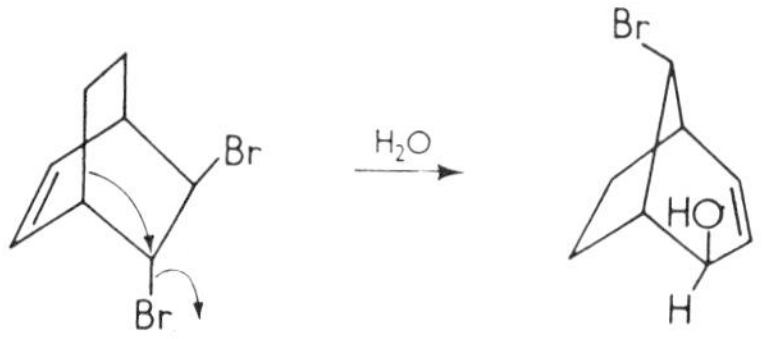

(272)   (273)

hydrogenolyzed to the *exo*(axial) alcohol (265a, X = OH), the stereochemistry of which was established later.[217,222] The stereochemistry of the hydroxyl function in the bromohydrin (273) is thus the same as that in the unsaturated alcohol (269c) derived from rearrangement of the amine (268); this suggests that the products from 272 are derived from intermediates (e.g., 274a,c,d) similar to those (270a,b, 271) which may be precursors of the products from 268.

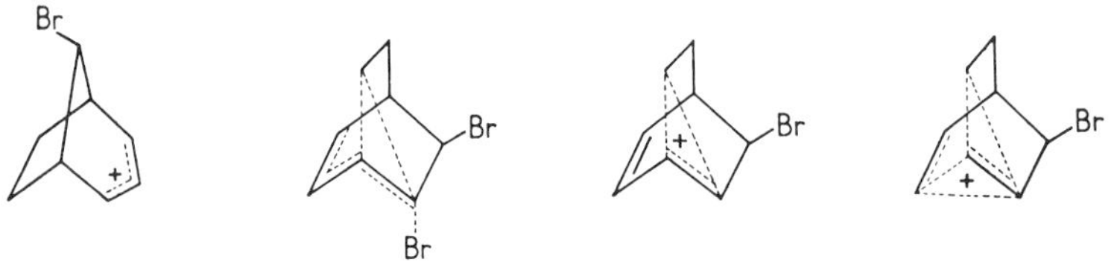

(274a)   (274b)   (274c)   (274d)

The dibromide (272) is 143 times as reactive as cyclopentyl bromide in solvolysis in 80% ethanol, despite the polar retardation provided by the adjacent bromine.[220] Since 2-bicyclo[2.2.2]octyl *p*-bromobenzenesulfonate is only about as reactive as cyclopentyl *p*-bromobenzenesulfonate,[213a,215,219] a rate-enhancing role is assigned[220] to the double bond of 272 in stabilizing the solvolysis transition state (274b) by electronic delocalization.

Electrophilic additions to bicyclooctadiene (281) are strikingly different from those to bicycloheptadiene (see page 198). These results[220,221] are summarized in Scheme 4. The differences in behavior are traceable[220,221] to

p-toluenesulfonate also results in complete rearrangement to the axial derivative of the bicyclo[3.2.1]octenyl system (269c). The rate of acetolysis is about 2×10^4 times that of *endo*-dehydronorbornyl *p*-toluenesulfonate, implying[219] anchimeric assistance in the solvolysis.

[220] A. Gagneux and C. A. Grob, *Helv. Chim. Acta*, 42, 1753 (1959).

[221] A. Gagneux and C. A. Grob, *Helv. Chim. Acta.*, 42, 2006 (1959).

[222] A. A. Youssef, M. E. Baum, and H. M. Walborsky, *J. Am. Chem. Soc.*, 81, 4709 (1959).

the preference for *endo* additiion to bicyclooctadiene, typified by the formation of the epoxide **275**; electrophilic addition to bicycloheptadiene occurs preferentially from the *exo* side. In bromine addition to bicyclooctadiene, the cation **276** (or its symmetrical variant, **277**) is presumably the first intermediate. Significantly, products with rearranged carbon skeleton are not

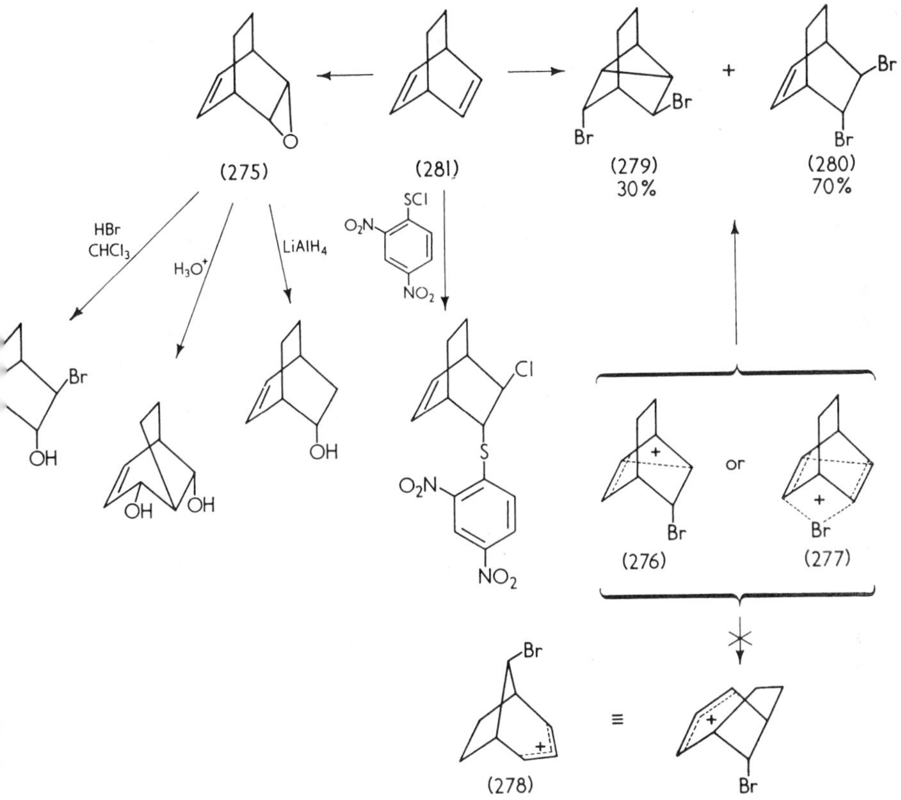

Scheme 4.

observed. Apparently, conversion of the cation **276** or **277** to the allylic ion **278** (which is merely an epimer of the cation (**274a**) that may be involved in solvolysis of **272**) is much slower than reaction with bromide ion to give **279** and **280**.

Several rearrangements of dibenzobicyclooctadienes are known.[223] The three bromo acids **282**, **283**, and **284** provide some interesting effects. Depending upon the conditions, these substances partition themselves into three

[223] W. R. Vaughan and A. C. Schoenthaler, *J. Am. Chem. Soc.*, **80**, 1956 (1958), and other papers by Vaughan and co-workers therein cited.

types of reaction products: (a) olefins resulting from dehalogenative decarboxylation, (b) unsaturated acid resulting from dehydrohalogenation, and

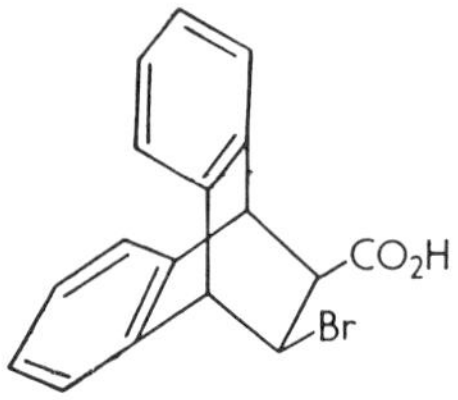

(282) 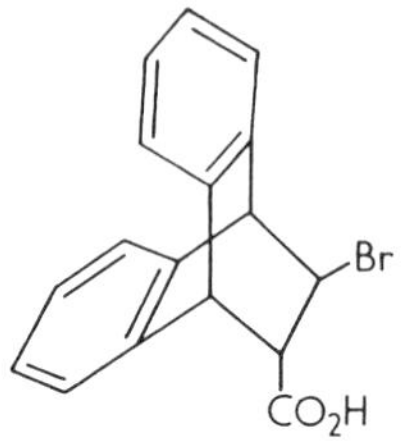   (283) 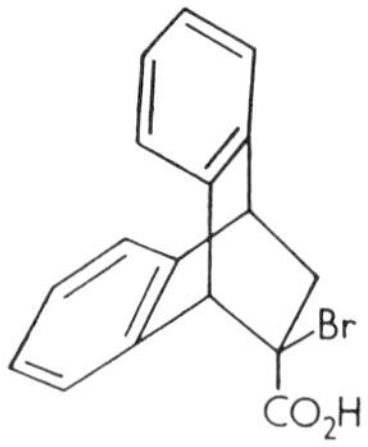   (284)

(c) lactone or hydroxy acid resulting from Wagner-Meerwein rearrangement. Table XV gives a portion of the results obtained.

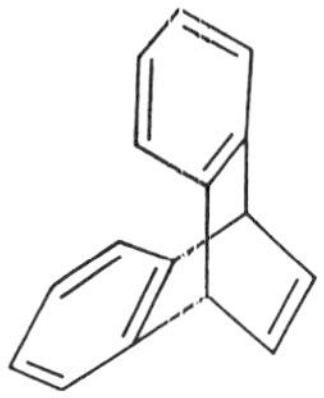

(285) 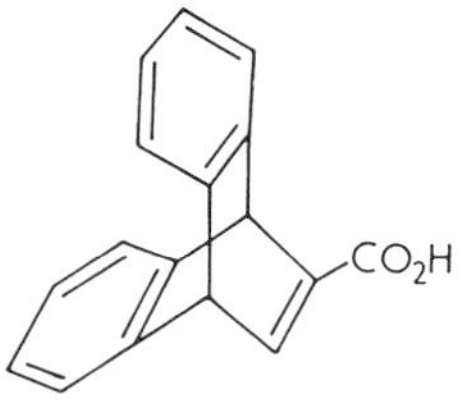   (286) 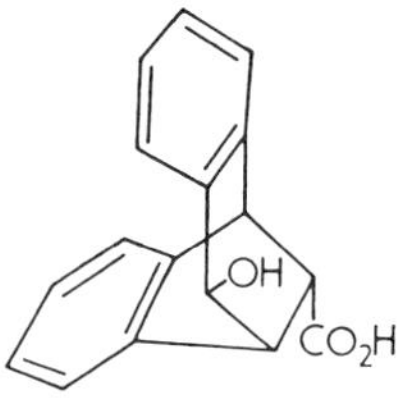   (287)
                                                  (287 a: OH config. as shown)
                                                  (287 b: epimeric OH)

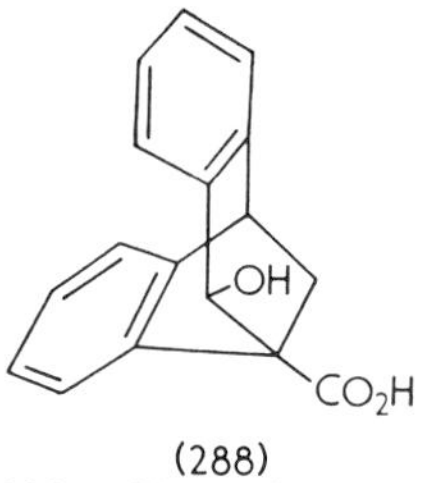

(288)   (289)
(288 a: OH config. as shown)
(288 b: epimeric OH)

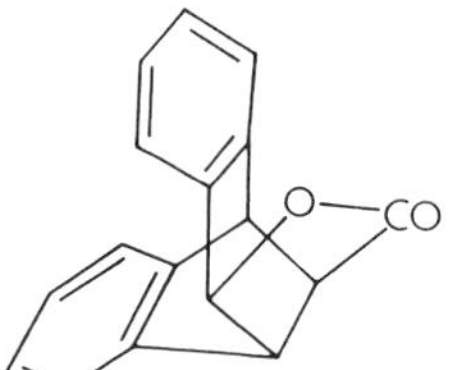

The formation of both epimers (287a and 287b) of the Wagner-Meerwein product from treatment of 283 with silver nitrate excludes a bridged cation (290) as the sole intermediate, since the latter would give only 287a. The product seems to derive from an "open" rearranged benzyl carbonium ion (291). This result is in accord with the behavior of other α,β-diphenyl-substituted carbonium ions, which in contrast to β-monosubstituted ions, frequently do not have the bridged "phenonium" structure (see Section 1).[223]

The same conclusions apply to the reaction of **284** with silver nitrate, which gives **288a** and **288b**. In contrast, Wagner-Meerwein rearrangement in aqueous

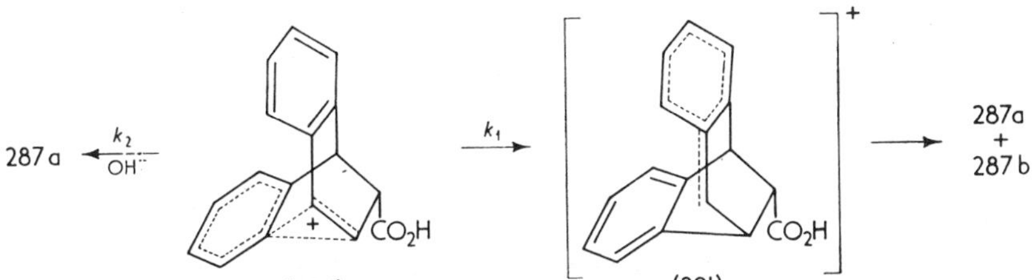

$$287a \xleftarrow{k_2}{OH^-} \qquad (290) \qquad \xrightarrow{k_1} \qquad (291) \qquad \longrightarrow \begin{array}{c} 287a \\ + \\ 287b \end{array}$$

alkali in both cases gives a single epimer; **283** gives only **287a**, and **284** gives only **288a**. The authors [223] explain this behavior in terms of a "phenonium"-bromide ion pair, which is attacked by silver ion to give rearranged ion, but undergoes exchange in the presence of base to give a "phenonium"-hydroxide

TABLE XV

Products of Reactions of Dibenzobicyclooctadiene Bromo Acids [223]

Reagent	Bromo acid	Observed type of reaction[a]	Yield, %	Product
10% aq. KOH	282	A	5	285
		B	95	286
	283	B	45	286
		C	55	287a
	284	C	100	288a
AgNO₃ in aq. acetone	282	A	19	285
		C	81	289
	283	C	100	287a and 287b
	284	C	100	288a and 288b

[a] A = dehalogenative decarboxylation; B = dehydrohalogenation; C = Wagner-Meerwein rearrangement.

ion pair, which is then assumed to collapse stereospecifically. An alternative interpretation, which avoids postulating ion pair phenomena in aqueous solution, is, however, equally compatible with the results. If the phenonium ion (**290**) is the first intermediate from **283**, it can be partitioned unimolecularly (with rate constant k_1) to rearranged ion **291** and ultimately to a mixture of **287a** and **287b**, or bimolecularly, by reaction with hydroxyl ion with rate constant k_2, directly to **287a**. The bimolecular process is expected to be faster in more basic solution, and the observed stereospecificity is therefore reasonable.

Dibenzobicyclo[2.2.2]octadiene 2,3-epoxide (**292**) is converted by formolysis and subsequent hydrolysis to the Wagner-Meerwein rearrangement product **293**.[224]

(292)   (293)

A. *Alternative Routes to Cations of the Bridged Bicyclooctane Series*

Ring Closures of Cycloheptenylcarbinyl and Cyclohexenylethyl Derivatives. As outlined in the discussion on p. 214, the 2-bicyclo[2.2.2]octyl and *exo*-2-bicyclo[3.2.1]octyl systems are connected in carbonium ion reactions through a common mesomeric cation **293d**. In the *endo*-2-bicyclo[3.2.1]octyl system, the cationic intermediate is symmetrical (**293b**), and gives rise to *endo*-2-bicyclo[3.2.1]octyl solvolysis product **293c** exclusively.

This distinction between the two kinds of cation appears to be maintained when the intermediates are generated by solvolytic ring closure. Acetolysis of Δ^4-cycloheptenylcarbinyl *p*-bromobenzenesulfonate **293a** gives an acetate product that is at least largely *endo*-2-bicyclo[3.2.1]octyl acetate (**293c**, X = OAc);[224a] the acetolysis rate constant is about 30 times as large as that of the saturated analog.[444a] In the absence of special factors, the latter substance would be expected to solvolyze more rapidly than **293a** because it does not have to contend with the polar-retarding effect of the double bond. The observed ratio of rates, therefore, suggests that the acetolysis of **293a** is anchimerically accelerated, assistance to heterolysis being provided by the π electrons of the double bond. The results are interpreted with the aid of the symmetrical mesomeric intermediate **293b**.[224a]

The isomeric unsymmetrical cation **293d** apparently is generated when Δ^3-cyclohexenylethyl *p*-bromobenzenesulfonate **293e** (X = OBs) is solvolyzed.[224b] In acetic acid, the product consists of 20% of acetate of unchanged carbon skeleton (**293e**, X = OAc), and 80% of a 54:46 mixture of 2-bicyclo-[2.2.2]octyl acetate **293f** (X = OAc) and 2-*exo*-bicyclo[3.2.1]octyl acetate **293g** (X = OAc), respectively; in formic acid, the same ratio (54:46) of bicyclooctyl products (as formate) is obtained, but the amount of Δ^3-cyclohexenyl-ethyl formate is very small. The 54:46 product distribution appears to be characteristic of the cation **293d**, since it is also observed in the acetolysis of a mixture of **293f** (X = OBs) and **293g** (X = OBs).[224b] The acceleration

[224] S. J. Cristol and R. K. Bly, 136th Meeting, ACS, Atlantic City, N. J., September, 1959, *Abstracts*.

[224a] G. Le Ny, *Compt. rend.*, **251**, 1526 (1960).

[224b] S. Winstein and P. Carter, *J. Am. Chem. Soc.*, **83**, 4485 (1961).

associated with anchimeric assistance by the double bond in the solvolysis of **293e** (X=OBs) is not very dramatic, the factor by which the rate exceeds that of the saturated analog being only about four in the case of acetolysis and ten in the case of formolysis. The true extent of the assistance to *ionization* (as distinct from gross solvolysis) cannot yet be assessed, since the amount of polar retardation by the double bond and the importance of ion-pair return are unknown.

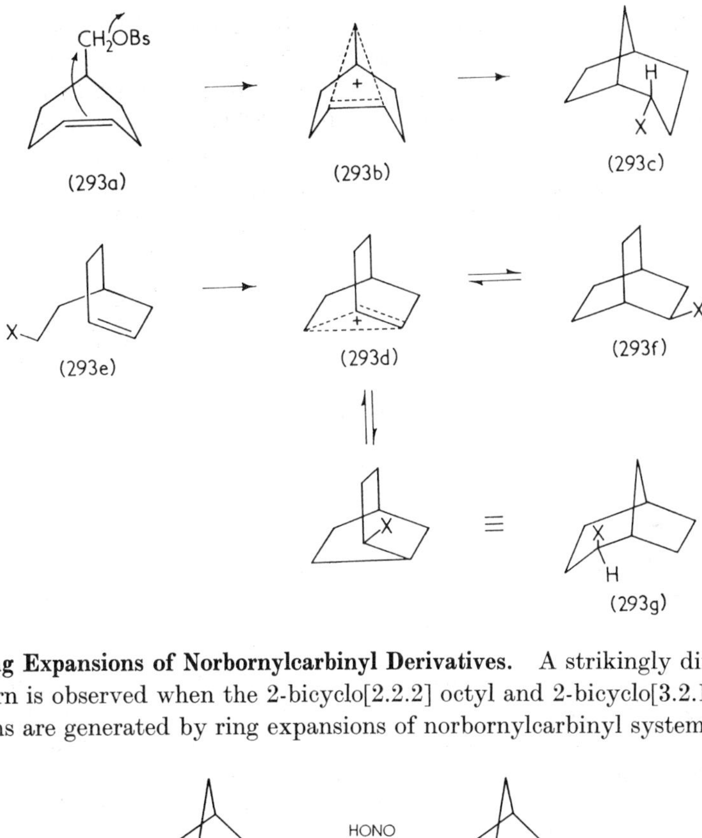

Ring Expansions of Norbornylcarbinyl Derivatives.   A strikingly different pattern is observed when the 2-bicyclo[2.2.2] octyl and 2-bicyclo[3.2.1]octyl cations are generated by ring expansions of norbornylcarbinyl systems. The

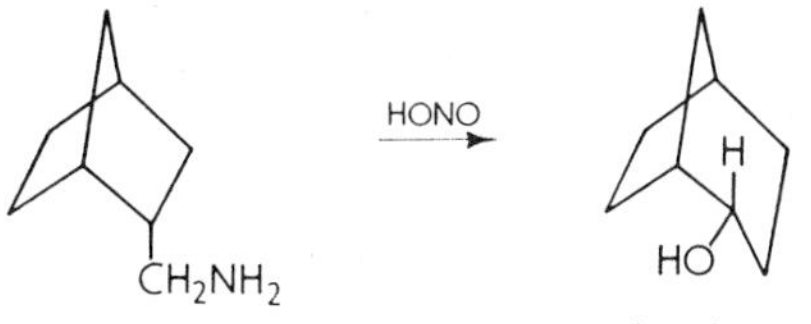

gross structural features of these rearrangements are discernible in studies of the nitrosative deamination of the epimeric 2-aminomethylnorbornanes, **294** and **296**.

The *endo*-amine **294**, in aqueous acetic acid, gives a 2-bicyclo[3.2.1]octa-nol[225] that is largely the *endo* (*equatorial*) isomer **295**, but contains also a

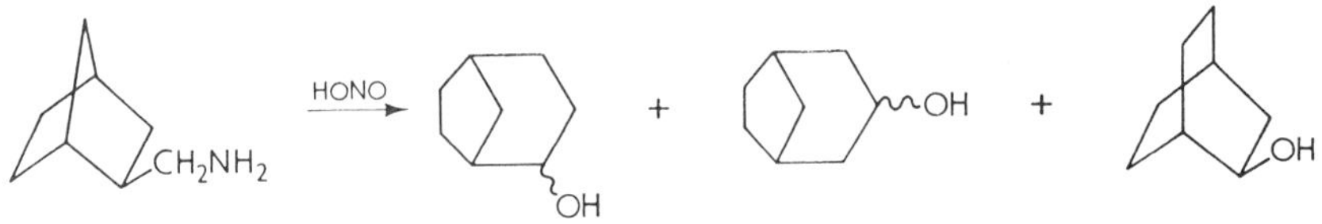

(296)   (297)   (298)   (299)

detectable quantity of the *exo* (*axial*) product **295a**.[222] The stereochemical composition of the product mixture is approximately reproduced in the acetates obtained when the corresponding *p*-bromobenzenesulfonate **294** ($NH_2 = OBs$) is solvolyzed in acetic acid-sodium acetate.[226] The *exo*-amine **296**, in acetic acid, gives acetates of three alcohols:[225] a 2-bicyclo[3.2.1]octanol (later shown[218] to be the *exo* (axial) isomer **295a**); 3-bicyclo[3.2.1]octanol **298** (stereochemistry unknown); and 2-bicyclo[2.2.2]octanol **299**.

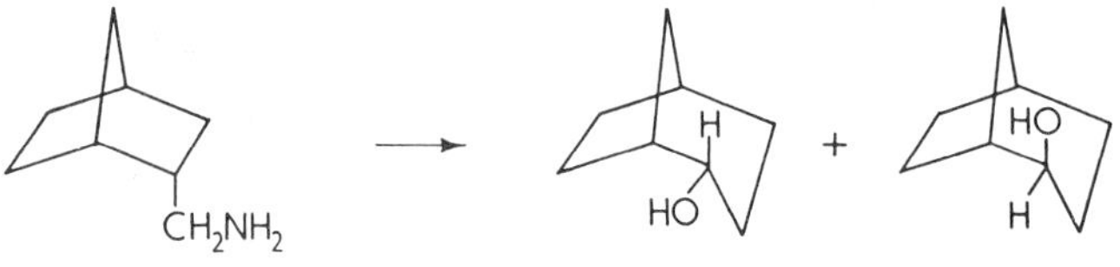

(294)   (295)   (295a)

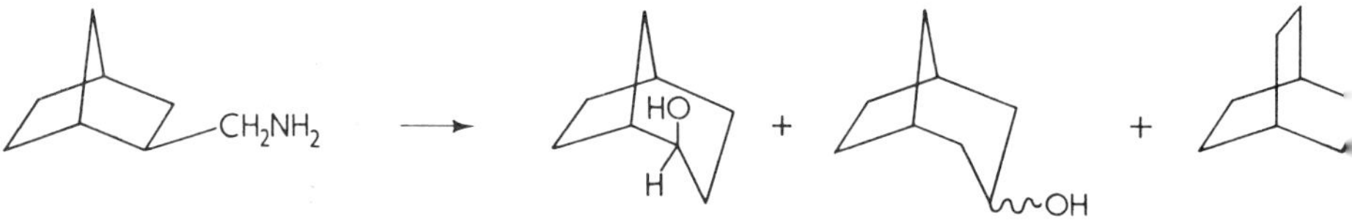

(296)   (295a)   (298)   (299)

The *formal* structural changes (without regard to the precise description of the intermediates) involve apparent single rearrangements in the conversions **300 → 301** in the *endo* series and **302 → 298a** in the *exo* series, and an apparent double rearrangement in the *exo* series, represented by **302 → 304**. The counterpart of the change **302 → 298a**, achieved by migration of the C_2—C_6 bond, seems to occur to the extent of, at most, a few tenths of 1% in the *endo* series.[227]

A study[218,226,227] of these rearrangements employing optically active start-

[225] K. Alder and E. Windemuth, *Ber.*, **71**, 2404 (1938); K. Alder and R. Reubke, *Chem. Ber.*, **91**, 1525 (1958); K. Alder, H. Krieger, and H. Weiss, *Chem. Ber.*, **88**, 144 (1955).

[226] J. A. Berson and P. Reynolds-Warnhoff, *J. Am. Chem. Soc.*, **84**, 682 (1962).

[227] J. A. Berson and P. Reynolds-Warnhoff, unpublished observations.

ing material provides some insights that are inaccessible in the racemic series, and reveals an extremely complex pattern.

From the *endo*-amine **294**, there are obtained [226] *optically active* **295** and **295a**. The symmetrical, optically inactive cation **306** ($\equiv$**293b**), previously postulated as an intermediate in the solvolysis of the *endo* (*equatorial*)-2-bicyclo[3.2.1]octyl derivative **295** (OH = OTs) and of the cycloheptenyl-carbinyl derivative **293a** (see p. 221), therefore cannot be the sole carbonium ion intermediate in the deamination of **294**, since purely racemic products would then have resulted.[226] The enantiomeric classical cations **305** and/or **305a** cannot be the sole intermediates either, since, although they can account for the formation of optically active products, these products would be

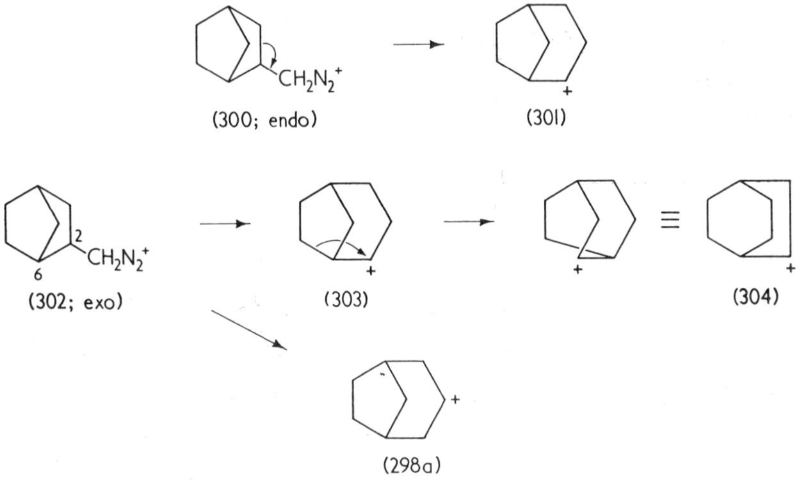

(300; endo)   →   (301)

(302; exo)   →   (303)   →   (304)

(298a)

formed with identical optical purities, a requirement in conflict with the observation [226] that product **295** is of lower optical purity than product **295a**. The data require that there be at least two different product-forming intermediates, and that the ratio of products **295/295a**, formed from each, be different. The simplest mechanism accommodating these requirements is that shown above the dotted line in Scheme 5.[226]

The nonclassical cation **306** can be replaced formally in the scheme by another species in which C₂ and C₄ are bridged by hydrogen, or conceivably both hydrogen-bridging and carbon-bridging might be involved. These alternatives are eliminated by position-labeling experiments.[227] The proposed scheme, with sequential formation of the cations (**305** → **306** → **305a**), cannot yet be distinguished experimentally from an alternative involving competitive formation of the cations (**306** ← **305** → **305a**), although the latter scheme would require the postulate of a transition state (for the **305** →

305a reaction) that has a structure similar to, if not actually identical with, that of a true product-forming intermediate **306**.

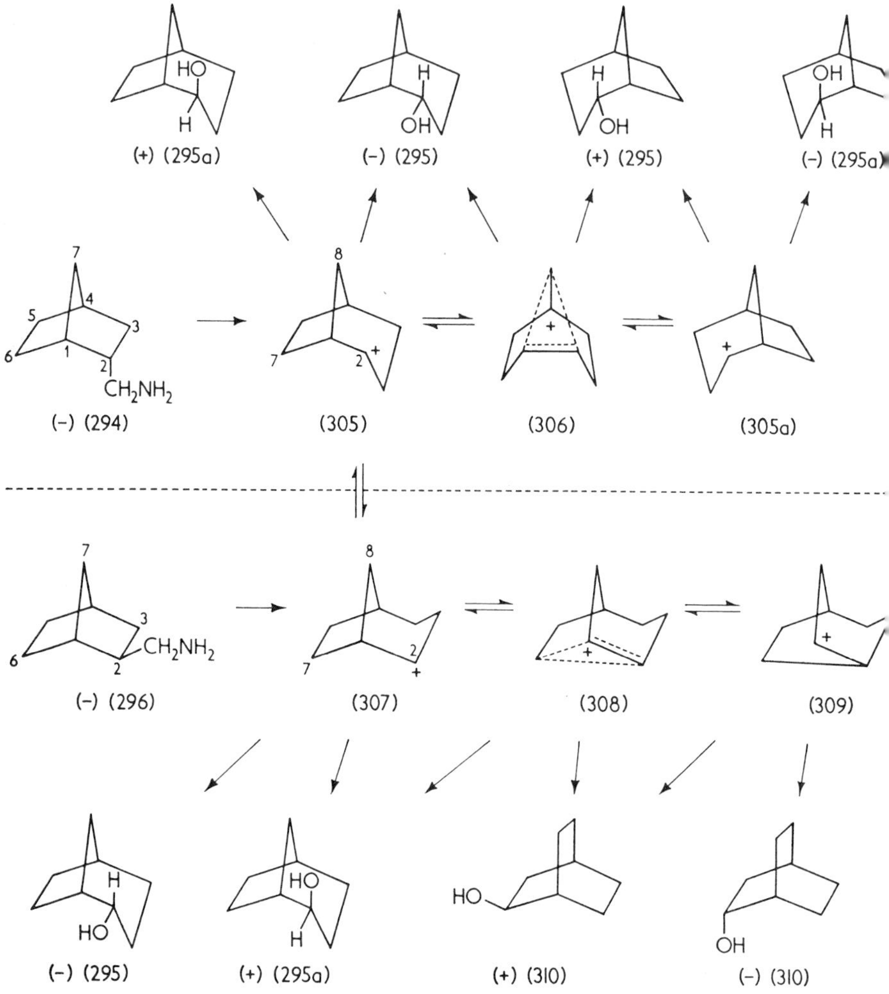

(+) (295a)   (−) (295)   (+) (295)   (−) (295a)

7
4
5
3
6   1
2
CH$_2$NH$_2$
(−) (294)   (305)   (306)   (305a)

8

7   2 +

7
3
6   2
CH$_2$NH$_2$
(−) (296)   (307)   (308)   (309)

8
2
7   +

H
HO
(−) (295)   (+) (295a)   (+) (310)   (−) (310)

HO
H

HO

OH

Scheme 5

There are indications [227] that a slow leak, possibly the chair-boat cyclo-hexane conformational isomerization **305 ⇌ 307** (Scheme 5), connects the *endo*-derived system with that originating in the *exo* isomer **296**. The latter gives optically active *axial* 2-bicyclo[3.2.1]octanol **295a** and optically active 2-bicyclo[2.2.2]octanol **310**. The optical purity of the **295a** formed from the *exo* amine **296** is different from that of the **295** or **295a** formed from the *endo* amine **294**. Thus, at least part of the discrepancy in optical purities of the

295 and **295a** formed in the latter reaction may arise from the formation of part of the **295a** by the path below the dotted line of Scheme 5. Supporting the interconnection of the *endo-* and *exo-*derived paths by the **305** $\rightleftharpoons$ **307** isomerization is the observation that a small amount ($\sim 7\%$) of 2-bicyclo-[2.2.2]octanol **310** is observed in the product mixture from **294**.[227] Similarly, a small amount ($\sim 3\%$) of *equatorial* 2-bicyclo[3.2.1]octanol **295** is observed[227] in the product mixture from the *exo* amine **296**, although it is not clear at present whether this is formed by a small amount of attack on the boat cation **307**, or by a preliminary isomerization to **305**, or both.

The 2-bicyclo[2.2.2]octanol **310** obtained from the *exo*-amine **296** is 37 to 51% racemized,[218] which shows that some of the product is formed from intermediates other than the optically active nonclassical cation **308**. The necessary optically inactive intermediate is formulated[218] as the classical 2-bicyclo[2.2.2]octyl cation **309**. The scheme for the rearrangement of **296** is written to conform to that for the companion *endo* amine **294**. The experimental error in the optical result of the acetolysis of 2-bicyclo[2.2.2]-octyl *p*-bromobenzenesulfonate (**310**, OH = OBs), 3 to 32% racemization (p. 214) and, in the present case, 37 to 51% racemization, is almost large enough to permit the possibility that the two results are the same. It remains to be seen whether this is indeed the case.

It seems likely that the multiple rearrangements observed with **294** and **296** are stepwise. The geometry of both amines makes it stereoelectronically unfavorable for migration of C_3 from C_2 to the CH_2 side chain to occur in concert with the movement of C_7 or C_6 from C_1 to a position between C_1 and C_2. In this respect, the situation is formally analogous to that in the solvolyses of *endo*-norbornyl arenesulfonates (heading 7A) which pass through a classical intermediate before proceeding to a mesomeric cation. The relative geometry of C_7 (or C_6) and C_3 in **294** (or **296**) is roughly the same as that of the arenesulfonate group and C_6 in the *endo*-norbornyl derivative.[218,226]

Once the classical cations (**305** from **294**, and **307** from **296**) are formed, conformational effects appear to be decisive in the choice of a group (C_8 or

(311a)   (311b)

C_7) for involvement in further rearrangement. That C_8 migration predominates in **305** and C_7 migration predominates in **307** is explicable on the ground that the geometry of the newly formed cyclohexane ring (chair in the case of 305, boat in the case of 307) places the empty p-orbital at C_2 in position to interact readily with only one bond in each case. This bond is the C_1—C_8 bond in 305 (cf. 311a) and the C_1—C_7 bond in 307 (cf. 311b).

II. REARRANGEMENTS OF MORE COMPLEX BRIDGED SYSTEMS

A particularly intricate set of rearrangements accompanies the solvolysis of the unsaturated fused double norcamphane derivative (314a). Acetolysis gives (in addition to unrearranged acetate 314b (four saturated acetates (317b, 318b, 319b, and 320b) as well as the "bird cage" saturated hydrocarbon 323. The p-bromobenzenesulfonates (317a, 318a, 319a, and 320a) also give mixtures of acetates upon acetolysis (see Table XVII).[228] From the structural point of view, the transannular interactions observed in the ring closure giving the "half cage" acetate 317b and the "bird cage" hydrocarbon 323 are particularly striking; the shifts of atomic positions associated with the formation of the Wagner-Meerwein bridged cation 322 bring C_a and C_b into close proximity, as is clearly discernible with molecular models.

The mechanisms of the various rearrangements are unusually complex, and the proposed interpretations[228] presumably will be amplified with respect to details. Nevertheless, sufficient evidence upon which to base at least an outline is already available. The rates of acetolysis (Table XVI) of 314a and its saturated analog, 316, are nearly the same. The double bond of 314a, being remote from the site of reaction, is not expected to produce a marked decrease in ionization rate, and in fact does not (cf. 313 versus 315). The near identity of the solvolysis rates of 314a and 316 is interpreted[228] as indicating the absence of any acceleration of solvolysis by the double bond. Ionization of 314a evidently is anchimerically assisted, the rate of solvolysis of this material exceeding that of the $endo$-p-bromobenzenesulfonate (313) by a factor of about 100. Of the two possible acetates from the Wagner-Meerwein bridged cation 322, only one, 314b, is formed. The isomer 321b is also missing from the solvolysis products of its corresponding trifluoroacetate, 321a.[229] The failure to form an $endo$-$endo$ fused system (321) is in accord with the behavior of the cation in the hydration of $endo$-dicyclopentadiene (324), which gives the exo-fused alcohol 325[230] (see heading 4D, but cf. heading 5B).

Ion 322 apparently is partitioned between at least two further rearrangement paths. By way of path A, it is connected with half cage acetate 317b, bird cage hydrocarbon 323, and rearranged acetate 320b. These three products

[228] L. de Vries and S. Winstein, *J. Am. Chem. Soc.*, **82**, 5363 (1960).

[229] (a) P. Bruck, D. Thompson, and S. Winstein, *Chem. & Ind. (London)*, **1960**, 590.
(b) P. Bruck, D. Thompson, and S. Winstein, *Chem. & Ind. (London)*, **1960**, 405.

are formed in the same relative proportions regardless of whether **314a** or **317a** is the starting material for acetolysis, a finding that suggests common

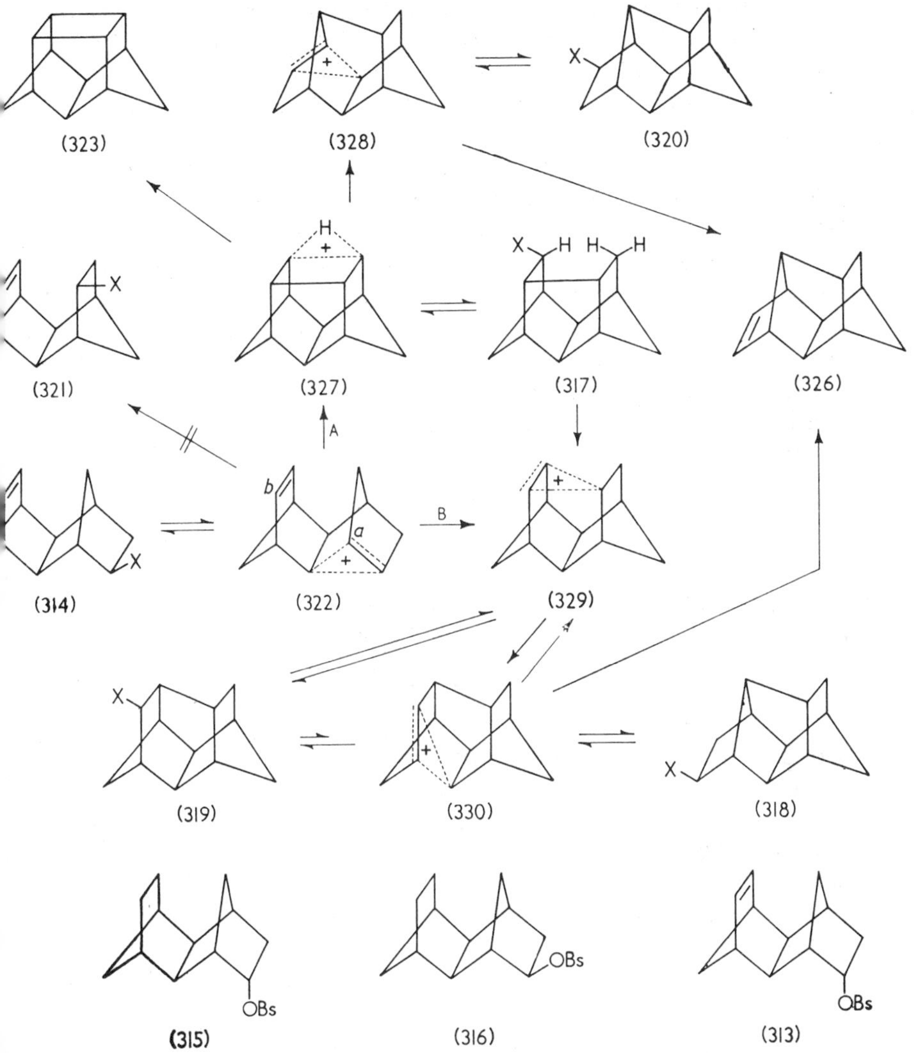

(323)   (328)   (320)

(321)   (327)   (317)   (326)

(314)   (322)   (329)

(319)   (330)   (318)

(315)   (316)   (313)

precursors. Significantly, acetolysis of **320a** does not give any **317b**, **314b**, or **323**, the sole products being unrearranged acetate **320b** and olefin **326**. Thus, the intermediates in the solvolysis of **320a** are not identical with those produced in the solvolyses of **314a** or **317a**. It is suggested that the hydrogen-bridged cation **327** rearranges irreversibly to the carbon-bridged cation **328**, which is then partitioned between **320b** and olefin **326**. Path B connects ion

322 with another set of products, **318b** and **319b**. Acetolysis of either of the corresponding bromobenzenesulfonates **318a** and **319a** gives mixtures of acetates **318b** and **319b** and olefin **326**, but the proportions of products are not independent of the starting material (see Table XVII), the **318b/319b** ratio being 73:27 from **318a** and 95:5 from **319a**. Also, **318a** gives some olefin **326** (5%), but **319a** does not, at least within the sensitivity of the methods of detection. This suggests that **318a** and **319a** pass over non-identical intermediates in their conversions to solvolysis products. It is suggested [228] that **319a** can solvolyze by two paths, one leading to ion **329** and the other to ion **330**, while **318a** ionizes only to **330**. A small difference in partition ratios between ions **329** and **330** would then account for the differences in product compositions.

It is not clear whether the structures representing the various bridged cationic intermediates are specifically correct or will require later modification. For example, ion **331** (≡**332**) may be a common intermediate for the formation of both **327** and **329** from **322**.[228] Further, it should be pointed out

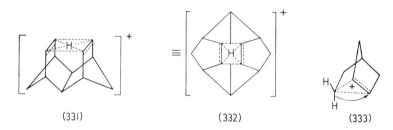

(331)   (332)   (333)

that the changes **322** → **329** and **329** → **330** involve *front-side* opening of a mesomeric bridge, in contrast to the more usual rear-side opening. An analogy is drawn [228] between this geometry and that prevailing in 6,2 hydride shifts (e.g., **333**) (heading 4). Nevertheless, it is an open question whether ions such as **334**, formed from **322** by vicinal 7,1 hydride shift (with *rear-side* opening of the mesomeric bridge), could not intervene and provide a pathway for formation of **329** by rear-side opening of the hydrogen bridge.

(322)   (334)   (329)

The role of ion pair return in this system has not yet been fully explored and the full extent of the enhancements of solvolysis rates by anchimeric assistance therefore is still uncertain. Nevertheless, some of these systems are exceptionally reactive (Table XVI); the unsaturated substance **321**, for

TABLE XVI
Relative Rates of Acetolysis at 25° [228-230]

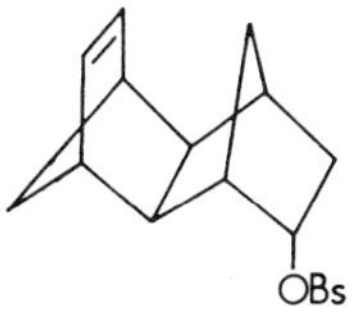

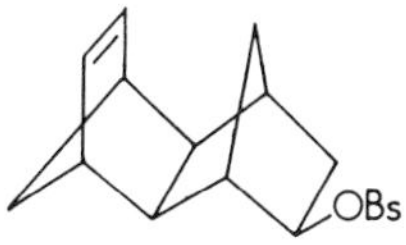

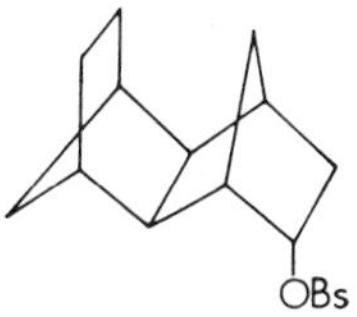

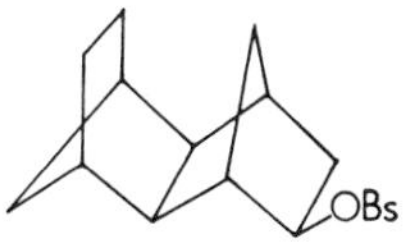

(313)
1.00

(314a)
1.2×10^2

(315)
3.0

(316)
66

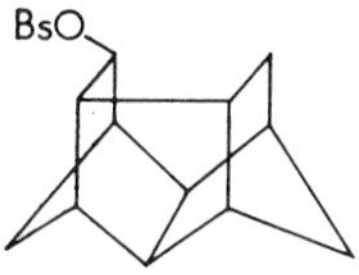

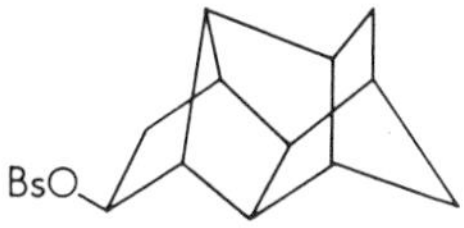

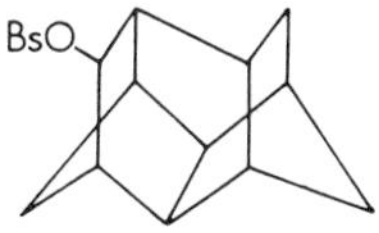

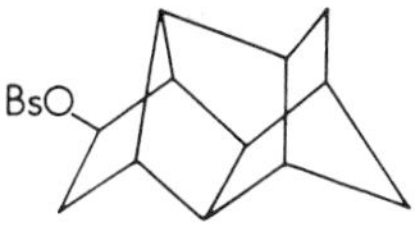

(317)
1.8×10^4

(318)
3.1×10^3

(319)
4.5×10^3

(320)
6.8×10^2

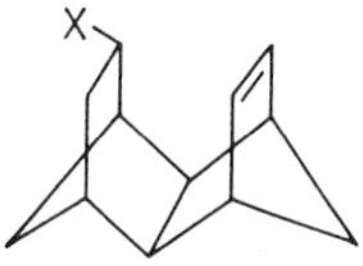

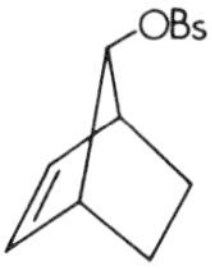

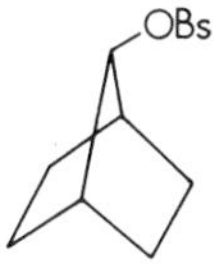

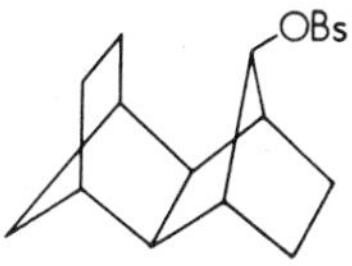

(321)
1.3×10^6 [a]

9.5×10^4

1.5×10^{-6}

(335)
$\sim 1 \times 10^{-2}$

Solvolysis of p-nitrobenzoate in 70% aqueous acetone relative to anti-7-norbornenyl p-nitrobenzoate in 70% aqueous acetone.

example, is even more reactive than the anti-7-norbornenyl system. Transannular hydrogen bridging (**317a → 327**) presumably provides anchimeric assistance to the solvolysis of **317a**, and direct evidence for similar bridging is provided by observations [231] in the solvolysis of **335a**. This substance is 10^4 times as reactive in acetolysis as 7-norbornyl p-bromobenzenesulfonate (see Table XVI), and the products are the Wagner-Meerwein pair of isomers **336**

[230] P. D. Bartlett and A. Schneider, J. Am. Chem. Soc., **68**, 6 (1946); P. D. Bartlett and R. S. Barnes, ACS 12th National Organic Chemistry Symposium, Denver, Colo., June, 1951, Abstracts, p. 1.

[231] S. Winstein and R. L. Hansen, J. Am. Chem. Soc., **82**, 6206 (1960); S. Winstein, private communication, 1960.

and **337** derived by transannular hydrogen shift. None of the unrearranged acetate **335b** is found. The deuterated analog **335c**, containing about 80% of 8 atoms of D per mole, solvolyzes about 30% slower than the parent com-

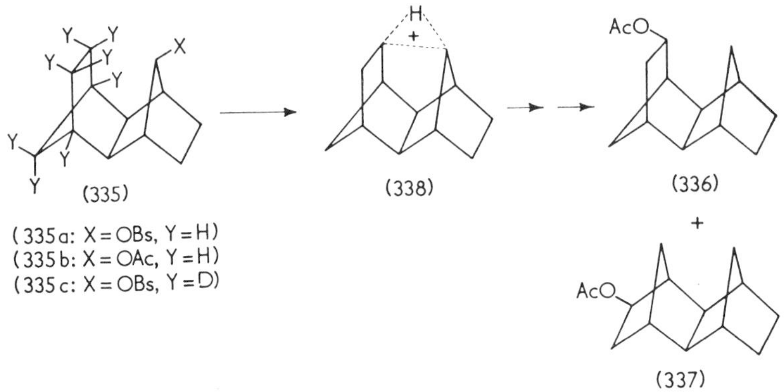

(335)

(335a: X = OBs, Y = H)
(335b: X = OAc, Y = H)
(335c: X = OBs, Y = D)

(338)

(336)

+

(337)

pound **335a**. This retardation is believed [231] too large to attribute to a secondary isotope effect at a center so remote from the reaction site. The facts are consistent with direct formation of the hydrogen-bridged cation **338**,[231]

TABLE XVII

Products from Acetolysis[a] of ROBs at 50° (in % of over-all composition of product)

	Hydrocarbons		Acetates				
ROBs	323	326	314b	317b	318b	319b	320b
314a	10	—	30.5	16	34	3.5	5.6
317a	35	< 1	—	37	12	2	14
318a	0	5	—	0	70	26	0
319a	0	< 1	—	0	95	5	0
320a[b]	0	6	—	0	0	0	94

[a] In the presence of 0.12M NaOAc.
[b] Acetolysis at 75°.

which, presumably through one or more additional intermediates, is eventually converted to **336** and **337**. (For other examples of transannular hydrogen bridging, see Section 9.)

The structures described here are readily subject to other transannular phenomena, as in the hydration of **339** [229] and the photoisomerization of

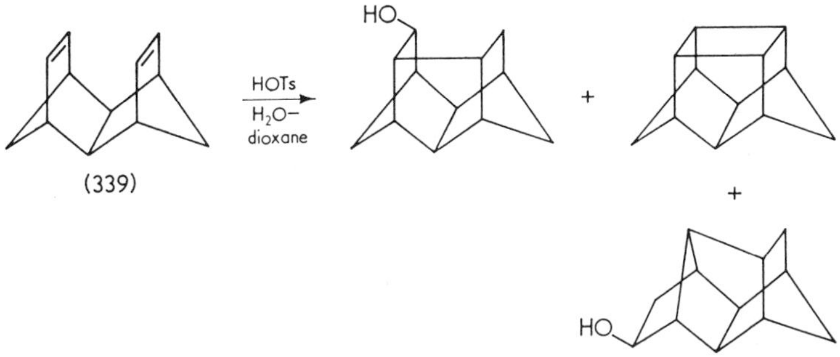

(339)

isodrin (**340**) to the hexachloro bird-cage structure **341**,[225a] among other examples.[229,232b,233]

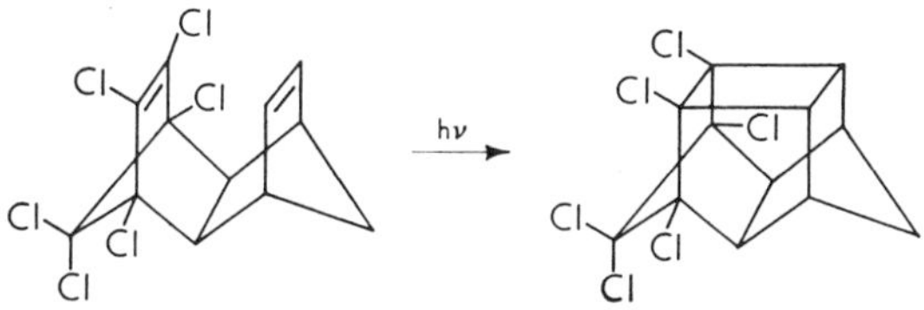

(340)   (341)

As a final example of transannular involvement of a double bond, there is the conversion of **342** to **343** and **344**.[234]

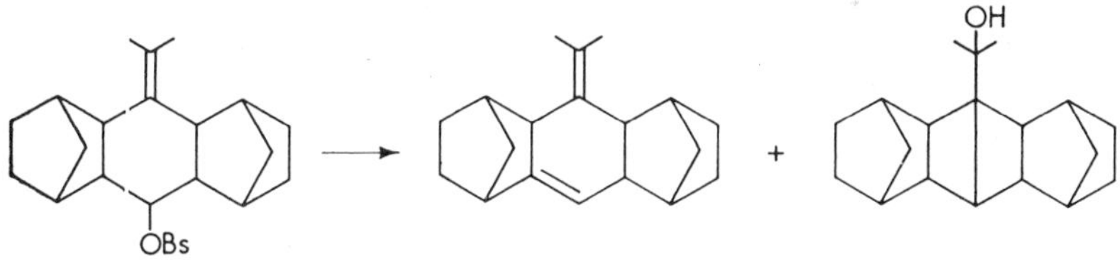

(342)   (343)   (344)

[232] (a) R. C. Cookson and E. Crundwell, *Chem. & Ind.* (*London*), **1958**, 1004, (b) **1959**, 703.

[233] S. B. Soloway, A. M. Damiana, J. W. Sims, H. Bluestone, and R. E. Lidov, *J. Am. Chem. Soc.*, **82**, 5377 (1960); R. E. Lidov and H. Bluestone, U.S. Patent 2,714,617 (to Shell Development Co.) (Oct. 2, 1955).

[234] S. Winstein and L. de Vries, ACS 15th National Organic Chemistry Symposium, Rochester, N. Y., June, 1957, *Abstracts*.

4

REARRANGEMENTS IN SMALL RING COMPOUNDS

RONALD BRESLOW

Columbia University, New York, New York

CONTENTS

I. INTRODUCTION

The chemistry of small ring compounds is replete with examples of rearrangements. The relief of ring strain is a powerful driving force in assisting ring openings and ring expansions in small—i.e., three- and four-membered—rings under conditions where larger ring compounds or aliphatic analogs retain their original carbon skeletons intact. Although examples of rearrangements may be found in small heterocyclic systems, we shall restrict our attention to cyclopropane and cyclobutane derivatives and will consider the types of reactions in which the rings themselves are converted to other skeleta, e.g., other rings or open chains. Thus, examples of rearrangements *leading* to small ring compounds will be omitted unless they are relevant to the discussion of the reverse, ring-opening, reaction. Furthermore, examples of such rearrangements in terpenes and steroids will be cited only infrequently, since these topics are treated elsewhere (Sections 3, 13, and 16).

Several other reviews on the chemistry of small rings are available which contain important material on rearrangements.[1-3]

2. THERMAL REARRANGEMENTS

A. Cyclopropane Derivatives

When cyclopropane is pyrolyzed at 400–500°, propylene is formed. This change has been the object of a number of careful studies, since it represents a particularly simple unimolecular gas-phase reaction. The overall change requires (a) ring opening, and (b) hydrogen shift, and most of the work done on the reaction[4] has been directed toward discovering which of these two processes is rate determining, or whether they are in some way simultaneous. Slater's theoretical treatment of unimolecular processes has been applied to this reaction,[4d] and it was concluded that the rate-determining step is not simply ring opening. This treatment has been criticized,[4h,4j] but, in spite of some disagreement about terminology, a fairly clear picture has emerged. The finding that cis and trans dideuterocyclopropane are thermally equilibrated more rapidly than either one is isomerized to propene[4g] shows that ring opening can occur without hydrogen shift, since an intermediate trimethylene diradical seems the most likely intermediate for this cis-trans isomerization. Similarly cis and trans dimethylcyclopropane are equilibrated more rapidly than either opens to a pentene.[5] Since the intermediate trimethylene undergoes predominant collapse to a cyclopropane again, the rate-determining step for propene formation must involve the migrating hydrogen atom as well. This is also indicated by the isotope effect on the rearrangement of hexadeuterocyclopropane.[4f] Because the preexponential factor in an Arrhenius treatment of the propene-forming reaction indicates a "loose" transition state, and because of the evidence cited above that

[1] E. Vogel, *Fortschr. chem. Forsch.*, **3**, 430 (1955).

[2] E. Vogel, *Angew. Chem.*, **72**, 4 (1960).

[3] R. A. Raphael in E. H. Rodd, ed., *Chemistry of Carbon Compounds*, Elsevier Publishing Co., 1953, IIA, pp. 11 ff.

[4a] T. S. Chambers and G. B. Kistiakowsky, *J. Am. Chem. Soc.*, **56**, 399 (1934).

[4b] E. S. Corner and R. N. Pease, *J. Am. Chem. Soc.*, **67**, 2067 (1945).

[4c] M. C. Flowers and H. M. Frey, *J. Chem. Soc. (London)*, **1960**, 2758.

[4d] N. B. Slater, *J. Chem. Soc. (London)*, **1961**, 606, and references therein.

[4e] W. E. Falconer, T. F. Hunter, and A. F. Trotman-Dickenson, *J. Chem. Soc. (London)*, **1961**, 609.

[4f] A. T. Blades, *Can. J. Chem.*, **39**, 1401 (1961).

[4g] B. S. Rabinovitch, E. W. Schlag, and K. B. Wiberg, *J. Chem. Phys.*, **28**, 504 (1958).

[4h] S. W. Benson, *J. Chem. Phys.*, **34**, 521 (1961).

[4i] F. T. Smith, *J. Chem. Phys.*, **29**, 235 (1958).

[4j] E. W. Schlag and B. S. Rabinovitch, *J. Am. Chem. Soc.*, **82**, 5886 (1960).

[5] M. C. Flowers and H. F. Frey, *Proc. Roy. Soc. (London)*, **260A**, 424 (1961).

trimethylene is available under these conditions, it seems that hydrogen migration in the diradical is the rate-determining process for ring opening. The calculated lifetime of this diradical is so short [4h] that failure to intercept it with radical scavengers is not surprising.

The thermal ring-opening reaction is rather unselective, 1 forming 2 and 3

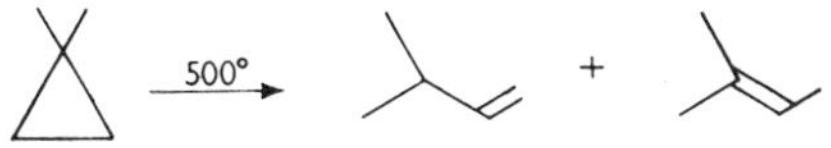

in about equal amounts.[6] In more highly strained systems [6a] ring cleavage is even easier, bicyclopentane (4) pyrolyzing to cyclopentene at 330°.[7]

A change which is very similar to the ring openings cited above occurs when spiropentane (4a) is pyrolyzed [7a] but, in this case, the postulated intermediate diradical (4b) undergoes migration of a carbon atom, rather than a

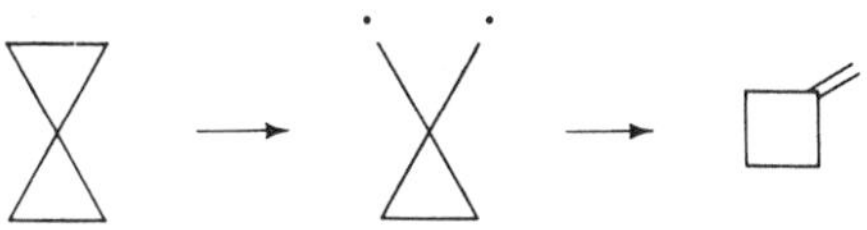

hydrogen. The activation energy for this process is smaller than for cyclopropane isomerization, presumably because there is more strain relief in this case, but the large preexponential factor again indicates a "loose" transition state consistent with the postulated 4b.

The pyrolysis of cyclopropene is similar to that of cyclopropane, methylacetylene being formed at ~400° [7b] by a process which formally requires ring opening to a diradical followed by hydrogen shift.

Vinylcyclopropanes undergo a somewhat different type of thermal rearrangement, in which a five-membered ring is formed. Thus, vinylcyclopropane itself is rearranged to cyclopentene,[8] and this reaction has been

---

[6] M. C. Flowers and H. M. Frey, *J. Chem. Soc. (London)*, **1959**, 3953.

[6a] See also R. Huisgen and G. Juppe, *Ber.*, **94**, 2332 (1961).

[7] R. Criegee and A. Rimmelin, *Chem. Ber.*, **90**, 414 (1957).

[7a] M. C. Flowers and H. M. Frey, *J. Chem. Soc. (London)*, **1961**, 5550.

[7b] K. B. Wiberg and W. J. Bartley, *J. Am. Chem. Soc.*, **82**, 6375 (1960).

[8] Cf. C. G. Overberger and A. E. Borchert, *J. Am. Chem. Soc.*, **82**, 1007 (1960).

studied kinetically.[8a] By contrast with the pyrolysis of cyclopropane, this isomerization has a normal preexponential factor, showing that the transition state does not involve appreciable loosening, and the activation energy is also considerably lower. This suggests that the rearrangement proceeds with simultaneous formation and cleavage of the appropriate carbon-carbon bonds, rather than by ring opening to a diradical with subsequent closure to product.

Pyrolysis of 2-vinyl-1,1-dichlorocyclopropane (5) affords the cyclopenta-diene derivative (6) with loss of HCl.[9] The mechanism of this reaction is clarified by the isolation of 7 from the products and the demonstration that it is probably an intermediate in the formation of 6. Because the chlorines would be expected to help stabilize a diradical intermediate such as 8, this particular rearrangement need not involve simultaneous bond making and bond breaking.

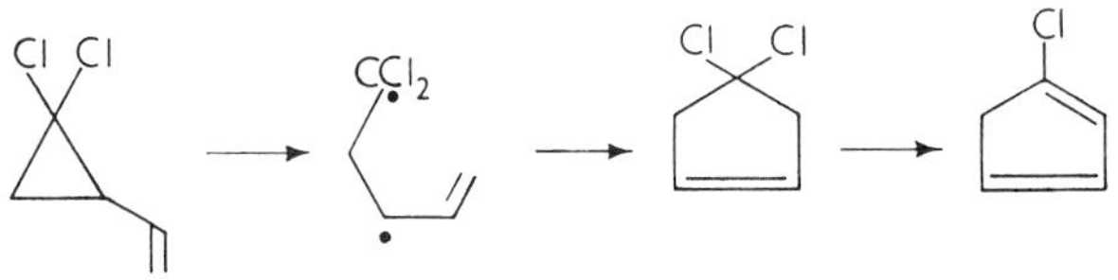

As might be expected if the rearrangement of vinylcyclopropane has a transition state which partially resembles the product, a vinyl cyclopropene derivative rearranges even more easily. Thus, vinyl triphenylcyclopropene (8a) rearranges to the cyclopentadiene derivative (8b) at only 180°.[9a]

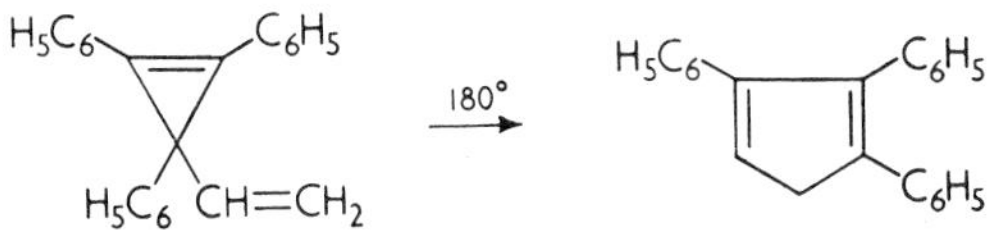

Divinylcyclopropanes also undergo ring-expanding rearrangements, and perhaps the most familiar examples are those in which norcaradiene deriva-tives rearrange to cycloheptatrienes under the conditions of their synthesis

[8a] M. C. Flowers and H. M. Frey, *J. Chem. Soc.* (*London*), **1961**, 3547.

[9] N. P. Neureiter, *J. Org. Chem.*, **24**, 2044 (1959).

[9a] A. Small and R. Breslow, unpublished work.

(eq. 1) (see also Section 11). An analogous situation obtains with divinyl-cyclopropane, for the *cis* isomer (**9**) cannot be isolated, rearranging under the

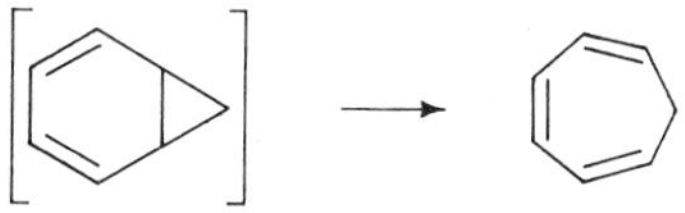

$$\left[\text{\qquad}\right] \longrightarrow \text{\qquad} \qquad (1)$$

conditions of its synthesis to cycloheptadiene (**10**).[10] The *trans* isomer affords the same product, but only when it is heated to 200°. This much greater ease of rearrangement of the *cis* compound shows that it is not first cleaving to a diradical, which then closes the seven-membered ring, but that the rearrangement is concerted, as shown. A concerted mechanism is much more difficult for the *trans* compound, which may indeed give a diradical in the first step.

$$\left[\text{\qquad}\right] \longrightarrow \text{\qquad}$$

(9)   (10)

An interesting choice between a concerted and a non-concerted mechanism has been made in the case of another small ring rearrangement. When Feist's ester (**11**) is heated, it rearranges to an isomer (**12**), and studies of the stereochemical result of pyrolyzing optically active **11** indicate that two mechanisms are operative.[11]

In the first mechanism there is a direct isomerization, as symbolized in equation 2. However, the loss of some optical activity in the recovered

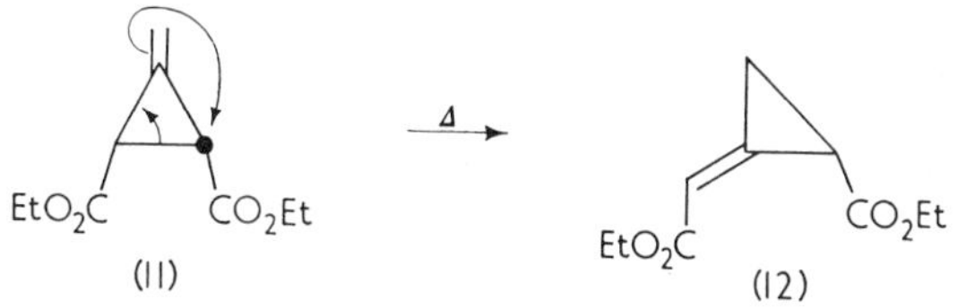

$$\text{} \xrightarrow{\Delta} \text{} \qquad (2)$$

EtO_2C CO_2Et EtO_2C CO_2Et

(11)   (12)

Feist's ester shows that there is also some equilibration through an open chain intermediate, which has been formulated as (**13**). A similar intermediate (**13a**) is indicated for the nonstereospecific Favorskii reaction which occurs in

---

[10] E. Vogel, K. H. Ott, and K. Gajek, *Annal.*, **644**, 172 (1961).

[11] E. F. Ullman, *J. Am. Chem. Soc.*, **82**, 505 (1960).

polar media,[11a] although in nonpolar solvents closure to the cyclopropanone occurs directly.[11b]

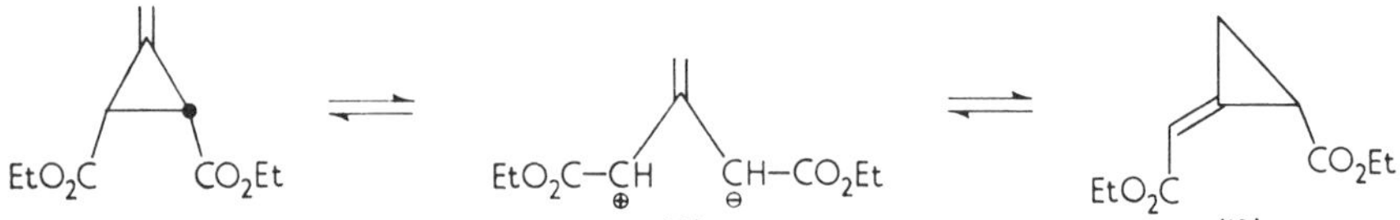

(11)   (13)   (12)

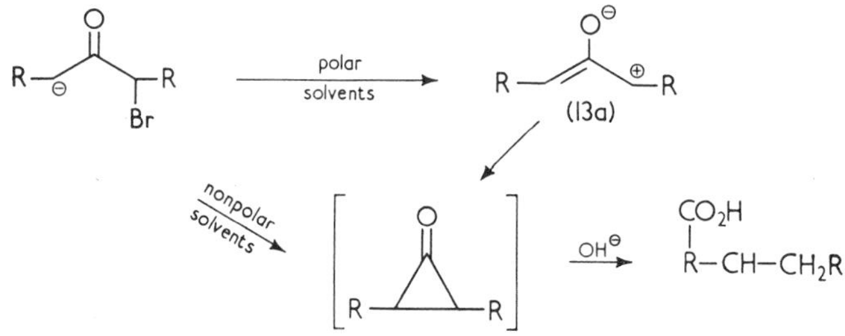

(13a)

A thermal rearrangement very similar to that of Feist's ester occurs when **13b** is heated.[11c] This example shows that the rearrangement does not require carbonyl substituents on the cyclopropane ring, but is probably in fact a very general reaction for methylenecyclopropanes.

(13b)

Closely related to the ring-opening isomerizations is the observation[12] that a vinyl cyclopropane derivative (**14**) will undergo the Diels-Alder reaction with maleic anhydride. This is an illustration of the type of

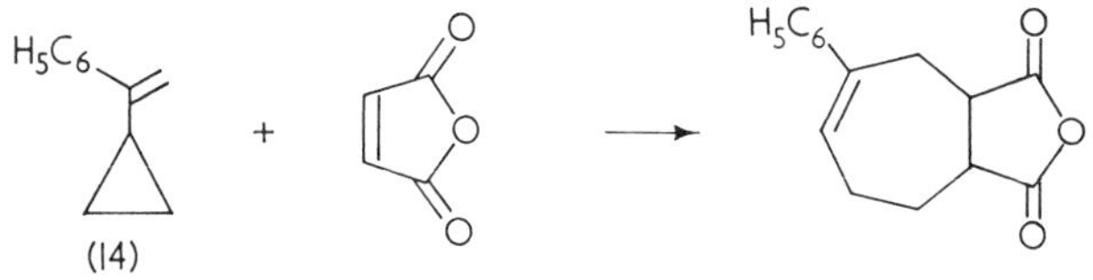

(14)

behavior which suggests that cyclopropane rings have some similarity to double bonds in their chemistry.

If the cyclopropane ring carries a carbonyl substituent instead of a vinyl

[11a] H. House and W. Gilmore, *J. Am. Chem. Soc.*, **83**, 3980 (1961).

[11b] G. Stork and I. Borowitz, *J. Am. Chem. Soc.*, **82**, 4307 (1960).

[11c] E. F. Ullman and W. J. Farshawe, *J. Am. Chem. Soc.*, **83**, 2379 (1961).

[12] S. Sarel and E. Breuer, *J. Am. Chem. Soc.*, **81**, 6522 (1959).

group, a ring-enlarging isomerization is also possible, and cyclopropyl carboxaldehyde (15) has been found to be in equilibrium with dihydrofuran (16) at high temperature.[13] This equilibrium and the previously mentioned

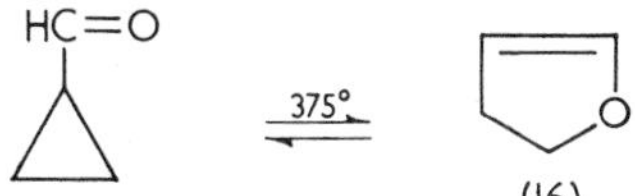

vinylcyclopropane isomerizations can explain the observation[14] that when 17 is heated it rearranges to 18, presumably through the cyclopropane intermediate (although an ionic mechanism is also possible).

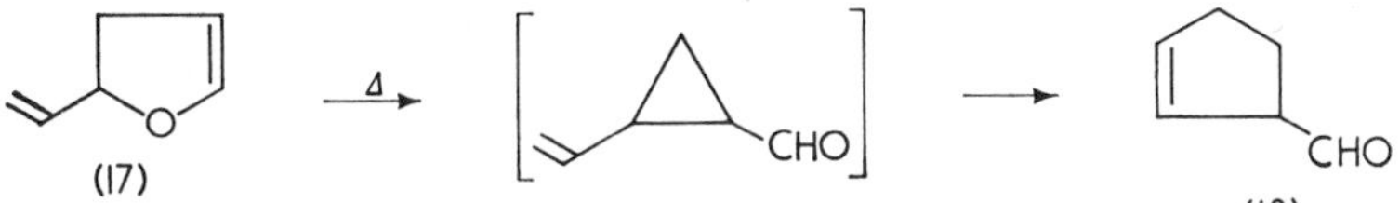

A similar process can occur in substances having an imino group instead of a carbonyl group. Thus it has been found that the imine 19 rearranges on heating at 170° to a pyrroline derivative (20).[15,16] This reaction does not seem to be reversible, probably because of further tautomeric isomerization of the enamine (20) to an imine, a Δ^1-pyrroline.

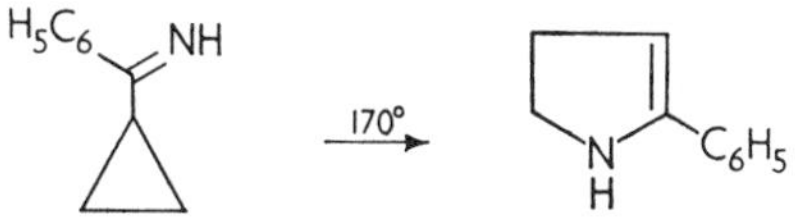

A very facile rearrangement of this type has been found in the cyclopropene series. While the above cyclopropane compound (19) was prepared via an addition of phenylmagnesium bromide to cyclopropyl cyanide, the reaction of triphenylcyclopropenyl cyanide (21) with phenyllithium, even at very low temperature, leads exclusively to tetraphenylpyrrole.[17] This process can be explained by the attack of the intermediate imine derivative on the cyclopropene ring, as shown; the great ease of this attack in the unsaturated series may reflect the greater strain relief expected, the greater susceptibility of the double bond to nucleophilic attack, and the formation of an

[13] C. L. Wilson, J. Am. Chem. Soc., 69, 3002 (1947).

[14] J. Wiemann and Sa-Le Thi Thuan, Bull. soc. chim. France, 1958, 199.

[15] J. B. Cloke, J. Am. Chem. Soc., 51, 1174 (1929).

[16] J. B. Cloke and J. C. Murray, J. Am. Chem. Soc., 68, 126 (1946).

[17] R. Breslow and R. Boikess, and M. Battiste, Tetrahedron Letters, No. 26, 42 (1960).

aromatic system in the rearrangement. Furthermore, the intermediate (**22**) from the reaction of the acid chloride of diphenylcyclopropenecarboxylic acid

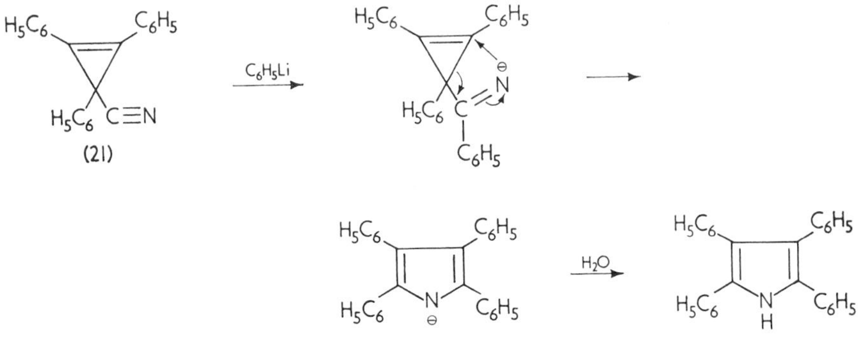

with diphenylcadmium rearranges to triphenylfuran at 60°, although at 0° it affords the expected phenyl ketone (which is not rearranged by diphenyl-cadmium at 60°).[17]

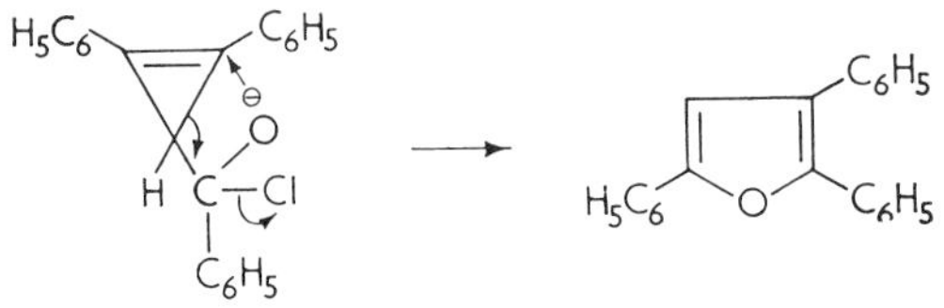

Somewhat similar "thermal" rearrangements of cyclopropene derivatives, albeit at low temperatures, occur to furnish six-membered rings. Thus the hydrazone (**23**) rearranges under the conditions of its synthesis to the dihydro-pyridazine (**24**), again by nucleophilic attack of nitrogen on the cyclopropene

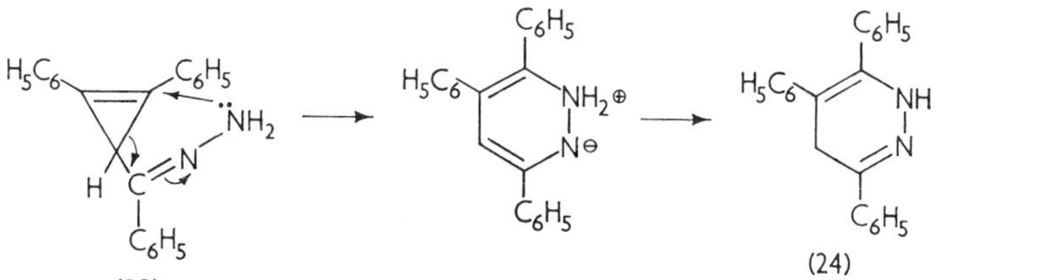

ring with formation of a stabilized intermediate ion.[17,18] Similarly, triphenyl-cyclopropenyl azide (**25**) rearranges under rather mild conditions to the triazine (**26**).[17,19,20]

18 R. Breslow and M. Battiste, unpublished work.
19 R. Breslow, unpublished work.
20 E. Chandross and G. Smolinsky, *Tetrahedron Letters*, No. 13, 19 (1960).

When the substituent on a cyclopropane ring is a carboxyl group, a five-membered heterocycle can also be formed, but in this case ionic intermediates

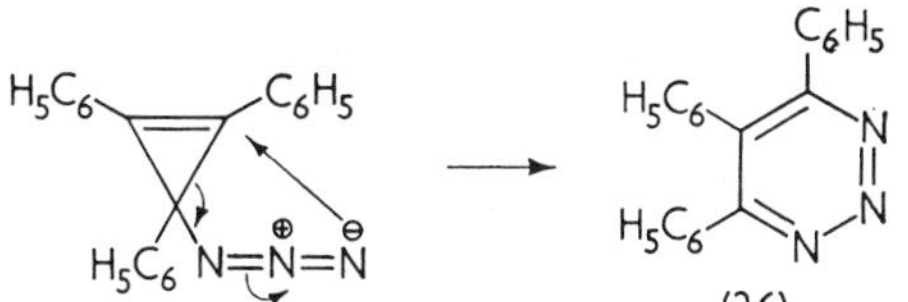

(25)   (26)

are almost certainly involved. One such rearrangement occurs when **27** is heated,[21] the product lactone (**28**) presumably arising through an intermediate such as **29**. Furthermore, the pyrolysis of the cyclopropene derivative

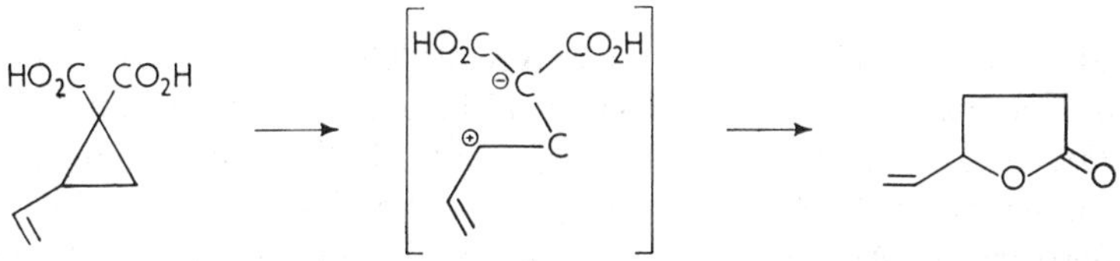

(27)   (29)   (28)

(**30**) to diphenylcrotonolactone (**31**) [22] almost certainly proceeds by an ionic mechanism, as suggested in equation 3, since the same rearrangement can occur at much lower temperatures in the presence of external acid catalysts.[18]

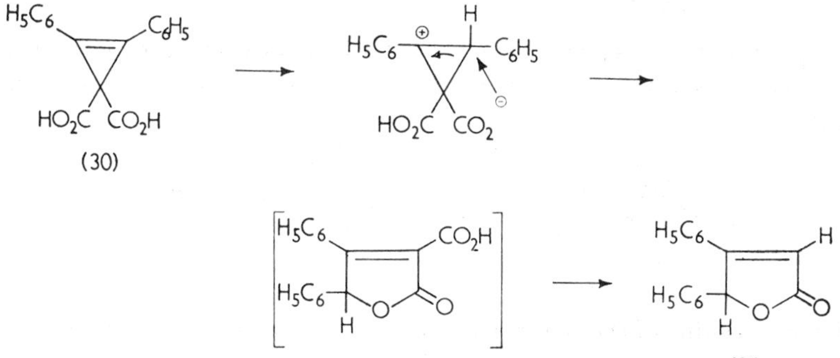

(30)

(3)

(31)

The contribution of acid-base catalysis to other "thermal" isomerizations of cyclopropane compounds is undoubtedly important, and the easy thermal isomerization of cyclopropanol (**32**) to propionaldehyde [23,24] may involve

[21] S. F. Birch, R. A. Dean, and N. J. Hunter, *J. Org. Chem.*, **23**, 1390 (1958).
[22] R. Breslow, R. Winter, and M. Battiste, *J. Org. Chem.*, **24**, 415 (1959).
[23] J. K. Magrane and D. L. Cottle, *J. Am. Chem. Soc.*, **64**, 484 (1942).
[24] G. W. Stahl and D. L. Cottle, *J. Am. Chem. Soc.*, **65**, 1782 (1943).

such catalysis, since the conversion can be strongly accelerated by base.[24,24a] The similar very facile rearrangement of triphenylcyclopropenol (33) to

(32)

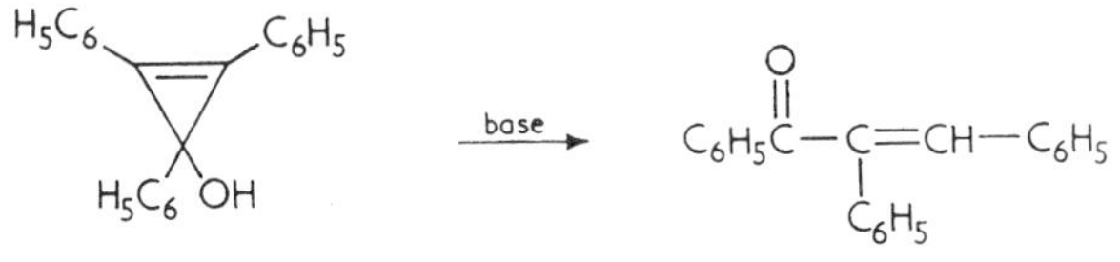

(33)

benzaldesoxybenzoin [25] is also base catalyzed.[26] The equilibrium in such ring-opening reactions of cyclopropanols would be expected to lie completely to the right, since a considerable amount of ring strain is relieved. None the less, it had been reported [27] that a mobile equilibrium exists in some α-ketoglutaric acid derivatives (34). The dilemma has been resolved by the finding [28]

(34)

that both structures assigned are wrong, 34 and its cyclopropane isomer being really stereoisomers of a trimethylene oxide dicarboxylic acid (35 and 35a).

(35)   (35a)

Under the heading of thermal rearrangements of cyclopropane derivatives, we should consider a few cases in which more deep-seated changes occur. Thus, the pyrolysis of acetoxycyclopropanecarboxylic acid (36) affords not a

[24a] Cf., however, C. H. de Puy, G. Dappen, and J. Hausser, *J. Am. Chem. Soc.*, **83**, 3156 (1961).

[25] R. Breslow and C. Yuan, *J. Am. Chem. Soc.*, **80**, 5991 (1958).

[26] R. Breslow and H. W. Chang, unpublished work.

[27] E. W. Lanfear and J. F. Thorpe, *J. Chem. Soc. (London)*, **123**, 1683 (1923).

[28] K. B. Wiberg and H. W. Holmquist, *J. Org. Chem.*, **24**, 578 (1959).

cyclopropene derivative, but rather acrolein and carbon monoxide in addition to the expected acetic acid.[29] Diphenylcyclopropenone (**37**), when heated,

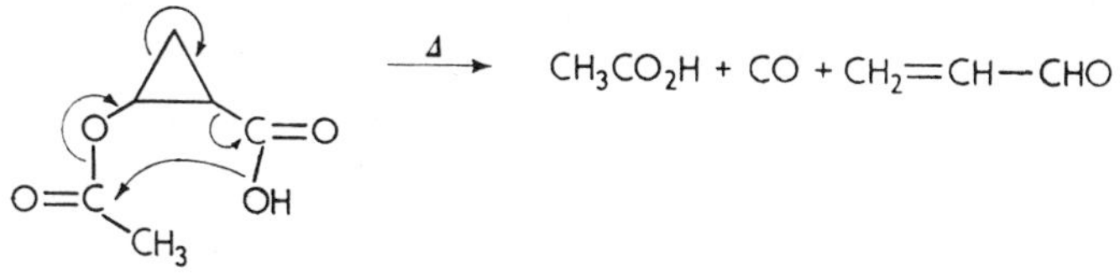

$$\xrightarrow{\Delta} CH_3CO_2H + CO + CH_2{=}CH{-}CHO$$

(36)

loses carbon monoxide to form diphenylacetylene,[30] although, interestingly, dipropylcyclopropenone has greater thermal stability.[31] Pyrolysis of the cyclopropylcyclopropene derivative **37a** affords the unusual products

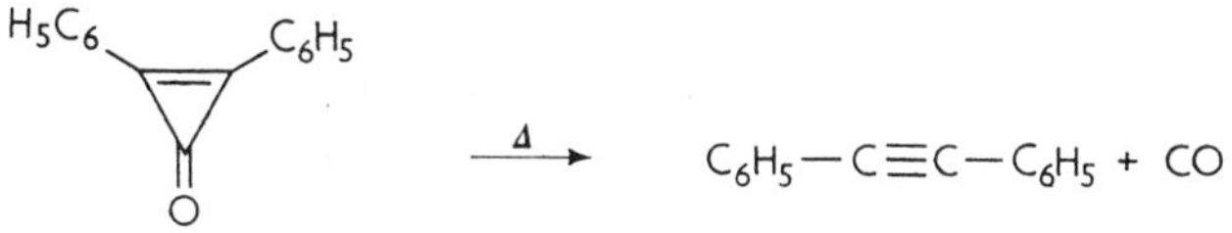

$$\xrightarrow{\Delta} C_6H_5{-}C{\equiv}C{-}C_6H_5 + CO$$

(37)

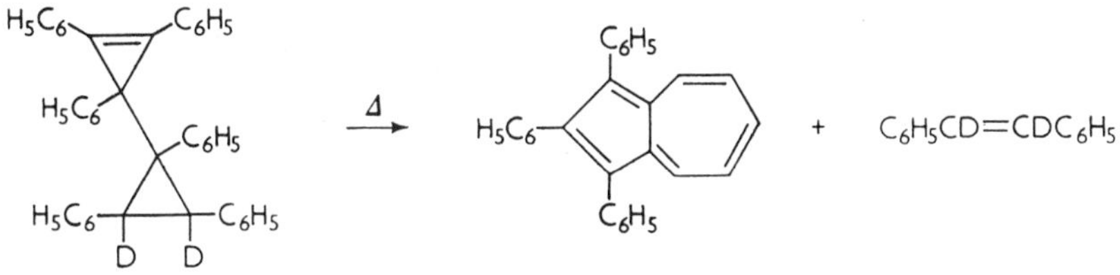

$$\xrightarrow{\Delta}$$

(37a)

$$+ \quad C_6H_5CD{=}CDC_6H_5$$

shown,[31a] and bis(triphenylcyclopropenyl) (**38**), on heating, rearranges to hexaphenylbenzene.[32] This process has been studied in some detail,[32a] and

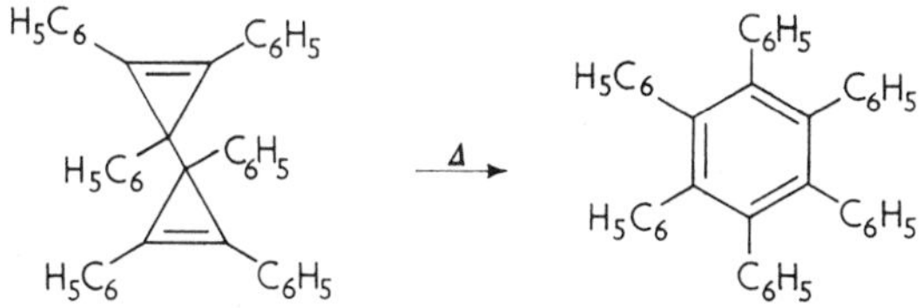

$$\xrightarrow{\Delta}$$

(38)

[29] K. Wiberg and R. Barnes, *J. Org. Chem.*, **23**, 299 (1958).
[30] R. Breslow, R. Haynie, and J. Mirra, *J. Am. Chem. Soc.*, **81**, 247 (1959).
[31] R. Breslow and R. Peterson, *J. Am. Chem. Soc.*, **82**, 4426 (1960).
[31a] R. Breslow and P. Dowd, unpublished work.
[32] R. Breslow and P. Gal, *J. Am. Chem. Soc.*, **81**, 4747 (1959).
[32a] R. Breslow and P. Gal, unpublished work.

an unusual mechanism seems to be indicated. Formally it is required simply that the two cyclopropene rings join by interaction of the two double bonds; the result would be a species with the carbon skeleton of hexaphenylbenzene, and electronic rearrangement would furnish the product. An intermediate corresponding to this simple scheme is symbolized as **39**, although

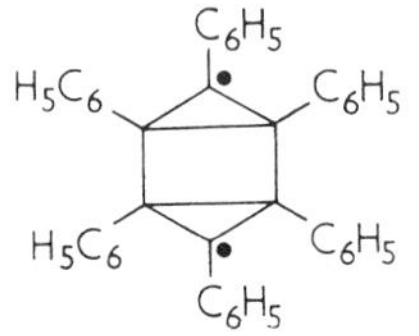

(39) 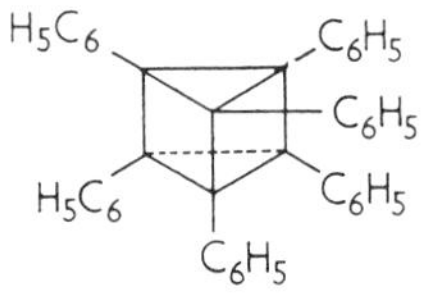   (40)

electronic rearrangement to the benzene could have started before the single bond is fully formed, so the classical diradical structure written may be symbolizing a considerably less classical intermediate. On the other hand, it is possible that not one but two bonds are formed by interaction of the olefins, in which case a prismatic intermediate (**40**) would be involved. A choice in

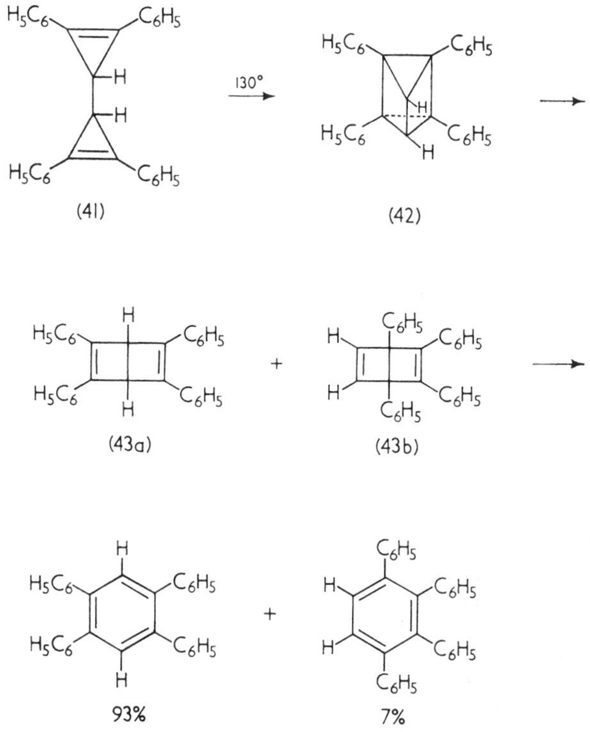

(41)   (42)

(43a)   +   (43b)

93%   +   7%

favor of the latter possibility has been made by the following experiment. A tetraphenylbiscyclopropene (**41**) was synthesized and thermally rearranged, and the product was a mixture of the 1,2,3,4- and 1,2,4,5-tetraphenylbenzenes. In the latter compound the two hydrogen-bearing carbons which were originally linked in the dimer are no longer joined, so the first mechanism suggested can be excluded. On the other hand, a mechanism proceeding from **41** to **42**, the prism, and thence through the bicyclohexadienes **43a** and **43b** to products, is in accord with the findings. As indicated, there is a rather large preference for the formation of the 1,2,4,5-tetraphenylbenzene isomer, and this can be rationalized in terms of the expectation that opening of **42** would go preferentially to **43a**. Although this mechanism is thus suggested by the data available, it cannot be considered as proven, of course.

Another unusual rearrangement of a closely related compound occurs when diphenylcyclopropenyl ether (**44**) is heated.[33] The mechanism of this process is still obscure.

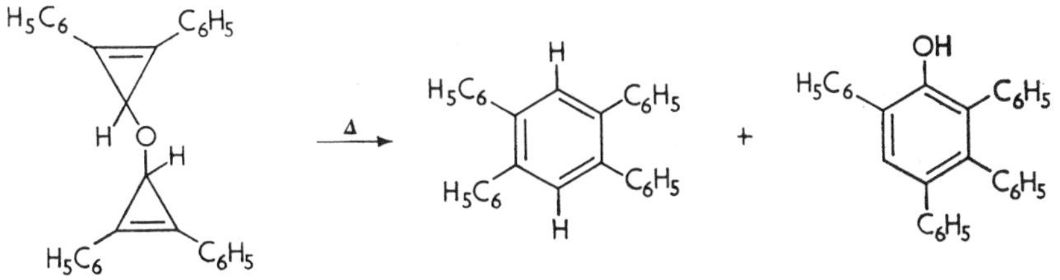

B. Cyclobutane Derivatives

The pyrolysis of substituted cyclobutanes results in fragmentation to ethylenes rather than simple isomerization to butene derivatives. The simplest example, pyrolysis of cyclobutane itself to two molecules of ethylene,[34] has received careful study. Again, as in the cyclopropane isomerization, a choice must be made between a two-step process, involving formation of tetramethylene diradical and subsequent cleavage, and a one-step process with simultaneous rupture of both bonds. The kinetic studies of this reaction[35] show that the entropy of activation is approximately $+9$ e.u., while the

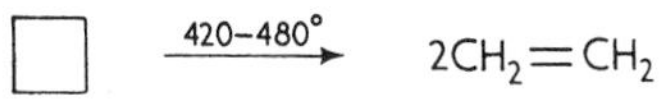

$$\square \xrightarrow{\;420\text{--}480°\;} 2CH_2 = CH_2$$

over-all cleavage of cyclobutane to two ethylene molecules under these conditions would involve a change of $+43$ e.u. From this, it is argued that the

[33] D. G. Farnum and M. Burr, *J. Am. Chem. Soc.*, **82**, 2651 (1960).
[34] C. T. Genaux and W. Walters, *J. Am. Chem. Soc.*, **73**, 4497 (1951).
[35] C. T. Genaux, F. Kern, and W. D. Walters, *J. Am. Chem. Soc.*, **75**, 6196 (1953).

transition state must closely resemble the starting cyclobutane rather than the product ethylenes. The estimated entropy change on cleavage of cyclobutane to tetramethylene diradical is $+15$ e.u., so the transition state could occur on the pathway to such a diradical but, of course, this type of argument does not establish the mechanism. However, as expected from these data, tetramethylene diradical, if it is an intermediate at all, must occur after the transition state, and this is consistent with the finding [35a,35b] that the interconversion of *cis* and *trans* 1,2-dimethylcyclobutanes is slower than their cleavage to propylene (and a smaller amount of ethylene and 2-butene).

Theoretical treatments of unimolecular reactions, such as the pyrolytic cleavage of cyclobutane, predict that the rate will fall off at very low pressures as energy transfer by collision becomes rate limiting.[35c] This is confirmed experimentally,[35] as is the prediction that the pressure dependence will be smaller in the pyrolysis of substituted cyclobutanes;[35d] a decreased pressure sensitivity has also been found in the pyrolysis of methylcyclopropane [35e] compared to cyclopropane. The same treatments predict that perdeuterocyclobutane will be less readily cleaved than will cyclobutane, due to a simple mass effect on the groups which are moving along the critical coordinate. This isotope effect has been found,[35f] and in magnitude it corresponds to that predicted from the Slater theory. Accordingly, the suggestion [4f] that this isotope effect demonstrates participation of hydrogen in the transition state seems unnecessary.

The ease of cleavage of cyclobutanes to ethylenes can be markedly affected by substituents, and **45**, for instance, cleaves to phenanthrene at a rather low temperature.[36]

(45)

As an extreme case it has been found that the unusual olefin **46** is in equi-

35a R. H. Gerberich and W. D. Walters, *J. Am. Chem. Soc.*, **83**, 3935 (1961).

35b H. R. Gerberich and W. D. Walters, *J. Am. Chem. Soc.*, **83**, 4884 (1961).

35c N. B. Slater, "Theory of Unimolecular Reactions," Cornell University Press, Ithaca, 1959.

35d S. M. F. Kellner and W. D. Walters, *J. Phys. Chem.*, **65**, 466 (1961).

35e J. P. Chesick, *J. Am. Chem. Soc.*, **82**, 3277 (1960).

35f J. Langrish and H. D. Pritchard, *J. Phys. Chem.*, **62**, 761 (1958).

36 G. Wittig, G. Koenig, and K. Clauss, *Ann.*, **593**, 127 (1955).

librium with **47** even at room temperature.[37,38] The cyclobutane is apparently comparable in stability to the olefin; at lower temperatures such equilibria will of course be shifted in this direction.

(46)   (47)

Fluorine atom substituents have a marked effect on the position of olefin-cyclobutane equilibria, an effect which is not well understood at the present time. Although many examples can be found of the use of fluorocarbons in cyclobutane syntheses by thermal reactions,[38a] two particularly striking cases will be mentioned here. Perfluorobutadiene (**48**) is converted by heating to the cyclobutane derivative (**49**), and this at somewhat higher temperature reacts further to form the unusual tricyclic compound **50**.[39] A similar thermal

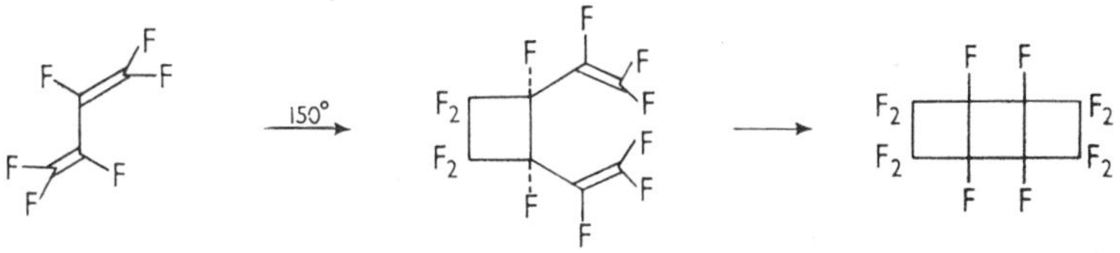

(48)   (49)   (50)

cyclization occurs with perfluoro-1,5-hexadiene (**51**), the bicyclohexane (**52**) being formed.[40]

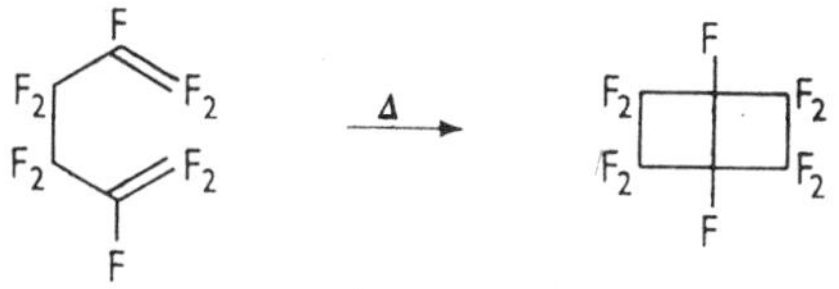

(51)   (52)

When the olefin component of the equilibrium is a cyclobutadiene derivative, then the dimer is favored, an example being the formation of **53** under the conditions of synthesis of its precursor (**54**).[41] Furthermore, while benzocyclobutadiene, during its formation, dimerizes to **55**,[42] in the presence

[37] K. Gundermann and R. Thomas, *Chem. Ber.*, **89**, 1263 (1956).
[38] K. Gundermann and R. Huchting, *Chem. Ber.*, **92**, 415 (1959).
[38a] J. D. Roberts and C. M. Sharts, *Organic Reactions*, Vol. XII, 1 (1962).
[39] M. Prober and W. T. Miller, *J. Am. Chem. Soc.*, **71**, 598 (1949).
[40] A. H. Fainberg and W. T. Miller, *J. Am. Chem. Soc.*, **79**, 4170 (1957).
[41] R. Criegee and G. Louis, *Chem. Ber.*, **90**, 417 (1957).
[42] M. Cava and D. Napier, *J. Am. Chem. Soc.*, **79**, 1701 (1957).

of nickel carbonyl the product is again a tricyclooctane derivative (**56**).[43] The tricyclooctadienes themselves are thermally unstable, except apparently in

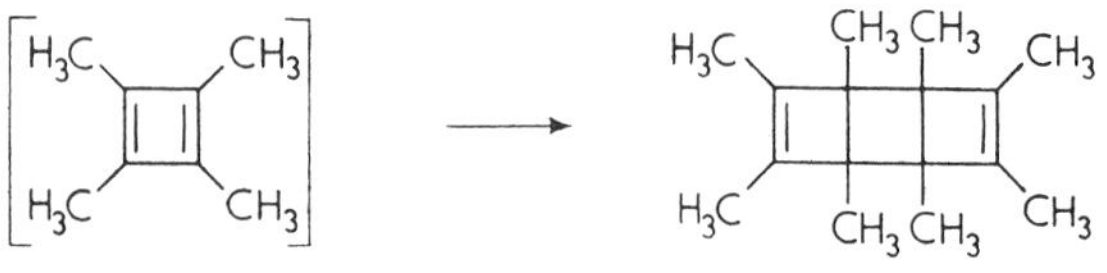

(54)   (53)

the fluorocarbon series, and at 150° **56** rearranges to dibenzocyclooctatetraene (**57**),[43] a process analogous to the pyrolysis of cyclobutane itself but occurring under much milder conditions. The benzene ring substituents may assist this

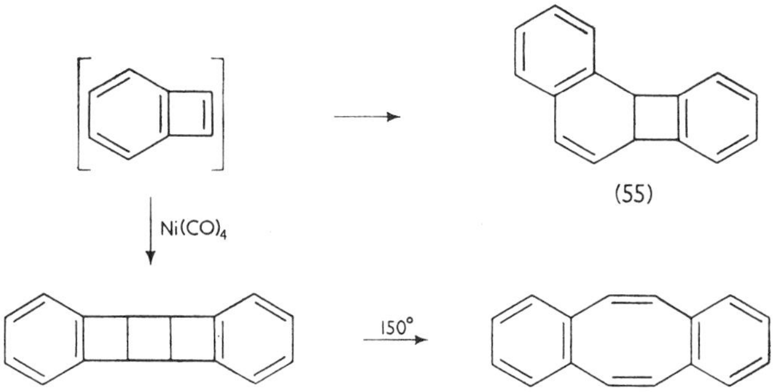

(55)

(56)   (57)

process, but it seems likely that a major extra factor in making the tricyclic cleavage so much easier is strain. For instance, **58** is cleaved to a cyclooctane derivative (**59**) at an even lower temperature than was used in the above example.[44] In some cases, rather more complex changes occur in the pyrolysis of tricyclooctadiene derivatives.[43a]

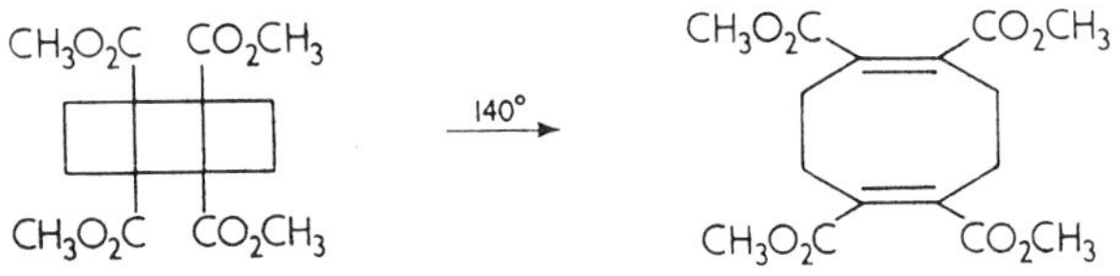

(58)   (59)

The pyrolysis of vinylcyclobutanes occurs differently, ring expansion rather than ring cleavage often being observed. This difference is similar to

---

[43] M. Avram, D. Dinu, and C. Nenitzescu, *Chem. & Ind.* (*London*), **1959**, 257.

[43a] R. Criegee, et. al., *Chem. Ber.*, **93**, 1553 (1960).

[44] E. Vogel and O. Roos, cited in E. Vogel, *Angew. Chem.*, **72**, 4 (1960).

that between vinylcyclopropanes and simple cyclopropanes. Pyrolysis of vinylcyclobutane itself (**60**) yields cyclohexene.[8] *cis*-Divinylcyclobutane (**61**)

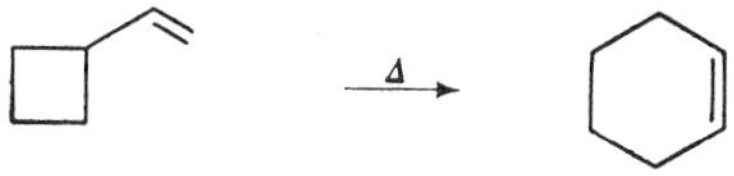

(60)

rearranges easily to cyclooctadiene,[45] but the *trans* isomer (**61a**), in this case, simply cleaves, and at a much higher temperature.[46] This difference furnishes

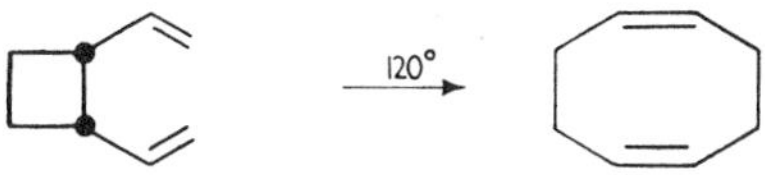

(61)

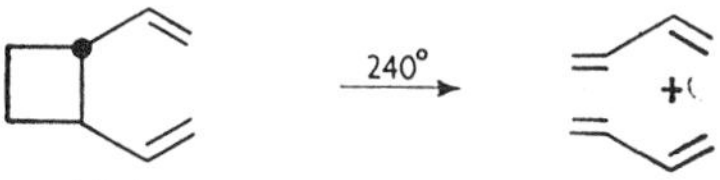

(61a)

evidence for the concerted nature of the *cis* rearrangement. Another example of this type of rearrangement is found in the chemistry of cyclooctatriene (**62**), which is in equilibrium with its bicyclic isomer even at 100°.[47]

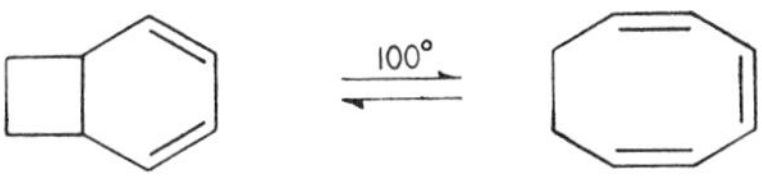

(62)

Cyclobutenes rearrange thermally to butadienes, and this explains the observation[48] that pyrolysis of **63** yields butadiene, not cyclobutene. The ease with which this rearrangement occurs depends on the nature of substituents, and, although the rearrangement of cyclobutene itself does not occur

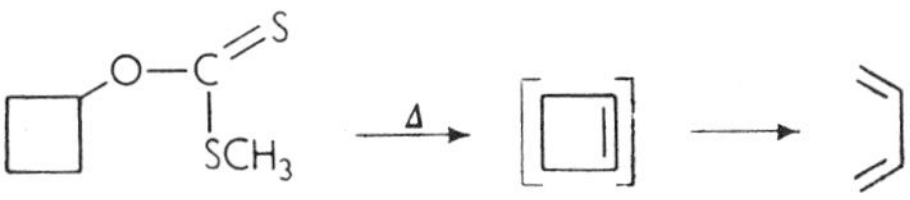

(63)

[45] E. Vogel, *Ann.*, **615**, 1 (1958).
[46] E. Vogel and K. Gajek, cited in E. Vogel, *Angew. Chem.*, **72**, 4 (1960).
[47] A. C. Cope, A. C. Haven, F. L. Ramp, and E. R. Trumbull, *J. Am. Chem. Soc.*, **74**, 4867 (1952).
[48] J. D. Roberts and C. W. Sauer, *J. Am. Chem. Soc.*, **71**, 3925 (1949).

under 200°, the diester (64) rearranges at 140°.[49] This illustrates the fact that the transition state for ring opening has appreciable product-like character,

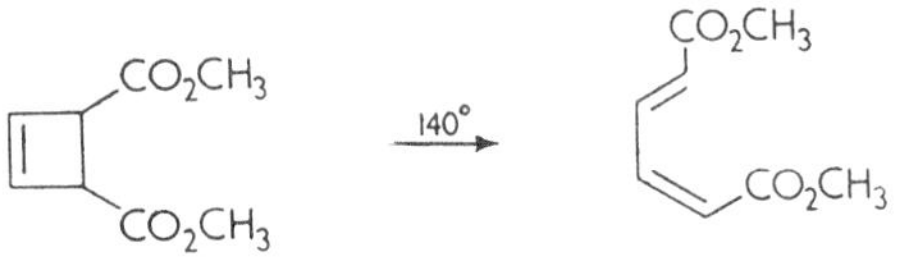

(64)

so that the development of effective conjugation in the product can assist the reaction. A further illustration of this factor is found in the observation [50] that 65 rearranges at a somewhat higher temperature, the net change in

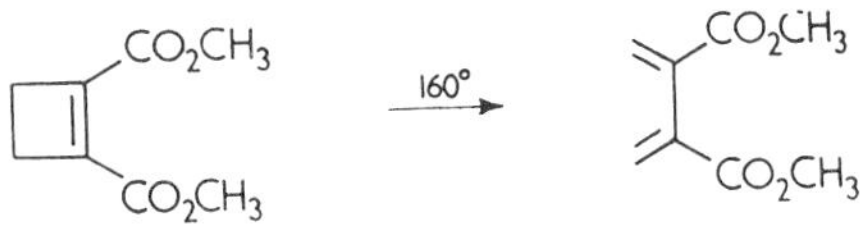

(65)

conjugation on going from starting material to product being somewhat less advantageous. The importance of the product structure in the transition state for such ring openings is seen in the contrast between the rather high temperatures required to rearrange 65a to tropylidene [50a] and the room temperature rearrangement of (postulated) 65b to the benzene.[50b] Ring opening

(65a)

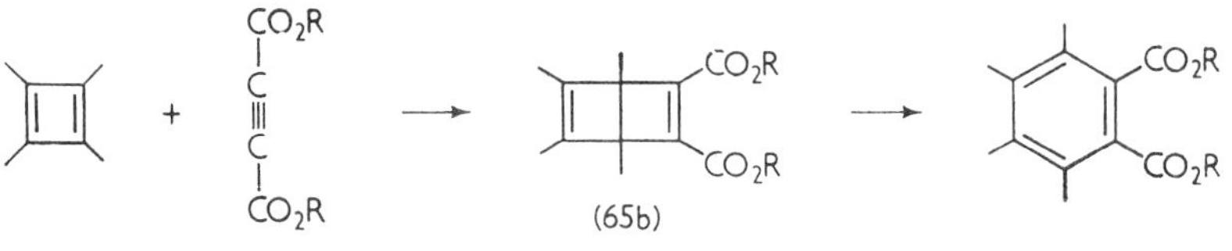

(65b)

at room temperature is also observed for 65d, the presumed intermediate in the conversion of 65c to 65e.[50c] As usual, fluorocarbons have a chemistry of

[49] E. Vogel, Angew. Chem., 66, 640 (1954).

[50] E. Vogel, Ann., 615, 14 (1958).

[50a] M. V. Evans and R. C. Lord, J. Am. Chem. Soc., 83, 3409 (1961).

[50b] C. E. Berkhoff, R. C. Cookson, J. Hudec, and R. O. Williams, Proc. Chem. Soc., 1961, 312.

[50c] R. Breslow and D. Kivelevich, unpublished work.

their own insofar as these equilibria are concerned. Perfluorocyclobutene (**66**) is in equilibrium with perfluorobutadiene, the cyclic compound being favored even at 500°.[51]

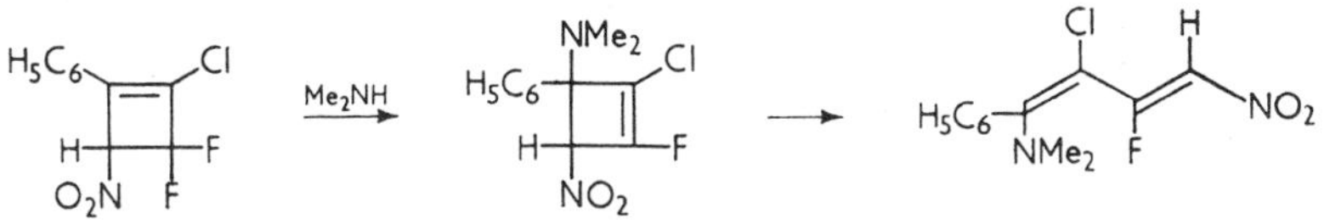

(65c)   (65d)   (65e)

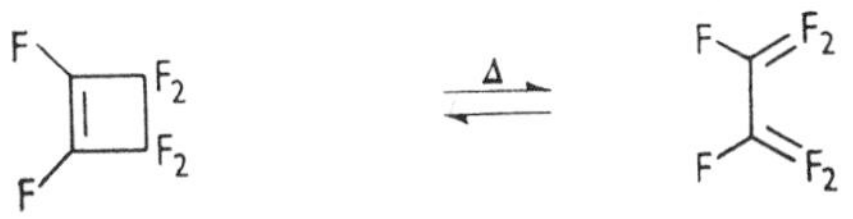

(66)

Another factor which can affect the position of this equilibrium is the presence of a fused benzene ring. Benzocyclobutenes exist principally in the cyclized form: isomerization to the butadiene form in this case involves the change of a benzene ring to an *o*-quinoid form, an *o*-xylylene. However, the properties of such compounds as diphenylbenzocyclobutene (**67**) suggest that there is an equilibrium, for **67** reacts with sulfur dioxide in refluxing carbon tetrachloride to form **68**.[52] Recent studies[53] show that the reaction of

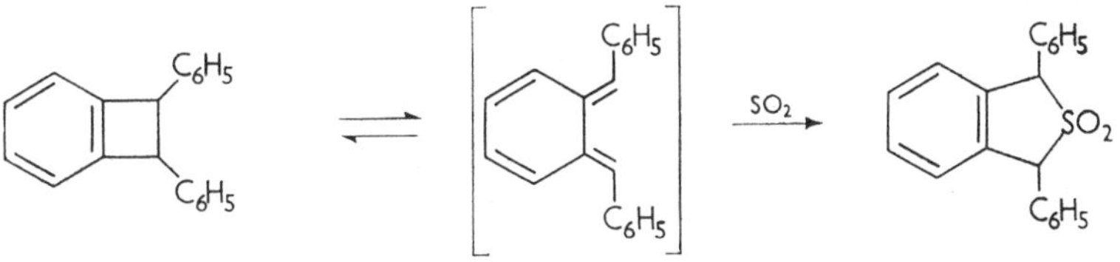

(67)   (68)

69 with iodide ion yields **71** by way of the intermediate **70**, which has been trapped with dienophiles. It would be expected that the position of an

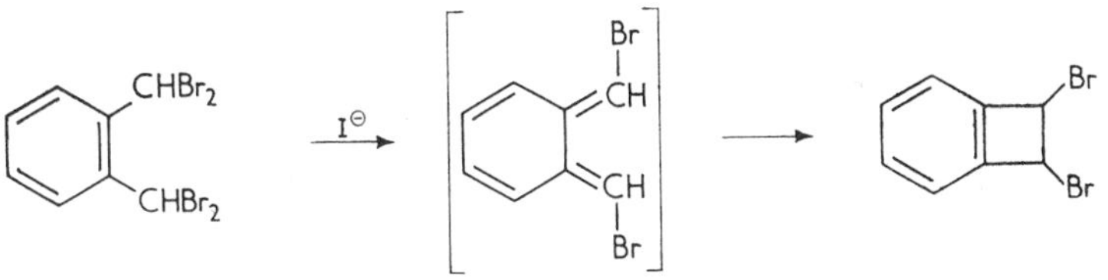

(69)   (70)   (71)

[51] R. N. Haszeldine and J. E. Osborne, *J. Chem. Soc. (London)*, **1955**, 3880.

[52] F. R. Jensen and W. E. Coleman, *J. Am. Chem. Soc.*, **80**, 6149 (1958); F. R. Jensen, W. E. Coleman and A. J. Berlin, *Tetrahedron Letters*, **1962**, 15.

[53] M. P. Cava, A. A. Deana, and K. Muth, *J. Am. Chem. Soc.*, **81**, 6458 (1959).

equilibrium between benzocyclobutene form and *o*-xylylene form could be affected by substituents. This is already clear in the chemistry of **67**, in which the extra phenyl groups stabilize the open form. An interesting example of another sort is furnished by the naphthalene compounds **71a** and **71b**. Both

(71a)   (71c)

(71b)   (71d)

are in equilibrium with open forms at high temperatures, but the relative reactivities of the two suggest that the **71a** to **71c** conversion occurs more readily than does the **71b** to **71d** isomerization. This is reasonable, since **71c** retains one benzenoid ring while **71d** is completely quinoid.[53a]

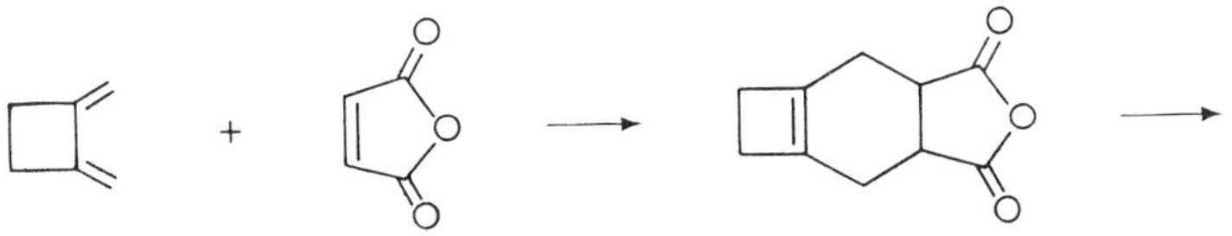

(73)

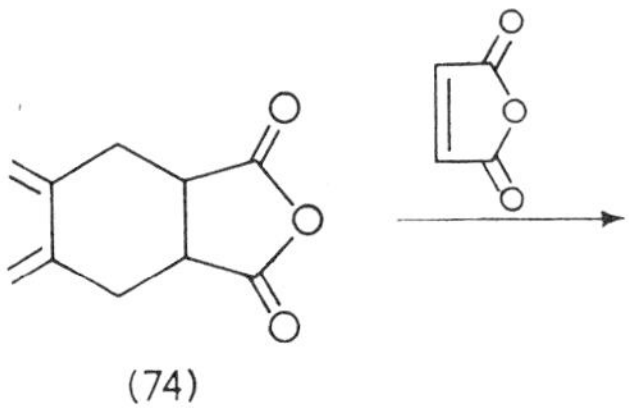

(74)

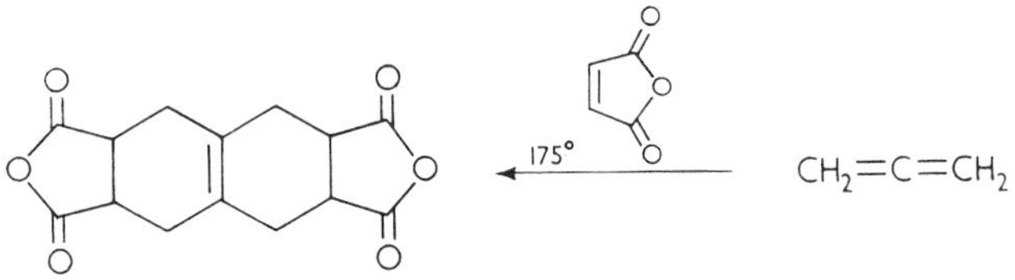

(72)

[53a] M. Cava, R. Shirley, and B. Erickson, *J. Org. Chem.*, **27**, 755 (1962).

An unusual reaction occurs between allene and maleic anhydride, the product being **72**.[54] Although this seems at first sight unrelated to the processes just discussed, the mechanism has been clarified by later studies [55] with dimethylenecyclobutane, the thermal dimerization product of allene, for the adduct **73** has been shown to react with maleic anhydride, via the intermediate **74**, to yield **72** as the final product.

Cyclobutenones could, in principle, be in equilibrium with butadiene derivatives, which in this case would also be ketenes. Such an equilibrium has been demonstrated for **75**; for the racemization of optically active **75** occurs through **76**, rather than by enolization. Furthermore, **75** is, in fact, formed when reactions are run which might be expected to yield **76**, the open isomer.[56]

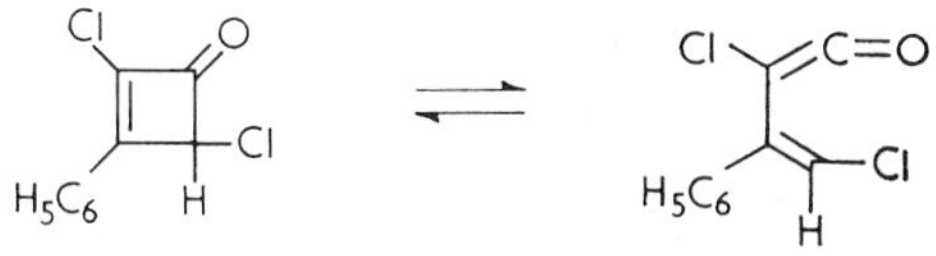

(75)   (76)

This reversible ring opening is intermediate in the hydrolysis of some cyclobutenone derivatives occurring in acetic acid, the process taking place through the ketene isomer.[57] The alkaline hydrolysis of cyclobutenones, however, involves a different mechanism and will be discussed later.

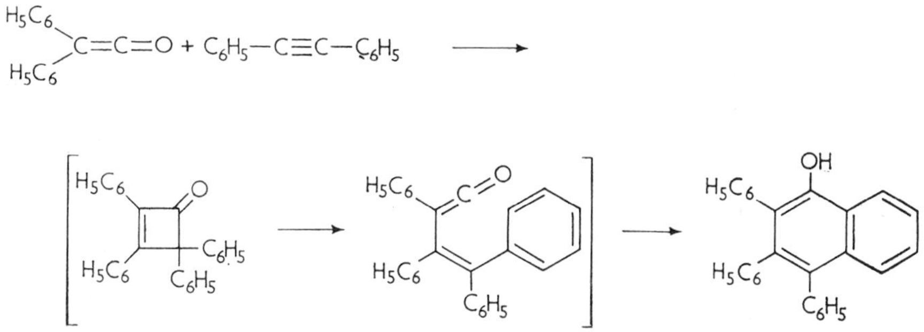

Finally, the thermal ring opening of a cyclobutenone must be involved in the reaction by which diphenylketene and diphenylacetylene form triphenylnaphthol,[58] although in this case the intermediate has not been trapped. A related reaction has been observed, however, in which diphenylketene

[54] K. Alder and O. Ackermann, *Chem. Ber.*, **87**, 1567 (1954).

[55] A. T. Blomquist and J. A. Verdol, *J. Am. Chem. Soc.*, **78**, 109 (1956).

[56] E. F. Jenny and J. D. Roberts, *J. Am. Chem. Soc.*, **78**, 2005 (1956).

[57] E. F. Silversmith, Y. Kitahara, M. C. Caserio, and J. D. Roberts, *J. Am. Chem. Soc.*, **80**, 5840 (1958).

[58] L. I. Smith and H. H. Hoehn, *J. Am. Chem. Soc.*, **61**, 2619 (1939), **63**, 1175, 1176, 1178, 1180, 1181 (1941).

reacts with ethoxypropyne to form the cyclobutenone derivative **77**, which on warming yields the naphthol **78**.[59]

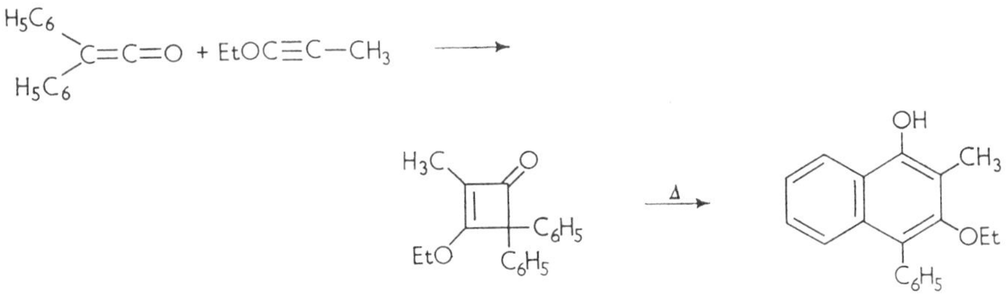

(77)   (78)

3. REARRANGEMENTS INVOLVING CARBONIUM IONS, AND ACID-CATALYZED REARRANGEMENTS

In this category will be included not only those reactions for which carbonium ion intermediates have been demonstrated, but also those for which such intermediates may be presumed on the basis of the reaction conditions.

A. Cyclopropane Derivatives

It is, of course, well known that cyclopropane rings may be opened with acid; the product with a proton acid HX is apparently, for cyclopropane, the normal propyl derivative $CH_3CH_2CH_2X$. This reaction has been studied kinetically,[60] and it seems clear that the process involves opening of a protonated cyclopropane ring to give a more or less solvated propyl cation, which then adds the anion. Some evidence for the reverse process, collapse of a propyl cation to cyclopropane, has also recently been obtained.[61] With Lewis acids, ring opening also occurs and the product may be either a polymer [61a] or a propane derivative.[62,62a]

$$\triangle \ + \ LiAlH_4 \ \longrightarrow \ Al(CH_2CH_2CH_3)_3 \qquad (4)$$

Ordinarily, fission occurs according to a modified Markownikoff rule in substituted cyclopropanes, the proton adding to the least substituted carbon

[59] J. F. Arens, *Angew. Chem.*, **70**, 631 (1958); cf. E. F. Jenny, K. Schenker, and R. B. Woodward, *Angew. Chem.*, **73**, 756 (1961).

[60] C. D. Lawrence and C. F. H. Tipper, *J. Chem. Soc. (London)*, **1955**, 713.

[61] P. Skell and I. Starer, *J. Am. Chem. Soc.*, **82**, 2971 (1960); M. S. Silver, *J. Am. Chem. Soc.*, **82**, 2972 (1960).

[61a] M. Yanagita, et al., *Rika Gaku Kenkyusho Hokoku*, **37**, 429 (1961).

[62] C. F. H. Tipper and D. A. Walker, *Chem. & Ind. (London)*, **1957**, 730.

[62a] R. Ya. Levina, V. N. Kostin, and T. K. Ustynynk, *J. Gen. Chem. (USSR)*, **30**, 383 (1960).

and cleavage occurring so as to leave the best carbonium ion.[62b] Although it had been suggested that in the acid cleavage of maaliane (**79**) a stereochemical requirement results in ring opening in violation of this rule,[63a] more

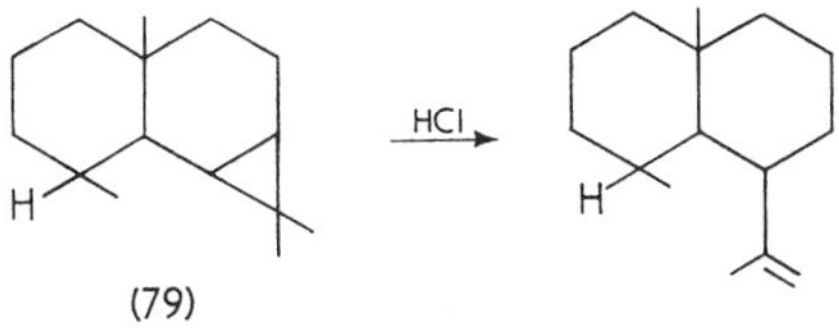

(79)

recent work shows that opening in an expected direction occurs.[63b] Thus no violation of the rule is yet known except under Friedel-Crafts conditions (see below).

An interesting rearrangement occurs when **80** is treated with acid, the product being an indane derivative (**81**).[64] This can be rationalized by postulating the expected ring opening, with subsequent hydride shifts equilibrat-

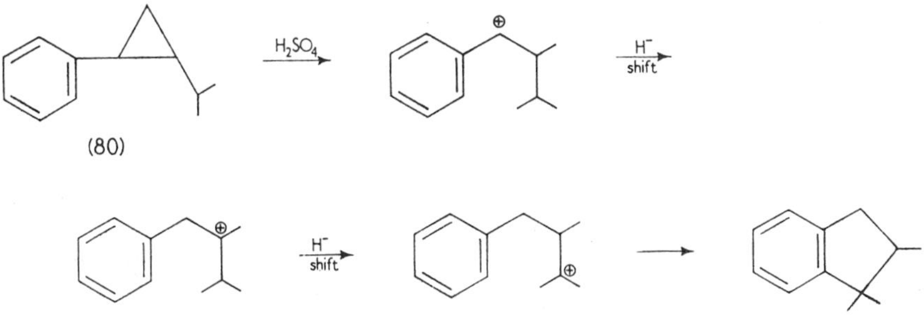

(80)

(81)

ing the three carbonium ions shown, which are all of comparable stability; the equilibrium is displaced by attack of the last ion on the benzene ring.

Cyclopropane derivatives can be components in Friedel-Crafts reactions, and in some cases the products are those normally expected from simple ring opening. Thus cyclopropane reacts with benzene, in the presence of aluminum chloride, to yield n-propylbenzene as the only product (eq. 5).[65] Furthermore,

$$\triangle + C_6H_6 + AlCl_3 \longrightarrow CH_3CH_2CH_2-C_6H_5 \qquad (5)$$

the cyclopropane ring can be the substrate for attack by a Friedel-Crafts complex, in contrast to its role above, and with acetyl chloride and aluminum

---

[62b] For a recent review, cf. A. Bhati, *Perfumery Essent. Oil Record*, **53**, 15 (1962).

[63] (a) G. Büchi and D. White, *J. Am. Chem. Soc.*, **79**, 750 (1957). (b) G. Büchi, M. Wittenau, and D. White, *J. Am. Chem. Soc.*, **81**, 1968 (1959).

[64] D. Davidson and J. Feldman, *J. Am. Chem. Soc.*, **66**, 488 (1949).

[65] L. Schmerling, *Ind. Eng. Chem.*, **40**, 2072 (1948).

chloride nortricyclene (82) is acetylated in the normal manner.[66] However, the acylation of cyclopropane itself gives curious results, the products being

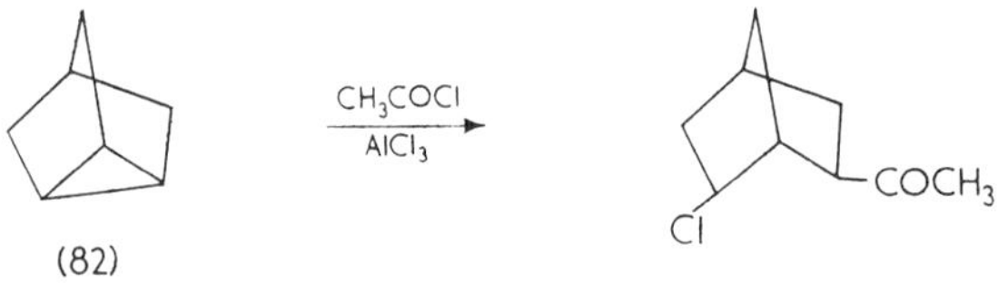

the expected ketone (83) plus an isomer (84) which is at first sight rather difficult to account for.[67] With 1,1-dimethylcyclopropane (85) this "abnormal" reaction is the exclusively occurring one, 86 being the only product.[68]

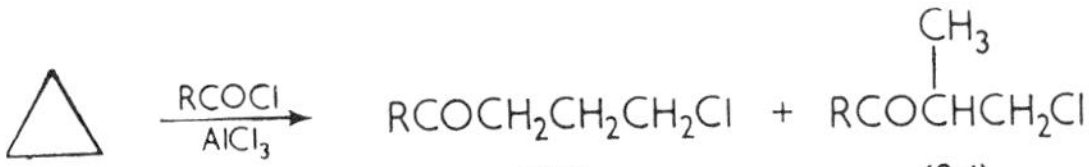

The mechanism operating to effect this skeletal rearrangement is not yet clear. Some of the obvious possibilities have been ruled out by the finding that neither the "normal" product nor an acylcyclopropane (e.g., 87) is an intermediate.[68]

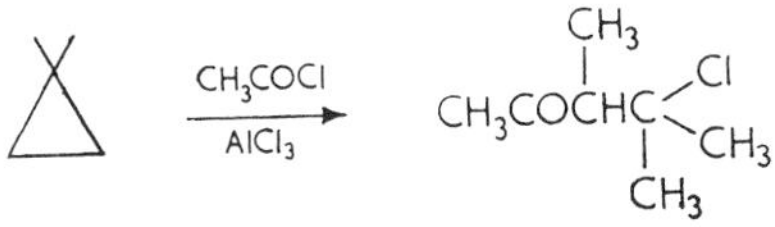

These ring openings have resulted from the attack of an external reagent on the single bond of a cyclopropane; the rearrangements observed in the chemistry of cyclopropyl cations and cyclopropylcarbinyl cation involve internal attack on these bonds. The cyclopropyl cation itself is not easily formed, because of ring strain, but when formed it readily rearranges, cyclopropyl tosylate (88)[69] yielding allyl acetate on acetolysis.[70]

[66] H. Hart and R. A. Martin, J. Org. Chem., 24, 1267 (1959).

[67] H. Hart and O. E. Curtis, J. Am. Chem. Soc., 79, 931 (1957).

[68] H. Hart and G. Levitt, J. Org. Chem., 24, 2161 (1959).

[69] J. D. Roberts and V. C. Chambers, J. Am. Chem. Soc., 73, 3176 (1951).

[70] J. D. Roberts and V. C. Chambers, J. Am. Chem. Soc., 73, 5034 (1951).

That the transition state for this solvolysis does not resemble the allyl cation very much, and that a more or less classical cyclopropyl cation may thus be

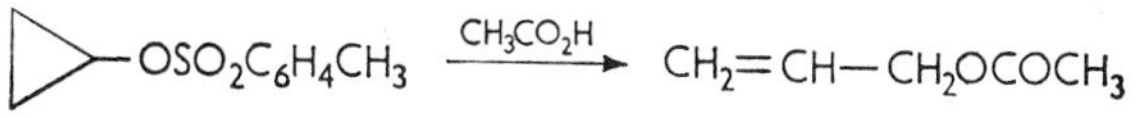

$$\text{▷}\!-\!OSO_2C_6H_4CH_3 \xrightarrow{CH_3CO_2H} CH_2\!=\!CH\!-\!CH_2OCOCH_3$$

(88)

involved as an intermediate, is indicated by the very slow rate of this reaction. There is a considerable geometrical difference between the allyl cation and the cyclopropyl cation, of course, so that they are by no means resonance forms of a common nonclassical cation.

The cyclopropyl cation can also be an intermediate in the acid-catalyzed rearrangements of cyclopropenes, the first step being protonation of the double bond. This is apparently involved in the polymerization of sterculic acid (89)[71] and in the acid-catalyzed rearrangement of diphenylcyclopropene carboxylic acid (90) to diphenylcrotonolactone.[71a] Such a ring opening is

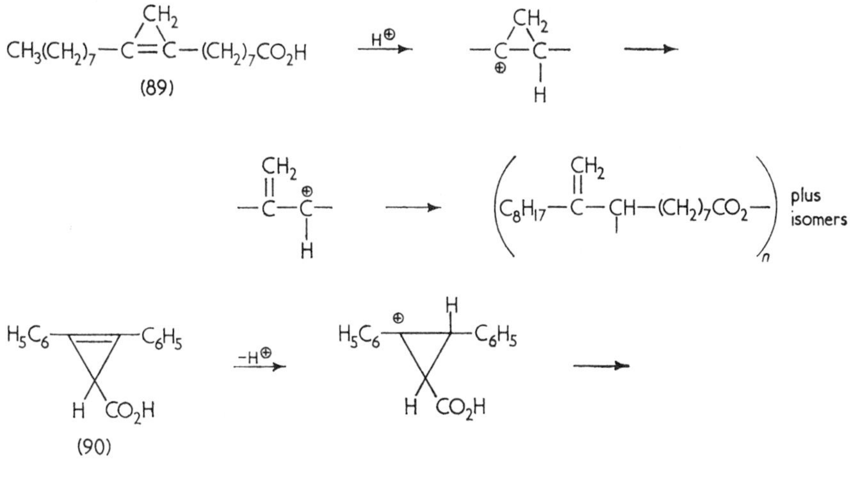

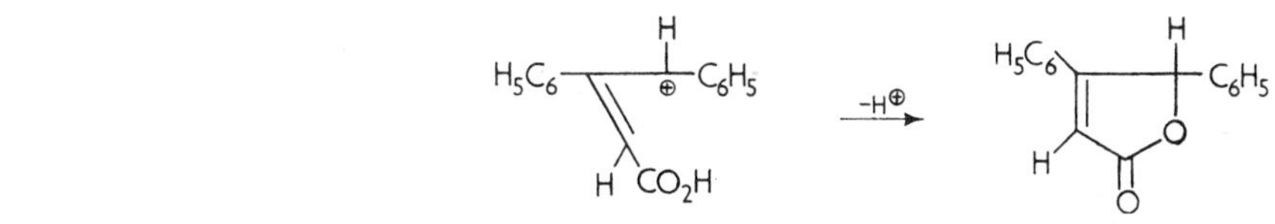

undoubtedly involved also in the rearrangment of triphenylcyclopropene to diphenylindene by acid;[71b] however, rearrangement does not always occur

[71] K. Rinehart, C. Tarimu, and T. Culbertson, *J. Am. Chem. Soc.*, **81**, 5008 (1959); K. Rinehart, S. Goldberg, C. Tarimu, and T. Culbertson, *J. Am. Chem. Soc.*, **83**, 225 (1961).

[71a] R. Breslow and M. Battiste, unpublished work.

[71b] P. Wolf, unpublished work.

during electrophilic addition to cyclopropenes, since cyclopropene itself reacts with bromine to give dibromocyclopropane.[71c] Although the solvolyses

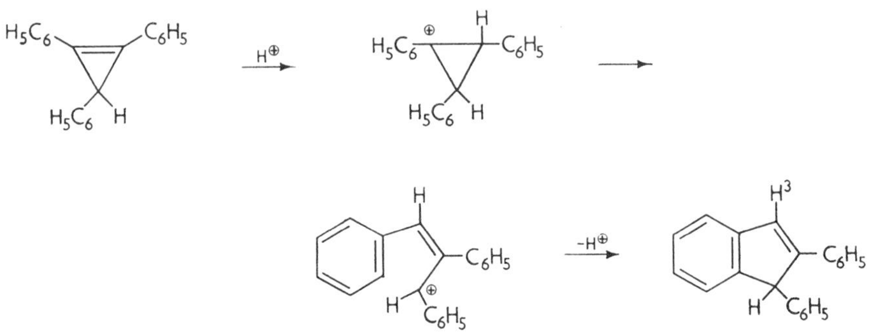

of cyclopropyl tosylate and cyclopropyl chloride are quite slow,[70] a number of dihalocyclopropane systems ionize more readily. Thus the adduct of dibromo-carbene and cyclopentene (91) rearranges under very mild conditions to 1,2-dibromo-2-cyclohexene (91a).[72] Although solvolyses of 91 and 91a in

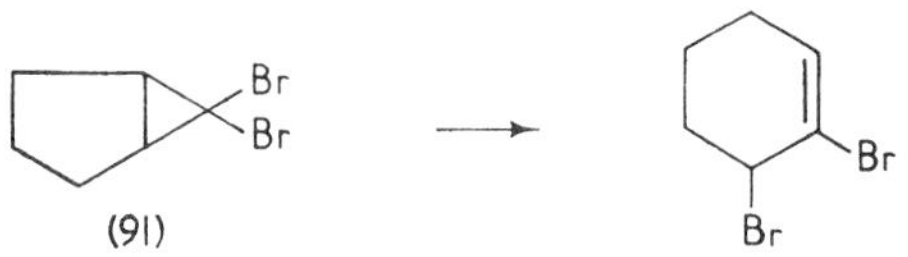

aqueous acetone both lead to the expected bromocyclohexenol, it was found that 91 with aqueous silver nitrate yielded only this alcohol, while 91a under the same conditions afforded, in addition, a substantial amount of nitrate ester; this interesting result suggests [72] that the carbonium ion formed from the two compounds is not quite the same.

The reaction of pyrrole with dichlorocarbene leads directly to chloro-pyridine (eq. 6), and a similar process involving the reaction of sodium

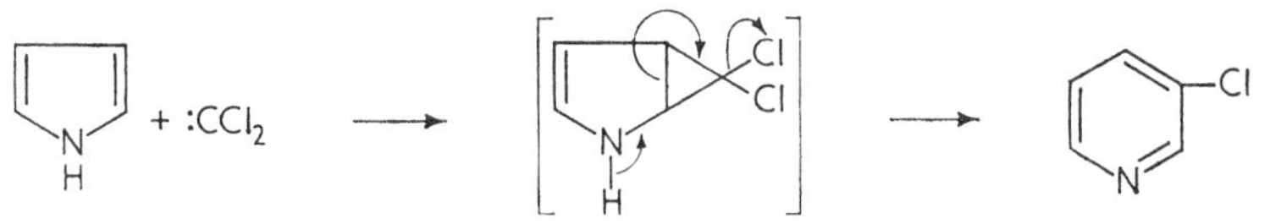

cyclopentadienide and chloroform yields directly chlorobenzene (eq. 7).[73] It might be thought that these rearrangements are unlikely to involve the

71c K. B. Wiberg and W. J. Bartley, *J. Am. Chem. Soc.*, **82**, 6375 (1960).

72 J. Sonnenberg and S. Winstein, *J. Org. Chem.*, **27**, 748 (1962), and references therein.

73 A. P. terBorg and A. F. Bickel, *Proc. Chem. Soc.* (*London*), **1958**, 283.

cyclopropyl cation, but instead proceed by attack by the electron pair from the nitrogen or from carbon (with the assistance of base) (eq. 8). However, the

$$\text{(7)}$$

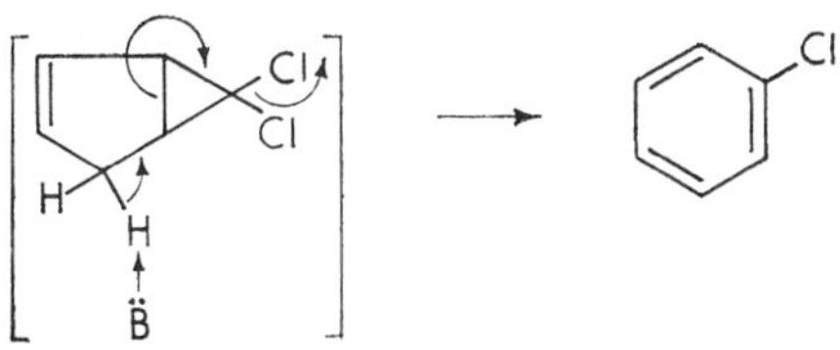

$$\text{(8)}$$

corresponding intermediate (**92**) has been isolated in the reaction of dichloro-carbene with indene, and it has been found that its rearrangement to chloro-naphthalene (**93**) is zero order in base.[74] This result suggests that the rate-controlling step involves ionization of the chlorine to afford the cation (**94**); it must be presumed that considerable delocalization of charge occurs

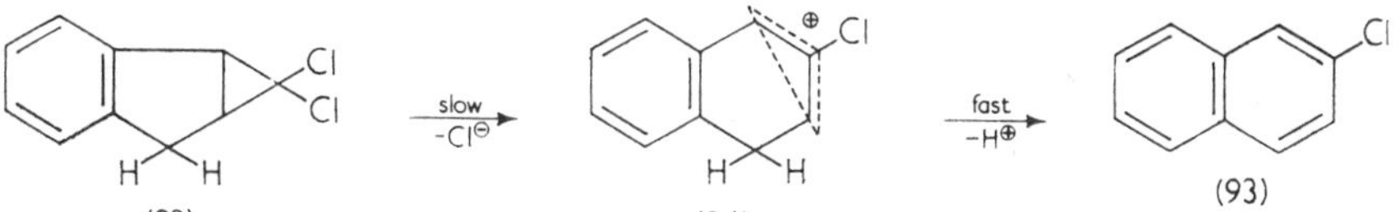

in the transition state in order that ionization proceed as readily as is observed. The generality of this mechanism remains to be explored.

Finally, mention should be made of a completely different rearrangement which the dichlorocarbene adduct of cycloheptatriene undergoes. When **95** is heated, the product is **96**.[73] This change can be simply formulated in terms of the already discussed isomerizations.

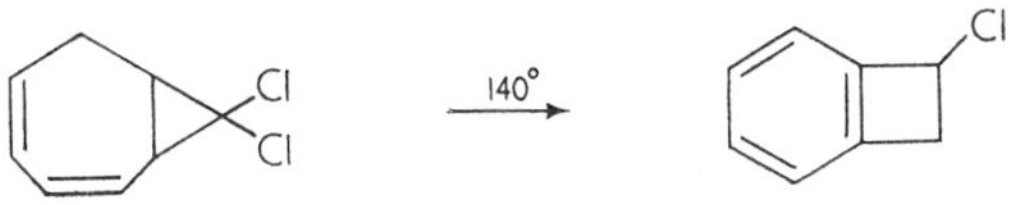

The Cyclopropylcarbinyl Cation.   The most interesting chemistry in small ring rearrangements involves the reactions of derivatives of the cyclopropyl-carbinyl cation (**97**). It might be expected that such a cation could undergo ring expansion to form the cyclobutyl cation (**98**), since thereby a primary

[74] W. E. Parham, H. E. Reiff, and P. Swartzentruber, *J. Am. Chem. Soc.*, **78**, 1437 (1956).

carbonium ion is transformed into a secondary cation and ring strain is also relieved. Alternatively, derivatives of **97** might undergo ring opening to derivatives of the allylcarbinyl cation (**99**), the driving force in this case

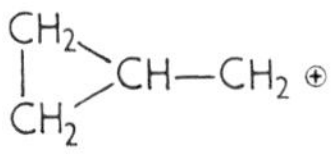

being only strain relief. In actual fact, the situation is more complicated than would be implied by either of these simple alternatives, and substituents play a major role in deciding the course of the rearrangements. As an example of the type of situation found in this series of rearrangements, the case of cyclopropyldimethylcarbinol (**100**) may be considered. When this compound is treated with HCl, the product is the ring-opened chloride (**101**),

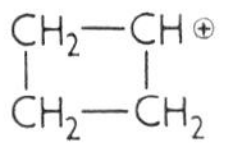

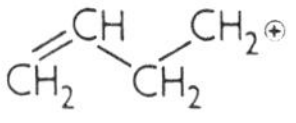

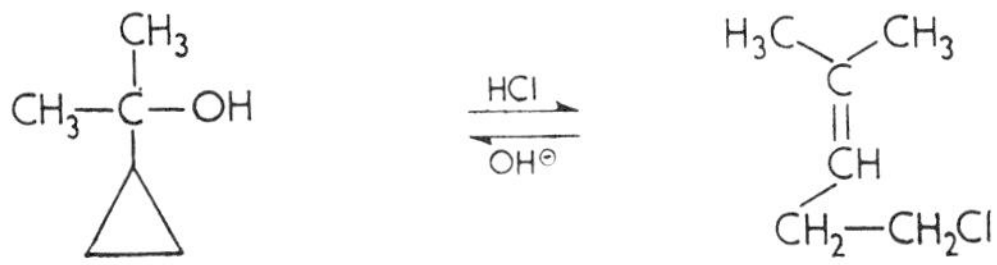

so here it seems clear that strain relief has caused the opening of the initially formed cyclopropylcarbinyl cation derivative. However, when **101** is hydrolyzed, the alcohol formed is **100** again.[75] If strain relief is the driving force for the first reaction, what can be the reason for the second?

Another interesting situation has been observed in deamination reactions. If cyclopropylcarbinylamine (**102**) is treated with nitrous acid, a mixture of products is obtained, and it was early noted that this mixture consists chiefly of cyclopropylcarbinol (**103**) and cyclobutanol (**104**) and that a similar mixture is formed when cyclobutylamine is deaminated.[76,77] More recently it has been found that precisely the same mixture is obtained from each reaction, the product containing a small amount of allycarbinol (**105**) in addition.[78] One

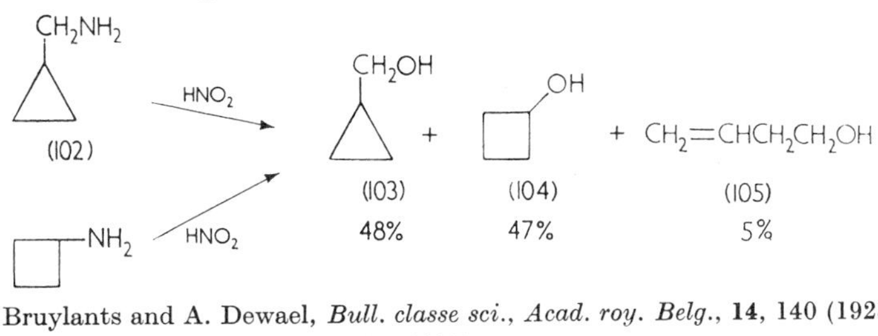

[75] P. Bruylants and A. Dewael, *Bull. classe sci., Acad. roy. Belg.*, **14**, 140 (1928).

[76] N. Demjanow, *Ber.*, **40**, 4393, 4961 (1907).

[77] R. Skrabal, *Monatsh.*, **70**, 420 (1937).

[78] J. D. Roberts and R. H. Mazur, *J. Am. Chem. Soc.*, **73**, 2509 (1951).

would expect cyclobutanol to be more stable than cyclopropylcarbinol, and this expectation has been confirmed by the quantitative conversion of **103** to **104** under equilibrating conditions.[79] The formation of an equal mixture of the two alcohols from either deamination reaction thus seems even more unusual, the reaction from cyclobutylamine in particular being another case in which the product is more strained than the starting material.

Considerable light has been shed on the reason for these striking results from a study of solvolysis reactions and rates, and although our primary concern in this chapter is not with reaction rates *per se*, kinetic studies have indicated the necessity of formulating some nonclassical intermediate ions for reactions such as those we have mentioned. The most striking experimental result is that cyclopropylcarbinyl chloride (**105**) is extremely reactive in solvolytic S_N1 reactions and is, in fact, forty times as reactive as is the allylic chloride (**106**);[78] of course, ordinary saturated primary halides are essentially inert in such solvolyses when compared to the allyl compounds. Work on related compounds has confirmed this high reactivity; cyclopropylcarbinyl benzenesulfonate (**107**) also solvolyzes very rapidly.[80,81] To be

sure, the high reactivity of **105** can be rationalized by generalizations about the olefinic character of a cyclopropane ring, but it is still striking that **105** is more reactive than the corresponding ethylenic compound (**106**). Cyclobutyl chloride is also unusual, solvolyzing one and a half times as rapidly as does **106**,[78] and thus being more reactive than is cyclopentyl chloride, contrary to what is to be expected from ring strain effects.[82]

The reaction products from the solvolyses of the cyclobutyl or cyclopropylcarbinyl chlorides are mixture of alcohols, and the mixture in each case is identical and is also identical with that obtained from the deaminations of the amines. Thus, whatever the reason for the high reactivity of these halides, it is likely to contain the reason for the formation of the same product mixture from both the cyclopropylcarbinyl and the cyclobutyl series. For the solvolyses to be fast, it seems that there must be some delocalization of charge in the intermediate carbonium ions, and a simple form in which this can

[79] M. C. Caserio, J. D. Roberts, and W. H. Graham, *Tetrahedron*, **11**, 171 (1960).
[80] C. G. Bergstrom and S. Siegel, *J. Am. Chem. Soc.*, **74**, 145 (1952).
[81] Cf. A. Streitwieser, *Chem. Revs.*, **56**, 571 (1956), for review.
[82] H. C. Brown and M. Borkowski, *J. Am. Chem. Soc.*, **74**, 1894 (1952).

occur involves a nonclassical ion (**108**), a bicyclobutonium ion.[83] Here a structure intermediate between a cyclopropylcarbinyl cation and a cyclo-butyl cation is suggested to be more stable than either classical ion, the ring

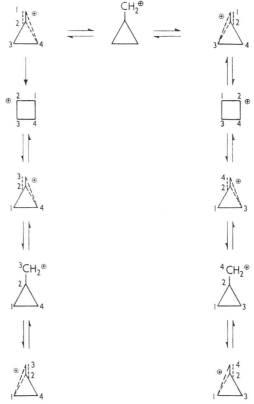

thus having partially expanded if the cyclopropyl compound is the starting material and partially contracted if the substrate is in the cyclobutyl series. Because the intermediate in such Wagner-Meerwein rearrangements has some positive charge on the migrating carbon, it can also be represented as having some of the character of the allylcarbinyl cation, and there is thus delocaliza-

[83] R. H. Mazur, W. N. White, D. A. Semenov, C. C. Lee, M. S. Silver, and J. D. Roberts, *J. Am. Chem. Soc.*, **81**, 4390 (1959).

tion of the charge over three carbon atoms, which apparently more than makes up for the strain in **108**. One of the "resonance forms" written for **108** is a cyclobutyl cation, although with unusual geometry. With normal geometry such a cation could, of course, collapse to **108** in either of two equivalent ways, since either methylene group adjacent to the methine carbon could begin to develop some charge in the cyclopropylcarbinyl resonance form. Thus it would be expected that six bicyclobutonium ions could be in rapid equilibrium, and the interchange between them can be represented simply, although actually it would be expected that no intermediate so classical as a true cyclobutyl or cyclopropylcarbinyl cation would intervene.

If this equilibration is very rapid, it is apparent that the three methylene groups of the original cyclopropylcarbinyl or cyclobutyl system become equivalent, and it might even be thought that the true nonclassical ion is none of the six bicyclobutonium ions written above, but is rather a tricyclobutonium ion (**109**) in which all three methylene groups are equivalent.[80,84] Some evidence for this is found in the reaction of cyclopropylcarbinyl chloride with Lucas' reagent, zinc chloride and HCl. Under these

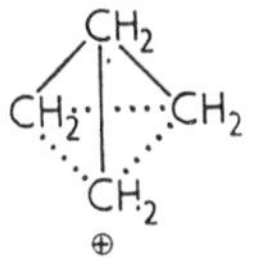

(109)

conditions the only product is allylcarbinyl chloride, since of the three related systems this open chain one has the least strain and is thus the ultimate product under vigorous equilibrating conditions. When the starting cyclopropyl compound is labeled with carbon-14 in the carbinyl group, the ^{14}C is found to be equally distributed in the three methylenes of the product (eq. 9).[83] The difficulty here is that under these equilibrating conditions there

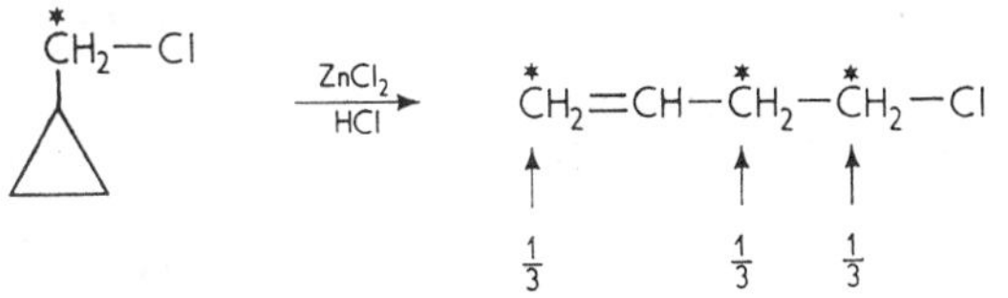

would be ample opportunity for rearrangements among the various bicyclobutonium ions described above, so it is not necessarily required that there be a single intermediate (**109**) in which all three methylenes are equivalent. For this reason an irreversible reaction, the deamination of labeled cyclopropylcarbinyl amine (**110**), was examined, and it was found that in the major

[84] J. D. Roberts and R. H. Mazur, *J. Am. Chem. Soc.*, **73**, 3542 (1951).

products, the cyclopropyl and cyclobutyl derivatives, the methylene groups have approached equivalence but have not attained it.[83] It thus seems that

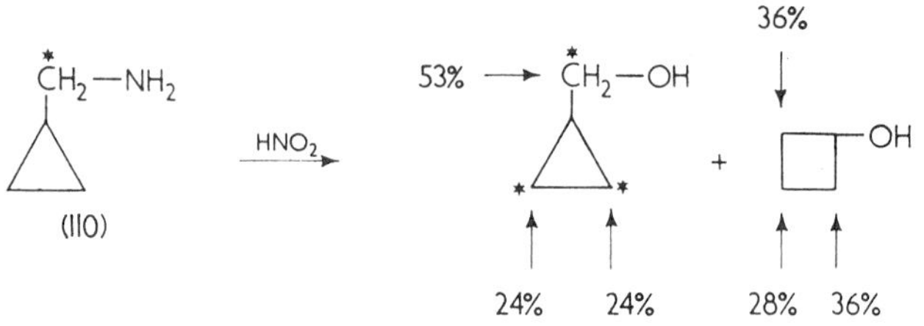

in the deamination reaction rearrangements occur among bicyclobutonium ion intermediates, and **109** is not the immediate product if it is involved at all. It will be apparent that unsymmetrical labeling in the product cyclobutanol, with the least label in the C_3 methylene group, is predicted if the initially formed bicyclobutonium ion does not have an opportunity to rearrange completely before it reacts with water. A similar interpretation can be attached to the excess of label in the carbinyl methylene group of the cyclopropylmethanol.

Although it seems clear that the mutual interconversion of cyclopropylcarbinyl and cyclobutyl compounds proceeds through the intermediates discussed, one might wonder about the relationship of these intermediates to the open chain compounds, the allylcarbinyl derivatives. It is found that deamination of allylcarbinylamine yields a mixture, including the derived alcohol and products **111** and **112** as well as small amounts of cyclopropylcarbinyl and cyclobutyl alcohol, which is quite different from that obtained

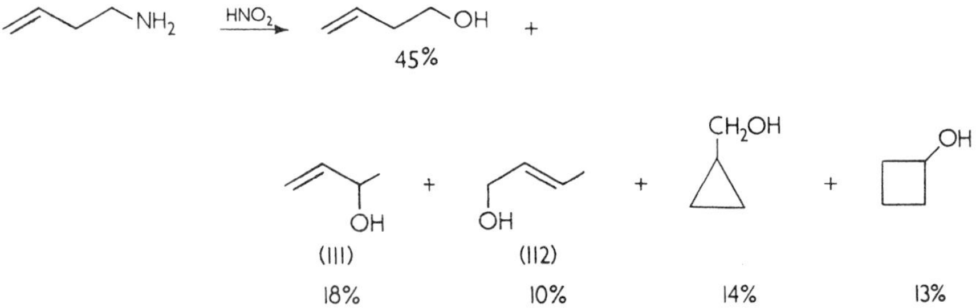

from the cyclic compounds.[78] The interpretation of this fact is clouded somewhat by uncertainty about the exact nature of carbonium ions derived from deaminations,[85] but it seems that the homoallyl cation is distinct from the bicyclobutonium ions, that it may be converted to them (as evidenced by the typical composition of the cyclopropylmethanol-cyclobutanol mixture), but

[85] For references, cf. ref. 83, fn. 15.

that it yields several products not found when the cyclic compounds are substrates. Again the cyclopropylcarbinol and cyclobutanol formed in this deamination reaction are derived from a mixture of equilibrating bicyclobutonium ions rather than a tricyclobutonium ion, for deamination of allylcarbinyl amine 1-^{14}C affords **103** and **104** in which the label is distributed almost equally among the methylene groups, but not quite.[85a] A slight excess of label is found in those positions expected if some of the first-formed bicyclobutonium ion is intercepted before equilibration is complete.

The presence of small amounts of **111** and **112** might be hard to detect along with the 5% of allylcarbinol in the deaminations or solvolyses of the cyclic compounds, but in the conversion of cyclopropylcarbinyl chloride to allylcarbinyl chloride with Lucas' reagent (eq. 10) no such rearrangement

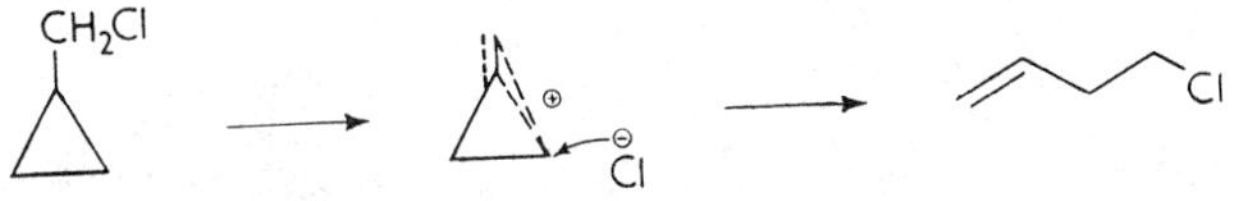

$$\text{(10)}$$

products were found. This suggests that the ring-opening reaction comes from attack by chloride ion on the bicyclobutonium ion, rather than by prior conversion of this ion to the classical homoallyl cation.

The exact composition of the mixture obtained when the bicyclobutonium ions react depends on the attacking reagent, and water showed no preference between the cyclopropylcarbinyl and the cyclobutyl modes of reaction. When cyclopropylcarbinol is treated with thionyl chloride, however, much less rearrangement takes place, the result being precisely the same mixture as is obtained from cyclobutanol (see eq. 11). This again demonstrates a common

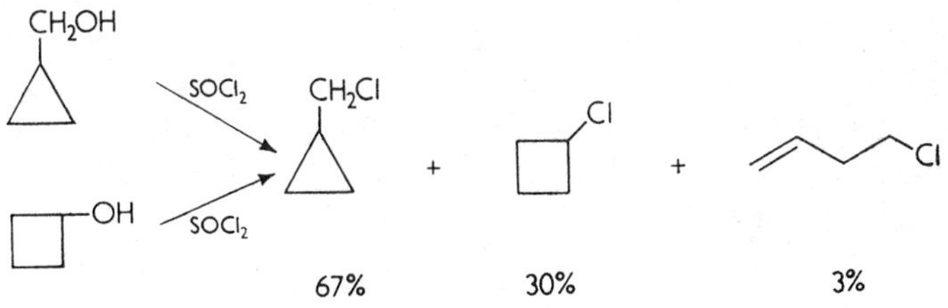

| | 67% | 30% | 3% |

$$\text{(11)}$$

intermediate, but shows also the preference by chloride ion for one mode of attack on that intermediate.[78] Allylcarbinol reacts with thionyl chloride to yield only the unrearranged chloride (eq. 12), but this need not involve a carbonium ion mechanism.

$$CH_2\!\!=\!\!CHCH_2CH_2OH \xrightarrow{SOCl_2} CH_2\!\!=\!\!CHCH_2CH_2Cl \qquad (12)$$

[85a] J. Renk and J. D. Roberts, *J. Am. Chem. Soc.*, **83**, 878 (1961).

The discussion so far has centered entirely on the parent compounds in the interconvertible set, but the exact structure of a bicyclobutonium ion would be expected to differ according to the substitution when carbon-substituted derivatives of cyclopropylcarbinyl cations are involved, and this effect of substitution can be rationalized perfectly well if the bicyclobutonium ion is considered to be a resonance hybrid of the three classical cations which contribute to it. Thus substituents which would stabilize one resonance form favor the products which are derived from that form, and this effect can lead to some striking results. The solvolysis of 1-methylcyclobutyl chloride (113) yields only the related alcohol (114), and the rate of this solvolysis is slower

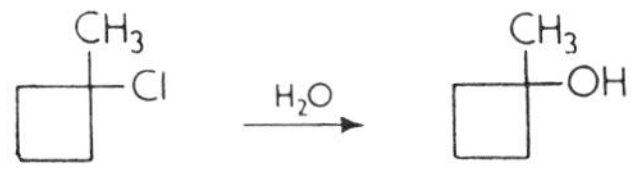

than that of the related cyclopentane compound, although, of course, it is faster than the solvolysis of cyclobutyl chloride itself.[82,85b] These two facts are explicable since the tertiary carbonium ions, in both the cyclobutyl and cyclopentyl series, are sufficiently good as classical ions that little extra stability derives from the special opportunity for bicyclobutonium ion formation with the four-membered ring. Consequently, classical ring strain effects play the dominant role here. Furthermore, the bicyclobutonium ion must have as its predominant resonance form this same cyclobutyl cation, because of the stabilizing effect of the methyl substituent on this form, and the positive charge is thus mostly localized on the methine carbon, which is then the site of reaction with water. It is not even clear to what extent one must invoke a nonclassical ion at all here, although it is hard to believe that nothing would be gained from a little delocalization of the type which was so important in the unsubstituted case. The same evidence on the structure of this substituted bicyclobutonium ion is found in the observation[83] that 114 is the exclusive product from the deamination of 115, and that the solvolysis

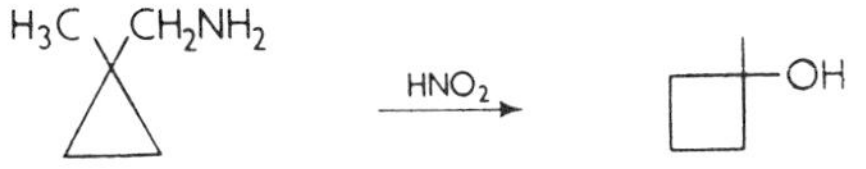

of the chloride corresponding to 115 also leads to 114. This latter solvolysis is accelerated 50 fold by the extra methyl group, showing that in the transition state there is appreciable transfer of the positive charge to the ring carbon.[85b]

[85b] E. F. Cox, M. C. Caserio, M. S. Silver, and J. D. Roberts, J. Am. Chem. Soc., 83, 2719 (1961).

When **115**, labeled in the α methylene group, was deaminated the product **114** was labeled chiefly in carbons 2 and 4, as expected from simple ring expansion.[85b] However, 3% of the radioactivity did end up in carbon 3. This result shows that even here, in a case in which the classical cyclobutyl cation might be invoked as the only required intermediate, some rearrangement of the type characteristic of bicyclobutonium ions is found.

The effects of substituents at other carbons are as expected.[85c] Substitution on the α-methylene group has a large effect on the rate; [85d] the transition state in a solvolysis usually occurs somewhat before the nonclassical carbonium ion, so the rate is most sensitive to substituents on the carbon which bears the leaving group. On the other hand, 2-phenylcyclopropylcarbinyl naphthalenesulfonate (**115a**) solvolyzes at almost the same rate as the un-

$$CH_2OSO_2C_{10}H_7$$

$$C_6H_5$$

(115a)

substituted compound.[85e] This suggests that little charge is transferred to the ring methylene groups, consistent with the idea that the allylcarbinyl cation is only a minor contributor to the structure of the hybrid ion, but the steric requirements for conjugation by phenyls and the opposing resonance and inductive effects of the phenyl group make this evidence somewhat ambiguous. The secondary isotope effect on the rate of solvolysis of cyclopropylcarbinylbenzenesulfonate deuterated in various positions has also been determined and, from the most recent work,[85f] it is concluded that the data are consistent with the postulated bicyclobutonium ion intermediate.

It is possible for substituted cyclopropylcarbinyl derivatives to show very high reactivity and yet yield unrearranged derivatives. Although an early report [80] that cyclopropylcarbinyl benzenesulfonate ethanolizes without rearrangement is unlikely to be correct (since the large excess of sodium alkoxide in the preparative reaction used for product study probably changes the mechanism to a direct displacement [79]), there are several cases in which undoubted S_N1 processes lead to unrearranged products.[85c,85d] One of the simplest involves the reaction of 1-cyclopropylethanol (**116**) with acidic

[85c] Cf., also, M. S. Silver, M. Caserio, H. Rice, and J. D. Roberts, *J. Am. Chem. Soc.*, **83**, 3671 (1961).

[85d] R. A. Sneen and A. C. Baron, *J. Am. Chem. Soc.*, **83**, 614 (1961).

[85e] R. A. Sneen, K. Lewandowski, I. Taha, and B. Smith, *J. Am. Chem. Soc.*, **83**, 4843 (1961).

[85f] S. Borcic, M. Nikoletic, and S. Sunko, *J. Am. Chem. Soc.*, **84**, 1615 (1962).

methanol, in which the ether (**117**) is formed very rapidly, although on standing in the reaction medium it is slowly rearranged further.[86] The very rapid reaction indicates that a special carbonium ion is being formed, presumably the bicyclobutonium ion (**118**), but in this case the methyl group favors one of

(116) (117) (118)

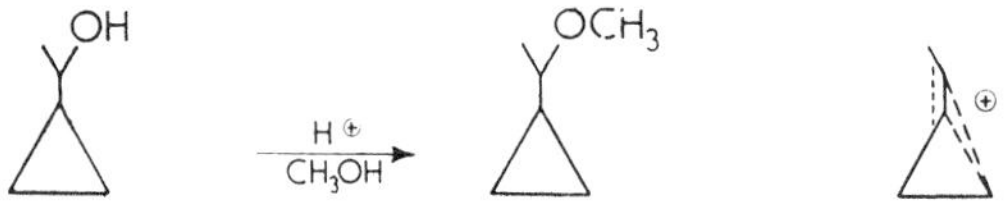

the cyclopropylcarbinyl contributors to the hybrid. This form occurs in only one of the three possible bicyclobutonium ions, hence that ion is favored. The substituent effect also results in predominant attack on that ion so as to produce **117**, the solvent again attacking the point of maximum charge.

A series of unusual solvolyses has been studied in which the cyclopropylcarbinyl canonical form is very strongly stabilized, the compounds involved being **119**, **120**, **121**, and **122**, and a related aliphatic tertiary carbinol derivative (**123**). Enormous accelerating effects were obtained from these extra substituents, the relative reactivities being as indicated under the formulas, for

(119) 23,500 (120) 124,000 (121) 246 (122) 60.7 (123) 1

(X = *p*-nitrobenzoate)

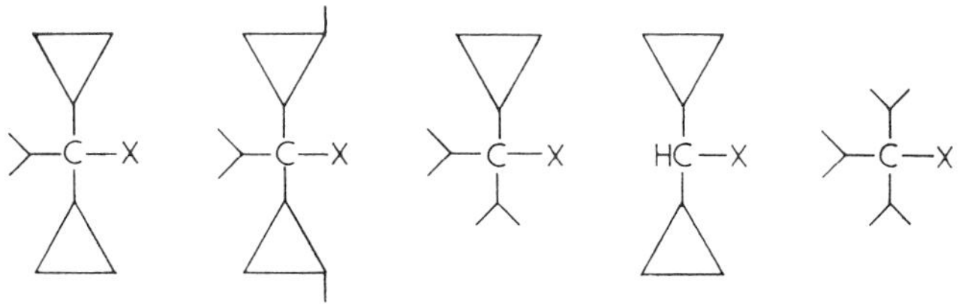

solvolysis in 80% aqueous dioxane.[87] Comparison of compounds **123**, **121**, and **119** indicates that a cyclopropyl group is much more effective than an isopropyl group in stabilizing the carbonium ion, and that a second cyclopropyl group adds half as much as the first, still a large effect. Comparison of **119** with **122** shows that even with two cyclopropyl groups contributing nonclassical stabilization an extra alkyl group adds a lot, the tertiary compound solvolyzing much more rapidly than the secondary one. It is interesting that **120** is more reactive than **119**. Ignoring a possible steric effect, this can be interpreted as indicating the contribution of the allylcarbinyl resonance

[86] R. G. Pearson and S. H. Langer, *J. Am. Chem. Soc.*, **75**, 1065 (1953).
[87] H. Hart and J. M. Sandri, *J. Am. Chem. Soc.*, **81**, 320 (1959).

form (124) to the nonclassical ion; this contribution must be small, however, for the effect of these two alkyl groups is small compared with that realized in

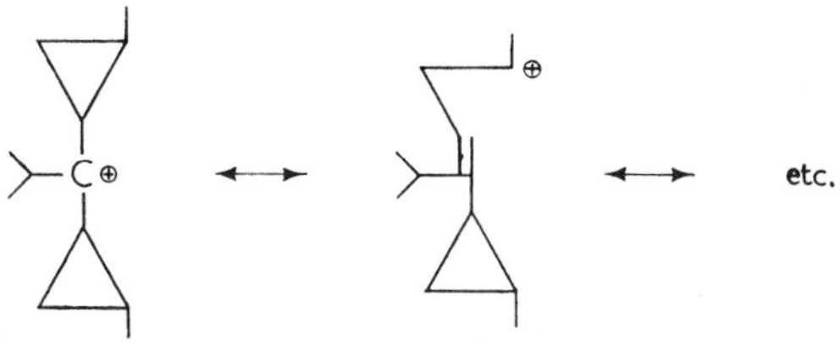

(124)

going from 122 to 119. The possibility that this small acceleration by the ring-substituting methyls is due entirely to steric interactions cannot be dismissed.

The products of the solvolysis of all these compounds are exclusively the unrearranged alcohols. Thus, here, too, there is evidence of considerable acceleration by cyclopropyl groups without the rearrangements which were observed in the unsubstituted cyclopropylcarbinyl compounds, but again this does not rule out bicyclobutonium ions as intermediates. The substitution is such as to stabilize the cyclopropylcarbinyl resonance form of the bicyclobutonium ion, either because that form is a tertiary carbonium ion (121) or because it is common to several bicyclobutonium ions. The stable products would in this case also be, of course, open chain isomers, and under some conditions the compounds discussed do rearrange irreversibly to allylcarbinyl isomers. This type of process represents an equilibration in which the ion pair forms and collapses many times, with the occasional irreversible collapse to the open chain compound resulting in eventual isomerization. Under nonequilibrating conditions, as in solvolysis to an unreactive alcohol, the important factor is apparently not the stability of the product but the stability of the transition states involved in the various possible modes of attack on the intermediate carbonium ion, and it seems that the prediction can be made by considering where the positive charge may best be localized.

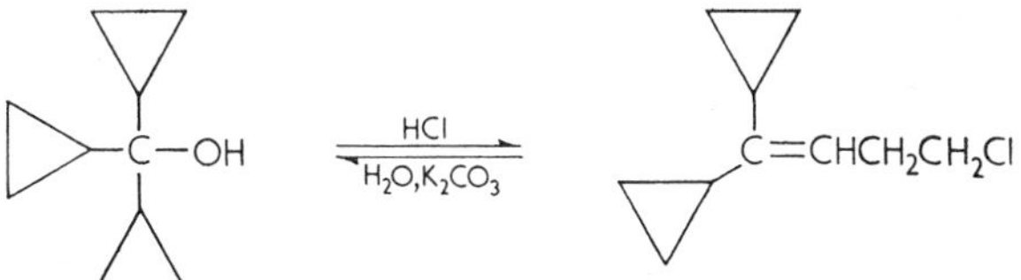

(125)   (126)

On this basis we can understand the observation [87] that tris(cyclopropyl)-carbonol (125) rearranges with HCl to the open compound (126), which may be solvolyzed back to 125. The situation here is simply that the HCl reaction is equilibrating, the more stable product being formed, but that the solvolysis occurs to form a nonclassical ion (**127**) which under nonequilibrating conditions reacts with water at the site of maximum positive charge (or rather, at

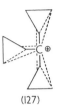

(127)

the site where the charge is best localized). This reaction is, of course, almost the same as that with which we started the discussion of these rearrangements, and the interconversions of **100** and **101** involve the same situation; that is, the ring opening occurs under equilibrating conditions, but the solvolysis is nonequilibrating. These solvolyses of the allylcarbinyl compounds suggest that the open chain compounds, under solvolysis conditions, furnish the same bicyclobutonium ions formed in the reactions of the cyclopropylcarbinyl or cyclobutyl derivatives. The unusual collection of products formed in the deamination of allylcarbinylamine represents reaction through a carbonium ion of such high energy that it is not normally available in a solvolysis, where only the more stable bicyclobutonium ion is permissible.

Although emphasis has so far been placed on interconversions among cyclopropylcarbinyl, cyclobutyl, and allylcarbinyl derivatives, a very common situation exists in which the cyclobutyl compounds play no role. Thus,

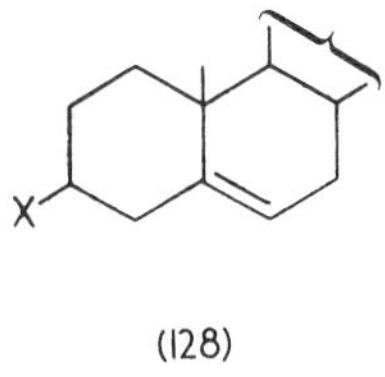

(128) 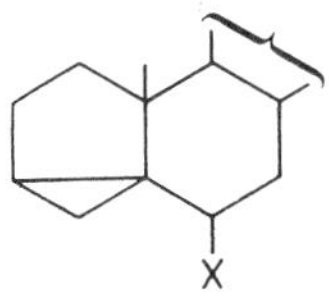   (129)

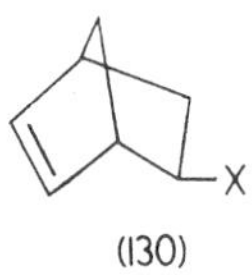

(130) 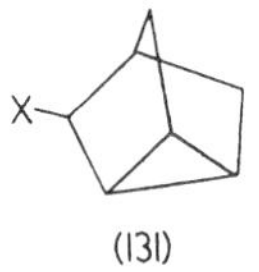   (131)

in the steroids, the interconversion of cholesteryl (**128**) and *i*-cholesteryl derivatives (**129**) occurs readily under some conditions, and such rearrangements have been extensively studied (see Section 16). Similar interconversions are observed between derivatives of the dehydronorbornyl (**130**) and nortricyclyl (**131**) systems (see Section 3). In these cases, stereochemistry prevents contribution of a cyclobutyl form. Accordingly the intermediate ions could be pictured either as distorted bicyclobutonium ions or, perhaps more properly, as homoallyl cations (**131a**). The significance of the various geometrical forms of **131a**, with and without the explicit consideration of 1,4

(131a)

interaction which makes them equivalent to bicyclobutonium ions, has been discussed by Winstein and Kosower.[88] They emphasize the fact that the ground state strain energy of compounds interconverted through such intermediate ions may play a dominant role in their relative reactivities. Thus, i-cholesteryl derivatives solvolyze enormously more rapidly than do the cholesteryl analogs, while nortricyclyl derivatives are less reactive than the related norbornenyl compounds; however, this difference in the relative reactivities of the cyclopropylcarbinyl and homoallyl compounds in the two series is not due to any special steric problems decreasing or increasing the opportunity for electron delocalization in the transition states. Instead, it can be ascribed almost entirely to the high stability of **128** compared with **129**, and the contrasting greater stability of the cyclopropane derivative **131** compared with **130**. A similar example of the effect of a fused ring system on the course of reaction of the cyclopropylcarbinyl cation is seen in the observation that deamination of **132** proceeds without rearrangement.[89] Here again the cyclobutyl cation is forbidden by the stereochemistry of the system.

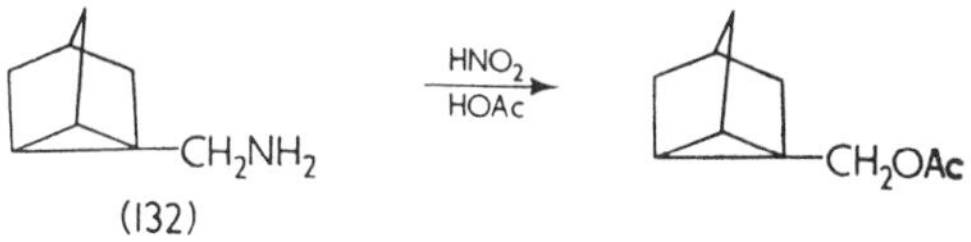

(132)

Under equilibrating conditions, even simple cyclopropylcarbinyl derivatives undergo ring opening; a particularly extensive series of studies is reported in the Russian literature.[90] The course of ring opening is ordinarily such as to produce the better carbonium ion (although at least one exception to

[88] S. Winstein and E. M. Kosower, *J. Am. Chem. Soc.*, **81**, 4399 (1959).

[89] H. Hart and R. A. Martin, *J. Am. Chem. Soc.*, **82**, 6362 (1960).

[90] Cf. T. A. Favorskaya, K. A. Kononova, and N. I. Titov, *Zhur. Obshcheĭ Khim.*, **29**, 2894 (1959), and previous papers.

this rule is known [91]). A recent study of the reaction of a series of cyclopropyl ketones (**133**) and carbinols (**134**) with acid reveals that the rate of ring opening is strongly affected by substituents on the ring as well as substituents

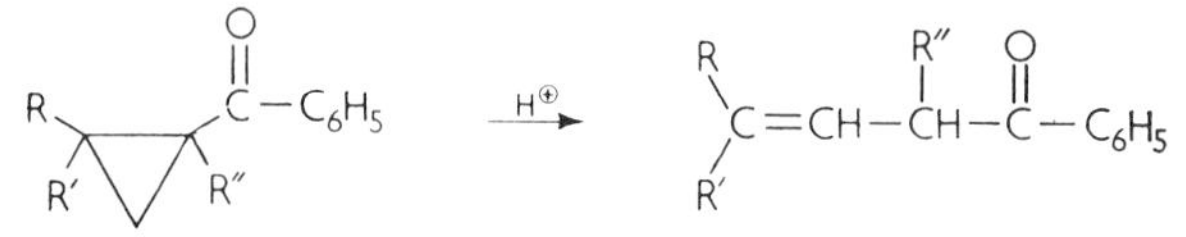

(133)

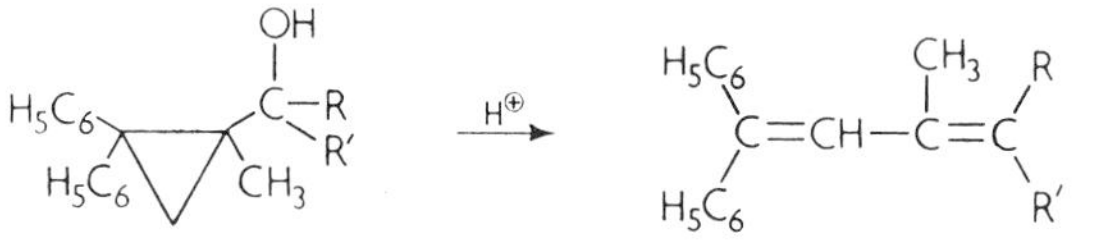

(134)

(in **134**) at the carbinyl carbon; [92] again the substituent effect is larger at the carbinyl carbon, the site of initial development of charge. Some evidence that the open chain cations ultimately formed can collapse to the cyclopropane compounds again was also obtained.

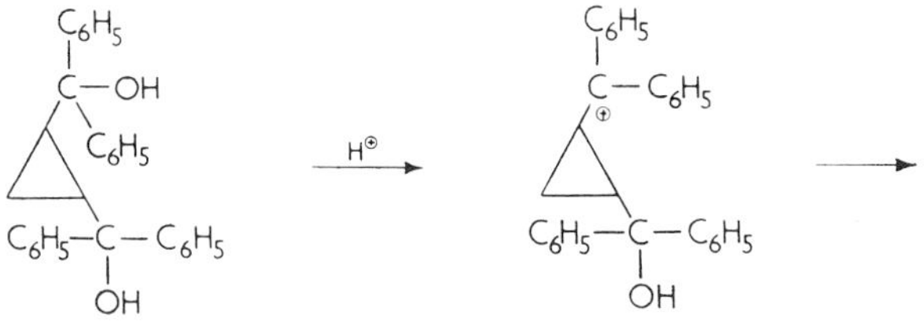

(135)

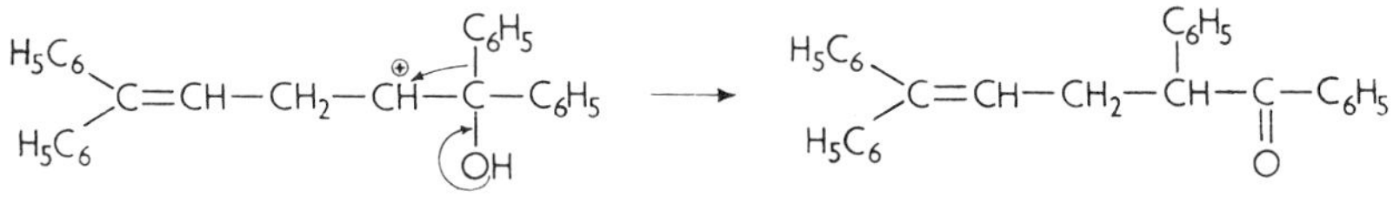

(136)

Treatment of **135** with acid leads to **136**, in this case with phenyl migration accompanying ring opening.[93]

The spiropentyl system is ambiguous, spiropentyl chloride (**137**) being

[91] S. Julia, M. Julia, and C. Huynk, *Bull. soc. chim. France*, **1960**, 174.

[92] H. M. Walborsky and L. Plonsker, *J. Am. Chem. Soc.*, **83**, 2138 (1961).

[93] R. A. Darby and R. E. Lutz, *J. Org. Chem.*, **22**, 1353 (1957).

related to both the cyclopropyl and the cyclopropylcarbinyl systems. It might be expected that the compound would solvolyze slowly, however, since the derived bicyclobutonium ion (138) is a hybrid of three carbonium ions which appear to be rather unstable; the solvolysis is in fact sluggish.[94] When spiropentyl amine (139) is deaminated, the products are 140 and 141; thus, while the reactivity of spiropentyl derivatives is similar to that of simple cyclopropanes, far more rearrangement occurs.

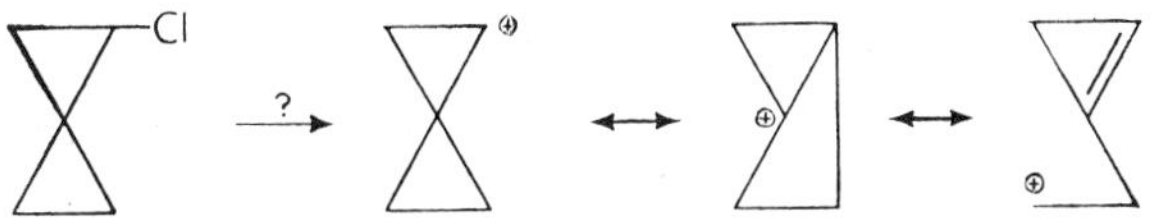

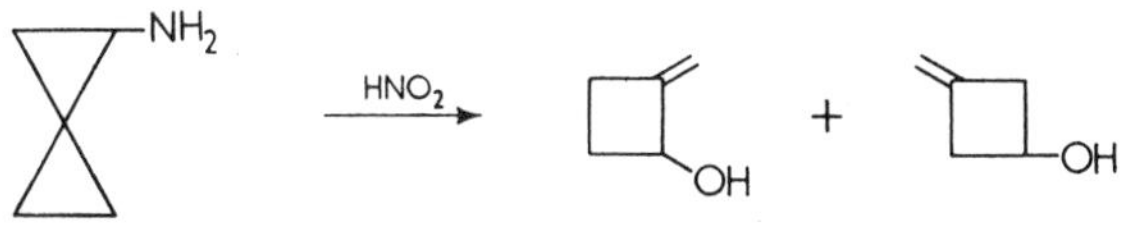

The cyclopropenylcarbinyl cation (142) is apparently very similar to the cyclopropylcarbinyl cation.[95] Thus the rate of solvolysis of diphenylcyclopropenylcarbinyl tosylate (143) is only three times that of the related saturated compound (143a), and is essentially the same as the extrapolated rate

for unsubstituted cyclopropylcarbinyl tosylate. The products are derived entirely from the cyclobutenyl cation (143b) which results from ring expansion, and at first sight it might have been expected that this possibility of ring expansion to 143b could have strongly affected the rate of solvolysis. Thus, by contrast with the cyclobutyl cation which contributes to the ordinary bicyclobutonium ion, 143b is a cyclobutenyl cation in which the positive charge is allylic, and is conjugated with a phenyl group as well. However, this

[94] D. E. Applequist and C. F. Fanta, J. Am. Chem. Soc., 82, 6393 (1961).
[95] R. Breslow, J. Lockhart, and A. Small, J. Am. Chem. Soc., 84, 2793 (1962).

conjugation is apparently almost negligible in the transition state for solvolysis, since the p-methoxy derivative of **143** solvolyzes only three times more rapidly. It has also been argued [95] that the change from **143** to **143b** involves

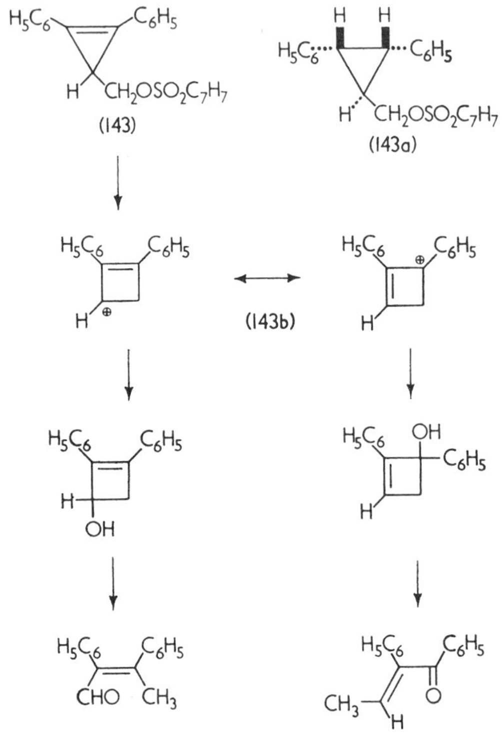

almost 20 kcal. more strain relief than the similar change in the saturated series. Assuming that there is no major effect of the double bond which counteracts these factors, it seems clear from this work that the transition state in the solvolysis of **143** is electronically and geometrically much closer to starting material than to the cyclobutenyl cation.

A similar process of ring expansion has been suggested for the first steps in the rearrangement of **144**.[96] Under a variety of conditions this compound dehydrates to the naphthalene (**144a**) and azulene (**144b**). This process can be rationalized by the following scheme, in which a variety of rearrangements are proposed which are similar to those just discussed. Classical forms of carbonium ions are drawn for simplicity, although it is recognized that in all of them considerably more delocalization of charge is probable. Intermediate **144c** is a phenonium ion, but it is also a cyclopropyl-

[96] R. Breslow and M. Battiste, *J. Am. Chem. Soc.*, **82**, 3626 (1960).

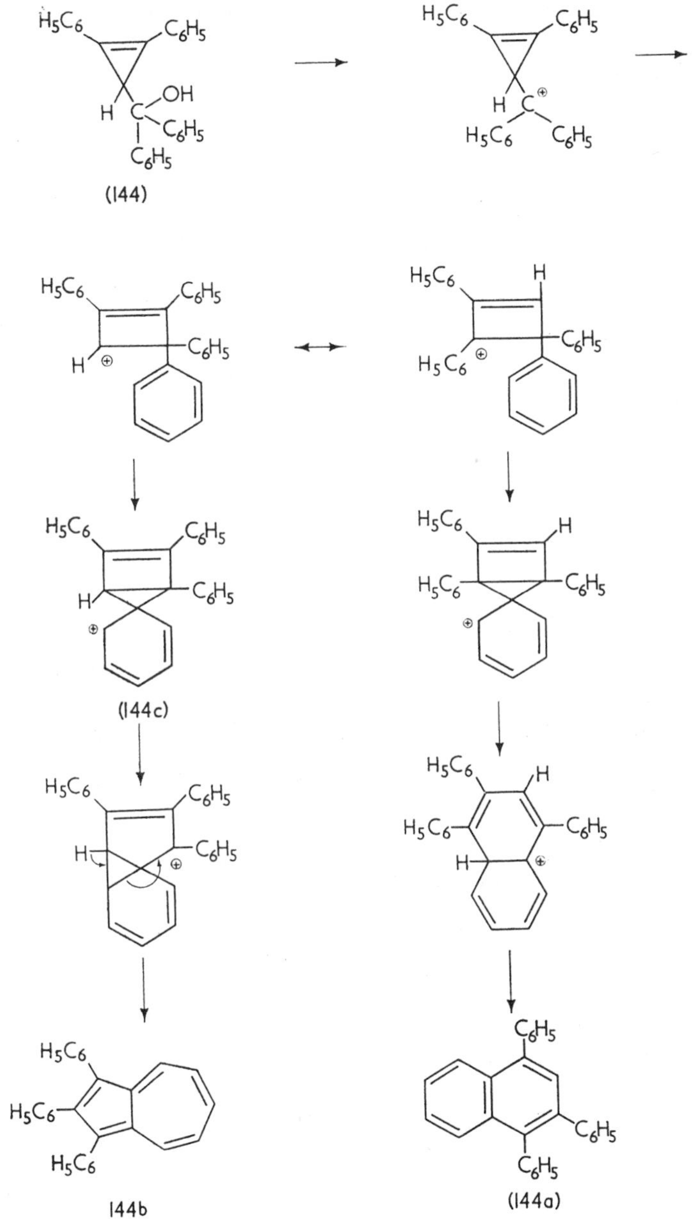

(144)

(144c)

144b

(144a)

carbinyl cation, as are all phenonium ions. Its rearrangement is thus not unreasonable, being really the isomerization of one bicyclobutonium ion to another, a process discussed earlier.

An additional piece of evidence in support of this mechanism has been obtained recently.[97] When triphenylcyclopropenyl bromide is treated with phenyldiazomethane, the first formed diazonium salt should ring-expand to a cyclobutenyl cation (144d). This is not identical with the previous cyclobutenyl cation, but it has the same phenonium ion (144c) postulated as an intermediate before, so it is interesting that triphenylazulene (144b) is formed in this reaction as well. However, with an excess of phenyldiazomethane 144d reacts further, the major product being pentaphenylcyclopentadiene.

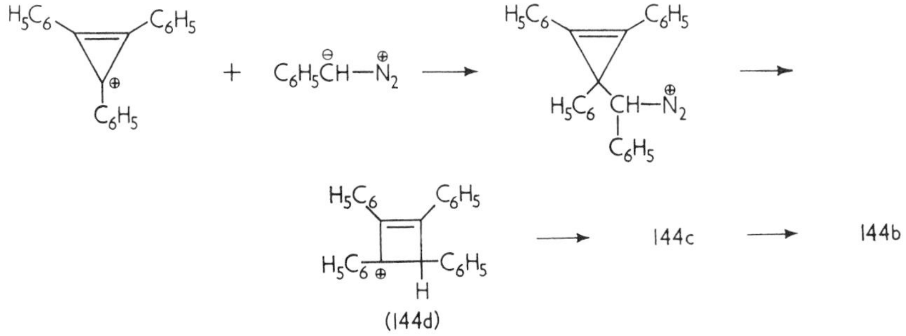

(144d)

B. Cyclobutane Derivatives

Rearrangements of the cyclobutyl cation have already been discussed in the previous section, but a few more cases are of interest. The reaction of methylenecyclobutane (145) with bromine yields some rearrangement products in addition to the expected adduct,[98] and although the amount of

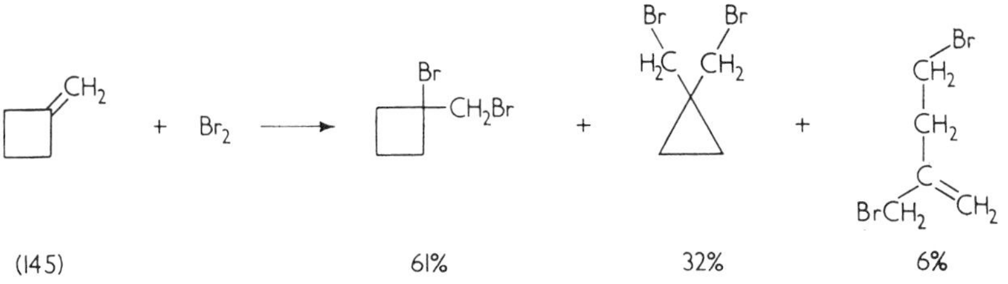

(145)   61%   32%   6%

cyclopropyl derivative formed is less than that from reactions of cyclobutanol derivatives, it is more than that from 1-methylcyclobutanol derivatives, discussed previously. That any rearrangement occurs is probably due to the lesser stabilizing effect of a bromomethyl group compared to a methyl, and the already demonstrated preference of halide ion, compared to water, for the cyclopropylcarbinyl mode of attack on bicyclobutonium ions. The reaction of diazocyclobutane (146) with carboxylic acids leads to equal mixtures

[97] R. Breslow and M. Mitchell, unpublished work.
[98] D. E. Applequist and J. D. Roberts, *J. Am. Chem. Soc.*, **78**, 874 (1956).

of the cyclobutyl and cyclopropylcarbinyl esters,[99] as expected if the bicyclobutonium ion is an intermediate and if carboxylate ion shows the same equal

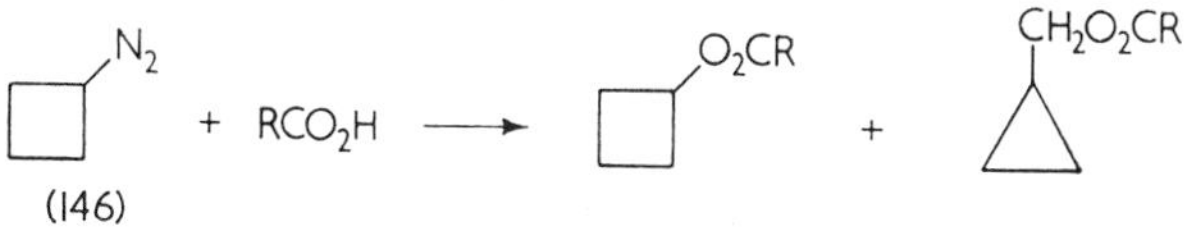

(146)

preference for the two major modes of attack on this ion which is shown by
water.

An interesting ring contraction occurs on lithium aluminum hydride
reduction of the bridged tosylate **146a**.[99a] The product cyclopropane presumably arises from a prior carbonium ion rearrangement in which strain
relief in **146a** furnishes much of the driving force. Another reaction in which
complete ring contraction occurs is the conversion of bromocyclobutanone
(**146b**) to cyclopropanecarboxylic acid.[99b] Although this resembles a Favorskii

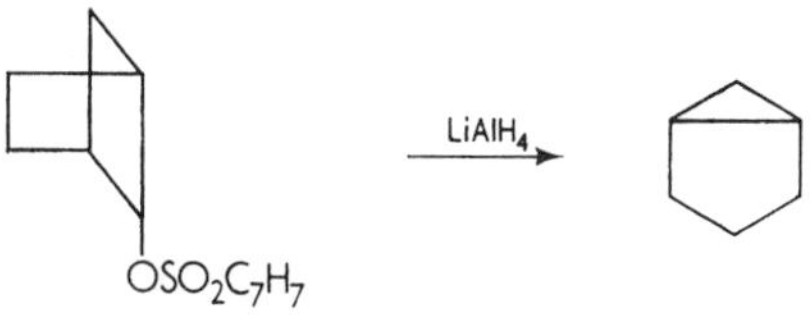

(146a)

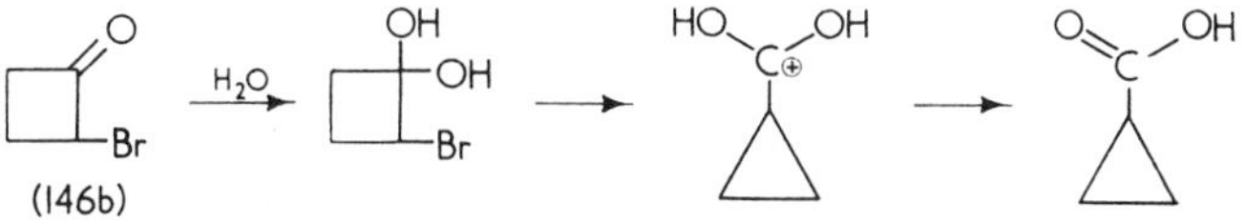

(146b)

reaction, in this case the rearrangement occurs even in neutral aqueous
solution; it seems likely that solvolytic rearrangement of the hydrate of **146b**
is involved. Here, of course, the driving force for complete ring contraction
is the formation of a protonated carboxyl group. Ring opening can become
the dominant reaction of a cyclobutyl cation if the resulting allylcarbinyl
cation is stabilized by some additional interaction, and this must explain the
solvolytic ring opening of **147** in an interesting cycloheptatriene synthesis.[100]

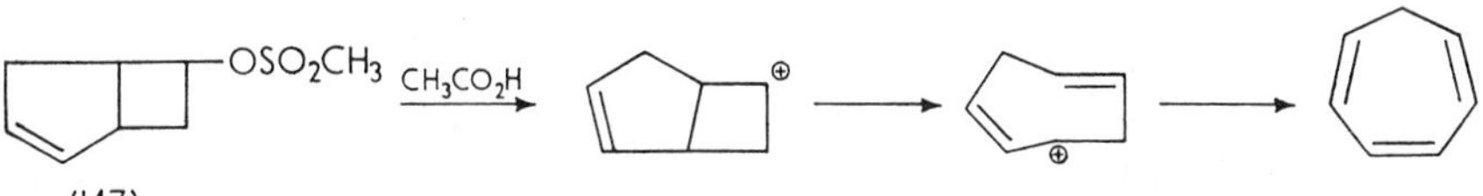

(147)

[99] D. E. Applequist and D. E. McGreer, *J. Am. Chem. Soc.*, **82**, 1965 (1960).

[99a] K. Wiberg, B. Lowry, and T. Colby, *J. Am. Chem. Soc.*, **83**, 3998 (1961).

[99b] J. Conia and J. Ripoli, *Compt. rend.* **251**, 1071 (1960); cf. also J. Conia and J. Ripoli, *Compt. rend.*, **252**, 423 (1961).

[100] H. L. Dryden and B. E. Burgert, *J. Am. Chem. Soc.*, **77**, 5633 (1955).

A similar ring opening occurs when methylenecyclobutanol (**146c**) is proton-ated,[100a] and as well when the *trans* cyclobutanedoil **146d** is treated with acid.[100b]

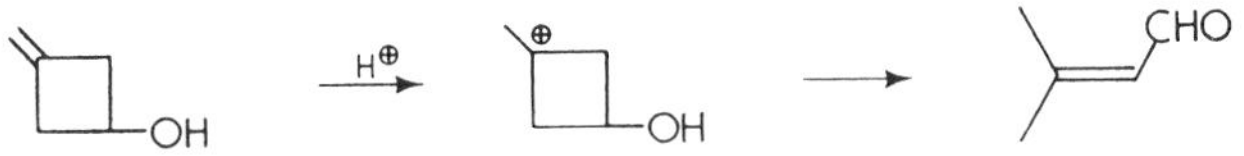

(146c)

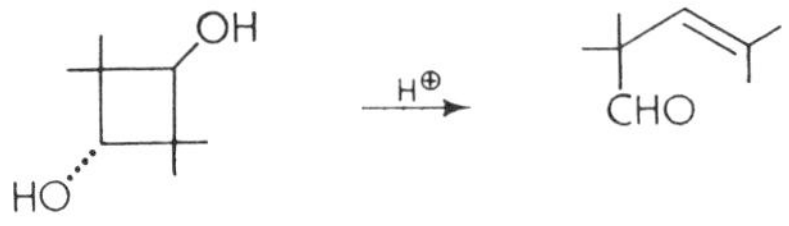

(146d)

Cyclobutylcarbinyl cations can also rearrange, but there is no evidence for any significant stabilization of these species by formation of nonclassical ions analogous to the bicyclobutonium ion. The deamination of cyclobutycarbinyl amine (**148**) yields cyclopentanol [101] and cyclobutylcarbinol (**149**) rearranges

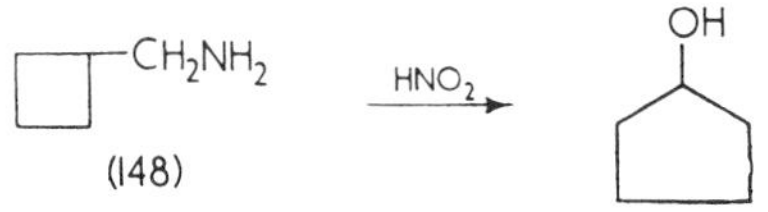

(148)

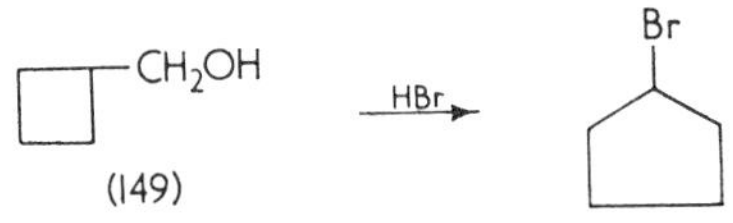

(149)

to cyclopentyl bromide with HBr.[101] Such rearrangements can occur under very mild conditions with suitable cyclobutane derivatives: isopropenyl-cyclobutane (**150**), on being chromatographed over silica gel, rearranges to **151** and **152**.[102] The latter compound arises from a Wagner-Meerwein methyl shift in the cyclopentyl cation intermediate.

The strong electrostatic effect of fluorine must account for the observation that **153** is deaminated without rearrangement, this being the unique case of such lack of rearrangement in a simple cyclobutylcarbinylamine deamina-tion.[103] The fluorines would destablize the cyclopentyl cation intermediate in

[100a] E. Kiefer and J. D. Roberts, *J. Am. Chem. Soc.*, **84**, 784 (1962).

[100b] R. Hasek, R. Clark, and J. Chaudet, *J. Org. Chem.*, **26**, 3130 (1961).

[101] N. J. Demjanov, *Ber.*, **40**, 4959 (1907).

[102] B. A. Kazanskii *et al.*, *Izvest. Akad. Nauk S.S.S.R.*, **1956**, 1421.

[103] D. R. Baer, *J. Org. Chem.*, **23**, 1560 (1958).

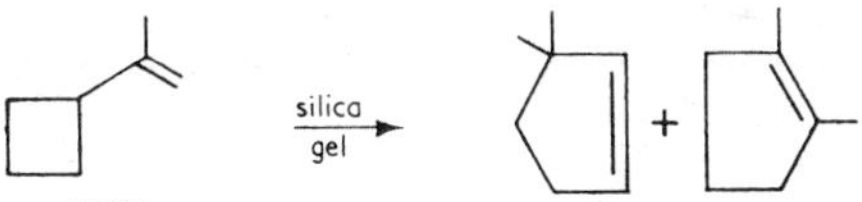

(150)   (152)   (152)

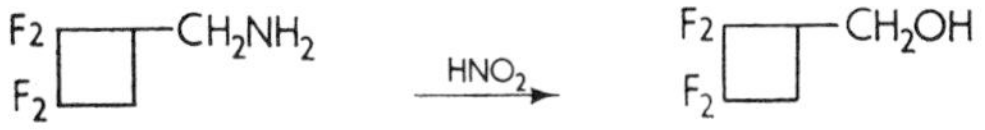

(153)

the rearrangement. In a related observation, it has recently been found that the carbinol **153a** is converted with HBr to an unrearranged bromide, and that the ring-expanded product is formed only under equilibrating conditions.[99a] Study of the acid-catalyzed dehydration of **154** shows that either rearrangement to **155** or simple dehydration to **156** can occur, depending on the conditions.[104]

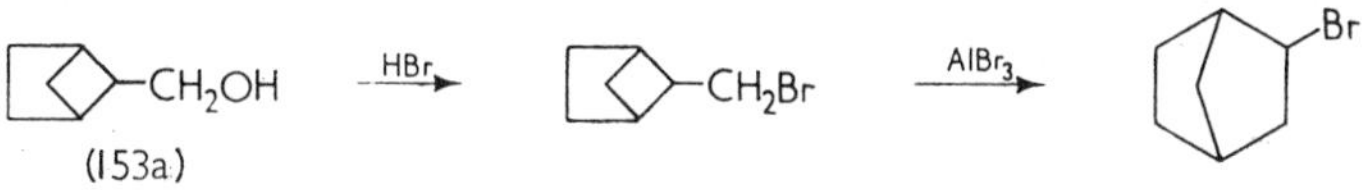

(153a)

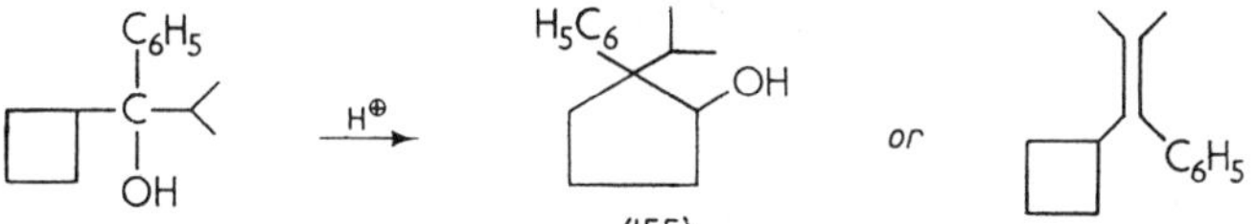

(154)   (155)   or   (156)

The normal ring-expanding rearrangement of cyclobutylmethyl cations has been used in a synthesis of pentalane derivatives, both in a simple form (eq. 13)[105] and in a more complex scheme (eq. 14),[106] where the reaction is

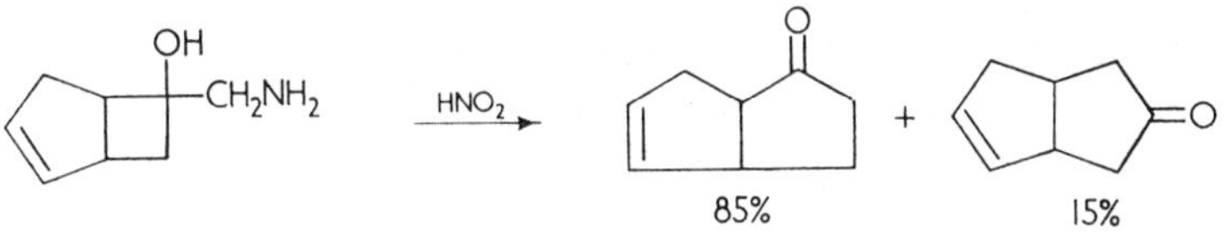

85%   15%   (13)

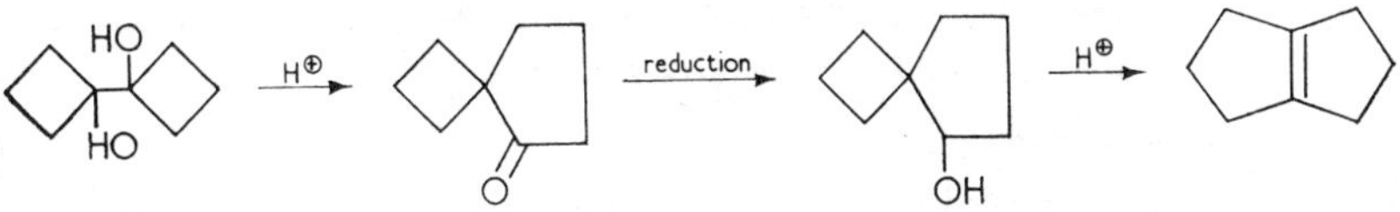

(14)

[104] T. A. Favorskaya and I. P. Yakovlev, *Zhur. Obshcheĭ Khim.*, **22**, 1816 (1952).
[105] J. D. Roberts and W. F. Gorham, *J. Am. Chem. Soc.*, **74**, 2278 (1952).
[106] E. Vogel, *Chem. Ber.*, **85**, 25 (1952).

used twice. Finally, such rearrangements can be part of more involved changes, a good example of which is furnished in the acid rearrangement of the caryophyllene oxide **157**.[107]

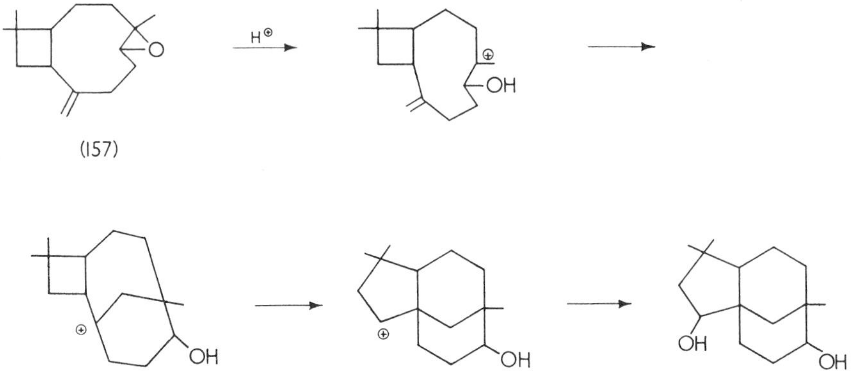

(157)

An acid-catalyzed rearrangement of a cyclobutane derivative is known which really does not fit in any of the categories so far discussed, but it illustrates the fact that many rearrangements found in larger ring or aliphatic compounds are also, of course, possible in small ring compounds. When cyclobutenone methyl ketal (**158**) is submitted to acid hydrolysis the products are **159**, **160**, and **161**,[108] the first being easily explicable from hydration of

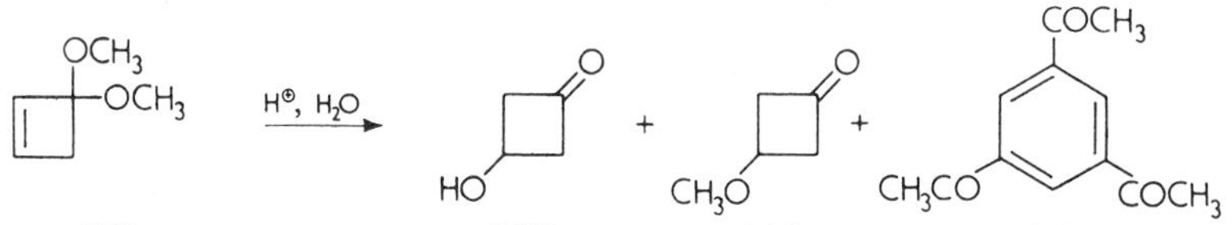

(158)   (159)   (160)   (161)

the cyclobutenone, and the second from allylic rearrangement during the hydrolysis of the ketal. The last occurs by ring opening of **159** via a reverse aldol reaction to form acetylacetaldehyde, which then condenses to the benzene derivative.

4. REARRANGEMENTS INVOLVING CARBANIONS, AND BASE-CATALYZED REARRANGEMENTS

A. Cyclopropane Derivatives

The cyclopropyl Grignard reagent, a derivative of the cyclopropyl anion, does not rearrange, but an interesting reaction occurs with 1,1-dibromo-

[107] D. H. R. Barton, A. Aebi, and A. S. Lindsey, *J. Chem. Soc. (London)*, **1953**, 3124.
[108] E. Vogel and K. Hasse, *Ann.*, **615**, 22 (1958).

cyclopropanes and magnesium, the product being an allene (eq. 15).[109] The
same rearrangement occurs with sodium metal, although with sodium in

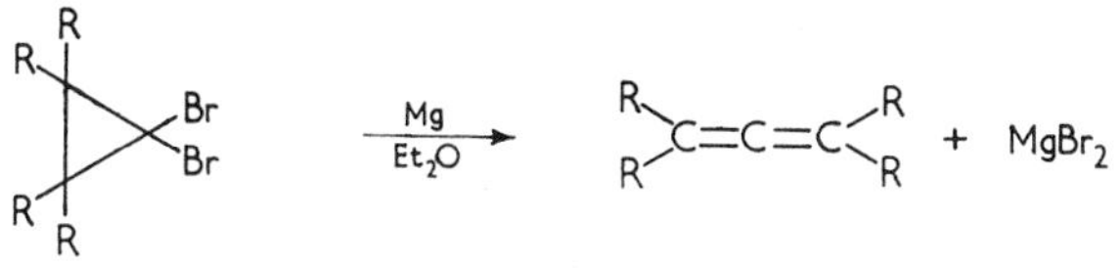

$$\text{(structure with Br, Br)} \xrightarrow[\text{Et}_2\text{O}]{\text{Mg}} \quad {}^{R}_{R}\!\!>\!\!C\!=\!C\!=\!C\!<^{R}_{R} \;+\; MgBr_2 \qquad (15)$$

alcohol these dihalides are simply reduced (eq. 16).[110] However, the reaction
of a geminal halide with a reducing metal is not typically an example of a
carbanion-forming reaction; the rearrangement in this case, for instance, may
well involve the carbene of cyclopropane.

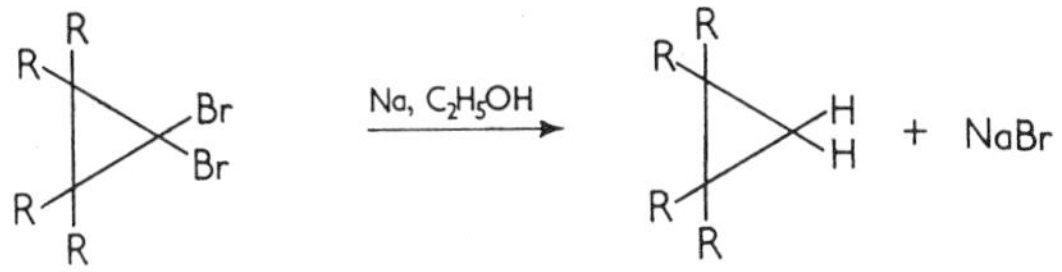

$$\text{(structure with Br, Br)} \xrightarrow{\text{Na, } C_2H_5OH} \quad \text{(structure with H, H)} \;+\; NaBr \qquad (16)$$

While the simple cyclopropyl Grignard reagent is stable, the Grignard
reagent derived from cyclopropylcarbinyl chloride is allylcarbinylmagnesium
chloride,[110a] a rearrangement product (eq. 17). Recent studies show that this

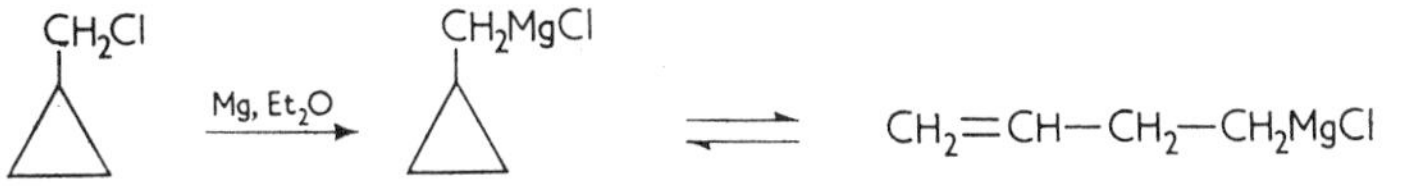

$$\overset{CH_2Cl}{\triangle} \xrightarrow{\text{Mg, Et}_2\text{O}} \overset{CH_2MgCl}{\triangle} \;\rightleftharpoons\; CH_2\!=\!CH\!-\!CH_2\!-\!CH_2MgCl \quad (17)$$

is in equilibrium with the cyclopropylcarbinyl isomer, but that they are
distinct compounds, the reagent *not* being some resonance hybrid of the
two.[111] Thus the situation is much less complex than is the case in the related
cation, and since there is an equilibrium we may expect rearrangement to
the less strained open isomers from various reactions which could involve
cyclopropylcarbinyl anions.

An early example of this was found in the reaction of **162** with base, for
instead of cyclization to a bicyclopentane derivative the reaction follows a
course of ring opening, with subsequent Dieckmann cyclization to **163**.[112]

[109] W. von E. Doering and P. M. La Flamme, *Tetrahedron*, **2**, 75 (1958); cf. J. T. Logan, *Tetrahedron Letters*, No. 5, 173 (1961).

[110] W. von E. Doering and A. K. Hoffmann, *J. Am. Chem. Soc.*, **76**, 6162 (1954).

[110a] J. D. Roberts and R. H. Mazur, *J. Am. Chem. Soc.*, **73**, 2509 (1951).

[111] M. S. Silver, P. R. Shafer, J. E. Nordlander, C. Rüchardt, and J. D. Roberts, *J. Am. Chem. Soc.*, **82**, 2647 (1960).

[112] O. Wallach, *Ann.*, **388**, 49 (1912).

Simple ring opening of this type is also seen in the conversion of **163a** to **163b** with base.[112a] A recent synthesis of cycloheptadienone (eq. 18) also utilizes

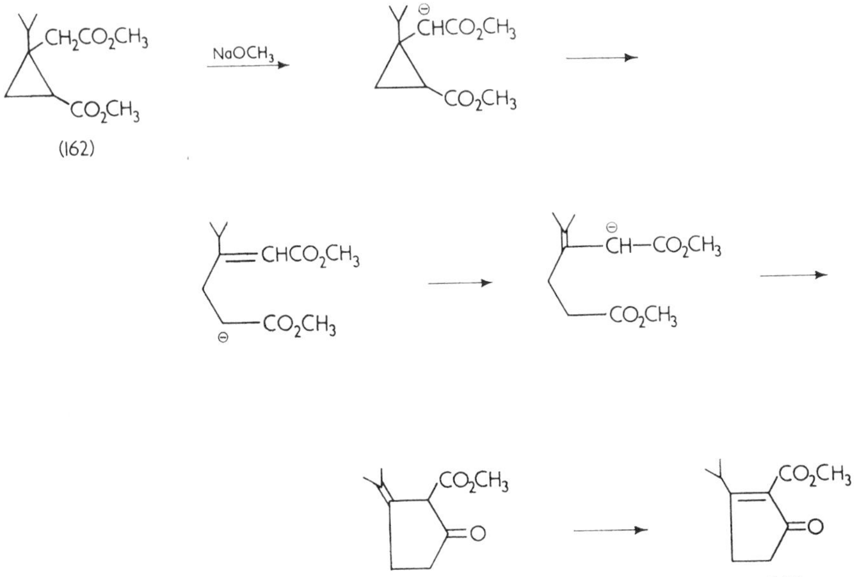

ring opening in which an enolate ion next to a cyclopropane ring undergoes rearrangement with formation of an open enolate ion, as in the above case. Here, however, the same carbonyl group is used to stabilize both the starting anion and the product anion, and the reaction could be considered to be just another example of the norcaradiene-to-cycloheptatriene isomerization.[113]

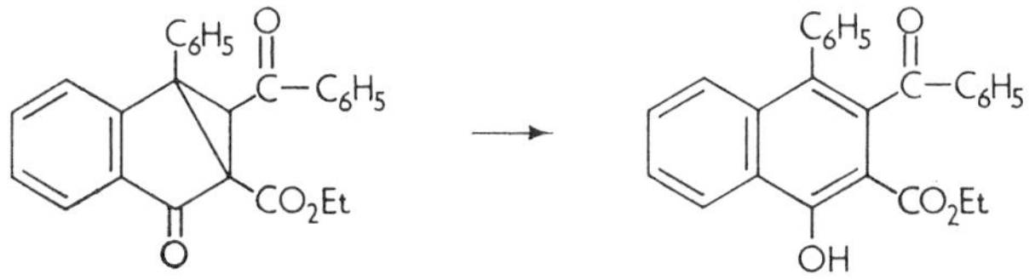

An analog of the Michael addition reaction is found when 1,1-cyclopropanedicarboxylic ester is reacted with sodiomalonic ester, ring opening occurring to form **164**.[114] A similar case, but involving attack on a vinylcyclopropane system, is found when **165** is reacted with malonate.[115] The products here

[112a] C. F. Koelsch, *J. Org. Chem.*, **26**, 1003 (1961).

[113] E. E. van Tamelen and G. T. Hildahl, *J. Am. Chem. Soc.*, **75**, 5451 (1953).

[114] W. A. Bone and W. H. Perkin, *J. Chem. Soc. (London)*, **67**, 108 (1895).

[115] R. P. Linstead, R. W. Kierstead, and B. C. L. Weedon, *J. Chem. Soc. (London)*, **1952**, 3616.

result either from conjugate addition to the entire system (166) or from attack on the cyclopropane ring alone (167).

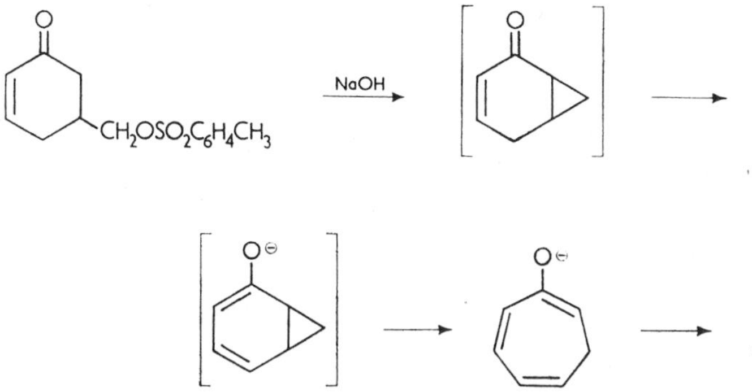

(18)

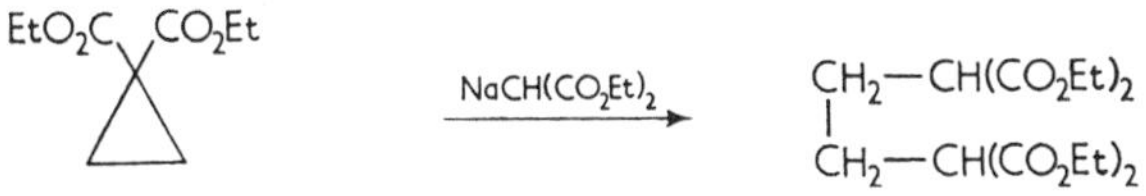

(164)

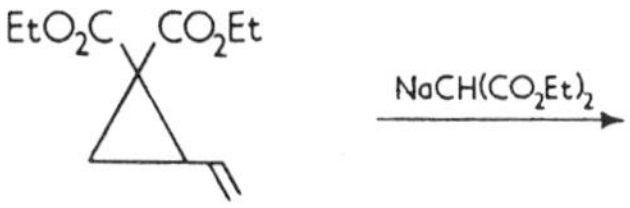

(165)

$$(EtO_2C)_2CH-CH_2-CH=CH-CH_2-CH(CO_2Et)_2 \quad + \quad CH_2=CH-CH-CH(CO_2Et)_2$$

                                                                                        $$CH_2-CH(CO_2Et)_2$$

(166)   (167)

When 2-nitrocyclopropyl ketones, such as 168, are treated with potassium hydroxide, the products are open chain diketones, in this case 169, and sodium nitrite.[116] The mechanism of this reaction was at first suggested to involve elimination of nitrite to form a cyclopropene derivative, which was then rearranged by base to an acetylene and thence to the product.[116]

Some support for this proposal is found in the observation that an authentic cyclopropene [116a] is formed when 170 is treated with sodium methoxide,[117]

[116] E. P. Kohler and L. I. Smith, J. Am. Chem. Soc., 44, 624 (1922).
[116a] R. Breslow, R. Winter, and M. Battiste, J. Org. Chem., 24, 415 (1959).
[117] S. F. Darling and E. W. Spanagel, J. Am. Chem. Soc., 53, 1117 (1931).

but an extensive series of investigations has been carried out on the diketone-forming reactions,[118] and it is now clear that the mechanism is as shown.

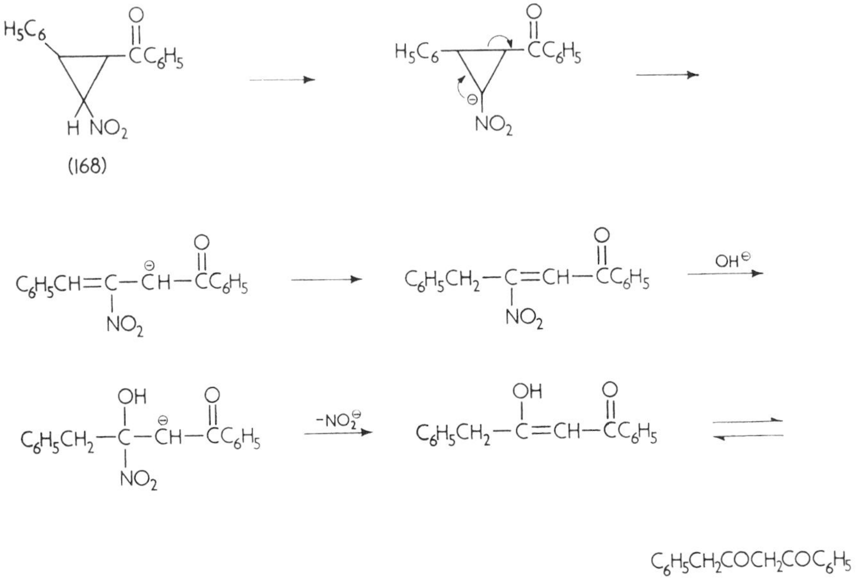

(168)

$$C_6H_5CH=C(NO_2)-\overset{\ominus}{C}H-\overset{O}{\overset{\|}{C}}C_6H_5 \longrightarrow C_6H_5CH_2-C(NO_2)=CH-\overset{O}{\overset{\|}{C}}C_6H_5 \xrightarrow{OH^\ominus}$$

$$C_6H_5CH_2-\overset{OH}{\overset{|}{C}}(NO_2)-\overset{\ominus}{C}H-\overset{O}{\overset{\|}{C}}C_6H_5 \xrightarrow{-NO_2^\ominus} C_6H_5CH_2-\overset{OH}{\overset{|}{C}}=CH-\overset{O}{\overset{\|}{C}}C_6H_5 \rightleftharpoons$$

$$C_6H_5CH_2COCH_2COC_6H_5$$

(169)

(170)

When triphenylcyclopropene (**171**) is treated with potassium amide, hexaphenylbenzene is formed.[119] This unusual change has been studied in some detail,[119a] and the following points have so far emerged. Under milder conditions a cyclopropylcyclopropene derivative (**172**) is the immediate product, and the two hydrogen atoms in this compound are both derived from the cyclopropene and not from solvent ammonia (revealed by deuterium labeling). Accordingly, the attack of amide does not take place on the cyclopropene hydrogen atom but, instead, there is presumably initial addition to the double bond. This is supported by the observation that

---

[118] L. I. Smith and V. A. Englehardt, *J. Am. Chem. Soc.*, **71**, 2676 (1949); L. I. Smith, W. L. Kohlhase, and R. J. Brotherton, *J. Am. Chem. Soc.*, **78**, 2532 (1956).

[119] R. Breslow and M. Battiste, unpublished work.

[119a] R. Breslow and P. Dowd, unpublished work.

reaction of cyclopropene 171 with lithium *p*-toluidide affords benzyldeoxy-benzoin.[119a] Rearrangement of 172 to hexaphenylbenzene can be pictured

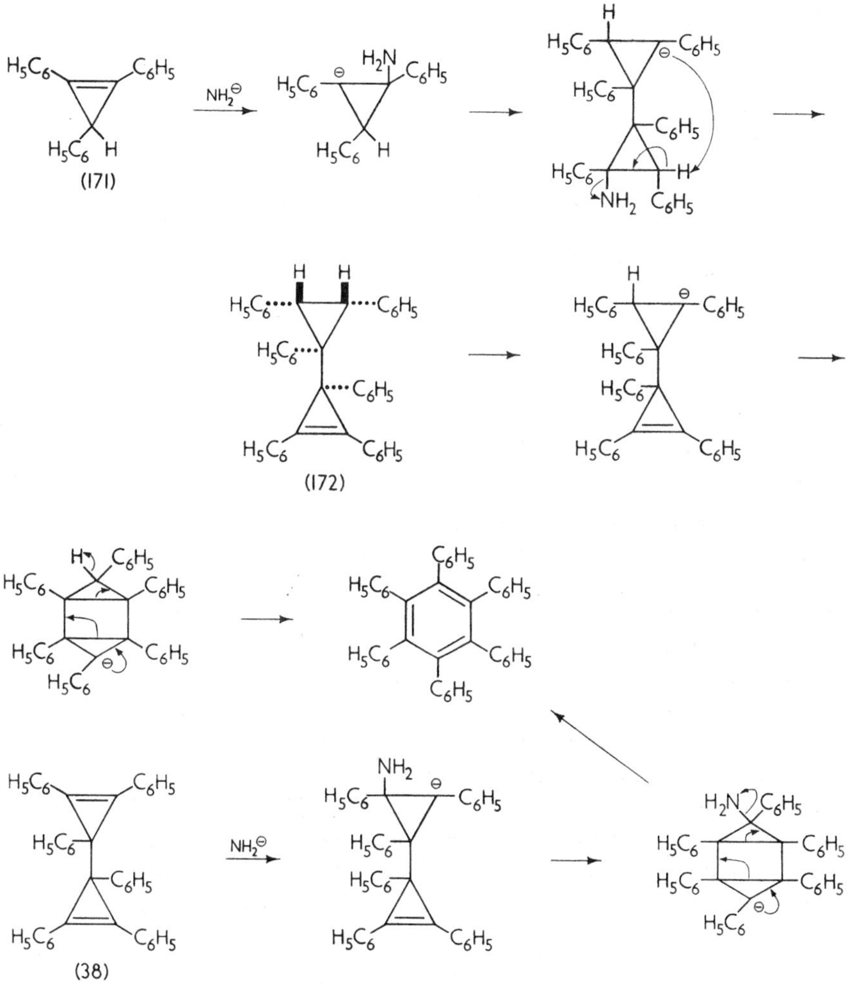

as shown, and this is again supported by analogy, in this case the low temperature rearrangement of 38 with potassium amide. Although this simple scheme accommodates the available data, it cannot of course be accepted without further evidence.

It is often observed that hydrogenolysis of a cyclopropane ring occurs in methylenecyclopropanes or in vinylcyclopropanes when the corresponding saturated derivatives are stable to ring cleavage. Although hydrogenation is not ordinarily considered to involve carbanion intermediates, it has been suggested that the opening occurs by transfer of a hydride ion from the hydrogenation catalyst to the double bond so as to yield a cyclopropyl carbanion,

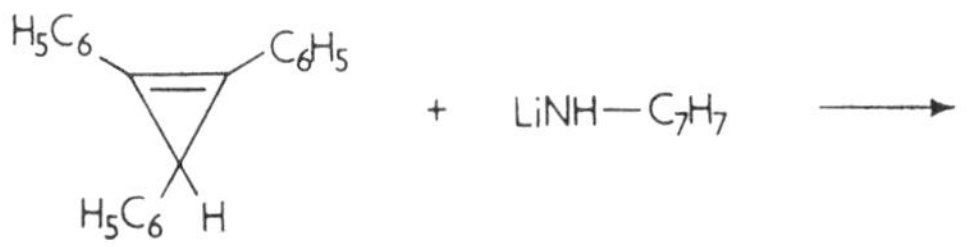

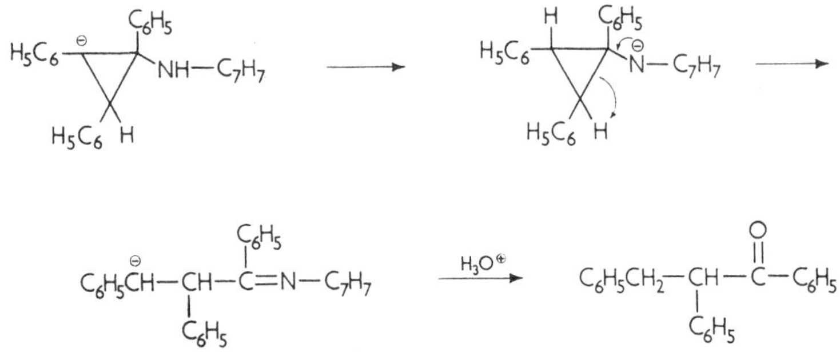

which then undergoes ring opening. The products observed with a variety of substrates can be accommodated on the basis of this mechanism.[120]

B. Cyclobutane Derivatives

Cyclobutyl bromide gives an unrearranged Grignard reagent with magnesium. Thus the interconversions found in the cation series among cyclobutyl, cyclopropylcarbinyl, and allylcarbinyl species are not mirrored with the anion.[110a] This is expected, since the interconversion of cyclopropylcarbinyl anion and cyclobutyl anion would involve alkyl migration to a carbanion, a process known to be energetically unfavorable. By contrast, the observed cyclopropylcarbinyl anion-butenyl anion interconversion involves addition of the carbanion to a vinyl group, an acceptable process.

Certain cyclobutenone derivatives can be opened with base, the phenyl-

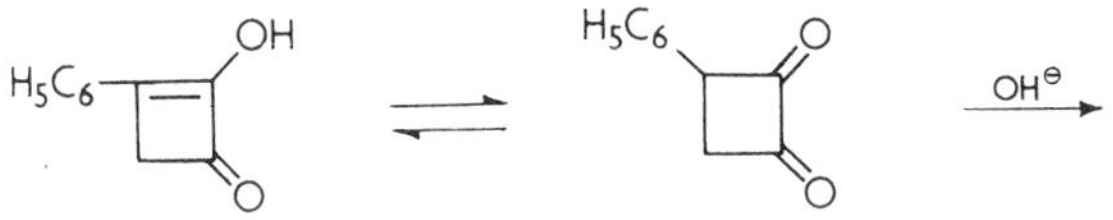

[120] E. F. Ullman, J. Am. Chem. Soc., 81, 5386 (1959).

hydroxycyclobutenone **173** [121] cleaving to **174**. Although a mechanism involving ring contraction prior to cleavage has been proposed,[122] there seems to be no reason to prefer it to the simpler alternative of direct cleavage. Similarly, phenylcyclobutenedione (**175**) is cleaved to **176**, [122] and here, too, a

(175)   (176)

direct cleavage mechanism seems adequate. However, the reactions of such ketones with bases are not always so simple, diphenylcyclobutenedione (**176a**) reacting with o-phenylenediamine to afford the unusual product **176b**.[122a]

(176a)   (176b)

Reaction of **177** with base leads to **178**,[123] and in this and related cases it has been demonstrated that the reaction occurs by direct attack on the substrate, as shown, although it will be remembered that this same ketone, in acetic

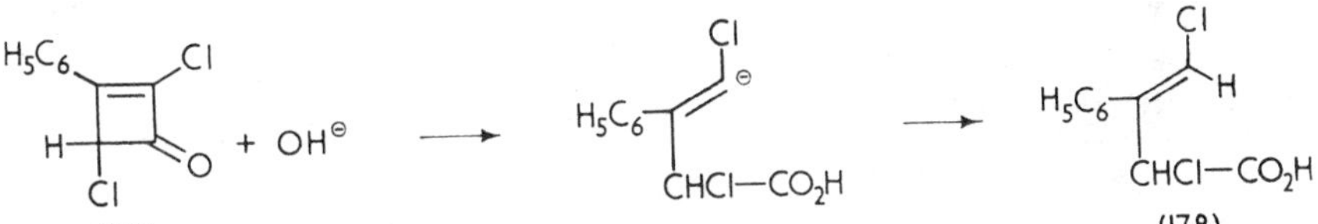

(177)   (178)

acid, cleaves via the ketene isomer.[123a] The mechanism here has been elucidated by carrying out the hydrolysis in deuterium oxide, when it is found that the product is **179**; [123a] it is apparent that reaction via the ketene

[121] E. F. Silversmith and J. D. Roberts, *J. Am. Chem. Soc.*, **80**, 4083 (1958).

[122] L. Skattebøl and J. D. Roberts, *J. Am. Chem. Soc.*, **80**, 4085 (1958); cf. also F. B. Mallory and J. D. Roberts, *J. Am. Chem. Soc.*, **83**, 393 (1961), for some related rearrangements.

[122a] A. T. Blomquist and E. A. LaLancette, *J. Am. Chem. Soc.*, **84**, 220 (1962).

[123] E. F. Silversmith and J. D. Roberts, *J. Am. Chem. Soc.*, **78**, 4023 (1956).

[123a] E. F. Silversmith, Y. Kitahara, M. C. Caserio, and J. D. Roberts, *J. Am. Chem. Soc.*, **80**, 5840 (1958).

intermediate would have afforded **180**. Interesting effects of the substituents on the mode of cleavage of such ketones have been observed.[123a]

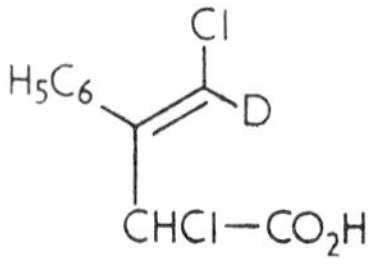

(179)

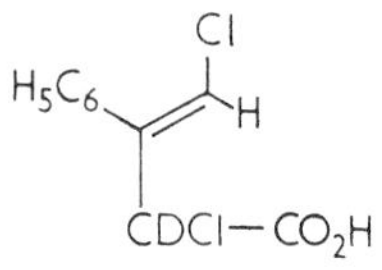

(180)

When a cyclobutylcarbinyl anion can undergo ring opening to generate a new anion which is reasonably stabilized, this process will occur. The base-catalyzed isomerization of photoisopyrocalciferol (**181**) is one example,[124]

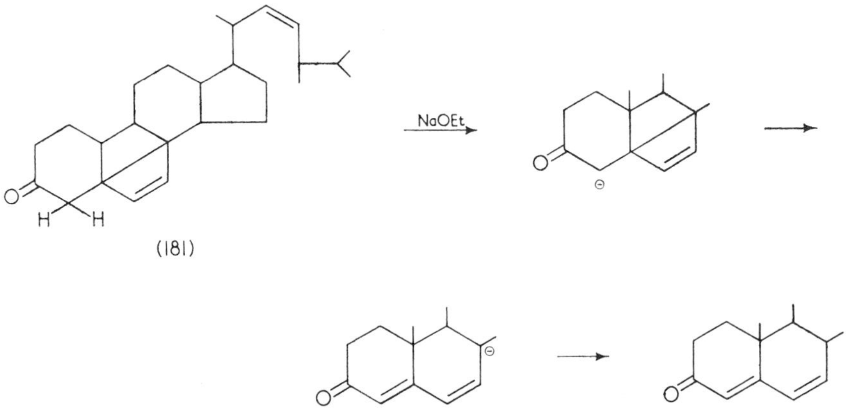

(181)

and a more complex case is represented by the isomerization of **181a** to **181b**, a base or nucleophile being required.[124a] The basic isomerization of chrysan-thenol (**181c**) is also of this mechanistic type.[124b]

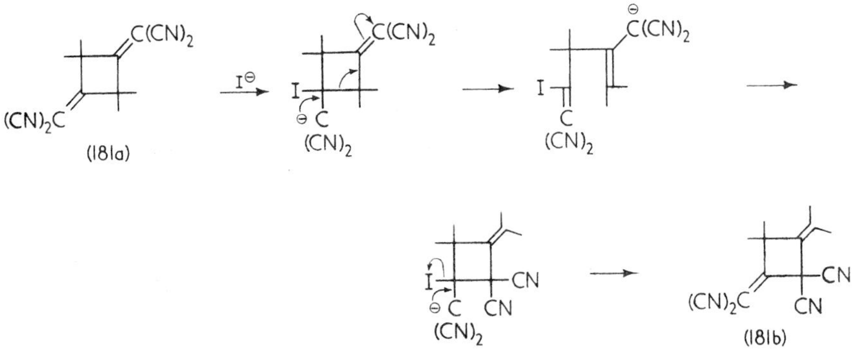

(181a)

(CN)$_2$C

(181b)

[124] W. G. Dauben and G. J. Fonken, *J. Am. Chem. Soc.*, **79**, 2971 (1957).
[124a] E. A. LaLancette and R. E. Benson, *J. Am. Chem. Soc.*, **83**, 4867 (1961).
[124b] J. Hurst and G. Whittam, *J. Chem. Soc.* (*London*), **1960**, 2864.

Finally, as an indication that some cyclobutenes can undergo considerably more obscure rearrangements than those so far mentioned, it should be noted that **182** is rearranged to **183** with base.[125]

(181c)

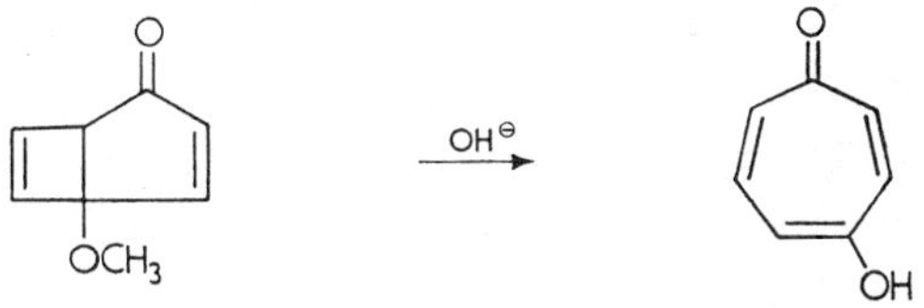

CHO

(182)   (183)

5. REARRANGEMENTS INVOLVING FREE RADICAL AND CARBENE INTERMEDIATES

The attack of a radical reagent on cyclopropane can lead to direct carbon-carbon bond rupture, as occurs in the reaction of atomic bromine with cyclopropane to produce methylene tribromide.[126] Also, the bicyclobutane derivative **184** undergoes free radical polymerization, probably by attack of a

(184)

radical on the diagonal bond.[127] However, a more common reaction is free radical substitution on cyclopropane, in which a cyclopropyl radical is the intermediate.

Photochemical chlorination of cyclopropane at moderate temperatures yields cyclopropyl chloride,[128] and vapor phase nitration of cyclopropane yields nitrocyclopropane.[129] There is also no rearrangement in the Huns-

---

[125] O. L. Chapman and D. J. Pasto, *J. Am. Chem. Soc.*, **81**, 5510 (1959).

[126] M. S. Kharasch, M. Fineman, and F. Mayo, *J. Am. Chem. Soc.*, **61**, 2139 (1939).

[127] K. B. Wiberg and R. P. Cinla, *J. Am. Chem. Soc.*, **81**, 5261 (1959).

[128] J. D. Roberts and P. H. Durstine, *J. Am. Chem. Soc.*, **67**, 1281 (1945).

[129] H. B. Hass and H. Schechter, *J. Am. Chem. Soc.*, **75**, 1382 (1953).

diecker reaction of silver cyclopropanecarboxylate (eq. 19),[130] and the pyrolysis of the peracid anhydride **185** in carbon tetrachloride affords unrearranged

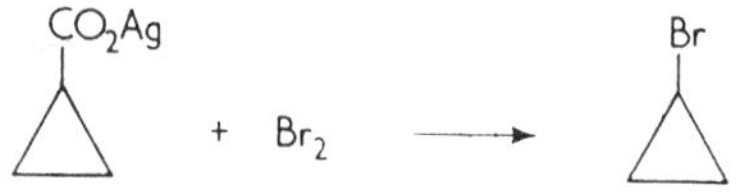

$$\text{(19)}$$

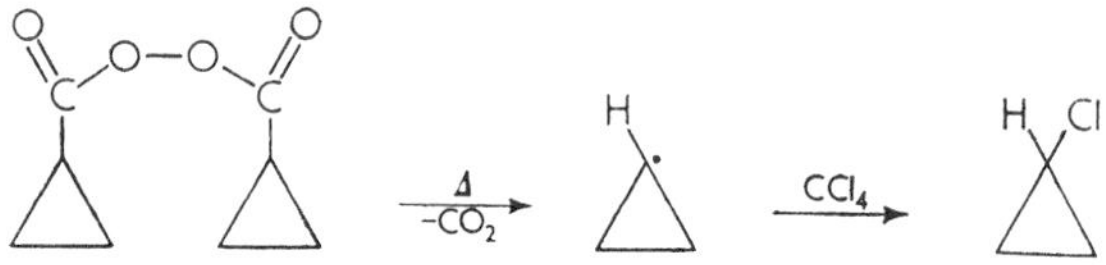

(185)

cyclopropyl chloride.[131] However, when the cyclopropyl radical is generated at 375° by the attack of a methyl radical on cyclopropane the products are derived from the allyl radical, the result of rearrangement (eq. 20).[132] The

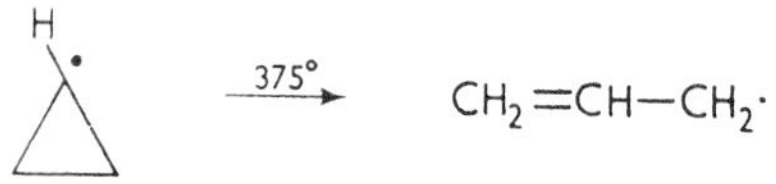

$$\xrightarrow{375°} \quad CH_2 = CH - CH_2 \cdot \qquad (20)$$

allyl radical is not the immediate product, and even though at first sight it seems to be just an electronic rearrangement product of the cyclopropyl radical the two differ in geometry as well, and are thus distinct species. As

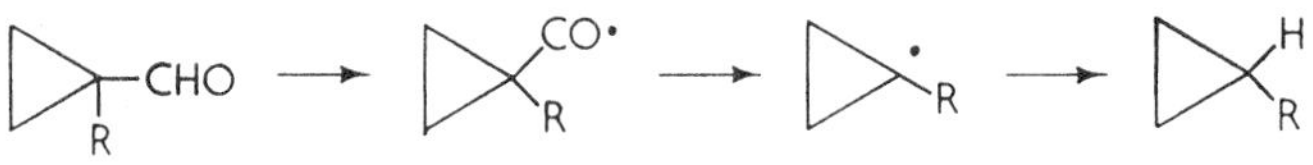

expected on this basis, cyclopropane is less reactive than larger ring compounds toward methyl radical,[132,133] since the transition state resembles the cyclopropyl radical. This is unstable because of strain, even though it may subsequently rearrange to the very stable allyl radical. A similar situation was discussed in the case of the related cations. The free-radical decarbonylation of 1-methylcyclopropanecarboxaldehyde at 140° occurs without rearrangement, as does that of the 1-phenyl derivative, but unsubstituted cyclopropanecarboxaldehyde does not decarbonylate; it is thus apparent that the cyclopropyl radical has an appreciable lifetime before rearrangement to the allyl radical even at this temperature.[133a] The failure of the unsub-

[130] J. D. Roberts and V. C. Chambers, *J. Am. Chem. Soc.*, **73**, 3176 (1951).

[131] H. Hart and D. Wyman, *J. Am. Chem. Soc.*, **81**, 4891 (1959).

[132] J. R. McNesby and A. S. Gordon, *J. Am. Chem. Soc.*, **79**, 825 (1957).

[133] A. F. Trotman-Dickenson and E. W. R. Steacie, *J. Chem. Phys.*, **19**, 329 (1951).

[133a] D. Schuster and J. D. Roberts, *J. Org. Chem.*, **27**, 51 (1962).

stituted compound to decarbonylate reflects again the instability of cyclo-propyl radical, an instability which can of course be decreased by substituents.

Some cases have been reported in which ring opening occurs at normal temperatures, although in these examples it is probably not the cyclopropyl radical which is rearranging. Kolbe electrolysis of cyclopropanecarboxylic acid yields allyl alcohol,[134] and reaction of the silver salt with iodine is reported to afford **186**, presumably from rearrangement leading to allyl iodide followed by reaction with further amounts of the silver salt and of iodine.[135]

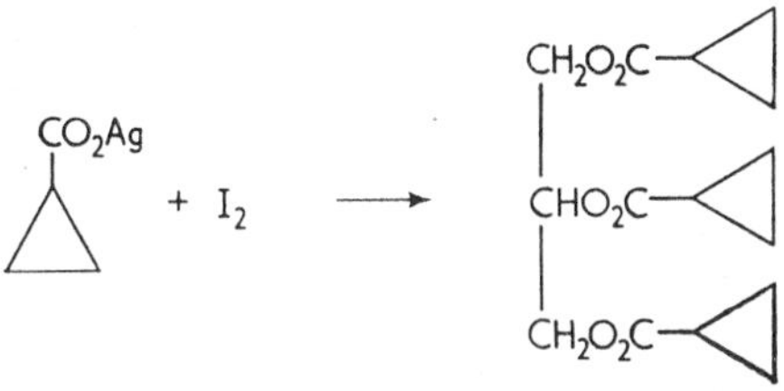

(186)

The situation with the cyclopropylcarbinyl radical is also complex, some reactions involving rearrangement and others not. Thus it is reported that photochemical chlorination of methylcyclopropane in the liquid phase (eq. 21)

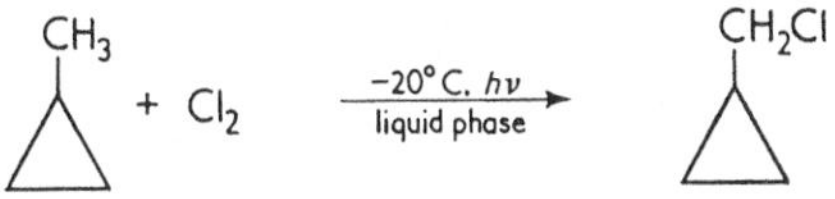

$$\text{(21)}$$

proceeds without much rearrangement, with substitution only on the methyl group.[136] On the other hand, in the vapor phase this same chlorination apparently leads to a mixture of products, including not only the expected chloride but also the product (**187**) from ring-opening rearrangement of the

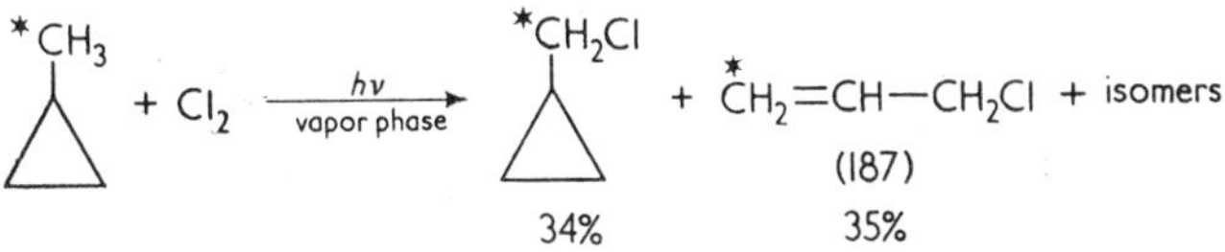

intermediate radical. In addition, other isomers were obtained which were suggested to be ring-chlorinated cyclopropanes.[136a] Chlorination of methyl-^{13}C-cyclopropane affords the normal and rearranged chlorides with the

[134] F. Fichter and H. Reeb, *Helv. Chim. Acta.*, **6**, 450 (1923).

[135] P. Lipp, J. Buchkremer, and H. Seeles, *Ann.*, **499**, 1 (1932).

[136] H. C. Brown and M. Borkowski, *J. Am. Chem. Soc.*, **74**, 1894 (1952).

[136a] J. D. Roberts and R. H. Mazur, *J. Am. Chem. Soc.*, **73**, 2509 (1951).

labels as shown. Thus no equilibration of the methylene groups could be detected, showing that the radical equivalent of a bicyclobutonium ion is certainly not formed.[136b] This ring opening has been observed in other systems, even under mild conditions, and photochemical chlorination of **188** affords exclusively the open compound **189** even at −80°.[137] Another interest-

(188) (189)

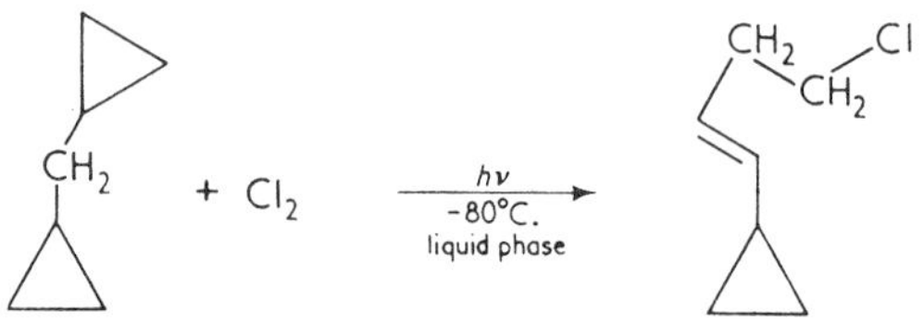

ing case occurs in the free radical chlorination of spiropentane (**190**), where the products are **191, 192, 193,** and **194.**[138] The first comes from the usual free radical substitution, with no rearrangement even though the intermediate (**195**) is both a cyclopropyl and a cyclopropylcarbinyl radical. How-

(190) (195) (191) (196)

(192) (193) (194)

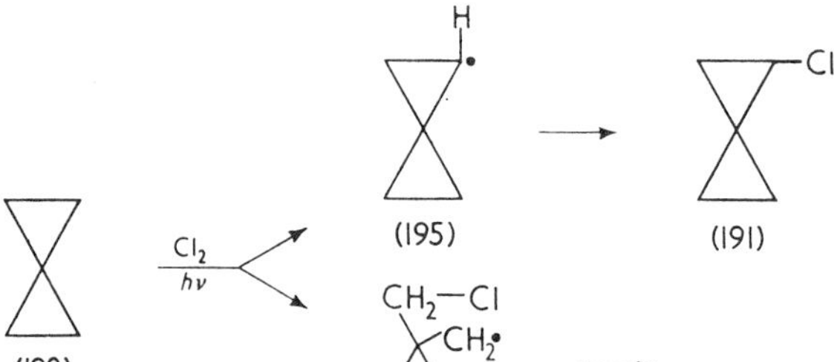

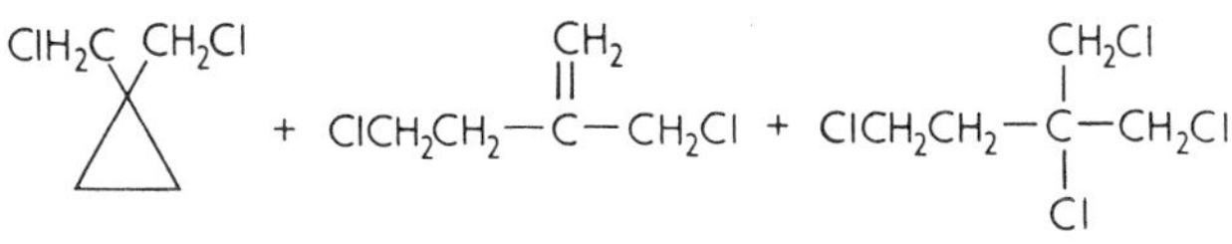

ever, the last three products are apparently derived from **196**, which is formed by ring-opening attack by a chlorine atoms. This may react with

[136b] E. Renk, P. Shafer, W. Graham, R. Mazur, and J. Roberts, *J. Am. Chem. Soc.*, **83**, 1987 (1961).

[137] H. Hart and D. Wyman, *J. Am. Chem. Soc.*, **81**, 4891 (1959).

[138] D. E. Applequist, G. F. Fanta, and B. W. Henrikson, *J. Am. Chem. Soc.*, **82**, 2368 (1960).

chlorine to yield **192**, or it may open, the other two products being formed in this latter way.

It is interesting that ring opening, but not ring expansion, occurs with the cyclopropylcarbinyl radical, as it also did with the anion; apparently the cyclobutyl radical is not in ready equilibrium with the cyclopropylcarbinyl or homoallyl radical. In this respect the radical and the anion are distinct from the cation, with its bicyclobutonium ion formulation, and further evidence on this point is furnished by the observation that chlorination of cyclobutane, under the same conditions as led to rearrangement with methylcyclopropane, furnishes only cyclobutyl chloride.[136a] As an additional example, the free radical decarbonylation of cyclopropyl acetaldehyde yields only the ring-opened 1-butene, but cyclobutane carboxaldehyde under the same conditions yields only cyclobutane.[139] None the less, it might be wondered whether the cyclopropylcarbinyl radical is especially stabilized by "resonance" between its classical form and the homoallyl radical. An interesting piece of evidence suggesting that this may be so is found in the observation that **197** decomposes to afford nitrogen—and, presumably, **198**—twenty-

$$NC-\underset{\underset{\triangle}{|}}{\overset{\overset{CH_3}{|}}{C}}-N{=}N-\underset{\underset{\triangle}{|}}{\overset{\overset{CH_3}{|}}{C}}-CN \quad \xrightarrow{\Delta} \quad \cdot\underset{\underset{\triangle}{|}}{\overset{\overset{CH_3}{|}}{C}}-CN$$

(197)   (198)

five times as rapidly as does the corresponding cyclopentane derivative.[140]

Only a modest amount of work has so far been done on the carbenoid rearrangements of small ring compounds. As was discussed earlier, reduction of 1,1-dihalocyclopropanes with metals affords allenes, presumably via a carbene intermediate, and allene was found as well from the decomposition of (intermediate) diazocyclopropane.[141] The same intermediate carbene has been prepared, and its rearrangement to allene observed, in two systems which formally add atomic carbon to ethylene (eq. 22).[142,143]

$$CH_2{=}CH_2 \quad + \quad \overset{\cdot\cdot}{\underset{\cdot\cdot}{C}} \quad \longrightarrow \quad \triangle \quad \longrightarrow \quad CH_2{=}C{=}CH_2 \quad (22)$$

Cyclopropylcarbene (**199**), the presumed intermediate in the pyrolysis of cyclopropyldiazomethane, yields chiefly cyclobutene, along with some

[139] D. Schuster, Ph.D. thesis, California Institute of Technology, 1960.

[140] C. G. Overberger and A. Lebovits, *J. Am. Chem. Soc.*, **76**, 2722 (1954).

[141] L. Friedman and H. Schechter, *J. Am. Chem. Soc.*, **83**, 3159 (1961).

[142] K. Bayes, *J. Am. Chem. Soc.*, **83**, 3712 (1961).

[143] C. MacKay, P. Polak, H. Rosenberg, and R. Wolfgang, *J. Am. Chem. Soc.*, **84**, 308 (1962).

products of fragmentation.[144] On the other hand, diazocyclobutane (**200**) yields chiefly methylenecyclopropane along with a small amount of cyclobutene from hydride shift.[144] Thus, as expected, the electron deficient carbene can undergo 1,2 alkyl migration; the two diazo compounds do not lead to the same products, of course, since migration of a single bond would not interconvert two carbenes.

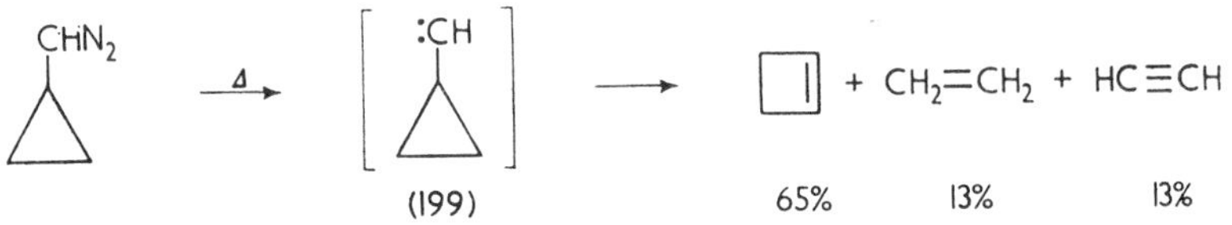

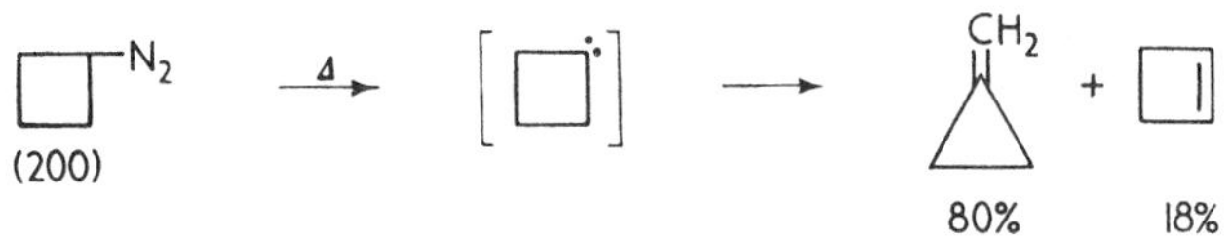

It is apparent from the reactions discussed that carbon-skeleton rearrangement is the rule rather than the exception in small-ring chemistry; this series gives the lie to the principle of minimal structural change. Confusing though this situation would have been during the early development of organic chemistry, it is undoubtedly responsible for the present burst of interest in small-ring compounds. These simple substances, with their complicated reactions, are worthy opponents against which to pit the skill of modern organic chemistry.

[144] L. Friedman and H. Schechter, *J. Am. Chem. Soc.*, **82**, 1002 (1960).

AROMATIC REARRANGEMENTS[1]

M. J. S. DEWAR

University of Chicago, Chicago,
Illinois

I. INTRODUCTION: THE π COMPLEX

Aromatic molecular rearrangements are reactions in which a group migrates from one position to another in an aromatic system or from a side chain into the nucleus. A rearrangement proper is a reaction in which the migrating group remains attached to the same nucleus throughout the reaction; reactions of this kind are often called intramolecular, to distinguish them from intermolecular or pseudorearrangements which take place by fission and recombination. Here we shall be concerned only with true (intramolecular) rearrangements.

A further distinction can be drawn on the basis of the number of positions

---

[1] Rearrangements not involving, at least obviously, discrete ionic or radical intermediates are dealt with elsewhere in this Part (Section 11).

of potential attachment of the migrating group. In a *monodentate* rearrangement the migrating group has only one point of possible attachment; halogen atoms and alkyl groups are of this type. In a *bidentate* rearrangement the migrating group has two possible points of attachment; in the rearranged product the migrating group is attached through a point different from that used in the parent compound. Reactions of this type, of which the Claisen rearrangement is the best-known example, normally involve cyclic transition states.[1] In a *polydentate* rearrangement the migrating group has three or more possible points of attachment; reactions of this type commonly give mixtures of products, in which the migrating group is attached to the substrate through one or the other of its potential points of attachment.

Monodentate rearrangements present two main problems. First, there is the theoretical problem of explaining how a migrating monodentate group can move from one part of a molecule to another without ever being completely detached. Groups of this type cannot by definition be attached simultaneously to two different positions in a molecule by normal bonds. Second, there is the experimental difficulty of establishing whether or not a given reaction involves a true intramolecular rearrangement.

The solution of the first problem was given [1a] some years ago in terms of MO theory. All these reactions are acid catalyzed; it is reasonable to suppose that the entity which undergoes rearrangement is a conjugate acid formed by protonation of the starting material. Now if one detached the migrating group (X) from this conjugate acid in the form of a positive ion (X^+), one would be left with a normal aromatic system, derived from the parent molecule by replacement of X by hydrogen. For example, the conjugate acid (**B**) from N-nitroaniline (**A**) could split into aniline and a nitronium ion (NO_2^+).

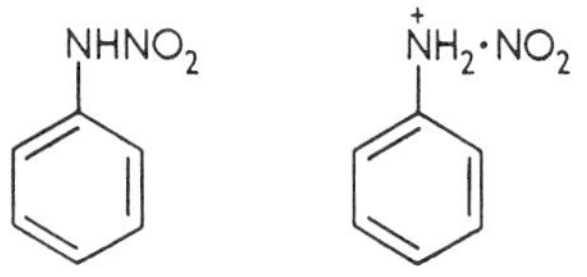

(A)   (B)

In this derived aromatic system the conjugated atoms are linked by π bonds, formed by electrons occupying delocalized π orbitals. It can easily be shown that such electrons should be free to form dative bonds to any acceptor, in the same manner as can the unshared pairs of electrons in water or an amine. For example, benzene should be able to form such a π *complex* with an acceptor X^+ by overlap of the vacant AO of d X^+ with the filled MO's of the ring (**C**).

[1a] M. J. S. Dewar, *J. Chem. Soc.* (*London*), **1946**, 406, 777; *The Electronic Theory of Organic Chemistry*, Clarendon Press, Oxford, 1949; *Bull. Soc. Chim.*, **18c**, 86 (1951); *Theoretical Organic Chemistry* (*Kekulé Symposium*), Butterworths, London, 1959, p. 179.

The geometry of the π complex $C_6H_6 \rightarrow X^+$ is of interest. Theory indicates that if the empty orbital of X^+ is a σ-type orbital (as it is in all the cases that concern us here), then X^+ must be attached off-axis to the benzene ring, above or below one edge, as indicated in **C**, and not along the six-fold axis as in **D**.

The π electrons used by benzene in forming a dative bond must be then occupying the MO or MO's of highest energy since electrons in such orbitals will be the least strongly bound. The highest occupied level is in fact degenerate, consisting of two MO's of like energy; each of these MO's has a node passing through the six-fold axis (Fig. 1). This means that if X^+ lies on that axis, it cannot interact with the electrons occupying the two vital MO's. This therefore is the one place where X^+ cannot be.

This argument does not apply if the empty orbital of X^+ has p- or d-type symmetry; in this case the six-fold axis is a very favorable location for X^+ (Fig. 1). This situation arises in the complexes formed by benzene with brom-

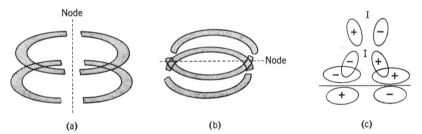

Figure 1.   (a) and (b) Highest occupied MO's of benzene; (c) orbital overlap in $C_6H_6I_2$ complex.

ine and iodine where the halogen molecule lies in line along the six-fold axis.[2]

This means that the conjugate acid $(ArXH)^+$ of our substrate ArX, instead of splitting off X^+, can rearrange directly to a π complex ArH $\rightarrow X^+$ in which the group X^+ is now held by a bond formed by interaction of one of its AO's with the π MO's of the aromatic system. As far as X is concerned, this bond will be a normal covalent bond; if X is an asymmetric alkyl group, its stereochemistry will be retained in the π complex. Thus in the π complex **C** the methyl carbon will retain a tetrahedral geometry; the symbol $C_6H_6 \rightarrow \overset{+}{C}H_3$ no

[2] R. S. Mulliken, *J. Am. Chem. Soc.*, **72**, 600 (1950).

more implies that the methyl group has the planar configuration of a carbonium ion than would the corresponding representation $Me_3N \rightarrow \overset{+}{C}H_3$ for the tetramethylammonium ion; this formulation is, of course, equivalent to the more conventional $Me_3\overset{+}{N}$—CH_3.

Since the bond holding X^+ is a dative covalent bond, albeit a rather unusual one, its strength should be comparable with the strength of covalent bonds in conventional dative complexes such as amine oxides or the ammonia–borine adduct. The isomerization of the conjugate acid $(ArXH)^+$ to a π complex, $ArH \rightarrow X^+$, should therefore require very little energy. This point needs emphasizing in view of the unfortunate misuse of the term π complex to describe loose polarization complexes such as the hydrogen-bound complexes formed from aromatic hydrocarbons and hydrogen chloride.[3] These (E) bear the same relation to true π complexes (G) that the analogous complexes (F) formed by ether with hydrogen chloride do to salts (H). This confusion has

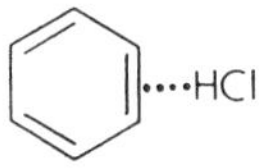

led certain authors to misunderstand the theoretical basis of π complex mechanisms for molecular rearrangements.

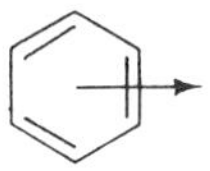

In the π complex $ArH \rightarrow X^+$, the group X^+ is held by a bond formed by interaction with the π electrons of the ring. Therefore X should be able to rove freely over the π electron cloud, the latter providing a kind of electronic railroad over which X can move from one part of the molecule to another without ever being detached from the parent aromatic ring. This provides a very attractive mechanism for intramolecular migrations of groups from one point to another in such a system.

The second problem, that of establishing whether or not a given rearrangement is intramolecular, is a much more difficult one. It has been commonly assumed that an acid test is provided by finding if cross-migration can occur; but this is incorrect. During the migration of a group from one point to another in a molecule, the system normally passes through intermediates of higher energy in which the migrating group is midway between its starting point and final destination. A reactive foreign molecule may capture the

[3] H. C. Brown and J. D. Brady, *J. Am. Chem. Soc.*, **74**, 3570 (1952).

migrating group from such an intermediate, even though it could not do so from the starting material or final product. The occurrence of cross-migrations is therefore no indication of the inter- or intramolecularity of a rearrangement; cross-migration is possible even for the intramolecular processes.

Conversely the nonexistence of cross-migration is no proof that a reaction is truly intramolecular. A molecule may undergo fission into two fragments (e.g., radicals) which recombine to form a product isomeric with the starting material. If the recombination is very fast, the fragments may be held together in a cage of solvent molecules (Franck-Rabinowitch effect) until they recombine. It is often extremely difficult to exclude the possibility of cage-effect mechanisms of this kind.

2. MONODENTATE REARRANGEMENTS: MIGRATION AROUND THE AROMATIC SYSTEM

A. The Jacobsen Rearrangement

The Jacobsen rearrangement consists of the migration of alkyl groups from one position to another in an aromatic system in the presence of acids. The original examples[4] were concerned with the migrations of methyl groups during sulfonation of polymethylbenzenes; for example, durene (1) on sulfonation gives prehnitenesulfonic acid (2). Numerous other examples are known; thus the octahydrophenanthrene (3) rearranges to the octahydroanthracenesulfonic acid (4). Similar rearrangements are observed[5] when

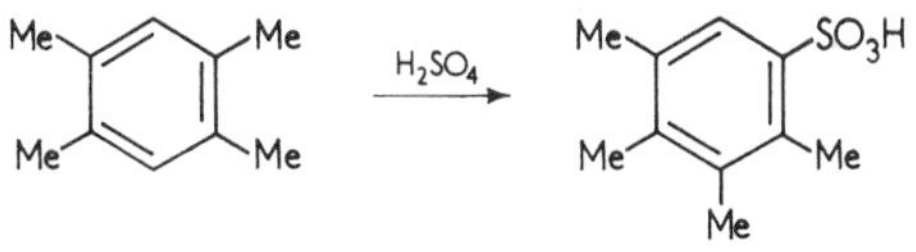

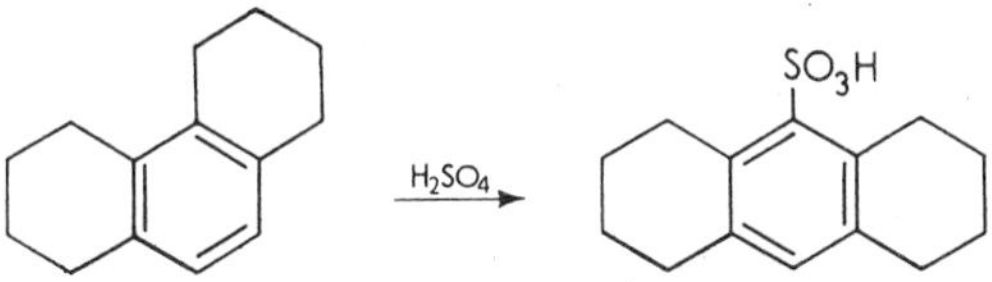

polymethylbenzenes are treated with boron trifluoride and anhydrous hydrogen fluoride; under these conditions the trimethylbenzenes are isomerized to mesitylene, the most basic isomer (see below).

[4] Cf. L. I. Smith, *Org. Reactions*, 1, 370 (1942).
[5] D. A. McCaulay and A. P. Lien, *J. Am. Chem. Soc.*, 74, 6246 (1952).

These reactions cannot be intermolecular; for methyl groups could be detached only in the form of derivatives (Me_2SO_4, $MeHSO_4$, MeF, etc.) which would not act as methylating agents under the conditions used in the reactions. The only reasonable mechanism seems to be one based on π complex intermediates (e.g., 5-7). Here rearrangement is brought about by the agent

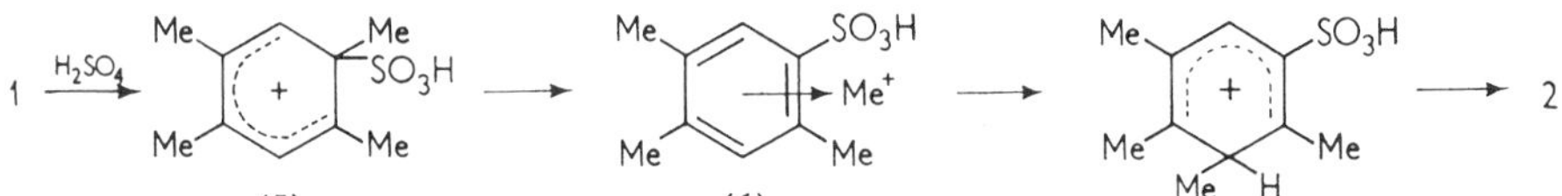

$(SO_3H)^+$ acting as a general acid. In the case of the HF–BF$_3$ reactions it is a protonated form of the hydrocarbon that rearranges. Formula 6 implies a π complex formed by interaction of CH_3^+ with 2,4,5-trimethylbenzenesulfonic acid.

In the simple treatment outlined above it was assumed that the π electron cloud of benzene is isotropic; this is equivalent to using a free electron MO picture of the π system. In actual fact the π electron density will fluctuate round the ring in sympathy with the periodic potential field due to the nuclei. There will be a real distinction between the forms 8 and 8a of the π complex formed by benzene with an acceptor X^+, depending on whether X^+ is attached at a point midway between two carbon atoms (8) or opposite one carbon atom (8a). The position is further complicated by the possibility of rearrangement of 8a into the quasi-classical benzenonium [6] ion (9) in which one carbon

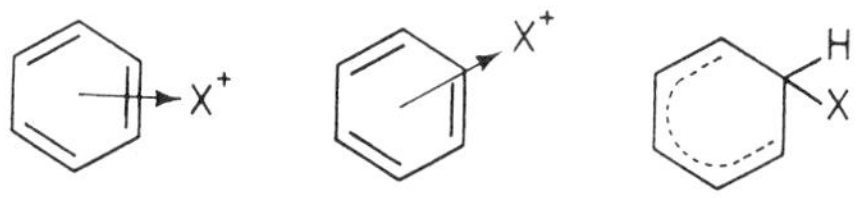

atom in the ring has changed its hybridization to sp^3 and adopted a tetrahedral geometry so that it no longer plays a part in the conjugated system.

The relative stabilities of these three structures have been studied by various workers: it now appears that 9 is the most stable form, but that 8 and 9 differ little in energy. Therefore the migration of a group X around a ring takes place in a series of hops from one benzenonium ion to another, via intermediate π complexes in which the ring recovers its planar configuration. The migrations take place very readily since the energy barriers between the benzenonium ions are small.

[6] W. von E. Doering, M. Saunders, H. G. Boynton, E. F. Wadley, W. R. Edwards, and G. Laber, *Tetrahedon*, 4, 178 (1958).

The best evidence that **9** is the stable form has been provided by the preparation [7] of salts of benzene and of its methyl derivatives containing ions $C_6H_7^+$, etc., which appear to be benzenonium ions (**9**, R = H). Two lines of evidence support this formulation. First, the ions are colored and their light absorption corresponds to that calculated [8] for the benzenonium ion structure. Second, the basicity of methylbenzenes depends [9] on the maximum number of methyl groups meta to one another; thus, 1,2,3- and 1,2,4-trimethyl-benzenes are little more basic than *m*-xylene but mesitylene is a much stronger base.

This would be expected if the conjugate acids are benzenonium ions; for the positive charge in **9** is concentrated on the position ortho-para to the methylene and **9** should therefore be stabilized most strongly by $-I$ groups such as methyl if they occupy these positions—and consequently if they are meta to one another.

This second argument is inconclusive as it stands, since there is no a priori reason for believing that methyl groups might not show a similar selectivity in their ability to stabilize the π complex (**8**). However, unpublished calculations by Dr. J. Burr have shown that this is not the case; methyl groups should stabilize **8** to a comparable degree no matter where they are attached.

A study [10] of the heptamethylbenzenonium ion (**10**) by NMR has shown that the methyl groups undergo rapid interchange; this indicates that the benzenonium (**10**) and π complex (**11**) forms of the ion must have very similar energies, as one would expect on theoretical grounds. (The relative stabilities of π complexes and benzenonium ions are discussed later in the article.)

(10)   (11)

One interesting feature of the Jacobsen rearrangement is the occurrence of cross-migration of alkyl groups; thus sulfonation of durene (**1**) gives some trimethyl- and pentamethylbenzenesulfonic acids, formed by migration of methyl from one nucleus to another. Since the reactions are undoubtedly intramolecular, this bears out the argument given above that cross-migration

[7] C. Reid, *J. Am. Chem. Soc.*, **76**, 3264 (1954); G. A. Olah and S. J. Kuhn, *J. Am. Chem. Soc.*, **80**, 6536, 6541 (1958).

[8] N. Muller, L. W. Pickett, and R. S. Mulliken, *J. Am. Chem. Soc.*, **76**, 4770 (1954).

[9] D. A. McCaulay and A. P. Lien, *J. Am. Chem. Soc.*, **73**, 2013 (1951).

[10] W. von E. Doering, M. Saunders, H. G. Boynton, H. W. Earhart, E. F. Wadley, W. R. Edwards, and G. Laber, *Tetrahedron*, **4**, 178 (1958).

of groups during a rearrangement cannot be taken as evidence that it is inter-molecular. In this case the cross-migration probably involves a transfer of alkyl from a benzenonium ion (**12**) to a foreign nucleus (**13**) by an S_N2

mechanism. It was pointed out some time ago [11] that the uncatalyzed benzyl-ation of anthracene by benzyl chloride must involve such an S_N2 process, and a similar mechanism has more recently been postulated [12] to account for certain alkylations of aromatic compounds by alkyl chlorides in presence of aluminum chloride.

The dienone-phenol rearrangement is a reaction which is analogous to the Jacobsen rearrangement. It concerns the conversion of a dienone (or semi-quinone) to a phenol by alkyl migration in the presence of acid. This is illus-trated by the earliest known example, the conversion of santonin to desmo-troposantonin (these transformations are discussed in detail in Section 16) and of **14** to **15**.

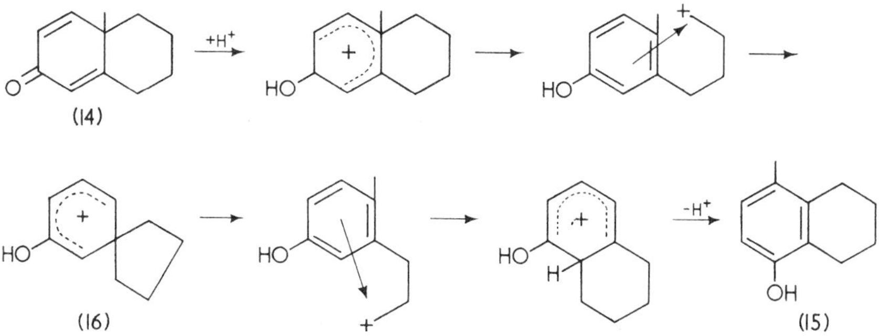

These reactions undoubtedly involve initial attachment of a proton to the dienone giving an intermediate which can be regarded as a hydroxy-benzeno-nium derivative; this, in turn, rearranges by alkyl migration. The mechanism, illustrated is supported by the observation [15] that the solvolysis of **17** gives **18** which is very similar to the postulated intermediate (**16**) (see Section 16).

[11] M. J. S. Dewar, *The Electronic Theory of Organic Chemistry*, Clarendon Press, Oxford, 1949, p. 180.

[12] H. Jungk, R. Smoot, and H. C. Brown, *J. Am. Chem. Soc.*, **78**, 2176, 2182, 2185 (1956).

[13] G. R. Clemo, R. D. Haworth, and E. Walton, *J. Chem. Soc.* (*London*), **1930**, 1110.

[14] R. B. Woodward and T. Singh, *J. Am. Chem. Soc.*, **72**, 494 (1950).

[15] S. Winstein and R. Baird, *J. Am. Chem. Soc.*, **79**, 756 (1957).

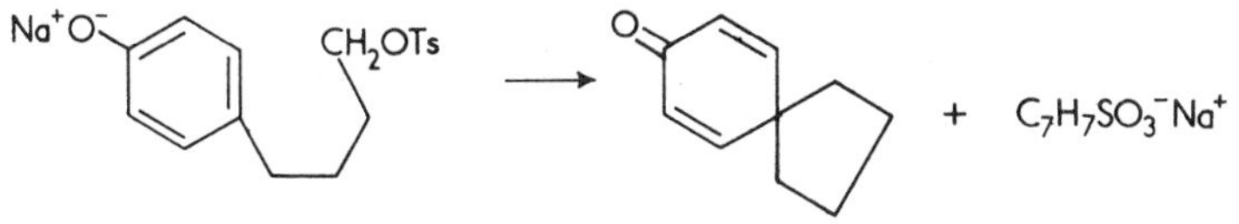

(17)　　　　　　　　(18)　　+　$C_7H_7SO_3^-Na^+$

B. Migrations of Alkyl Groups During the Fischer Indole Synthesis

Fischer reactions on hydrazones derived from 2,6-dimethylphenylhydrazine lead to indole derivatives by methyl migration; reactions of this kind have been studied in some detail by Carlin and his collaborators. For example[16] the acetophenonehydrazone (19) on treatment with zinc chloride gives 2-phenyl-4,7-dimethylindole (20). Here again a benzenonium intermediate

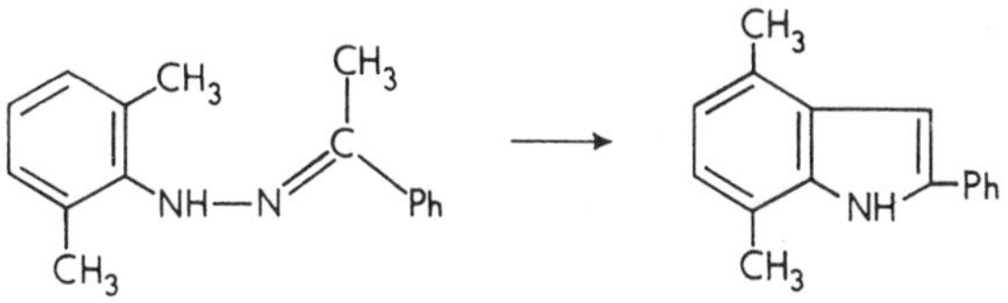

(19)　　　　　　　　　(20)

(21) seems to be involved, in view of the generally accepted mechanism of the Fischer reaction. This mechanism was confirmed by isolation[17] of the cyclo-hexenone derivative (23) which must have been formed from the intermediate 22 as shown.

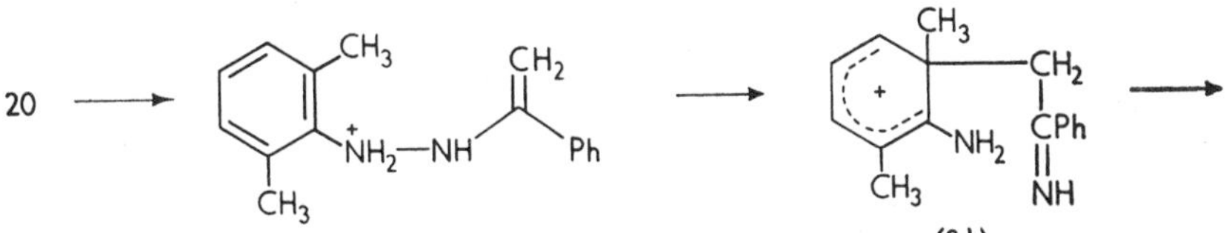

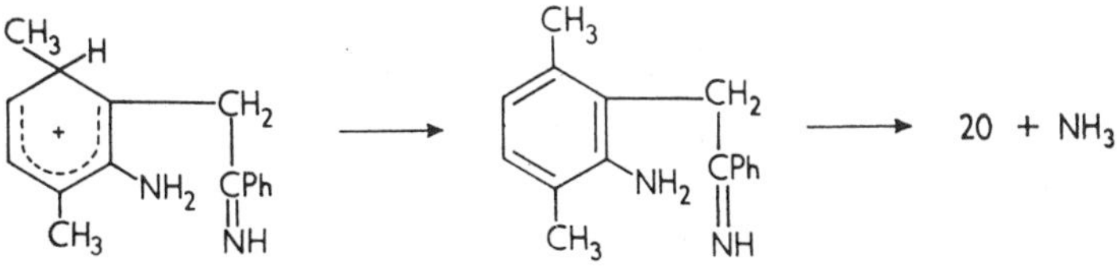

Carlin and Moore[18] have found an interesting variant of this reaction. Fischer rearrangement of the mesitylhydrazone (24) gave 5,6,7-trimethyl-tetrahydrocarbazole (25) in which a 1,4 shift of methyl had taken place.

[16] R. B. Carlin, W. O. Henley, and D. P. Carlson, *J. Am. Chem. Soc.*, **79**, 5712 (1957).
[17] R. B. Carlin and D. P. Carlson, *J. Am. Chem. Soc.*, **81**, 4673 (1959).
[18] R. B. Carlin and M. S. Moore, *J. Am. Chem. Soc.*, **81**, 1259 (1959).

Carlin and Moore postulate a direct 1,4 shift of methyl across the ring, but this seems very unlikely. No reasonable structure can be written [18a] for the

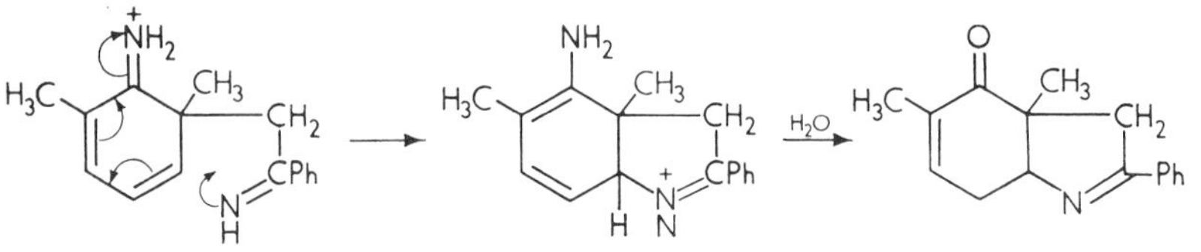

(22)   (23)

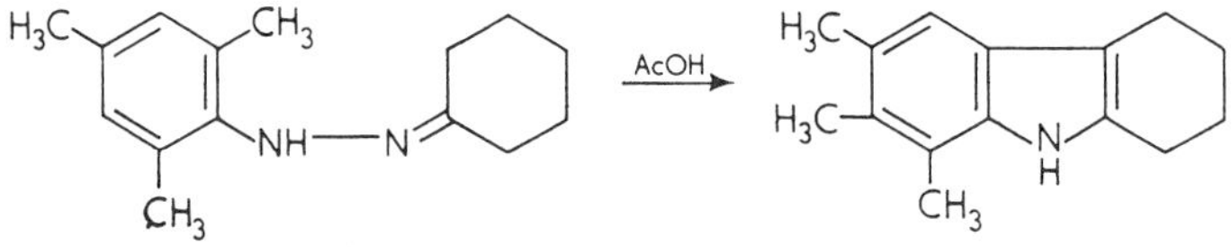

(24)   (25)

transition state for such a 1,4 shift and no analogies are known. It seems much more probable that the reaction takes place by a series of 1,2 shifts, as in the rearrangement of the dienone (**14**) to the phenol (**15**). The first step will be formation, from **24**, of the intermediate **26**; this rearranges by 1,2 shifts of methyl via **27** and **28** to **29** which by loss of a proton and ammonia forms the product (**25**). The problem is to explain why the benzenonium ion (**27**) does not itself lose a proton, giving a 4-methylindole derivative analogous to **20**. There are three reasons why the two compounds should behave so differently. First, there will be a steric interaction between the bulky cyclohexyl group in **27** and the migrating methyl; this will encourage further migration. No such steric effects are present in the case of **22**. Second, the extra methyl group will stabilize **27**, being ortho to the methylene group of a benzenonium ion, and so will discourage removal of a proton from it. Finally, the two reactions were carried out with different catalysts and solvents; this could very well have

---

[18a] In the transition state the migrating methyl would be halfway between the 1 and 4 carbon atoms. In such a structure the benzene ring could not be coplanar, for, as we have seen, the orbitals of benzene are not able to bind alkyl groups attached along the six-fold axis. The only possibility would be a boat configuration cyclohexadiene structure of the type

with the migrating methyl held by a three-center bond; this is clearly very unlikely.

influenced the relative rates of rearrangement and proton loss from **22** and from **27**.

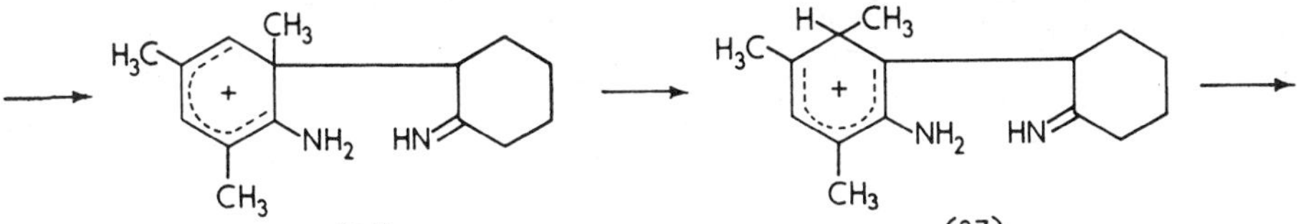

(26)   (27)

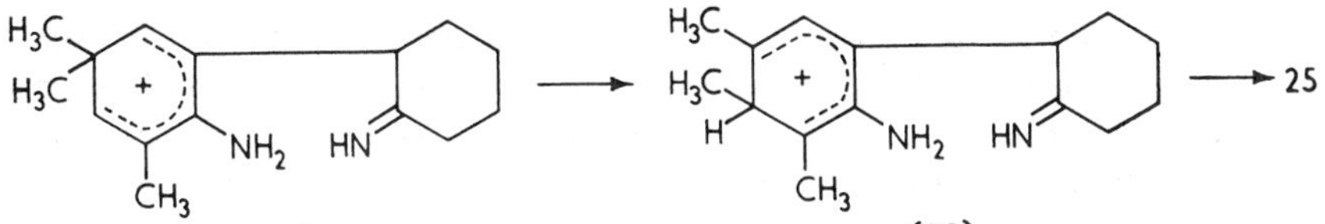

(28)   (29)

C. Halogen Migration

A number of reactions are known in which halogens appear to migrate around aromatic rings, but it is not known whether or not any of these are true intramolecular rearrangements. A typical example is the Reverdin rearrangement [19] where migration of iodine occurs during nitration of *p*-iodo-anisole (**30**). Robinson [20] claimed that the reaction is intermolecular on the

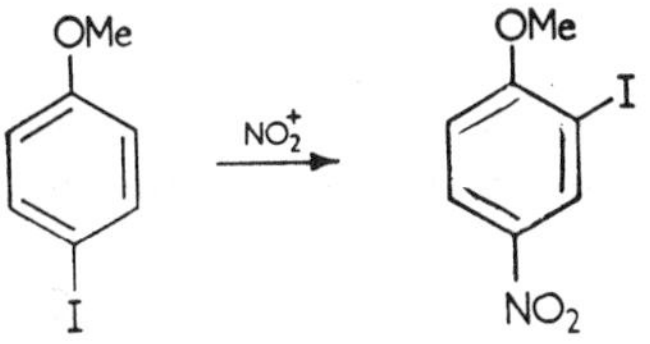

(30)   (31)

grounds that cross-migration of iodine can occur; 2,4-diiodoanisole is formed during the reaction. We have seen, however, that such evidence is inconclusive.

Another reaction of the same type is the formation [21] of 5,7-dichloroindole (**33**) as one product in the Fischer reaction of 2,6-dichlorophenylhydrazone (**32**). Here again the mechanism is uncertain. It is quite possible that reactions of this kind are intermolecular, involving a preliminary removal of halogen

[19] F. Reverdin, *Ber.*, **29**, 1000 (1896).

[20] G. M. Robinson, *J. Chem. Soc.* (*London*), **109**, 1078 (1916).

[21] R. B. Carlin and E. E. Fisher, *J. Am. Chem. Soc.*, **70**, 3421 (1948); R. B. Carlin and L. Amoros-Marin, *J. Am. Chem. Soc.*, **81**, 730 (1959).

as either a positive ion (I^+, Cl^+) or a hypohalite, although an intramolecular mechanism seems on the whole more likely.

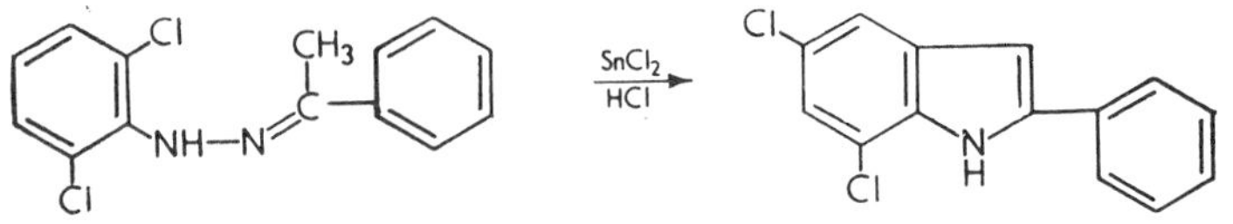

(32)   (33)

3. MONODENTATE REARRANGEMENTS: MIGRATION OF GROUPS FROM THE SIDE CHAIN TO THE NUCLEUS

The other main class of monodentate aromatic rearrangements involves the acid-catalyzed migration of a group from the side chain of an aromatic compound into the ring. In the majority of these reactions it is the group initially attached to the nitrogen of an aromatic amine or to the oxygen of a phenol that migrates. A number of N-substituted anilines rearrange in this way to ortho or para-substituted anilines (eq. 1). Similar rearrangements are

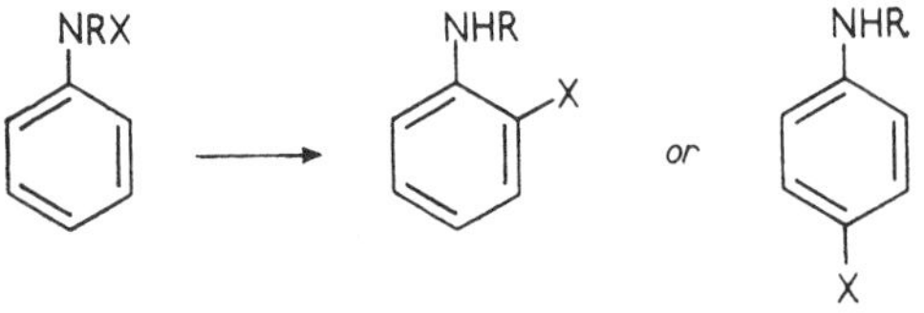

$(X = alkyl, NO, ArN{=}N{-}, halogen, NO_2)$

also known in the case of aryl esters (Fries rearrangement) and aryl alkyl ethers (e.g., eq. 2). Most of these reactions are now known to be intermole-

cular, involving a preliminary removal of the migrating group to form an aniline or phenol which then undergoes electrophilic substitution. This has long been known to happen in the rearrangement of diazoaminobenzene (eq. 3). Some, however, are intramolecular; and it will be convenient first to

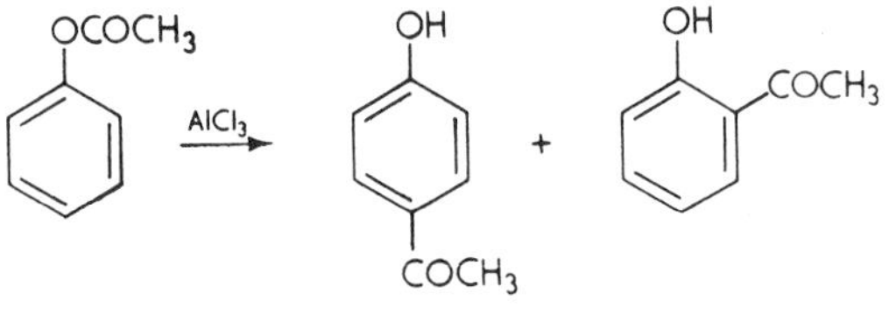

$$PhNH{\cdot}N{=}N^Ph \xrightarrow{H^+} PhNH_2 + Ph\overset{+}{N}{\equiv}N \longrightarrow PhN{=}N{-}\!\!\!\left\langle\!\!\!\bigcirc\!\!\!\right\rangle\!\!\!-NH_2 \quad (3)$$

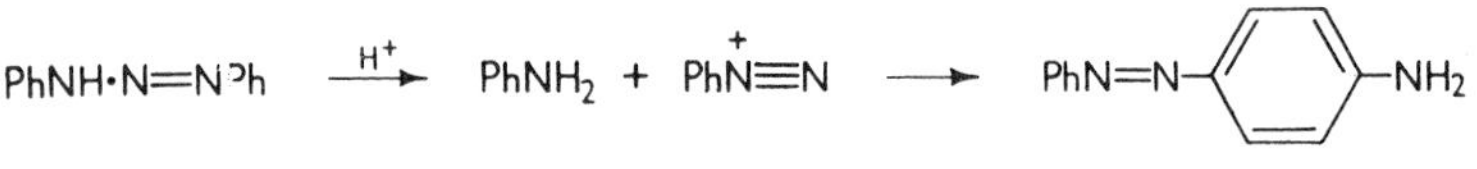

consider how intramolecular migration can occur in such cases from the side chain to distant points on the adjacent benzene ring.

Consider the rearrangement of an aniline derivative, PhNRX. The first step in the reaction will presumably be formation of the ion (**34**) by reaction with the acid catalyst. Removal of X^+ from this ion would leave a normal aniline derivative, C_6H_5NHR, in which the π orbitals cover nitrogen as well as the six carbon atoms in the ring. These π electrons could be used to form a dative bond to X^+. Consequently **34** should be able to rearrange by a series of 1,2 shifts via π complex intermediates.

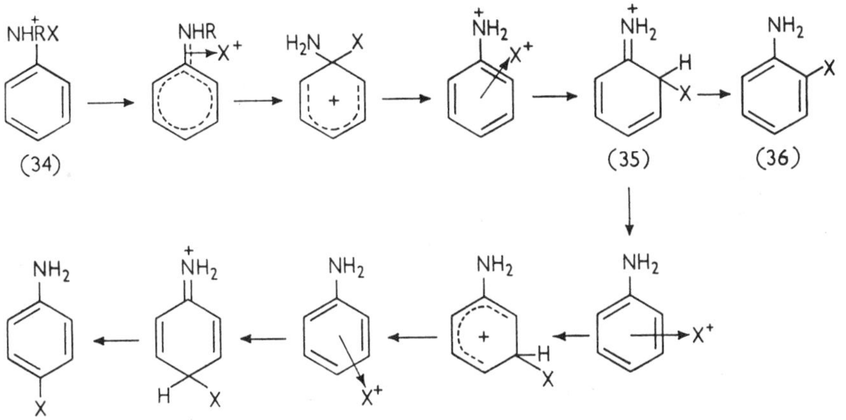

(34)   (35)   (36)

(39)   (38)   (37)

The benzenonium ions (**35**, **37**, and **38**) are identical with the intermediates postulated by current theory [22] for electrophilic substitution of aniline by the ion X^+. Of these **35** and **38** are much the more stable, having the $-E$ amino group in positions ortho or para to the saturated carbon atom. Indeed, since a $-E$ substituent should have no stabilizing effect in the meta positions of a benzenonium ion, but should stabilize the corresponding π complex strongly, it is likely that **37** is not a stable intermediate at all, but rather a transition state for the interconversion of **35** and **38**. Theory [23] suggests that **38** should be more stable than **35**, accounting for the fact that electrophilic substitution takes place mainly para in aniline derivatives. The changes in potential energy during the rearrangement **34** $\rightarrow$ **39** are therefore probably as represented in Figure 2.

Now in the rearrangement the system has to pass *through* the o-aminobenzenonium ion intermediate (**35**) in order to reach the para isomer (**38**). Loss of a proton from **35** to form the stable ortho rearrangement product (**36**)

[22] Cf. M. J. S. Dewar, *Record Chem. Progr.*, **19**, 1 (1958).
[23] M. J. S. Dewar, *J. Chem. Soc. (London)*, **1949**, 463.

is likely to be facile; if it happens, the system is stabilized and the migrating group never has a chance to get to the para position. The rearrangement of PhNRX should therefore give a much higher proportion of ortho isomer than substitution of the corresponding aniline derivative, PhNHR, by X$^+$.

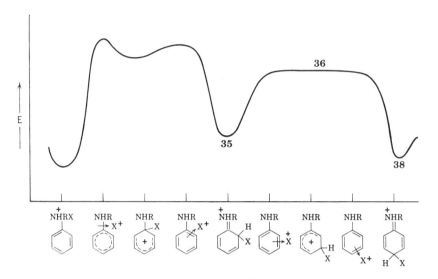

Figure 2. Variation in potential energy of PhN̄HRX during rearrangement by the π-complex mechanism.

This is an interesting conclusion since it suggests a possible method for distinguishing experimentally between inter- and intramolecular mechanisms for such rearrangements. An acid-catalyzed intermolecular rearrangement of PhNRX involves a splitting off of X as X$^+$ or its equivalent followed by electrophilic substitution of the PhNHR simultaneously formed. Such a process should give products with the low ortho/para ratio characteristic of electrophilic substitution in aniline; an intramolecular rearrangement of PhNHX should give a much higher proportion of ortho product.

A. Rearrangements of N-Substituted Anilines

A number of N-substituted anilines undergo acid-catalyzed rearrangements to ortho- or para-substituted anilines; the known reactions of this type are listed in Table I, together with the main rearrangement products. These results, in combination with the theoretical considerations given above, suggest that the N-nitroaniline rearrangement alone is intramolecular. The available evidence is in agreement with this conclusion.

TABLE I

Products from Acid-Catalysed Rearrangements of Various N-Substituted
Aniline Derivatives

Aniline derivative	Migrating group	Main product
PhNH—N=NPh	—N=NPh	Para
PhNHOH	OH	Para
PhNBrCOR	Br	Para
PhNClCOR	Cl	Para
PhNH·alkyl	Alkyl	Para
PhNR·NO	NO	Para
PhNHNO₂	NO₂	Ortho
PhNHSO₃H	SO₃H	?

1. The rearrangements of diazoaminobenzenes have long [24] been known to be intermolecular, involving fission and diazo coupling (eq. 4).

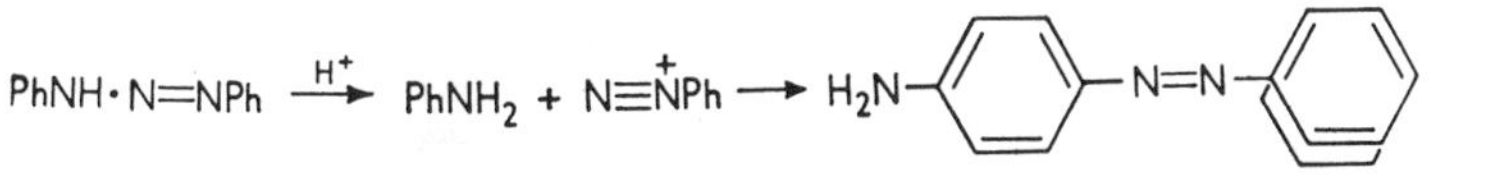

$$PhNH \cdot N{=}NPh \xrightarrow{\ H^+\ } PhNH_2 + N{\equiv}\overset{+}{N}Ph \longrightarrow H_2N{-}\!\!\!\bigcirc\!\!\!-N{=}N{-}\!\!\!\bigcirc \quad (4)$$

2. Yukawa [25] has given good reasons for believing that the rearrangement of phenylhydroxylamine (**40**) to p-aminophenol (**41**, R = H) is intermolecular. When the reaction was carried out in methanol or ethanol, the product was the corresponding p-methoxy- or p-ethoxyaniline (**41**, R = Me or Et), although

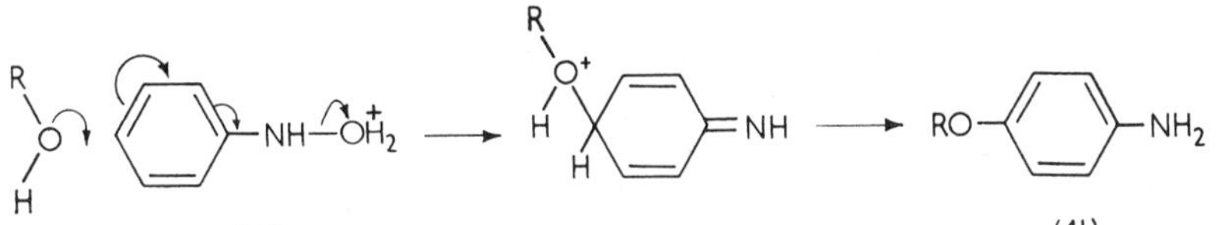

$$(40) \qquad\qquad (41)$$

p-aminophenol itself is not alkylated under the conditions used. The alkoxy group must therefore be derived from the solvent, the mechanism being that indicated in equation 5, a kind of S_N' reaction. (There is no evidence to show whether the reaction is of S_N2' type, or takes place in stages via an intermediate PhNH.) This conclusion was confirmed by Heller, Hughes, and Ingold [26] who showed that in the rearrangement of **40** in water enriched in ¹⁸O, complete exchange of oxygen with the solvent took place.

3. The rearrangements of N-chloro- and N-bromoacylanilides in water are

[24] Cf. H. V. Kidd, *J. Org. Chem.*, **2**, 198 (1937).

[25] Y. Yukawa, *J. Chem. Soc. Japan, Pure Chem. Sect.*, **71**, 547, 603 (1950).

[26] H. F. Heller, E. D. Hughes, and C. K. Ingold, *Nature*, **168**, 909 (1951).

specifically catalyzed by the corresponding hydrogen halides and have long been known [27] to take place by an intermolecular mechanism (eq. 6). The

$$\text{Ph}\overset{+}{\text{N}}\text{HAc}\text{—Cl }\ \bar{\text{Cl}} \longrightarrow \text{PhNHAc} + \text{Cl}_2 \longrightarrow \text{Cl}\text{—}\langle\text{—}\rangle\text{—NHAc} + \text{HCl} \qquad (6)$$

corresponding rearrangement in aprotic solvents shows general acid catalysis, and its mechanism was for some time in doubt; [27a] a detailed study by Dr. P. J. Couzens [28] has shown the rearrangements of N-bromoacetanilide to be mechanistically intermolecular under these conditions, although the reaction shows a number of interesting and unusual features.

4. The mechanism of the Hofmann rearrangement is still uncertain, particularly that of the Hickinbottom modification where metal halides are used as catalysts in place of normal acids. It seems very likely that the normal reaction, carried out by fusing a salt of the amine, takes place by an intermolecular carbonium ion mechanism:

$$\text{Ph}\overset{+}{\text{N}}\text{H}_2\text{R} \rightarrow \text{PhNH}_2 + \text{R}^+ \rightarrow \text{RC}_6\text{H}_4\text{NH}_2 \qquad (7)$$

The S_N1 heterolysis of the anilinium ion should be assisted by the highly polar medium and high temperature. The by-products commonly formed (olefins, alkyl halides, etc.) would be expected if carbonium ions were intermediates, while groups which are known to rearrange when set free in the form of carbonium ions do in fact give rearranged products; thus N-isobutylaniline rearranges to *tert*-butylaniline.

The mechanism of the Hickinbottom modification is certainly different since alkyl groups (e.g., isobutyl) migrate unchanged. However it seems very likely that the reaction is still intermolecular, involving nuclear alkylation of one molecule of aniline by the metal halide complex of another (e.g., eq. 8).

$$\underset{+}{\text{PhNH}}\overset{\bar{\text{C}}\text{oCl}_2}{\text{—R}}\ \langle\bigcirc\rangle\text{—NHR} \longrightarrow \text{PhNHC}\bar{\text{o}}\text{Cl}_2 + \overset{R}{\underset{H}{\times}}\langle\text{—}\rangle\text{=}\overset{+}{\text{NHR}} \qquad (8)$$

This would bring the reaction into line with the Friedel-Crafts alkylations of aromatic hydrocarbons with primary alkyl chlorides which also take place without rearrangement and probably involve [12] a similar S_N2 mechanism.

5. The mechanism of the Fischer-Hepp rearrangement of N-nitrosoanilines

[27] Cf. K. J. P. Orton, F. G. Soper, and G. Williams, *J. Chem. Soc. (London)*, **1928**, 998.

[27a] M. J. S. Dewar, *J. Chem. Soc. (London)*, **1946**, 406, 777; *The Electronic Theory of Organic Chemistry*, O.U.P., Oxford, 1949; *Bull. Soc. Chim.*, **18c**, 86 (1951); *Theoretica Organic Chemistry (Kekulé Symposium)*, Butterworths, London, 1959, p. 179.

[28] P. J. Couzens, Ph.D. thesis, London, 1960.

to p-nitrosoanilines is commonly assumed to be intermolecular, although there is in fact no definite evidence concerning its mechanism, apart from the inconclusive information that cross-migration can take place.

6. The rearrangement of N-nitroaniline is, however, intramolecular. This was indicated by early work which showed that the products from the rearrangement of N-nitroaniline differed from those obtained by nitrating aniline under the same conditions. This work has recently been repeated by Hughes and Jones[29] whose results are shown in Table II. Nitration gave

TABLE II

Proportions of Isomers Formed[29] by Rearrangement of N-Nitroaniline, and by Nitration of Aniline, in Sulfuric Acid Monohydrate at Its Freezing Point

	Isomer, %		
	Ortho	Meta	Para
Rearrangement of PhNHNO$_2$	93	0	7
Nitration of PhNH$_2$	6	34	59

comparable amounts of m- and p-nitranilines, the former by nitration of anilinium ion, the latter by the much more facile reaction of the minute amount of free aniline present in the strongly acid medium. The fact that the rearrangement produced no detectable amount of m-nitroaniline indicates that it was completely intramolecular, even the p-nitroaniline being formed by an intramolecular route. This conclusion was confirmed by Brownstein, Bunton, and Hughes[30,31] who showed by using ^{15}N as a tracer that no exchange of nitro groups took place between the nitroaniline and the added nitric acid during the rearrangement.

The facts that the rearrangement gives both o- and p-nitroanilines by an intramolecular route, and that o-nitroaniline is the main product, are, of course, entirely consistent with an intramolecular π complex mechanism.

Hughes and Jones[29] suggested an alternative bidentate mechanism for the reaction, based on the accepted mechanism for the Claisen rearrangement. They suppose that the monoacid salt (42) of the N-nitroaniline first isomerizes to a salt (43) of N-phenylhydroxylamine nitrite, which then rearranges via a cyclic transition state. This mechanism is unsatisfactory for several reasons.

First, there is no analogy for the initial isomerization of 42, and such a reaction seems both unlikely and contrary to the known chemistry of nitroamide

[29] E. D. Hughes and G. T. Jones, $J. Chem. Soc.$ ($London$), 1950, 2678.
[30] S. Brownstein, C. A. Bunton, and E. D. Hughes, $J. Chem. Soc.$ ($London$), 1958, 4354.
[31] S. Brownstein, C. A. Bunton, and E. D. Hughes, $Chem. \& Ind.$ ($London$), 1956, 981.

derivatives. Conversion of a nitro compound to an isomeric nitrite would be strongly endothermic, and such reactions have never been observed.

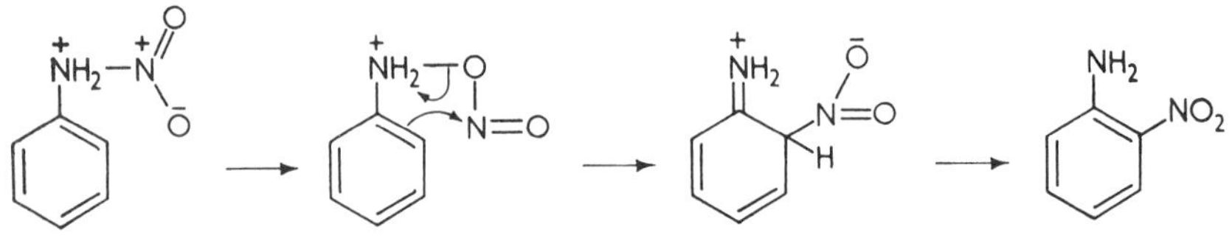

(42)   (43)

Second, if such an isomerization could nevertheless take place here, similar reactions should be equally possible in the case of nitroamides which cannot rearrange. Since nitrous esters are extremely easily hydrolyzed, one would expect such an isomerization to be followed by hydrolysis to a substituted hydroxylamine and nitrous acid. Such reactions have never been reported. Secondary nitroamines, and N-acylnitroamides, are hydrolyzed quantitatively to the amine or amide and nitrous acid, a reaction of analytical value. Mono-N-alkylnitroamines decompose quantitatively on treatment with strong acid by route 9.

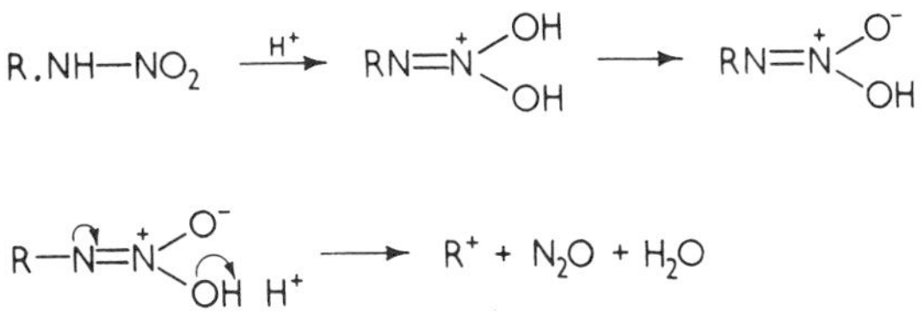

(9)

Third, the suggested mechanism does not account for the formation of p-nitroaniline by an intramolecular route from N-nitroaniline.

This last difficulty was met by Brownstein, Bunton, and Hughes[30] by a modification of the mechanism, making it analogous to the known[32] bidentate mechanism for the para Claisen rearrangement. This modification, however, merely gets one out of the frying pan into the fire. There are no known examples of a nitrous ester isomerizing to a nitro compound under any conditions, let alone in strong sulfuric acid solution; the esters 44 and 46 would be expected to hydrolyze immediately and quantitatively under such conditions to nitrous acid and tautomeric forms of o- or p-aminophenol. (It used to be thought that alkyl nitrites isomerized to nitro compounds at high temperatures, but recent work[33] has shown this to be incorrect.)

[32] H. Schmidt and K. Schmidt, Helv. Chim. Acta, 36, 489 (1953); K. Schmidt, W. Haegele, and H. Schmidt, Helv. Chim. Acta, 37, 1908 (1954); H. Conroy and R. A. Firestone, J. Am. Chem. Soc., 75, 2530 (1953).

[33] Cf. N. Kornblum and E. P. Oliveto, J. Am. Chem. Soc., 71, 226 (1949).

7. It was long believed that the sulfonation of aniline by baking its sulfate took place by the formation and rearrangement of N-phenylsulfamic acid, $PhNHSO_3H$; but Illuminati [34] has shown that the sulfamic acid does not rearrange under normal conditions.

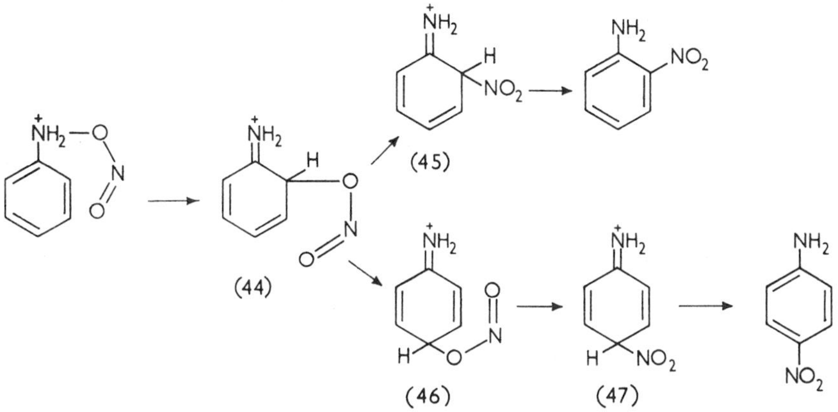

(44)

(45)

(46)

(47)

B. Rearrangements of Alkyl Aryl Ethers

When treated with acid catalysts, alkyl aryl ethers rearrange to mixtures of alkylphenols. Most of these reactions have been carried out under heterogeneous conditions with aluminum chloride as catalyst, or under homogeneous conditions in a solution of sulfuric acid or zinc chloride in acetic acid or of aluminum bromide in some solvent such as chlorobenzene. There has been much confusion concerning the mechanisms of these reactions, and recent work [35] has shown that many of the statements in the earlier literature are incorrect.

In most cases a complex mixture of mono-, di-, and trialkylphenols is formed which can be analyzed only by the use of modern techniques, in particular infrared spectroscopy; this has been taken as evidence that the reactions are intermolecular, taking place by dealkylation followed by realkylation (e.g., eq. 10). Alkylation of phenol under conditions similar to

those used in the rearrangement gives a mixture of the same individual products, and rearrangement of n-butyl ethers gives exclusively sec-butyl-phenols; [35] moreover, rearrangement of optically active sec-butyl phenyl

[34] G. Illuminati, *J. Am. Chem. Soc.*, **78**, 2603 (1956).
[35] M. J. S. Dewar and N. A. Puttnam, *J. Chem. Soc.* (*London*), **1959**, 4080, 4086, 4090.

ethers gives inactive products.[36] Both these observations are consistent with an intermolecular carbonium ion mechanism such as equation 10.

Sprung and Wallis [36] found, however, that rearrangement of optically active *sec*-butyl phenyl ether with sulfuric acid in acetic acid gave optically active *sec*-butylphenol. This work was confirmed by Diassi,[37] who moreover oxidized (eq. 11) the mixture of *sec*-butylphenols to optically active valeric

$$C_4H_9 \cdot C_6H_4OH \xrightarrow{\text{O}} C_4H_9 \cdot COOH \qquad (11)$$

acid, of known configuration, and so established that the reaction had involved retention of configuration. From the values reported by Diassi for the rotations of the *sec*-butyl phenyl ether and the valeric acid formed by rearrangement and oxidation one can calculate [35] that 24% of the *sec*-butyl groups in the rearrangement product had retained their configuration and 76% had racemized.

Sprung and Wallis also showed that in the intermolecular migration of *sec*-butyl from optically active *sec*-butyl mesityl ether (48) to *p*-cresol (49), under

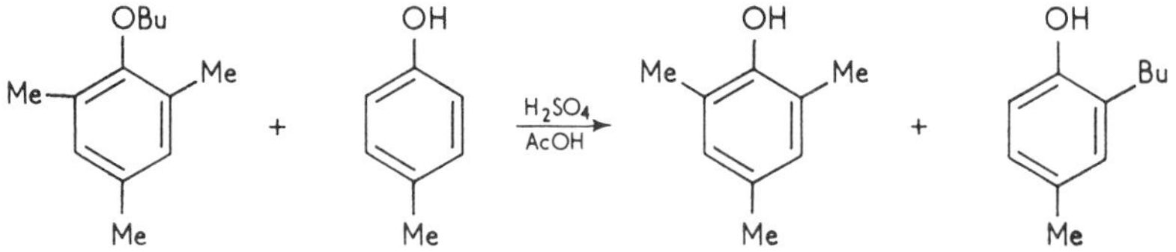

(48)   (49)   (50)

conditions similar to those used in the rearrangement, complete racemization took place; although rearrangement of optically active *sec*-butyl *p*-tolyl ether (51) gave optically active 2-*sec*-butyl-*p*-cresol (50). The retention of activity

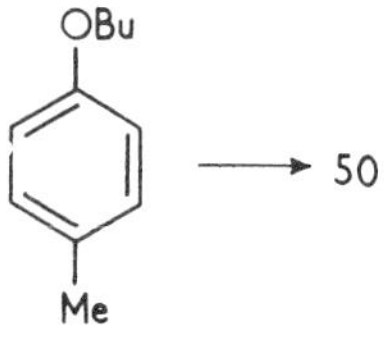

(51)

in the rearrangement therefore suggests strongly that the reaction must have been at least partly intramolecular.

---

[36] Sprung and Wallis, *J. Am. Chem. Soc.*, **56**, 1715 (1934); cf. Gilbert and Wallis, *J. Org. Chem.*, **5**, 184 (1940).

[37] Personal communication from Dr. P. A. Diassi.

The intermolecular reaction presumably takes place as follows:

$$PhO\overset{+}{\underset{Bu}{\diagup}}\overset{H}{\diagup} + AcOH \rightarrow PhOH + BuOAc \tag{12}$$

$$PhOH + BuO-CMe{=}\overset{+}{O}H \rightarrow BuC_6H_4OH + AcOH \tag{13}$$

Each of these reactions is a nucleophilic substitution on butyl; the loss of configuration implies that one or both are of S_N1 type.

In all the cases that have been studied, a true intramolecular migration of alkyl takes place with complete retention of configuration.[37a] This would be expected on theoretical grounds; for in the intermediate π complexes the alkyl group is still covalently linked to the rest of the molecule and so has no opportunity to racemize. Diassi's work therefore indicates that the rearrangement of sec-butyl phenyl ether must take place by two different mechanisms; about three-quarters of the ether rearranges by an intermolecular route (eqs. 12 and 13) with complete racemization, and about one-quarter by an intramolecular route with complete retention of configuration.

This suggestion has been confirmed [35] by a detailed study of the products of rearrangement of sec-butyl phenyl ether and of alkylation of phenol with sec-butanol in sulfuric–acetic acids. Although the same individual products are formed in both reactions, the proportions differ; in particular the ortho/para ratio in the mono-sec-butylphenol fraction is much higher for the product from the rearrangement (Table III). This indicates very clearly that not all the reactions can take place by an intermolecular route; for the realkylation

TABLE III

Ortho/Para Ratios in Mono-sec-butylphenol Fraction from sec-Butylation of Phenol or Rearrangement of sec-Butylphenyl Ether under Homogeneous Conditions

Reaction	Reactants	Ortho/para ratio in mono-sec-butyl-phenol fraction
Alkylation of phenol	sec-BuOH, PhOH, H_2SO_4/AcOH	0.54
Rearrangement of ether	sec-BuOPh, H_2SO_4/AcOH	1.04
Rearrangement of ether	sec-BuOPh, $AlBr_3$/PhCl	11.5
Rearrangement of PhNHNO₂	$H_2SO_4 \cdot H_2O$	13
(Calculated for rearrangement of sec-BuOPh, 76% intermolecular, 24% intramolecular)		0.98

[37a] M. J. S. Dewar, *The Electronic Theory of Organic Chemistry*, Clarendon Press, Oxford, 1949.

stage (eq. 13) would give the same ortho/para ratio as simple alkylation of phenol.

Part of the rearrangement must be taking place by some alternative route leading mainly to o-sec-butylphenol; this could well be intramolecular rearrangement by a π complex mechanism (eq. 14). If one assumes that the

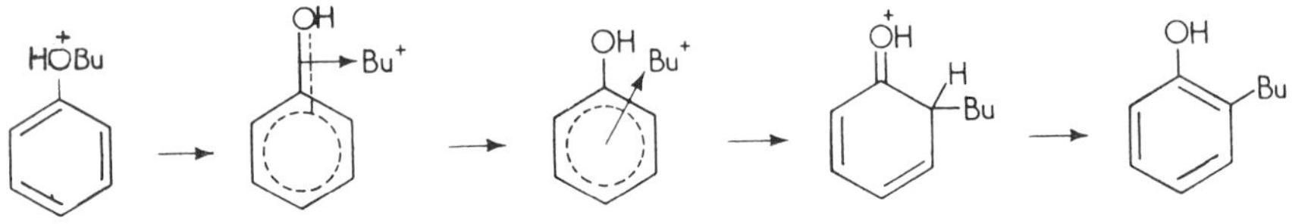

ortho/para ratio in the product from this reaction is the same as that found in the intramolecular rearrangement of N-nitroaniline (Table III), and if one assumes from Diassi's results that 76% of the rearrangement of the ether is intermolecular, 24% intramolecular, one estimates (Table III) an ortho/para ratio of 0.98 for the rearrangement of sec-butyl phenyl ether in sulfuric–acetic acids, agreeing with the experimental value within the limits of experimental error.

This argument was further supported[35] by a study of the rearrangement of sec-butyl phenyl ether with aluminum bromide in chlorobenzene. Tarbell and Petropoulos[38] have shown that the rearrangement of benzyl phenyl ether (52) under these conditions gives exclusively o-benzylphenol (53) with

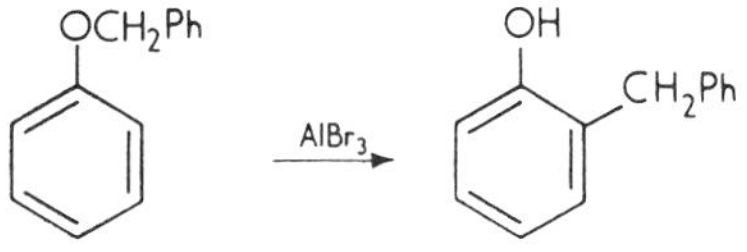

no detectable amount of the para isomer; and Hart and Elia[39] have reported that rearrangement of optically active α-methylbenzyl p-tolyl ether (54) with aluminum bromide gave 2-(α-methylbenzyl)-4-methylphenol (55) with 75%

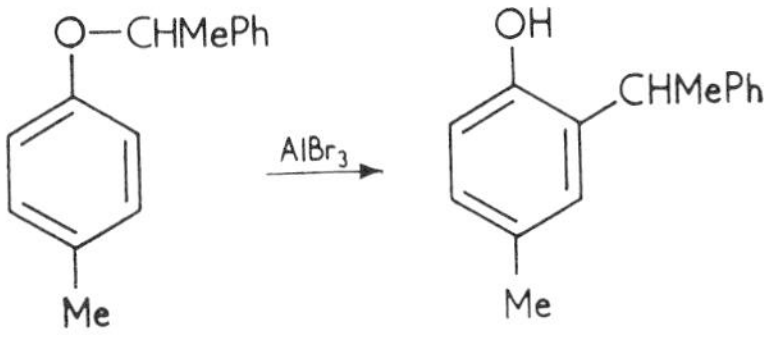

---

[38] Tarbell and Petropoulos, J. Am. Chem. Soc., **74**, 244 (1952).
[39] Hart and Elia, J. Am. Chem. Soc., **76**, 3031 (1954).

retention of optical activity. These observations show clearly that the rearrangements are intramolecular, and suggest that homogeneous solutions of aluminum bromide may be particularly good catalysts for bringing about intramolecular rearrangements. We found indeed that the rearrangement of sec-butyl phenyl ether with aluminum bromide in chlorobenzene gave mainly o-sec-butylphenol, the ortho/para ratio (11.5) being very close to that for the rearrangement of N-nitroaniline (Table III). The intramolecular nature of this reaction was further indicated by the absence of di- and trialkylphenols in the rearrangement product and by the failure of phenol to react with sec-butyl bromide at a significant rate under the same conditions.

With this information we were able to unravel the complex reactions undergone by butyl phenyl ethers with solid aluminum chloride as catalyst. The products from the rearrangements of both the n-butyl and sec-butyl ethers, and from alkylation of phenol with 1- or 2-chlorobutane, contained a variety of mono-, di-, and tri-sec-butylphenols; the n-butyl groups underwent complete isomerization during the reaction. The mixtures of product from alkylation of phenol with either chloride were identical; but the rearrangement products contained slightly different proportions of the various products, and the proportions varied when the amount of catalyst was altered. Data for the ortho/para ratios in the monobutylphenol fractions are listed in Table IV.

TABLE IV

Ortho/Para Ratios in Products from Butylation of Phenol or Rearrangement of Butyl Phenyl Ethers in the Presence of Solid Aluminum Chloride

Reactants	Moles catalyst	Ortho/para ratio
PhOH + n-BuCl	1	0.20
PhOH + sec-BuCl	1	0.20
sec-BuOPh	1	0.24
sec-BuOPh	$\frac{1}{2}$	0.33
n-BuOH	1	0.33
n-BuOH	$\frac{1}{2}$	0.76

The fact that more ortho isomer is formed in the rearrangements than in the alkylations would not in itself be significant, since the reactions are heterogeneous and unpredictable steric effects could arise on the catalytic surface; but this would not account for the differences between the n- and sec-butyl ethers or for the effect of varying the amount of catalyst. The only reasonable explanation seems[35] to be that the rearrangements are in fact partly intramolecular. As we have seen, a homogeneous solution of aluminum bromide in a nonpolar solvent (chlorobenzene) specifically catalyzes rearrangement by an intramolecular π complex mechanism, presumably because the preliminary ionization involved in an intermolecular carbonium ion mechanism (eq. 10) is too difficult in a nonpolar solvent. Now aluminum chloride is appreciably soluble in ethers; the part of the catalyst dissolved in the butyl phenyl ether should then bring about an intramolecular rearrangement leading mainly to *o*-butylphenol. The rate of this reaction will be independent of the amount of catalyst used, since there is always undissolved catalyst present and the ether therefore contains a saturated solution. Reducing the amount of catalyst will, however, reduce the rate of the intermolecular rearrangement which takes place on the surface of the solid; reducing the amount of catalyst therefore increases the relative importance of the intramolecular rearrangement and so increases the ortho/para ratio. The higher ortho/para ratio in the case of the *n*-butyl ether can be ascribed to a greater solubility of aluminum chloride in the less hindered ether.

Two facts remain to be explained; (*a*) the formation of *sec*-butylphenols from *n*-butyl phenyl ether under conditions where the ortho/para ratio indicates extensive intramolecular reaction and (*b*) the complete racemization [36] of optically active *sec*-butyl phenyl ether during rearrangement. Both can be explained in terms of a rapid reversible ionization of the ether on the polar surface of the aluminum chloride, i.e.

$$PhOBu + AlCl_3 \rightleftharpoons PhO\overline{Al}Cl_3 + Bu^+ \tag{15}$$

The recombination of Bu^+ and $PhO\overline{Al}Cl_3$ to the ether should be faster than their reaction to form alkylphenols (eq. 10) since the negative charge in PhO^- is mostly concentrated on oxygen. If reaction 15 is fast compared with the homogeneous rearrangement, only racemic *sec*-butylphenols will be formed from butyl phenyl ethers. The failure of *n*-butyl phenyl ether to rearrange to *n*-butylphenols by a π complex mechanism is in any case not surprising; the migratory aptitude of *n*-alkyl groups is much less than that of *sec*-alkyl; and indeed *n*-butyl phenyl ether is only very slowly attacked by aluminum bromide in chlorobenzene under conditions where the *sec*-butyl ether rearranges rapidly.

In summary, the rearrangements of alkyl aryl ethers can take place by both inter- and intramolecular routes, the former favoring para migration, the latter ortho migration. The intramolecular rearrangements, which almost certainly take place by the π complex mechanism, are interesting in view of the suggestion [40] that reactions of this kind can only be intramolecular if they involve a bidentate mechanism. Here we have true intramolecular rearrangements where no bidentate mechanism is possible.

C. Fries Rearrangement

The Fries rearrangement involves conversion of aryl esters to acylphenols under the influence of Friedel-Crafts catalysts (e.g., eq. 16). The mechanism

[40] C. K. Ingold, *Mechanism and Structure in Organic Chemistry*, G. Bell, London, 1953.

of these reactions is still uncertain. Cullinane, Evans, and Lloyd [41] have claimed that the rearrangement of p-tolyl acetate (56) to 2-hydroxy-5-

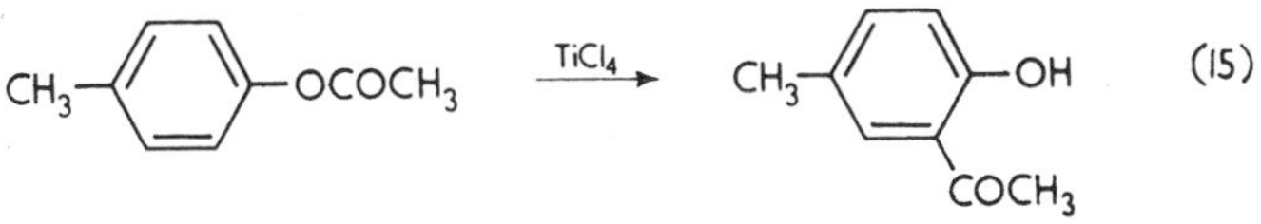

(15)

(56)   (57)

methylacetophenone (57), catalyzed by titanium tetrachloride, is intramolecular on the grounds that the rate of rearrangement is finite at the start of the reaction.

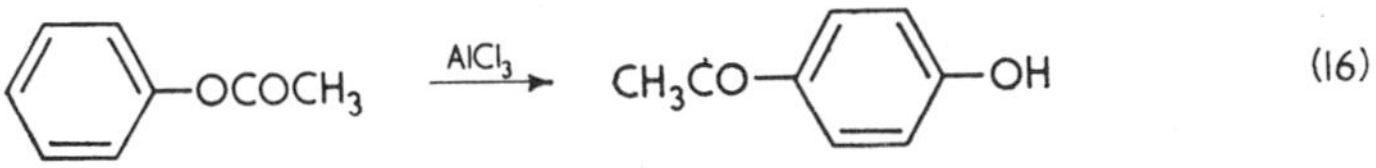

(16)

If the rearrangements were intermolecular, taking place via an intermediate acetylium ion, i.e.,

$$C_7H_7OCOCH_3 + TiCl_4 \rightarrow C_7H_7O\bar{T}iCl_4 + CH_3\overset{+}{C}O \qquad (16)$$

$$C_7H_7OH + CH_3\overset{+}{C}O \rightarrow CH_3CO \cdot C_7H_6OH \qquad (17)$$

The rate of formation of 57 would be given by

$$d[57]/dt = k[CH_3\overset{+}{C}O][C_7H_7OH] \qquad (18)$$

and would be zero at zero time when the concentrations of the intermediates (p-cresol and acetylium) are zero.

This argument would only be valid if the measurements of rates were infinitely accurate. If the amount of 57 formed is plotted against time, a curve of the form of Figure 3 will be obtained; there is an induction period, during which the concentrations of the intermediates build up to their steady-state values. The induction period will be such that extrapolation of the final linear part (AB) of the curve to zero time gives an intercept (C) on the concentration axis differing from zero by an amount approximately equal to the steady-state concentrations of the intermediates. If these concentrations are small, the induction period may be too small to be detected by feasible methods. Now acetylium is extremely reactive; the rate of reaction 17 must be very great and the steady-state concentrations correspondingly small. The fact

[41] N. M. Cullinane, A. G. Evans, and E. T. Lloyd, *J. Chem. Soc.* (*London*), **1956**, 2222; cf. N. M. Cullinane and B. F. R. Edwards, *J. Chem. Soc.* (*London*), **1957**, 3016.

that no induction period could be observed is therefore no evidence against the intermolecular mechanism.

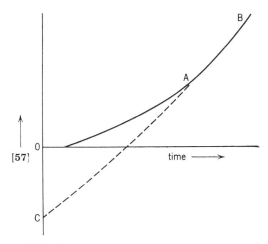

Figure 3.   Induction period in intermolecular Fries rearrangement.

This argument is made even stronger by the possibility that $CH_3\overset{+}{C}O$ may react with **56**. In the workup procedure used by Cullinane, Evans, and Lloyd, **58** would have been hydrolyzed to the normal Fries product (**57**). This

$$56 \ + \ CH_3\overset{+}{C}O \ \longrightarrow \ CH_3-\!\!\!\underset{\underset{COCH_3}{|}}{\bigcirc}\!\!\!-OCOCH_3$$

(58)

reaction, which Cullinane, Evans, and Lloyd do not seem to have considered, would further reduce the steady-state concentration of $CH_3\overset{+}{C}O$ and so make the induction period even smaller.

The only other evidence concerning the mechanism of the Fries rearrangement is that provided by the isomer distribution in the products. Here the evidence is conflicting. Phenyl acetate itself gives predominantly p-hydroxyacetophenone, suggesting that the reaction is intermolecular; but Crawford [42] has reported that phenyl isovalerate (**59**) rearranges to a mixture of 40% o- (**60**) and 11% p- (**61**) hydroxyphenyl isobutyl ketones, although acylation of phenol with isovaleryl chloride under the same conditions gives exclusively

[42] R. J. Crawford, *Disc. Abstracts*, **17**, 501 (1959).

the para isomer (**61**); this observation seems to suggest that the rearrangement is at least partly intramolecular.

(59)

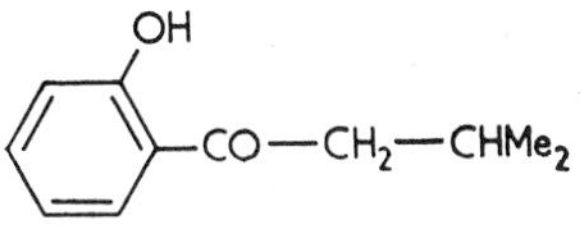

(60)

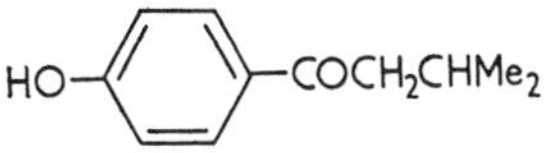

(6I)

Stabilities of π Complexes. The evidence indicates that aromatic π complexes are less stable than the isomeric arenonium ions; this contrasts with the aliphatic series where the evidence suggests that π complexes (**62**) are inherently more stable than the isomeric carbonium ions (**63**). Thus every

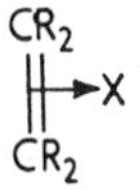

(62) 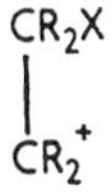   (63)

case so far studied of electrophilic addition to olefins has given exclusively *trans* adducts, implying that cations add to olefins to give π complexes rather than carbonium ions, while addition of cations to aromatic hydrocarbons has invariably given arenonium ions.

One would expect **62** to be inherently more stable than **63**. The heat (ΔH) of conversion of **63** to **62** can be written:

$$\Delta H = E_{C=C} + E_\pi - E_{C-C} - E_{CX} \tag{19}$$

where $E_{C=C}$, E_{C-C}, and E_{CX} are the corresponding bond energies, and E_π is the energy liberated when the olefin $R_2C=CR_2$ combines with X^+ to form **62**. Substituting standard values [37a] for $E_{C=C}$ and E_{C-C}, we find that ΔH is positive, and **62** consequently more stable than **63**, if

$$E_\pi > E_{CX} - (E_{C=C} - E_{C-C})$$
$$E_\pi > E_{CX} - 64 \text{ kcal./mole} \tag{20}$$

Since the bond between the ethylene unit and X^+ in **62** should be comparable in strength with other covalent bonds, the theoretical descriptions being very similar, this condition will certainly be met for all bonds other than CF, and possibly CH.

The situation is very different in the comparison of the π complex (**64**) with the benzenonium ion (**65**). The condition that **64** is the more stable is:

$$E_{\pi}' > E_{CX} - \delta E_{\pi}$$

where E'_{π} is the heat of formation of **64** from benzene and X$^+$, and δE_{π} is the difference in π energy between benzene and **62**. One might expect $E'_{\pi} < E_{\pi}$,

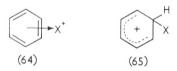

(64)   (65)

since in **64** X$^+$ only overlaps with part of the MO's of benzene, while in **62** it overlaps with the whole of the ethylenic π MO; calculation confirms this. Likewise δE_{π} is probably less than the difference (64 kcal./mole) between $E_{C=C}$ and E_{C-C}. It is therefore not surprising that the π complex should here be the less stable form.

Migratory Aptitudes.   Since monodentate intramolecular rearrangements normally take place via π complex intermediates, the ease of migration of a group depends on the ease with which it can take up the bridging position in a π complex. Now in the "classical" structures **63** and **65** the group X is attached to a single carbon atom by a covalent bond formed by sharing of a pair of electrons between two atoms; X will therefore be neutral, apart from small charges imposed by polarity of the C—X bond. In the π complexes **62** and **64**, however, X is held by a bond formed by sharing of n electrons ($n = 2$ or 6) between ($n + 1$) atoms; here X has a significant positive charge, regardless of any additional effects due to uneven sharing of electrons. Therefore X is more positive in the π complexes than in the isomeric classical structure, and so X should migrate more easily, the lower its affinity for electrons. Therefore alkyl groups should show the order of migratory aptitude CH_3 < primary < secondary < tertiary, and $+I$ substituents should lower the migratory aptitude. This is well known to be the case in aliphatic rearrangements; it also seems to be true in aromatic ones. Thus **64** rearranges by ring migration (effectively migration of a primary alkyl group) rather than by methyl migration; and trichloromethyl groups never migrate except by bidentate mechanisms.[43]

The situation is different,[43a] however, in the case of phenyl groups. If the

[43] R. L. Tse and M. S. Newman, *J. Org. Chem.*, **21**, 638 (1956); M. S. Newman and L. L. Wood, *J. Am. Chem. Soc.*, **81**, 6450 (1959); M. S. Newman, J. Eberwein, and L. L. Wood, *J. Am. Chem. Soc.*, **81**, 6454 (1959).

[43a] M. J. S. Dewar, *Bull. soc. chim.*, **18c**, 86 (1951).

bonding between phenyl and the adjacent unsaturated system in a π complex
(**66** or **67**) were no different from that in analogous π complexes involving

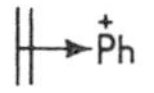

(66) 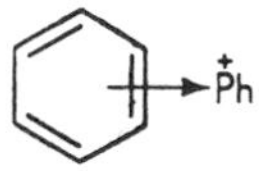   (67)

alkyl groups, one would expect the migratory aptitude of phenyl to be less
than that of alkyl; for the phenyl group forms bonds through an sp^2 hybrid
orbital, and not only are such bonds stronger [44] than the corresponding bonds
formed by saturated carbon (thus making the term E_{CX} in equations 19 and
20 larger) but also the binding energy of an sp^2 orbital is greater, and the
effective electronegativity of an unsaturated group consequently greater,
than that of a saturated group. In fact, however, phenyl shows a *greater*
migratory aptitude than alkyl in aliphatic carbonium ion rearrangements;
this is due [43a] to the possibility of an additional dative bond in a π complex
involving a bridging phenyl due to interaction of the filled π orbitals of the
phenyl group with the empty antibonding π MO of the olefin **68**. The corre-

Normal dative bond   Reverse dative bond

(68)

sponding reverse dative bond in **67** must, however, be much weaker (by a factor of two according to simple MO calculation) because of the less efficient
overlap. Therefore aryl groups may well migrate less readily than alkyl in
aromatic rearrangements; no such migration of aryl has as yet been observed.

4. POLYDENTATE REARRANGEMENTS

A. Rearrangements of the Benzidine Type

Hydrazobenzene (**69**) and its derivatives are converted by acid into one or
more of five different rearrangement products (**70–74**); part of the hydrazine
also undergoes disproportionation to the corresponding amine and azo compound (**75**). At least two different products are formed in any given case,
except for a few diarylhydrazines which disproportionate exclusively.

[44] M. J. S. Dewar and H. N. Schmeising, *Tetrahedron*, 5, 166 (1959).

The main products in most cases are benzidines, diphenylines, or o-semi-dines; only in a few exceptional cases are o-benzidines or p-semidines formed

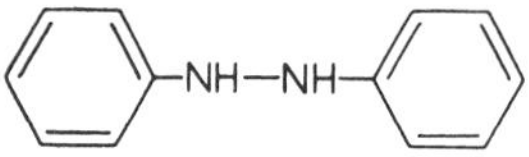

(69)

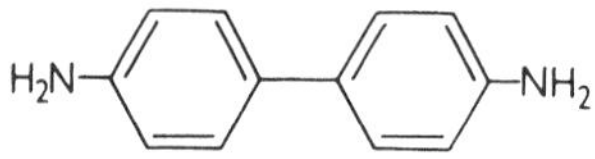

Benzidine
(70)

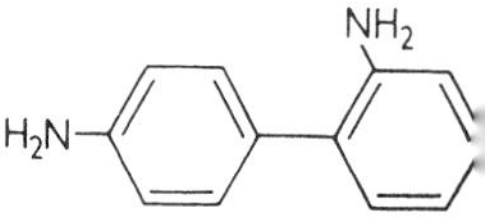

Diphenyline
(71)

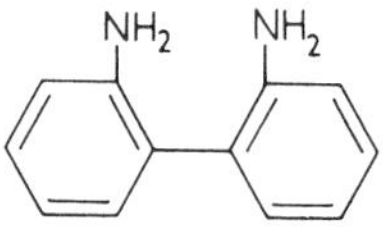

o-Benzidine
(72)

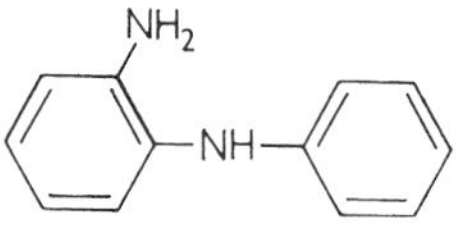

o-Semidine
(73)

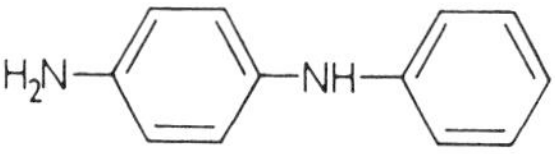

p-Semidine
(74)

$2 ArNH_2 + ArN = NAr$

(Disproportionation)
(75)

in significant amounts. Recent work [45] has, however, indicated that the re-action products may be more complex than has been commonly supposed; thus the rearrangement of hydrazobenzene itself gives small but isolable amounts of o-benzidine and o- and p-semidines in addition to the main products, benzidine ($\sim 70\%$) and diphenyline ($\sim 30\%$).

Hydrazonaphthalenes also rearrange on treatment with acid, but in this case o-benzidines are commonly the main products and diphenylines are not formed. Thus the rearrangement of α-hydrazonaphthalene (76) gives a mix-ture of the o-benzidine (77) and the benzidine (78), the former predominating.

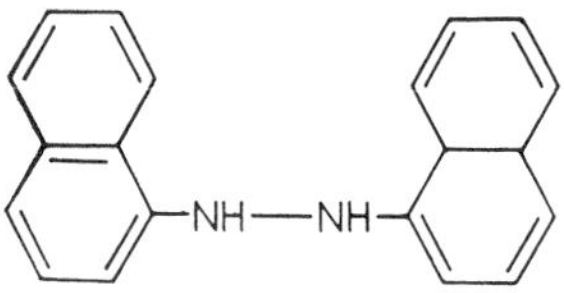

(76)

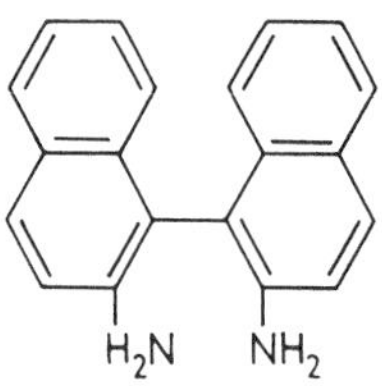

(77)

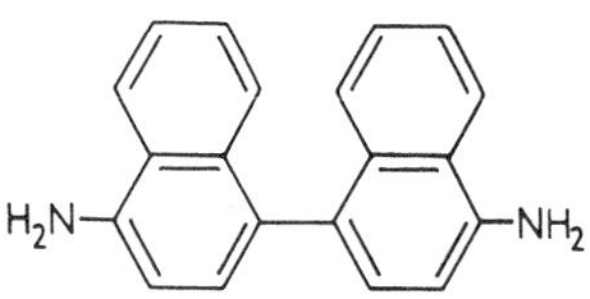

(78)

The reactions seems to be intramolecular since there is apparently no inter-change of aryl groups between different molecules of hydrazo compound

[45] M. Večeră, J. Casparič, and J. Petránek, *Chem. Listy*, **51**, 911 (1957).

during the reaction. The most definite evidence for this was provided by Wheland and Schwartz [46] who showed by a tracer method that the rearrangement of 2-ethoxy-2-methylhydrazobenzene (**79**) gave no *o*-tolidine (**80**), and by Smith, Schwartz, and Wheland [47] who showed that the rearrangement of a mixture of 2-methylhydrazobenzene (**81**) marked with ^{14}C and of *o*-hydrazotoluene (**82**) gave *o*-tolidine (**80**) free from radioactivity.

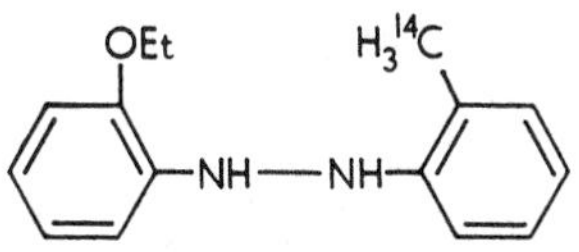

(79) 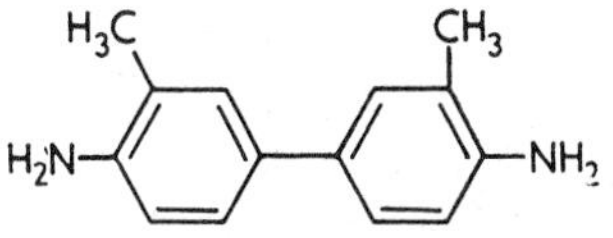   (80)

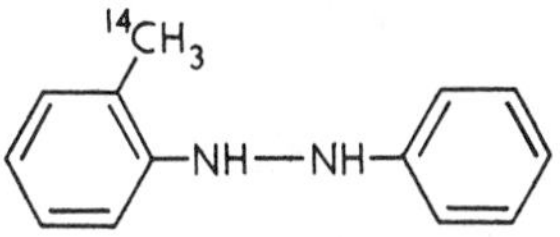

(81) 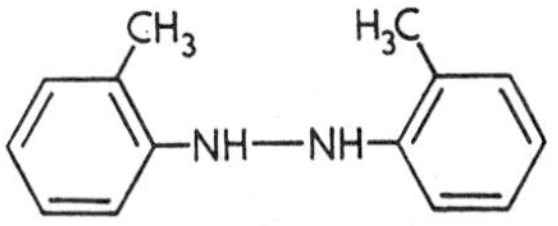   (82)

It seems to be generally agreed that the rearrangements all follow a common mechanism; they certainly seem to show the same acid dependence since the proportions of rearrangement products are unaffected by the concentration of the catalyzing acid. This has been shown for the rearrangements of hydrazobenzene itself,[48] and of its 4,4'-dimethyl [49] and 4-chloro [50] derivatives.

Since the products are formed by linkage of the two aniline fragments through one of four positions in each, the reactions may be classed as polydentate rearrangements.

The main product from the rearrangement of a given hydrazobenzene derivative may be predicted by applying three simple rules.[51] The first action of the acid must be to convert the hydrazobenzene to its monoacid salt; this will be formed by attachment of a proton to the more basic nitrogen atom. The relative basicities of the two nitrogen atoms can be deduced from the basicities of the two aniline derivatives that would be formed by hydrogenolysis of the N—N bond. Denote by A the benzene ring adjacent to the more basic nitrogen, and by B the other ring. Then:

1. The preferred order of products is benzidine > diphenyline ≫ semidine.

[46] G. W. Wheland and J. R. Schwartz, *J. Chem. Phys.*, **17**, 425 (1949).

[47] D. H. Smith, J. R. Schwartz, and G. W. Wheland, *J. Am. Chem. Soc.*, **74**, 2282 (1952).

[48] R. B. Carlin, R. G. Nelb, and R. C. Odioso, *J. Am. Chem. Soc.*, **73**, 1002 (1951).

[49] R. B. Carlin and G. S. Wick, *J. Am. Chem. Soc.*, **80**, 4023 (1958).

[50] D. J. Morley, M.Sc. thesis, London, 1953.

[51] M. J. S. Dewar, *Nature*, **176**, 784 (1945).

2. A diphenyline is the main product only if ring A has a free para position; the diphenyline is formed by linkage to an ortho position of ring B.

3. If a semidine is formed, ring A carries the free amino group.

Thus if both para positions are free, the main product is a benzidine; hydrazobenzene itself gives 70% benzidine together with 30% diphenyline.

If the para position in ring B is blocked, the main product is a diphenyline; thus p-chlorohydrazobenzene (**83**) gives mainly the diphenyline (**84**). Here the substituted ring is ring B, p-chloroaniline being less basic than aniline.

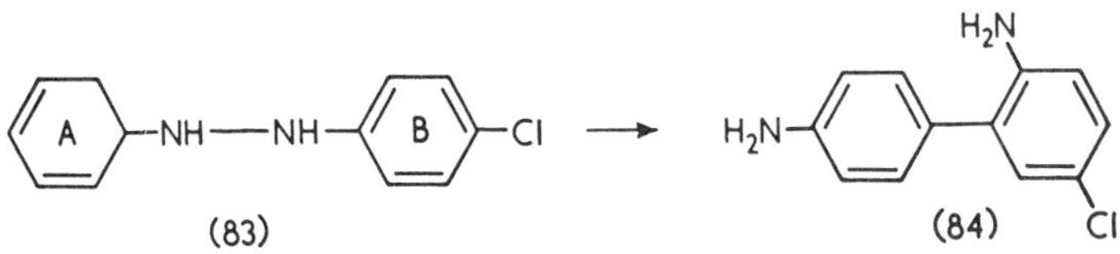

(83)   (84)

In p-methylhydrazobenzene (**85**), however, the substituted ring is ring A, p-toluidine being a stronger base than aniline; here the main product is the o-semidine (**86**) in which ring A carries the free amino group.

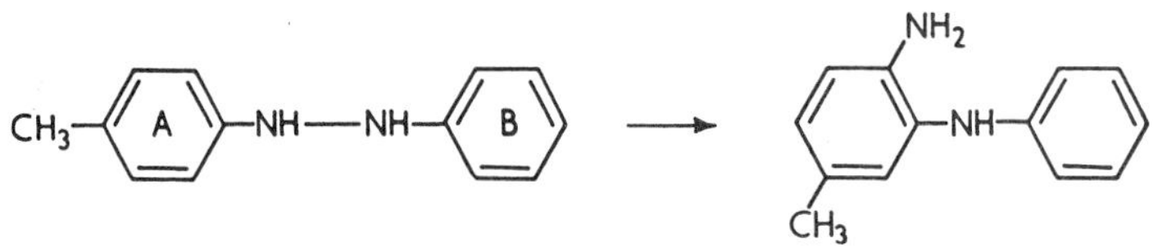

(85)   (86)

The only known exceptions to these rules occur in certain anomalous reactions leading to o-benzidines or p-semidines as major products; these will be considered in detail later.

The situation in the α-hydrazonaphthalene (**76**) series is different; as we have seen, the preferred order of products is o-benzidine > benzidine ≫ semidine, no diphenyline being formed. Rearrangement of β-hydrazonaphthalene (**87**) gives exclusively the o-benzidine (**77**).

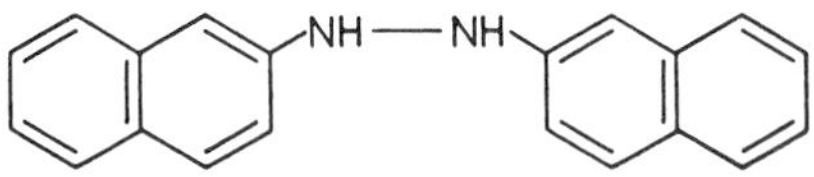

(87)

These reactions present an interesting theoretical problem. Even in the *cis* form of hydrazobenzene, the para positions are 4.3 A. apart; during the rearrangement a bond is formed between these positions without the two halves of the molecule at any time drifting apart. How can this come about?

The early mechanisms of Hughes and Ingold [52] and Robinson [53] ignored this stereochemical difficulty. An ingenious modification of the Robinson mechanism was proposed by Hammick and Mason,[54] but this apart from other difficulties [54a] could not account for the semidine rearrangement. Only three intrinsically acceptable mechanisms have been proposed for the rearrangement; according to the first, the reaction is mechanistically intermolecular, but the intermediate fragments are prevented from separating by the Franck-Rabinowitch cage effect; the second mechanism, proposed by Brownstein, Bunton, and Hughes,[54b] involves cyclic transition states; the third mechanism [51,54a,54c] represents the reaction as an intramolecular π complex process.

Cage Effect Mechanism. This mechanism has been widely discussed but does not seem to have appeared in print. It postulates a rate-determining fission of the second conjugate acid (88) of hydrazobenzene into a pair of ion radicals (89) which recombine to form one or other product. This mechanism is superficially very attractive. The ion radical (89) is isoconjugate with the benzyl radical (90) in which the odd electron occupies a nonbonding MO concentrated on the methylene carbon and the positions ortho and para to it; the coefficients of AO's in this MO are shown in (91). Dimerization of two ion

(88) (89) (90) (91)

radicals (89) should take place through one of these positions in each radical: in this way one or other of the observed rearrangement products 70–74 would be formed. The initial fission of 88 should take place readily since the resonance energy of the ion radical (89), relative to benzene, must be comparable with that of benzyl [55a] (~ 25 kcal./mole); fission of 88 to 89 should therefore lead to an increase in resonance energy of the order of 40–50 kcal./mole. The effective N—N bond strength in 89 must therefore be very low since the N—N bond energy is only [55b] 60 kcal./mole.

[52] E. D. Hughes and C. K. Ingold, *J. Chem. Soc. (London)*, **1941**, 606.

[53] R. Robinson, *J. Chem. Soc. (London)*, **1941**, 220.

[54] D. L. Hammick and S. F. Mason, *J. Chem. Soc. (London)*, **1946**, 638.

[54a] M. J. S. Dewar, *The Electronic Theory of Organic Chemistry*, O.U.P., Oxford, 1949.

[54b] S. Brownstein, C. A. Bunton, and E. D. Hughes, *Chem. & Ind. (London)*, **1956**, 981.

[54c] M. J. S. Dewar, *J. Chem. Soc. (London)*, **1946**, 406, 777; *Bull. Soc. Chim.*, **18c**, 86 (1951); *Theoretical Organic Chemistry (Kekulé Symposium)*, Butterworths, London, 1959, p. 179.

[55a] M. Szwarc, *Discussions Faraday Soc.*, **10**, 336 (1951).

[55b] M. Szwarc, *Proc. Roy. Soc. (London)*, **A198**, 267 (1949).

A further argument for the cage effect mechanism is provided by the oxidation [56] of dimethylaniline to tetramethylbenzidine (**92**) by lead dioxide; this almost certainly takes place by the process of equation 21, the crucial step being the dimerization of the N,N-dimethyl derivative of the ion radical (**89**).

$$PhNMe_2 + PbO_2 \rightarrow (PhNMe_2)^+$$

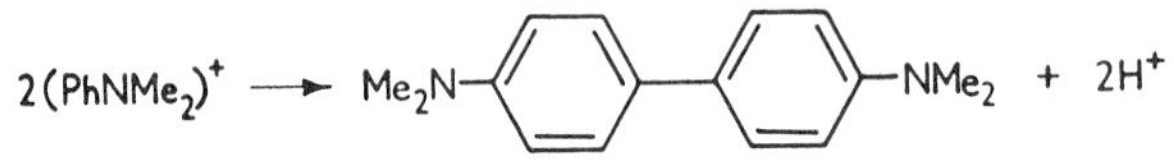

$$2(PhNMe_2)^+ \longrightarrow Me_2N-\overset{}{\bigcirc}-\overset{}{\bigcirc}-NMe_2 + 2H^+ \qquad (21)$$

(92)

The occurrence of disproportionation can also be very easily explained as a side reaction of the ion radicals (**89**):

$$Ph\overset{+}{N}H_2 + PhNH \cdot NHPh \rightarrow Ph\overset{+}{N}H_3 + Ph\overset{\cdot}{N} \cdot NHPh$$

$$Ph\overset{+}{N}H_2 + Ph\overset{\cdot}{N} \cdot NHPh \rightarrow Ph\overset{+}{N}H_3 + PhN{=}NPh$$

This mechanism is, however, refuted by the following considerations. First, it cannot account for the course of the rearrangement of α-hydrazonaphthalene (**76**) where the o-benzidine (**77**) and the benzidine (**78**) are formed but no diphenyline. One would have to postulate that the ion radicals (**93**) can

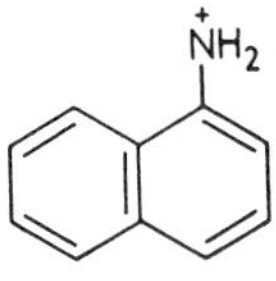

(93)

dimerize by o,o' linkage, or by p,p' linkage, but never by o,p' linkage, which would be unreasonable. Second, one cannot account for the product rules without making numerous *ad hoc* assumptions. Consider the reaction of the unsubstituted ion radical (**90**). The fact that hydrazobenzene (**69**) gives mostly benzidine (**70**), together with diphenyline (**71**) but no semidine, would imply that the order of reactivity of the positions in **89** is $p > o \gg N$. However in the rearrangement of p-methylhydrazobenzene (**85**) the main product is the semidine (**86**); here the ion radical (**89**) reacts preferentially through nitrogen, the order of reactivity being $N \gg o,p$. Inconsistencies of this kind cannot be avoided in any mechanism that does not keep a clear structural distinction between rings A and B of the hydrazobenzene right up to the product-determining stage; this distinction would be automatically lost in the second

[56] Cf. W. Michler and H. Pattinson, *Ber.*, **17**, 115 (1884).

conjugate acid (88) of hydrazobenzene—and still more so in the ion radicals (89) formed by its fission.

A third difficulty is that of explaining why 4,4'-diphenylhydrazobenzene (94) does not rearrange at all, the sole products of reaction with acid being [57] the corresponding amine and azo compound. This cannot be due to any subtle electronic effect of the phenyl substituents; for 2,2'-diphenylhydrazobenzene (95) rearranges normally to a benzidine, and 4-phenylhydrazobenzene (96) gives the semidine (97). The failure of 94 to rearrange must be steric in origin; and the *p*-phenyl substituents could not possibly hinder the dimerization of the ion radical (97) to a semidine.

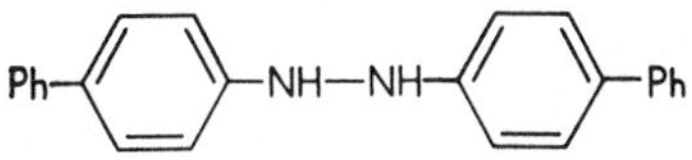

(94) 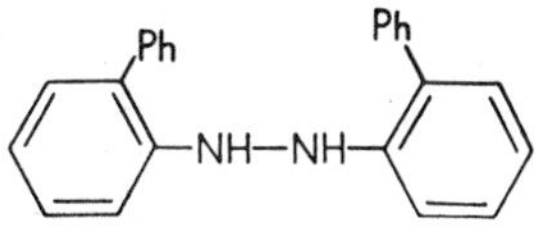   (95)

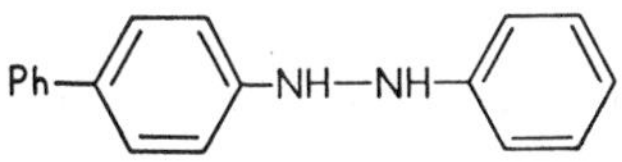

(96) 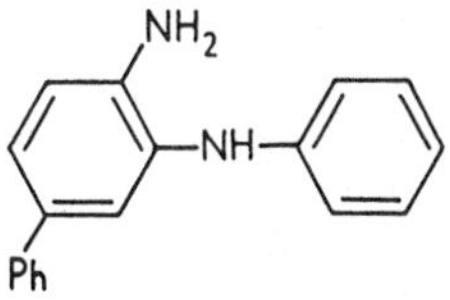   (97) 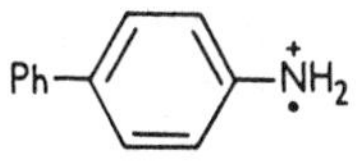   (98)

There are moreover several purely theoretical objections that make the cage effect mechanism very unlikely. First, there are no analogies for the cage effect operating in the case of ions, and it is difficult to see how it could do so in the case of ions of like charge. The coulomb repulsion between two ions of like charge in contact with one another is of a different order of magnitude from the van der Waals adhesions of neutral molecules; forces of this kind could not possibly hold ions together against their mutual repulsion.

Second, if the rearrangement products are formed by dimerization of ion radicals (89), it is difficult to see why the intermediate in the dispro-portionation reaction does not also combine with 89 to form products that are not in fact observed; e.g.,

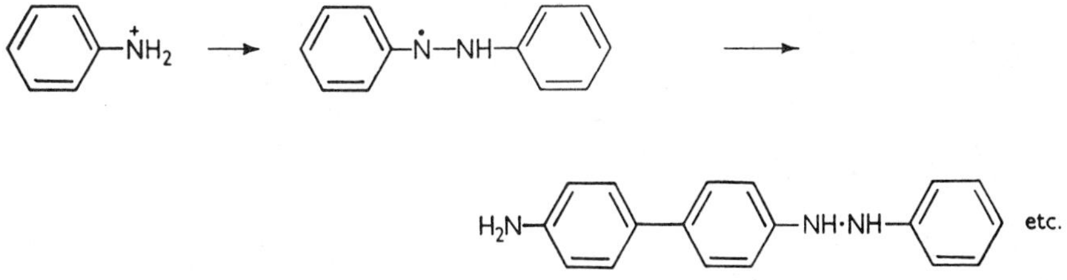

[57] G. Friebel and B. Rassow, *J. prakt. Chem.*, [2]**63**, 449 (1901).

Third, the fact that semidines are not formed preferentially would be difficult to explain; for the odd electron density in **89** is greatest on nitrogen,

$$2 \; \text{C}_6H_5\text{-}\overset{+}{N}H_2 \longrightarrow \text{(99)} \tag{25}$$

and the mode of dimerization to **99** would clearly be more exothermic than the formation of **100** since **99**, unlike **100**, is aromatic.

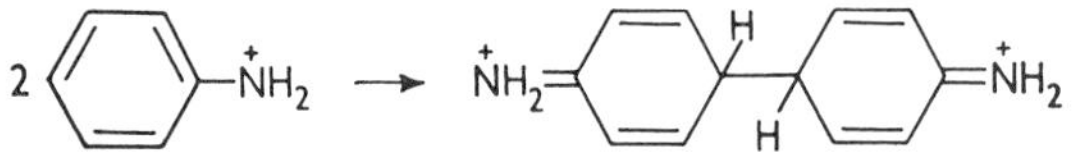

$$2 \; \text{C}_6H_5\text{-}\overset{+}{N}H_2 \longrightarrow \text{(100)} \tag{26}$$

It is particularly significant that the thermal rearrangement [58] of diaryl-hydrazines, which very probably does take place by a cage effect mechanism, gives the products that would be expected on the basis of the arguments developed above. Thus hydrazobenzene (**69**) gives almost exclusively a mixture of *o*- and *p*-semidines (**73** and **74**), while α-hydrazonaphthalene (**76**) gives

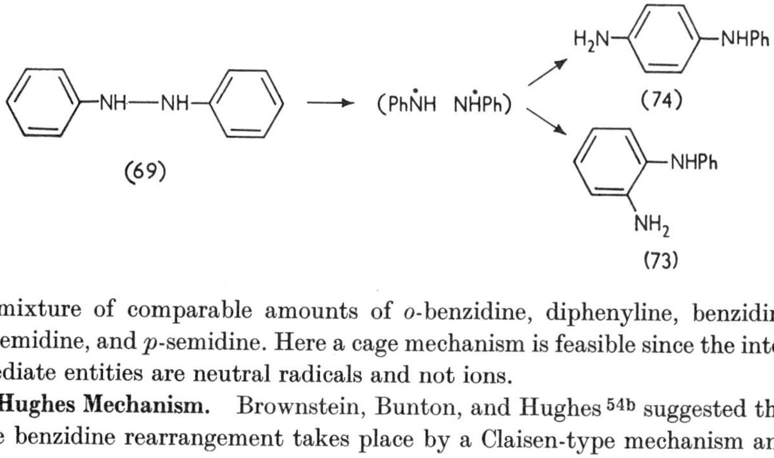

a mixture of comparable amounts of *o*-benzidine, diphenyline, benzidine, *o*-semidine, and *p*-semidine. Here a cage mechanism is feasible since the intermediate entities are neutral radicals and not ions.

Hughes Mechanism. Brownstein, Bunton, and Hughes [54b] suggested that the benzidine rearrangement takes place by a Claisen-type mechanism ana-

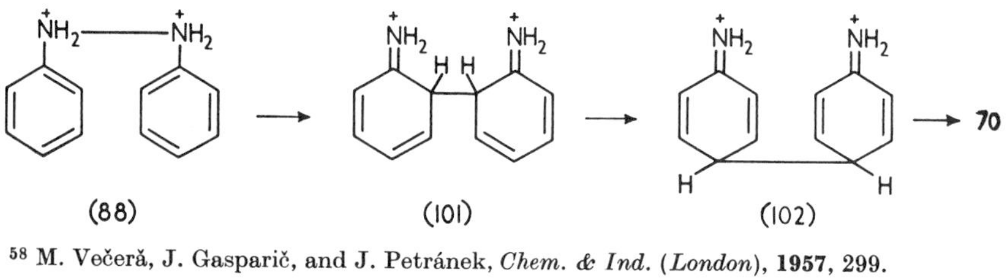

[58] M. Večeřá, J. Gasparič, and J. Petránek, *Chem. & Ind.* (*London*), **1957**, 299.

logous to the one suggested by them for the formation of p-nitroaniline by rearrangement of N-nitroaniline (**44** → **47**), i.e., via **101** and **102**. This mechanism does not, as it stands, explain the formation of the other rearrangement products, but this can be done by an obvious extension. Rotation about the central bond in **101** can bring appropriate pairs of positions opposite each other, allowing allylic rearrangements to intermediates analogous to **102**. This is illustrated in Scheme 1, which shows diagrammatic projections of the rotational isomers of **102** and indicates how they give rise to the various products.

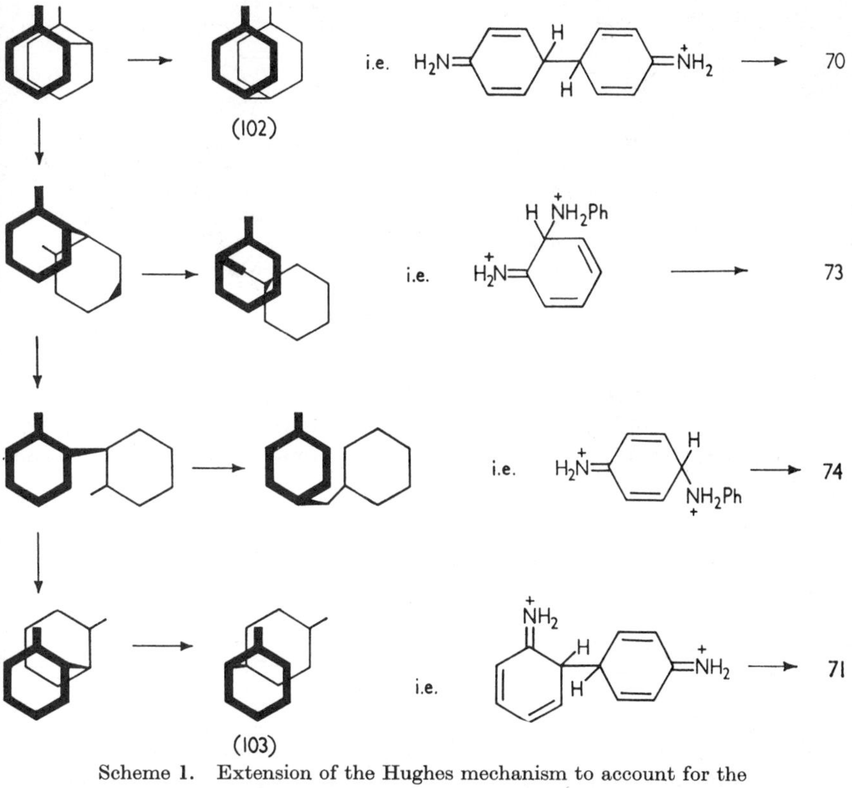

Scheme 1.   Extension of the Hughes mechanism to account for the
formation of products other than benzidene.

One immediate consequence of this mechanism is that it allows a diphenyline to form *only* if ring B has both ortho positions free; for the rearrangement **88** → **101** will certainly take place preferentially to unsubstituted ortho positions, from analogy with the Clasien rearrangement where o-allylphenols are formed exclusively whenever there is a free ortho position, and the rearrangement of **102** to a diphenyline via the intermediate (**103**) leads to linkage through the second ortho position. This explains very nicely why α-hydrazonaphthalene (**76**) fails to give a diphenyline, although it gives both *o*- and *p*-benzidines, and also suggests a simple test of the Hughes mechanism. Rearrangement of a hydrazobenzene in which ring B carries substituents in the 2 and 4 positions, e.g., 2,4-dichlorohydrazobenzene (**104**), should according to the product rules give a diphenyline, in this case **105**; but such a reaction should not occur if the Hughes mechanism is correct. The product should be either the *o*-benzidine (**106**) or a semidine (**107**). One example of

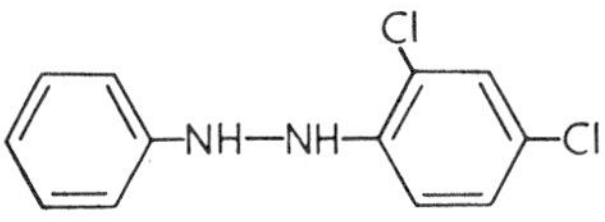

(104) 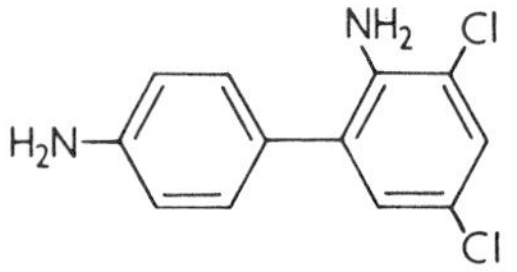 (105)

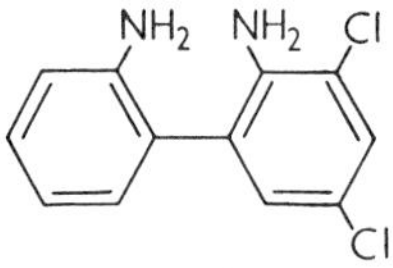

(106) 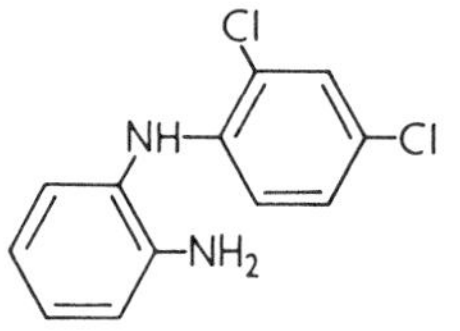 (107)

this kind has been reported;[59] it is stated that 2-ethoxy-5,2′,4′-trimethyl-hydrazobenzene (**108**) gives the diphenyline (**109**) as a major product. However the structure of the product was not rigorously determined; it could have been the *o*-benzidine (**110**).

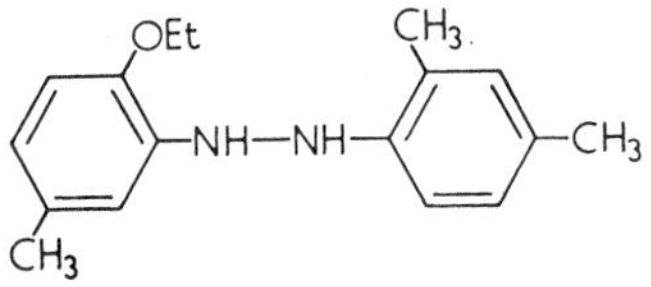

(108) 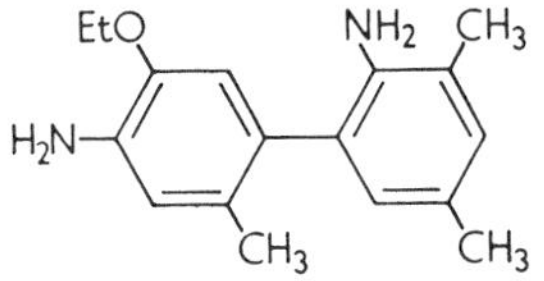 (109) 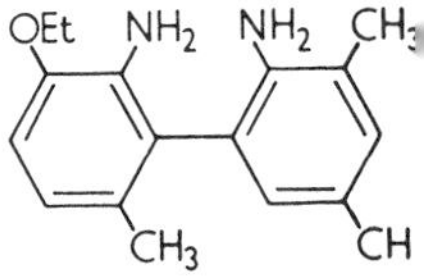 (110)

There are in any case serious objections to the Hughes mechanism. First, it cannot account in any simple way for the product rules; this must be true of any mechanism where the second conjugate acid (**88**) of hydrazobenzene is an intermediate. Second, it cannot account for the failure of 4,4′-diphenyl-hydrazobenzene (**94**) to rearrange. At first sight it might appear that the phenyl groups could interfere with the formation of **101** from **88**, but examination of models shows that this is not the case. The rings in **101** are not parallel and the positions para to nitrogen can remain well apart during the conversion of **89** to **101**, as shown.

[59] P. Jacobsen, *Ann.*, **428**, 76 (1922).

Worst of all is the problem of explaining why **101** does not immediately lose two protons to form *o*-benzidine (**72**) rather than undergo further rearrange-

ment. In the Claisen rearrangement ortho migration is invariably the main reaction whenever it is possible—i.e., when one of the positions ortho to allyloxy is free. In the rearrangement of hydrazobenzene, *o*-benzidine is formed only in traces. This cannot be explained as any kind of steric effect, or effect of mutual repulsion of the charged $\overset{+}{N}H_2$ groups, since these effects operate equally well in the rearrangement of α-hydrazonaphthalene (**76**) where *o*-benzidine is in fact the main product. It is also difficult to see why if **101** rearranges at all, it does not do so predominantly to the more stable isomers such as (**99**), which would lead to semidines, rather than to the less stable biquinonoid intermediates that lead to benzidine or diphenyline.

There are also a number of minor observations that are very difficult to explain on the basis of the Hughes mechanism; for example, the fact [60] that 3,3'-dimethylhydrazobenzene gives only benzidine and no diphenyline on rearrangement.

The π Complex Mechanism. The third mechanism marked the first application of molecular orbital ideas to molecular rearrangements [51,54a,54c] and the inception of the π complex concept. It was pointed out that heterolysis of the N—N bond in the first conjugate acid (**111**) of hydrazobenzene would give aniline (**112**) and a positive ion, (PhNH)[+]. If the nitrogen atom in this ion retains its unshared pair of electrons, the structure of the ion will be one (**113**)

derived from aniline by the loss of a proton and two π electrons. One of the π MO's that is filled with a pair of electrons in aniline is left empty in the ion (**113**). Consequently aniline and the ion (**113**) should be able to form a stable sandwich-like π complex (**114**), being held together by a dative bond in which the highest filled orbital of aniline acts as donor and the corresponding empty

[60] R. B. Carlin and R. C. Odioso (M), *J. Am. Chem. Soc.*, **76**, 2345 (1954).

MO of (113) as acceptor. Since these orbitals must be almost identical in shape, the overlap between them should be very good. The strength of this dative π bond should therefore be comparable with the strengths of other dative covalent bonds, e.g., that in the $\overset{+}{N}H_3$–$\overset{-}{B}F_3$ complex. (This point needs emphasizing; for, as was pointed out above, the term π complex has been misused to describe weak complexes of other kinds, and this misuse has led a number of authors to dismiss the possibility of π complex mechanisms for rearrangements.)

Since the N—N bond in (111) is weak, the π complex (114) should differ little from 111 in energy. Consequently it should require little energy to fold up the monoacid salt (111) of hydrazobenzene into the isomeric π complex (114). In the π complex (114), the para positions have been brought together; unfolding of the π complex and linkage of the para carbon atoms can lead to the double quinonoid structure (115), which can lose protons to form benzi-

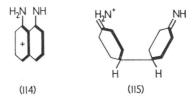

(114)   (115)

dine. Not only does this mechanism account for the intramolecular conversion of 111 to benzidine, but it does so by a route involving only intermediates of low energy; one can therefore easily understand why rearrangement of this kind takes place with such extraordinary ease. The rearrangement of hydrazobenzene in strong acid is complete in a fraction of a second at room temperature.

The π complex (114) can also react in other ways. It should be possible to twist one benzene ring relative to the other in 114 without much weakening the π bond between them. In this way 114 can be converted to the rotational

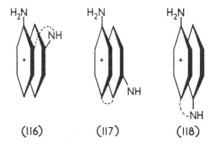

(116)   (117)   (118)

isomers 116, 117, and 118, which can unfold as indicated to give o-semidine, diphenyline, and p-semidine, respectively.

Now the two orbitals mainly involved in π complex formation between **112** and **113** are concentrated on the nitrogen atoms and the positions ortho and para to them; orbital overlap will therefore be best in isomer **114**, which should therefore be the most stable. Since **114** is also the first-formed intermediate and is the precursor of benzidine, it is not surprising that benzidine is the main product in cases where both para positions are free. The next most stable π complex should be the diphenyline precursor (**117**) where the o,p-position of the rings are adjacent; the other isomers (**116** and **118**) should be much less stable.

Since the rates of formation of benzidine, diphenyline, and semidine should run parallel to the concentrations of their precursors, we have a simple explanation of the first orientation rule (benzidine > diphenyline $\gg$ semidine). These qualitative arguments are supported by MO calculations which further indicate that **118** should be much the least stable of the four isomers; this explains why p-semidine can so easily be formed.

One can even explain why p-semidines *are* formed in certain cases. They are formed only when one ring of the hydrazobenzene carries a strong $-E$ group such as acetamido in the para position. In this case the π complex will be built up from the fragments **119** and **120**; but here the aniline moiety (**119**) is symmetrical, having two $-E$ substituents (NH, NHAc) para to each other. Consequently the initial π complex (**121**) and the 180° isomer (**122**) are now of comparable energies, the NH of the $C_6H_5NH^+$ moiety in each case being opposite one or other of the exocyclic atoms in **119**. Here a p-semidine can be formed by the linkage indicated in **122**.

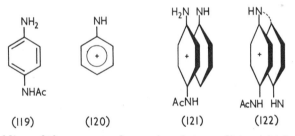

(119)	(120)	(121)	(122)

The unfolding of these π complexes gives intermediates which are similar to the benzenonium ion intermediates [60a] formed in electrophilic substitution of aniline (cf. **115**), which can be written more familiarly as **123**, and the

(123)   (124)

[60a] Cf. M. J. S. Dewar, *Record Chem. Progr.*, **19**, 1 (1958).

benzenonium ion intermediate (**124**) for para substitution in aniline (**123**) is simply a special case of **124** with $X = C_6H_5NH$. The unfolding can therefore be regarded as an electrophilic substitution of the aniline component by the ion $(C_6H_5NH)^+$. Since aniline substitutes mainly para, for reasons which are well understood,[60b] we can account for the fact that **114** unfolds to benzidine rather than to *o*-benzidine, and also for the second orientation rule (that diphenylines are formed only if ring A has a free para position).

The differences between the hydrazonaphthalenes and hydrazobenzenes are also easily explained. In this case the first-formed π complex has no axial symmetry; rotation of one ring relative to the other is therefore inhibited and so no diphenylines can be formed. The failure of 4,4′-diphenylhydrazobenzene (**94**) to rearrange can, of course, be ascribed to steric hindrance; the bulky para substituents prevent the salt of the hydrazobenzene from folding up into a π complex. (Note that one would not expect an extended π complex (**125**)

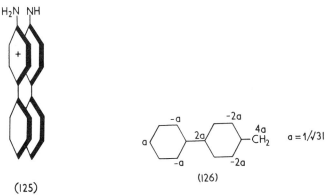

(125)

(126)

to be formed in this case; the highest occupied orbital of 4-aminodiphenyl is concentrated almost entirely in the ring adjacent to the amino group, and the weak attractive interactions between the terminal rings due to the π complex overlap would be swamped by the mutual repulsion of the many other π electrons in the system. This is illustrated by the AO coefficients (**126**) in the relevant MO for the isoconjugate *p*-phenylbenzyl system; the MO is seen to be mostly concentrated on the ring carrying the methylene group.)

One further factor remains to be explained, however. Hammond and Shine [61] found that the rearrangement of hydrazobenzene is second order with respect to acid, indicating that two protons are involved in the rate-determining step. They concluded that the second conjugate acid, $Ph\overset{+}{N}H_2.\overset{+}{N}H_2Ph$, forms first and rearranges by a first-order reaction to the products; since hydrazobenzene is a very weak base, the concentration of the second con-

[60b] M. J. S. Dewar, *J. Chem. Soc.* (*London*), **1949**, 463.
[61] G. S. Hammond and H. J. Shine, *J. Am. Chem. Soc.*, **72**, 220 (1950).

jugate acid will be proportional to the square of the hydrogen ion concentration, and so likewise will be the rate of rearrangement.

This, of course, would not affect the π complex mechanism if it were the second conjugate acid of hydrazobenzene that folds up into a π complex; but there is a much more attractive alternative.[61a,62] If the π complex is formed reversibly from the first conjugate acid (111), and if the rate-determining step involves attack by a second proton on the π complex, the over-all order

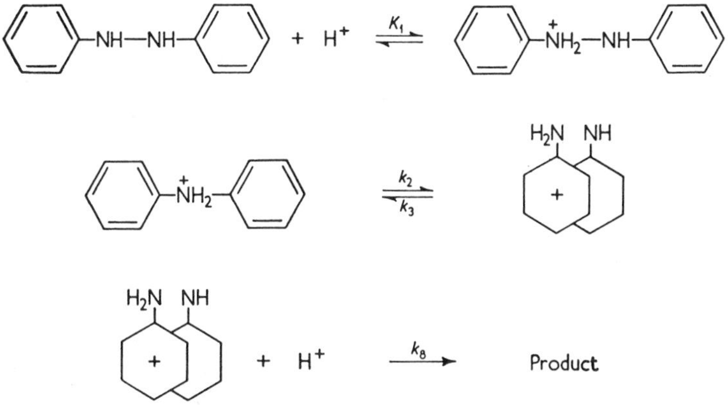

Scheme 2.

of the reaction with respect to acid can well be two. This can be written as shown in Scheme 2. This scheme gives for the over-all rate of reaction:

$$\text{Rate} = K_1 k_2 k_8 [\text{HAB}][\text{H}^+]^2 / (1 + K_1[\text{H}^+])(k_3 + k_8[\text{H}^+]) \tag{22}$$

where $\text{HAB} = $ hydrazobenzene. Since hydrazobenzene is an extremely weak base, the equilibrium between it and its conjugate acid will be well over to the side of the base under the mildly acid conditions used in the rate measurements; this corresponds to the condition

$$K_1[\text{H}^+] \ll 1 \tag{23}$$

If in addition the π complex reverts much more rapidly to hydrazobenzene than it reacts to form the product, so that equilibrium between the π complex and hydrazobenzene is almost attained

$$k_8[\text{H}^+] \ll 1 \tag{24}$$

If equations 23 and 24 hold, the rate expression (22) reduces to:

$$\text{Rate} = (K_1 k_2 k_8 / k_3)[\text{HAB}][\text{H}^+]^2 \tag{25}$$

which is second order with respect to acid.

[61a] M. J. S. Dewar, *Theoretical Organic Chemistry* (*Kekulé Symposium*), Butterworths, London, 1959, p. 179.

[62] M. J. S. Dewar, *Ann. Repts. on Progr. Chem.* (*Chem. Soc. London*), **48**, 126 (1951).

This mechanism has the advantage of maintaining a distinction between the two nitrogen atoms up to the product-determining stage. The rules for the products indicate strongly that this is the case; they depend on a clear distinction between the more and less basic halves of the hydrazobenzene. If the reaction involved an initial formation of the diacid salt, this distinction would be lost. Furthermore the modified π complex mechanism rests on a very reasonable physical basis. In hydrazobenzene the two PhNH units are neutral and do not attract one another. In the monoacid salt, one unit carries a positive charge; there will now be a polarization force between the two units, encouraging the molecule to fold up into a π complex. Addition of a second proton gives a dipositive ion in which the two positively charged aniline groups must repel one another very strongly; it is therefore very reasonable that addition of this second proton should occur only with synchronous unfolding of the π complex into a rearrangement product.

Carlin and Odioso [63] have found that the order with respect to acid of the rearrangement of o-hydrazotoluene (**127**) is less than two; over a moderate

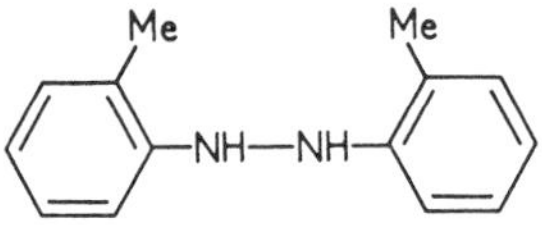

(127) 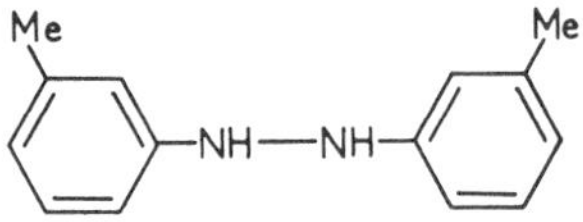   (128)

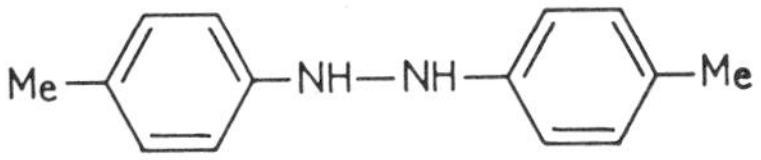

(129)

range of acid concentration the order appeared to be 1.6. They explained this result on the basis of the mechanism proposed by Hammond and Shine, [61] supposing that it is the diacid salt of hydrazobenzene that rearranges, following the scheme (HAB = hydrazobenzene);

$$HAB + H^+ \rightleftharpoons HAB \cdot H^+ \qquad \text{equilibrium constant } K_1$$
$$HAB \cdot H^+ + H^+ \rightleftharpoons HAB \cdot 2H^+ \qquad \text{equilibrium constant } K_2$$
$$HAB \cdot 2H^+ \rightarrow \text{product} \qquad \text{rate constant } k$$

Since the second dissociation constant, K_2, must be extremely small, the rate will be given by

$$\text{Rate} = kK_1K_2[HAB][H^+]^2/(1 + K_1[H^+]) \qquad (26)$$

Under conditions where $K_1[H^+]$ is negligible compared with unity, so that only a very small fraction of the hydrazobenzene is converted even to the mono-

[63] R. B. Carlin and R. C. Odioso, *J. Am. Chem. Soc.*, **76**, 100 (1954).

acid salt, this is approximately proportional to $[H^+]^2$; if, however, $K_1[H^+] \sim 1$, the apparent order will fall, approaching unity when $K_1[H^+] \gg 1$. Carlin and Odioso suppose that the $-I$ o-methyl groups in **126** make it more basic than hydrazobenzene, so that $K_1[H^+]$ becomes appreciable.

This explanation is unsatisfactory for two reasons. Table V lists the dissociation constants of aniline and the three toluidines; it will be seen that

TABLE V

Comparison of pK_B for Substituted Anilines with Order with respect to Acid for the Rearrangement of Corresponding Hydrazobenzenes

Substituent	10^{10} K_B for $ArNH_2$	Order with respect to acid for rearrangement of $ArNH \cdot NHAr$
(H)	4.6	2.0
o-Me	3.3	1.6
m-Me	5.5	2.0
p-Me	20	2.0

o-toluidine is the weakest of the four bases. The basicities of the hydrazotoluenes (**127, 128,** and **129**) must run parallel to those of the toluidines; therefore o-hydrazotoluene should be the least basic, and its rearrangement should show the highest order with respect to acid. Likewise the order should be least for the para isomer. In fact, the orders with respect to acid for the rearrangements of the meta and para isomers are in each case two,[60],[63a] which is inconsistent with the explanation given by Carlin and Odioso. Their mechanism also fails to explain another curious feature, the fact that both o- and m-hydrazotoluenes (**127** and **128**) give exclusively [60],[63] benzidines on rearrangement; no diphenylines are formed, although the rearrangement of hydrazobenzene itself gives as much as 30% of diphenyline.

All these points can be explained in terms of the π complex mechanism. The complete scheme is given in Scheme 3, π_1, π_2, π_3, and π_4 representing, respec-

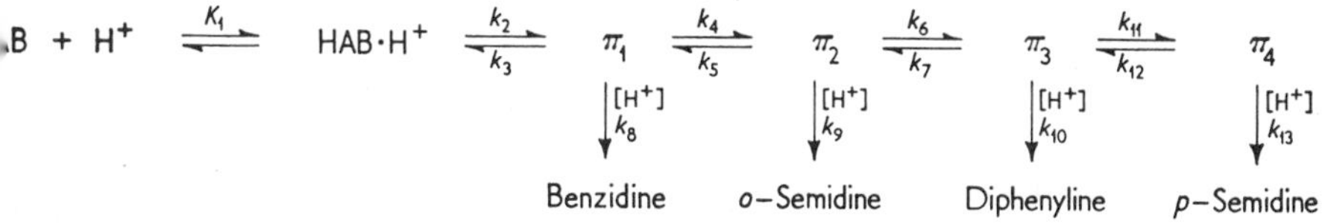

$$B + H^+ \underset{}{\overset{K_1}{\rightleftharpoons}} HAB \cdot H^+ \underset{k_3}{\overset{k_2}{\rightleftharpoons}} \pi_1 \underset{k_5}{\overset{k_4}{\rightleftharpoons}} \pi_2 \underset{k_7}{\overset{k_6}{\rightleftharpoons}} \pi_3 \underset{k_{12}}{\overset{k_{11}}{\rightleftharpoons}} \pi_4$$

$$\pi_1 \xrightarrow[k_8]{[H^+]} \text{Benzidine} \qquad \pi_2 \xrightarrow[k_9]{[H^+]} o-\text{Semidine} \qquad \pi_3 \xrightarrow[k_{10}]{[H^+]} \text{Diphenyline} \qquad \pi_4 \xrightarrow[k_{13}]{[H^+]} p-\text{Semidine}$$

Scheme 3.

tively, the four isomeric forms **114, 116, 117,** and **118** of the π complex. Methyl substituents will accelerate the product-forming reactions since these are effectively electrophilic substitutions; methylation therefore increases k_8, k_9, k_{10}, k_{13}.

[63a] R. B. Carlin and G. S. Wick, *J. Am. Chem. Soc.*, **80**, 4023 (1958).

Now the rate of conversion of π_1 to benzidine, and the rate of isomerization to π_2, are given by

$$d[\text{benzidine}]/dt = k_8[\pi_1][\text{H}^+] \tag{27}$$

$$d[\pi_2]/dt = k_4[\pi_1] \tag{28}$$

If $k_2[\text{H}^+] \gg k_3$, none of the π_1 will isomerize; consequently, nothing but benzidine will be formed in the rearrangement. Since methylation will increase k_8, but not k_4, it is not surprising to find that the hydrazotoluenes, unlike hydrazobenzene, give benzidine as the sole rearrangement product. A further factor in the case of the meta isomer could be steric hindrance in the π_3 configurations (**130** and **131**) that lead to diphenyline; in each case the methyl group in one ring is opposite to the methyl or amino group in the other.

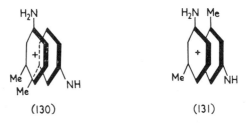

(130)   (131)

If isomerization of π_1 does not occur, and if $K_1[\text{H}^+] \ll 1$, the rate of formation of benzidine is given (cf. eq. 22) by

$$d[\text{benzidine}]/dt = K_1 k_2 k_8[\text{HAB}][\text{H}^+]^2/(k_3 + k_8[\text{H}^+]) \tag{29}$$

Methyl substituents should increase k_8; if $k_8[\text{H}^+] \sim k_3$, the order with respect to acid will fall. This apparently happens in the case of o-hydrazotoluene.

Why, then, is the order normal for the meta and para isomers? The unfolding reaction in the case of the meta isomer gives rise to a sterically hindered di-ortho-substituted diphenyl; this steric hindrance could decrease k_8 sufficiently for $k_8[\text{H}^+]$ to be no longer comparable with k_3. In the case of the para isomer the situation is different since only semidine can form, at a rate given by

$$d[\text{semidine}]/dt = K_1 k_2 k_4 k_9[\text{HAB}][\text{H}^+]^2/(k_3 k_5 + (k_3 + k_4)k_9[\text{H}^+]) \tag{30}$$

The order with respect to acid falls if the second term in the denominator becomes comparable with the first. Suppose first that $k_3 \gg k_{-1}$. The condition for falling acid dependence is then

$$(k_4/k_5)k_9[\text{H}^+] \sim k_3 \tag{31}$$

But $k_4 \ll k_5$, since π_2 is much less stable than π_1; this is the reason why semidines are formed only as a last resort when rearrangement to benzidine or diphenyline is restricted. Comparison with equation 29 shows that it is much harder for the acid dependence to be reduced in the case of the semidine rearrangement since, other things being equal, k_9 and k_{10} are likely to be comparable.

The same conclusion follows if $k_3 \ll k_{-1}$; here the condition for reduced acid dependence is

$$k_9[\text{H}^+] \sim k_5 \tag{32}$$

This again will be a difficult condition to meet since k_4 is likely to be large.

In short, the acid dependence of the p-hydrazotoluene rearrangement is normal for the same reason that the semidine rearrangement is inherently slow—i.e., the instability of the appropriate form π_2 of the π complex.

One last point remains. Bunton, Ingold, and Mhala[64] have produced evidence that seems to support the mechanism proposed by Hammond and Shine,[64a] in which the second conjugate acid (88) of hydrazobenzene is formed reversibly and rearranges in the rate-determining step by a first-order reaction. Their evidence is based on the fact that a plot of the logarithm of the rate against the Hammett acidity function, H_0, gives a straight line, of slope 2.6, and that the rate in deuterium oxide is about four times greater than in water.

The first line of evidence is not convincing. It is now well recognized that the rate of a reaction can be proportional to H_0 even if it involves a rate-determining proton transfer rather than a preliminary reversible protonation. The second argument is more cogent. Changing the solvent from water to deuterium oxide should increase the basicity of hydrazobenzene and so increase K_1 and K_2 in equations 22 through 31, but it should also decrease the terminal rate constants k_8, k_9, k_{10}, and k_{13} in the π complex mechanism. The Hammond mechanism (eq. 26) would therefore predict a considerably higher rate in D_2O; the π complex mechanism (cf. 25) seems to make no clear prediction, since the net result would depend on the interplay of two opposing effects. The fact that there is such a large rate increase in D_2O (factor of four) certainly seems to support the Hammond-Shine mechanism.

However it has been observed[64a,64b] that several of these rearrangements show general acid catalysis. This provides conclusive proof that a rate-determining proton transfer is involved. The work of Bunton, Ingold, and Mhala must therefore be taken as one further indication of the uncertainties in arguments based on isotope effects. One factor which may have influenced the rate in D_2O, and which those authors apparently overlooked, is that rapid exchange must have taken place between the imino hydrogen and the solvent, so that the rearranging entity in D_2O was not hydrazobenzene, but

[64] C. A. Bunton, C. K. Ingold, and M. M. Mhala, *J. Chem. Soc. (London)*, **1957**, 1906.
[64a] G. S. Hammond and H. J. Shine, *J. Am. Chem. Soc.*, **72**, 220 (1950).
[64b] D. J. Morley, M.Sc. thesis, London, 1953.

7,7'-dideuterohydrozobenzene, PhND·NDPh. The effect of this cannot be predicted at present.

There is a further piece of evidence that has a bearing on the mechanism. Hauser and Murrell [66] have observed that Wurster's blue perchlorate (**133**)

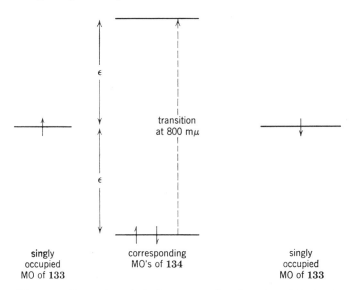

(133)   (134)

forms a diamagnetic dimer at low temperatures, with a new absorption band at 800 mμ. This must be formulated as a π complex (**134**), precisely analogous to the π complex that would be formed by folding up the second conjugate acid, $Ph\overset{+}{N}H_2 \cdot \overset{+}{N}H_2Ph$ of hydrazobenzene.

singly occupied MO of **133**   corresponding MO's of **134**   singly occupied MO of **133**

Figure 4. Formation of **134** from **133** and explanation of the band at 800 mμ.

The formation of **134** can be represented, in MO terms, as being due to an interaction of the two singly occupied MO's of the component units (**133**) to form two extended MO's, one of lower and one of higher energy, of which the lower accommodates the two electrons in question (Fig. 4).

[65] K. H. Hauser and J. N. Murrell, *J. Chem. Phys.*, **27**, 500 (1957).

The splitting of the levels in (**134**) will be approximately symmetrical. They will lie at equal increments, ϵ, of energy above and below the singly occupied level of **133**. The total binding energy between the two benzene units in **134** will therefore be 2ϵ.

The new band at 800 mμ can be ascribed to a transition between these two MO's in **134**; Figure 4 indicates that the corresponding energy difference is also 2ϵ. This indicates that the bond energy between the units (**133**) in **134** is approximately 40 kcal./mole, confirming the idea that bonds in such π complexes must be comparable in strength with normal covalent bonds. (This conclusion is further supported by the complete parallel between the formation of **134** from two molecules of **133** and that of a diatomic molecule such as I_2 from two atoms and by the fact that the new band in the spectrum of **134** appears in the same region as the corresponding N—V transition of I_2, indicating that the bond strengths are similar.)

Nevertheless **134** is quite unstable, its heat of formation from **133** being only about 2 kcal./mole. The reason for this is clear: the coulomb repulsion between two ions (**133**) of like charge must be very great at distances short enough to allow formation of a covalent bond between them. The repulsion would certainly be of the order of 40 kcal./mole so that **134** is only just stable.

Now this argument shows two things. First, the type of π bond postulated in the π complex theory is seen to be indeed a very strong one, comparable in strength with normal covalent bonds. Second, the coulomb repulsion between two $Ar\overset{+}{N}H_2\cdot$ units is enough to balance out the covalent bond so that the π complex $(Ar\overset{+}{N}H_2)_2$ is unstable. This provides very strong support for the π complex mechanism in the form indicated above; for it suggests that no stable π complex intermediate could be formed from the second conjugate acid of hydrazobenzene, and also that protonation of the singly charged π complex (**114**) would force the rings apart.

B. *Other Rearrangements that may be Analogous to the Benzidine Rearrangement*

It was pointed out above that the rearrangements of benzyl phenyl ether (**135**) to *o*-benzylphenol (**138**) in the presence of aluminum bromide are almost

(135)　　　　　(136)　　　　　(137)　　　　　(138)

certainly intramolecular. These reactions may be simple π complex rearrangements analogous to the corresponding rearrangement of *sec*-butyl phenyl ether; but there is an intriguing possibility [65a] that the aromatic ring of the benzyl group may play a specific role in the reaction, the intermediate π complexes being sandwich-like structures (**136** and **137**) isoconjugate with those (**114** and **116**) involved in the semidine rearrangement. This suggests that similar mechanisms may also operate in the case of other molecules when two aromatic rings are linked by a pair of atoms (e.g., **139–141**). Intramolecular

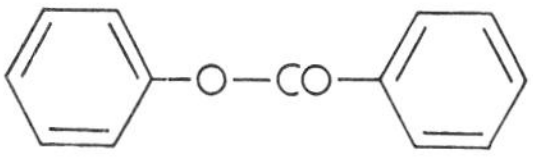

(139) 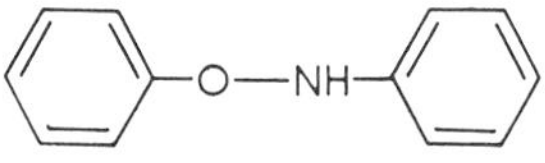   (140) 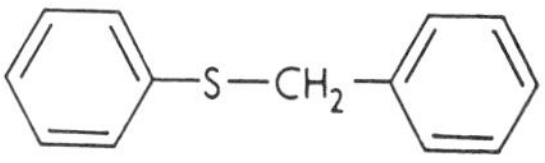   (141)

rearrangements of this kind should be most favorable in reactions carried out in homogeneous solution in a nonpolar solvent, e.g., with aluminum bromide in chlorobenzene. Shine and Beer [66] have given some inconclusive evidence that diphenyl disulfide undergoes a benzidine-like rearrangement to 4,4'-biphenylthiol in sulfuric acid; otherwise the field has been scarcely touched.

5. SUMMARY

Our knowledge of these interesting reactions has increased greatly in recent years, but much remains to be done. The most striking development has been the discovery that some aromatic rearrangements are genuinely intramolecular and their interpretation in terms of recent theoretical ideas. The field of rearrangements in general, and of aromatic rearrangements in particular, has been transformed by the application of quantum theory; the success of the molecular orbital approximation in this field has been one of its most striking achievements.

[65a] M. J. S. Dewar, *Theoretical Organic Chemistry (Kekulé Symposium)*, Butterworths, London, 1959, p. 179.

[66] H. J. Shine and J. L. Beer, *Chem. & Ind. (London)*, **1957**, 565.

6

BASE-CATALYZED REARRANGEMENTS

H. E. ZIMMERMAN
University of Wisconsin, Madison,
Wisconsin

CONTENTS

I. MESOMERIC ANIONS AND ENOLATES

A. Protonation of Mesomeric Anions

An unusually fascinating phenomenon is the formation of unstable tautomers by protonation of mesomeric anions. Probably the simplest example is
the kinetically controlled protonation of nitroalkane conjugate bases to
afford aci-nitro compounds as unstable but initially formed products. Thus,[1,2]
acidification of the lithium conjugate base (1) of 1-nitro-2-phenylcyclohexane
affords[1] the ephemeral but isolable 1-aci-nitro-2-phenylcyclohexane (2). The

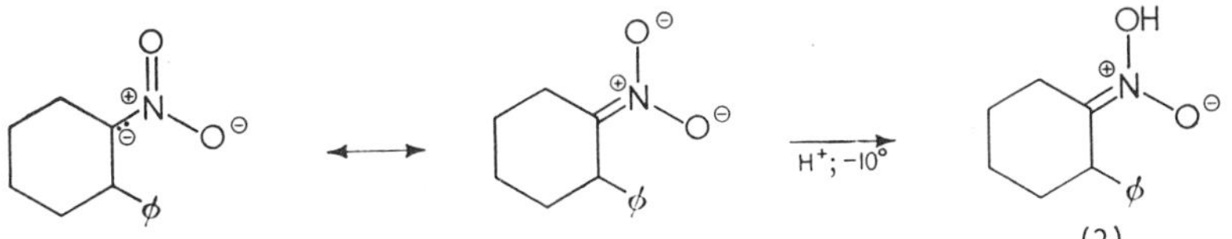

(1)   (2)

---

[1] H. E. Zimmerman and T. E. Nevins, *J. Am. Chem. Soc.*, **79**, 6559 (1957).

[2] For other examples see A. F. Holleman, *Rec. trav. chim.*, **14**, 121 (1895); A. Hantzsch
and O. Schultze, *Ber.*, **29**, 699, 2253 (1896); A. Hantzsch, *Ber.*, **45**, 89 (1912).

more stable nitro tautomer, 1-nitro-2-phenylcyclohexane, resulting from protonation at C_1, is formed much more slowly and results only under conditions where the protonation of the first-formed *aci*-nitro tautomer (2) is reversible. That prototopic attack on the oxygen atom of anion 1 is faster than on C_1 can be attributed to the greater electronegativity of the oxygen atom and the consequently greater electron density at this atom compared to C_1. The transition state for the highly exothermic neutralization process comes early, according to Hammond's principle,[3] and hence little covalent bonding has ensued. As a result, the lowest energy transition state has the electron-deficient proton as close as possible to the p orbital of highest electron density.

A more complex case obtains when the mesomeric anion is stabilized by an additional double bond; the literature holds many examples in which a β,γ-unsaturated carbonyl compound results on acidification, under mild conditions, of an enolate common both to this tautomer and to the more stable α,β-unsaturated isomer. A representative case [4] is that of enolate anion 3, the common conjugate base of cholest-4-en-3-one (4) and cholest-5-

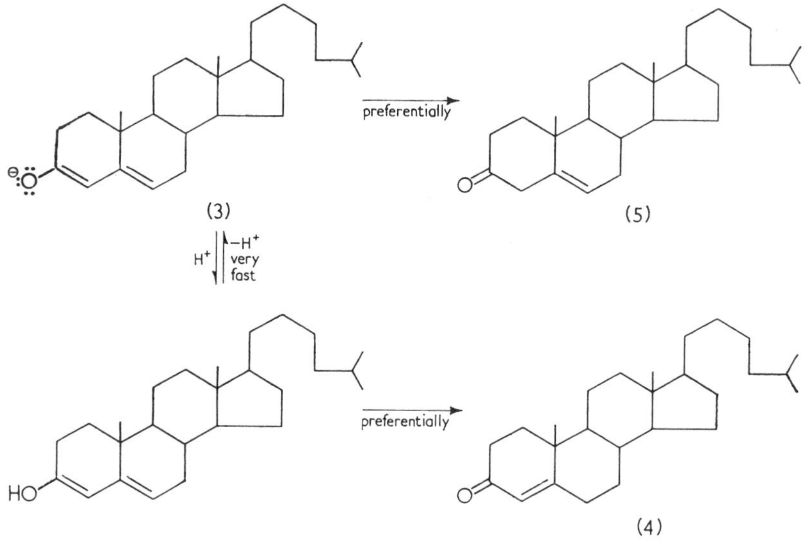

[3] G. S. Hammond, *J. Am. Chem. Soc.*, **77**, 334 (1955).

[4] For further cases see E. Bauer, *Ann. chim.*, [9]**1**, 343 (1914), regarding the enolates of 1-benzoyl-2-phenylcyclopentene and 1-benzoyl-2-phenylcyclo-hexene; M. S. Kharasch and P. O. Tawney, *J. Am. Chem. Soc.*, **63**, 2308 (1941), concerning the enolate of isophorone, formed from isophorone and methylmagnesium bromide in the presence of ferric chloride; W. E. Hugh and G. A. R. Kon, *J. Chem. Soc. (London)*, **1930**, 775, for the behavior of the enolate of diethyl cyclopentylidenemalonate. In each case the unconjugated unsaturated carbonyl product results from acidification of the enolate.

en-3-one (5), which has been known [5-7] for some time to afford the unconjugated and less stable isomer 5 on careful acidification. Evidence that it is indeed the enolate (3) and not the neutral enol which protonates to afford the unstable product has more recently been obtained [8] by studying the product composition, corrected for small amounts of equilibration, resulting when enolate 3 is quenched with buffers of varying pH. At pH's near 8 where the enolate would be expected to be the predominant species, cholest-5-en-3-one does indeed predominate, to the extent of 98%. However, as the quenching buffer pH is decreased, the amount of cholest-4-en-3-one formed increases much more rapidly than can be explained on the basis of equilibration of initially formed cholest-5-en-3-one. This result accords with the expectation that at lower pH's more neutral enol and less enolate will be present and that the enol, in contrast to the enolate, protonates at the end of the conjugated system.[9]

Of particular interest is the final protonation step of the Birch reduction. According to its most commonly accepted mechanism [10,11] the final step of the reduction of benzene involves the protonation of the mesomeric carbanion 6. While a priori any of carbon atoms 1, 3, or 5 of carbanion 6 might have

(6)

been protonated, it is actually the central position of the pentadienyl carbanion moiety which is attacked, affording [10,12] 1,4-dihydrobenzene as the

[5] B. Belleau and T. F. Gallagher, J. Am. Chem. Soc., 73, 4458 (1951).

[6] A. J. Birch, P. Hextall, and J. A. K. Quartey, Australian J. Chem., 6, 445 (1953).

[7] W. Dauben et al., J. Am. Chem. Soc., 73, 4463, 4496 (1951).

[8] R. M. Paufler and H. E. Zimmerman, unpublished results; R. M. Paufler, Ph.D. Thesis, Northwestern University, 1960.

[9] It will be noted that the cation produced by addition of a proton to the end of the π system (i.e., at C_6) of the neutral enol gives an intermediate with three contributing resonance structures, while attack at C_4 gives a cation with only two structures; the former and the transition state leading to it will be of lower energy for this reason. The protonation of the enolate, leading directly to a neutral species, is not subject to such control.

[10] A. Krapcho and A. A. Bothner-By, J. Am. Chem. Soc., 81, 3658 (1959). However, also note J. F. Eastham, C. Keenan, and H. Secor, J. Am. Chem. Soc., 81, 6523 (1959), and A. Krapcho and A. Bothner-By, J. Am. Chem. Soc., 82, 751 (1960).

[11] A. J. Birch and D. Nasipuri, Tetrahedron, 6, 150 (1959); A. J. Birch and H. Smith, Quart. Revs. (London), 12, 17 (1958).

[12] W. Hückel, and U. Wörffel, Chem. Ber., 88, 338 (1955).

major Birch reduction product. This interesting result receives no theoretical rationale in terms of the charge distribution of anion **6** as given by the simple LCAO molecular orbital theory, for the negative charge is predicted [13] to be equally distributed among carbon atoms 1, 3, and 5. However, the simple LCAO MO theory assumes equal overlap between atoms 1 and 2, 2 and 3, etc. Simple qualitative resonance considerations lead to the expectation that bonds 1–2 and 4–5 should be shorter and involve greater overlap than bonds 2–3 and 3–4; this is because in two of the three resonance structures for **6** bonds 1–2 and 4–5 are double, while in only one of the three are bonds 2–3 and 3–4 double. The simple LCAO MO theory itself, while naive in predicting charge distribution, does agree with the resonance theory in giving a higher π bond order for bonds 1–2 and 4–5 than for 2–3 and 3–4. Now it is easily shown [14] that the LCAO MO prediction of charges, when unequal overlap is taken into account, is given by the expression:

$$q_1/q_3 = S_{23}^2/S_{12}^2$$

where q_1 and q_3 are the charges at carbon atoms 1 and 3, and S_{12} and S_{23} are the overlap integrals for π bonds 1–2 and 2–3, respectively. Therefore, since $S_{12} > S_{23}$, it is immediately seen that the electron density at C_3 is higher than at C_1, rationalizing the preferential attack of a positive species at the central position of the pentadienyl carbanion system. The charge densities and π bond orders calculated by successive approximation are given in Table I; [15]

TABLE I

Charge Densities Calculated for the Pentadienyl Carbanion by Successive LCAO MO Approximation with Changing Bond Orders [15]

Approximation	q_1	q_2	q_3	P_{12}	P_{23}
First	0.333	0.000	0.333	0.788	0.578
Second	0.317	0.000	0.365	0.802	0.564
Third	0.316	0.000	0.368	0.802	0.562

[13] This prediction is most easily arrived at by the method of nonbonding molecular orbitals as described by H. C. Longuet-Higgins, *J. Chem. Phys.*, **18**, 265 (1950); *Proc. Chem. Soc. (London)*, **1957**, 157; and M. J. S. Dewar, *J. Am. Chem. Soc.*, **74**, 3341, 3345 (1952); M. J. S. Dewar, *Prog. in Org. Chem.*, **2**, 1 (1953).

[14] This derives simply from solution of the secular equation, with or without neglect of overlap, making the approximation that the resonance integral is proportional to the overlap integral.

[15] These results were obtained by the method described by N. Muller and R. S. Mulliken, *J. Am. Chem. Soc.*, **80**, 3489 (1958), and N. Muller, L. W. Pickett, and R. S. Mulliken, *J. Am. Chem. Soc.*, **74**, 4770 (1954), except that no adjustment of coulomb integrals was made and overlap was neglected.

here the π bond orders resulting from each approximation were used to obtain the overlap integral for the next iteration.[16]

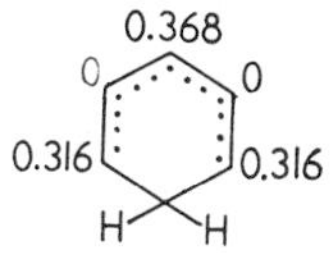

(6)

The importance of charge density in controlling rates of protonation has been considered by a number of authors.[3,17,19] Ingold [18] has correctly pointed out that of two possibilities the protonation process requiring less electronic reorganization will have a lower energy of activation. On the other hand, the suggested rule "When a proton is supplied by acids to the mesomeric anion of weakly ionizing tautomers of markedly unequal stability, then the tautomer which is most quickly formed is the thermodynamically least stable" is not invariably, although very frequently, correct. For example, Russell [19] has found that neutralization of α,α-dimethylbenzylpotassium (7) with a variety of deutero acids results in preferential attack at the α carbon atom, although significant amounts of ortho and para attack occur when protonation is by deuterium chloride in ether. Here even the simple LCAO MO treatment predicts a markedly heavy electron density at the α carbon atom.[20] Protonation thus proceeds again by attack on the most electron-rich position, although in this example it is the most stable tautomer **9** formed in preference (rather

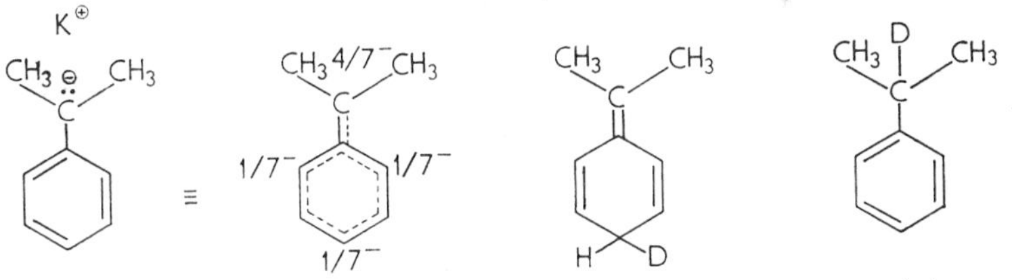

(7a)   (7b)   (8)   (9)

[16] Hammond has considered [3] the last stage of the Birch reduction, using the LCAO MO method with assumption of equal overlap. While pointing out the importance of a high charge density at the center being protonated, he has noted the inability of the charge density predicted by the simple model to account for the observed protonation.

[17] In a classic paper relating rates of ionization and recombination to equilibrium constants of pseudo acids, R. G. Pearson and R. Dillon, *J. Am. Chem. Soc.*, **75**, 2439 (1953), have emphasized the importance of this factor.

[18] C. K. Ingold, *Structure and Mechanism in Organic Chemistry*, Cornell University Press, Ithaca, N.Y., 1953, pp. 565–66.

[19] G. Russell, *J. Am. Chem. Soc.*, **81**, 2017 (1959).

[20] Cf. H. C. Longuet-Higgins, *Proc. Chem. Soc.* (*London*), **1957**, 160.

than, for example, 8). Clearly prototopic attack at the α carbon atom involves less electron reorganization than attack at any of the ortho or para positions where electrons are less available.[21,22]

Related to the course of protonation of mesomeric carbanions, is that of radical anions, for example, those which result from introduction of one electron into the π system of aromatic compounds. Evidence has been presented[10,11] that the protonation of such radical anions is the rate-limiting step in the Birch reduction. In view of the course of this reaction, in which electron-donating substituents such as methoxyl, alkyl, or amino groups tend to appear on the double bonds of the 1,4-dihydrobenzene products,[23] one must conclude that protonation of the radical anion derived from, say, anisole must proceed preferentially ortho or meta to the methoxyl group, following Path A or Path B. In this connection the electron distribution of the

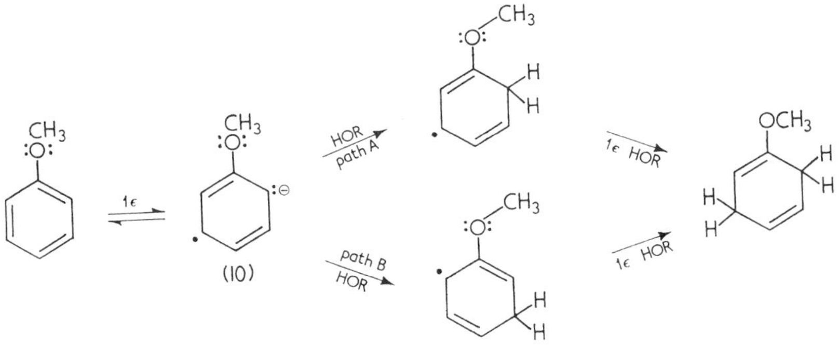

radical anion **10** is especially pertinent. The results of LCAO calculations[24] shown in Figure 1 indicate the ortho position to be most electron rich.

Similarly, the species (**11**) generated by ortho protonation should be of lower energy than that formed by meta protonation (i.e., **12**), since only in the former can the odd electron interact electronically with the methoxyl

[21] Note also H. F. Herbrandson and D. S. Mooney, *J. Am. Chem. Soc.*, **79**, 5809 (1957), and examples cited therein.

[22] The course of protonation of organometallics having a largely covalent carbon-metal bond and not involving a relatively free carbanion will not be considered here.

[23] A. J. Birch, *J. Chem. Soc. (London)*, **1944**, 430.

[24] The molecular orbitals, on which the charge distribution calculation was based, derive from unpublished results of the author with Vernon Sandel. In these calculations α_0 was taken as $\alpha_C + 2.7\beta$ and β_{OC} was taken as $0.6 \beta_{CC}$. The charge densities in parentheses were calculated using the molecular orbitals given for phenol by K. Nishimoto and R. Fujishiro, *Bull. Chem. Soc. Japan*, **31**, 1036 (1958); cf. H. E. Zimmerman, *Tetrahedron*, **16**, 169 (1961), for further discussion and the results of more recent calculations on anisole and the dimethoxybenzene systems.

group.[25] On the other hand, viewpoints differing from the above have been presented,[10,11] and an experimental test is desirable.[26]

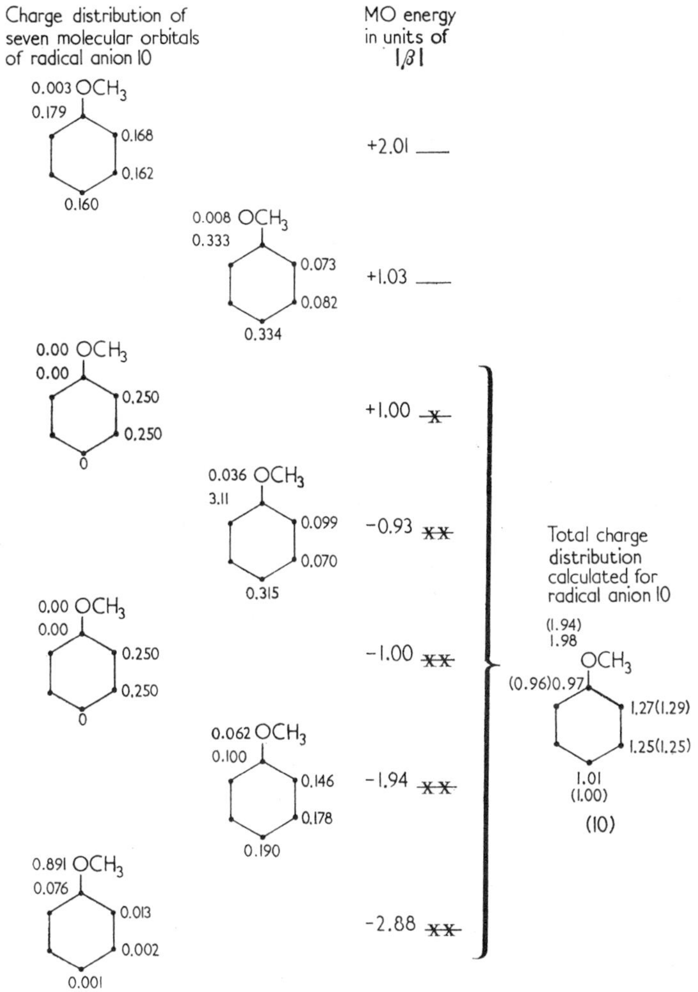

Charge distribution of seven molecular orbitals of radical anion 10

MO energy in units of $|\beta|$

0.003 OCH$_3$
0.179
0.168
0.162
0.160

$+2.01$ ___

0.008 OCH$_3$
0.333
0.073
0.082
0.334

$+1.03$ ___

0.00 OCH$_3$
0.00
0.250
0.250
0

$+1.00$ ―x―

0.036 OCH$_3$
3.11
0.099
0.070
0.315

-0.93 ―xx―

0.00 OCH$_3$
0.00
0.250
0.250
0

-1.00 ―xx―

0.062 OCH$_3$
0.100
0.146
0.178
0.190

-1.94 ―xx―

0.891 OCH$_3$
0.076
0.013
0.002
0.001

-2.88 ―xx―

Total charge distribution calculated for radical anion 10

(1.94)
1.98
OCH$_3$
(0.96)0.97
1.27(1.29)
1.25(1.25)
1.01
(1.00)
(10)

Figure 1.

[25] The stabilizing effect of a methoxyl group by conjugation with an odd electron-bearing center is well known. Conjugation of an atom which has two π electrons (here the methoxyl group) with an odd alternant free radical (here the pentadienyl moiety) leads in the first approximation to interaction of the atomic p orbital of the former and the nonbonding MO of the latter with splitting about the center of gravity of the two original MO's. There are formed an MO of lower energy than the lower energy original MO and an MO of higher energy than the higher original MO. Conjugation leading to these two new MO's is energetically favorable, since two electrons go into the lower and only one

(11)
Odd electron can appear
on the methoxyl–bearing
carbon.

(12)
Odd electron cannot
appear on the methoxyl–
bearing carbon atom.

B. Stereochemistry of Carbanion and Related Reactions

Because carbanions and enolates are intermediates in so many organic reactions, the stereochemical behavior of these species has been of more than average concern. Unfortunately, in many cases of interest the precise nature of the carbanion undergoing reaction is obscure. Considering organometallic compounds of groups I and II metals, one finds a wide range of ionic character. The organopotassium and organosodium compounds are clearly ionic, being salt-like; for example, these do not dissolve in the organic solvents. In contrast are the organomagnesium compounds where the carbon-metal bond is largely covalent. Organolithium compounds seem to be intermediate between these extremes. The alkyllithiums are essentially covalent, dissolving in nonpolar organic solvents; nevertheless, they are associated.[27] An interesting borderline case is triphenylmethyllithium. This compound crystallizes from ether as orange-red needles as a dietherate; on heating to 90° under vacuum it loses the two ether molecules to form unsolvated, pale solid triphenylmethyllithium. The solvated orange-red modification can be regenerated by treatment with ether.[28] The orange-red form is clearly ionic, having the color characteristic of the sodium and potassium analogs, while the nonsolvated species would seem to be covalent.

Just as none of these organometallic compounds might be termed examples of "free" carbanions—being covalently bonded, or tied up in an ion pair or ion aggregate and perhaps solvated—it would appear equally true that carbanions generated as unstable intermediates do not exist as individual, free anions. Nevertheless, especially for reactions in relatively polar media, the ionic nature of the reaction intermediate is often quite clear and one may focus attention on the carbanion moiety with consideration of its environment only when forced and allowed by experimental reality.

---

into the upper of the two new orbitals. Cf. M. J. S. Dewar, *Electronic Theory of Organic Chemistry*, Oxford University Press, London, 1948, p. 243.

[26] It should be noted that the above molecular orbital considerations predict that the dianion, resulting from introduction of two electrons into anisole, would preferentially ortho protonate. In certain cases it may actually be the dianion which is involved in reduction.

[27] E.g., G. Wittig, F. J. Meyer, and G. Lange, *Ann.*, **571**, 186 (1951).

[28] A. v. Grosse, *Ber.*, **59**, 2652 (1926).

First selecting saturated carbanions for consideration, we note that it was Barton who first suggested [29] that protonation of such tetrahedral anions tends to proceed with the carbanion in its more stable conformation to afford the more stable product. Thus both 5α-chlorocholestane (**13**) and 5β,6α-dibromocholestane (**14**) on lithium–liquid ammonia (Wilds' reagent) [30] reduction give cholestane as the sole saturated product. [28] It is clear that, to the extent that the two compounds (**13** and **14**) reduce by the same mechanism, as seems very likely, the carbon-5 configuration of the products of reduction is unrelated to that of the reactants and the reaction is nonstereospecific; [31] it is, however, quite stereoselective, [31] there being a strong preference for formation

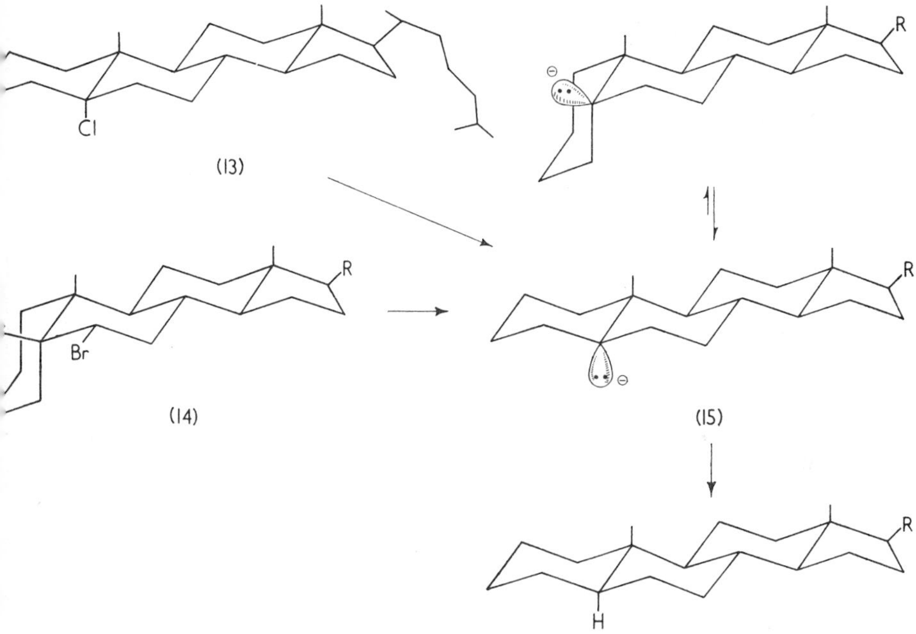

[29] D. H. R. Barton and C. H. Robinson, *J. Chem. Soc.* (*London*), **1954**, 3045.

[30] A. L. Wilds and N. A. Nelson, *J. Am. Chem. Soc.*, **75**, 5360, 5366 (1953).

[31] A "stereospecific" reaction has been defined as one in which there is *some* relationship between reactant and product configurations; the relationship may be retention of configuration, inversion, or any other by which one isomer of reactant goes to one isomer of product while the second isomer of reactant gives the other isomer of product. Stereospecificity is not necessarily complete. A "stereoselective" reaction, according to these definitions, is one in which there is no relationship between reactant and product configurations, both reactants giving the same product distribution, and where there is nevertheless a preferential formation of one of the possible stereoisomeric products due to some driving force. Cf. H. E. Zimmerman, L. Singer, and B. S. Thyagarajan, *J. Am. Chem. Soc.*, **81**, 108 (1959), fn. 16; H. E. Zimmerman, and L. Ahramjian, *J. Am. Chem. Soc.*, **81**, 2086 (1959), fn. 23.

of one of the possible epimeric products (i.e., cholestane rather than copro-stane). The lack of stereospecificity suggests intervention of carbanion **15** which protonates in its "cholestanoid" conformation. Since the reactions were run in liquid ammonia, a relatively polar solvent, the above discussion in terms of a discrete carbanion may not be too idealized.

Cram and co-workers[32] have studied the base-catalyzed hydrogen-deuterium exchange of 2-phenylbutane and α-phenethyl methyl ether. When the reactions were run with potassium *tert*-butoxide in deuterated *tert*-butyl alcohol, the exchange of deuterium for hydrogen at the benzylic position proceeded with over 80% retention of configuration. On the other hand, when the solvent consisted largely of dimethylsulfoxide, the exchanged product was racemized. These results were rationalized with a picture in which the initially formed species (**16**) is unsymmetrically solvated; the side

$$\phi-\overset{\overset{\displaystyle OCH_3}{|}}{\underset{\underset{\displaystyle CH_3}{|}}{C}}-H \quad + \quad K^{\oplus}\overset{\ominus}{O}-t\text{-Bu} \quad + \quad DO-t\text{-Bu} \longrightarrow$$

$$\left[\phi-\overset{\overset{\displaystyle OCH_3}{|}}{\underset{\underset{\displaystyle CH_3}{|}}{C}}:^{\ominus} \quad \begin{matrix} K^{\oplus} & O-t\text{-Bu} \\ & D \\ & HO-t\text{-Bu} \end{matrix} \right] \longrightarrow \phi-\overset{\overset{\displaystyle OCH_3}{|}}{\underset{\underset{\displaystyle CH_3}{|}}{C}}-D \quad \overset{\oplus}{K} \quad \overset{\ominus}{O}-t\text{-Bu}$$

(16) $+HO-t\text{-Bu}$

of the carbanion from which the proton is lost has in proximity not only the *tert*-butyl alcohol molecule formed in the abstraction process but also the potassium cation and at least one molecule of deuterated *tert*-butyl alcohol solvating this cation. The deuterated solvent molecule associated with the potassium cation delivers the deuteron from the side of the molecule which originally lost the proton. In the more polar dimethylsulfoxide a symmetri-cally solvated carbanion (**17**) results prior to protonation. This example

$$\text{dimethyl sulfoxide} \cdots \cdots \overset{\overset{\displaystyle \phi}{\diagdown}\,\,\overset{\displaystyle OCH_3}{\diagup}}{\underset{\underset{\displaystyle CH_3}{|}}{C}\,\!\!{:}^{\ominus}} \cdots \cdots \text{dimethyl sulfoxide}$$

(17)

[32] D. J. Cram, C. Kingsbury, and B. Rickborn, *J. Am. Chem. Soc.*, **81**, 5835 (1959). Papers dealing with related processes will not be considered here; but references are given in the present paper. For more recent studies on hydrogen exchange, see E. J. Corey and E. T. Kaiser, *J. Am. Chem. Soc.*, **83**, 490 (1961); O. J. Cram and co-workers, *J. Am. Chem. Soc.*, **83**, 3678 (1961) and following papers; and H. L. Goering, D. L. Towns, and B. Dillmar, *J. Org. Chem.*, **27**, 736 (1962).

emphasizes that in considering the stereochemistry of carbanion reactions as influenced by the geometry of the carbanion molecule itself, one must make certain that a carbanion intermediate with behavior independent of the configuration of its precursor is actually involved. In the steroid example studied by Barton and cited above, this was indeed the case, since the same product distribution resulted from starting material independent of the configuration of the reactant 5-halosteroid (i.e., **13** or **14**).

Barton, in the paper discussed above, considered the stereochemistry of the lithium–liquid ammonia reduction of α,β-unsaturated ketones. He pointed out that in the many available examples of lithium–liquid ammonia reduction of α,β-unsaturated ketones the configuration at the β carbon atom of the product was that of the more stable stereoisomer; for example, cholestanone (**21**) results from cholest-4-en-3-one (**18**). The mechanism was pictured as involving introduction of two electrons into the π system to give a dianion (e.g., **19**) whose β carbon atom is basic enough to abstract a proton from ammonia (pKa ~ 34); the β carbon atom was considered to be tetrahedral and to protonate in its favored cholestanoid conformation (here **19**) affording nolate anion (**20**) which remains until the addition of ammonium chloride

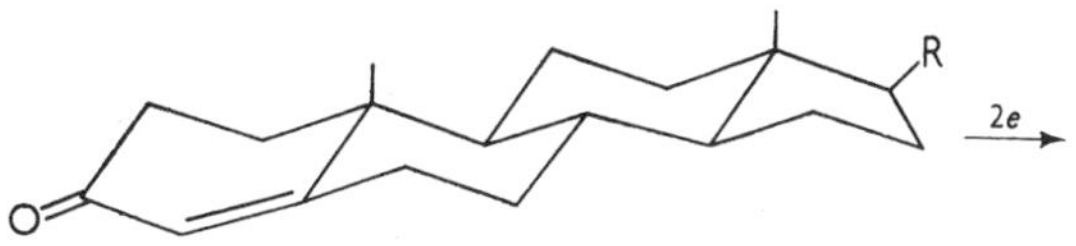

(18)

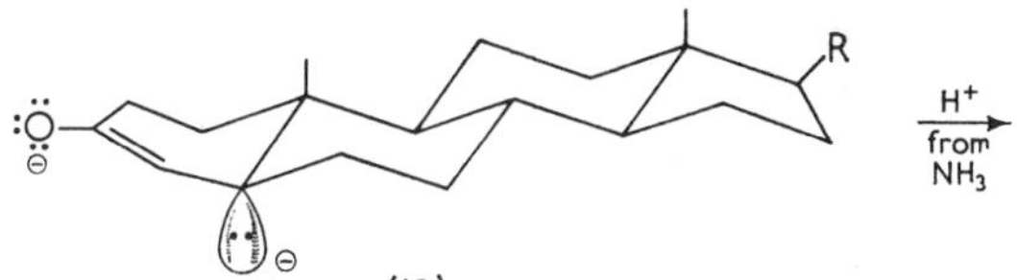

(19)

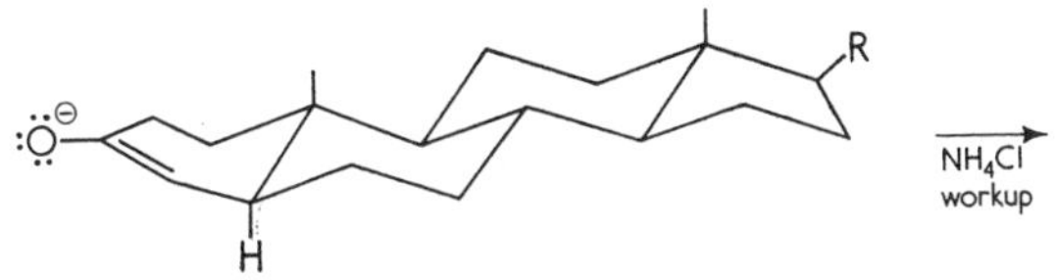

(20)

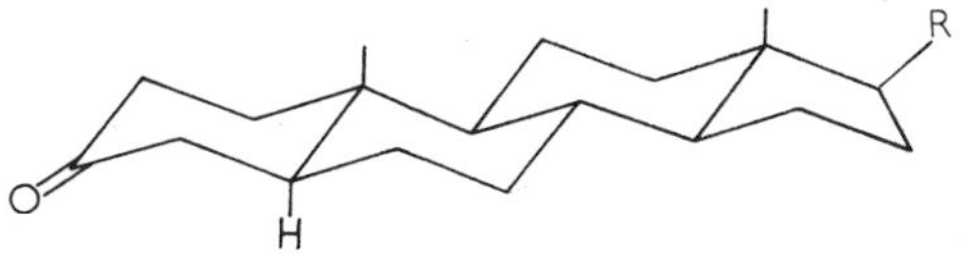

(21)

during workup. The corresponding enol is then formed which ketonizes to afford cholestanone product (**21**). In the few cases where an asymmetric center was generated at the α carbon atom during the reaction, the conditions of workup were fairly drastic, and thus the formation of the stable configuration at this center in these products could not be interpreted as having mechanistic significance.[33] The important conclusion deriving from this study of unsaturated ketone reduction by lithium–liquid ammonia was that in the transition state for protonation of the β carbon atom, the hybridization at this atom approximates sp^3 (i.e., tetrahedral). It should be noted that it is alternatively possible that it is the one electron adduct, a radical anion, which is actually protonated; a second electron would then be introduced.

More recently, additional information has been obtained bearing on the stereochemistry of the β protonation process in these metal-ammonia reductions.[34] Stork has shown that the most stable of stereoisomers differing in the β carbon configuration is not invariably formed. Thus the reduction of 7,10-dimethyl-6-methoxy-1(9)-decal-2-one (**22**) affords the *trans*-decalone derivative (**29**), although as noted by Stork the *cis*-decalone derivative in conformation **31** is without doubt of lower energy, having fewer axial group–ring methylene interactions as well as missing the 1,3-diaxial methyl: methoxyl interference of the *trans* product. Stork noted that these results suggest the requirement for overlap of the β carbon orbital with the enolate system in the transition state. Such overlap is possible only where the β carbon orbital being protonated is axial in the ring containing the enolate system. This overlap criterion is satisfied by transition states **23** and **24** but not **25**; of the former two, **23** is the more stable transoid transition state and leads to the observed product **29**. Hence the Barton-Stork rule for β carbon stereochemistry in the metal-ammonia reduction of unsaturated ketones predicts product formation by protonation of the more stable dianion conformer having the β carbon orbital axial in the enolate containing ring.

Two aspects of the above example are of special interest. First, intuitively one would guess that there would be only weak interaction of the β carbon electron pair and accompanying negative charge with the already electron-rich enolate system. Second, the sp^3 hybridization of the β carbon atom is interesting, since maximum overlap of an orbital, such as that of the β carbon, with an adjacent π system is obtained with sp^2 hybridization, although as the protonation proceeds the hybridization must in any event approach tetrahedral. In contrast, a number of examples to be discussed later involve protonation transition states which approximate sp^2 hybridiza-

---

[33] Cf. G. E. Arth, G. I. Poos, R. M. Lukes, F. M. Robinson, W. F. Johns, M. Feurer, and L. H. Sarett, *J. Am. Chem. Soc.*, **76**, 1715 (1954).

[34] G. Stork and S. D. Darling, *J. Am. Chem. Soc.*, **82**, 1513 (1960).

tion. The two points, anticipated minimal delocalization and sp^3 hybridization of the transition state and the dianion, must be related. In regard to the

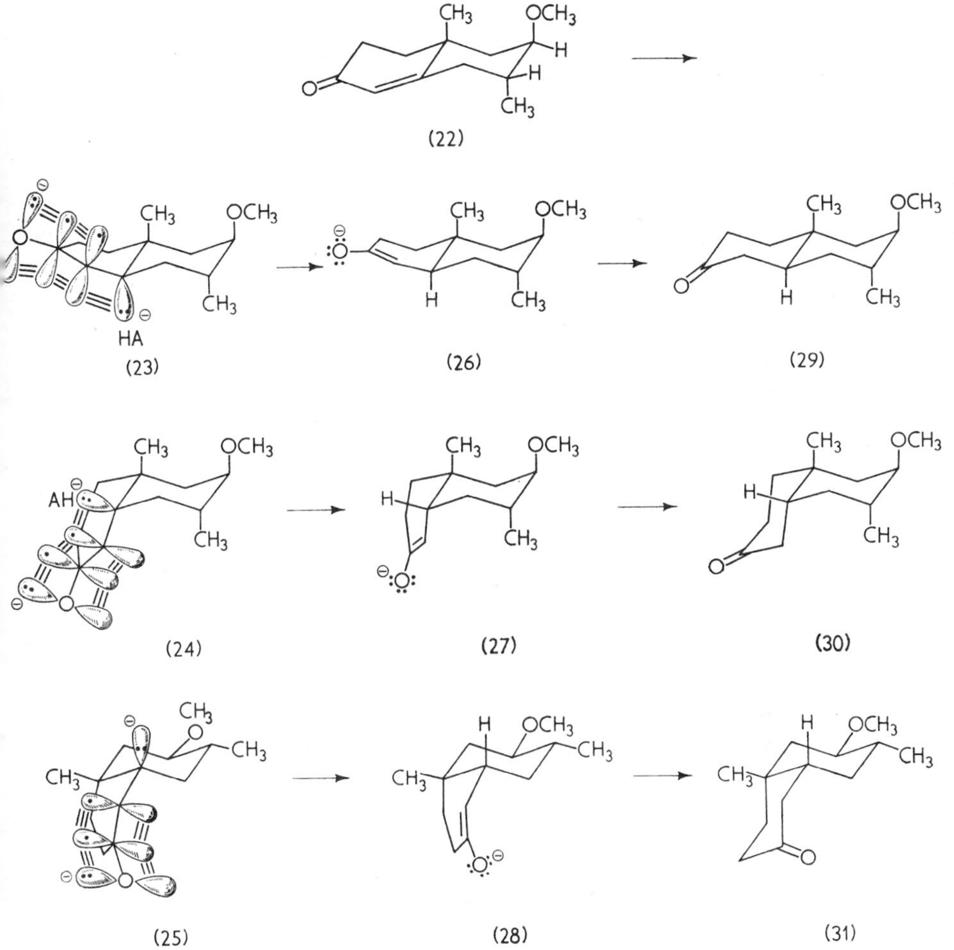

(22)

(23)   (26)   (29)

(24)   (27)   (30)

(25)   (28)   (31)

former, the molecular orbital results of Figure 2 are instructive. It is noted that of the six π electrons of a dianion, such as **23**, the last two must be placed in an antibonding orbital. The net result of this unhappy state is that the π energy lost in localizing two electrons on the end carbon atom is small (less than half) compared, for example, to the π localization energy of an enolate. It is still apparently large enough to account for the overlap requirement noted by Stork. Thus, not only is it clear that considerably more π energy is lost in protonation of an enolate than of the dianion, but another result may be seen. Where a carbanion is not stabilized by electron delocalization the preferred hybridization is sp^3; and, in the present case with delocalization being

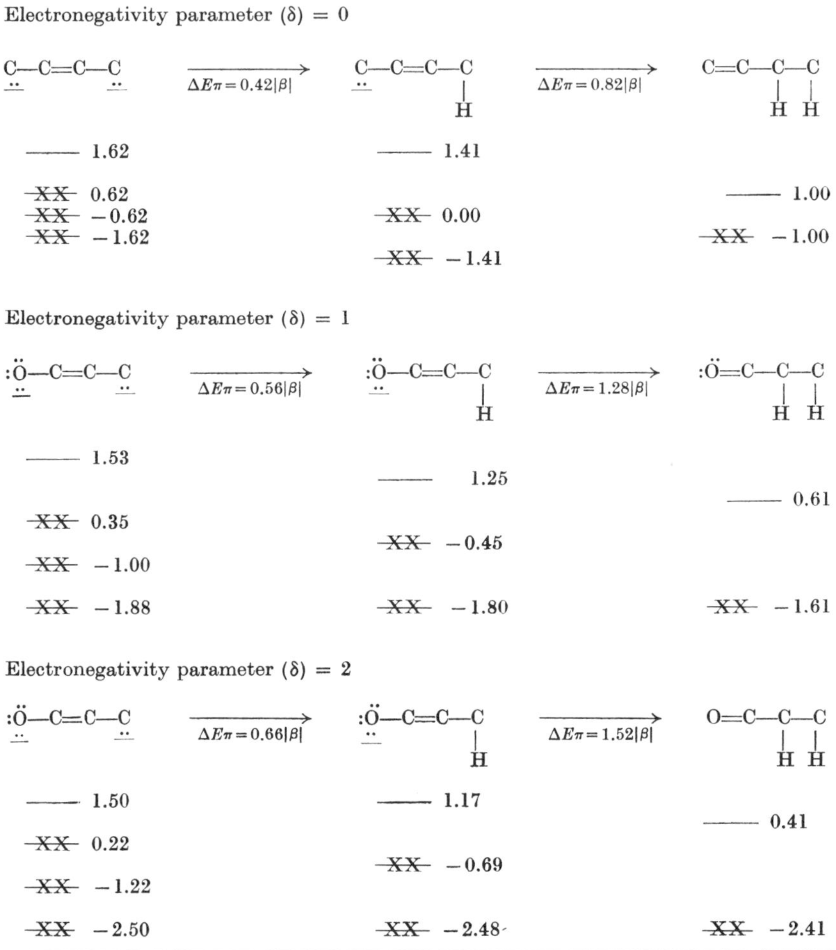

Electronegativity parameter $(\delta) = 0$

$$C\!-\!C\!=\!C\!-\!C \quad \xrightarrow{\Delta E\pi = 0.42|\beta|} \quad C\!-\!C\!=\!C\!-\!C \quad \xrightarrow{\Delta E\pi = 0.82|\beta|} \quad C\!=\!C\!-\!C\!-\!C$$

—— 1.62   —— 1.41

XX 0.62
XX −0.62   XX 0.00   —— 1.00
XX −1.62

XX −1.41   XX −1.00

Electronegativity parameter $(\delta) = 1$

$$:\!\ddot{O}\!-\!C\!=\!C\!-\!C \quad \xrightarrow{\Delta E\pi = 0.56|\beta|} \quad :\!\ddot{O}\!-\!C\!=\!C\!-\!C \quad \xrightarrow{\Delta E\pi = 1.28|\beta|} \quad :\!\ddot{O}\!=\!C\!-\!C\!-\!C$$

—— 1.53   —— 1.25

XX 0.35   —— 0.61

XX −1.00   XX −0.45

XX −1.88   XX −1.80   XX −1.61

Electronegativity parameter $(\delta) = 2$

$$:\!\ddot{O}\!-\!C\!=\!C\!-\!C \quad \xrightarrow{\Delta E\pi = 0.66|\beta|} \quad :\!\ddot{O}\!-\!C\!=\!C\!-\!C \quad \xrightarrow{\Delta E\pi = 1.52|\beta|} \quad O\!=\!C\!-\!C\!-\!C$$

—— 1.50   —— 1.17

XX 0.22   —— 0.41

XX −1.22   XX −0.69

XX −2.50   XX −2.48   XX −2.41

Figure 2. π Localization energies in protonation of dianions and monoanions.

less important than in an enolate, one is not surprised at a greater tendency toward sp^3 character than in the enolate.

Considering now the situation where a mesomeric anion, heavily stabilized by delocalization, is protonated—one finds as an especially clear example the protonation of the conjugate base (1) of 1-nitro-2-phenylcyclohexane.[34a] When

[34a] H. E. Zimmerman and T. E. Nevins, *J. Am. Chem. Soc.*, **79**, 6559 (1957).

the conjugate base (**1**), obtained from either *cis*- or *trans*-1-nitro-2-phenyl-cyclohexane (**32** and **33**, respectively), in aqueous alcoholic solution is acidified with sulfuric acid, there precipitates the relatively unstable *aci*-nitro tautomer (**2**), mentioned earlier. This substance failed to tautomerize to the more stable isomers when allowed to react in ethanolic sulfuric acid, ethanol alone, or chloroform. In contrast, it underwent a facile tautomerization when treated with an ethanolic lithium acetate–acetic acid buffer designed to convert the *aci*-nitro tautomer (**2**) heavily to its conjugate base while leaving an ample supply of proton donors in solution. This result strongly suggests, in agreement with kinetic evidence presented by Pearson [35] for the nitroethane system, that *aci*-nitro–nitro tautomerism proceeds by protonation of the conjugate base rather than of the *aci*-nitro tautomer itself.

Having been convinced that it is the mesomeric anion, the conjugate base **1**, whose stereochemistry of protonation must be considered, one may turn his attention to the interesting fact [35a] that this protonation process affords *cis*-1-nitro-2-phenylcyclohexane (**32**) as the almost exclusive product. This is very clearly an example of kinetically controlled formation of the thermodynamically less stable of two possible stereoisomers from a common precursor. The lithium acetate–acetic acid buffer, while sufficiently basic to remove a proton from the relatively acidic *aci*-nitro precursor, is not basic enough to remove a proton from the 1-nitro-2-phenylcyclohexane isomers once formed and hence cannot effect their equilibration. However, when *cis*-1-nitro-2-phenylcyclohexane (**32**) is treated with a catalytic quantity of sodium bicarbonate in refluxing ethanol, it is virtually completely isomerized to the more stable *trans* isomer **33**, thus demonstrating the thermodynamics of the system. It is

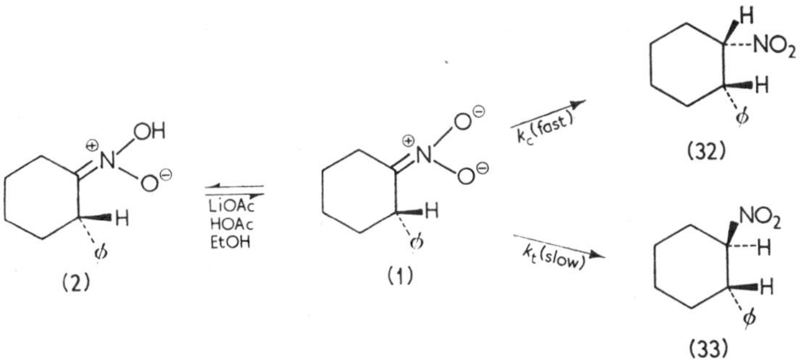

only superficially surprising that the anion **1**, which preferentially protonates to afford the less stable *cis* isomer **32**, is the intermediate involved in the equilibration of this *cis*-1-nitro-2-phenylcyclohexane (**32**) to the more stable *trans* stereoisomer **33**. This is readily seen when the energetics as depicted

[35] R. G. Pearson and R. L. Dillon, *J. Am. Chem. Soc.*, **72**, 3574 (1950).

in the free energy diagram of Figure 3 are considered. Any given molecule of *aci*-nitro anion **1**, given one chance to tautomerize, will prefer to surmount

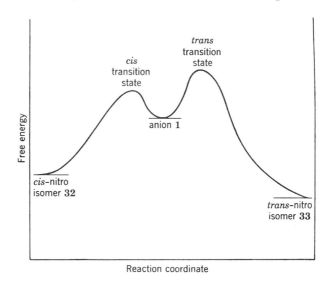

Figure 3.

the lower barrier corresponding to the *cis* transition state to afford *cis*-1-nitro-2-phenylcyclohexane; this is control by kinetics. On the other hand, when reversible ionization is allowed, each molecule of *cis* product formed may lose a proton to reform *aci*-nitro anion **1** and have another chance to protonate. In fact, each *cis* molecule will be repeatedly reionized. Since the rate of formation of *trans* product **33** is finite, eventually some *aci*-nitro anions will protonate to form this isomer; and this will continue until the equilibrium favoring the more stable *trans* product is established; this represents thermodynamic control.

Free energy diagrams merely serve as convenient bookkeeping devices to record kinetic and thermodynamic observation. We have recorded the kinetic preference for formation of *cis*-1-nitro-2-phenylcyclohexane (**32**) without explaining the reason why the barrier or transition state interposed between anion **1** and *cis* product **32** is of lower energy than the transition state leading to *trans* isomer **33**. The suggestion has been made by the present author [35a] that the transition state for the protonation process approximates in geometry the *aci*-nitro anion **1** itself.[36] Inspection of the two possible transition

[35a] H. E. Zimmerman and T. E. Nevins, *J. Am. Chem. Soc.*, **79**, 6559 (1957).

[36] This picture is idealized. Clearly a certain amount of rehybridization towards sp^3 has taken place by the time the transition state has been reached.

states, **34** and **35**, differing in which lobe of the p orbital adjacent to the nitro group is attacked, reveals that prototopic attack from below is severely

Transition state (34) if bonding from HA above (preferred)

Transition state (35) if from below

(32)

sterically hindered by the axial hydrogen atoms at carbons 3 and 5 while attack from above is relatively unhindered. Thus transition state **34** is preferred despite the fact that following the energy maximum, as the proton becomes more tightly bonded, the hybridization at carbon atom 1 changes from close to sp^2 toward sp^3 with the result that the nitro group is bent downward into an axial conformation. One might say that the molecule in the transition state is unaware of its later fate and that this later energetically unfortunate state is of no kinetic consequence since the energy factors in the transition state are controlling.

It should be noted that a second rationalization might be entertained and cannot be completely dismissed, especially since in one limit it merges into the above mechanistic picture. This possibility is that the protonation transition state is really better described as sp^3 and that the preferred formation of *cis* product derives from a transition state in which the proton donor and its solvent shell represent an entity effectively larger than the nitro group and therefore prefer to bond equatorially at the expense of the nitro group becoming axial. The main objection to this picture in its extreme version is that it fails to account for the kinetically preferred formation of the more stable stereoisomer in cases (*vide supra* and later) where a strongly electron-delocalizing group is not present.

The nitro anion example presented above is especially clear-cut because the species undergoing protonation is identified (i.e., the anion), and as a result a reasonably accurate picture of the transition state is possible. In the related process in which unstable enols ketonize to afford the corresponding carbonyl isomer, the picture is not as straightforward, although the stereochemical results and implications are analogous. Thus there exist a number of available pathways for enolization and therefore, owing to microscopic reversibility, for the ketonization process. The subject of enolization has received much attention,[37] and the present consideration will be confined to that relevant to the subject under discussion. One important process in enolization is hydroxide removal of the α hydrogen atom of the ketone and transfer of a hydrogen atom from water to the ketone oxygen atom; [37] hence one allowed ketonization process is the microscopic reverse, the removal of the enol proton by hydroxide with protonation of the incipient enolate by water. A second enolization process, catalyzed by acetic acid, involves a pre-equilibrium formation of the ketone oxonium ion followed by a rate-limiting removal of the α hydrogen atom by acetate; [37a] the microscopic reverse ketonization process here is the protonation of the enol by acetic acid to leave the protonated ketone. In analogous fashion one may envision protonation of the enol by oxonium ion as the reverse of the hydronium ion-catalyzed enolation process, and a number of other possible ketonization processes, in addition to these, may be pictured. For example, a process in which the enolate itself is protonated, in direct analogy to the *aci*-nitro to nitro tautomerism mechanism, is a real possibility; the existence of such a pathway implies that under the same environmental conditions the base-catalyzed enolization process of ketones would proceed by hydroxide removal of an α hydrogen atom with formation of enolate rather than leading directly to enol, as in the termolecular process mentioned above, which requires both hydroxide *and* water. [38]

Despite the kinetic complexity of the ketonization process one finds the stereochemistry of a large number of reactions proceeding via enolic intermediates to fall into patterned behavior. It was first noted by the present author [39] that the kinetically controlled ketonization of enols, occurring as unstable intermediates in a large number of organic reactions, frequently leads preferentially to the less stable of two stereoisomers differing in configuration of the carbon atom protonated in the ketonization process; furthermore, it was pointed out in this initial study [35a] that an important factor in controlling ketonization is steric accessibility of the proton donor to the two lobes of the p orbital of the essentially sp^2-hybridized enolic carbon atom being protonated. Thus, *cis*-1-benzoyl-2-phenylcyclohexane (36) is the almost exclusive product resulting from the conjugate addition of phenylmagnesium

[37] Cf. (a) R. P. Bell, *The Proton in Chemistry*, Cornell University Press, Ithaca, N.Y., 1959, pp. 148 ff. (b) V. Gold, *Ann. Repts. on Progr. Chem. (Chem. Soc. London)*, **56**, 51 (1959). (c) C. G. Swain, A. J. DiMilo, and J. P. Cordner, *J. Am. Chem. Soc.*, **80**, 5983 (1958). (d) C. G. Swain, E. C. Stivers, J. F. Reuwer, Jr., and L. J. Schaad, *J. Am. Chem. Soc.*, **80**, 5885 (1958).

[38] The question of direct formation of enolate in base-catalyzed ketone reactions is discussed by J. Hine. [38a] Also P. D. Bartlett [38b] discusses the logical difficulty in assuming that an enolate anion, in rapid equilibrium with enol, cannot be directly formed from ketone but must arise only by a termolecular process giving enol and subsequent ionization.

[38a] J. Hine, *Physical Organic Chemistry*, McGraw-Hill, New York, 1956, p. 224.

[38b] P. D. Bartlett in (Sir) A. Todd, ed., *Perspectives in Organic Chemistry*, Interscience, New York–London, 1956, p. 23.

[39] H. E. Zimmerman, *J. Org. Chem.*, **20**, 549 (1955).

bromide to benzoylcyclohexene, a reaction unambiguously proceeding by way of the magnesium enolate **38** and subsequently on acidification via the enol **39**. The same stereoisomer (**36**) results from the acetone–dilute hydriodic acid debromination [39] of 1-bromo-1-benzoyl-2-phenylcyclohexane (**40**). That the same enolic intermediate **39** occurs in this reaction is a logical consequence of microscopic reversibility. The acid-catalyzed chlorination, bromination, and iodination of ketones are known [40] to occur by prior enolization of the ketone followed by rapid attack of halogen on the enolic intermediate; this is a reaction in which ketone plus halogen yields halo ketone plus hydrogen halide. The debromination reaction presently under discussion is one of hydrogen halide plus halo ketone giving ketone plus halogen, the reverse [41] of halogenation; and the principle of microscopic reversibility [42] requires that the debromination mechanism be the precise reverse of halogenation and necessarily proceed by way of the enol. There is experimental verification that

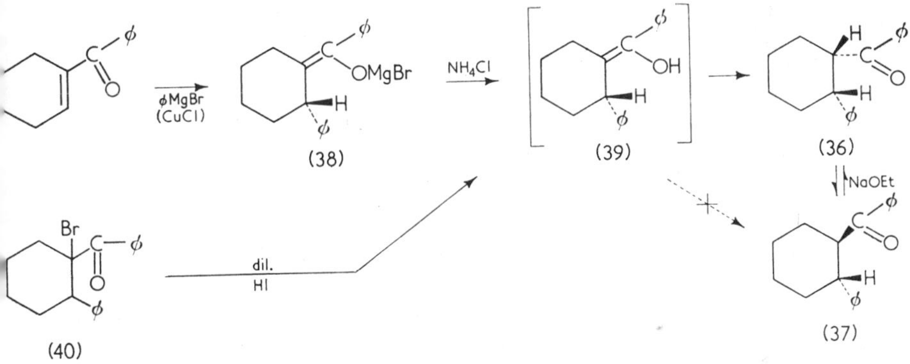

the kinetically favored *cis*-1-benzoyl-2-phenylcyclohexane (**36**), obtained in ketonization of the enol **39**, is actually thermodynamically less stable in the sodium ethoxide-catalyzed equilibration of **36** to the *trans* isomer **37**. This is not unexpected, since in *trans*-1-benzoyl-2-phenylcyclohexane (**37**) both phenyl and benzoyl groups can attain equatorial conformations.

As in the case of the tautomerism of 1-*aci*-nitro-2-phenylcyclohexane (**1**) to afford *cis*-1-nitro-2-phenylcyclohexane (**32**), ketonization to give *cis* ketone in the present example is attributed [39] to steric hindrance to approach of the

[40] Cf. L. Zucker and L. P. Hammett, *J. Am. Chem. Soc.*, **61**, 2791 (1939); L. P. Hammett, *Physical Organic Chemistry*, McGraw-Hill, New York, 1940, p. 231; also note J. Hine, *Physical Organic Chemistry*, McGraw-Hill, New York, 1956, p. 198, for further references and discussion.

[41] Debromination by hydriodic acid is only the reverse of (e.g.) bromination in approximation, since the environmental conditions differ somewhat; nevertheless, the approximation is relatively good.

[42] Cf. A. A. Frost and R. G. Pearson, *Kinetics and Mechanism*, Wiley, New York, 1953, p. 202.

proton donor to one lobe of the α carbon p orbital as a result of van der Waals interference by axial hydrogen atoms at carbons 3 and 5. The free energy diagram (Fig. 4) used to record the kinetic and thermodynamic facts of this system parallels that of Figure 3 for the 1-nitro-2-phenylcyclohexane case.

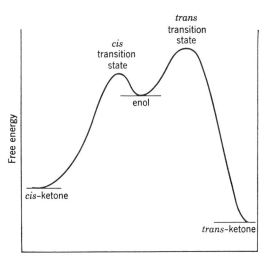

A further relevant observation made in this investigation[39] of the 1-benzoyl-2-phenylcyclohexane system relates to the ease of bromination of the *cis* and *trans* ketones (**36** and **37**). While *cis*-1-benzoyl-2-phenylcyclohexane (**36**) was readily brominated in acetic acid with formation of 1-bromo-1-benzoyl-2-phenylcyclohexane, *trans*-1-benzoyl-2-phenylcyclohexane (**37**) was so resistant to bromination that the acetic acid solvent instead reacted. This behavior prettily accords with the energetics of the system as outlined in Figure 4. Thus, since the rate-limiting step of bromination is enolization and

Figure 4.

since a high energy transition state is interposed between *trans* ketone **37** and enol **39**, while only a relatively low energy transition state exists between *cis* ketone **36** and enol **39**, the failure or success of bromination may be related to the ease of enolization, a process expected to be much easier for *cis* ketone **36** than for the *trans* isomer **37**.[43]

A similar situation was observed [44] for the 1-acetyl-2-phenylcyclohexane system. The desired unstable enol was generated by the same methods as described above, conjugate addition of phenylmagnesium bromide (here to acetylcyclohexene) and dilute hydriodic acid debromination of 1-bromo-1-acetyl-2-phenylcyclohexane; additionally, debromination was effected using zinc and a proton donor. As before, ketonization led predominantly to *cis* product. Further substantiation of the interpretation given above for the reluctance of *trans*-1-benzoyl-2-phenylcyclohexane to brominate was revealed in the acetic acid bromination of *cis*- and *trans*-1-acetyl-2-phenylcyclohexanes, *cis*-1-Acetyl-2-phenylcyclohexane (**40**) brominated smoothly, giving 1-bromo-2-acetyl-2-phenylcyclohexane (**42**); bromination of the ketone at the tertiary ring α carbon atom rather than the methyl group is expected, since Cardwell has shown unsymmetrically substituted ketones to brominate preferentially with acid catalysis at the more alkylated α position, enolization in this direction being more rapid.[45] Strikingly, however, bromination of *trans*-1-acetyl-2-phenylcyclohexane (**41**) yielded *trans*-1-bromoacetyl-2-phenylcyclohexane (**43**). Clearly, the usually facile acid-catalyzed enolization toward the tertiary

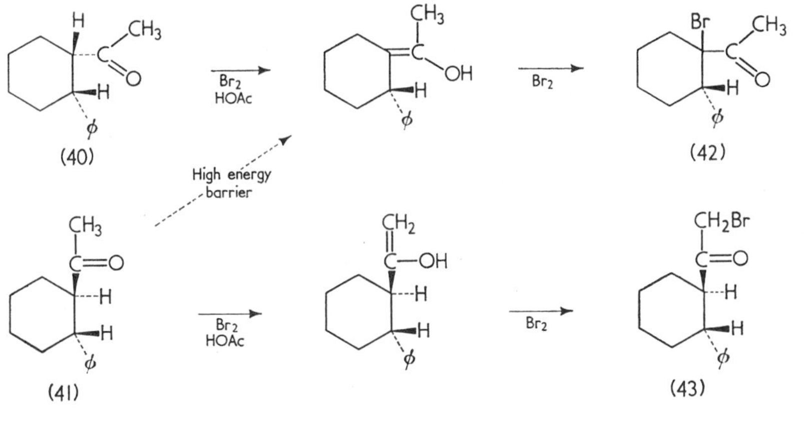

α carbon atom in this case is blocked by the high energy transition state between *trans* ketone **41** and enol.

Of particular interest is the enol of 2-methyl-3-phenylindanone.[46] In this

[43] An added factor is the lower energy ground state of the more stable *trans* ketone.
[44] H. E. Zimmerman, *J. Am. Chem. Soc.*, **79**, 6554 (1957).
[45] H. Cardwell and A. Kilner, *J. Chem. Soc. (London)*, **1951**, 2430.
[46] H. E. Zimmerman, *J. Am. Chem. Soc.*, **78**, 1168 (1956).

case both stereoisomers of 2-bromo-2-methyl-3-phenylindanone were available. Acetone–dilute hydriodic acid debromination of *cis* and *trans* isomers (**44** and **45**) was found to afford a mixture of 76% *cis*-2-methyl-3-phenylindanone (**46**) and 34% *trans*-2-methyl-3-phenylindanone (**47**) independent of

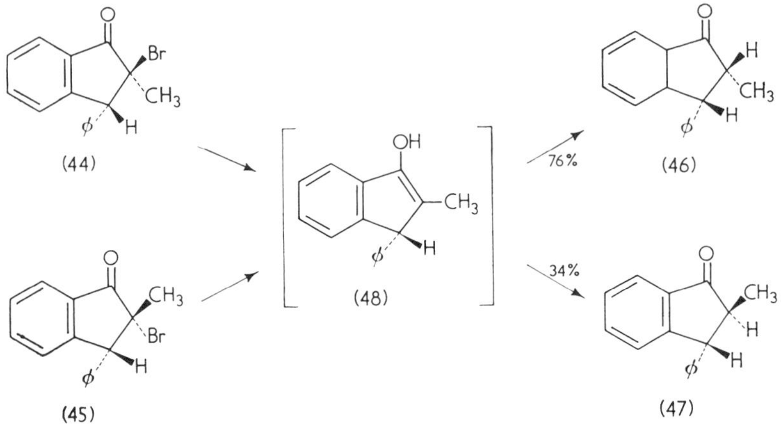

configuration of the bromo ketone utilized. That the product distribution is the same from the two bromo ketone stereoisomers employed constitutes strong evidence for the common, enolic intermediate **48** and against any alternative stereospecific electrophilic substitution mechanism. This is a good example of a nonstereospecific reaction which exhibits some stereoselectivity (see page 353 fn. 31). The stereoselectivity observed is attributed to a preference for prototopic attack on the side of the enolic π system *trans* to the phenyl group at C_3.

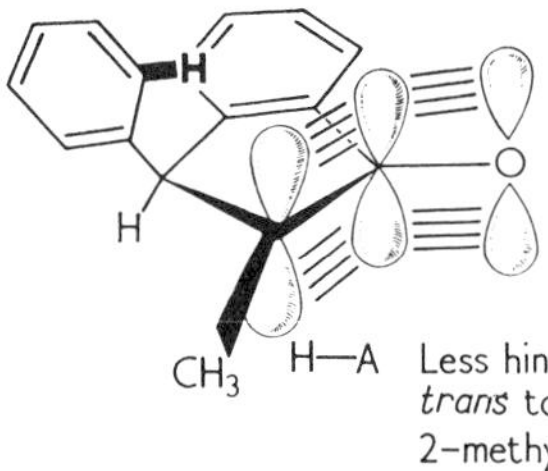

Less hindered attack from below, *trans* to C_3 phenyl, gives *cis* – 2-methyl-3-phenylindanone.

In the same study[46] the lithium–liquid ammonia reduction of 2-methyl-3-phenylindone (**49**) was investigated. It was noted that the stereochemistry at the α carbon atom of the product of such reductions is determined in a final ketonization step and that if the conditions employed for the α protonation step are nonequilibrating, the configuration introduced at this position will be governed by the usual factors controlling the stereochemistry of ketonization.

It was found that by addition of the liquid ammonia solution of the enolate **50** to a large excess of saturated aqueous ammonium chloride a maximum of

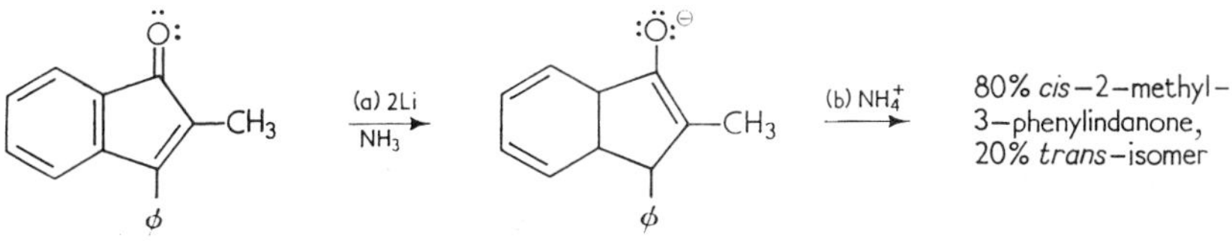

(49)   (50)

80% of *cis*-2-methyl-3-phenylindanone (**46**) was obtainable.[47] Under the usual conditions of reduction [46a] in which a proton source is added to the liquid ammonia solution, the more stable *trans* product was obtained as a result of equilibration. An interesting and more recent example of control of the lithium–liquid ammonia reduction of unsaturated ketones by ketonization of the initially formed enol has been provided by Birch and co-workers.[48] In this study the enolate **52**, formed by the two-electron reduction of

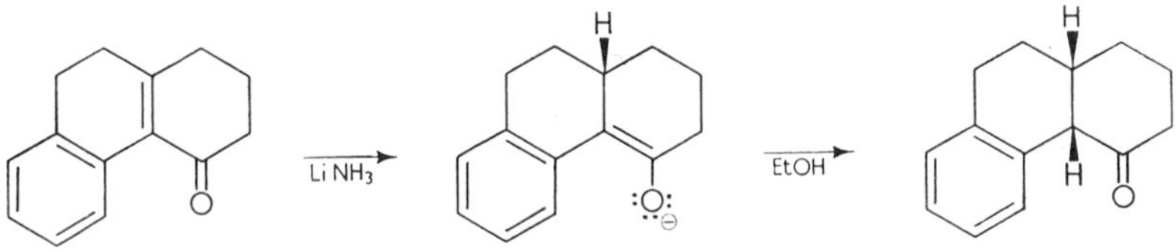

(51)   (52)   (53)

[46a] Cf. D. H. R. Barton and C. H. Robinson, ref. 29.

[47] It is appropriate here to make a general, somewhat philosophical comment on the justifiability of interpreting small kinetic preferences and changes in kinetic preferences, perhaps less than ten-fold. It has often been suggested that because a kinetic preference of ten to one corresponds to a difference in transition state free energies of only 1.4 kcal./mole, one is not justified in attempting to rationalize such one-sided product distributions.

Clearly these variations, seemingly small in kcal./mole language, are of major importance to the organic chemist. From a synthetic viewpoint a 90% yield is a considerably different result than a 10% yield. Furthermore, the problem itself is intrinsically of interest. The question is merely whether such observations are capable of interpretation.

When in a given reaction or set of related reactions one finds a repetitious and consistent kinetic preference for one of several a priori possible reaction modes, it is reasonable to interpret this as evidence for a repetitiously and consistently operating driving force. Especially in the case of reaction of one intermediate to afford one of several isomers (tautomers or stereoisomers), energetically small but observationally important driving forces become dominant and amenable to interpretation, for here the grosser features by which transition states and products usually differ now disappear.

[48] A. J. Birch, H. Smith, and R. E. Thornton, *J. Chem. Soc.* (*London*), **1957**, 1339.

unsaturated ketone **51**, was protonated with ethanol to yield the less stable *cis* stereoisomer **53**.[49]

A number of further examples of kinetic control of the stereochemistry of ketonization have been published,[50-54] and the principles set forth in the original publication on the subject[39] have been applied by a considerable number of investigators to rationalize the stereochemistry of reactions proceeding via unstable enolic intermediates. This literature will be reviewed elsewhere.

A different type of control of ketonization has been reported by Corey and Sneen.[55] These authors focused their attention on endocyclic cyclohexane enols and found a driving force favoring axial attack of the proton donor in analogy to the preference for axial attack of electron-deficient bromine suggested earlier by Corey[56] for the bromination of ketones. Corey pointed out that in the attack of an electrophile on the enolic system of an endocyclic cyclohexane ring a smooth transition to product is favored by overlap considerations when the attack is axial rather than equatorial. Thus the orbitals involved in formation of an axial bond are nearly parallel with the carbonyl

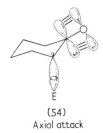

(54)   (55)
Axial attack   Equatorial attack

[49] The lability of the less stable ketonization product will vary from system to system. Thus the less stable isomer **53** was isolated despite the inverse workup procedure in which sodium ethoxide is an inevitable artifact when ethanol is added to the enolate. At the other extreme is the reduction of an unsaturated aldehyde, reported by Inhoffen *et al.*,[49a] where the equilibrium product distribution resulted despite inverse workup with addition of the liquid ammonia enolate solution to excess aqueous ammonium chloride. Similarly, in unpublished work with A. Mais the present author has found the lithium–liquid ammonia reduction of 1-octalone to give amounts of *cis*-1-decalone varying with the rapidity of workup even under inverse decomposition; a maximum of 42% was observed.

[49a] H. H. Inhoffen, K. Irmscher, G. Friedrich, D. Kampe, and O. Berges, *Chem. Ber.*, **92**, 1772 (1959).

[50] H. E. Zimmerman and H. J. Giallombardo, *J. Am. Chem. Soc.*, **78**, 6259 (1956).

[51] H. E. Zimmerman and T. W. Cutshall, *J. Am. Chem. Soc.*, **80**, 2893 (1958).

[52] H. E. Zimmerman and W. Chang, *J. Am. Chem. Soc.*, **81**, 3634 (1959).

[53] H. E. Zimmerman and A. Mais, *J. Am. Chem. Soc.*, **81**, 3644 (1959).

[54] H. E. Zimmerman and T. W. Cutshall, *J. Am. Chem. Soc.*, **81**, 4305 (1959).

[55] E. J. Corey and R. A. Sneen, *J. Am. Chem. Soc.*, **78**, 6271 (1956).

[56] E. J. Corey, *J. Am. Chem. Soc.*, **75**, 2301 (1953); **76**, 175 (1954).

carbon p orbital, and the bonding electrons may be delocalized (cf. **54**); the orbitals involved in formation of an equatorial bond are close to perpendicular to the carbonyl carbon p orbital (cf. **55**). Supporting this picture was the report by Corey and Sneen that the ketonization of 3β-acetoxycholest-6-en-7-ol (**57**), generated by debromination of the corresponding α-bromo ketone (**56**) with zinc and a proton donor, could be followed by use of a deuterium tracer and that axial attack was favored.

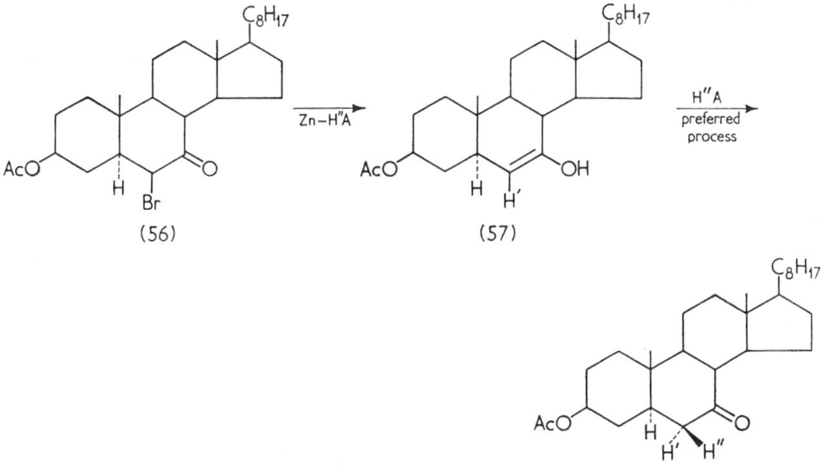

It is important to note that the steric control of ketonization described by Zimmerman and the stereoelectronic control of ketonization reported by Corey are not discordant theoretically in the least. The enolic systems discussed above in which steric hindrance to approach of the proton donor is controlling did not include endocyclic cyclohexane enols and are not subject to stereoelectronic control; in these cases, continued overlap of orbitals is equally possible for the two possible modes of protonation (cf. eq. 1).

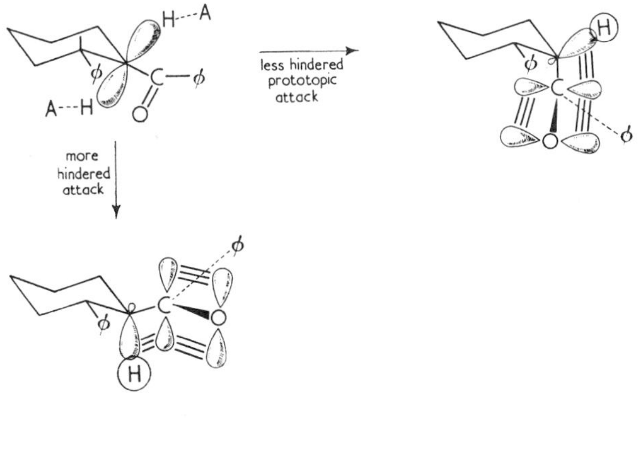

(1)

Where stereoelectronic, or overlap, factors are operative, as in the special case of endocyclic cyclohexane enols, the stereoelectronic driving force will either cooperate with or oppose the driving force due to steric hindrance to approach of the proton donor. As has been pointed out,[57] in the latter event, the net stereochemical outcome will depend on the magnitude of the steric effects characteristic of the given system relative to the stereoelectronic driving force.[58]

An example illustrating the several driving forces influencing the stereo-chemistry of ketonization is the 1,9-enol of 1-decalone.[53] The enol itself has available two conformations: **58**, resembling *trans*-decalin, and **59**, resembling *cis*-decalin. There are two possible transition states derived from each of these conformations, since the proton donor may attack either from above the ring structure, *cis* to the C_{10} hydrogen atom, or from below the ring, *trans* to this hydrogen atom. In two transition states, **61** and **62**, the protonation process is axial with respect to enolic ring.[59] Transition state **61** affords *trans*-1-decalone

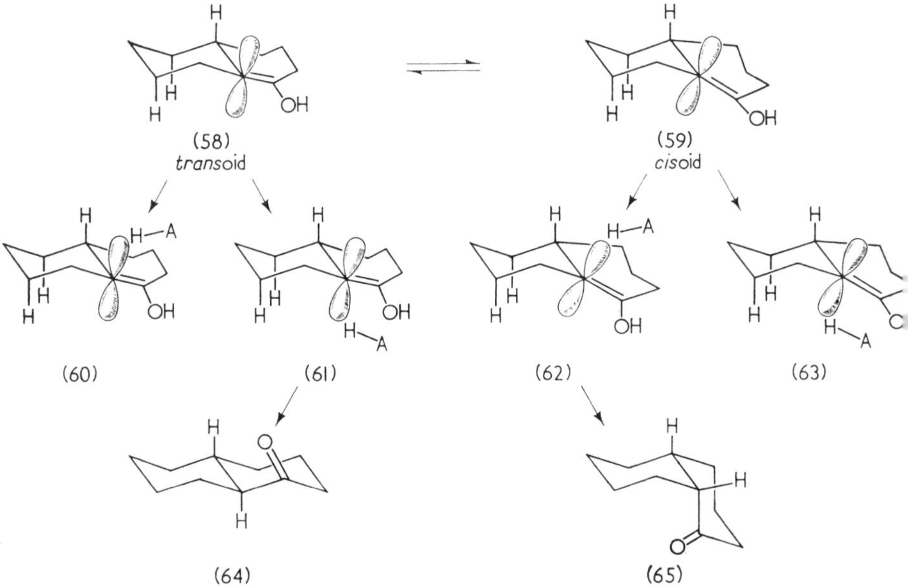

(58)
transoid

(59)
cisoid

(60)   (61)   (62)   (63)

(64)   (65)

[57] H. E. Zimmerman and W. Chang, *J. Am. Chem. Soc.*, **81**, 3634 (1959), fn. 8.

[58] Although the realm of the present chapter is taken not to include alkylation of enolates and bromination of enols, the problems are closely related. For some recent views on stereoelectronic control of halogenation of ketones, see R. Villotti, H. J. Ringold, and C. Djerassi, *J. Am. Chem. Soc.*, **82**, 5693 (1960); R. Mauli, H. J. Ringold, and C. Djerassi, *J. Am. Chem. Soc.*, **82**, 5494 (1960); C. Djerassi, N. Finch, R. C. Cookson, and C. W. Bird, *J. Am. Chem. Soc.*, **82**, 5488 (1960).

[59] Also, **60** is a *trans*-decalin type of conformation, but would have to lead to *cis*-1-

(64), while 62 gives *cis*-1-decalone (65). Experimentally it was found that the enol, generated from the 9-bromo-1-decalones with zinc and a proton donor, ketonized preferentially to *cis*-1-decalone when a bulky proton donor was used, while increasing amounts of *trans*-1-decalone were formed as the size of the proton donor decreased. With acetic acid as the donor more *trans* than *cis* product resulted. This was interpreted as evidence that transition state 62 has smaller van der Waals repulsions between proton donor and axial hydrogen atoms of the nonenolic ring while transition state 61 is conformationally of lower energy.

A suitable example to cite to conclude the discussion of protonation stereochemistry is the reaction of the conjugate base (66) of 1-benzenesulfonyl-2-phenylcyclohexane.[60] Here it was observed that, in striking contrast to the stereochemistry of protonation of exocyclic enols and *aci*-nitro compounds, the more stable *trans* sulfone (68) was kinetically preferred, although the relative amounts of *cis* product (67) increased with increasing bulk and acid

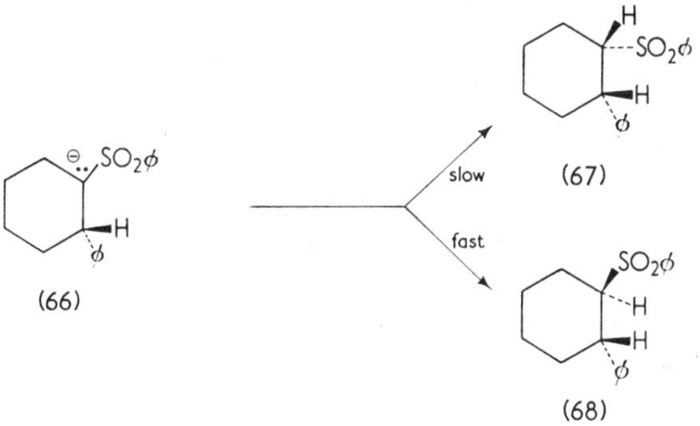

strength of the proton donor. These results were attributed to a decreased importance of resonance interaction of the bonding electron pair with the sulfone stabilizing group contrasted with nitro. Such decreased electron delocalization results in a situation paralleling that of saturated carbanions where the choice is between two essentially tetrahedral transition states.

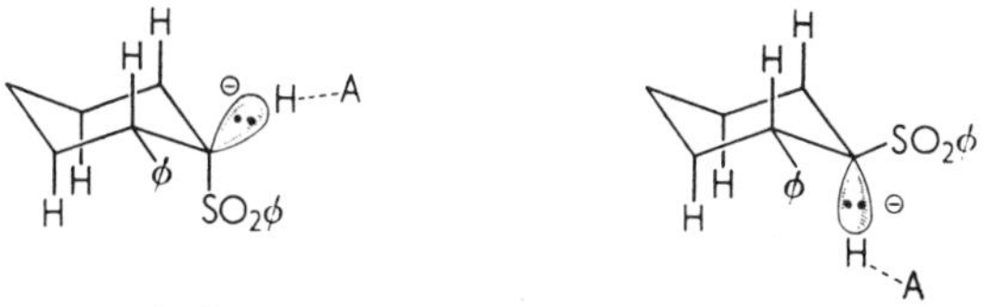

decalone, while 63 which has a *cis* type of conformation, would lead to *trans*-1-decalone. Collapse to chair form product requires conformational changes with at least temporary formation of ˘eclipsed conformations.

[60] H. E. Zimmerman and B. S. Thyagarajan, *J. Am. Chem. Soc.*, **80**, 3060 (1958).

Here **70**, giving *trans* sulfone product, is of lower energy than **69** since the larger benzenesulfonyl group has the equatorial conformation.

2. 1,2 ANIONIC MIGRATION REACTIONS AND RELATED REARRANGEMENTS

Rearrangements have received more than average attention in organic chemistry, and this is not surprising. As a rule the relatively low energy carbon-carbon σ bonds of an organic reactant molecule remain undisturbed in organic reactions; organic chemistry is usually the chemistry of functional groups, large carbon moieties (phenyl, methyl, ethyl, etc.) surviving chemical change. When carbon-carbon bonds are broken during reaction, as in rearrangements, the chemist's interest is aroused.

Of the rearrangement reactions, without doubt the nucleophilic 1,2 shift, in which a group migrates from one atom to an adjacent electron-deficient atom, has received the most attention. Much less studied are 1,2 free radical rearrangements in which the migrating group moves to an atom bearing an odd electron. Probably least studied and least well understood are the electrophilic 1,2 shifts in which the migration is to an adjacent atom bearing an unshared electron pair and negative charge. Electrophilic rearrangements investigated include oxygen to carbon migrations (the Wittig rearrangement), nitrogen to carbon migrations (the Stevens rearrangement), and more recently uncovered carbon to carbon migrations. These will be considered in turn along with related rearrangement reactions.

A. The Wittig Rearrangement

The first examples of this rearrangement were reported in 1924 by Schörigen[61a] and in 1928 by Schlenk and Bergmann.[61b] Schörigen studied the reaction of sodium with ethers and reported the isolation of rearrangement products, although generally in poor yield. For example, benzhydryl phenyl ether on treatment with sodium at 100° gave small amounts of triphenylcarbinol along with other products (eq. 2). Benzyl phenyl ether under the same conditions gave about 30% of benzhydrol.

$$\phi_2CH-O-\phi \xrightarrow[\text{Na 100°}]{} \phi_3COH$$

$$\phi CH_2-O-\phi \xrightarrow[\text{Na 100°}]{} \phi_2CHOH \qquad (2)$$

It will be clear from later discussion that this rearrangement must have been effected by strong bases present rather than by sodium itself.

[61] (a) P. Schorigen, *Chem. Ber.*, **57**, 1634 (1924), **58**, 2028 (1925), **59**, 2510 (1926). (b) W. Schlenk and E. Bergmann, *Ann.*, **464**, 35 (1928). Complete experimental details are lacking. No mention of solvent, mode of workup, or yield is made.

Schlenk and Bergmann reported that treatment of benzophenone dimethyl-ketal with sodium afforded 1,1-diphenylethanol. These researchers pictured the reaction as proceeding via **71**, which rearranges to **72**. Similarly, treatment

$$\phi_2C\overset{OCH_3}{\underset{OCH_3}{\big<}} + 2Na \rightarrow \phi_2C-O-CH_3 + NaOCH_3 \rightarrow \phi_2\overset{CH_3}{\underset{|}{C}}-ONa \rightarrow \phi_2\overset{CH_3}{\underset{|}{C}}OH$$

(71)   (72)

$$\phi_2\overset{|}{\underset{|}{C}}-\overset{|}{\underset{|}{C}}\phi_2 + 2Na \rightarrow 2\phi_2\overset{|}{\underset{|}{C}}Na \rightarrow \phi_3C-ONa \rightarrow \phi_3COH$$

Na

(73)   (74)

of benzopinacol diphenyl ether with sodium gave triphenylcarbinol. The formation of **72** from **71** and of **74** from **73** was attributed to the "great affinity of sodium for oxygen," or in modern terms to the driving force for formation of a more stable anion. Following these early reports [61] the rearrangement of conjugate bases of benzylic ethers has been elegantly and thoroughly investigated by Wittig and co-workers.

In 1942, Wittig and Löhmann [62] found that although benzyl phenyl ether (**75**) gave mainly 1,1,2-triphenylethane on treatment with phenyllithium in

$$\phi CH_2O\phi \xrightarrow[Et_2O]{\phi Li} \phi_2CH-CH_2\phi$$

(75)

ether, benzyl methyl ether (**76**) rearranged to 1-phenylethanol (**79**), and dibenzyl ether (**80**) gave 1,2-diphenylethanol. Wittig [62] pictured the reaction

$$\phi CH_2-O-CH_3 \xrightarrow[Et_2O]{\phi Li} \phi\overset{|}{\underset{Li}{C}}H-O-CH_3 \rightarrow \phi\overset{CH_3}{\underset{|}{C}}H-OLi \xrightarrow{workup} \phi\overset{CH_3}{\underset{|}{C}}HOH$$

(76)   (77)   (78)   (79)

as being initiated by abstraction of the relatively acidic benzylic α hydrogen atom to afford the conjugate base which then rearranged to a more stable alkoxide anion. In a later study Hauser and Kantor [63] effected the same rearrangement of dibenzyl ether using potassium amide in liquid ammonia. In addition to 1,2-diphenylethanol (**83**) as the major product these researchers

$$\phi CH_2-O-CH_2\phi \xrightarrow[Et_2O]{\phi Li} \phi\overset{|}{\underset{Li}{C}}H-O-CH_2\phi \rightarrow \phi\overset{CH_2\phi}{\underset{|}{C}}H-OLi \xrightarrow{workup} \phi\overset{CH_2\phi}{\underset{|}{C}}HOH$$

(80)   (81)   (82)   (83)

[62] G. Wittig and L. Löhmann, *Ann.*, **550**, 260 (1942).
[63] C. R. Hauser and S. W. Kantor, *J. Am. Chem. Soc.*, **73**, 1437 (1951).

isolated both toluene and benzaldehyde as minor products. Hauser postulated an intramolecular displacement mechanism for formation of **83** and a competing elimination reaction for formation of the benzaldehyde and toluene. That it was not anion **82** (metal = K) which was β eliminating to give these products was indicated by the stability of **82** under reaction conditions. Hauser also noted that it is unlikely that benzylpotassium and benzaldehyde are intermediates in formation of **82** since benzylpotassium would be expected

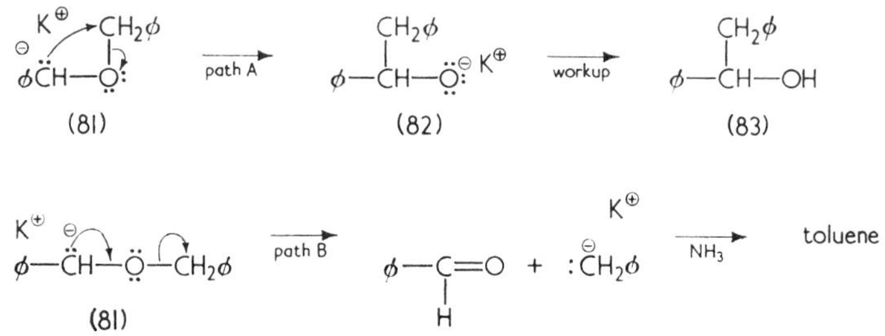

to react much more rapidly with ammonia to give toluene than to add to benzaldehyde and the reaction of toluene and benzaldehyde with potassium amide in toluene was found not to give **83**. Similarly, the cleavage-readdition mechanism seems unreasonable for the rearrangements effected with organolithium bases, for as has been noted by Wittig and by Hauser the carbonyl fragment would be expected to react at least to some extent with the organolithium compound used but such products are never found.[63a]

There is some evidence on migration aptitudes in the Wittig rearrangement. Wittig and co-workers[64] studied the rearrangement of a sequence of 9-fluorenyl ethers in tetrahydrofuran using phenyllithium as the proton

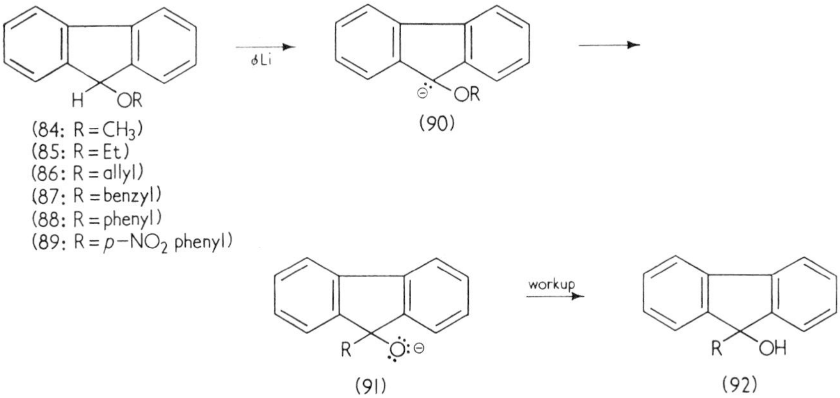

(84: R = CH₃)
(85: R = Et)
(86: R = allyl)
(87: R = benzyl)
(88: R = phenyl)
(89: R = p-NO₂ phenyl)

[63a] However, cf. footnote 74a.
[64] G. Wittig, H. Döser, and I. Lorenz, *Ann.*, **562**, 192 (1949).

abstractor. The allyl (86) and benzyl (87) ethers rearranged spontaneously at room temperature to give 80 and 90% yields of tertiary carbinol after workup. The methyl (84) and ethyl (85) ethers did not rearrange appreciably at this temperature, but did rearrange at 100° to give 43 and 13% yields of 9-methyl-9-fluorenol and 9-ethyl-9-fluorenol, respectively. The phenyl ether (88) on treatment with phenyllithium at room temperature did give a red color, indicative of formation of anion 90 (R = ϕ), but only starting material could be isolated from the reaction; at 100° difluorenylidene and phenol were formed. In the case of the p-nitrophenyl ether (89) rearrangement was effected at 100° by use of sodium methoxide in methanol; unfortunately, the reactivity could not be studied under conditions strictly comparable to those used for the other ethers. From this data Wittig has postulated the following sequence of decreasing migratory aptitudes: allyl, benzyl > methyl, ethyl, p-nitrophenyl > phenyl.[65] Wittig postulated the bridged species 93 as an intermediate in the p-nitrophenyl migration.[66]

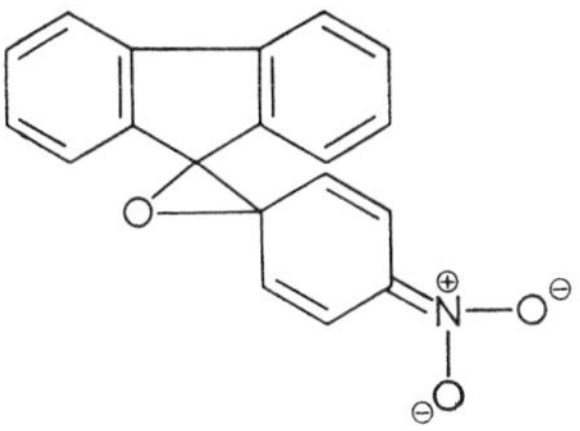

(93)

Hauser's study [63] also provided evidence on the migratory aptitudes in the rearrangement. The conjugate bases of a series of benzyl ethers were formed using potassium amide in liquid ammonia and the rearrangement effected by refluxing the suspension of the potassium base in ether. The relative ease of isomerization was found to be benzyl > sec-butyl > neopentyl, phenyl. Hauser noted that this sequence is that for bimolecular displacement of the corresponding halides by basic anions and suggested the $S_N i$ type mechanism discussed earlier.

In another study bearing on migration aptitudes in the Wittig rearrangement, Curtin and co-workers [67,68] investigated the base-catalyzed rearrangement of several desyl ethers. Curtin and Leskowitz [67] found that benzhydryl desyl ether (94), on treatment with ethanolic potassium hydroxide, affords α-benzhydrylbenzoin (95) along with further transformation products. Curtin and Proops [68] reported benzyl desyl ether (96) under the same conditions to

[65] G. Wittig, Angew. Chem., 66, 10 (1954).
[66] G. Wittig, Experientia, 14, 389 (1958).
[67] D. Y. Curtin and S. Leskowitz, J. Am. Chem. Soc., 73, 2633 (1951).
[68] D. Y. Curtin and W. R. Proops, J. Am. Chem. Soc., 76, 494 (1954).

rearrange to give 33% of α-benzylbenzoin (97) together with 17% of α-benzyl-phenylcarbinol and 34% of benzoic acid, products reasonably postulated as arising from initially formed 100. In contrast, under the same reaction conditions phenyl desyl ether (98) was largely unchanged. p-Nitrophenyl desyl ether (99), when treated with methanolic potassium hydroxide, gave none of the simple rearrangement product; however, there were isolated products which might have arisen from this under the reaction conditions. On the basis of the above results Curtin suggested migration aptitudes in the order: phenyl < p-nitrophenyl, benzyl < benzhydryl.

$$\phi C\!-\!CH\phi\!-\!O\!-\!R \rightarrow \phi C\!-\!\overset{\ominus}{C}\phi\!-\!O\!-\!R \rightarrow \phi C\!-\!\overset{R}{\underset{|}{C}}\phi\!-\!\overset{..\ominus}{\underset{..}{O}}: \rightarrow \phi C\!-\!\overset{R}{\underset{|}{C}}\phi\!-\!OH$$

(94: R = ϕ_2CH—)　　　　　　　　　　　　　　　　(95: R = ϕ_2CH—)
(96: R = ϕCH$_2$—)　　　　(100)　　　　　　　(97: R = ϕCH$_2$—)
(98: R = ϕ—, no reaction)
(99: R = p—NO$_2\phi$—)

Wittig obtained[69-71] further information on the ability of phenyl to migrate. It was found that benzhydryl phenyl ether did not rearrange with phenyllithium or butyllithium in ether. However, the potassium conjugate base (101, M = K), obtained with potassium piperidide or potassium

$$\phi_2CH\!-\!O\!-\!\phi \rightarrow \phi_2\overset{M\oplus}{\underset{..\ominus}{C}}\!-\!O\!-\!\phi \rightarrow \phi_3C\!-\!\overset{\ominus}{\underset{..}{O}}\!:\!\overset{\oplus}{M} \xrightarrow[H_2O]{} \phi_3C\!-\!OH$$

(101)

amide in liquid ammonia, did rearrange in good yield to afford triphenyl-carbinol when heated either dry or in ether. In tetrahydrofuran phenyl-lithium and butyllithium were effective; 85–93% of triphenylcarbinol was isolable after 50 hours at 40°. Also, in this study the reaction of the lithium conjugate base (101, M = Li) was found to be unimolecular, as expected on the basis of the proposed mechanism.

In a later study[72] Wittig compared the rates of rearrangement of benz-hydryl methyl ether (102, R = CH$_3$) and benzhydryl tert-butyl ether (102, R = tert-butyl) and found the migration of tert-butyl to be slower than methyl.

$$\phi_2CH\!-\!O\!-\!R \xrightarrow[\text{THF and workup}]{\phi Li \text{ in}} \phi_2CR\!-\!OH$$

(102)

[69] G. Wittig and R. Clausnizer, Ann., 588, 145 (1954).

[70] G. Wittig and E. Stahnecker, Ann., 605, 69 (1957).

[71] Cf. the review by G. Wittig, Experientia, 14, 389 (1958).

[72] G. Wittig and H. Schlör, Suomen Kemistilehti, 31, 2 (1958); Chem. Zentr., 130, 12183 (1959).

Most recent have been studies by Cram [73] and Stevens.[74,74a] Cram investigated the stereochemistry of an elimination reaction which often competes with the base-catalyzed rearrangement of ethers. He found that treatment of optically active benzyl 2-phenyl-2-butyl ether (103) with potassium N-methylanilide in N-methylaniline afforded 2-phenylbutane with predominant retention of configuration. Cram considered the possibility that the cleavage resulted from Wittig rearrangement of the ether (103) followed by β elimination of the resulting carbinol (104) as its conjugate base (105). It was found that the cleavage of carbinol 104 under similar conditions also gave 2-phenylbutane with predominant retention of configuration.

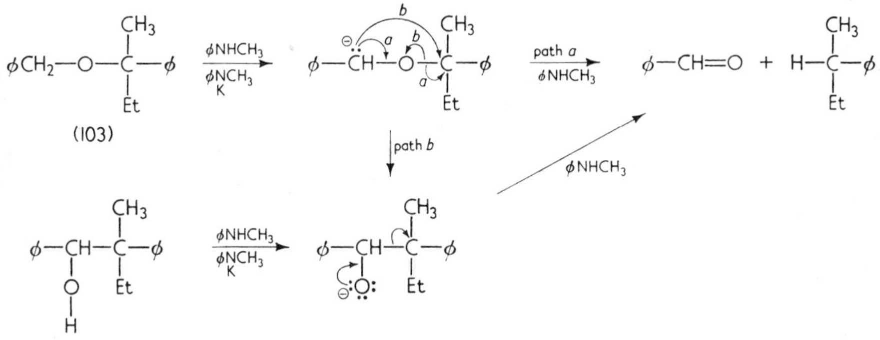

Stevens and co-workers [74] reported that reaction of not only 9-fluorenyl but-2'-enyl (106) ether but also 9-fluorenyl 1'-methylallyl (107) ether with potassium hydroxide affords 9-but-2'-enyl-9-fluorenol as the major product. It would thus appear that one ether (106) rearranges by the normal mechanism while the other (107) yields product by a cyclic mechanism, at least in so far as the currently accepted [74a] intramolecular mechanism is correct.

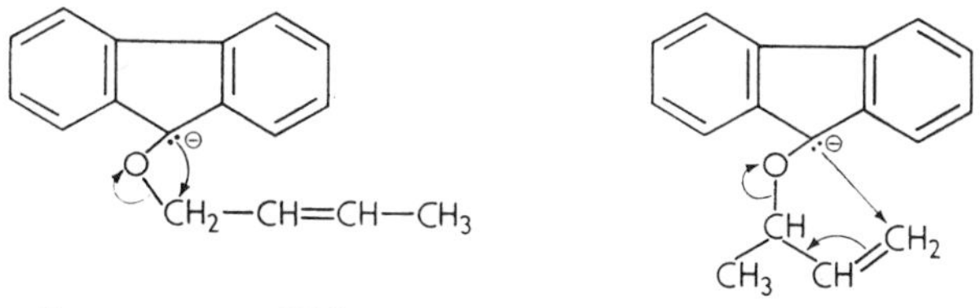

Rearrangement of 106   Rearrangement of 107

[73] D. J. Cram, C. A. Kingsbury, and A. Langemann, $J. Am. Chem. Soc.$, 81, 5785 (1959).

[74] J. Cast, T. S. Stevens, and J. Holmes, $J. Chem. Soc.$ ($London$), 1960, 3521.

[74a] For very recent evidence of cleavage recombination occurring under certain circumstances, see U. Schollköpf and W. Fabian, $Ann.$, 642, 1 (1961); P. Lansbury and V. Pattison, Abstr. Am. Chem. Soc., March 1962 meeting, p. 20–O, $J. Org. Chem.$, 27, 1933 (1962). The latter authors found the intramolecular mechanism to predominate in ether, and tetrahydrofuran to favor cleavage-recombination.

B. The Stevens Rearrangement

The Wittig rearrangement involves migration from oxygen to carbon. The Stevens rearrangement, which will now be considered, involves migration from nitrogen to carbon.

Stevens and co-workers [75,76] in 1928 and 1930 provided the first examples of this rearrangement. It was found that phenacylbenzyldimethylammonium bromide (108) rearranged under aqueous alkaline conditions to yield α-dimethylamino-β-phenylpropiophenone (109), a product arising from benzyl

$$\phi C-CH_2-\overset{\overset{\displaystyle CH_2\phi}{|}}{\underset{\oplus Br\ominus}{N}Me_2} \overset{OH^-}{\longrightarrow} \phi C-\overset{\overset{\displaystyle CH_2\phi}{|}}{CH}-NMe_2$$

$$\underset{\displaystyle O}{\|} \qquad\qquad \underset{\displaystyle O}{\|}$$

(108)   (109)

migration from nitrogen to carbon. In this early work Stevens demonstrated the intramolecularity of the reaction by rearranging a mixture of m-bromo-phenacylphenyldimethylammonium bromide and p-bromophenacylphenyl-dimethylammonium bromide and showing that no crossed products resulted. Much more recently Stevens [77] has shown that the α-dimethylamino-β-phenylpropiophenone (112) isolated from the rearrangement of a mixture of phenacylbenzyldimethylammonium bromide (110) and p-bromophenacyl-benzyl-^{14}C-dimethylammonium bromide (111) contains no [14]C. Since the rearrangement rates of 110 and 111 are very close, both compounds are

$$\phi C-CH_2-\overset{\overset{\displaystyle CH_2\phi}{|}}{N}Me_2 \qquad\qquad \phi C-\overset{\overset{\displaystyle CH_2\phi}{|}}{CH}-NMe_2 \quad \text{(no }^{14}\text{C incorporation)}$$

$$\underset{\displaystyle O}{\|} \qquad \underset{\oplus}{} \quad Br\ominus \qquad\qquad \underset{\displaystyle O}{\|}$$

(110)   (112)

$$\xrightarrow{\quad OH^- \quad}$$

$$p\text{-}Br\phi C-CH_2-\overset{\overset{\displaystyle ^{14}CH_2\phi}{|}}{N}Me_2 \qquad\qquad p\text{-}Br\phi C-\overset{\overset{\displaystyle ^{14}CH_2\phi}{|}}{CH}-NMe_2$$

$$\underset{\displaystyle O}{\|} \qquad \underset{\oplus}{} \quad Br\ominus \qquad\qquad \underset{\displaystyle O}{\|}$$

(111)

reacting at the same time without transfer of the migrating benzyl group from one molecule to another. Stevens found that electron-withdrawing para substituents on the migrating benzyl ring increase the rate of rearrangement, while electron donors tend to decrease the rate: p-MeO $(0.76) < p$-Me $(1.06) < p$-Cl $(2.65) < p$-NO$_2$ (73). He suggested that the rearrangement proceeds by

[75] T. S. Stevens, E. M. Creighton, A. B. Gordon, and M. MacNicol, J. Chem. Soc. (London), 1928, 3193.

[76] T. S. Stevens, J. Chem. Soc. (London), 1930, 2107.

[77] R. A. W. Johnstone and T. S. Stevens, J. Chem. Soc. (London), 1955, 4487.

formation of the enolate-ylid conjugate base (e.g., **113**) of the quaternary salt followed by generation of the benzylcarbanion immonium ion pair (**114**) which collapses rapidly internally. Intermediate **114** was suggested by the

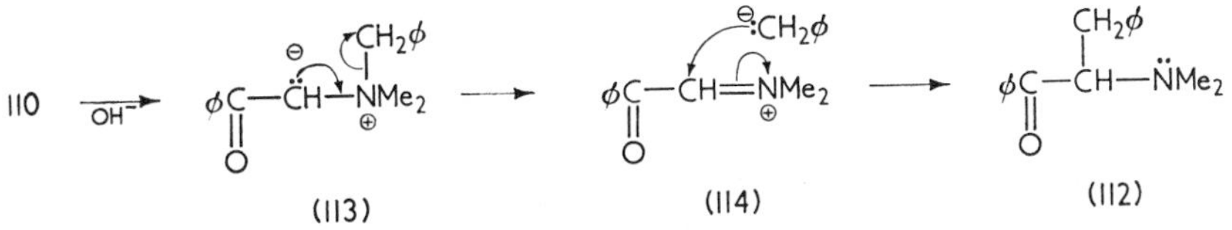

reactivity trend observed on para substitution of the migrating benzyl group, qualitatively paralleling stabilization of benzyl carbanions by para substituents.

Some further observations bearing on the reaction mechanism were made by Stevens and co-workers. First, since use of a second mole of alkali causes only a slight further increase in rate while a third mole has even less effect, Stevens [78] suggested that the proton abstraction is relatively complete by the time a slight excess of alkali has been added. Additional evidence on this point was found [79] in the effect of substituents on the phenacyl ring. *p*-Methoxyl increases the rate slightly while *m*-nitro decreases it mildly, again indicating that ease of formation of the conjugate base (e.g., **113**) is not dominant. Second, Stevens found that the reaction rate is solvent dependent. The rates are increased in the sequence MeOH < EtOH < *n*-PrOH < *i*-PrOH.[79] One may conclude from this that the transition state must have less charge separation than the ground state, which here would seem to be the conjugate base **113**. This is not unreasonable since, whatever the intimate details of the migration process, the unlike charges are being dissipated.

In 1932 Stevens reported an example in which proton removal is not facilitated by a carbonyl group.[80] Dibenzyldimethylammonium chloride (**115**) was found to afford desyldimethylamine (**116**) on fusion with sodamide at 140–150°. A related example involving methyl migration was reported by

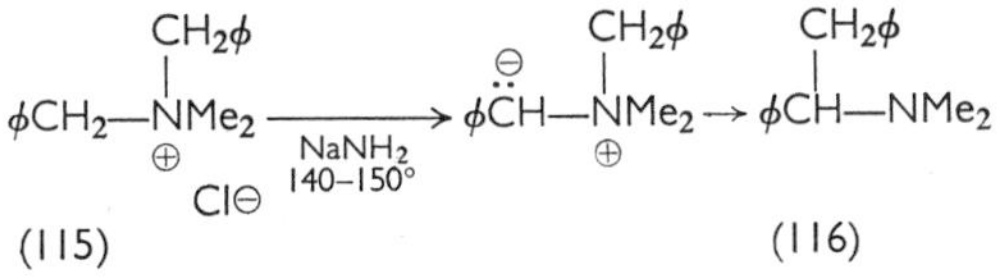

Hughes and Ingold.[81,82] Hofmann pyrolytic treatment of benzhydryltri-

[78] J. L. Dunn and T. S. Stevens, *J. Chem. Soc. (London)*, **1932**, 1926.

[79] T. Thomson and T. S. Stevens, *J. Chem. Soc. (London)*, **1932**, 55.

[80] T. Thomson and T. S. Stevens, *J. Chem. Soc. (London)*, **1932**, 1932.

[81] E. D. Hughes and C. K. Ingold, *J. Chem. Soc. (London)*, **1933**, 71.

[82] Cf. J. L. Dunn and T. S. Stevens, *J. Chem. Soc. (London)*, **1934**, 279, for examples of phenacyl, allyl, and phenylpropargyl migration.

methylammonium hydroxide (117) was found to yield 1,1-diphenylethyl-dimethylamine as one of the several products.

$$\phi_2CH\overset{\oplus}{-}NMe_3 \rightarrow \phi_2\overset{\overset{\displaystyle Me}{|}}{C}-NMe_2$$
$$OH\ominus$$
$$(117)$$

Very relevant to detailed mechanism of the migration process of the Stevens rearrangement are three papers. Campbell, Houston, and Kenyon [83] in 1947 showed that the Stevens rearrangement of optically active phenacyl-α-phenylethyldimethylammonium bromide (118) proceeds with α-phenylethyl migration to afford two diastereomers of α-dimethylamino-β-phenylbutyro-phenone (119) and that each of these diastereomers is optically active. This result meant that the group migrating does so with either retention or inversion of configuration.

In 1951 Hauser and Kantor [84] in a critical analysis of the problem suggested that the Stevens rearrangement proceeds by an intramolecular nucleophilic displacement process. These authors noted a qualitative relationship between

$$-\overset{\ominus}{\underset{|}{C}}-\overset{C}{\underset{|\oplus}{N}}- \longrightarrow -\overset{C}{\underset{|}{C}}-\overset{|}{\underset{|}{N}}-$$

the ease of migration of para-substituted benzyl groups and the rates of bimolecular displacement of the corresponding benzyl chlorides by iodide ion.

Confirmation of this view was convincingly provided by Brewster[84a] who showed that the rearrangement to d-α-dimethylamino-β-phenylbutryo-phenone (119) occurs with retention of configuration of the α-phenylethyl

$$\phi\overset{\overset{\displaystyle MeCH\phi}{|}}{\underset{\underset{\displaystyle O}{||}}{C}}-CH_2\overset{\oplus}{-}NMe_2 \underset{\overline{OH}}{\longrightarrow} \phi\overset{\overset{\displaystyle MeCH\phi}{|}}{\underset{\underset{\displaystyle O}{||}}{C}}-\overset{\ominus}{C}H\overset{\oplus}{-}NMe_2 \longrightarrow \phi\overset{\overset{\displaystyle MeCH\phi}{|}}{\underset{\underset{\displaystyle O}{||}}{C}}-CH-NMe_2$$
$$Br^{\ominus}$$
$$(118) \hspace{6cm} (119)$$

group. Thus the side of the asymmetric carbon atom of the α-phenylethyl group originally bonded to nitrogen remains bonded throughout the migration.

The original description (114) of Stevens may be considered to be accurate if one realizes that the bonding between the migrating moiety and the re-

[83] A. Campbell, A. H. Houston, and J. Kenyon, *J. Chem. Soc.* (*London*), **1947**, 93.

[84] C. R. Hauser and S. W. Kantor, *J. Am. Chem. Soc.*, **73**, 1437 (1951).

[84a] J. H. Brewster and M. W. Kline, *J. Am. Chem. Soc.*, **74**, 5179 (1952).

mainder of the molecule is strong; **114** seems likely, then, to be an important contributor to the transition state.

Wittig has contributed a number of interesting examples to the chemistry of the Stevens rearrangement. Generally, Wittig has studied weaker acids than most of those considered above and therefore used stronger bases and aprotic media. For example, the reaction of benzyltrimethylammonium bromide (**120**) with phenyllithium in ether was shown by Wittig and co-workers[85] to give α-phenylethyldimethylamine (**121**). The same reaction of benzhydryltrimethylammonium bromide (**122**) not only gave the Stevens type product (**123**), but also provided evidence for the formation of the product **124** resulting from ortho attack. The latter type reaction is considered in detail in connection with the Sommelet rearrangement (see below).

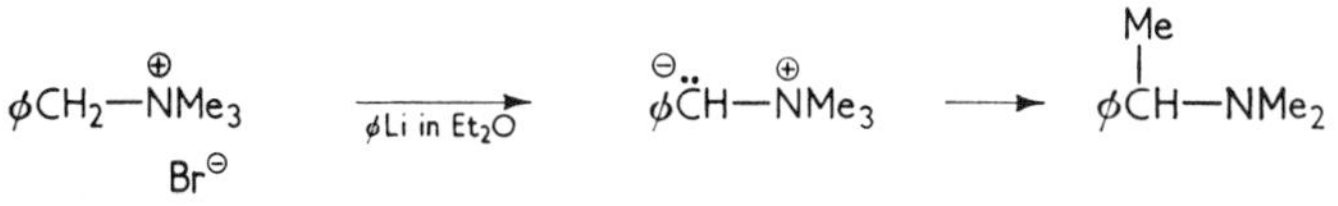

φCH2—N⊕Me3 Br⊖
φLi in Et2O
φC⊖H—N⊕Me3
Me
φCH—NMe2

(120) (121)

φ2CH—N⊕Me3 Br⊖
φLi in Et2O
Me
φ2C—NMe2
φ
CH2
CH2NMe2

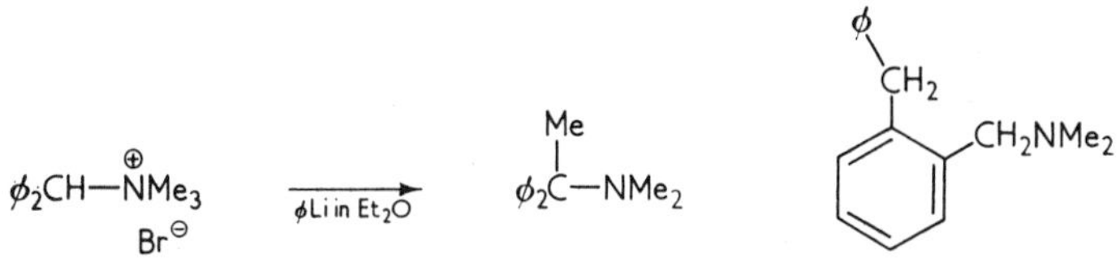

(122) (123) (124)

In Wittig's examples it may be noted that the reaction involves proton abstraction from the benzyl or benzhydryl group, to give a resonance-stabilized species, followed by methyl migration; an alternative a priori possibility of proton abstraction from the less acidic methyl group followed by benzyl or benzhydryl migration was not observed. Another pertinent example[86] is the rearrangement of 9-fluorenylbenzyldimethylammonium bromide (**125**). On treatment with phenyllithium in ether or sodium methoxide in methanol the red color of the ylid conjugate base (**126**) appeared and then

Me2N⊕ H
CH2—φ
φLi Et2O
or
NaOCH3
CH3OH
:⊖
Me2N⊕
CH2φ
Me2N CH2φ

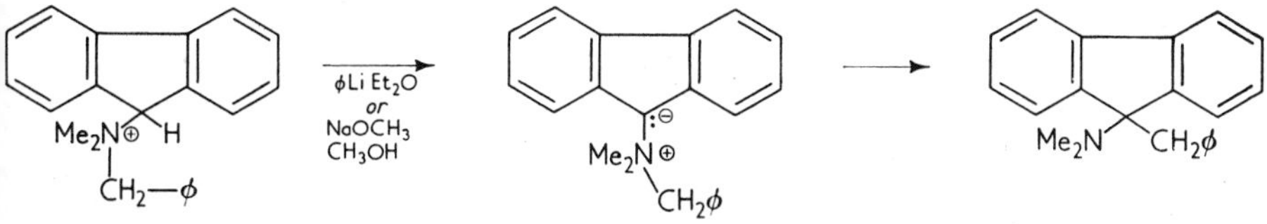

(125) (126)

[85] G. Wittig, R. Mangold, and G. Felletschin, *Ann.*, **560**, 117 (1948).

[86] G. Wittig and G. Felletschin, *Ann.*, **555**, 133 (1944); cf. also G. Wittig, *Angew. Chem.*, **63**, 15 (1951).

disappeared as the rearrangement proceeded to give 9-dimethylamino-9-benzylfluorene in nearly quantitative yield. Again the rearrangement proceeds via the more stable (**126**) of two possible ylid intermediates.

To the extent that an extrapolation from the Wittig rearrangement and from the Stevens rearrangement of phenacylammonium salts is valid, one would predict that, other things being equal, benzyl should migrate more readily than methyl. However, other things are not equal, since the stability of the two ylid intermediates will not in general be the same. Where the *ylid* stability and the migratory aptitude factors oppose one another, it thus appears to be ylid stability considerations which dominate.

Three further examples reported by Wittig are of interest (eqs. 3–5):

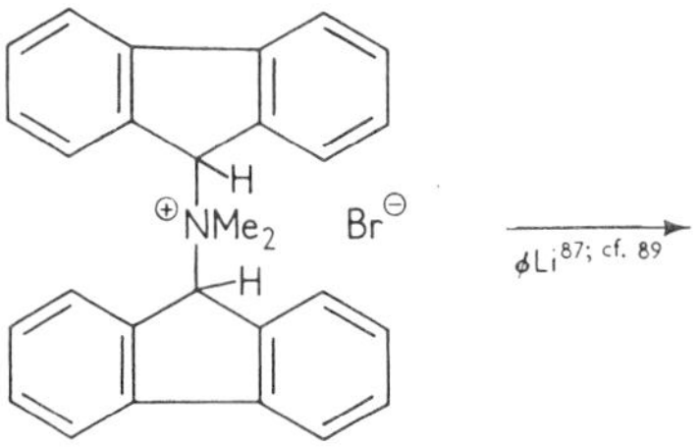

(3)

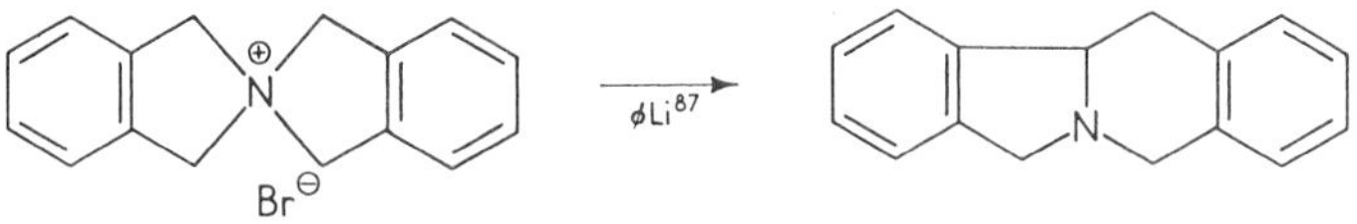

(4)

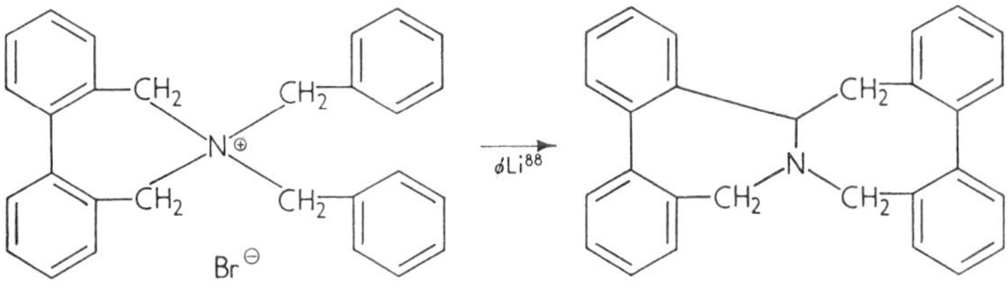

(5)

C. The Sommelet Rearrangement

A related rearrangement reaction often accompanies or actually supersedes the Stevens rearrangement of quaternary ammonium salts. Sommelet in 1937 reported the first example of this rearrangement.[90] He found that benzhydryl-trimethylammonium hydroxide (**127**) in a desiccator over phosphorus pen-

[87] G. Wittig, H. Tenhaeff, W. Schoch, and G. Koenig, *Ann.*, **572**, 1 (1951).

[88] G. Wittig, G. Koenig, and K. Clauss, *Ann.*, **593**, 127 (1955).

[89] W. R. Bamford and T. S. Stevens, *J. Chem. Soc.* (*London*), **1952**, 4675.

[90] M. Sommelet, *Compt. rend.*, **205**, 56 (1937); *Chem. Zentr.*, **II**, 2986 (1937).

toxide rearranged in sunlight to give (o-benzylbenzyl)dimethylamine (**124**). Since **127** would not absorb light of wavelength above 290 mμ and since ordi-

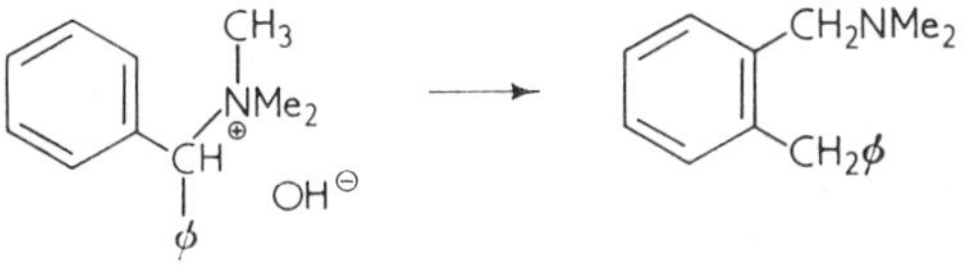

(127)   (124)

nary glassware absorbs what little radiation sunlight has below 300 mμ, one might suspect that the sunlight employed facilitated the reaction mainly by raising the temperature. Somewhat supporting this view is the fact that Sommelet was able to obtain the same product by heating the quaternary hydroxide to 145°; however, the yield was poor.

In 1948 Wittig[85] observed the same rearrangement as a side reaction in the Stevens rearrangement of benzhydryltrimethylammonium bromide (**122**) discussed earlier. On treatment with phenyllithium, **122** afforded not only the Stevens rearrangement product but also a base, $C_{29}H_{29}N$. Wittig showed that this base could be degraded, using potassium-sodium alloy, to diphenyl-methane and **124**; he suggested that **124** arises from a Sommelet rearrangement and is then benzhydrylated to give the observed $C_{29}H_{29}N$. Wittig pictured the reaction as proceeding by rearrangement of the less stable of two possible ylids, **128**.

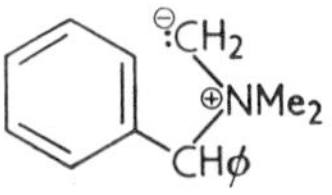

(128)

Two years later, in 1950, Wittig[87] described the reaction of dibenzyl-dimethylammonium bromide (**129**) with phenyllithium in ether. Under these conditions both the Stevens and the Sommelet rearrangement products, desyldimethylamine (**130**) and (o-methylbenzhydryl)dimethylamine (**131**),

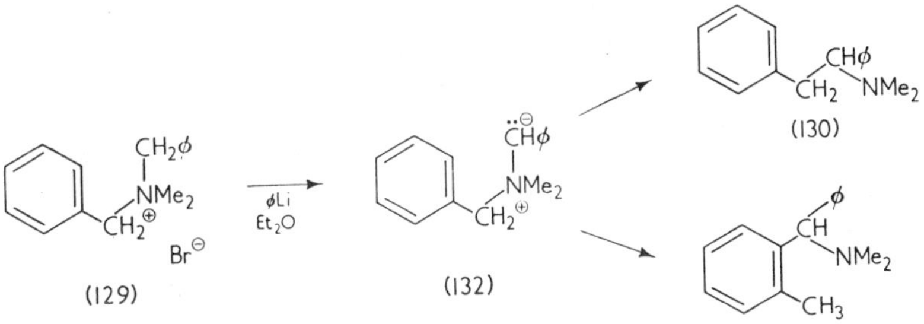

(129)   (132)   (130)

(131)

result. Wittig suggested that both products arise by rearrangement from the ylid **132**.

Most striking was the finding by Hauser in 1951 [91] that Sommelet type rearrangement products can be obtained essentially exclusively in many cases with the use of sodium or potassium amide in liquid ammonia. Thus benzyltrimethylammonium iodide (**133**) affords (o-methylbenzyl)dimethylamine (**134**). Benzhydryltrimethylammonium iodide (**135**) gives (o-benzylbenzyl)dimethylamine (**124**) in 96% yield under these conditions, in contrast with Wittig's finding that the same quaternary cation gives both Stevens and Sommelet products with phenyllithium in ether. Dibenzyldimethylammonium chloride (**136**) under Hauser's conditions gives **131**. As noted above, Wittig's

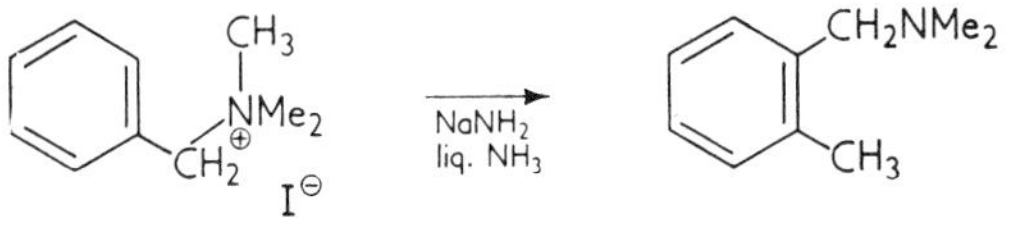

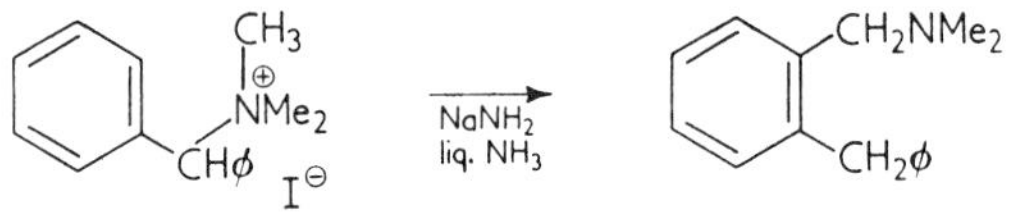

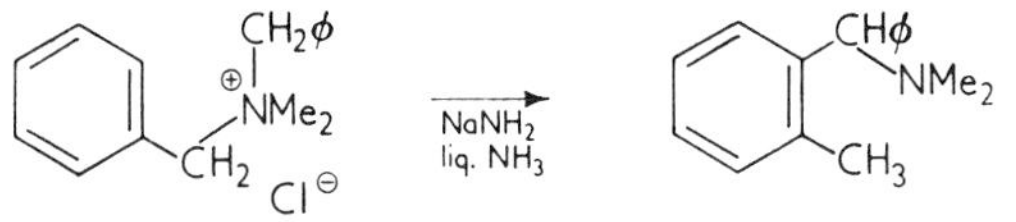

phenyllithium conditions give both rearrangement products, **130** and **131**. Thomson and Stevens in work discussed earlier reported only 1,2 shift product to result at 145° with fused sodamide. Hauser suggested a reaction mechanism which involves nucleophilic attack of the ylid carbon at the ring position ortho to the benzylammonium moiety; in the case of the rearrangement of **133** the ylid intermediate (**137**) is the less stable of the two possible ylid conjugate bases. It may be noted that the reaction here leads to product in which the

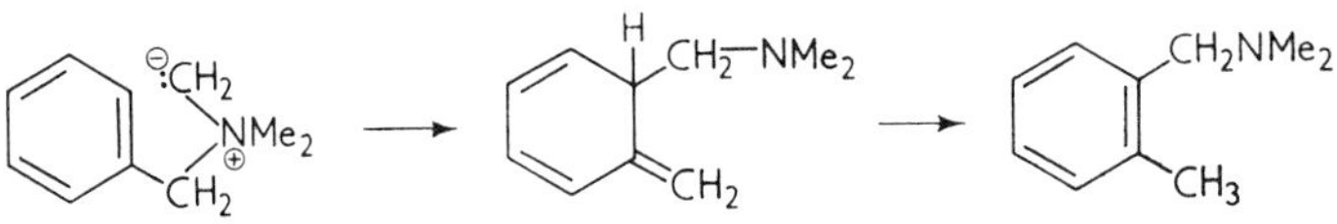

[91] S. W. Kantor and C. R. Hauser, *J. Am. Chem. Soc.*, **73**, 4122 (1951).

benzylic methylene is converted to methyl and a dimethylaminomethyl group is introduced ortho to the original benzylic methylene group. Hauser showed that the process can be continued around the ring by successively remethylating the rearrangement product and then repeating the sodamide treatment (eq. 6):

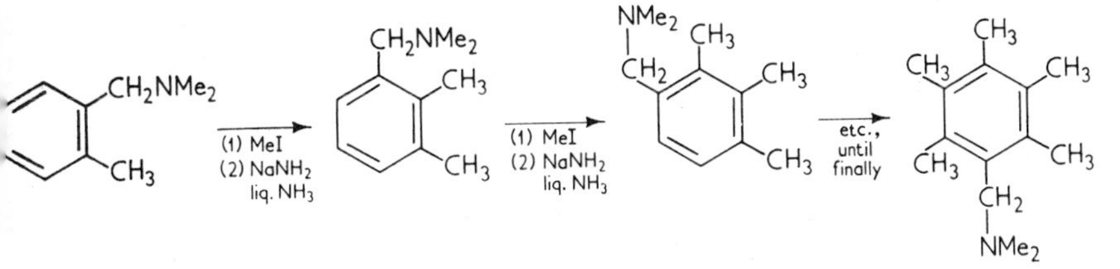

(6)

A clue to the factors controlling whether the Stevens or the Sommelet rearrangement occurs in a given circumstance derives from research by Hauser and by Wittig. Hauser noted [92] that in general an elevation in temperature favors the Stevens 1,2 shift over the Sommelet rearrangement. He suggested that the increasing amount of Stevens rearrangement observed in the reaction of the dibenzyldimethylammonium ion (**136**), as the conditions are changed in the sequence: sodamide in liquid ammonia, phenyllithium in ether, fused sodamide at 145°, probably derives from a temperature effect. Hauser found that only Stevens product results when potassium amide is used in refluxing toluene. The case of **136** (or **129**) is especially interesting, since, as Hauser noted, both the Stevens and Sommelet rearrangement processes originate from the same ylid precursor, **132**.

Wittig [93] investigated the rearrangement of **138** as a function of reaction

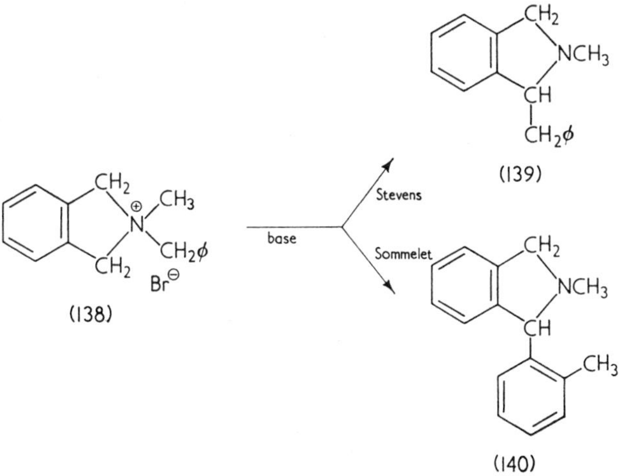

(139)

(138)

(140)

[92] C. R. Hauser, S. W. Kantor, and W. R. Brasen, *J. Am. Chem. Soc.*, **75**, 2660 (1953).
[93] G. Wittig and H. Streib, *Ann.*, **584**, 1 (1953).

conditions. He found decreasing yields of Sommelet rearrangement products and increasing yields of Stevens products as the temperature increased. Most significant is the reaction using phenyllithium at 25° in ethyl ether compared to that at 120° in butyl ether. Although the base itself is the same in the two experiments, at 25° only Sommelet product could be isolated, while at 120° Stevens but no Sommelet product was obtained. Although the total yields, especially at the higher temperatures, are sometimes low, the trend with temperature is evident (cf. Table II).

TABLE II

Sommelet versus Stevens Rearrangement of **138** [93]

	Type of product isolated	
Conditions	Sommelet **(140)**	Stevens **(139)**
NaNH$_2$, liquid NH$_3$, −33°	87%	a
ϕLi, Et$_2$O, 20–30°	69%	a
NaOEt, EtOH, 80°	b	44%
ϕLi, Bu$_2$O, 120°	b	41%
Hofmann decomposition, 180°	b	33%[c]

[a] No Stevens product isolated.

[b] No Sommelet product isolated.

[c] Some N-methylisoindole obtained as well.

That the Sommelet rearrangement proceeds in phenylethyl and more complex systems may be seen in examples provided by Hauser (eqs. 7 and 8):

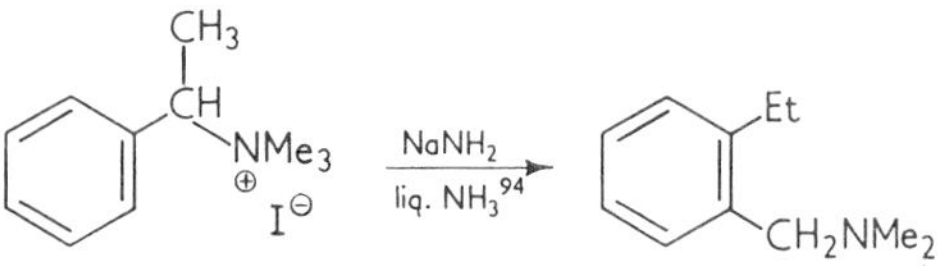

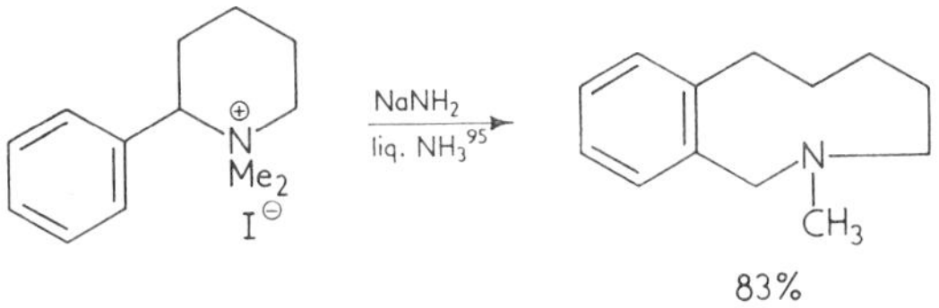

$$(7)$$

$$(8)$$

[94] C. R. Hauser and A. J. Wienheimer, *J. Am. Chem. Soc.*, **76**, 1264 (1954).

[95] D. Lednicer and C. R. Hauser, *J. Am. Chem. Soc.*, **79**, 4449 (1957).

Support for Hauser's picture of attack of the ylid carbon at the ortho position is found in the reaction of 2,4,6-trimethylbenzyltrimethylammonium iodide to afford product, which, unlike the examples discussed thus far, cannot tautomerize to regenerate the aromatic ring (eq. 9).[96-98]

The temperature dependence of the product distribution, with Sommelet rearrangement tending to be preferred at lower temperatures, is interesting; and an interpretation is possible. In general, the ratio of rate constants for two competing reactions is controlled by the difference in activation free energies per degree absolute. For the case at hand

$$\ln (k_{so}/k_{st}) = \Delta F_{st}^{\ddagger}/RT - \Delta F_{so}^{\ddagger}/RT = \Delta\Delta F_{st-so}^{\ddagger}/RT$$

where the subscripts so and st refer to Sommelet and Stevens. Thus if the Stevens reaction has a larger activation free energy at a given temperature than the Sommelet rearrangement, then $\Delta\Delta F_{st-so}^{\ddagger} > 0$, $(k_{so}/k_{st}) > 1$, and the Sommelet reaction dominates. If the converse is true, $\Delta\Delta F_{st-so}^{\ddagger} < 0$, $(k_{so}/k_{st}) < 1$ and the Stevens rearrangement will dominate. Furthermore, $\Delta\Delta F_{st-so}^{\ddagger}/RT$ may be dissected into temperature-dependent and temperature-independent components:

$$\Delta\Delta F_{st-so}^{\ddagger}/RT = \Delta\Delta H_{st-so}^{\ddagger}/RT - \Delta\Delta S_{st-so}^{\ddagger}/R$$

If the enthalpies of activation are not heavily temperature dependent, then at low temperatures the first term becomes large and the ratio of rates is controlled by $\Delta\Delta H_{st-so}^{\ddagger}/RT$. Since at low temperatures we know k_{so}/k_{st} tends to become > 1, we deduce that $\Delta\Delta H_{st-so}^{\ddagger}/RT$ and hence $\Delta\Delta H_{st-so}^{\ddagger}$ become positive. Conversely, at high temperatures the first term becomes small and the ratio of rates is controlled by $\Delta\Delta S_{st-so}^{\ddagger}/R$. Since at high temperatures we observe that k_{so}/k_{st} tends to become < 1, we conclude that $\Delta\Delta S_{st-so}^{\ddagger}$ is positive.

That $\Delta\Delta S_{st-so}^{\ddagger}$ is positive—that is, the entropy of activation is more positive for the Stevens than for the Sommelet rearrangement—is not surprising. Using ylid **132** as an example one notes that rotational freedom is frozen only

96 C. R. Hauser and D. N. van Eenam, *J. Org. Chem.*, **23**, 865 (1958).
97 C. R. Hauser and D. N. van Eenam, *J. Am. Chem. Soc.*, **79**, 5512 (1957).
98 C. R. Hauser and D. N. van Eenam, *J. Am. Chem. Soc.*, **79**, 6280 (1957).

about the ylid C—N bond in the Stevens transition state (141), while in the Sommelet reaction a five-membered ring (142) is being formed, freezing rotation about three σ bonds.

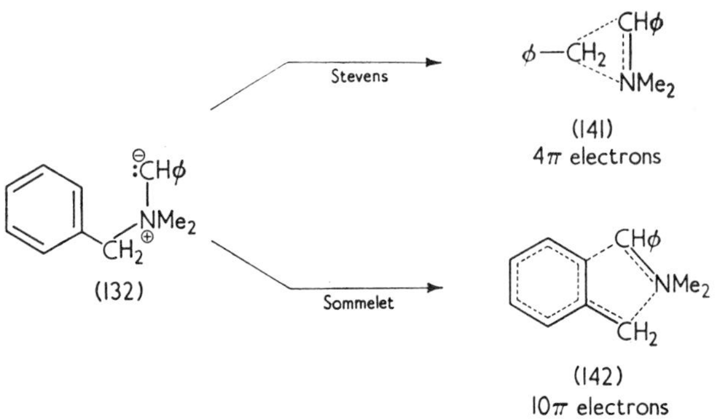

Why $\Delta\Delta H^{\ddagger}_{st-so}$ should be positive is an intriguing but less than obvious matter. One notes that transition states 141 and 142 differ mainly in whether the ylid carbon is bonded to the benzyl methylene or to the benzyl ortho carbon.

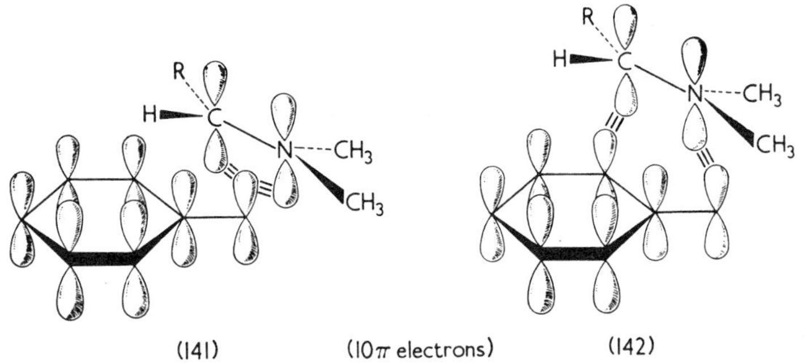

An approximation of the relative energies of 141 and 142 is possible. For simplicity, conjugation of R, which is actually phenyl, is neglected, although the actual extent of interaction by phenyl will not be precisely the same for the two transition states. One notes that each of the two systems may be considered to derive from juxtaposition of two moieties, the benzyl carbanion (143) and the immonium species (144). The molecular orbital energy levels for the separated fragments are readily obtained from the Hückel LCAO MO approach.[99] These are given in units of $|\beta|$ in Table III. For a first approximation one may assume that fusion of the benzyl carbanion and immonium

[99] The coulomb integral for nitrogen is taken as $\alpha + \beta$.

cation fragments leads to interaction of only the highest filled molecular orbital of the benzyl carbanion and the lowest vacant MO of the immonium species.

TABLE III

Molecular Orbital Energy Levels of Isolated and Merged Benzyl Carbanion and Immonium Cation Species **141** and **142**[a]

Benzyl carbanion **143**	Immonium ion **144**	Merged species **141** or **142**
2.10 ——		—— 2.10
1.26 ——		—— 1.26
1.00 ——		—— 1.00
		⋯—— E_+
	0.62 —— ⋯	
0.00 –•–•–⋯⋯		⋯–•–•– E_-
−1.00 –•–•–		–•–•– −1.00
−1.26 –•–•–		–•–•– −1.26
	−1.62 –•–•–	
		–•–•– −1.62
−2.10 –•–•–		–•–•– −2.10

[a] The energies are in units of the absolute value of β. The levels are filled with the ten available electrons.

It is easily shown that interaction of two such orbitals will lead to two new energy levels of energies E_+ and E_-. These energies are given by

$$E_\pm = \tfrac{1}{2}\left\{ E_U + E_L \pm \left[(E_U - E_L)^2 + 4\left(\sum_{i,j} C_{iU}C_{jL}H_{ij} \right)^2 \right]^{1/2} \right\}$$

where E_U and E_L are the energies of the upper and lower MO's interacting, C_{iU} is the LCAO coefficient for atom i in the upper energy MO, and C_{jL} is the coefficient for atom j in the lower energy MO. H_{ij} is the exchange integral for atoms i and j, and it is a function of the extent of overlap of the atomic orbitals at atoms i and j. Inspection of this equation shows that the term $\left(\sum_{i,j} C_{iU}C_{jL}H_{ij} \right)^2$ controls the amount of interaction between the molecular orbitals "mixed"—that is, the amount of splitting of the two new levels about the average of the original two MO energies. If this term is zero, then the equation affords E_U and E_L, the original energies, as solutions, and there is no interaction of the original MO's U and L. As the term under consideration becomes larger, the splitting increases and the energy E_- of the new lower level becomes less than E_L while the higher energy level E_+ becomes greater than E_U.

The energy of E_- is of interest, since as seen in Table III this is used to accommodate the two highest energy electrons of the merged species. The knowledge of the energy E_- for the Stevens species **141** compared to that of the Sommelet species **142** leads to an estimate of the relative energy of the two total transition states. The two molecular orbitals, the benzyl nonbonding MO at zero and the immonium antibonding MO at 0.62, whose interaction is to be considered are pictured as **143′** and **144′**. Here the LCAO coefficients for

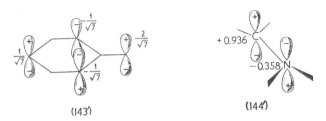

(143′)   (144′)

these MO's are indicated near each atom; these give the weighting of the indicated p orbitals in the MO's and the plus and minus signs in each lobe of the p orbitals indicate the sign of the wave function in the various lobes. Where no p orbitals are drawn, the coefficients are zero. A comparison of the $\left(\sum_{i,j} C_{iU}C_{jL}H_{ij}\right)^2$ term for the two transition states can now be easily made. For the Stevens species **141** this term is $[(-0.358)(2/\sqrt{7})H_{\alpha N}+(0.936)$ $(-1\sqrt{7})H_{oy}]^2$, while for **142** the term is $[(-0.358)(2/\sqrt{7})H_{\alpha N}+(0.936)$ $(2/\sqrt{7})H_{\alpha y}]^2$, where the subscripts α, N, o, and y signify, in order, the benzylic α carbon, the nitrogen, the ortho carbon, and the ylid carbon. It is seen that the term for the Stevens species **141** is larger since it contains two terms of the same sign which are summed and squared while the term for the Sommelet species **142** contains two terms of opposite sign which are summed and squared.[100] Another way of saying this, but more qualitatively, is that the antibonding orbital of the immonium ion has the positive lobe of the p orbital nitrogen down and can overlap with the upper, positive lobe of the α carbon of the benzyl nonbonding MO. However, the p orbital at the ylid carbon has its negative lobe down, and this lobe can overlap favorably only with the negative lobe on the ortho carbon facing upward. Overlap of the lower lobe of the ylid carbon p orbital with the upper lobe of the benzylic α carbon atom is antibonding owing to overlap of wave functions of differing signs; this makes a negative contribution to the energy-splitting term. We conclude that E_- is

[100] The H_{ij}'s in the present problem will not differ enough to change this conclusion.

lower for the Sommelet species and that the transition state species' energy as a whole is lower.

D. Carbon to Carbon Anionic Migration

It was noted by Wittig in 1955 [101] that, although many examples of electrophilic rearrangements were known in which migration is from nitrogen to carbon or oxygen to carbon, no case of carbon to carbon electrophilic migration exactly paralleling the well-known nucleophilic 1,2 shifts of carbonium ions had been established. Such a rearrangement had been reported much earlier by Wooster and Mitchell; [102] however, it was shown to be in error by Hughes in 1951. [103]

In 1957 in independent studies Grovenstein [104] and Zimmerman [105] uncovered an example of an electrophilic carbon to carbon 1,2 shift. It was found in these two studies that 1,1,1-triphenyl-2-chloroethane (145) on treatment with sodium rearranged to 1,1,2-triphenylethylsodium (147). The

$$\phi_3C-CH_2Cl \xrightarrow[2Na]{} \phi_3C-CH_2{:}^{\ominus}Na^{\oplus} \rightarrow \phi_2\overset{..}{C}-CH_2\phi$$
$$+NaCl \qquad \ominus$$
$$(145) \qquad\qquad (146) \qquad Na^{\oplus}\ (147)$$

driving force for this rearrangement is clearly the formation of a resonance-stabilized carbanion, 147, from 146 in which the negative charge is localized on a saturated carbon atom. At the time it was by no means clear that the rearrangement was actually proceeding by the carbanion mechanism indicated in the equation above, since other mechanistic possibilities remained. For example, a free radical rearrangement could be envisioned differing from the carbanion mechanism in that only one electron, rather than two, would be introduced prior to phenyl migration, with the second electron being subsequently transferred. In these initial studies, attempts to stop the re-

$$\phi_3C-CH_2-Cl \xrightarrow[Na\cdot]{} \phi_3C-CH_2\cdot \rightarrow \phi_2C-CH_2\phi \xrightarrow[Na\cdot]{} \phi_2C-CH_2\phi$$
$$+NaCl \qquad\qquad \bullet \qquad\qquad \overset{..}{\oplus}Na$$
$$(145) \qquad\qquad\qquad\qquad (147)$$

action at the triphenylethylsodium (146) stage, and thus to demonstrate the intermediacy of this species, were fruitless. Subsequently, further studies by Grovenstein and by Zimmerman have shown the carbanion mechanism to be correct.

[101] G. Wittig and R. Clausnizer, *Ann.*, **588**, 145 (1955).

[102] C. Wooster and N. Mitchell, *J. Am. Chem. Soc.*, **52**, 1042 (1930).

[103] J. Charlton, I. Dostrovsky, and E. Hughes, *Nature*, **167**, 987 (1951).

[104] E. Grovenstein, Jr., *J. Am. Chem. Soc.*, **79**, 4985 (1957).

[105] H. E. Zimmerman and F. J. Smentowski, *J. Am. Chem. Soc.*, **79**, 5455 (1957).

In the study by Zimmerman [106] the behavior of 2,2-diphenylpropyl metallic derivatives was investigated. The magnesium derivative was found to be stable, even in refluxing dioxane; carbonation afforded the acid **148** of unrearranged skeleton. The lithium derivative, 2,2-diphenylpropyllithium (**149**), was relatively stable at 0°, being carbonated to afford the same unrearranged acid (**148**). However, most exciting was the observation that this lithium reagent rearranged at an appreciable rate in refluxing ether to afford 1-methyl-1,2-diphenylpropyllithium (**150**) which on carbonation gave 2-methyl-2,3-diphenylpropionic acid (**151**). While 2,2-diphenylpropylmagnesium chloride

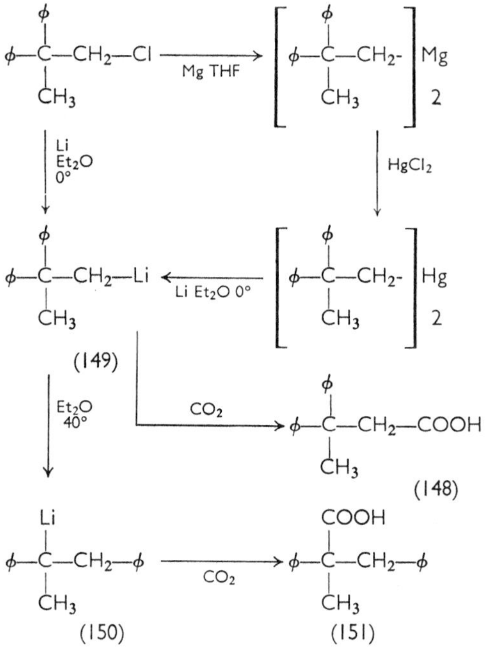

would not rearrange, and while 2,2-diphenylpropyllithium was stable at 0° although rearranging at 40°, the reaction of bis(2,2-diphenylpropyl)mercury with potassium in tetrahydrofuran even after a short reaction time gave only the rearranged acid (**151**) on carbonation. This suggested that 2,2-diphenylpropylpotassium (**152**) rearranged very quickly to give 1-methyl-1,2-diphenylpropylpotassium (**153**). The facility in rearrangement in the organometallic

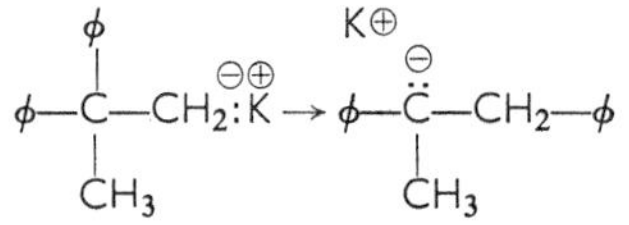

[106] H. E. Zimmerman and A. Zweig, *J. Am. Chem. Soc.*, **83**, 1196 (1961).

series Mg < Li < K was attributed to the increasing ionic nature of the carbon to metal bonds in this sequence.

Of considerable interest was the migration of a phenyl rather than a methyl group despite the fact that methyl migration would have led to a more stable carbanion. Further evidence on the nature of the rearrangement was obtained by Zimmerman [106] from a study of the relative tendency of phenyl versus p-tolyl groups to migrate. In the rearrangement of 2-phenyl-2-p-tolylpropyllithium (154) phenyl was found to migrate in preference to p-tolyl to afford carbanion 155 in preference to 156. This result was interpreted as in accord with the postulated carbanion rearrangement mechanism. One would expect the half-migrated phenyl rearrangement species 157 to be of lower energy than the p-tolyl counterpart 158, since electron delocali-

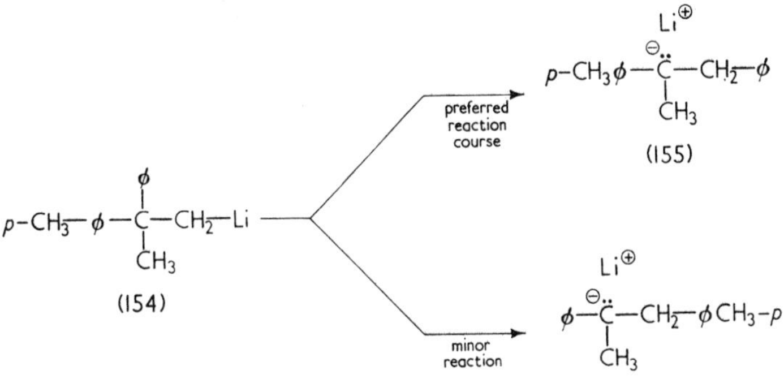

zation toward the para position of the p-tolyl ring of 158 should be inhibited by the presence of the electron-donating methyl group. We note again that the rearrangement proceeds to form the less stable of possible carbanions (i.e., 155) in which the electron pair is stabilized by the p-tolyl group rather than by the more efficient phenyl group as in 156. The most stable possible carbanion product (159) resulting from methyl migration was not observed.

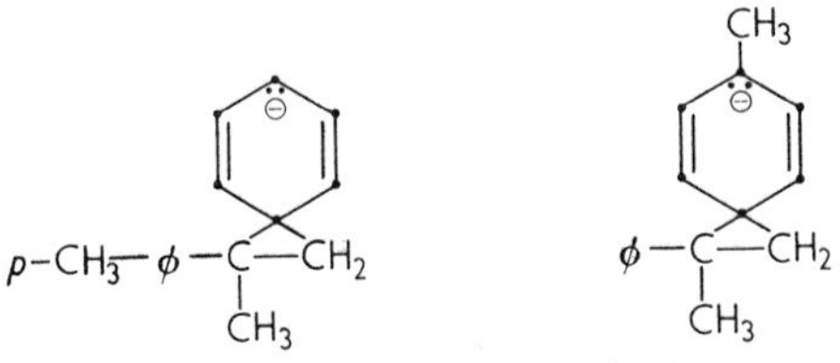

In a contemporary and independent study, Grovenstein [107] showed that

[107] E. Grovenstein, Jr., and L. P. Williams, Jr., J. Am. Chem. Soc., 83, 412, 2537 (1961).

even at $-66°$ potassium reacts with 1,1,1-triphenyl-2-chloroethane to give 1,1,2-triphenylethylpotassium (**161**) as the only detectable monopotassium

$$p\text{-}CH_3\phi\text{—}\overset{\displaystyle\phi}{\underset{\displaystyle\ominus Li\oplus}{\overset{..}{C}}}\text{—}CH_2CH_3$$
(159)

derivative. In contrast, 2,2,2-triphenylethyllithium was found to be stable at these low temperatures but was found to rearrange above zero. The difference

$$\phi_3C\text{—}\overset{\ominus}{C}H_2^{..}:K\oplus \xrightarrow[-60°]{} \overset{K\oplus}{\phi_2\overset{\ominus}{C}}\text{—}CH_2\phi$$
(160)   (161)

$$\phi_3C\text{—}CH_2\text{—}Li \xrightarrow[0°]{} \overset{Li\oplus}{\phi_2\overset{\ominus..}{C}}\text{—}CH_2\phi$$
(162)   (163)

in ease of migration was again interpreted on the basis of the pronounced ionic character of the carbon-potassium bond. Thus the viewpoints of Grovenstein [107] and Zimmerman [106] are in agreement.

A second example reported by Grovenstein [107] is also of considerable interest. The reaction of 1-chloro-2,2,3-triphenylpropane (**164**) at $-65°$ in tetrahydrofuran was found to give 2,2,3-triphenylpropyllithium (**165**). This at $0°$ underwent benzyl rather than phenyl migration to afford 1,1,3-triphenyl-propyllithium (**166**). The structures of the organometallic derivatives were

$$\overset{\displaystyle CH_2\phi}{\underset{\displaystyle (164)}{\phi_2C\text{—}CH_2Cl}} \xrightarrow[-65°]{Li\ THF} \overset{\displaystyle CH_2\phi}{\underset{\displaystyle (165)}{\phi_2C\text{—}CH_2\text{—}Li}} \xrightarrow[0°]{} \overset{Li\oplus}{\underset{\displaystyle (166)}{\phi_2\overset{\ominus..}{C}\text{—}CH_2CH_2\phi}}$$

proved, as before, by carbonation. Grovenstein noted that the migration of benzyl in preference to phenyl is in accord with a carbanion mechanism and has analogy in the Wittig rearrangement of ethers where, as noted on page 375, benzyl migrates especially readily.

In the report by Zimmerman and Zweig [106] the energetics of carbon to carbon migration was considered using LCAO molecular orbital calculations. Five situations were described: A, alkyl migration between adjacent, non-phenyl-bearing carbon atoms; B, phenyl migration between adjacent, non-phenyl-bearing carbon atoms; C, alkyl migration from a phenyl-bearing carbon atom to an adjacent nonphenyl-bearing carbon atom; D, phenyl migration from a phenyl-bearing carbon atom to a nonphenyl-bearing carbon atom; and lastly, E, phenyl migration from a carbon atom bearing two phenyl groups to a nonphenyl-bearing carbon atom. In each case the simple LCAO molecular orbital theory was applied to the half-migrated species as well as to the nonbridged ion or radical from which the half-migrated species might, at least in principle, have originated. The energies of these two species were then compared.

The molecular geometry and the orbitals, whose linear combination was used in the calculation, are pictured for each of the first four half-migrated species—**A**, **B**, **C** and **D**—as well as for the related non-bridged species **A'**, **B'**, **C'**, and **D'**. The two species in **E** differ from **D'** and **D**, respectively, only in having an additional phenyl group at C_1. In each case, A through D, the migration is from C_1 to C_2, and the atom actually bonded to atoms 1 and 2 in the bridged species is designated a. In the cases of alkyl migration (A and C) the hybridization at atom a is taken as sp^3, while in the cases of phenyl migration (B, D, and E) the hybridization is taken as sp^2. The molecular orbitals obtained for species **A** through **D** are given in Table IV.

The lowest energy molecular orbitals of each species are used to accommodate, in pairs, all electrons available for delocalization. Also the two σ electrons of the C_1—C_a bond of each parent species are included as these become delocalized in the bridging process. In the nonbridged species these electrons are placed in a localized low energy σ-bonding orbital. Additionally available are any (number n) electrons—0, 1, or 2—originally in the $C_2\,p$ orbital of the parent species. If $n=0$, the parent species is a carbonium ion; if $n=1$, the species is a free radical; while, if $n=2$, it is a carbanion. In Table IV and in the equations below these n electrons are represented by an asterisk.

For each type system, A through E, an energy of bridging may be calculated. The dependence of the bridging energy on the type of system— A, B, C, D, E—as well as on the type of species involved—carbonium ion $(n=0)$, free radical $(n=1)$, or carbanion $(n=2)$—is of interest. A reasonable assumption is that the bridging energy will be inversely related to the ease of migration. For carbonium ion $(n=0)$ migration the theory predicts that migration will increase in facility in the sequence: A (alkyl migration from unactivated to unactivated carbon) $<C$ (alkyl migration from phenyl-substituted to unactivated carbon) $< B$ (phenyl migration from unactivated to unactivated carbon) $< D$ (phenyl migration from phenyl-bearing to unactivated carbon) $< E$ (phenyl migration from doubly phenyl-substituted

---

[108] The value of β is left unassigned since there is no general agreement on its magnitude. Values from -16.5 to close to -50 kcal./mole have been suggested.

[109] S. Winstein, B. K. Morse, E. Grunwald, K. C. Schreiber, and J. Corse, *J. Am. Chem. Soc.*, **74**, 1113 (1952) and S. Winstein and H. Marshall, *J. Am. Chem. Soc.*, **74**, 1120 (1952). Simonetta and Winstein [109a] have carried out an interesting calculation in which the energetic importance of phenyl participation with a cationic center is assessed as ~ 4.7 kcal./mole without involvement of the σ bond bearing the phenyl group; here β was taken as -20 kcal./mole.

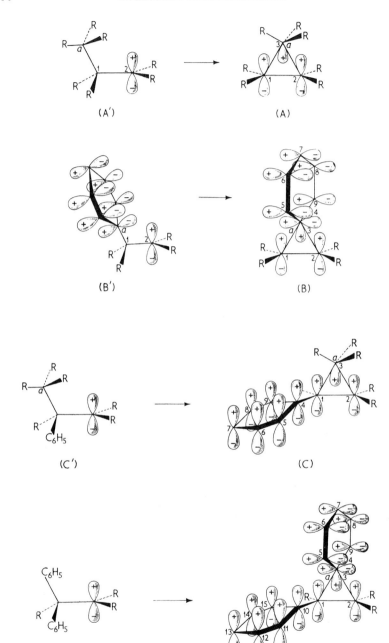

(A′)   (A)

(B′)   (B)

(C′)   (C)

(D′)   (D)

TABLE IV

Molecular Orbital Reaction Diagram[a]

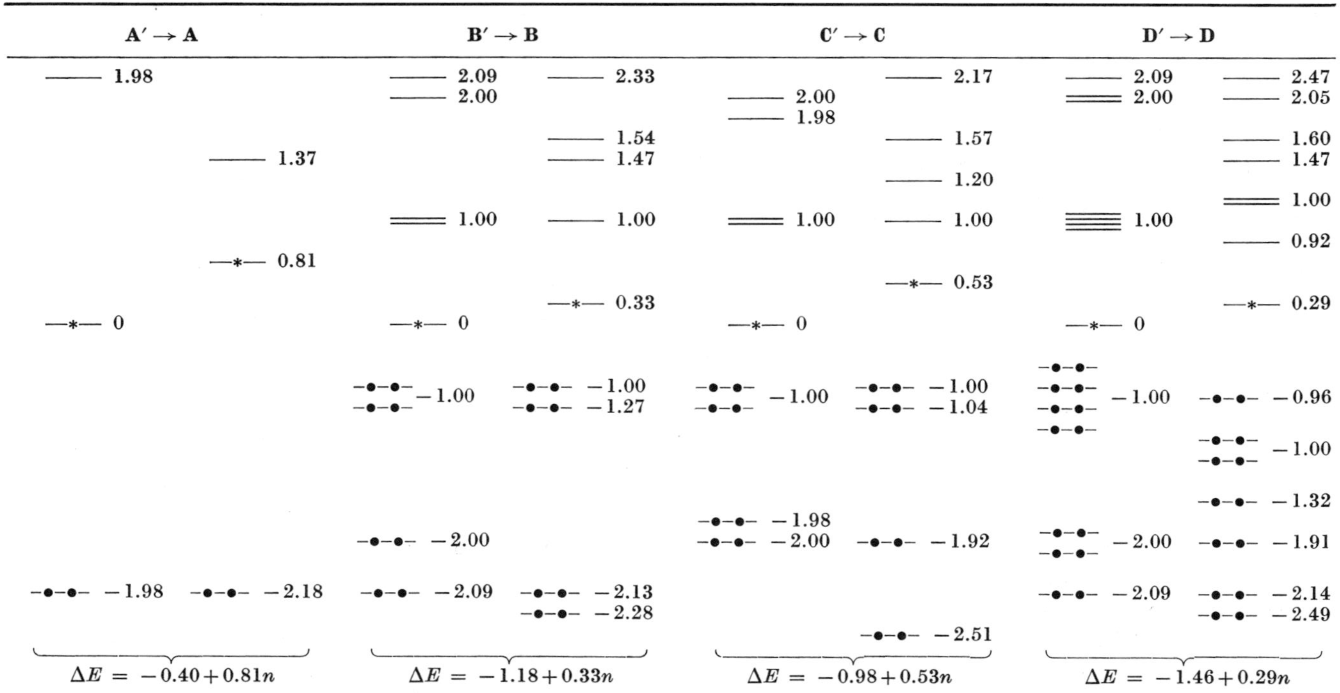

$A' \rightarrow A$	$B' \rightarrow B$	$C' \rightarrow C$	$D' \rightarrow D$
	2.09	2.17	2.47
	2.00		2.05
		2.00	2.09
		1.98	2.00
1.98	2.33		
	1.54	1.57	1.60
	1.47		1.47
		1.20	
	1.00	1.00	1.00
1.37			1.00
			0.92
*0.81	*0.33	*0.53	*0.29
*0	*0	*0	*0
	−1.00	−1.00	−0.96
	−1.27	−1.04	−1.00
			−1.00
			−1.32
	−2.00	−1.92	−1.91
−1.98	−2.09	−1.98	−2.00
−2.18	−2.13	−2.00	−2.09
	−2.28	−2.51	−2.14
			−2.49
$\Delta E = -0.40 + 0.81n$	$\Delta E = -1.18 + 0.33n$	$\Delta E = -0.98 + 0.53n$	$\Delta E = -1.46 + 0.29n$

[a] Each dot represents one electron; each asterisk represents n electrons (zero, one, or two). The molecular orbital energies are in units of $|\beta|$.

carbon to unactivated carbon); this sequence accords with observed reactivity sequences [109] in solvolytic and rearrangement reactions.

For each extra electron added to systems A through E it is clear that the bridging process becomes less advantageous. In the case of free radical

A: $\overset{R}{\underset{}{\diagdown}} C - \overset{*}{C}$ $\xrightarrow{\dfrac{E=(-0.40 + 0.81n)|\beta|}{\text{kcal./mole}}}$ (figure) $(2 + n)$ electrons[cf. 108]

B: $\overset{H_5C_6}{\underset{}{\diagdown}} C - \overset{*}{C}$ $\xrightarrow{\dfrac{E=(-1.18 + 0.33n)|\beta|}{\text{kcal./mole}}}$ (figure) $(8 + n)$ electrons

C: $\overset{R}{\underset{H_5C_6}{\diagup}} \overset{\diagdown}{C} - \overset{*}{C}$ $\xrightarrow{\dfrac{E=(-0.98 + 0.53n)|\beta|}{\text{kcal./mole}}}$ (figure) $(8 + n)$ electrons

D: $\overset{H_5C_6}{\underset{H_5C_6}{}} C - \overset{*}{C}$ $\xrightarrow{\dfrac{E=(-1.46 + 0.29n)|\beta|}{\text{kcal./mole}}}$ (figure) $(14 + n)$ electrons

E: $\overset{H_5C_6}{\underset{H_5C_6}{}} H_5C_6 - C - \overset{*}{C}$ $\xrightarrow{\dfrac{E=(-1.87 + 0.26n)|\beta|}{\text{kcal./mole}}}$ (figure) $(20 + n)$ electrons

rearrangements, where $n = 1$, alkyl migration between unactivated carbon atoms is especially unfavorable (ΔE for case A $= +0.41\ |\beta|$). In the remaining cases migration may be predicted to occur with increasing ease in the order $C < B < D < E$. These predictions are consonant with the observed reluctance of alkyl groups and the known ability of phenyl groups to migrate in free radical arrangements.[110,111]

Having found the molecular orbital calculations to be at least qualitatively reliable in the instances of carbonium ion and free radical rearrangements, it remains to apply these calculations to the problem at hand, namely, carbanion rearrangements. One finds that in case A, that of alkyl migration between unactivated carbon atoms, $1.22\ |\beta|$ is required to effect bridging; thus simple alkyl migration of carbanions is the most energetically unfavorable of cases. Even in case C, where the alkyl group migrates from a phenyl-bearing carbon atom, the bridging energy is unfavorable by $0.08\ |\beta|$.

[109a] M. Simonetta and S. Winstein, *J. Am. Chem. Soc.*, **76**, 18 (1954).

[110] F. H. Seubold, Jr., *J. Am. Chem. Soc.*, **75**, 2532 (1953).

[111] For further references and discussion, see J. Hine, *Physical Organic Chemistry*, McGraw-Hill, New York, 1956, p. 446.

Contrariwise, for phenyl migration (cases B, D, and E) the half-migrated species is of lower energy than the free unbridged carbanion. For migration between nonactivated carbon atoms (case B) 0.52 $|\beta|$ is gained in the bridging process, while for migration from a phenyl-bearing to a nonphenyl-bearing carbon atom (case D) the bridging process is favored by 0.88 $|\beta|$. The most favorable case of phenyl migration is in case E where the shift is from a carbon atom retaining two phenyl groups.

In connection with the electrophilic rearrangements discussed thus far, there is a point to be considered. This is the apparent differing migratory aptitudes in the Wittig and Stevens rearrangements compared to the Grovenstein-Zimmerman type rearrangement. In the Wittig rearrangement it appeared that methyl migration proceeds more readily than phenyl, while in the 1,2 carbon to carbon anionic rearrangement phenyl proved to migrate more readily than methyl. One possible rationalization is that the differing behavior is due to differences in the stability of the anion generated in the rearrangement process. One may, as Hauser has noted,[111a] picture the Wittig and Stevens rearrangements to be internal nucleophilic displacements of the negative carbon on the migrating group; the departing groups for these two rearrangements are alkoxide and substituted amine. Intuitively and with ordinary nucleophilic displacements in mind, one finds the greater reactivity of methyl versus phenyl to be reasonable, for simple displacements on an unactivated phenyl ring do not proceed readily. In the case of the carbon to carbon migrations a much poorer anion departs, namely, a carbanion. With a poor departing anion, unable to absorb much of the negative charge derived from the attacking anion, the phenyl group with its π system is more able to absorb this charge in the transition state than methyl. Thus the dichotomy of migratory aptitudes is not unreasonable.

E. The Truce-Smiles Rearrangement

The Smiles rearrangement involves an intramolecular nucleophilic substitution reaction illustrated by equation 10.[112] Many interesting variations have been uncovered by Smiles and his co-workers, and the reaction has been

(10)

[111a] C. R. Hauser and S. W. Cantor, *J. Am. Chem. Soc.*, **73**, 1437 (1951).

[112] F. Galbraith and S. Smiles, *J. Chem. Soc. (London)*, **1935**, 1234.

reviewed by Bunnett.[113] Despite its interest, the ordinary Smiles rearrangement will not be discussed here, since carbanions are not involved.

An interesting rearrangement related to the Smiles reaction and pertinent to the present text has been described by Truce.[114] Truce showed that treatment of mesityl phenyl sulfone (167) with butyllithium in refluxing ether affords, after working up, an excellent yield of 2-benzyl-4,6-dimethylbenzenesulfonic acid (170). Similarly, mesityl p-tolyl sulfone (171) yields 172, thus indicating that the rearrangement occurs by displacement of the arylsulfonyl group at the ring position originally bonded to sulfur.

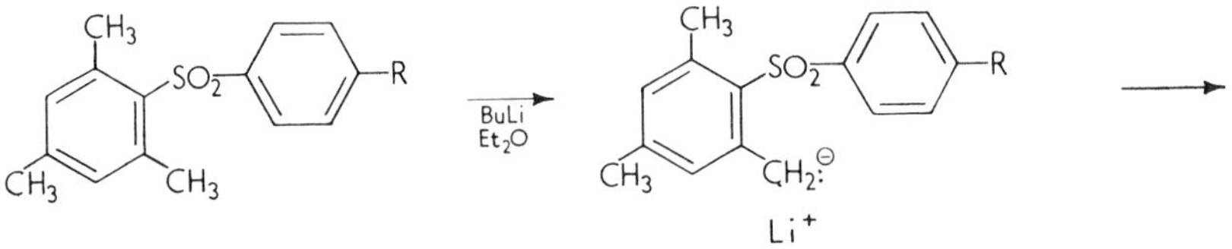

(167: R = H)
(171: R = CH₃)

(168)

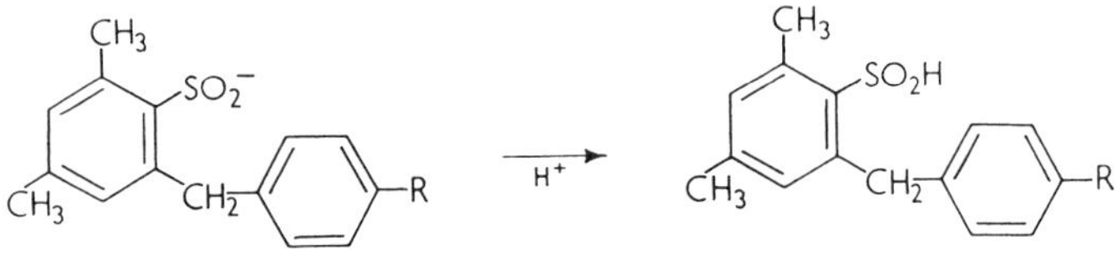

(169: R = H)

(170: R = H)
(172: R = CH₃)

It may be seen that the Truce-Smiles reaction is mechanistically related to the Stevens, Wittig, and Grovenstein-Zimmerman type rearrangements; it differs mainly in having a five-membered ring transition state rather than a three-membered one. The Truce-Smiles rearrangement is of further interest in that it provides additional cases of phenyl migration under relatively mild conditions.

3. BASE-CATALYZED α ELIMINATION REARRANGEMENT REACTIONS

A base-catalyzed α elimination reaction may be defined operationally as one in which a proton and an anionoid species are lost from the same carbon atom. This contrasts with the more common β elimination reactions in which a proton is removed from the carbon atom β to the departing anion. Many,

[113] J. F. Bunnett and R. E. Zahler, Chem. Revs., 49, 362 (1951).

[114] W. E. Truce and co-workers, J. Am. Chem. Soc., 80, 3625 (1958); see also W. E. Truce and W. J. Ray, Jr., J. Am. Chem. Soc., 81, 481, 484 (1959), for further examples and discussion.

but by no means all, base-catalyzed α elimination reactions involve divalent carbon intermediates. Probably the best known and most thoroughly studied example is the basic hydrolysis of chloroform. Although a number of early researchers had suggested a mechanism in which the elements of hydrogen chloride are removed from chloroform to afford dichlorocarbene (**173**) as an

$$
\underset{\underset{Cl}{|}}{\overset{\overset{Cl}{|}}{Cl-C-H}} + OH^- \quad \rightleftharpoons \quad \underset{\underset{Cl}{|}}{\overset{\overset{Cl}{|}}{Cl-C:^{\ominus}}} + H_2O
$$

$$
\underset{\underset{Cl}{|}}{\overset{\overset{Cl}{|}}{Cl-C:^{\ominus}}} \quad \underset{\xrightarrow{\text{rate limiting}}}{} \quad \underset{\underset{Cl}{|}}{\overset{\overset{Cl}{|}}{C:}} + Cl^-
$$
(173)

$$
\underset{\underset{Cl}{|}}{\overset{\overset{Cl}{|}}{C:}} + OH^- \quad \longrightarrow \quad CO + HCOO^-
$$
(173)

intermediate, it was the thorough and elegant research of Hine[115] which clearly established the intermediacy of this substance and the details of the reaction mechanism.

α Elimination Reactions of Alkyl Halides and Related Compounds. Striking demonstration of the presence of dichlorocarbene in the base-catalyzed reactions of chloroform, as postulated by Hine and discussed above, is found in the elegant and pioneering work of v. E. Doering and Hoffmann.[116] Dichlorocarbene (**174**) generated from chloroform and potassium *tert*-butoxide was trapped by cyclohexene to give dichloronorcarane (**175**). Closs[117] has shown that the still less stable species, chlorocarbene (**176**), can be obtained from the reaction of butyllithium with methylene chloride and trapped to give chloronorcarane (**177**). The series is completed with the example described by Friedman.[118] Low yields of norcarane could be isolated from the reaction

[115] J. Hine, *J. Am. Chem. Soc.*, **72**, 2438 (1950); J. Hine and A. M. Dowell, Jr., *J. Am. Chem. Soc.*, **76**, 2688 (1954). Cf. J. Hine, R. J. Rosscup, and D. C. Duffey, *J. Am. Chem. Soc.*, **82**, 6120 (1960), for Paper XXII and references to intermediate papers in this series of investigations.

[116] W. v. E. Doering and A. K. Hoffman, *J. Am. Chem. Soc.*, **76**, 6162 (1954).

[117] G. L. Closs and L. E. Closs, *J. Am. Chem. Soc.*, **82**, 5723 (1960); G. L. Closs and G. M. Schwartz, *J. Am. Chem. Soc.*, **82**, 5729 (1960).

[118] L. Friedman and J. G. Berger, *J. Am. Chem. Soc.*, **82**, 5758 (1960).

of phenylsodium with methyl chloride in the presence of cyclohexene. Here α elimination affords carbene itself.[119]

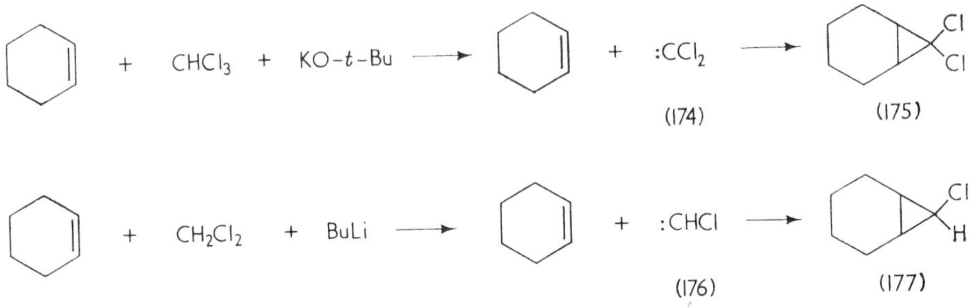

(174)   (175)

(176)   (177)

A related α elimination reaction was reported by Wittig and R. Polster [120] and Franzen and Wittig.[121] Wittig and Polster had noted that the reaction of organolithium reagents with tetramethylammonium bromide affords a conjugate base reasonably formulated as **178**. On heating with ethylene glycol dimethyl ether, **178** yielded trimethylamine and polymethylene, presumably as a result of the formation of the free ylid **179**. In accord with this

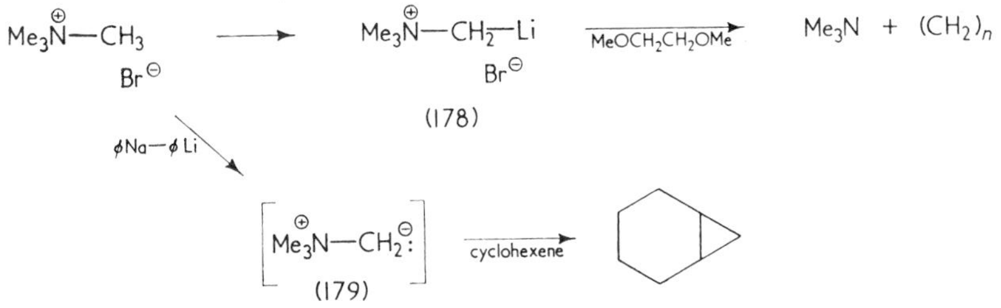

picture were the findings that attempted preparation of the sodium analog of **178** led only to trimethylamine and polymethylene. More recently Franzen and Wittig were able to obtain 5–18% of norcarane from the reaction of tetramethylammonium bromide with phenyllithium-phenylsodium in the presence of cyclohexene, thus demonstrating the presence of carbene.

Some very interesting reactions of halides were reported by Whitmore and

---

[119] S. M. Luck et al.[119a] have presented evidence that α elimination occurs to some extent in the potassium amide–liquid ammonia elimination of primary halides. α elimination is said to occur partially with n-octyl bromide-2-d_2 but not with n-octyl bromide-1-d_2.

[119a] S. M. Luck, D. G. Hill, A. T. Stewart, Jr., and C. R. Hauser, J. Am. Chem. Soc., **81**, 2784 (1959).

[120] G. Wittig and R. Polster, Ann., **599**, 1 (1956).

[121] V. Franzen and G. Wittig, Angew. Chem., **72**, 417 (1960).

co-workers.[122] It was noted that the reaction of sodium or ethylsodium with neopentyl chloride affords 1,1-dimethylcyclopropane (180) as a major product.

$$CH_3-\underset{\underset{CH_3}{|}}{\overset{\overset{CH_3}{|}}{C}}-CH_2-Cl \xrightarrow{EtNa} CH_3-\underset{\underset{CH_3}{|}}{\overset{\overset{CH_2}{|}}{C}}-CH_2$$

(180)

Similarly, reaction of sodium or ethylsodium with neophyl chloride was found to yield 1-phenyl-1-methylcyclopropane and 1-phenyl-2-methyl-2-propene (181).

$$\phi-\underset{\underset{CH_3}{|}}{\overset{\overset{CH_3}{|}}{C}}-CH_2-Cl \xrightarrow{EtNa} \phi-\underset{\underset{CH_3}{|}}{\overset{\overset{CH_2}{|}}{C}}-CH_2 + \underset{\underset{CH_3}{|}}{\overset{\overset{CH_2}{||}}{C}}-CH_2\phi$$

(181)

More recently, Kirmse and v. E. Doering [123] have studied the reactions of *n*-propyl chloride, *n*-butyl chloride, and isobutyl chloride with sodium. Cyclopropane was shown to constitute 4% of the C_3H_6 fraction in the first example. In the second case, methylcyclopropane was found to the extent of 7% in the C_4H_8 fraction together with 86% of 1-butene and small amounts of the 2-butenes. In contrast, isobutyl chloride affords 35% of methylcyclopropane, while, as noted by Whitmore, neopentyl chloride gives mainly dimethylcyclopropane. Kirmse and v. E. Doering found that the reaction of α,α-dideuterated isobutyl chloride yields monodeuterated methylcyclopropane, a result consistent with an α elimination mechanism in which a carbene is formed and then ring formation results by insertion of the carbene carbon between the carbon and hydrogen of a methyl group (eq. 11). These

$$CH_3-\underset{\underset{H}{|}}{\overset{\overset{CH_3}{|}}{C}}-CD_2-Cl \xrightarrow[\substack{\text{present}}]{\text{RNa species}} CH_3-\underset{\underset{H}{|}}{\overset{\overset{CH_3}{|}}{C}}-\underset{D}{C}: \rightarrow CH_3-\underset{\underset{H}{|}}{\overset{\overset{CH_2}{|}}{C}}-CDH$$

(11)

researchers noted that a γ elimination, in which a proton is abstracted from a methyl group while chloride is lost from the α carbon atom, would lead to product containing two deuterium atoms. Also of interest is the observation

[122] F. C. Whitmore, A. H. Popkin, and J. R. Pfister, *J. Am. Chem. Soc.*, **61**, 1616 (1939); F. C. Whitmore, A. H. Popkin, H. I. Bernstein, and J. P. Wilkins, *J. Am. Chem. Soc.*, **63**, 124 (1941); F. C. Whitmore and H. D. Zook, *J. Am. Chem. Soc.*, **64**, 1783 (1942); F. C. Whitmore, C. A. Weisgerber, and A. C. Shabica, Jr., *J. Am. Chem. Soc.*, **65**, 1469 (1943).

[123] W. Kirmse and W. v. E. Doering, *Tetrahedron*, **11**, 266 (1960).

that the isobutylene was formed to the extent of 67% by α elimination and 33% by β elimination.

A related α elimination reaction was reported by Zimmerman and Smentowski.[124] In this study it was found that treatment of 1-chloro-2,2,2-triphenylethane (**182**) with amylsodium at 35° affords triphenylethylene. Unlike the formation of **181** from neophyl chloride reported in Whitmore's study, this is unambiguously an α elimination with phenyl migration.

$$\phi_3C—CH_2—Cl + amylsodium \rightarrow \phi_2C{=}CH\phi + pentane + NaCl$$
(182)

The base-catalyzed Stieglitz rearrangement [125] presents a similar example of α elimination with aryl migration. In this reaction trityl chloramines and bromoamines are treated with base to give benzophenone N-arylimines. In these studies, the relative extent of migration of phenyl versus p-chlorophenyl was reported to be very close to statistical. Pinck and Hilbert [126] found that

$$\phi_3C—NHCl \xrightarrow[\text{or NaOCH}_3 \text{ in CH}_3\text{OH}]{\text{soda lime 100-200°}} \phi_2C{=}N\phi$$

the rearrangements of 9-methyl-, 9-phenyl-, and 9-α-naphthyl-9-fluorenyl-chloramines afford the corresponding 9-substituted phenanthridines (**183**).

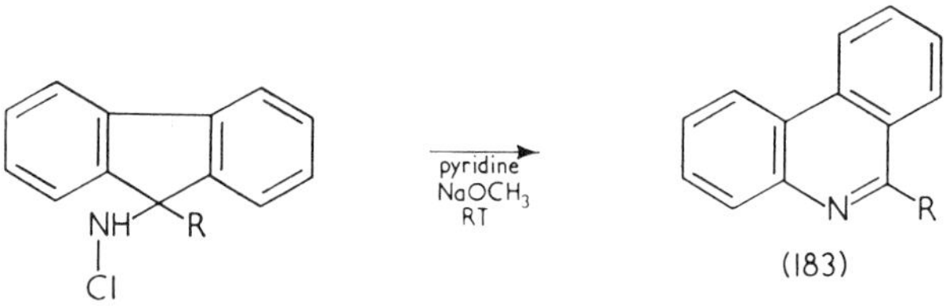

In these base catalyzed α elimination reactions occurring with rearrangement there are two extreme a priori mechanisms which might be envisioned. One might picture, at one extreme, a 1,2 carbanion shift followed by β elimination; e.g.,

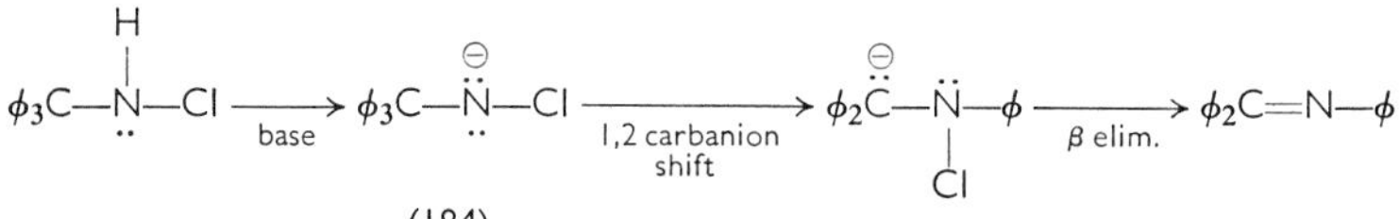

(184)

[124] H. E. Zimmerman and F. J. Smentowski, *J. Am. Chem. Soc.*, **79**, 5455 (1957).

[125] The base-catalyzed version was investigated largely by two of Stieglitz's students.[125a]

[125a] I. Vosburgh, *J. Am. Chem. Soc.*, **38**, 2081 (1916); A. F. Morgan, *J. Am. Chem. Soc.* **38**, 2095 (1916).

[126] L. A. Pinck and G. E. Hilbert, *J. Am. Chem. Soc.*, **59**, 8 (1937).

Alternatively, at the other extreme one might picture loss of chloride from conjugate base **184** prior to rearrangement to give a divalent species (carbene or nitrene) which then undergoes rearrangement to product.

$$\phi_3C-\overset{\ominus}{\underset{\cdot\cdot}{N}}-Cl \xrightarrow[\text{chloride}]{\text{loss of}} \phi_3C-\overset{\cdot\cdot}{\underset{\cdot\cdot}{N}} \rightarrow \phi_2C{=}N\phi$$

Between these extremes are gradations in which migration and loss of chloride are synchronized to varying extents. Which is actually the best description for each rearrangement will have to derive from future studies.

One case where information bearing on this question is available is the α elimination reaction of diarylhaloethylenes to give tolans as originally described in 1894.[127,128]

$$Ar_2C{=}CHX \xrightarrow[\text{base}]{} ArC{\equiv}CAr$$

Bothner-By [129] prepared *cis*- and *trans*-1-*p*-bromophenyl-1-phenyl-2-bromo-ethylenes-*1*-14*C* (**185** and **186**) and studied the extent of migration of each

$$\begin{array}{c}
\underset{Ar''}{\overset{Ar'}{\diagup}}{}^{14}C{=}C\underset{Br}{\overset{H}{\diagdown}} \xrightarrow[\text{t-BuOH}]{\text{KO-t-Bu}} \underset{Ar''}{\overset{Ar'}{\diagup}}{}^{14}C{=}\overset{\ominus}{\underset{Br}{\overset{\cdot\cdot}{C}}} \rightarrow Ar''{-}^{14}C{\equiv}C{-}Ar'
\end{array}$$

(185: Ar′ = ϕ; Ar″ = *p*-Brϕ)
(186: Ar′ = *p*-Brϕ; Ar″ = ϕ)

aryl group as a function of its stereochemistry. It was observed that the main course of the reaction involves migration of the aryl group *cis* to hydrogen and *trans* to the departing bromine. Bothner-By suggested that the first step of the reaction is proton removal to give a vinyl carbanion capable of holding its geometry and that this carbanion then undergoes an aryl migration concerted with the loss of bromide. Curtin and co-workers [130] studied the similar rearrangement of *cis*- and *trans*-1-phenyl-1-*p*-chlorophenyl-2-bromoethylenes-*1*-14*C* with butyllithium as the base. It was found, in agreement with Bothner-By, that the aryl group *trans* to bromine is the one that migrates. As both Bothner-By and Curtin have noted, the stereospecificity of the reaction rules

[127] P. Fritsch, *Ann.*, **279**, 319 (1894); W. Buttenberg, *Ann.*, **279**, 327 (1894); H. Wiechell, *Ann.*, **279**, 337 (1894).

[128] For more recent references and discussion of the reaction, see T. L. Jacobs, *Org. Reactions*, **5**, 40 (1949); Bothner-By;[129] Curtin *et al.*[130]

[129] A. A. Bothner-By, *J. Am. Chem. Soc.*, **77**, 3293 (1955).

[130] D. Y. Curtin, E. W. Flynn, and R. F. Nystrom, *J. Am. Chem. Soc.*, **80**, 4599 (1958); D. Y. Curtin, E. W. Flynn, R. F. Nystrom, and W. H. Richardson, *Chem. & Ind.* (*London*), **1957**, 1453.

out the carbene **187** as a reasonable reaction intermediate, for it is unlikely that such an intermediate could hold its configuration.

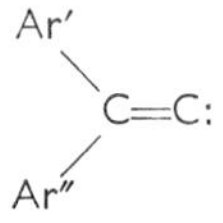

$$\begin{array}{c} Ar' \\ \diagdown \\ C{=}C: \\ \diagup \\ Ar'' \end{array}$$

(187)

In conclusion it should be stated that there are indeed many additional base-catalyzed rearrangement reactions in the literature. Some of these, as the Favorskii rearrangement [131] (see also Section 16) and the benzilic acid rearrangement,[132] have recently been reviewed and therefore have not been discussed. Since all base-catalyzed rearrangements could not possibly be covered in any single chapter, the topics considered here were chosen because of their pertinence to the main theme of carbanion rearrangements and because of their special interest to the author.

[131] A. Kende, *Org. Reactions*, **11**, 261 (1960).
[132] S. Selman and J. F. Eastham, *Quart. Revs. (London)*, **14**, 221 (1961).

7

FREE RADICAL REARRANGEMENTS

CHEVES WALLING
Columbia University, New York,
New York

I. INTRODUCTION

The intensive study of reactions proceeding through free radical intermediates makes up a relatively new branch of organic chemistry. As a consequence, our knowledge of free radical rearrangements is considerably less extensive than that of rearrangements involving carbonium ions or other species with open sextets of electrons. Nevertheless, enough information is now at hand so that one can say with considerable certainty that (at least at ordinary temperatures) free radicals show much less tendency to undergo rearrangement than do more electron-deficient species. Furthermore, such rearrangements which do occur can be classified into a small number of types, defined either by the over-all structural change or by the nature of the individual steps involved.

407

As far as over-all structural changes are concerned, any definition of a "rearrangement" is rather a loose one, and we will restrict ourselves for the most part to rearrangements of carbon skeletons (including cyclizations and ring openings), double bond migrations, and interchange of substituents within the same molecule. From the point of view of understanding the nature of radical rearrangements, however, classification on the basis of individual steps is more illuminating, and this, in turn, requires some brief comments on radical reactions in general. For a more detailed discussion the reader is referred to the author's monograph on the subject.[1]

For the purpose of organic chemistry, a free radical may be defined as a species with one or more unpaired electrons. With a few exceptions such as triphenylmethyl or highly substituted phenoxyl radicals, such species exist in solution or in the gas phase only as transient reaction intermediates, since they are rapidly destroyed by bimolecular reactions leading to either coupling or disproportionation. Like other transient intermediates, radicals are produced by suitable combinations of reagents and conditions during the course of a reaction. These include the thermal dissociation of molecules (e.g., peroxides, azo compounds, etc.) with weak covalent bonds, photochemical dissociation of suitable molecules, oxidation-reduction processes, the impact of high energy radiation, and even mechanical rupture of covalent bonds.

Once formed, radicals rapidly disappear by coupling or disproportion as mentioned above, usually within a fraction of a second. However, within this time they may undergo 1,2 shifts of substituents:

$$R_1R_2R_3C\text{—}\overset{\bullet}{C}H_2 \rightarrow R_1R_2\overset{\bullet}{C}\text{—}CH_2R_3 \tag{1}$$

take part in displacement reactions:

$$R_1\cdot + X\text{—}R_2 \rightarrow R_1\text{—}X + R_2\cdot \tag{2}$$

or add to double bonds or other centers of unsaturation:

$$R\cdot + CH_2\text{=}CHR \rightleftharpoons R\text{—}CH_2\text{—}\overset{\bullet}{C}HR \tag{3}$$

Such additions are frequently reversible, leading to radical decompositions. Thus the decomposition of the acetoxy radical into CO_2 and the methyl radical

$$CH_3COO\cdot \rightarrow CH_3\cdot + CO_2 \tag{4}$$

might be thought of as the reverse of the (hypothetical) addition of methyl to CO_2.

Reactions such as 1 through 4 lead to the transformation, rather than the destruction, of radicals, and the products, being in turn capable of further reaction, can make up the propagating steps in free radical chain reactions. Through such chains a single initial radical may lead to the formation of

[1] C. Walling, *Free Radicals in Solution*, Wiley, New York, 1957.

hundreds (or even millions) of molecules of product, making this class of reactions one of the most interesting, and certainly synthetically most useful, in free radical chemistry.

A 1,2 shift such as shown in equation 1 represents the simplest type of free radical rearrangement, but over-all rearrangements may also be observed by suitable combinations of intramolecular and intermolecular displacements, additions, and decompositions (usually as parts of radical chain processes). Also, since allylic radicals are delocalized systems

$$\dot{C}H_2-CH{=}CHR \leftrightarrow CH_2{=}CH-\dot{C}HR$$

which can undergo displacement or addition reactions at either end of the allylic system, their formation as transient intermediates can often lead to allylic rearrangements in the course of radical reactions.

Finally, it is a reasonably safe generalization that free radicals, once formed, show reactions and properties which are essentially independent of their mode of formation, and are remarkably independent of the media in which they exist. Enough contradictions exist in the literature, however, so that both of these statements require some justification. Unequivocal evidence exists, chiefly from the work of Russell,[2] that specific solvent effects produce dramatic changes in the reactivity of halogen atoms, but no phenomena of comparable magnitude have been demonstrated for the reactions of carbon radicals. The situation in regard to the properties of the "same" radical produced from different sources is a bit more obscure. In a number of cases rather different final products have been reported from radicals generated in different ways, and this has led to the question of just how "free" free radicals may be. Unfortunately, as far as the writer is aware all such cases are suspect on one of two grounds. Either radicals may have been produced at different *rates* in the systems under comparison, altering the competition between reactions of different kinetic order in radicals, or oxidation-reduction systems were involved which could lead to ionic as well as radical species. Indeed, the possibility of such a competition between radical and nonradical processes (or the alternation of radical and nonradical steps in an over-all reaction) poses one of the most difficult questions in the interpretation of radical reactions in general. A number of examples will appear in the course of our discussion, and it will be seen that in some cases the observed rearrangements do not appear to involve radical intermediates in the rearrangement step at all.

2. 1,2 SHIFTS

A. Aryl Migrations

In 1947 Winstein and Seubold[3] investigated the di-*tert*-butyl peroxide-initiated decarbonylation of β-phenylisovalyraldehyde. They obtained 90%

[2] G. A. Russell, *J. Am. Chem. Soc.*, **79**, 2977 (1957), and subsequent papers.
[3] S. Winstein and F. H. Seubold, Jr., *J. Am. Chem. Soc.*, **69**, 2916 (1947).

CO, and 70% of a 1:1 mixture of *tert*-butyl- and isobutylbenzenes, and interpreted the result in terms of the competing steps in the sequence shown in equations 5–8, involving in equation 7 the rearrangement of the intermediate

$$\phi-\underset{\underset{CH_3}{|}}{\overset{\overset{CH_3}{|}}{C}}-CH_2\overset{O}{\overset{\|}{C}}\cdot \ \rightarrow \ \phi-\underset{\underset{CH_3}{|}}{\overset{\overset{CH_3}{|}}{C}}-CH_2\cdot + CO \tag{5}$$

$$\phi-\underset{\underset{CH_3}{|}}{\overset{\overset{CH_3}{|}}{C}}-CH_2\cdot + \phi-\underset{\underset{CH_3}{|}}{\overset{\overset{CH_3}{|}}{C}}-CH_2CHO \rightarrow \phi-\underset{\underset{CH_3}{|}}{\overset{\overset{CH_3}{|}}{C}}-CH_3 + \phi-\underset{\underset{CH_3}{|}}{\overset{\overset{CH_3}{|}}{C}}-CH_2-\overset{O}{\overset{\|}{C}}\cdot \tag{6}$$

$$\phi-\underset{\underset{CH_3}{|}}{\overset{\overset{CH_3}{|}}{C}}-CH_2\cdot \ \xrightarrow{\ \ \ } \ \phi-CH_2-\underset{\underset{CH_3}{|}}{\overset{\overset{CH_3}{|}}{C}}\cdot \tag{7}$$

$$\phi-CH_2-\underset{\underset{CH_3}{|}}{\overset{\overset{CH_3}{|}}{C}}\cdot + \phi-\underset{\underset{CH_3}{|}}{\overset{\overset{CH_3}{|}}{C}}-CH_2CHO \rightarrow \phi-CH_2-\underset{\underset{CH_3}{|}}{\overset{\overset{CH_3}{|}}{C}}H + \phi-\underset{\underset{CH_3}{|}}{\overset{\overset{CH_3}{|}}{C}}-CH_2\overset{O}{\overset{\|}{C}}\cdot \tag{8}$$

"neophyl" radical by a 1,2 shift of phenyl. Subsequently Seubold[4] showed that the decarbonylation and rearrangement are successive steps and that the neophyl radical has independent existence by comparing the products obtained in pure (6.4 M) aldehyde and in 1M solution in chlorobenzene. Under these conditions the ratio of isobutyl- to *tert*-butylbenzene increased from 1.3 to 4.0, but remained essentially temperature independent, indicating that equations 6 and 7 have comparable activation energies. The concentration dependence of the rearrangement has recently been investigated in more detail by Ruechardt[4a] who finds that the ratio of rate constants for reaction 7:reaction 6 is 2.76 at 130° and 3.25 at 144.5°. His similar measurements on a series of para-substituted β-phenylisovaleraldehydes are discussed under heading 2D.

Such decarbonylations provide a convenient technique for generating radicals of known structure and have been widely used in studying the possibility of rearrangements. Curtin and Hurwitz[5] have examined a series of β-phenyl-substituted aldehydes with the results shown in equations 9–12. The first three examples (eqs. 9–11) all yielded products with rearranged structures, although the product isolated from equations 9–11 represents the result of chain termination by radical coupling, rather than the anticipated product of the chain

[4] F. H. Seubold, Jr., *J. Am. Chem. Soc.*, **75**, 2532 (1953).

[4a] C. Ruechardt, *Chem. Ber.*, **94**, 2599 (1961).

[5] D. Y. Curtin and M. J. Hurwitz, *J. Am. Chem. Soc.*, **74**, 5381 (1952).

decarbonylation. In a subsequent paper Curtin and Kauer[6] demonstrated that the absence of observable rearrangement in reaction 12 was not the

$$\phi_3CCH_2CHO \xrightarrow{-CO} \phi_2CHCH_2\phi \qquad (9)$$

$$\phi_3C—CH(CH_3)CHO \xrightarrow{-CO} \phi_2CH—CH(CH_3)\phi + \phi_2C{=}C(CH_3)\phi \qquad (10)$$

$$\phi_2C(CH_3)CH_2—CHO \xrightarrow{-CO} \phi—CH_2—\overset{\overset{\displaystyle CH_3}{|}}{C}—\overset{\overset{\displaystyle CH_3}{|}}{C}—CH_2 \qquad (11)$$

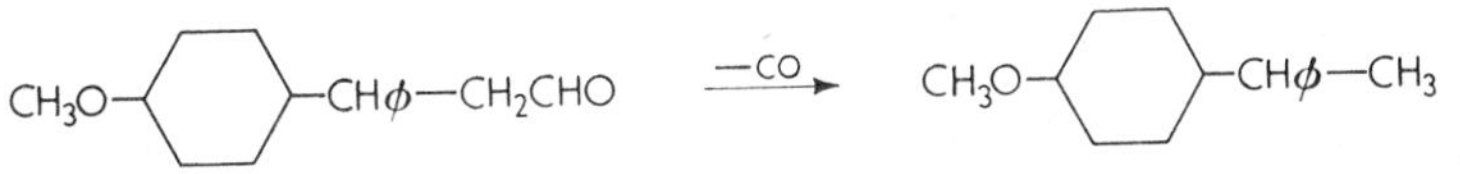

$$(12)$$

result of a competing hydrogen migration, since the β-deutero compound yielded only 1-anisyl-1-phenylethane-1-d. The occurrence of similar phenyl migrations in cyclic systems has been demonstrated by Wilt and Philip[7] in reactions 13 and 14. Their results again support the idea of the rearrangement

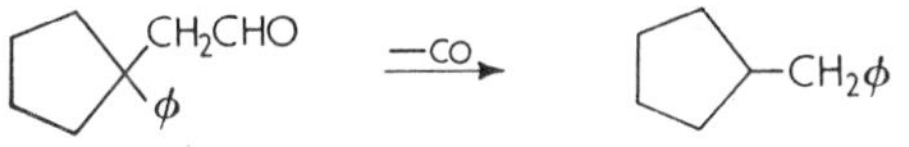

$$(13)$$

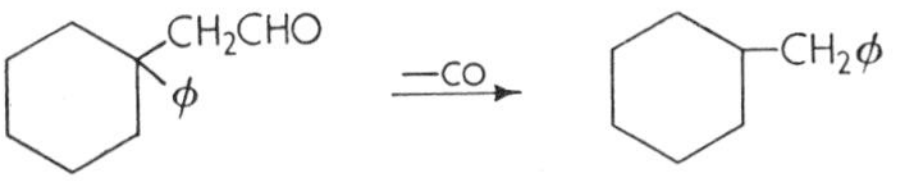

$$(14)$$

being a separate step competing with hydrogen abstraction by the unrearranged radical from aldehyde or other substrate. In reaction 13 the percentage of rearranged hydrocarbon increased from 63 to 92% on dilution of the aldehyde to 1M with chlorobenzene, and decreased to under 3% on addition of 20% benzyl mercaptan which permits the very rapid competing reaction 15.

$$(15)$$

Under the same conditions, rearrangement of the cyclohexylacetaldehyde was found to be more extensive than that of the cyclopentyl derivative, although the latter showed a higher over-all rate of decarbonylation. These results Wilt and Philip explained in terms of both a more favorable conformation for the rearrangement in the first case and a more rapid rate of the competing hydrogen abstraction in the latter. Recently these studies have

[6] D. Y. Curtin and J. C. Kauer, *J. Org. Chem.*, **25**, 880 (1960).

[7] J. W. Wilt and H. Philip, *J. Org. Chem.*, **24**, 441 (1959), **25**, 891 (1960).

been extended to a fused ring system.[7a] Decarbonylation of (1-methyltinanyl) acetaldehyde gives both 1,1-dimethylindane (65%) and 2-methyltetralin (35%). Here, the rearrangement seems to be somewhat retarded by the rigid nature of the ring system.

In all the foregoing examples, rearrangement converts a primary alkyl radical into a more stable tertiary or benzyl radical. That such a driving force is not required has been shown by Slaugh[8] who has investigated the decarbonylation of ^{14}C-labeled β-phenylpropionaldehyde (eq. 16). By determining

$$\phi—CH_2{}^{14}CH_2CHO \xrightarrow{-CO} \phi CH_2{}^{14}CH_3 + \phi{}^{14}CH_2CH_3 \qquad (16)$$

the position of the ^{14}C label in the resulting ethylbenzene Slaugh concluded that 2.3% rearrangement took place at 150–155° and 4.2% at 165–175° and that rearrangement was significantly reduced by the addition of thiophenol. By carrying out the reaction in the presence of tritium-labeled thiophenol and demonstrating the absence of α-tritioethylbenzene in the product, the occurrence of any hydrogen shift was also ruled out.

If our postulate about the identical reactivity of the same radical produced by different methods is indeed correct, rearrangements of β-aryl radicals should also be observed when they are produced by other means, providing only that they have long enough lives for rearrangement to compete with hydrogen abstraction or similar processes. In 1944 Urry and Kharasch[9] reported that 2-methyl-2-phenylpropyl chloride (neophyl chloride) on treatment with phenylmagnesium bromide in the presence of cobaltous bromide yielded *tert*-butyl- and isobutylbenzenes, 2-methyl-3-phenyl-1-propene, and 2-methyl-1-phenyl-1-propene, together with dimeric products and biphenyl, and suggested that the products containing the isobutylbenzene skeleton resulted from the same radical rearrangement shown in equation 7. Since this work antedates that of Winstein and Seubold, it very properly represents the first report of this type of radical rearrangement, but the aldehyde case was here cited first for reasons given below.

The general class of Grignard reagent reactions catalyzed by heavy metal salts has been extensively investigated by Kharasch and his students,[10] and the remarkable series of results they have obtained have been explained as radical processes involving basic sequences such as

$$RMgX + CoX_2 \rightarrow RCoX + MgX_2$$
$$RCoX \rightarrow CoX + R\cdot$$
$$CoX + R'X \rightarrow CoX_2 + R'\cdot$$

[7a] J. W. Wilt and C. A. Schneider, *J. Org. Chem.*, **26**, 4191 (1961).

[8] L. H. Slaugh, *J. Am. Chem. Soc.*, **81**, 2262 (1959).

[9] W. H. Urry and M. S. Kharasch, *J. Am. Chem. Soc.*, **66**, 1438 (1944).

[10] M. S. Kharasch and O. Reinmuth, *Grignard Reactions of Nonmetallic Substances*, Prentice-Hall, New York, 1954.

While it is certainly correct that traces of heavy metal salts profoundly influence the course of Grignard reactions, and that many of the products (particularly dimers of the radicals postulated above) are those expected from free radical intermediates, this class of reaction remains ill defined, and seems to the writer to provide a good example of the difficulty mentioned earlier, since it is not clearly demonstrated that *all* of the products result necessarily from radical reactions. Thus Wilds and McCormack have proposed an alternative scheme involving the formation of metallic cobalt,[11] some of the steps may well be heterogeneous, and the formation of carbonium ion intermediates (and their subsequent reactions) by oxidation-reduction processes cannot at present be excluded. In the case of aryl migrations, however, results parallel those in more clear-cut purely radical reactions. In addition to the case cited, Urry and Nicolaides [12] have observed similar amounts of rearrangement in the decarbonylation of β-p-tolylisovaleraldehyde and the reaction of ethylmagnesium bromide and $CoCl_2$ with p-methylneophyl chloride. More recently, Smith and Anderson [13] have studied the reaction of the Grignard reagents from 2-phenylpropyl bromide and 2-phenylethyl bromide with $CoBr_2$. In the first case a 17% yield of C_9 hydrocarbons was obtained containing 15% n-propylbenzene, 8% allylbenzene, and 17% β-methylstyrene together with unrearranged material. In the second, the mixture of ethylbenzene and styrene produced was shown, by ^{14}C labeling and degradation, to be 20% rearranged.

Rearrangements of radicals produced by the attack of peroxide fragments on hydrocarbons have recently been observed by Pines and Pillai [14] who decomposed di-*tert*-butyl peroxide in *tert*-butylbenzene, *tert*-amylbenzene, and cumene. With *tert*-butylbenzene at reflux, 7.1% isobutylbenzene was obtained, presumably via the sequence shown in equations 17–19, followed

$$(CH_3)_3C—O—O—C(CH_3)_3 \rightarrow 2(CH_3)_3CO\cdot \tag{17}$$

$$(CH_3)_3C—O\cdot \rightarrow CH_3COCH_3 + CH_3\cdot \tag{18}$$

$$(CH_3)_3CO\cdot (\text{or } CH_3\cdot) + \phi C(CH_3)_3 \rightarrow \phi \overset{\overset{\displaystyle CH_3}{\displaystyle |}}{\underset{\underset{\displaystyle CH_3}{\displaystyle |}}{C}} —CH_2\cdot + C_4H_9OH \text{ (or } CH_4) \tag{19}$$

by rearrangement of the neophyl radical and subsequent hydrogen abstraction by the rearranged product. Similarly, *tert*-amylbenzene gave 10.4%

[11] A. L. Wilds and W. B. McCormack, *J. Org. Chem.*, **14**, 45 (1949). For further discussion of the complications in these reactions, see. W. B. Smith, *J. Org. Chem.*, **26**, 4206 (1961); and F. W. Frey, Jr., *J. Org. Chem.*, **26**, 5187 (1961).

[12] W. H. Urry and N. Nicolaides, *J. Am. Chem. Soc.*, **74**, 5163 (1952).

[13] W. B. Smith and J. D. Anderson, *J. Am. Chem. Soc.*, **82**, 656 (1960).

[14] H. Pines and C. N. Pillai, *J. Am. Chem. Soc.*, **82**, 2921 (1960).

2-phenyl-3-methylbutane, and cumene 1.6% n-propylbenzene. Traces of isobutyl-benzene were also detected on treatment of *tert*-butylbenzene with benzoyl and acetyl peroxides.

The rearrangement of neophyl-type radicals from the decomposition of azo compounds of the structure **1** has been studied by Overberger and Gainer.[15]

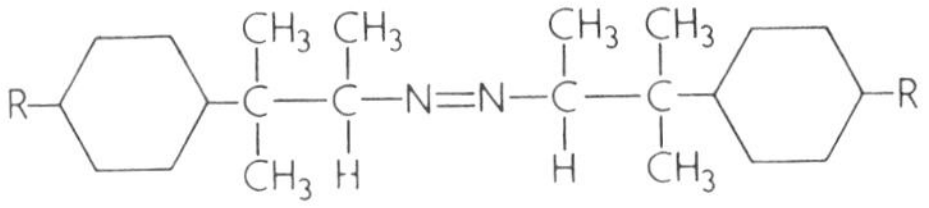

$$R = H, CH_3O—, CH_3CONH_2—$$

(1)

At 255° in diphenyl ether all decomposed at approximately the same rate, indicating no participation of the aryl group in the step of radical formation. The rather complex mixture of products from the case of $R = H$ was investigated with the conclusion that at least 23% rearrangement had occurred (eq. 20). Rearrangement of a similar radical during radical addition to

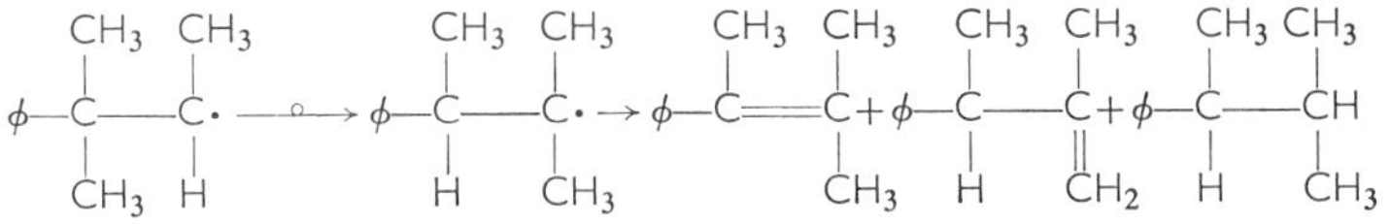

(20)

3,3-diphenyl-1-butene also occurs under some conditions[16] and again illustrates the importance of radical lifetimes and the rates of competing steps. Peroxide-initiated addition of n-butyl mercaptan or thioacetic acid at 80° gives only unrearranged product

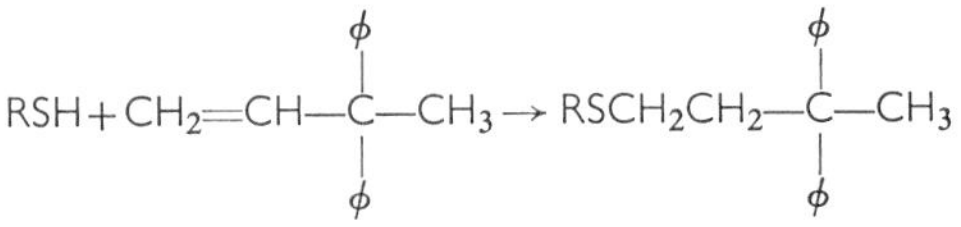

(21)

On the other hand, addition of n-butyraldehyde gives rearranged ketone via the sequence

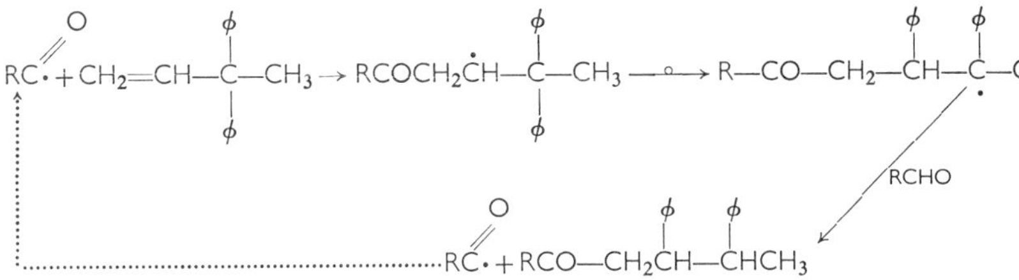

(22)

The difference is in keeping with the known much higher rate of alkyl radical attack on the RS—H bond of mercaptans compared with attack on the

[15] C. G. Overberger and H. Gainer, *J. Am. Chem. Soc.*, **80**, 4561 (1958).
[16] J. Weinstock and S. N. Lewis, *J. Am. Chem. Soc.*, **79**, 6243 (1957).

RCO—H bond of aldehydes and parallels the mercaptan inhibition of re-arrangements in decarbonylation reactions mentioned earlier.

Aryl migrations are not commonly observed during free radical halo-genations proceeding through the chain-carrying steps

$$X \cdot + RH \rightarrow HX + R \cdot \qquad (23)$$

$$R \cdot + X_2 \rightarrow RX + X \cdot \qquad (24)$$

because of the great rapidity and low activation energy of reaction 24. Thus liquid phase chlorination of *tert*-butylbenzene gives solely neophyl chlor-ide.[17,18] However, by carrying out the reaction at 190–245° in the gas phase, under conditions where halogen concentration is relatively low and the elevated temperature facilitates the higher activation energy rearrangement, Ingold and his co-workers[19] were able to obtain detectable quantites of 3-phenyl-2-methylpropyl chloride among the products and also demonstrated some rearrangement in the gas phase nitration of *tert*-butylbenzene.[20]

A much more striking example of rearrangement occurring in the gas phase at elevated temperatures has recently been described by Slaugh and Raley.[21] In their technique, alkylbenzenes are heated at 400–525° in the presence of organic halides or sulfur derivatives, which decompose into radicals capable of reversible hydrogen abstraction. Best results were obtained with alkyl bromides. As an example, in the presence of 2 mole % benzyl bromide cumene (2) was found to undergo 53% reaction to products containing 81% *n*-propyl-benzene (3). The key to the reaction is the reversibility of the hydrogen

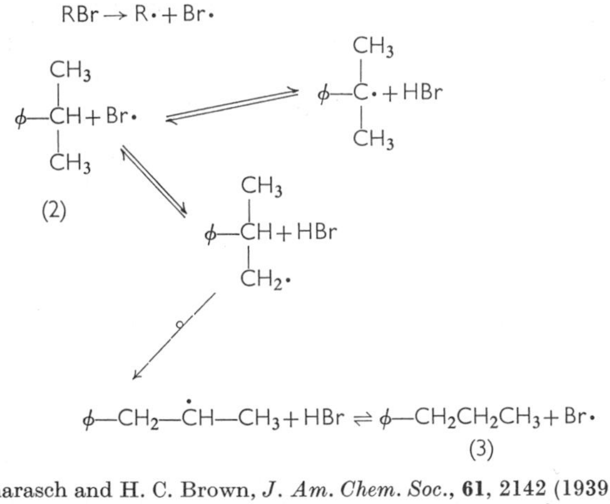

[17] M. S. Kharasch and H. C. Brown, *J. Am. Chem. Soc.*, **61**, 2142 (1939).

[18] H. C. Brown and G. A. Russell, *J. Am. Chem. Soc.*, **74**, 3995 (1952).

[19] J. D. Backhurst, E. D. Hughes, and C. K. Ingold, *J. Chem. Soc. (London)*, **1959**, 2742.

[20] H. C. Duffin, E. D. Hughes, and C. K. Ingold, *J. Chem. Soc. (London)*, **1954**, 2734.

[21] L. H. Slaugh and J. H. Raley, *J. Am. Chem. Soc.*, **82**, 1259 (1960).

abstraction by bromine atoms, and it should be noted that, while the preferred point of bromine atom attack is certainly the tertiary C—H, enough attack on primary C—H must occur at these temperatures to bring about the rearrangement. Comparable conversions of *tert*-butylbenzene to isobutylbenzene were also observed, although the isomerization of *sec*-butylbenzine to *n*-butylbenzene gave lower yields. Analogous rearrangements have also been observed in a less well-defined reaction by passing alkylbenzenes over copper turnings at 479–528° and very high pressures,[22] and it is noteworthy that in both cases the isomerizations occur in the opposite direction from that usually observed in low temperature carbonium ion processes.

Aryl migration to oxygen has been observed in the radical decomposition of triarylmethyl peroxides, the rearrangement usually being followed by dimerization as in the case of triphenylmethyl peroxide [23]

$$\phi_3C—O—O—C\phi_3 \rightarrow 2\phi_3C—O\cdot \rightarrow 2\phi_2\dot{C}—O\phi \rightarrow \phi O—\overset{\overset{\phi}{|}}{C}—\overset{\overset{\phi}{|}}{C}—O\phi$$

In the thermal decomposition of *p*-nitrophenyldiphenylmethyl hydroperoxide, which is believed to go by a similar path, Bartlett and Cotman [24] obtained evidence that the *p*-nitro group migrates in preference to phenyl, in contrast to the situation in nonsterically controlled rearrangements involving carbonium ions. A similar preference for *p*-nitrophenyl migration has also been noted by Curtin and Kauer [6] in the decarbonylation of β-*p*-nitrophenyl-β,β-diphenylpropionaldehyde. Kharasch and his students [25] have investigated the migratory aptitude of different aryl groups in a series of triarylmethyl *tert*-butyl peroxides, and *p*-biphenyl and α-naphthyl were found to migrate some six times as readily as phenyl and *p*-tolyl.

The foregoing examples show that the existence of radical rearrangements occurring via 1,2 shifts of aryl groups is well established. The probable nature of the transition states involved and the contrast with the nonrearrangement of most other types of groups are discussed on page 427.

B. Alkyl and Hydrogen Migrations

At present the preponderance of evidence indicates that 1,2 shifts of alkyl or hydrogen do not occur to a detectable extent during the lifetime of radicals in well-defined systems at ordinary temperatures. In most of the cases where

[22] V. N. Ipatieff, B. Kvetinskas, E. E. Meisinger, and H. Pines, *J. Am. Chem. Soc.*, **75**, 3323 (1953).

[23] H. Wieland, *Ber.*, 2553 (1911).

[24] P. D. Bartlett and J. D. Cotman, Jr., *J. Am. Chem. Soc.*, **72**, 3095 (1950).

[25] M. S. Kharasch, A. C. Poshkus, A. Fono, and W. Nudenberg, *J. Org. Chem.*, **16**, 1458 (1951).

they have been reported, alternate explanations are available for the observed results, or the radical nature of the reaction is in doubt.

As in the case of aryl migrations, aldehyde decarbonylation reactions (generally carried out using di-*tert*-butyl peroxide as an initiator for the chain reaction at 120–140°) provide one of the best and most popular tests. Seubold [26] has found no rearranged hydrocarbon in the decarbonylation of β,β-dimethylvaleraldehyde, cyclopentylacetaldehyde, and cyclohexanecarboxaldehyde. Similarly Doering *et al.*[27] obtained no rearrangement in the decarbonylations of methylethylisobutylacetaldehyde (**4**), although the optically active aldehyde yielded inactive 2,4-dimethylhexane (providing good evidence for a free radical intermediate), or of bicyclo[2.2.2]octane-2-carboxaldehyde (**5**) and apocamphane-1-carboxaldehyde (**6**). Very recently, Berson [28] has also obtained negative evidence for rearrangement with camphane-2-carboxaldehyde (**7**). A more complex rearrangement of the same

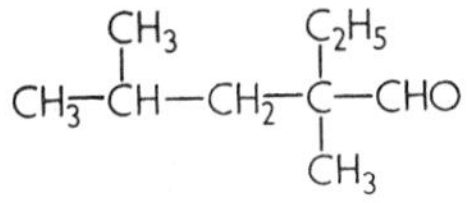

$$CH_3-\overset{\overset{\displaystyle CH_3}{|}}{CH}-CH_2-\overset{\overset{\displaystyle C_2H_5}{|}}{\underset{\underset{\displaystyle CH_3}{|}}{C}}-CHO$$

(4) 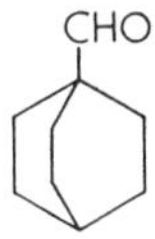　　　　(5) 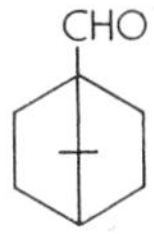　　　　(6) 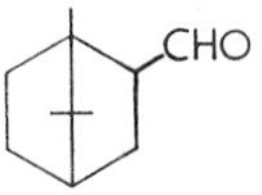　　　　(7)

intermediate radical occurring at a higher temperature does not appear to involve a 1,2 shift and is discussed under heading 4. Structures **5–7** are particularly interesting since they involve the formation of free radicals in bridged ring systems of the type known to undergo particularly facile carbonium ion rearrangements.

Radicals produced in such systems by other means also fail to undergo 1,2 shifts or to give evidence for "nonclassical" radicals. Cristol [29] has added thiocresol to norbornylene to give only unrearranged *exo*-2-norbornyl *p*-tolyl thioether via the sequence

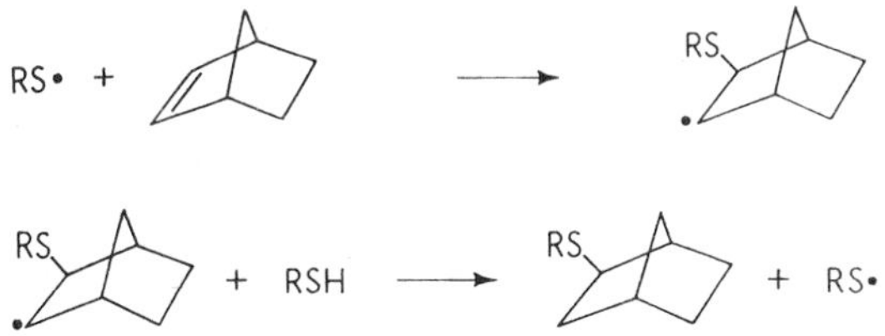

(25)

[26] F. H. Seubold, Jr., *J. Am. Chem. Soc.*, **76**, 3732 (1954).

[27] W. E. Doering, M. Farber, M. Sprecher, and K. B. Wiberg, *J. Am. Chem. Soc.*, **74**, 3000 (1952).

[28] J. A. Berson, C. J. Olson, and J. S. Walia, *J. Am. Chem. Soc.*, **82**, 5000 (1960).

[29] S. J. Cristol and G. D. Brindell, *J. Am. Chem. Soc.*, **76**, 5699 (1954).

and Berson and Jones [30] have obtained similar results with the substituted norbornylenes **8** and **9**

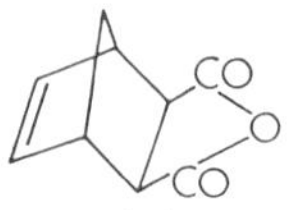

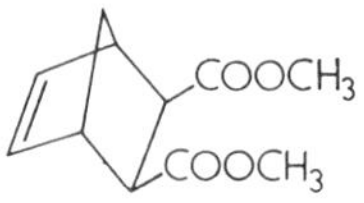

Numerous examples of radical additions to noncyclic olefins are, of course, also known, and in no case do rearranged products arise with evidence for alkyl migration. As an example, the radical addition of HCl to *tert*-butyl-ethylene [31] gives 1-chloro-3,3-dimethylbutane via the sequence

$$Cl\cdot + CH_2{=}CH{-}C(CH_3)_3 \to ClCH_2\overset{\cdot}{C}H{-}C(CH_3)_3 \qquad (25a)$$

$$ClCH_2\overset{\cdot}{C}H{-}C(CH_3)_3 + HCl \to ClCH_2CH_2C(CH_3)_3 + Cl\cdot \qquad (25b)$$

in spite of a driving force for the rearrangement which would convert a secondary to a tertiary radical and the fact that reaction 25b is endothermic by approximately 9 kcal. and accordingly must be relatively slow. Finally, extensive data [32] on the decomposition of *tert*-alkoxy radicals, where R's are alkyl, show breakdown to ketone and alkyl radical

$$R_3C{-}O\cdot \to RCOR + R\cdot$$

rather than alkyl migration

$$R_3C{-}O \to R_2\overset{\cdot}{C}{-}OR$$

Similar negative evidence exists for 1,2 shifts of hydrogen. The cases of decarbonylation of β-p-anisyl-β-phenylpropionaldehyde [32a] and β-phenyl-propionaldehyde [32b] have already been cited. Brown and Russell [18] have shown by using deuterium-labeled material that no rearrangement of the isobutyl radical to *tert*-butyl occurs during the photochlorination of isobutane, and Kornblum has demonstrated that no rearrangement such as equation 26

$$\begin{array}{c} R_1 \\ \diagdown \\ HC{-}O\cdot \\ \diagup \\ R_2 \end{array} \;{\nrightarrow}\; \begin{array}{c} R_1 \\ | \\ \cdot C{-}OH \\ | \\ R_2 \end{array} \qquad (26)$$

of alkoxy radicals can be detected. Thus, decomposition of optically active 2-octyl nitrite at 100° in the liquid phase gives 2-octanol with retention of

[30] J. A. Berson and W. M. Jones, *J. Am. Chem. Soc.*, **78**, 6045 (1956).

[31] G. G. Ecke, N. C. Cook, and F. C. Whitmore, *J. Am. Chem. Soc.*, **72**, 1511 (1950).

[32] C. Walling, *Free Radicals in Solution*, Wiley, New York, 1957, pp. 469–74; J. K. Kochi, *J. Am. Chem. Soc.*, **84**, 1193 (1962).

[32a] D. Y. Curtin and J. C. Kauer, *J. Org. Chem.*, **25**, 880 (1960).

[32b] L. H. Slaugh, *J. Am. Chem. Soc.*, **81**, 2262 (1959).

configuration (intervention of a *sec*-octyl radical in the process would be expected to lead to racemized material).[33] Similarly, thermal decomposition of optically active α-phenylethyl-*tert*-butyl peroxide in the presence of thiophenol as a hydrogen donor yields active α-phenylethyl alcohol.[34]

Turning now to cases where arguments for 1,2 shifts of alkyl or hydrogen have been advanced, Kharasch, Liu, and Nudenberg[35] have reported that gas phase bromination of 2,2,4,4-tetramethylpentane yields 4-bromo-2,2,3,4-tetramethylpentane

$$CH_3-\underset{\underset{CH_3}{|}}{\overset{\overset{CH_3}{|}}{C}}-CH_2-\underset{\underset{CH_3}{|}}{\overset{\overset{CH_3}{|}}{C}}-CH_3 + Br_2 \rightarrow CH_3-\underset{\underset{CH_3}{|}}{\overset{\overset{CH_3}{|}}{C}}\overset{\overset{CH_3}{|}}{CH}-\underset{\underset{Br}{|}}{\overset{\overset{CH_3}{|}}{C}}-CH_3 + HBr \qquad (27)$$

The product was identified by treatment with $AgNO_3$ to yield 2,3,4,4-tetramethyl-1-pentene, and the writer has suggested[36] that the rearrangement actually occurred at this step. This deduction seems to have been confirmed by Backhurst[37] who has reinvestigated both the chlorination and bromination of 2,2,4,4-tetramethylpentane and has found only products with unrearranged carbon skeletons.

Kharasch[35] has also reported the same sort of rearrangement (eq. 28) on

$$CH_3-\underset{\underset{CH_3}{|}}{\overset{\overset{CH_3}{|}}{C}}-CHCl-\underset{\underset{CH_3}{|}}{\overset{\overset{CH_3}{|}}{C}}-CH_3 \xrightarrow[CoBr_2]{RMgBr} CH_3\underset{\underset{CH_3}{|}}{\overset{\overset{CH_3}{|}}{C}}-CH_2-\underset{\underset{CH_3}{|}}{\overset{\overset{CH_3}{|}}{C}}-CH_3 + CH_2=\underset{\underset{CH_3}{|}}{\overset{\overset{CH_3}{|}}{C}}-CH-\underset{\underset{CH_3}{|}}{\overset{\overset{CH_3}{|}}{C}}-CH_3 \quad (28)$$

treating 3-chloro-2,2,4,4-tetramethylpentane with isopropylmagnesium bromide in the presence of $CoBr_2$ since the product contained both unrearranged alkane and rearranged olefin. As well, hydrogen shifts have been reported in the $CoCl_2$-catalyzed reaction of 3-phenylpropyl chloride with *n*-butylmagnesium bromide since the products include both 2-butene and β-methylstyrene.[38] Kharasch has interpreted these as arising from the disproportionation reactions of rearranged radicals, but again the radical nature of all of the steps in these metal-catalyzed processes would seem to need further demonstration.

The electrolysis of the salts of carboxylic acids leads to oxidation of the carboxylate anion at the anode with the formation of CO_2 and dimers of the

[33] N. Kornblum and E. Oliveto, *J. Am. Chem. Soc.*, **71**, 226 (1949).

[34] N. Kornblum and H. E. De La Mare, *J. Am. Chem. Soc.*, **74**, 3079 (1952).

[35] M. S. Kharasch, Y. C. Liu, and W. Nudenberg, *J. Org. Chem.*, **19**, 1150 (1954), **20**, 680 (1955).

[36] C. Walling, *Free Radicals in Solution*, Wiley, New York, 1957, p. 373.

[37] J. D. Backhurst, *J. Chem. Soc. (London)*, **1959**, 3497.

[38] M. S. Kharasch, F. L. Lambert, and W. H. Urry, *J. Org. Chem.*, **10**, 298 (1945).

hydrocarbon residue (the Kolbe reaction). Major side reactions include the formation of nondimeric paraffins and olefins and in addition esters, alcohols, and ethers often involving the solvent (the Hofer-Moest reaction). The scope of the Kolbe process has been reviewed by Weedon,[39] and Finkelstein and Petersen[40] have recently reported considerably improved yields of dimers when the electrolysis is carried out in dimethylformamide instead of in water or methanol, the usual solvents. It is generally agreed that the Kolbe reaction is a radical process involving the steps

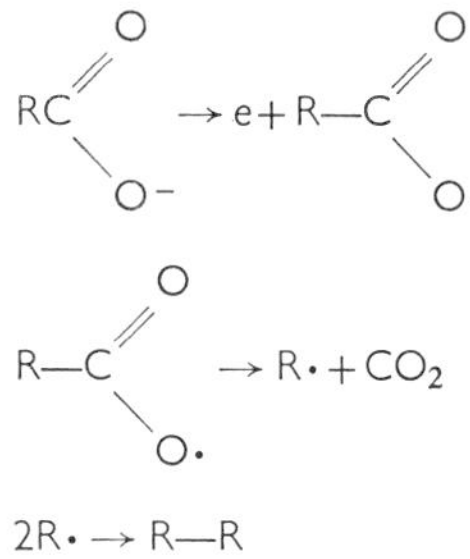

$$RC\underset{O^-}{\overset{O}{\diagdown}} \rightarrow e + R\text{---}C\underset{O\cdot}{\overset{O}{\diagdown}}$$

$$R\text{---}C\underset{O\cdot}{\overset{O}{\diagdown}} \rightarrow R\cdot + CO_2$$

$$2R\cdot \rightarrow R\text{---}R$$

and the scheme has been supported by recent observations of the addition of the alkyl radicals produced to butadiene[41,42] and their initiation of the polymerization of vinyl acetate, methyl methacrylate, and similar monomers.[43]

The Hofer-Moest reaction path giving alcohols, ethers, and esters is harder to reconcile with a radical process, since the usual mode of radical attack on methanol is

$$R\cdot + CH_3OH \rightarrow RH + \cdot CH_2OH$$

In 1957 the writer suggested[44] that Hofer-Moest products arise from further anodic oxidation of the intermediate radical and are the result of carbonium ion processes,

$$R\cdot \rightarrow e + R^+ \xrightarrow{R'OH} ROR$$

$$R' = \text{---}OH, \text{---}OCH_3 \text{---}OCOR$$

a proposal which has recently been amplified by Corey et al.[45]

[39] B. C. L. Weedon, Quart. Revs. (London), 6, 380 (1952).

[40] M. Finkelstein and R. C. Petersen, J. Org Chem., 25, 139 (1960).

[41] R. V. Lindsey, Jr., and M. L. Peterson, J. Am. Chem. Soc., 81, 2073 (1959).

[42] W. B. Smith and H. G. Gilde, J. Am. Chem. Soc., 81, 5325 (1959).

[43] W. B. Smith and H. G. Gilde, J. Am. Chem. Soc., 82, 659 (1960).

[44] C. Walling, Free Radicals in Solution, Wiley, New York, 1957, p. 581.

[45] E. J. Corey, N. L. Bauld, R. T. La Londe, J. Casanova, Jr., and E. T. Kaiser, J. Am. Chem. Soc., 82, 2645 (1960).

Rearrangements interpretable as 1,2 shifts of alkyl groups have sometimes been observed during electrolyses, but it is significant that *they are restricted to the Hofer-Moest products*. Thus Muhs [46] has electrolyzed 1-methylcyclo-hexaneacetic acid, obtaining 58% unrearranged dimer, 13% 1-methylcyclo-heptylmethyl ether, and 11% 1-methylcycloheptene, presumably via the carbonium ion rearrangement (eq. 29). Similarly, 1-methylcyclopentylacetic

$$\text{(29)}$$

acid gives unrearranged dimer plus 1-methylcyclohexene and 1-methyl-cyclohexyl methyl ether, and *tert*-butylacetic acid gives unrearranged dimer plus C_5 olefin and *tert*-amyl methyl ether. Additional examples have been cited by Corey.[45] In the case of β-aryl-substituted carboxylic acids, rearrange-ment of the intermediate radical might be anticipated, although it has not been unequivocally observed. Urry [47] has electrolyzed β-phenylisovaleric acid and has reported unrearranged dimer, but some olefin and alkane with the isobutylbenzene structure. Breederveld and Kooyman [48] have carried out the electrolysis in the presence of much acetate ion and shown that both the dimer and the product of cross-coupling with methyl radicals, *tert*-amylbenzene, have unrearranged structures. With triphenylmethylacetic acid a different type of rearrangement occurs (see heading 4).

The possibility of 1,2 shifts of hydrogen in high temperature gas phase reactions of simple hydrocarbon radicals was suggested by Kossickoff and Rice in 1943,[49] and has occasionally been cited to explain the products of thermal and photochemical processes. Such reactions have been extensively studied, but their supposed simplicity has proved to be somewhat illusory, since the radicals involved frequently react at comparable rates by a variety of parallel low activation energy paths, producing rather indiscriminate mixtures of products. As a result, the details of many processes are only now being unscrambled. To cite a recent example, Gordon and McNesby [50] have studied the reaction of methyl radicals (obtained by the photolysis of acetone) with ethylene at 300–500° and observed that the major product (49–64%) is

---

[46] M. A. Muhs, *Thesis*, University of Washington, 1954.

[47] W. H. Urry, Abstracts of Papers, 12th National Organic Chemistry Symposium (1951), p. 36.

[48] H. Breederveld and E. C. Kooyman, *Rec. trav. chim.*, **76**, 297 (1957).

[49] H. Kossickoff and F. O. Rice, *J. Am. Chem. Soc.*, **65**, 590 (1953).

[50] A. S. Gordon and J. R. McNesby, *J. Chem. Phys.*, **31**, 853 (1959); see also *J. Chem. Phys.*, **33**, 1882 (1960).

propylene, which, they suggest, arises from the sequence

$$CH_3 \cdot + C_2H_4 \rightarrow CH_3CH_2CH_2 \cdot$$

$$CH_3CH_2CH_2 \cdot + C_2H_4 \rightarrow CH_3CH_2CH_2CH_2CH_2 \cdot$$

$$CH_3CH_2CH_2CH_2CH_2 \cdot \rightarrow CH_3CH_2CH_2\overset{\cdot}{C}HCH_3$$

$$CH_3CH_2CH_2\overset{\cdot}{C}HCH_3 \rightarrow C_2H_5 \cdot + C_3H_6$$

While their reaction involves a 1,2 shift, it could also be the result of a cyclic intramolecular hydrogen abstraction (eq. 30). Such a process would occur

$$CH_3-C\overset{\overset{\displaystyle H}{|}}{\underset{CH_2}{\diagdown}}\overset{\cdot CH_2}{\underset{\diagup}{CH_2}} \rightarrow CH_3-\overset{\cdot}{C}H\overset{\overset{\displaystyle CH_3}{}}{\underset{CH_2}{\diagdown}}CH_2 \rightarrow C_2H_5 \cdot + C_3H_6 \qquad (30)$$

most easily through a five- or six-membered transition state and should occur more readily with a secondary than with a primary hydrogen in view of these authors' observation that n-butyl radicals apparently do not isomerize. A strictly comparable reaction is believed to account for the short chain branching that occurs in ethylene polymerization (see heading 5).

A high temperature alkyl migration has been suggested by Rust and Collamer [51] to account for the formation of traces of 2-methyl-1-butene, 2-methyl-2-butene, and 2,5-dimethylhexene in the complex mixture of olefins and other products obtained during the oxidation of isooctane at 450–470°. While they consider it less likely, they nevertheless recognize that these olefins could also arise from radical additions to isobutylene (a major product of the reaction). As far as the writer is aware, similar ambiguities are involved in all other reported high temperature rearrangements.

At the other end of the temperature scale, Ayscough, Ivin, O'Donnell, and Thomson [51a] have investigated the electron-spin resonance spectra of radicals produced in the solid state at $-196°C$ by γ-irradiation of alkyl halides, and conclude, on the basis of spectral changes, that isobutyl radicals rearrange to $tert$-butyl radicals by a process with a rate constant of approximately 0.1 days^{-1}. A similar rearrangement of n-propyl to isopropyl was reported, but whether these extremely slow reactions could compete with other radical processes at higher temperatures remains to be shown. Another interpretation of an over-all rearrangement on irradiation of alkyl halides has been given by Benson and Willard,[51b] and is discussed under heading 2C.

[51] F. F. Rust and D. O. Collamer, *J. Am. Chem. Soc.*, **76**, 1055 (1954).

[51a] P. B. Ayscough, K. J. Ivin, J. M. O'Donnell, and C. Thomson, Fifth International Symposium on Free Radicals, Uppsala (1961). preprints, p. 4–1.

[51b] H. L. Benson, Jr., and J. E. Willard, *J. Am. Chem. Soc.*, **83**, 4672 (1961).

As a final example of a reported rearrangement, Reutov and Shatkina [52] have decomposed α-^{14}C-labeled butyryl peroxide in CCl_4, isolated the resulting n-propyl chloride, and degraded it to acetic acid, reporting that the acetic acid retains some 4% of the original ^{14}C activity. However, since the activity was subsequently shown to be in the CH_3 group of the acetic acid, the reaction does not represent a 1,2 shift, but intramolecular hydrogen abstraction.

C. Halogen Migrations

Good evidence for 1,2 shifts of chlorine in radicals containing trichloromethyl groups exists, chiefly from the studies of Nesmeyanov and his colleagues. In 1941 Kharasch [53] reported that the peroxide- and light-catalyzed addition of HBr to 3,3,3-trichloropropene gave a product different from the known 1,1,1-trichloro-2-bromopropane, which he considered to be 1,1,1-trichloro-3-bromopropane. Subsequently this material has been prepared by another route, and Nesmeyanov [54] has shown that the addition product is actually 1,1,2-trichloro-3-bromopropane, suggesting that it is formed via the sequence

$$Br\cdot + CH_2{=}CH-CCl_3 \rightarrow CH_2Br-\overset{\cdot}{C}H-CCl_3$$

$$CH_2Br-\overset{\cdot}{C}H-CCl_3 \xrightarrow{\quad} CH_2BrCHCl\overset{\cdot}{C}Cl_2$$

$$CH_3BrCHCl\overset{\cdot}{C}Cl_2 + HBr \rightarrow CH_3BrCHClCHCl_2 + Br\cdot$$

Radical additions of mercaptans [55] and bromine [56] to trichloropropene also give rearranged products

$$RSH + CH_2 = CH-CCl_3 \rightarrow RSCH_2CHCl-CHCl_2$$

$$Br_2 + CH_2 = CH-CCl_3 \rightarrow CH_2Br-CHCl-CCl_2Br$$

while addition of CCl_3Br [57] gives a mixture of products which can be accounted for by the scheme shown. Three products were isolated:

[52] O. A. Reutov and T. N. Shatkina, *Izvest. Akad. Nauk S.S.S.R., Otdel. Khim. Nauk*, **1959**, 1960; *Tetrahedron*, **18**, 305 (1960).

[53] M. S. Kharasch, E. H. Rossin, and E. K. Fields, *J. Am. Chem. Soc.*, **63**, 2558 (1941).

[54] A. N. Nesmeyanov, R. K. Freidlina, and V. I. Firstov, *Izvest. Akad. Nauk S.S.S.R., Otdel. Khim. Nauk*, **1951**, 505.

[55] A. N. Nesmeyanov, R. K. Freidlina, R. G. Petrova, and A. B. Terent'ev, *Doklady Akad. Nauk S.S.S.R.*, **127**, 575 (1959).

[56] A. N. Nesmeyanov, R. K. Freidlina, and V. N. Kost, *Tetrahedron*, **1**, 241 (1957).

[57] A. N. Nesmeyanov, R. K. Freidlina, and L. I. Zakharin, *Doklady Akad. Nauk S.S.S.R.*, **81**, 199 (1951).

$$CCl_3 \cdot + CH_2{=}CH{-}CCl_3$$

$$CCl_3CH_2CHCl{-}\dot{C}Cl_2 \xrightarrow{CCl_3Br} CCl_3CH_2CHClCCl_2Br$$

$$CCl_3CH_2{-}\dot{C}H{-}CCl_3$$

$$(10)$$

$$CCl_3CH_2\dot{C}H{=}CCl_2 + Cl \cdot$$

$$(11)$$

$$C_3H_3Cl_3$$

$$CCl_3\dot{C}HCH_2Cl$$

$$CCl_3Br$$

$$CCl_2BrChClCH_2Cl \quad or \quad CCl_3CHBrCH_2Cl$$

$$(12a) \qquad\qquad (12b)$$

10, the result of the usual rearrangement; **11**, the olefin resulting from chlorine atom loss from either the rearranged or unrearranged radical; and **12**. The structure of **12** was not unequivocally determined, so its formation might or might not have involved a further rearrangement.

Rearrangements during radical additions to analogs of trichloropropene have also been noted, e.g., with 1,1,1-2-methyl-trichloropropene (eq. 31) [58] 2,3,3,3-tetrachloropropene (eq. 32), [59] and 2,3,3-trichloropropene (eq. 33). [59]

$$HBr + CH_2{=}\overset{\overset{\displaystyle CH_3}{|}}{C}{-}CCl_3 \xrightarrow{Bz_2O_2} CH_2Br{-}\overset{\overset{\displaystyle CH_3}{|}}{C}Cl{-}CHCl_2 + CHBr{=}\overset{\overset{\displaystyle CH_3}{|}}{C}{-}CHCl_2 +$$

$$(59\%)$$

$$CH_2Cl{-}\overset{\overset{\displaystyle CH_3}{|}}{\underset{\underset{\displaystyle Cl}{|}}{C}}{-}CHCl_2$$

$$(31)$$

$$HBr + CH_2{=}CCl{-}CCl_3 \rightarrow CH_2Cl{-}CCl{=}CCl_2 + CH_2Br{-}CCl{=}CCl_2 + CH_2Cl{-}CCl_2{-}CHCl_2$$

$$(32)$$

$$HBr + CH_2{=}CCl{-}CHCl_2 \rightarrow CH_2Br{-}CCl_2{-}CHCl_2 + CH_2Cl{-}CCl_2{-}CHCl_2 \qquad (33)$$

In these cases the variety of products evidently arises from sequences similar to those producing **10–12** in addition to simple rearrangement. [59a] Nesmey-

[58] A. N. Nesmeyanov, R. K. Freidlina, and A. B. Belyavskii, *Izvest. Akad. Nauk S.S.S.R., Otdel. Khim. Nauk*, **1959**, 1028.

[59] R. K. Freidlina, V. N. Kost, M. Y. Khorlina, and A. N. Nesmeyanov, *Doklady Akad. Nauk S.S.S.R.*, **128**, 316 (1959).

[59a] Nesmeyanov and his group are still actively investigating halogen atom shifts in radical reactions. For additional examples, see R. K. Freidlina, V. N. Kost, and T. T. Vasileva, *Doklady Akad. Nauk S.S.S.R.*, **137**, 1358 (1961); R. K. Freidlina, V. N. Kost, M. V. Khorlina, and A. N. Nesmeyanov, *Doklady Akad. Nauk S.S.S.R.*, **137**, 341 (1961); M. V. Khorlina and V. N. Kost, *Doklady Akad. Nauk S.S.S.R.*, **137**, 1133 (1961); and R. K. Freidlina, A. B. Terentev, R. G. Petrova, and A. N. Nesmeyanov, *Doklady Akad. Nauk S.S.S.R.*, **138**, 859 (1961).

anov has also reported [56] that irradiation of 2-bromo-3,3,3-trichloropropene leads to its quantitative isomerization to 1,1,2-trichloro-3-bromopropene. The isomerization also occurs spontaneously on standing and is inhibited by hydroquinone or dimethylaniline, indicating it is a radical chain process. Nesmeyanov here proposes the plausible sequence

$$Br\cdot + CH_2{=}CBr{-}CCl_3 \rightarrow BrCH_2{-}\overset{\cdot}{C}Br{-}CCl_3 \xrightarrow{\quad} BrCH_2{-}CClBr{-}\overset{\cdot}{C}Cl_2$$

$$\cdots\cdots Br\cdot + BrCH_2{-}CCl{=}CCl_2 \tag{34}$$

Even more striking examples of radical chain processes which seem explicable only in terms of 1,2 halogen shifts have been described by Urry and Eiszner [60] in the photochemical reaction of diazomethane and many polyhalomethanes. Typical is the reaction with CCl_4 which gives pentaeritritol tetrachloride, $C(CH_2Cl)_4$, in 60% yield. The reaction is evidently a radical chain since a quantum yield of 300 at 0° has been observed, and Urry suggests the sequence shown in equation 35. If correct, this is perhaps the most complex

$$\cdot CCl_3 + CH_2N_2 \rightarrow N_2 + CCl_3CH_2\cdot \xrightarrow{\quad} \cdot CCl_2CH_2Cl$$

$$\searrow CH_2N_2$$

$$\cdot CH_2CCl_2CHCl + N_2 \tag{35}$$

$$N_2 + ClCH_2{-}\overset{\overset{\displaystyle \cdot CH_2}{|}}{\underset{\underset{\displaystyle Cl}{|}}{C}}{-}CH_2Cl \xleftarrow{CH_2N_2} ClCH_2\overset{\cdot}{C}ClCH_2Cl$$

$$ClCH_2{-}\overset{\overset{\displaystyle CH_2Cl}{|}}{\underset{\underset{\displaystyle CH_2Cl}{|}}{\overset{\cdot}{C}}} \xleftarrow{CH_2N_2} ClCH_2{-}\overset{\overset{\displaystyle CH_2Cl}{|}}{\underset{\underset{\displaystyle CH_2Cl}{|}}{C}}{-}CH_2\cdot \xrightarrow{CCl_4} {-}C(CH_2Cl)_4 + \cdot CCl_3$$

radical chain sequence on record, but it is supported by the observation that possible stable intermediates, CCl_3CH_3 and CCl_3CH_2Cl, are not attacked by diazomethane. Similar products are obtained with bromotrichloromethane, chloroform, and methyl trichloroacetate [60]

$$CCl_3Br + 4CH_2N_2 \rightarrow BrCH_2C(CH_2Cl)_3 \quad (40\%)$$

$$CHCl_3 + 4CH_2N_2 \rightarrow CH_3C(CH_2Cl)_3 \quad (45\%)$$

$$CCl_3COOCH_3 + 3CH_2N_2 \rightarrow (CH_2Cl)_3CCOOCH_3 \quad (60\%)$$

but more highly brominated and iodinated methanes react differently,[61] e.g.

$$CBr_4 + 2CH_2N_2 \rightarrow CH_2Br_2 \quad (25\%) + CH_2{=}CBr_2 \quad (25\%)$$

---

[60] W. H. Urry and J. R. Eiszner, J. Am. Chem. Soc., 75, 5822 (1952).
[61] W. H. Urry, J. R. Eiszner, and J. W. Wilt, J. Am. Chem. Soc., 79, 918 (1957).

Since quantum yields are high, another chain is involved, and Urry proposes the sequence

$$CBr_3\cdot + CH_2N_2 \rightarrow N_2 + CBr_3\dot{C}H_2$$

$$N_2 + \dot{C}H_2Br \xleftarrow{\ CH_2N_2\ } Br\cdot + CBr_2{=}CH_2 \qquad (36)$$

$$\downarrow CBr_4$$

$$CH_2Br_2 + \cdot CBr_3$$

Evidently, here bromine atom elimination from the $CBr_3CH_2\cdot$ radical occurs more rapidly than rearrangement, in keeping with the general observation that bromine atom addition to double bonds is a more easily reversible process than is chlorine atom addition (the importance of such reversible additions is discussed further under heading 3A). At lower temperatures the competition between bromine atom rearrangement and elimination apparently becomes more favorable. Skell, Allen, and Gilmour report that, at $-78°$, *tert*-butyl hypochlorite chlorination of both *n*- and isopropyl bromides gives 1-bromo-2-chloropropane, and, similarly, both iso- and *tert*-butyl bromides give 1-bromo-2-chloro-2-methylpropane, suggesting Scheme 1.[61a]

$$C_4H_9O\cdot + CH_3CHBrCH_3 \rightarrow C_4H_9OH + \cdot CH_2CHBrCH_3$$

$$\cdot CH_2CHBrCH_3 \xrightarrow{\ \ \ } CH_2BrCHCH_3$$

$$CH_2BrCHCH_3 + C_4H_9OCl \rightarrow CH_2BrCHClCH_3 + C_4H_9O\cdot$$

Scheme 1.

As a final example of a reaction which now appears to involve a 1,2 shift of halogen, the isomerization of alkyl halides brought about by high energy radiation should be cited. Superficially, such reactions would appear to involve hydrogen or alkyl migration, but the isomerization of *n*-propyl chloride has recently been studied by Benson and Willard, who find that it is a chain that proceeds with G values up to 150, which is inhibited by I_2 and requires the presence of HCl. They propose Scheme 2.[61b]

$$Cl\cdot + CH_3CH_2CH_2Cl \rightarrow HCl + CH_3\dot{C}HCH_2Cl$$

$$CH_3\dot{C}HCH_2Cl \xrightarrow{\ \ \ } CH_3CHClCH_2\cdot$$

$$CH_3CHClCH_2\cdot + HCl \rightarrow CH_3CHClCH_3 + Cl\cdot$$

Scheme 2.

[61a] P. S. Skell, R. G. Allen, and N. G. Gilmour, *J. Am. Chem. Soc.*, **83**, 504 (1961).

[61b] H. L. Benson, Jr., and J. E. Willard, *J. Am. Chem. Soc.*, **83**, 4672 (1961); a somewhat different scheme, less well documented but also involving a halogen shift, has been advanced by R. H. Wiley, C. H. Jarbue, J. R. Harrell, and D. J. Parish, *Radiation Research*, **13**, 479 (1960).

The rearrangement suggested in Scheme 2 is the reverse of that usually observed, and must be highly reversible. However, since the reaction of alkyl radicals with HCl is endothermic, it is probably much faster with a primary than with a secondary radical (which would simply regenerate starting material). Accordingly, occurrence of the last step shifts the rearrangement equilibrium to the right.

D. Transition States in 1,2 Shifts

An understanding of the occurrence and nonoccurrence of 1,2 shifts in radical systems necessarily requires some knowledge of the structures and energies of the transition states involved. If the rearrangement is truly intramolecular, it must pass through some triangular arrangement of groups

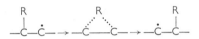

which represents either the transition state or a metastable intermediate of relatively high energy and short life. Further, if such a triangular arrangement actually represents a lower energy path than simple dissociation and recombination, it must be stabilized by delocalization of the odd electron in a manner which, in terms of resonance structures, might be depicted as

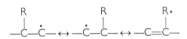

In molecular orbital terms, the equivalent statement is that the odd electron and the electron pair of the bond which is shifting must occupy delocalized three-center orbitals constructed from p orbitals of the two carbons and, depending upon its structure, a p or s orbital of the migrating group. The simple molecular orbital treatment first developed by Hückel[62] gives a qualitative picture of the energetics of such orbitals, stating that they will consist of a single low-lying bonding orbital and two higher energy nonbonding orbitals which are degenerate (of the same energy) if the triangular arrangement is symmetric. In the case of carbonium ion rearrangements only two electrons are involved and both can be accommodated in the bonding orbital, with the result that such bridged intermediates are easily formed, as is discussed in detail in other sections of this volume. The radical case, however, requires that the third electron must occupy a higher energy nonbonding orbital. As a consequence, it should be less stable in respect to either the initial or the rearranged radical. As we have seen, there is no conclusive evidence for the easy occurrence of 1,2 shifts where the migrating group is alkyl or hydrogen.

[62] E. Hückel, *Z. Physik*, **70**, 207 (1931).

A remarkable parallel exists between these conclusions and observations and the behavior of the closely analogous cyclopropene systems which have been elegantly examined by Breslow. Here one again has a triangular arrangement of centers, but now held together by a complete system of covalent σ bonds. The cyclopropene carbonium ion **14** can be prepared and isolated in

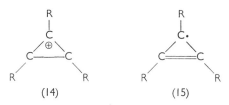

the form of a number of salts, and systems where R = aryl are not notably more stable than where R = alkyl.[63,64] Breslow finds that there is no indication of any marked stability of the radical **15**. No dissociation of the dimer of triphenylcyclopropene can be detected,[65] and polarographic reduction of **14** requires a much higher potential than does the triphenylmethyl cation.[66]

In the case where the migrating group is aryl and shifts are actually observed, it must be noted that additional structures are available to the bridged intermediate, e.g. **13**, which contains a covalent cyclopropane ring

and a radical stabilized by allylic resonance. Further, the limited data on relative migratory aptitude for different aryl groups show little effect of p-methyl,[66a,66b] but facilitated migration of p-nitrophenyl,[32a,66c] naphthyl[66b] and biphenyl[66b] groups. All of these are structures which should permit a further delocalization of the radical, both as would be predicted from the structures which can be drawn, and as is indicated experimentally by a comparison of the reactivities of benzene, toluene, nitrobenzene, naphtha-

[63] R. Breslow and C. Yuan, *J. Am. Chem. Soc.*, **80**, 5991 (1958).

[64] R. Breslow and H. Höver, *J. Am. Chem. Soc.*, **82**, 2644 (1960).

[65] R. Breslow and P. Gal, *J. Am. Chem. Soc.*, **81**, 4747 (1959).

[66] R. Breslow, W. Bahary, and W. Reinmuth, *J. Am. Chem. Soc.*, **83**, 1763 (1961).

[66a] W. H. Urry and N. Nicolaides, *J. Am. Chem. Soc.*, **74**, 5163 (1952).

[66b] M. S. Kharasch, A. C. Poshkus, A. Fono, and W. Nudenberg, *J. Org. Chem.* **16**, 1458 (1951).

[66c] P. D. Bartlett and J. D. Cotman, Jr., *J. Am. Chem. Soc.*, **72**, 3095 (1950).

lene, and biphenyl toward radical attack,[67] e.g., by methyl or phenyl radicals, where products of similar structure are initially formed (eq. 37). Recently,

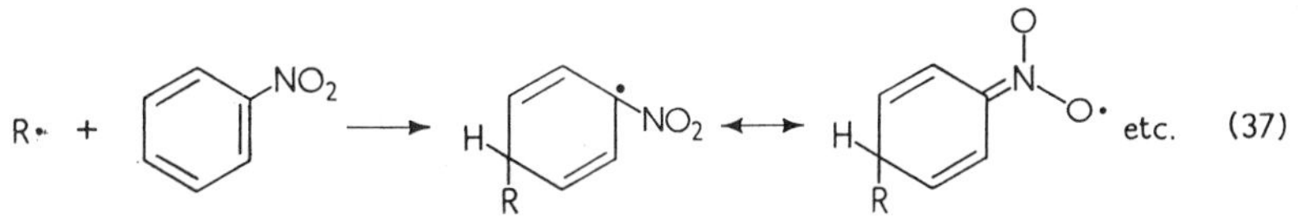

$$R\cdot + \quad \longrightarrow \quad \longleftrightarrow \quad \text{etc.} \quad (37)$$

Ruechardt [67a] has attempted a quantitative comparison of migratory aptitudes in the decarbonylation of β-arylisovaleraldehydes by measuring the yields of rearranged product in each case as a function of aldehyde concentration. This method involves the plausible assumption that the rates of reaction of unrearranged hydrocarbon radical with aldehyde is independent of para substituents in the aryl group, and yields the sequence p-Cl-phenyl, 1.82; phenyl, 1.0; p-tolyl, 0.65; p-anisyl, 0.35; corresponding to a Hammett ρ value of approximately 1. Since p-methyl and p-methoxy would be expected to stabilize an odd electron in the aryl ring (cf. 15a), this result indicates

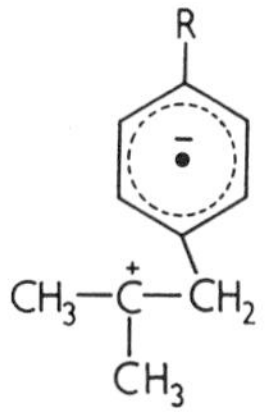

(15a)

that a polar effect is important in the rearrangement, and additional resonance structures such as 15a must be considered as contributing to the transition state.

Even here in the case of aryl migration there is no evidence for a bridged species of lower energy than the initial or rearranged radical. As we have seen, in aldehyde decarbonylations CO loss and rearrangement are not concerted processes. The fact that the extent of rearrangement in β-phenylisovaleraldehyde decarbonylation is almost temperature independent [67b] indicates that it has the same activation energy as hydrogen abstraction from another aldehyde molecule, approximately 7 kcal. In the case of β-phenylpropionaldehyde,

---

[67] For summaries of such reactions, see C. Walling, *Free Radicals in Solution*, Wiley, New York.

[67a] C. Ruechardt, *Chem. Ber.*, **94**, 2609 (1961).

[67b] F. H. Seubold, Jr., *J. Am. Chem. Soc.*, **75**, 2532 (1953); C. Ruechardt, *Chem. Ber.*, **94**, 2599 (1961).

where the extent of rearrangement increases with temperature,[67c] the activation energy for rearrangement must be even larger. Since the bridged intermediate either *is* the transition state—or closely resembles it—these activation energies should represent the extent of its instability relative to the unrearranged radical.

The problem of explaining the case of occurrence of halogen migration in radical reactions is somewhat more complicated, and both alternatives, a *bona fide* 1,2 shift

and a dissociation followed by addition

$$-\overset{\overset{\displaystyle X}{|}}{C}-\overset{\displaystyle \cdot}{C}- \longrightarrow \; C{=}C + X\cdot \longrightarrow -\overset{\displaystyle \cdot}{C}-\overset{\overset{\displaystyle X}{|}}{C}-$$

must be considered, since many cases of β elimination of halogen from radicals to olefins are known, for example, in the *cis-trans* isomerizations discussed under heading 3A. However, in the cases cited in the preceding section, evidence seems to favor a true bridged intermediate. Thus in the mercaptan additions to trichloropropene, halogen attack on mercaptan

$$Cl\cdot + RSH \longrightarrow HCl + RS\cdot$$

should be an extremely rapid competing process, leading to quite different products. Again, the CCl_4–diazomethane reaction seems altogether too clean-cut for a sequence involving dissociation-readdition; and in the CBr_4–diazomethane reaction, where dissociation apparently does occur, entirely different products result.

The arguments given above concerning bridged intermediates suggest that additional structures must also be available to the bridged halogen intermediate, and ones involving an expanded valence shell for chlorine

$$-\overset{\overset{\displaystyle Cl}{|}}{C}-\overset{\displaystyle \cdot}{C}- \longrightarrow -\overset{}{C}\overset{:\ddot{C}l:}{\diagup \diagdown}\overset{}{C}- \longrightarrow -\overset{\displaystyle \cdot}{C}-\overset{\overset{\displaystyle Cl}{|}}{C}- \qquad (38)$$

seem likely, since good evidence exists for similar expanded valence shells in radical reactions involving sulfur and phosphorus.

If the intermediate in equation 38 represents a structure of only slightly higher energy than the initial and rearranged radicals, the possibility also exists that it represents a structure of *lower* energy—i.e., that β-halo radicals actually possess a bridged "nonclassical" structure. This idea was originally

[67c] L. H. Slaugh, *J. Am. Chem. Soc.*, **81**, 2262 (1959).

proposed by Goering [68] to account for the stereospecific *trans* radical addition of HBr to 1-substituted cyclhexenes. Although it has been generally discounted for a number of reasons, including the comparably stereospecific addition of other radicals, it has received recent support from an examination of the electron-spin resonance spectra of β-bromoalkyl radicals trapped at low temperatures.[68a]

3. CIS-TRANS ISOMERIZATIONS AND ALLYLIC REARRANGEMENTS

A. Cis-Trans Isomerization

Although not generally classed as rearrangements, *cis-trans* isomerizations deserve some mention because of their bearing on allylic rearrangements discussed below. Many examples are known to occur in the presence of traces of free radicals, so it is evident that some sort of a radical chain process for the isomerization is possible. The simplest scheme (eq. 39) which can be pictured

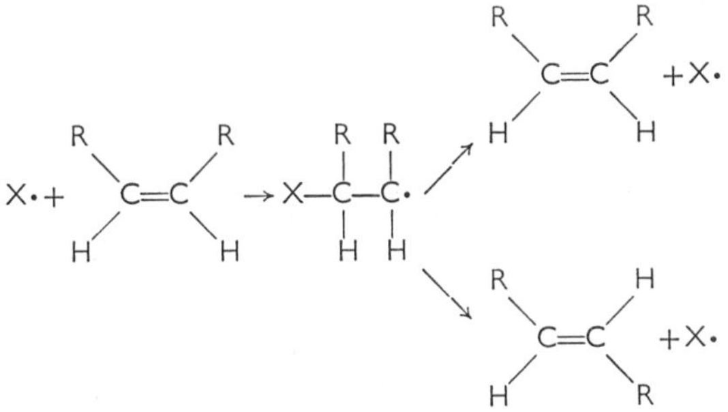

$$\text{X}\cdot + \underset{\text{H}}{\overset{\text{R}}{\diagup}}\text{C}=\text{C}\underset{\diagdown\text{H}}{\overset{\diagup\text{R}}{}} \rightarrow \text{X}-\underset{\underset{\text{H}}{|}}{\overset{\overset{\text{R}}{|}}{\text{C}}}-\underset{\underset{\text{H}}{|}}{\overset{\overset{\text{R}}{|}}{\text{C}}}\cdot \tag{39}$$

involves the reversible addition of a radical to the double bond and regeneration of the other isomer upon redissociation. The classic investigation which provides the key to what is going on is that of Noyes, Dickinson, and Schomaker [69] who studied the rates of exchange and isomerization in the reaction of radioactive iodine atoms and the diiodoethylenes, finding that the two processes had activation energies of 8 and 12 kcal., the exchange proceeding about 100 times as rapidly as the isomerization under their conditions. Evidently something must happen to the intermediate radical before dissociation can lead to isomerization, and this is believed to be rotation around the single bond (eq. 40). In this formulation the radical is indicated as having a

[68] H. L. Goering, P. I. Abell, and B. F. Aycock, *J. Am. Chem. Soc.*, **74**, 3588 (1952).

[68a] P. A. Abell and L. H. Piette, *J. Am. Chem. Soc.*, **84**, 916 (1962).

[69] R. M. Noyes, R. G. Dickinson, and V. Schomaker, *J. Am. Chem. Soc.*, **67**, 1319 (1945).

planar structure. While most evidence now supports this view, which has become commonly accepted, it should be noted that an easily inverted pyramidal structure would here lead to the same conclusions.

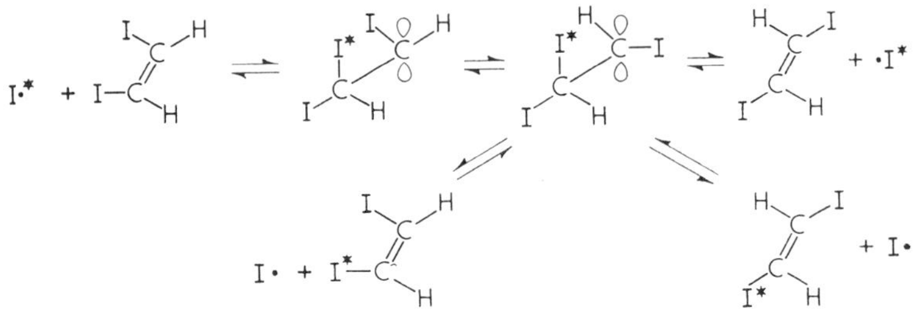

$$\tag{40}$$

Similar results have been observed with bromine atoms and *cis*-dibromoethylene,[70] although here the difference in rate between exchange and isomerization is smaller, presumably because of the higher activation energy of the dissociation process. Many other examples of such isomerizations by bromine or iodine atoms are known, and the literature has been reviewed by Mayo and Walling[71] and Walling.[72]

Cis-trans isomerization during radical addition of mercaptans to 2-butene has been demonstrated by Sivertz[73] and by Walling and Helmreich,[74] and in phosphine additions by Pellon.[75] All these processes can be formulated in the same manner as equation 40. The general requirement for reversibility of addition (and accordingly isomerization) is that the radical addition step be no more than slightly exothermic, and that the dissociation process require little activation energy above its endothermicity. Reversibility of addition is also favored by the fact that, in general, addition involves considerable loss of entropy in the system. The close relation between over-all energetics and observed cases of isomerization (and numerous reactions where dissociation must plainly occur) renders unlikely an alternative scheme, which has often been discussed,[71] in which direct transfer of halogen or other group from the intermediate radical to another olefin molecule occurs

$$XCHR\!-\!\overset{\cdot}{C}HR + CHR\!=\!CHR \rightarrow CHR\!=\!CHR + XCHR\!-\!\overset{\cdot}{C}HR \tag{41}$$

[70] H. Steinmetz and R. M. Noyes, *J. Am. Chem. Soc.*, **74**, 4141 (1952).

[71] F. R. Mayo and C. Walling, *Chem. Revs.*, **27**, 351 (1940).

[72] C. Walling, *Free Radicals in Solution*, Wiley, New York, 1957, p. 302. For a recent study of *cis-trans* isomerization of polybutadiene by bromine atoms and thiyl radicals, see M. A. Golub, *J. Polymer Sci.*, **25**, 373 (1957), *J. Am. Chem. Soc.*, **80**, 1794 (1958), and subsequent papers.

[73] R. H. Pallen and C. Sivertz, *Can. J. Chem.*, **35**, 723 (1957).

[74] C. Walling and W. Helmreich, *J. Am. Chem. Soc.*, **81**, 1144 (1959).

[75] J. Pellon, *J. Am. Chem. Soc.*, **83**, 1915 (1961).

In all reactions of this sort, isomerization competes with the over-all addition process, e.g., with the reaction

$$R'SCHR—\overset{\cdot}{C}HR + R'SH \rightarrow R'SCHRCH_2R + R'S\cdot$$

Accordingly, it is most complete when only traces of mercaptan are present and is favored by increasing temperature, since the dissociation has a higher activation energy.

Cis-trans isomerization by NO or NO_2 (which are free radicals) also appear to involve their reversible addition. The mechanisms of sulfur- and selenium-catalyzed isomerizations are less clear, and it should be pointed out that polar processes analogous to equation 40 are also possible. Thus acid-catalyzed *cis-trans* isomerizations presumably involve reversible proton additions, either to the double bond or to a neighboring carbonyl group.

B. Allylic Rearrangements Involving Hydrogen Abstraction

Allylic C—H bonds are relatively weak, having dissociation energies of 77 kcal. or less, and undergo ready radical attack, often in preference to addition to the neighboring double bond. The resulting allylic radical has a delocalized structure and, in a subsequent step in a radical chain reaction, often gives a product in which a double bond shift has occurred, i.e., the general equation 42. In fact, the occurrence of such a mixture of products is

$$X\cdot + CH_2{=}CH{-}CH_2R \rightarrow HX +$$

$$\begin{array}{ccc} CH_2{=}CH{-}\overset{\cdot}{C}HR & CH_2{=}CH{-}CHYR & \\ \updownarrow & \xrightarrow{XY} \quad and & +X\cdot \quad (42) \\ \overset{\cdot}{C}H_2{-}CH{=}CHR & CH_2Y{-}CH{=}CHR & \end{array}$$

often taken as supporting evidence for a radical chain process, while, conversely, complete isomerization or complete retention of double bond position (best with both allylic isomers) implies that some other process is taking place.

Many examples of such allylic rearrangements are known. Thus in autoxidations which proceed via the chain

$$R\cdot + O_2 \rightarrow RO_2\cdot$$

$$RO_2\cdot + RH \rightarrow ROOH + R\cdot$$

1,2-dimethylcyclohexane[76] yields two isomeric hydroperoxides (**16a** and **16b**)

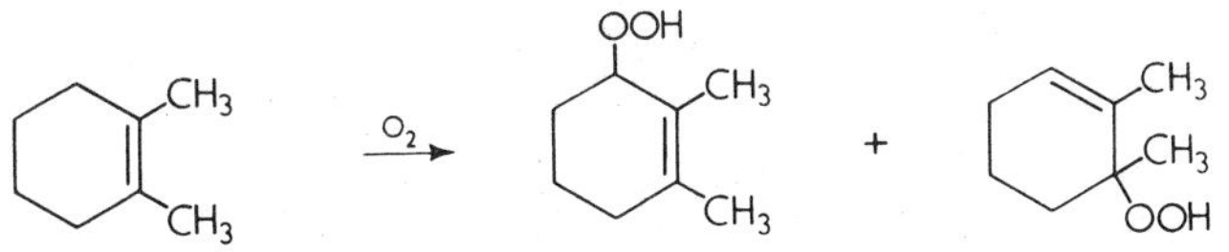

(16a)   (16b)

[76] E. H. Farmer and D. A. Sutton, *J. Chem. Soc.* (*London*), **1946**, 10.

while methyl linoleate, with a 1, 4-diene structure($-CH=CH-CH_2-CH=CH-$) gives chiefly hydroperoxide in which the double bonds are now conjugated.[77] Additional examples are cited by Bolland[78] and by Walling.[79]

Allylic bromination by N-bromosuccinimide appears to be a radical chain process involving the steps

$$\text{(image: succinimidyl radical)} \quad N\cdot + RH \longrightarrow \text{(image: succinimide)} \quad NH + R\cdot \qquad (43a)$$

$$R\cdot + \text{(image: N-bromosuccinimide)} \quad NBr \longrightarrow RBr + \text{(image: succinimidyl radical)} \quad N\cdot \qquad (43b)$$

and often leads to rearranged products. As an example, Bateman and Cunneen[80] found that 1-octene yields 17% 3-bromo-1-octene, 39% *cis*-1-bromo-2-octene, and 44% *trans*-1-bromo-2-octene. Again, bromination of *cis*- and *trans*-crotononitriles and allyl cyanide gives the same mixture of *cis*- and *trans*-γ-bromocrotononitriles, in the last case together with much α,β-dibromobutyronitrile.[81] Such results are unfortunately complicated by the fact that allylic bromides themselves undergo a very facile allylic isomerization as discussed on page 440.

Allylic chlorides are much more stable, and the recent finding that *tert*-butyl hypochlorite is a very efficient radical-halogenating agent,[82] which also brings about allylic halogenation of, rather than addition to, most olefins,[82] now gives a much clearer picture of both allylic rearrangements in radical systems and the stereochemistry of the intermediate allylic radicals.

With *tert*-butyl hypochlorite, halogenations may be carried out in nonpolar solvents at temperatures between -80 and $100°$, most conveniently using photoinitiation, and proceed via the sequence

$$t\text{-}C_4H_9O\cdot + RH \rightarrow t\text{-}C_4H_9OH + R\cdot$$
$$R\cdot + t\text{-}C_4H_9OCl \rightarrow RCl + t\text{-}C_4H_9O\cdot$$

with the *tert*-butoxy radical acting as the chain carrier.[82] Walling and Thaler[83] found that chlorination of 1- and 2-butenes yields 3-chloro-1-butene and *cis*-

---

[77] J. L. Bolland and H. P. Koch, *J. Chem. Soc. (London)*, **1945**, 445.

[78] L. Bateman, *Quart. Revs. (London)*, **8**, 147 (1954).

[79] C. Walling, *Free Radicals in Solution*, Wiley, 1957, ch. 9.

[80] L. Bateman and J. I. Cunneen, *J. Chem. Soc. (London)*, **1950**, 941.

[81] P. Couvreur and A. Bruylants, *Bull. soc. chim. Belges*, **61**, 253 (1952); cf. W. J. Bailey and J. Bello, *J. Org. Chem.*, **20**, 525 (1955).

[82] C. Walling and B. B. Jacknow, *J. Am. Chem. Soc.*, **82**, 6108 (1960).

[83] C. Walling and W. Thaler, *J. Am. Chem. Soc.*, **83**, 3877 (1961).

and *trans*-1-chloro-2-butenes, together with a small amount of addition to the double bond to give β-chloro-*tert*-butyl ethers. However, the ratio of products varies significantly with the starting olefin, as shown in Table I.

TABLE I

tert-Butyl Hypochlorite Chlorination of Butenes

	Products (%)		
	3-Chloro-1-butene	*cis*-1-Chloro-2-butene	*trans*-1-Chloro-2-butene
1-Butene	31	21–28	41–49
trans-2-Butene	27	0	73
cis-2-Butene	37	63	0

These results, which are inconsistent with a single common allylic radical in the three cases, may be interpreted by the scheme shown in equation 44,

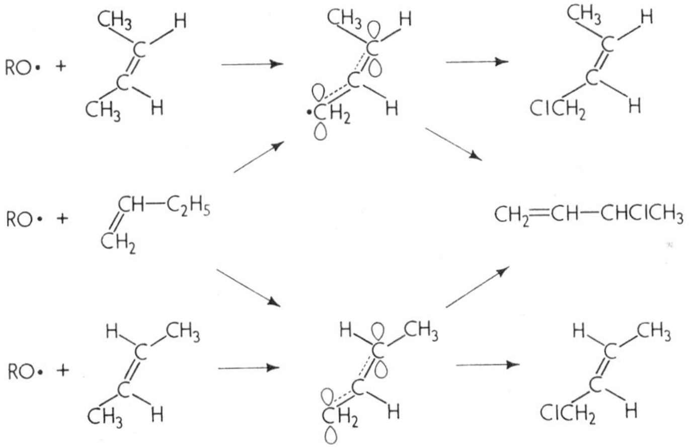

$$CH_2{=}CH{-}CHClCH_3 \qquad (44)$$

which assumes that *cis* and *trans* allylic radicals are distinguishable species which retain their integrity during the reaction. *Cis*-2-butene and *trans*-2-butene in this formulation give rise to *cis* and *trans* allylic radicals which not only yield solely the *cis* and *trans* isomers of 1-chloro-2-butene, respectively, but, as they are intrinsically different species, different ratios of 1-chloro-2-butenes and 3-chloro-1-butene. 1-Butene, which can yield either radical (as discussed further below), gives an intermediate distribution of products. Investigations of additional olefins of the general structure CH₃CH=CHR show that, with large R groups, steric hindrance may decrease the stability of *cis* allylic radicals to the point where isomerization occurs to the *trans* form.

While *cis*-2-butene gives solely the *cis* isomer of 1-chloro-2-butene, even at 100°, *cis*-2-pentene at 100° gives some *trans*-1-chloro-2-pentene, but none at 40°. When R = *tert*-butyl (4,4-dimethyl-2-pentene), the *cis* isomer gives half *trans* product at 40°, but none at −78°.

In the 1-olefin case, it is suggested that the distribution of *cis* and *trans* allylic radicals is determined by the conformation of the olefin at the moment of reaction, since hydrogen abstraction, a low activation energy process, probably occurs faster than rotational interconversion of the different possible conformations (eq. 45). Obviously, the larger the group R, the more

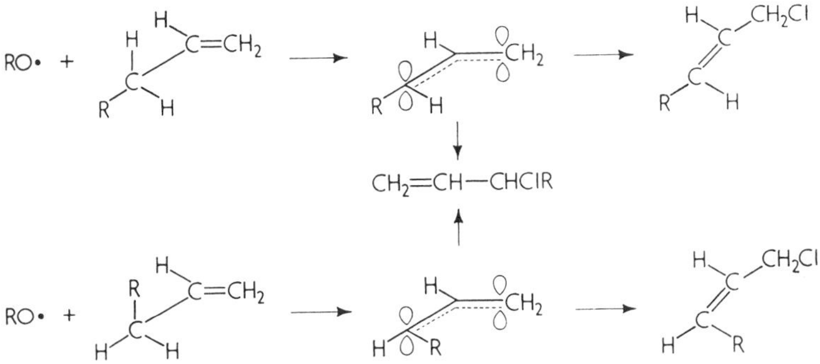

$$ (45) $$

the upper (*trans*) conformation will be favored. In keeping with this picture, the percentage of *trans* isomer in the 1-chloro-2-olefin increases from $65 \pm 5\%$ with 1-butene to 75% with 1-pentene and 100% with 4,4-dimethyl-1-pentene.

Attack on C_4 of 2-pentene presents a more complex stereochemical problem, since here three allylic radicals (**17–19**) are possible. Radicals **17**

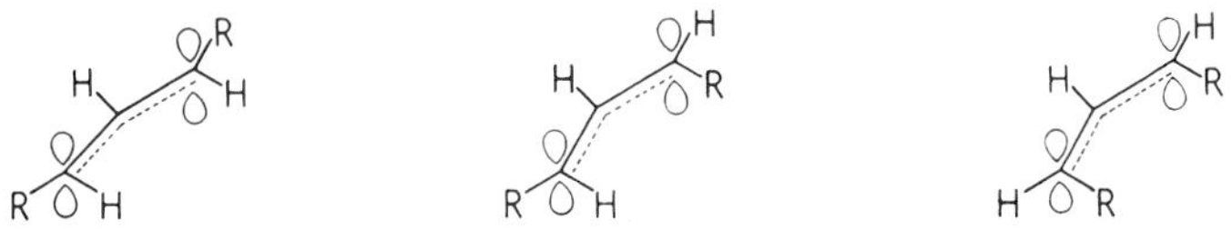

(17)   (18)   (19)

(*trans-trans*) and **18** (*trans-cis*) can arise from *trans*-2-pentene, while **18** and **19** (*cis-cis*) can come from *cis*-2-pentene. Since **17** can yield only *trans*-4-chloro-2-pentene, **19** only the *cis* isomer, and **18** a mixture, the observation that at 40° *trans*-2-pentene gives 4-chloro-2-pentene which is 86% *trans*, while *cis*-2-pentene gives 4-chloro-2-pentene which is only 57% *trans*, is consistent. This interpretation shows that a path exists for *cis-trans* isomerization via allylic radicals, even though the radicals themselves retain their stereochemistry. It further predicts that, under these conditions, *cis-trans* isomerization will be observed only in those products which have also undergone rearrangement.

Since olefin stability increases with increasing substitution, it might be expected that allylic radicals will tend to react at that end of the three-carbon system which produces the most highly substituted double bond in the product, a course which is also favored on steric grounds. Results with *tert*-butyl hypochlorite in general support this view. Thus 69% 1-chloro 2-olefin is produced from 1-butene, 94% from 4,4-dimethyl-1-pentene, and 83% from 3-methyl-1-butene.

Although the situation with *tert*-butyl hypochlorite seems well established, how general these conclusions are for other radical reactions involving allylic remains to be determined.

One group of rather remarkable reactions in which allylic rearrangements are frequently observed, but in which the detailed mechanism is still unsettled, is a series of processes investigated by Kharasch and his group in which peroxides were reacted with olefins (and other substrates) in the presence of traces of transition metal salts, notably copper halides. As examples, *tert*-butyl hydroperoxide and 1-octene yielded 1-*tert*-butylperoxy-2-octene and 3-*tert*-butylperoxy-1-octene,[84] and benzoyl peroxide and 1-octene gave similar mixtures of phenyloctenes and benzoyloxyoctenes.[85] Similarly, *tert*-butyl perbenzoate reacts suitable olefins to yield allylic esters, e.g. with 1-octene[86] or allyl benzene and β-methylstyrene,[87] while with norbornadiene the reaction takes a different course to give 7-*t*-butoxy-norbornadiene.[88]

The mechanism of these processes was first discussed by Kharasch in terms of "complexed radicals." An alternative sequence, illustrated for the reaction of *tert*-butyl peracetate and cyclohexene (which gives 3-acetoxycyclohexene in high yield), is that shown in equations 45a–45e, involving only steps well established in other radical processes.

Reliable experimental data on which mechanistic decisions can be made are just recently beginning to emerge for these reactions and, in particular, there has been considerable confusion as to the distribution of allylic isomers obtained in some systems. Kharasch and Sosnovsky[86] originally stated that *tert*-butyl perbenzoate reacted with 1-octene to give solely 3-benzoyloxy-1-octene, and Denney reported that both allylbenzene and β-methylstyrene gave allylic benzoates without rearrangements. Both reports now appear to be in error,[89] and Kochi, in a detailed study, has shown that 1-butene and

[84] M. S. Kharasch and A. Fono, *J. Org. Chem.*, **24**, 72 (1959).

[85] M. S. Kharasch and A. Fono, *J. Org. Chem.*, **24**, 606 (1959).

[86] M. S. Kharasch and G. Sosnovsky, *J. Am. Chem. Soc.*, **80**, 756 (1959).

[87] D. B. Denney, D. Z. Denney and G. Feig, *Tetrahedron Letters*, **No. 15**, 19 (1959).

[88] P. R. Story, *J. Org. Chem.*, **26**, 287 (1961).

[89] A. Zavitsas, unpublished work at Columbia University; also D. B. Denney, private communication.

cis- and *trans*-2-butene give essentially the same mixture of allylic isomers.[89a] Such an observation is a requirement of the sequence shown in equations 45a–45c for which Kochi argues strongly.

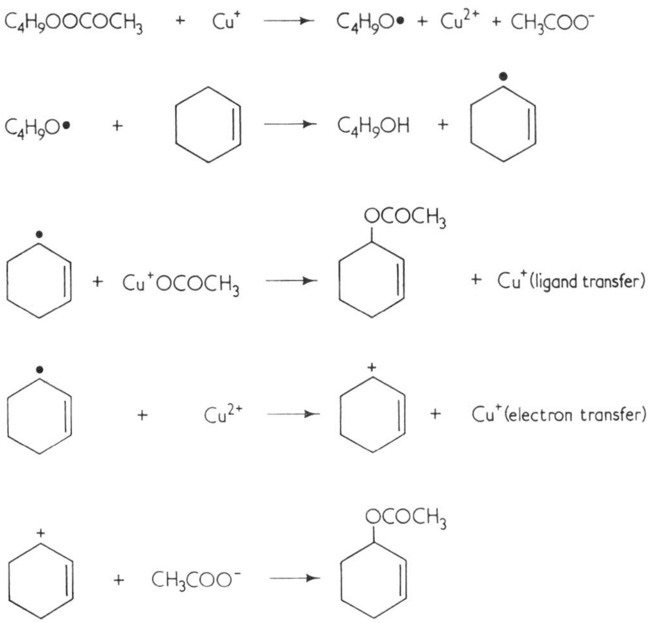

$$C_4H_9OOCOCH_3 \quad + \quad Cu^+ \quad \longrightarrow \quad C_4H_9O\bullet \; + \; Cu^{2+} \; + \; CH_3COO^- \qquad (45a)$$

$$(45b)$$

$$+ \; Cu^+OCOCH_3 \quad \longrightarrow \qquad + \; Cu^+ (\text{ligand transfer}) \qquad (45c)$$

$$+ \quad Cu^{2+} \quad \longrightarrow \qquad + \; Cu^+ (\text{electron transfer}) \qquad (45d)$$

$$+ \; CH_3COO^- \quad \longrightarrow \qquad \qquad (45e)$$

Interestingly, the products from the butenes are usually 85 to 90% 3-acyloxy-1-butenes and only 10 to 15% 1-acyloxy-2-butenes—a distribution of allylic isomers quite different from that observed in radical halogenation with *tert*-butyl hypochlorite.[83] Kochi has recently reported that isomer distribution is sensitive to the nature of the copper ion coordination.[89b] Thus, with α,α'-bipyridyl complexes, 55 to 60% 1-acyloxy-2-butenes are obtained, and he suggests that the differences arise from different contributions from ligand transfer (eq. 45c) and electron transfer processes (eqs. 45d–45e). Story's result with norbornadiene can also be accommodated by the sequence shown in equations 45a–45c, since *tert*-butoxy radicals from *tert*-butyl hypochlorite apparently add to norbornadiene, and oxidation of an intermediate radical could yield a carbonium ion capable of rearranging to the product with proton loss.

[89a] J. K. Kochi, *J. Am. Chem. Soc.*, **84**, 774 (1962).
[89b] J. K. Kochi, *J. Am. Chem. Soc.*, **84**, 3271 (1962).

C. Allylic Rearrangements involving Double Bond Additions

Radical addition to a conjugated diene gives rise to an allylic radical

$$R\cdot + CH_2 = CH-CH = CH_2 \rightarrow RCH_2CH-\dot{C}H-CH = CH_2 \leftrightarrow RCH_2CH = CH-\dot{C}H_2$$

which can react further at either end of the three-carbon allylic system (1,2 or 1,4 addition). The system which has been studied in the greatest detail (because of its practical importance) is that arising in the polymerization of butadiene.[90] Here the product contains both 1,2 and *cis* and *trans*-1,4 units.

Although the fraction of 1,2 units remains approximately 20%, the ratio of *trans*- to *cis*-1,4 units increases strikingly as the temperature is lowered, with a significant corresponding change in the physical properties of the polymer. Whether this change in *cis/trans* ratio arises from changes in the conformational distribution of butadiene or from *cis-trans* isomerization of the intermediate allylic radical at higher temperatures has not been unequivocally shown. However, the opportunity for isomerization is certainly more favorable than in the *tert*-butyl hypochlorite chlorinations discussed in the previous section, since the competing chain propagation step is here relatively slow.

Substitution in the 2 or 2,3 positions of butadiene increases the amount of 1,4 structural units in the product (88% in polyisoprene and 97% in chloroprene), as does copolymerization of butadiene with other monomers. Simple radical additions to butadiene also give chiefly 1,4 products, for example, in reactions with mercaptans,[91] CCl₃Br,[92] alkyl radicals,[92a] or *tert*-butyl hypochlorite.[92b]

In molecules containing suitable allylic substituents, allylic rearrangements may occur without intermediate formation of an allylic radical via the sequence

$$X\cdot + CH_2{=}CH-CH_2Y \rightarrow X-CH_2-\dot{C}H-CH_2Y \rightarrow X-CH_2-CH{=}CH_2 + Y\cdot$$

[90] Results are summarized by F. E. Condon, *J. Polymer Sci.*, **11**, 139 (1953).

[91] H. R. Snyder, J. M. Stewart, R. E. Allen, and R. J. Dearborn, *J. Am. Chem. Soc.*, **68**, 1422 (1946).

[92] M. S. Kharasch, E. Simon, and W. Nudenberg, *J. Org. Chem.*, **18**, 328 (1953).

[92a] W. B. Smith and J. L. Massingill, *J. Am. Chem. Soc.*, **83**, 4301 (1961).

[92b] J. K. Kochi, *J. Am. Chem. Soc.*, **84**, 2785 (1962). Copper-catalyzed additions of peresters, however, give chiefly 3-acyloxy-4-*tert*-butoxy-1-butenes.

The fragments Y which would be eliminated should evidently be of the same structures as undergo reversible addition in the *cis-trans* isomerizations discussed under heading 2A, e.g., Br-, I-, RS-, etc. Thus Cain and Noyes [93] have shown that, in the exchange of radioactive iodine with ^{14}C-labeled allyl iodide, $CH_2{=}CH{-}{}^{14}CH_2I$, isomerization accompanies exchange. However, the process is evidently a bit more complicated than is indicated by the sequence shown above, since the rate of isomerization is only about 50% of the rate of exchange. A similar scheme accounts for the facile equilibration of the allylic bromides

$$CH_2{=}CH{-}CHBrCH_3 \rightleftharpoons CH_2BrCH{=}CHCH_3$$

occurring in the presence of bromine atoms generated from HBr and peroxides first studied by Kharasch.[94] Although such reactions have not been studied extensively, the apparent ease with which they occur makes it questionable whether, in any radical reaction yielding an allylic bromide, the product distribution observed represents the initial kinetically determined ratio of allylic bromides or is the result of subsequent equilibration brought about by traces of bromine atoms. Examples of such reactions are NBS brominations, and additions of HBr, Br$_2$, and CCl$_3$Br to 1,3-dienes mentioned above.

4. REARRANGEMENTS INVOLVING RING OPENINGS AND CLOSINGS

Cleavage of a hydrocarbon radical to a smaller radical and an olefin

$$RCH_2{-}CH_2{-}\dot{C}HR \rightarrow RCH_2\cdot + CH_2{=}CHR$$

is a well-established step in hydrocarbon pyrolyses and in polymer degradation at elevated temperatures. When the system is a cyclic one, the over-all result may be rearrangement from a cyclic to a noncyclic structure, and, in strained molecules, the cleavage may take place under relatively mild conditions. A simple example occurs in the radical addition of CCl$_4$ to β-pinene (**20**),[95,96] which gives a rearranged product in high yield.

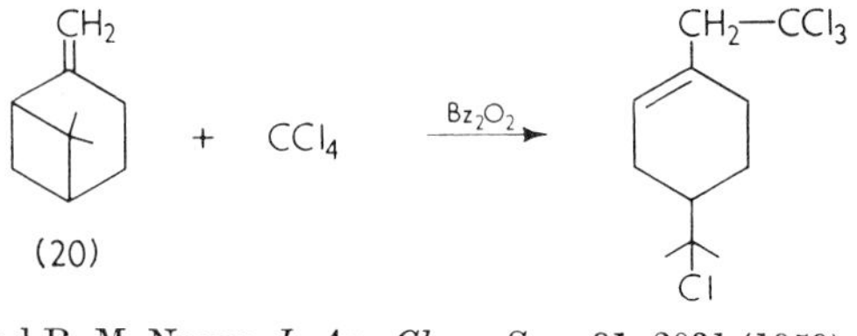

[93] W. P. Cain and R. M. Noyes, *J. Am. Chem. Soc.*, **81**, 2031 (1959).

[94] M. S. Kharasch, E. T. Margolis, and F. R. Mayo, *J. Org. Chem.*, **1**, 393 (1936).

[95] D. M. Oldroyd, G. S. Fisher, and L. A. Goldblatt, *J. Am. Chem. Soc.*, **72**, 2407 (1950).

[96] G. DuPont, R. Dulou, and G. Clement, *Bull. soc. chim. France*, **1950**, 1056, 1115; *Compt. rend.*, **236**, 2512 (1953).

The proposed reaction scheme is shown via the sequence in equation 46. The driving force for the rearrangement must be the relief of strain in opening

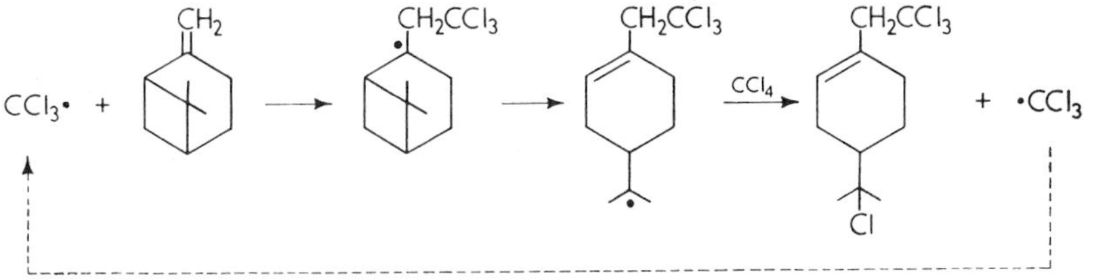

the four-membered bridged ring of the pinane skeleton, and the conclusion that the addition and ring opening are successive rather than concerted processes is supported by the observation that, while the addition of chloral leads to a similar rearrangement,[97] thiolacetic acid gives chiefly unrearranged addition products.[98] Here the very high rate of radical attack on the RS—H bond greatly shortens the lifetime of the radical formed in the initial addition and decreases its chances of rearrangement as in the decarbonylation reactions discussed under heading 2A.

A similar ring opening of the pinane skeleton has also been invoked to explain the complex mixture of products including carvomenthene and limonene obtained in the autoxidation of pinane and decomposition of the resulting peroxidic reaction product.[99]

Ring opening of a cyclopropyl ring attached to a carbon bearing a free radical has also been observed. Decarbonylation of cyclopropylacetaldehyde yields 1-butene as the major product via the sequence shown in equation 47.

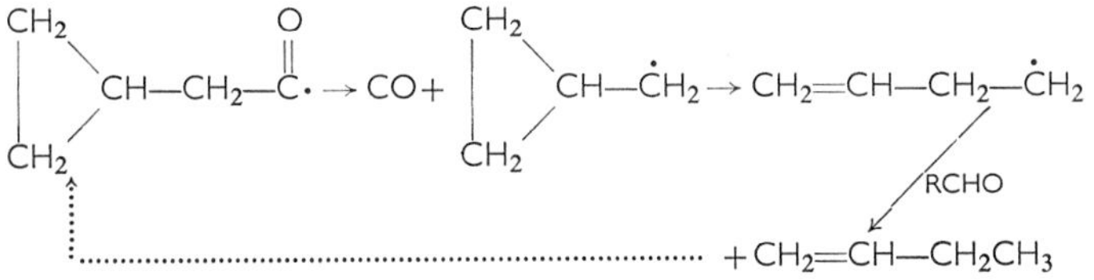

Dimethylcyclopropylacetaldehyde similarly gives 2-methyl-2-pentene, but, when benzyl mercaptan is added to the system to shorten the lifetime of the intermediate radical, unrearranged isopropylcyclopropane is obtained as well.[100] Similarly, chlorination of methylcyclopropane gives a complex mixture of products including both cyclopropylmethyl chloride and

[97] M. Vilkas, G. Du Pont, and R. Dulou, *Bull. soc. chim. France*, **1955**, 799.

[98] F. G. Bordwell and W. A. Hewett, *J. Am. Chem. Soc.*, **79**, 3493 (1957).

[99] G. A. Schmidt and G. S. Fisher, *J. Am. Chem. Soc.*, **81**, 445 (1959).

[100] D. I. Schuster, Thesis, California Institute of Technology, 1960.

4-chloro-1-butene (eq. 48).[101] Using ^{13}C labeled starting materials, the ^{13}C distribution is that shown, consistent with the scheme given, and providing no evidence for a "nonclassical" intermediate which could permit a further scrambling of the carbon skeleton.[101]

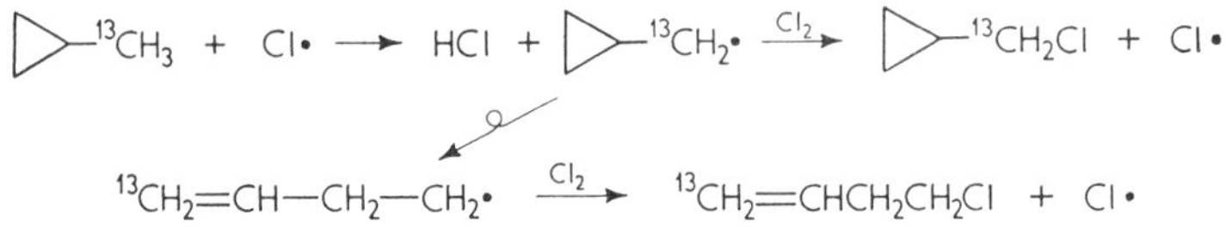

$$\tag{48}$$

Ring opening also occurs when methylcyclopropane and 1,1-dimethyl-cyclopropane are chlorinated with *tert*-butyl hypochlorite. In the former, some cyclobutyl chloride is also produced, presumably by reclosure of the intermediate allyl-carbinyl radical to the cyclobutyl radical.[104]

In contrast to these results, cyclopropyl radicals appear to be quite stable toward ring opening. Treatment of the silver salts of *cis-* and *trans*-2-methyl-cyclopropanecarboxylic acids with bromine gives the same mixture of *cis-* and *trans*-2-methylcyclopropyl bromides,[102] and decarbonylation of 1-methyl- and 1-phenylcyclopropanecarboxaldehydes gives solely methyl- and phenyl-cyclopropanes.[103] Similarly, *tert*-butyl hypochlorite chlorinates cyclopropane to cyclopropyl chloride in high yield.[104] Ring opening, however, may be extensive in halogen atom reactions. Roberts and Dirstine reported in 1945 that gas-phase chlorination of cyclopropane gives almost exclusively cyclopropyl chloride except at very high temperatures.[104a] However, recent work [104] shows that the liquid-phase photochemical reaction at 0° gives, chiefly, 1,3-dichloropropane. Chlorination of spiropentane (eq. 49) also gives a complex mixture of products, which Applequist [104b] accounts for as shown

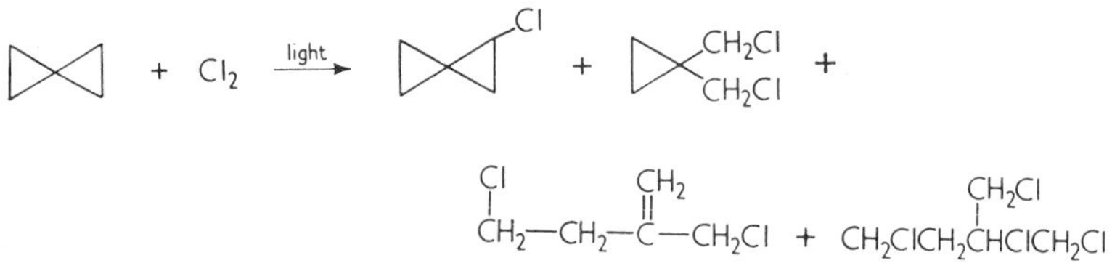

$$\tag{49}$$

[101] E. Renk, P. R. Shafer, W. H. Graham, R. H. Mazur, and J. D. Roberts, *J. Am. Chem. Soc.*, **83**, 1987 (1961).

[102] D. E. Applequist and A. H. Peterson, *J. Am. Chem. Soc.*, **82**, 2372 (1960).

[103] D. I. Schuster and J. D. Roberts, *J. Org. Chem.*, **27**, 51 (1962).

[104] C. Walling and P. S. Fredricks, *J. Am. Chem. Soc.*, **84**, 3326 (1962).

[104a] J. D. Roberts and P. H. Dirstine, *J. Am. Chem. Soc.*, **67**, 1281 (1945).

[104b] D. E. Applequist, G. F. Fanta, and B. W. Henrikson, *J. Am. Chem. Soc.*, **82**, 2368 (1960).

in equation 50. Analogous ring openings by bromine [104c] and iodine atoms [104d] have been reported, and all belong to the rather rare group of radical displacements on carbon.

$$Cl\cdot\ +\ \bowtie\ \longrightarrow\ \bigtriangleup\!\!\!{}^{CH_2\cdot}_{CH_2Cl} \qquad (50)$$

An interesting ring opening and isomerization of N-bromosuccinimide to β-bromopropionyl isocyanate

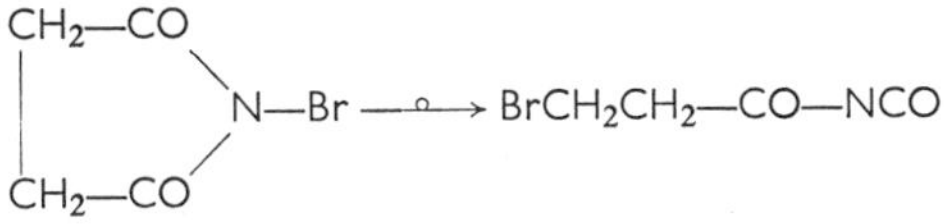

$$\begin{matrix} CH_2\!\!-\!\!CO \\ | \qquad\qquad N\!\!-\!\!Br \xrightarrow{} BrCH_2CH_2\!\!-\!\!CO\!\!-\!\!NCO \\ CH_2\!\!-\!\!CO \end{matrix}$$

has been noted as a side reaction during NBS brominations.[105,106] Although the conditions reported for the rearrangement are somewhat contradictory, its occurrence has been confirmed in this laboratory,[107] and the sequence (eq. 51) proposed by Martin and Bartlett [106] appears plausible, particularly

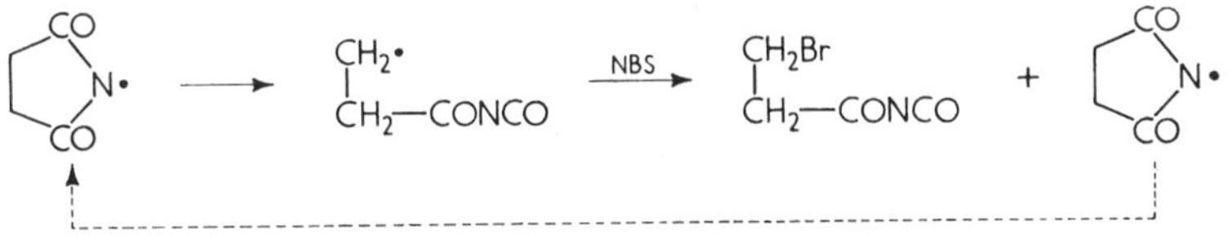

$$\qquad (51)$$

since the rearrangement appears to occur only in systems deficient in easily brominated substrate which would consume the succinimide radicals in equation 51 before they can rearrange.

A rather analogous scheme (eq. 52) accounts for the thermal isomerization

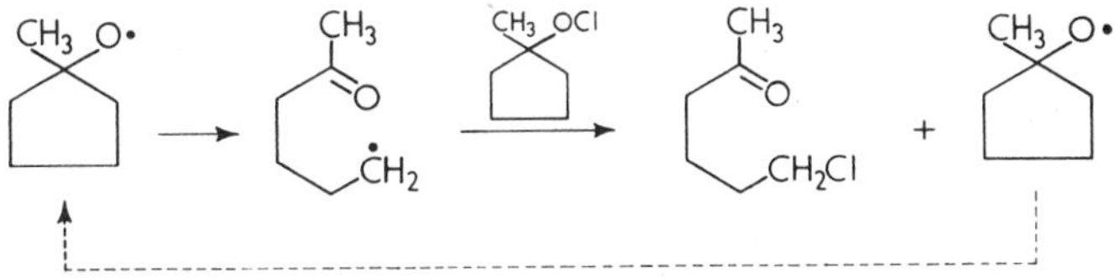

$$\qquad (52)$$

[104c] M. S. Kharasch, M. Z. Fineman, and F. R. Mayo, *J. Am. Chem. Soc.*, **61**, 2139 (1939).

[104d] R. A. Ogg, Jr., and W. J. Priest, *J. Chem. Phys.*, **7**, 736 (1939); S. W. Benson, *J. Chem. Phys.*, **34**, 521 (1961).

[105] H. W. Johnson, Jr., and D. E. Bublitz, *J. Am. Chem. Soc.*, **79**, 753 (1957); **80**, 3150 (1958).

[106] J. C. Martin and P. D. Bartlett, *J. Am. Chem. Soc.*, **79**, 2533 (1957).

[107] A. Rieger, unpublished work.

of 1-methylcyclopentyl hypochlorite to methyl δ-chlorobutyl ketone, reported by Cairns and Englund.[108] Another type of ring opening, in which the driving force is again the formation of a carbonyl group, has been proposed by Huyser[108a] to account for the isomerization of 2-methoxytetrahydropyran to methyl valerate, catalyzed by di-*tert*-butyl peroxide at 125°:

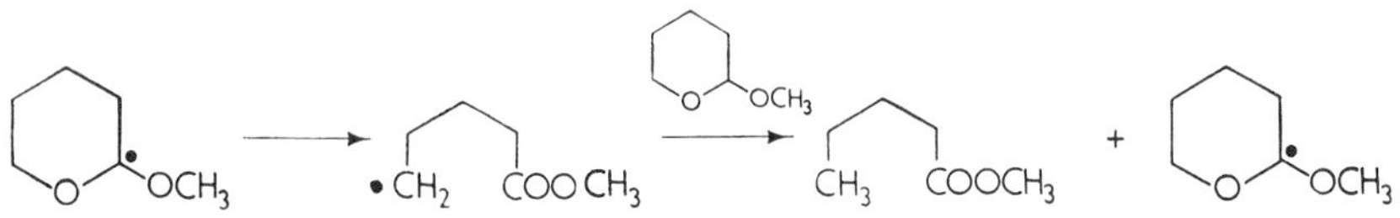

In the presence of 1-octene, some methyl tridecanoate is produced via

Similarly, Wallace and Gritter[108b] find that tetrahydrofuran, heated with 1-octene in the presence of di-*tert*-butyl peroxide, gives 40.6% 4-dodecanone, and suggest the sequence

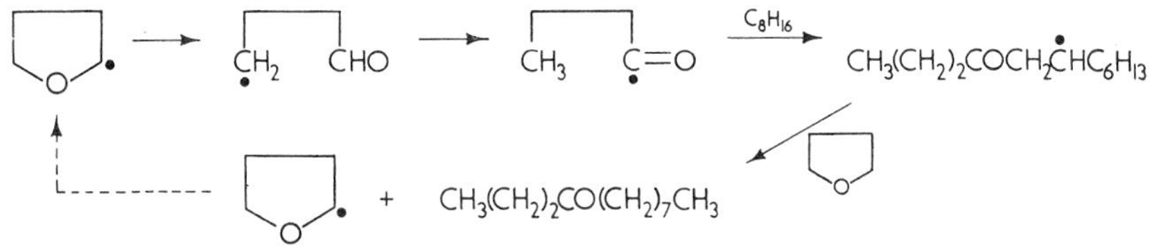

Here, the ring opening is followed by an intramolecular hydrogen transfer, of the sort discussed further under heading 5.

Opening of three-membered rings should occur with even greater ease. Although ethylene oxide and propylene oxide can be photochlorinated by *tert*-butyl hypochlorite at low temperatures to give the chloroepoxides in good yield,[104] Gritter and Wallace[108c] report that reaction with 1-octene at 150° in the presence of di-*tert*-butyl peroxide gives 2-decanone, by a reaction analogous to those just discussed. Interestingly, some 5-hydroxy-2-hexanone

[108] T. L. Cairns and B. E. Englund, *J. Org. Chem.*, **21**, 140 (1956). Examples with other sized rings are given by J. W. Wilt and J. W. Hill, *J. Org. Chem.*, **26**, 3523 (1961).

[108a] E. S. Huyser, *J. Org. Chem.*, **25**, 1820 (1960).

[108b] T. J. Wallace and R. J. Gritter, *J. Org. Chem.*, **26**, 5256 (1961).

[108c] R. J. Gritter and T. J. Wallace, *J. Org. Chem.*, **26**, 282 (1961).

was also reported to be formed by a process involving radical displacement on carbon.

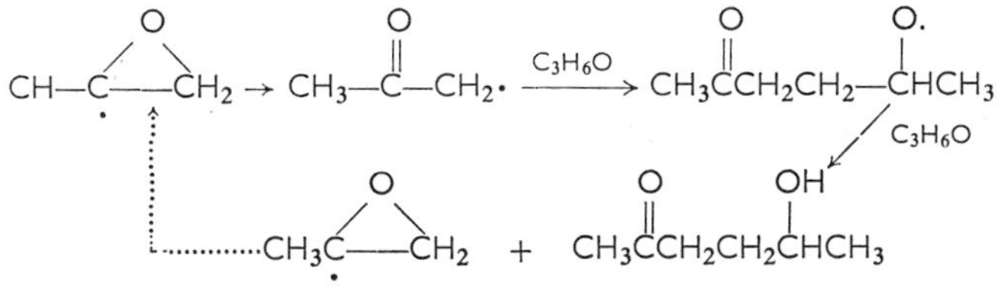

Lastly, isophorone oxide has been found by Reusch and Johnson[108d] to undergo a thermal rearrangement

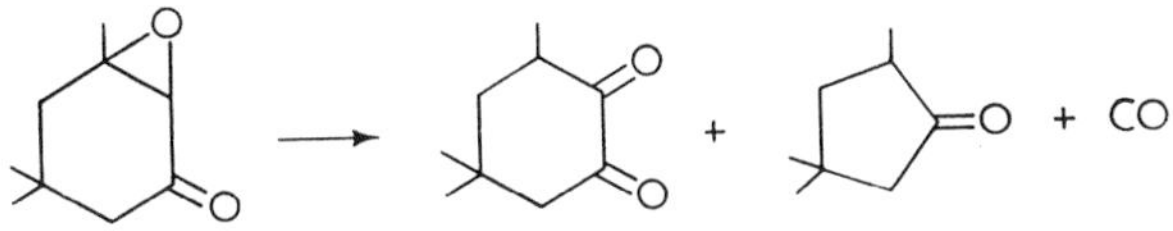

by what appears to be a free radical chain process, although several formulations are possible for the intermediate steps.

Turning next to ring closures, which are essentially the reverse of the type of process just considered, addition of p-thiocresol to norbornadiene was found by Cristol[109] to give both rearranged and unrearranged products (eq. 53). Again, evidence for the sequence given, and for the absence of an

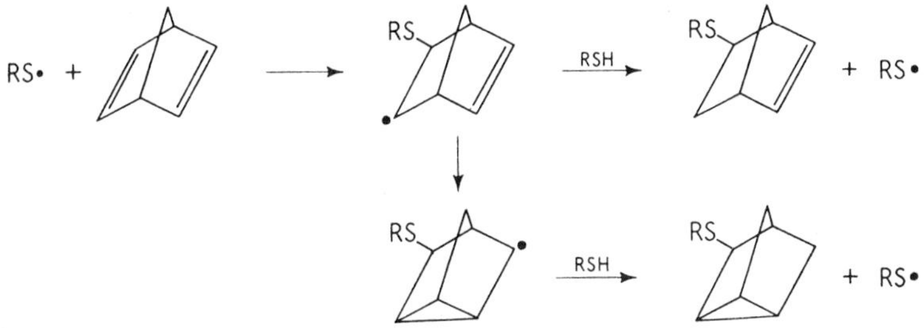

(53)

intermediate stable "nonclassical" radical, was supplied by the finding that the ratio of rearranged to unrearranged product increased as the p-thiocresol concentration was reduced to lengthen the lifetime of the initial hydrocarbon radical.

A rather less well-defined cyclization may accompany radical additions to nonconjugated dienes and is often of importance in their polymerization. Evidence for processes of this sort was pointed out in rather general terms by the writer in 1945[110] as accounting for the failure of systems such as methyl

[108d] W. Reusch and C. K. Johnson, *J. Am. Chem. Soc.*, **84**, 1759 (1962).
[109] S. J. Cristol, G. D. Brindell, and J. A. Reeder, *J. Am. Chem. Soc.*, **80**, 635 (1958).
[110] C. Walling, *J. Am. Chem. Soc.*, **67**, 441 (1945).

methacrylate–ethylene dimethacrylate to form gels at the point predicted by simple statistical theory. This idea was further developed by Gordon[111] and has attracted attention more recently chiefly through the work of Butler[112] and Marvel,[113] who have defined in some detail the type of diene structures in which such cyclizations are important. As an example, Butler[112] found that polymerization of diallyldimethylammonium bromide yields a water-soluble polymer, presumably consisting largely of piperidine rings, via the sequence shown in equation 54. As might be anticipated, the reaction is most successful

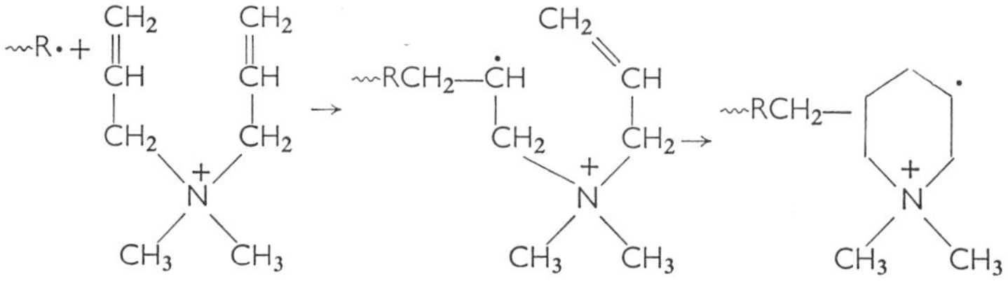

$$\text{(54)}$$

with 1,6-diene structures which permit the formation of six-membered rings.

Recently Berson[113a] has described a reaction which is formally a Wagner-Meerwein rearrangement but which he believes proceeds through ring opening followed by closure. Pyrolysis of 2-azocamphane at 255–290° yields a complex mixture of products including some isocamphane, ascribed to the sequence shown in equation 55. In support of this scheme, qualitatively the same mix-

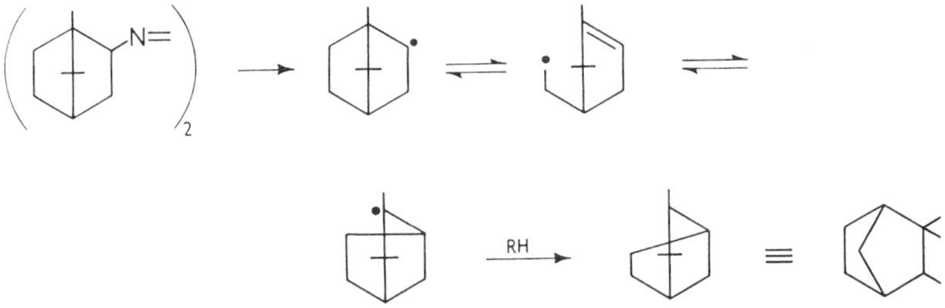

$$\text{(55)}$$

$$\text{(56)}$$

ture of products results from the decomposition of the azo compound (eq. 56), which should yield initially the second radical in the sequence shown

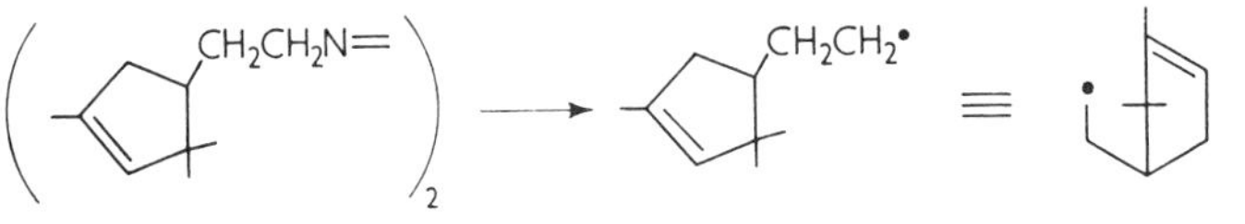

[111] M. Gordon, *J. Chem. Phys.*, **22**, 610 (1954), and subsequent papers.

[112] G. B. Butler and R. J. Angelo, *J. Am. Chem. Soc.*, **79**, 3128 (1957), and subsequent papers.

[113] C. S. Marvel and R. D. Vest, *J. Am. Chem. Soc.*, **79**, 5771 (1957); subsequent papers are reviewed by G. B. Butler, *J. Polymer Sci.*, **48**, 279 (1960).

[113a] J. A. Berson, C. J. Olson, and J. S. Walia, *J. Am. Chem. Soc.*, **82**, 5000 (1960).

in equation 55. Another series of reactions seemingly involving an intermediate ring, and formally analogous to the 1,2 shifts of aryl groups discussed under heading 2A, has been reported briefly by Winstein.[114] Decarbonylation of 5-methyl-5-phenylhexanal yielded a mixture of products, accounted for by the sequence shown in equation 57. The rearranged product 21 arises from a

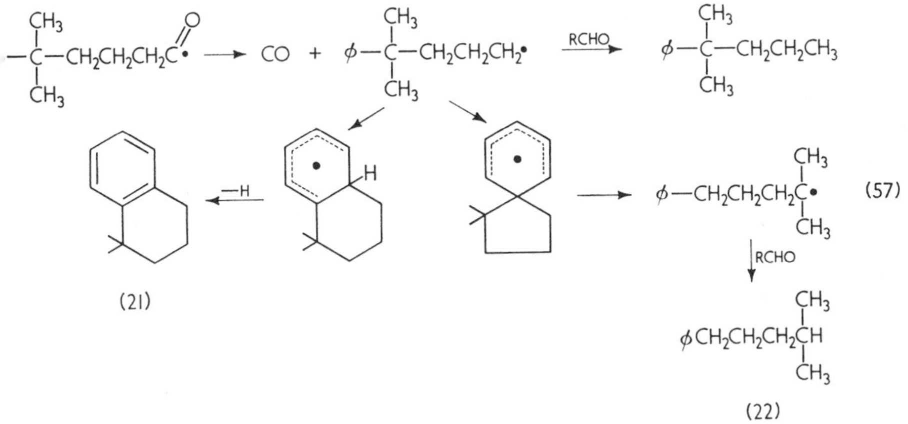

(57)

1,5 phenyl shift, and the bridged intermediate may represent either a transition state or more likely a relatively high energy intermediate. The nature of the H loss which gives 22 is unknown and could be either a radical disproportionation or oxidation during workup of a dihydro compound.

The scope of this sort of aryl shift seems to have had little further study. However, Breederveld and Kooyman [114a] have reported that electrolysis of β,β,β-triphenylpropionic acid yields phenyl β,β-diphenyl-β-methoxypropionate and have suggested a similar cyclic intermediate to account for the phenyl shift.

5. MISCELLANEOUS REARRANGEMENTS IN OPEN CHAIN SYSTEMS

Several radical reactions in open chain systems (other than the 1,2 shifts discussed under heading 2) are known which can properly be classified as rearrangements since they involve shifts of atoms or functional groups. Thus the rearrangement of α-alkoxystyrenes (eq. 58), first reported by Claisen,[115] has

$$\phi-\underset{\underset{OR}{|}}{C}=CH_2 \xrightarrow{200°} \phi-COCH_2R \qquad (58)$$

[114] S. Winstein, R. Heck, S. Lapporte, and R. Baird, *Experientia*, 12, 138 (1956).

[114a] H. Breederveld and E. C. Kooyman, *Rec. trav. chim.*, 76, 297 (1957).

[115] L. Claisen, *Ber.*, 29, 2931 (1896).

been reinvestigated by Wiberg and Rowland [116] who found that the reaction is induced by di-*tert*-butyl peroxide at 135° and, when R is optically active *sec*-butyl, leads to inactive product. Both findings are consistent with the chain shown in equation 59. The over-all reaction is thus analogous to the

$$R\cdot + CH_2{=}\overset{\underset{|}{OR}}{C}{-}\phi \rightarrow RCH_2{-}\overset{\underset{|}{OR}}{\underset{\cdot}{C}}{-}\phi \rightarrow RCH_2CO\phi + R\cdot \qquad (59)$$

radical-induced allylic rearrangements of heading 3C. A comparable sequence has been used by Stacey, Sauer, and McKusick [117] to account for the radiation-

$$R{-}SO_2{-}\overset{\underset{|}{CH_3}}{N}{-}CH{=}CH_2 \rightarrow CH_3NH{-}CH{=}CHSO_2R \qquad (60)$$

induced isomerization of N-alkyl-N-vinylsulfonamides, e.g., equation 60. Since the reaction shows G values of over 10^4, it is obviously a radical chain, and the authors propose the sequence shown in equation 61 in which the last step is a nonradical process

$$RSO_2\cdot + CH_2{=}CH{-}\overset{\underset{|}{CH_3}}{N}{-}SO_2R \rightarrow RSO_2CH_2{-}\overset{\underset{|}{CH_3}}{\underset{\cdot}{C}}H{-}\overset{\underset{|}{CH_3}}{N}{-}SO_2R$$

$$\cdots\cdots\cdots\cdots RSO_2\cdot + RSO_2CH_2{-}CH{=}NCH_3$$

$$RSO_2CH_2{-}CH{=}NCH_3 \rightarrow RSO_2CH{=}CH{-}NHCH_3 \qquad (61)$$

A class of rearrangements of rapidly increasing synthetic interest involves intramolecular hydrogen abstraction by a radical attached to a hydrocarbon chain of suitable length. The best known example occurs in the Hofmann-Löffler reaction, the over-all course of which involves the conversion of an N-haloamine to a pyrrolidine by irradiation in acid solution, followed by treatment with base, e.g., equation 62. A recent study by Corey and Hertler [118]

$$CH_3\overset{\underset{|}{Cl}}{N}{-}n{-}C_5H_{11} \xrightarrow[\text{(2) base}]{\text{(1) } h\nu,\ \text{acid}} \qquad (62)$$

has confirmed in detail Wawzonek's proposal [119] that the acid reaction is a radical chain process with the propagating sequence shown in equation 63 followed by ring closure to the pyrrolidine on addition of base. Attack on C_4

[116] K. B. Wiberg and B. I. Rowland, *J. Am. Chem. Soc.*, **77**, 1159 (1955).

[117] F. W. Stacey, J. C. Sauer, and B. C. McKusick, *J. Am. Chem. Soc.*, **81**, 987 (1959).

[118] E. J. Corey and W. R. Hertler, *J. Am. Chem. Soc.*, **82**, 1657 (1960).

[119] S. Wawzonek and P. J. Thelen, *J. Am. Chem. Soc.*, **71**, 2118 (1950).

is preferred, since the transition state is a quasi-six-membered ring but, with longer chain amines, small amounts N-substituted piperidines are also produced.

$$
\begin{array}{c}
\underset{\underset{+\,\cdot}{|}}{\overset{H}{\underset{|}{R-N}}}-CH_2CH_2CH_2CH_2CH_3 \rightarrow R-\overset{H}{\underset{|}{\overset{|}{N}}}{}^{+}-CH_2CH_2CH_2\overset{\cdot}{C}HCH_3 \xrightarrow{R_2NHCl}
\end{array}
$$

$$
R-\overset{H}{\underset{H}{\overset{|}{N}}}{}^{+}-CH_2CH_2CH_2\overset{\overset{Cl}{|}}{C}HCH_3
$$

$$
R-\overset{H}{\underset{+\,\cdot}{\overset{|}{N}}}-CH_2CH_2CH_2CH_2CH_3 \qquad (63)
$$

The Hofmann-Löffler reaction occurs smoothly only in strongly acid medium, and Corey suggests that the intramolecular reaction is favored for the radical ion, since intermolecular reaction between two positively charged species is unlikely. This being as it may, a number of facile intramolecular reactions of *uncharged* alkoxy radicals have recently been described. One group involves the intramolecular rearrangement of long-chain hypochlorites to δ-chloroalcohols by a photo- (or thermally) induced chain process.[120a–120c] To take the case of the hypochlorite from 2-methyl-2-hexanol, the reactions are

$$
\begin{array}{l}
\overset{\displaystyle CH_3}{\underset{\displaystyle CH_3}{C_4H_9\overset{|}{\underset{|}{C}}-O\cdot}} \nearrow CH_3COCH_3 + C_4H_9\cdot \xrightarrow{C_7H_{15}OCl} C_4H_9Cl + C_4H_9C(CH_3)_2O\cdot \\[2em]
\rightarrow CH_3\overset{\cdot}{C}HCH_2CH_2C(CH_3)_3OH \xrightarrow{C_7H_{15}OCl} CH_3CHClCH_2CH_2C(CH_3)_3OH \\
\qquad\qquad\qquad\qquad\qquad\qquad\qquad\qquad\qquad + C_4H_9C(CH_3)_2O\cdot \\[1.5em]
\searrow^{RH} C_4H_9C(CH_3)_2OH + R\cdot \xrightarrow{C_7H_{15}OCl} RCl + C_4H_9C(CH_3)_2O\cdot \qquad (64)
\end{array}
$$

It is evident that the intramolecular process competes both with β scission and attack on other hydrogen donors RH which may be either other hypochlorite molecules or added hydrocarbon substrates. The conclusion that the process leading to δ-chloroalcohol is indeed an intramolecular process is shown by the observation that the ratio of yields of δ-chloroalcohol (76 to

[120a] F. D. Greene, M. L. Savitz, H. H. Lau, F. D. Osterholtz, and W. N. Smith, *J. Am. Chem. Soc.*, **83**, 2196 (1961).

[120b] C. Walling and A. Padwa, *J. Am. Chem. Soc.*, **83**, 2207 (1961).

[120c] M. Akhtar and D. H. R. Barton, *J. Am. Chem. Soc.*, **83**, 2213 (1961).

80%) and of n-butyl chloride (13 to 15%) is independent of hypochlorite concentration in inert solvents. Strikingly, the yield of δ-chloroalcohol is hardly diminished when the reaction is carried out in cyclohexane as solvent, indicating a very real preference for intramolecular over intermolecular hydrogen abstraction.[120d] Although these processes occur best with *tert*-hypochlorites, reasonable yields of δ-chloroalcohols can also be obtained from *prim*- and *sec*-hypochlorites under suitable conditions.[120d,120e]

An alternate way of producing alkoxy radicals, which then undergo an intramolecular hydrogen abstraction, is by the photolysis of nitrites. This technique has been applied by Barton et al.[121] to the steroid series, and is elegantly demonstrated in the photolysis of the nitrite ester of 3β-acetoxy-5α-pregnan-20β-ol (23) to give the 18-oximino compound (24) in 34% yield.

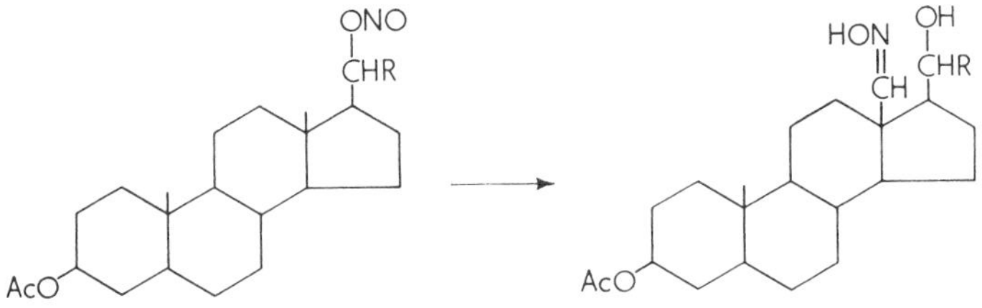

(23)   (24)

Apparently the reaction occurs via the nonchain radical process (eq. 65) followed by the well-established nitroso rearrangement

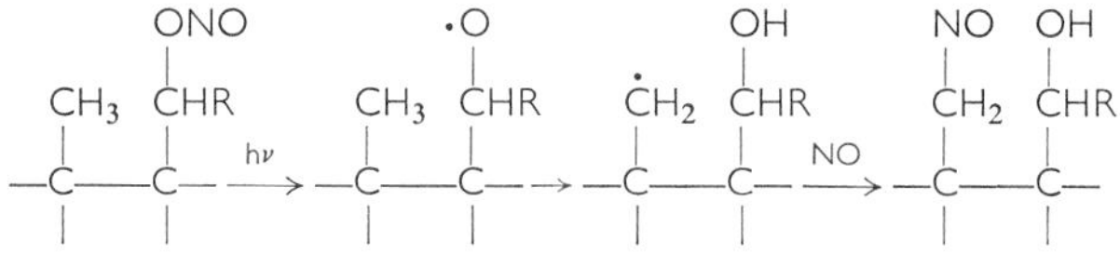

$$RCH_2NO \rightarrow RCH{=}NOH$$

A rather less well-defined example of intramolecular hydrogen abstraction occurs as a complication in vinyl polymerization, and appears to account for the formation of many short branches during the high temperature, high pressure free radical polymerization of ethylene.[121a] As a final example

[120d] A. Padwa and C. Walling, unpublished work.

[120e] E. L. Jenner, *J. Org. Chem.*, **27**, 1031 (1962).

[121] D. H. R. Barton, J. M. Beaton, L. E. Geller, and M. M. Pechet, *J. Am. Chem. Soc.*, **82**, 2640 (1960); **83**, 4076 (1961). For application of the same scheme to the synthesis of aldosterone acetate, see D. H. R. Barton and J. M. Beaton, *J. Am. Chem. Soc.*, **82**, 4083 (1960).

[121a] M. J. Roedel, *J. Am. Chem. Soc.*, **75**, 6110 (1953); W. M. D. Bryant and R. C. Voter, *J. Am. Chem. Soc.*, 6113; F. W. Billmeyer, Jr., *J. Am. Chem. Soc.*, 6118.

of an open chain rearrangement, a number of autoxidations of halogenated ethane and ethylene derivatives yield acid chlorides by a process which must

$$\underset{\overset{|}{CH_2}}{\overset{\cdot}{\sim}CH_2} \quad \underset{\overset{|}{CH_2}}{\overset{\cdot}{CH_2}} \rightarrow \underset{\overset{|}{C_5H_{11}}}{\overset{\cdot}{\sim}\overset{\cdot}{CH}} \xrightarrow{C_2H_4} \underset{\overset{|}{C_5H_{11}}}{\sim CH-CH_2\overset{\cdot}{CH_2}} \quad \text{etc.} \qquad (65a)$$

have involved rearrangement at some step. As an example, the chlorine-sensitized autoxidation of tetrachloroethylene gives trichloroacetyl chloride [122]

$$CCl_2{=}CCl_2 + \tfrac{1}{2}O_2 \xrightarrow[h\nu]{Cl_2} CCl_3COCl$$

several mechanisms have been proposed for this and similar reactions,[123] and their exact path is still in some doubt.

6. PHOTOCHEMICAL REARRANGEMENTS

Absorption of ultraviolet (or even visible) light by a molecule imparts to it sufficient energy to dissociate covalent bonds with the formation of free radicals. Such dissociation occurs readily with halogen molecules, many peroxides and azo compounds, and even simple carbonyl compounds such as acetone. The resulting fragments can be used to induce radical chain reactions, including the sorts of free radical rearrangements discussed in previous sections.

Dissociation is not, however, a necessary consequence of light absorption, and, with more complicated molecules, a variety of chemical transformations may result (including rearrangements). Often these photochemical reactions yield structures which are difficult to obtain by other means, and their synthetic applications have been reviewed in detail by Schönberg.[124] More recently Barton [125] and Schenck [126] and many others have made important extensions of these photochemical techniques. Photochemical rearrangements have been reviewed by Mayo.[126a]

At present, the detailed mechanisms of many of these photochemical reactions are only partially understood. Typically they involve unsaturated molecules, often with carbonyl groups or one or more carbon-carbon double

[122] R. A. Dickinson and J. A. Leermakers, J. Am. Chem. Soc., 54, 3852 (1932).
[123] C. Walling, Free Radicals in Solution, Wiley, New York, 1957.
[124] A. Schönberg, Präparative organische Photochemie, Springer-Verlag, Berlin, 1958.
[125] D. H. R. Barton, Helv. Chim. Acta., 42, 2604 (1959).
[126] G. O. Schenck, Z. Elektrochem., 64, 997 (1960).
[126a] P. de Mayo, in R. A. Raphael, E. C. Taylor, and H. Wynberg, eds., Advances in Organic Chemistry, Vol. II, Interscience, New York–London, 1960, p. 367.

bonds. Initial light absorption by such molecules is believed to involve excitation of an electron in a π orbital or in an unshared pair to an excited singlet state. This excited state very quickly loses its energy by fluorescence, thermal degradation, or chemical reaction, or it may pass to a longer-lived triplet state which in turn may emit light (phosphorescence), react, or dissipate its energy thermally. Since the triplet state is a diradical, any reactions in which it is involved may be considered radical processes, even though cleavage of the molecule into radical fragments does not take place. There is good reason to believe that many of the oxidation-reduction or addition reactions which occur between photoexcited molecules and various substrates are such radical reactions.[126,127]

On the other hand, the situation in regard to processes which lead simply to rearrangement of the photoexcited molecule is much less clear. Because of this uncertainty, discussion here will be limited to some relatively simple cases to illustrate the types of rearrangement which occur and the systems in which they take place, recognizing that the role of radical intermediates remains to be established.

Photolysis of saturated ketones of sufficient complexity leads to both radical and "molecular" decomposition, e.g., equation 66. The reaction,

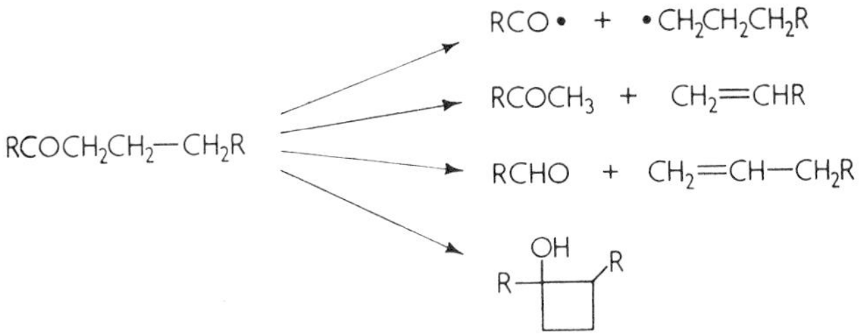

forming cyclobutanol derivatives, is properly a rearrangement. Although it is a minor path with most ketones, it has recently been found to occur in almost quantitative yield with a number of α,β-diketones, and is here believed to involve a triplet intermediate.[127a] As an example, 5,6-decadione is converted to 2-butyl-3-ethyl-2-hydroxycyclobutanone as the sole product on 12 hour exposure to sunlight:

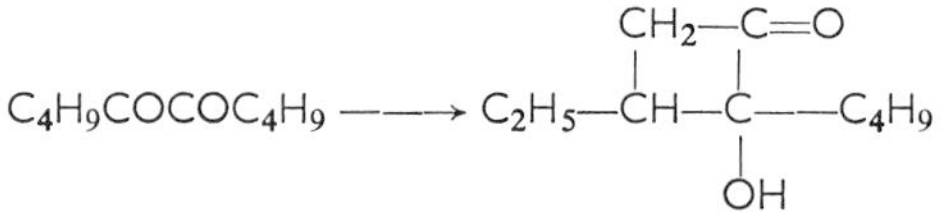

[127] G. S. Hammond and W. M. Moore, *J. Am. Chem. Soc.*, **81**, 6334 (1959); W. M. Moore, G. S. Hammond, and R. P. Foss, *J. Am. Chem. Soc.*, **83**, 2788 (1961).

[127a] W. H. Urry and D. J. Trecker, *J. Am. Chem. Soc.*, **84**, 118 (1962).

With cyclic ketones, all molecular decompositions amount to a rearrangement. Thus cyclopentanone (eq. 67) and cyclohexanone (eq. 68) give unsatu-

(67)

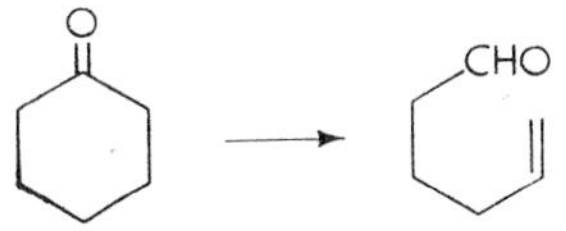

(68)

rated aldehydes,[128] while with camphor (eq. 69), both types of molecular cleavage occur.[128] Monoolefins (and also polyenes) undergo *cis-trans* isomerization in the presence of light of suitable wavelength, since the photoexcited state is able to undergo rotation at the site of the double bond. Similar

(69)

isomerization occurs with azo compounds and oximes. Since *cis* and *trans* isomers have different absorption spectra, choice of a suitable wavelength of light can by "optical pumping" lead to a product containing more of the unstable isomer than would result from thermal equilibration. Many such isomerizations have been reviewed by Schönberg [124] and by Wyman.[129]

In cyclic dienes where the double bonds are held in close proximity, bond shifts may occur in the photoexcited state to yield cage-like structures. Thus carvone (25) is converted to carvonecamphor (26) the structure of which has

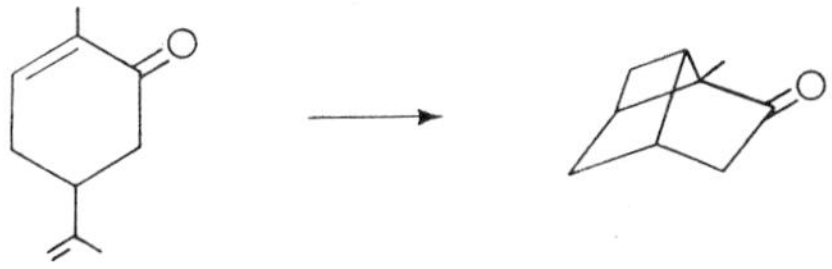

(25)   (26)

been established by Buchi and Goldman,[130] and norbornadiene-2,3-dicarboxylic acid (27) to a highly bridged isomer (28).[131] Recently Cookson [132] has

[128] R. Srinivasan, *J. Am. Chem. Soc.*, **81**, 1546, 2601, 2604 (1959).

[129] G. M. Wyman, *Chem. Revs.*, **55**, 628 (1955).

[130] G. Buchi and I. M. Goldman, *J. Am. Chem. Soc.*, **79**, 4741 (1957).

[131] S. J. Cristol and R. L. Snell, *J. Am. Chem. Soc.*, **76**, 5000 (1954).

[132] R. C. Cookson, E. Crundwell, and J. Hudec, *Chem. & Ind.* (*London*), **1958**, 1003, 1004.

described a variety of similar processes. In some polyunsaturated systems ring opening occurs. Thus Barton [125] found that irradiation of 6,6-dimethyl-

cyclohexa-2,4-dienone (**29**) in the presence of water yields an open chain acid, presumably by hydration of the intermediate ketene (**30**), while cyclohexa-1,3-

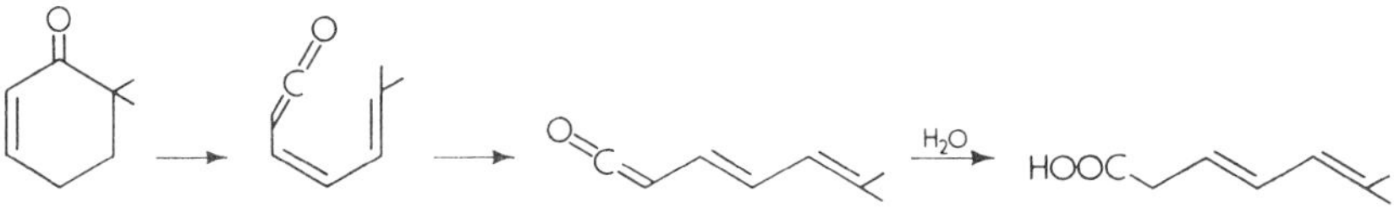

diene opens similarly to 1,3,5-hexatriene. As a result of his studies, Barton suggests that ring systems of $2n$ members with $(n-1)$ conjugated double bonds will in general open to give products with n double bonds. On the other hand, odd-membered ring systems should be expected to undergo bridge-forming reactions.

It is really in the photochemistry of certain natural products and related compounds that photorearrangements reach their full development, starting (chronologically) with the conversion of ergosterol to calciferol, and including a variety of other reactions in the steroid, santonin, and colchicine series. Examples are given in the general references cited,[124–126a] and further discussion will be found in Sections 13 and 16.

Recently, two developments have occurred which should prove useful in the unraveling of photochemical rearrangements. First, Zimmerman [133] has proposed a general scheme for interpreting photochemical rearrangements in terms of electron shifts in excited states, and used it to explain the rearrangement of 4,4-diphenylcyclohexadienone to 6,6-diphenylbicyclo[3.1.0]hex-3-en-2-one and 2,3-diphenylphenol:

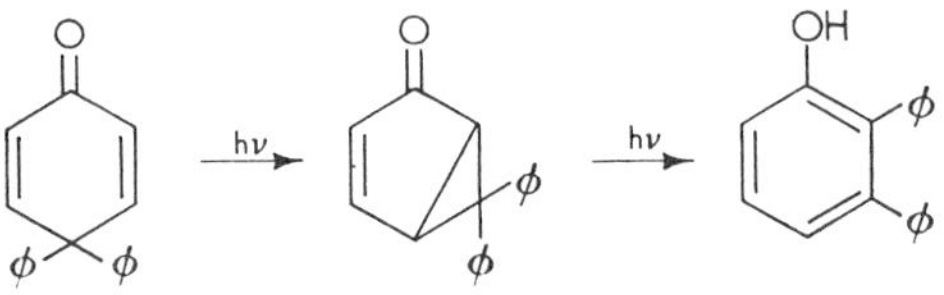

[133] H. E. Zimmerman and D. I. Schuster, *J. Am. Chem. Soc.*, **83**, 4486 (1961).

Second, Hammond[134-136] has demonstrated conclusively that benzophenone and a number of related ketones, which are converted photochemically to their triplet states in high yields, readily undergo energy transfer with a variety of molecules to convert them to their triplet states. In some cases, the subsequent reaction of these molecules results in rearrangement, which can thus be considered a radical process. As examples, piperylenes undergo *cis-trans* isomerization,[134] and norbornadiene is converted to quadricyclene [135] by a reaction analogous to that producing **28**. Many extensions of this technique are certainly to be expected. Interestingly, *ortho*-alkylbenzophenones have been found by Yang and Rivas [137] to undergo an internal rearrangement to an enol intermediate which can be trapped by reaction with dimethyl acetylenedicarboxylate:

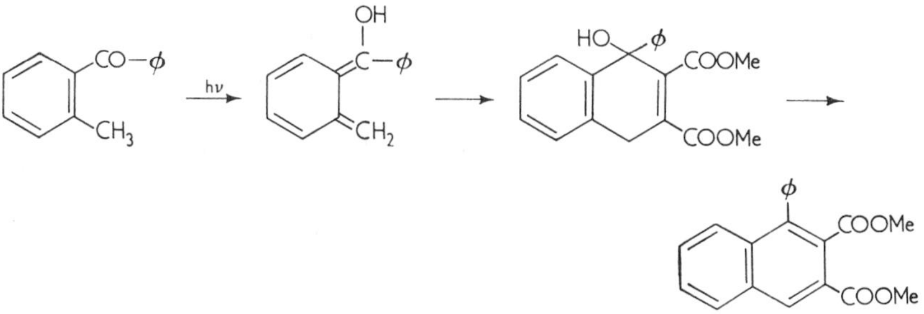

It is noteworthy that while, as we have seen, benzophenone acts as a photosensitizer for many reactions, *ortho*-hydroxy benzophenones are used as UV stabilizers for a variety of plastics, etc. It may be that energy is here dissipated by some similar reversible isomerization.

---

[134] G. S. Hammond, P. A. Leermakers, and N. J. Turro, *J. Am. Chem. Soc.*, **83**, 2395, 2396 (1961).

[135] G. S. Hammond, N. J. Turro, and A. Fischer, *J. Am. Chem. Soc.*, **83**, 4674 (1961).

[136] K. R. Kopecky, G. S. Hammond and P. A. Leermakers, *J. Am. Chem. Soc.*, **83**, 2397 (1961); **84**, 1015 (1962).

[137] N. C. Yang and C. Rivas, *J. Am. Chem. Soc.*, **83**, 2213 (1961).

8 | REARRANGEMENTS INVOLVING MIGRATION TO AN ELECTRON-DEFICIENT NITROGEN OR OXYGEN

PETER A. S. SMITH
University of Michigan, Ann Arbor
Michigan

I. INTRODUCTION

The rearrangements considered in this Section arise from a molecular cleavage accompanied by a structural change in one of the fragments. This change, a migration of a group from a neighboring atom, takes place so as to avoid the generation of an atom of a first period element with only a sextet of electrons in its valency shell. Ions and ionization need not be involved, although they often are. Whether the electron-deficient atom actually occurs as a discrete entity, or whether its formation is prevented by migration in concert with the cleavage, cannot always be said, and all such cases are considered together.

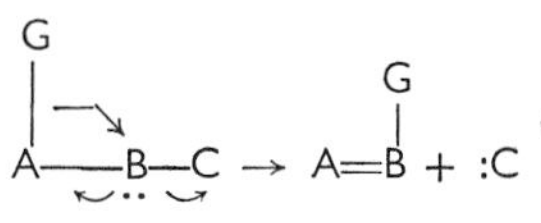

$$A\text{---}B\text{---}C \rightarrow A\text{==}B + :C \quad \begin{cases} G = \text{migrating group} \\ A = \text{migration origin} \\ B = \text{migration terminus} \\ C = \text{leaving group} \end{cases}$$

457

An electron-deficient carbon atom in the present sense may be a carbene if it is dicoordinate or a carbonium ion if tricoordinate. The rearrangements accompanying the actual or potential formation of carbonium ions are considered elsewhere in this volume, particularly in Sections 1 and 3, but the particular case of the rearrangement of α-diazo ketones, which is related to carbene formation, is included here because of its mechanistic similarity to the more widely studied nitrogen counterpart, the Curtius rearrangement. This Section thus treats of migrations to a nitrogen atom, migrations to an oxygen atom, and migrations to a carbon atom under certain related circumstances; migrations to other elements are in principle possible, but have not yet been observed unequivocally. The migrating group leaves from a carbon atom in most cases, but this is not a requirement. All the migrations occur between vicinal atoms, however. The site of attachment on the migrating group is usually a carbon atom, but it may be a nitrogen atom, or the unique case of hydrogen. Migrations in which a bond to an oxygen, sulfur, or other atom is broken and a new one formed are in principle possible, but unambiguous examples of them have not yet been reported.

The rearrangements in this Section are arranged according to the kind of atom at the migration terminus, the structure of the rearranging system with respect to unsaturation, the nature of the cleavage reaction, and the nature of the migrating group, in that order of precedence. Since the number of examples of such rearrangements is enormous, no attempt has been made at an encyclopedic coverage; on the other hand, the effort has been made to discuss representative examples of every type reported up to the time of going to press.

Nomenclature. Rearrangements in which a group migrates from carbon to nitrogen are known for alkyl, aralkyl, aryl, alkylidene, and acyl derivatives of appropriate nitrogen compounds. These may be azides, hydroxylamines, or haloamines. These functions, being energy rich, provide the driving force for the rearrangements by ejecting a species of uncommon stability, such as N_2, H_2O, and anions of strong acids. Most of the rearrangements have well-known names, although some of these names are ambiguous in one way or another.

Azide rearrangements are known for all the carbon structure types just mentioned, but bear different names. The rearrangement of alkyl and aralkyl azides (eq. 1) was discovered by T. Curtius;[1] it is sometimes called a Schmidt

$$(C_6H_5)_2CHN_3 \xrightarrow{\text{H}^+} C_6H_5\text{—CH}\text{=}N\text{—}C_6H_5 + N_2 \tag{1}$$

rearrangement, but this is unfortunate since K. F. Schmidt did not work with alkyl and aralkyl azides as such. His related work came twenty years after

[1] T. Curtius and S. Darapsky, *J. prakt. Chem.*, [2] **63**, 428 (1901).

that of Curtius, and the term "Schmidt reaction" is universally accepted for two other azide reactions already. It is not a widely discussed rearrangement, however, and a specific name does not seem to be needed. The rearrangement of aryl azides (eq. 2), only recently recognized, is likewise nameless. Re-

$$\text{(diagram: phenyl azide } \xrightarrow[\text{C}_6\text{H}_5\text{NH}_2]{\Delta} \text{ product with } NH{-}C_6H_5 \text{ group)} \quad + \quad N_2 \qquad (2)$$

arrangements of alkylidene azides are for the most part associated with the hypothetical (but highly probable) intermediates $R_2C{=}N{-}N_2^+$. They are believed to be formed when ketones or aldehydes are treated with hydrogen azide and a strong acid catalyst; rearrangement ensues according to equation 3. This reaction is a member of a group known as Schmidt reactions,[2] which are characterized as reactions between various organic compounds and hydrogen azide in the presence of strong acid. The other principal members of this group are the reactions with carboxylic acids (eq. 4), which lead to amines having one less carbon atom, and those with olefins and alcohols (eq. 5), which lead to the same aldimines and ketimines as are formed from alkyl and aralkyl azides.

$$R{-}CO{-}R \xrightarrow[\text{H}_2\text{SO}_4]{\text{HN}_3} \left[\begin{array}{c} R{-}C{-}R \\ \| \\ N{-}N_2^+ \end{array} \right] \xrightarrow{\text{H}_2\text{O}} R{-}CO{-}NH{-}R + N_2 \qquad (3)$$

$$R{-}COOH \xrightarrow[\text{H}_2\text{SO}_4]{\text{HN}_3} RNH_2 + N_2 + CO_2 \qquad (4)$$

$$R_3COH \xrightarrow[\text{H}_2\text{SO}_4]{\text{HN}_3} R_2C{=}N{-}R + N_2 \qquad (5)$$

The rearrangement of acyl azides (eq. 6) is known as the Curtius rearrangement.[3] It differs from the Schmidt reaction on carboxylic acids in that iso-

$$RCON_3 \rightarrow R{-}NCO + N_2 \qquad (6)$$

lated acyl azides are a distinct stage, and the rearrangement does not require acid catalysis (although it is susceptible to it). The appearance of isocyanates as the first isolable products also distinguishes the Curtius rearrangement from the Schmidt reaction as ordinarily carried out.

Rearrangements of hydroxylamines are known with aralkyl, alkylidene, and acyl derivatives. The rearrangement of triarylmethylhydroxylamines to ketimines (eq. 7) is called the Stieglitz rearrangement, but it is not a widely known reaction. Alkylidene hydroxylamines (oximes) are, by contrast, quite

[2] H. Wolff, *Org. Reactions*, **3**, Chapt. 8 (1946).
[3] P. A. S. Smith, *Org. Reactions*, **3**, Chapt. 9 (1946).

well known for the Beckmann rearrangement[4] (eq. 8) which they undergo. Acyl hydroxylamines undergo a rearrangement (eq. 9) analogous to the Curtius rearrangement, known as the Lossen rearrangement.[5] A variant in which the acyl group is a carbonimidyl group, thus giving rise to an amidoxime structure in one of its tautomeric forms, is called the Tiemann rearrangement (eq. 10).

$$Ar_3CNHOH \xrightarrow{PCl_5} Ar_2C=N-Ar \tag{7}$$

$$R_2C=NOH \xrightarrow{H_2SO_4, etc.} RCONHR \tag{8}$$

$$R-CO-NHOH \xrightarrow[base]{ArSO_2Cl} RNCO \tag{9}$$

$$R-C\overset{\displaystyle NH}{\underset{\displaystyle NHOH}{\big<}} \xrightarrow[base]{ArSO_2Cl} RNHCONH_2 \tag{10}$$

A close relative of the Beckmann rearrangement is the base-catalyzed conversion of O-sulfonyl oximes to α-amino ketones via azirenes; it is known as the Neber reaction (eq. 11).

$$R-CH_2-\underset{\underset{N-OSO_2Ar}{\|}}{C}-R \xrightarrow{OH^-} \left[R-\underset{\diagdown}{CH}-\underset{\diagup}{C}-R \right] \to R-\underset{\underset{NH_2}{|}}{CH}-\underset{\underset{O}{\|}}{C}-R \tag{11}$$

Rearrangement of haloamines is known in all structural classes. That of N-trityl haloamines was discovered by Stieglitz and Morgan[6] shortly after their discovery of the analogous hydroxylamine rearrangement, and is sometimes included in the term "Stieglitz rearrangement," along with the rearrangement of trityl azides. Alkylidene haloamines (N-halo ketimines) were for some time thought to be intermediates in the Beckmann rearrangement catalyzed by phosphorus pentachloride; they were eventually synthesized, however, but the early workers were not able to induce rearrangement. It was demonstrated much later by Theilacker[7] that a rearrangement (eq. 12) can be accomplished; it is generally considered to be a variant of the Beckmann rearrangement, and bears no special name.

The major haloamine rearrangement is that of the acyl derivatives, the well-known Hofmann rearrangement[8] of haloamides (eq. 13). While this designation is unambiguous and widely used, it should be noted that the

[4] W. Z. Heldt and L. G. Donaruma, *Org. Reactions*, **11**, Chapt. 1 (1960).

[5] H. L. Yale, *Chem. Revs.*, **33**, 209 (1943).

[6] A. T. Morgan, *J. Am. Chem. Soc.*, **38**, 2095 (1916).

[7] W. Theilacker and H. Mohl, *Ann.*. **563**, 99 (1949).

[8] E. S. Wallis and J. F. Lane, *Org. Reactions*, **3**, Chapt. 7 (1946).

terms "Hofmann reaction" and "Hofmann degradation" are sometimes used. The first term should be avoided, as it is ambiguous, being widely used to describe the Hofmann elimination reaction of quaternary amines.

$$Ar_2C{=}NCl \xrightarrow{SbCl_5} Ar{-}\underset{\underset{Cl}{|}}{C}{=}N{-}Ar \qquad (12)$$

$$R{-}CO{-}NHX \xrightarrow{OH^-} R{-}NH_2 + CO_3{}^{2-} + X^- \qquad (13)$$

Rearrangements of hydrazines analogous to those of hydroxylamines have long been sought. Although some suggestive observations have been made, nothing completely parallel to the Stieglitz, Beckmann, or Lossen rearrangement has been firmly established. Two closely related reactions have been reported, however: the rearrangement of hydrazones when nitrosated in strong acid [9] (eq. 14), which probably actually involves the same alkylidene azide ion as in the Schmidt reaction, and the conversion of quaternary hydrazones to α-amino ketones [10] (eq. 15), which is analogous to the alkali-induced Neber rearrangement of O-acyl oximes. No other names are used for these reactions.

$$Ar_2{-}C{=}NNH_2 \xrightarrow[HNO_2]{H_2SO_4} ArCONHAr \qquad (14)$$

$$R{-}CH_2{-}\underset{\underset{N{-}N^+(CH_3)_3}{\|}}{C}{-}\!\!-R \xrightarrow{OH^-} \left[R{-}CH{-}\underset{N}{\overset{\diagdown\diagup}{C}}{-}R \right] \rightarrow R{-}CH{-}\underset{\underset{NH_2}{|}}{C}OR \qquad (15)$$

A point of historical interest regarding the foregoing nomenclature should be mentioned. The second decade of the twentieth century saw an awakening of interest in reaction mechanism, and with it came the realization of the fundamental similarity in the rearrangements just mentioned. An effusion of papers resulted, affirming and extending the concept of rearrangements involving "univalent nitrogen." It soon became sophisticated practice to refer to *all* of them by the single name "Beckmann" rearrangement. However, as information accumulated, it became evident that the rearrangement of oximes, the classical Beckmann rearrangement, could not proceed through such an intermediate, owing to the stereospecificity observed in it. This put the proponents of the grand view in the unhappy position of having to declare that only the classical Beckmann is not a true Beckmann rearrangement. The use of the overextended name rapidly went out of fashion, but has left its mark in the journal and abstract indexes of the period, which are still capable of misleading the unwary. It is a valuable caution against generalizing too much and too soon.

[9] D. E. Pearson, K. N. Carter, and C. M. Greer, *J. Am. Chem. Soc.*, **75**, 5905 (1953).
[10] P. A. S. Smith and E. E. Most, Jr., *J. Org. Chem.*, **22**, 358 (1957).

Rearrangements involving migration from carbon to oxygen are in principle possible with analogs of all the foregoing nitrogen groupings, but are clearly established only for peroxides. The rearrangement of alkyl and aralkyl hydroperoxides gives rise to phenols or alcohols and ketones (eq. 16) and is of considerable commercial importance, but it has not acquired a name. An alkylidene peroxide rearrangement analogous to the Schmidt reaction on ketones and aldehydes is also well known; it is known as the Baeyer-Villiger reaction [11] (eq. 17). Acyl peroxides may rearrange to give aryl carbonate derivatives (eq. 18), in analogy to the Curtius, Hofmann, and Lossen reactions, but the reaction is unnamed.

$$R_3C\text{---}O\text{---}OH \rightarrow R_2CO + ROH \tag{16}$$

$$R\text{---}CO\text{---}R \xrightarrow{H_2O_2} R\text{---}O\text{---}CO\text{---}R \tag{17}$$

$$R\text{---}CO\text{---}O\text{---}O\text{---}COR \rightarrow R\text{---}O\text{---}CO\text{---}O\text{---}COR \tag{18}$$

2. CARBON TO NITROGEN REARRANGEMENTS

A. Systems in which the Carbon Skeleton Is Saturated or Aromatic: Azides, Hydroxyl-Amines, Haloamines

The functional groups that cleave so as to induce migration from carbon to nitrogen are azides, hydroxylamines, and haloamines, from which, respectively, nitrogen, derivatives of hydroxyl, or halides are cleaved in the initiating step (eq. 19). The cleavage may be brought about by heat alone or may be catalyzed by acid or base (but usually not by both).

$$R_3C\text{---}N{=}N_2 \qquad R_3C\text{---}NH\text{---}OH \qquad R_3C\text{---}NH\text{---}X \tag{19}$$
$$R_2C{=}N\text{---}R$$

Azides. The first example of this sort of behavior in an alkyl derivative was reported by Curtius and Darapsky,[1] who observed the decomposition of benzyl azide as catalyzed by warm 1:1 sulfuric acid, or concentrated hydrochloric acid. In this compound both phenyl and hydrogen are in a position to migrate, and products from both processes were found (eq. 20). Phenyl migration would give formaldehyde anil, hydrolyzed by the medium to aniline (isolated in 15% yield) and formaldehyde, while hydrogen migration would give benzaldimine, hydrolyzed to benzaldehyde (isolated in 19% yield) and ammonia. Reduction to benzylamine, presumably by formaldehyde, also occurred extensively. In contrast, decomposition of benzyl azide in the absence of acid (in p-xylene, p-cymene, or dimethylaniline) required higher

[11] C. H. Hassall, *Org. Reactions*, **9**, Chapt. 3 (1957).

temperatures (> 150°) and gave no products of phenyl migration.[12] p-Methyl-benzyl azide gave similar results.

$$C_6H_5CH_2N_3 \xrightarrow{H_2SO_4} (C_6H_5CH=NH) \text{ and } (C_6H_5N=CH_2) \rightarrow C_6H_5CHO,$$

$$C_6H_5NH_2, CH_2O, C_6H_5CH_2NH_2, \text{ and } C_6H_5NH_2 \cdot CH_2O \text{ condensation polymer} \quad (20)$$

These early observations illustrate two general points: strong acids are powerful catalysts for the decomposition of azides (with concomitant rearrangement), and the purely thermal, uncatalyzed decomposition may give products qualitatively different from those of the acid-catalyzed reaction. Unfortunately, there has been no comparative study made of the two processes.

That purely thermal decomposition of azides can result in rearrangement was demonstrated by Senior,[13] working with Stieglitz, who demonstrated that triarylmethyl azides are converted in part into benzophenone anils at temperatures in the neighborhood of 200° (eq. 21). Azides of this type, however, are virtually inert to strong acids [14] (see p. 464). Thermal decomposition is usually not smooth and the yields of anils are considerably less than the yields of nitrogen.

$$Ar_3CN_3 \xrightarrow{\sim 200°} Ar_2C=N-Ar \quad (21)$$

$$\downarrow \text{Conc. acids}$$

$$Ar_3COH + HN_3$$

The effect of substituents on the relative amounts of migration of phenyl groups was considered by Senior, who found that a p-chloro group appeared to have little effect on the migration aptitude; his experiments were far from quantitative, however. This subject was investigated in detail by Saunders and Ware [13b] much later. They worked with the para substituents $(CH_3)_2N-$, CH_3O-, CH_3-, $Cl-$, and NO_2-, and obtained yields of benzophenone anils of 43 to 75% by heating the azides at 185° for two hours without a solvent. The extents of migration decreased in the order given, but the range was small: from 6.7 to 0.2 relative to unsubstituted phenyl. The range appeared to be somewhat reduced in dibutyl carbitol solution.

The kinetics of nitrogen evolution were determined in dibutyl carbitol, and were found to be even less sensitive to substituents, varying over a $2\frac{1}{2}$-fold range, and to be first order. All substituents increased the rate, and the results could not be correlated by a Hammett equation. The enthalpies and entropies

---

[12] T. Curtius and G. Ehrhart, *Ber.*, **55**, 1559 (1922).

[13] (a) J. K. Senior, *J. Am. Chem. Soc.*, **38**, 2718 (1916). (b) W. H. Saunders and J. C. Ware, *J. Am. Chem. Soc.*, **80**, 3328 (1958). (c) R. H. B. Galt, J. D. Loudon, and D. B. Sloan, *J. Chem. Soc. (London)*, **1958**, 1588.

of activation varied linearly with each other, a commonly observed phenomenon in a substituent series. The enthalpy was least for p-$(CH_3)_2N$— and greatest for p-Cl— and p-NO_2—, and varied from 25.4 to 34.3 kcal./mole; the entropies ranged, in the reverse order, from −22.5 to −4.6 e.u./mole. The authors interpreted these results to mean that there is partial assistance by the migrating aryl group in the loss of nitrogen, giving a pseudo three-membered ring transition state in which the retained nitrogen is relatively negative and the migrating group positive. This would be consistent with the effect of substituents on the enthalpy of activation; if the separation of charge orients solvent molecules around the transition state in proportion to the extent of charge separation (and thus of participation), the effect on the entropy of activation could be accounted for. The rates were slightly faster in more polar solvents.

Thermal rearrangement of triarylmethyl azides may accomplish ring expansion, as in the case of 9-(α-naphthyl)-9-fluorenyl azide (1), which Pinck and Hilbert [14] converted to 9-(α-naphthyl)phenanthridine (2) in good yield

(1)   (2)

by heating for 10 minutes at 194°. 9-Phenyl-9-fluorenyl azide [15] behaves similarly. The relief of strain in the five-membered ring and the formation of a new aromatic ring that can conjugate with the 9-aryl group probably account for the fact that these fluorenyl azides rearrange so much more readily than triphenylmethyl azide. However, when there is a hydrogen in the 9 position instead of an aryl group, ring expansion does not occur, and fluorenone imines are formed instead; 1,2-benzo-,[15] 2-nitro-,[16] and unsubstituted [17] 9-fluorenyl azides have been found to do this. With catalysis by sulfuric acid at only 25°, on the other hand, ring expansion by aryl migration nevertheless occurs, and the isomeric phenanthridines are formed. Expansion of a six-membered ring by thermal decomposition of a triarylmethyl azide does not occur nearly so readily. 9-Phenyl-9-xanthyl azide gives much xanthone anil along with the isomeric oxazepine (eq. 22); and 9-phenyl-

[14] (a) M. M. Coombs, *J. Chem. Soc. (London)*, **1958**, 4200. (b) L. A. Pinck and H. E. Hilbert, *J. Am. Chem. Soc.*, **59**, 8 (1937).

[15] C. L. Arcus, R. E. Marks, and M. M. Coombs, *J. Chem. Soc. (London)*, **1957**, 4064.

[16] C. L. Arcus and M. M. Coombs, *J. Chem. Soc. (London)*, **1954**, 4319.

[17] C. L. Arcus and R. J. Mesley, *J. Chem. Soc. (London)*, **1953**, 178.

thiaxanthyl azide and its 3',2-dinitro derivative give small yields of the analogous thiazepines, but 9-phenyl-2-nitro- and 9-phenyl-2-nitro-7-methyl-thiaxanthyl azides gave only thiaxanthone anils in 86 and 74% yields, respectively.[13c] When there are fluorine atoms instead of hydrogen on the

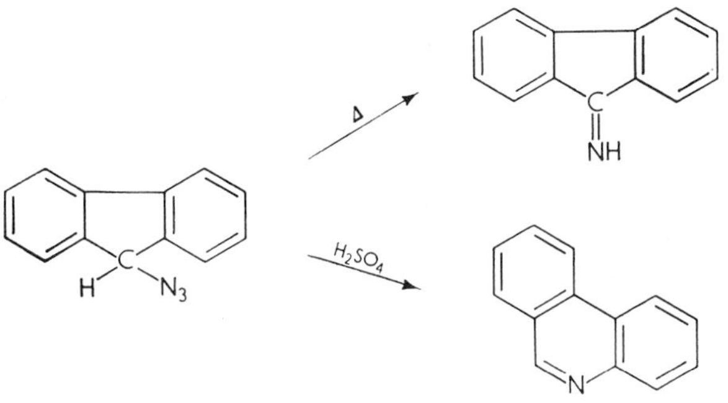

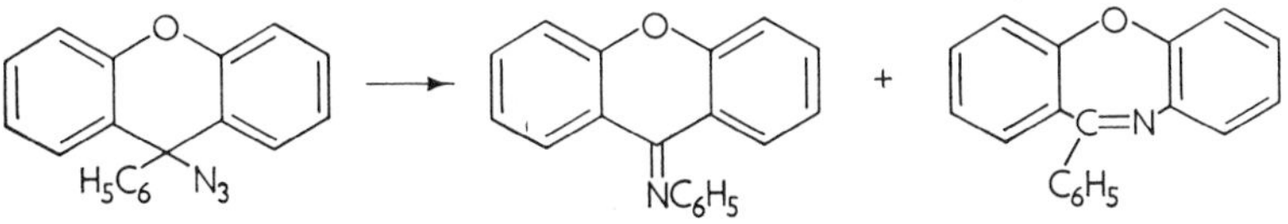

(22)

α carbon of an azide, carbon skeleton rearrangement can occur to the exclusion of migration of fluorine,[18a] although attachment of a fluorine to nitrogen occurs when perfluoropropenyl azide is heated[18b] (eq. 23).

$$CF_3CF_2CHFCF_2\text{—}N_3 \rightarrow CF_2\text{=}N\text{—}CHFCF_2CF_3 + N_2 \qquad (23)$$

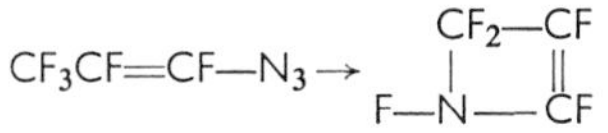

Aryl azides may also rearrange when heated[19] or when photolyzed[20] giving azepine derivatives. When phenyl azide was originally heated in boiling aniline, a small amount of a solid, dibenzamil, was obtained,[21] but its true nature was not recognized until much later. It was eventually characterized as an anilinoazepine (3). In the absence of aniline, the pyrolysis of aryl azides usually gives amorphous, apparently polymeric products or amines by

[18] (a) I. L. Knunyants, E. G. Bykhovskaya, and V. N. Frosin, *Doklady Akad. Nauk S.S.S.R.*, **132**, 357 (1960). (b) I. L. Knunyants and E. G. Bykhovskaya, *Doklady Akad. Nauk S.S.S.R.*, **131**, 1338 (1960).

[19] (a) R. Huisgen, *Angew. Chem.*, **67**, 756 (1955). (b) R. Huisgen, D. Vossius, and M. Appl, *Chem. Ber.*, **91**, 1, 12 (1958).

[20] W. E. Doering and R. Odum, unpublished results; R. Odum, doctoral dissertation, Yale University, 1953.

[21] L. Wolff, *Ann.*, **394**, 59 (1912).

hydrogen abstraction from the environment. However, when cyclization is possible other products may be obtained, as with o-azidobiphenyls,[22] which

$$\text{C}_6\text{H}_5\text{-N}_3 \;+\; \text{C}_6\text{H}_5\text{NH}_2 \;\xrightarrow{\;\Delta\;}\; \text{(azepine-NH-C}_6\text{H}_5\text{)} \;+\; \text{N}_2$$

(3)

give carbazoles. Kinetics have been studied in aniline [23] and in other solvents; [24] they are uniformly first order, although a drift may be manifested in the later stages. The rates of decomposition of meta-substituted aryl azides are quite independent of the electronic character of substituents, which suggests that the simple ejection of nitrogen, prior to rearrangement, is the rate-determining step. Huisgen formulates the reaction as proceeding through the bicyclic intermediate (4), whose formation involves electrophilic

$$\text{C}_6\text{H}_5\text{-N}_3 \;\longrightarrow\; \text{C}_6\text{H}_5\text{-N} \;\longrightarrow\; \text{(bicyclic)}$$

(4)

attack on the ortho position, a process that should, if the two steps were concerted, make the evolution of nitrogen sensitive to substituents.

Acid-catalyzed decomposition of aryl azides does not result in rearrangement; aniline derivatives are formed.[25]

Most of the studies on alkyl and aralkyl azide rearrangements have been concerned with the acid-catalyzed reactions. In addition to the studies with separately prepared azides, additional information is available from the Schmidt reaction on alcohols or olefins; both processes will be discussed together. Justification for doing so comes from two types of observations. When alcohols are treated with hydrogen azide and a strong acid, the corresponding azide may be formed along with the rearrangement products, as in the case of 9-tert-butylfluorenol,[26] or may even be formed in high yield to the exclusion of rearrangement. In such cases, it has generally been found that stronger acidity or higher temperatures will bring about complete rearrangement, whether one starts with the alcohol or azide. With lower acidity, such

[22] P. A. S. Smith and B. B. Brown, J. Am. Chem. Soc., **73**, 2435 (1951).

[23] M. Appl and R. Huisgen, Chem. Ber., **92**, 2961 (1959).

[24] P. A. S. Smith and J. H. Hall, J. Am. Chem. Soc., **84**, 480 (1962).

[25] P. A. S. Smith and B. B. Brown, J. Am. Chem. Soc., **73**, 2438 (1951).

[26] (a) C. L. Arcus and E. A. Lucken, J. Chem. Soc. (London), **1955**, 1634. (b) M. M. Coombs, J. Chem. Soc. (London), **1958**, 3454.

as that given by trichloroacetic acid, the reaction of tertiary and benzylic alcohols with hydrogen azide may be made a useful preparation method for azides.[27] When rearrangement may involve either of two equivalently situated but different groups, mixtures of isomeric rearrangement products are to be expected. Several such systems have been investigated by the Schmidt reaction on the alcohol[16] and through the separately prepared azide;[28] mixtures of the same composition, within experimental error, were produced.

The effect of substituents on the products produced from 9-fluorenols or 9-fluorenyl azides has been investigated by Arcus and Lucken.[26] They observed a marked influence of substituents on the direction of ring expansion to phenanthridines, even when the substituents were too far from the 9 position to have any steric influence. Their results, summarized in equation 24,

⟨R⟩	⟨Yield, %⟩	⟨Yield, %⟩
2-NO$_2$	3%	97%
3-NO$_2$	6	94
2-CH$_3$O	32	68
2-CH$_3$	53	47
3-CH$_3$	100	—
2-NH$_2$	—	100

(normalized percentage ratios; actual yields mostly 50–90%)

show that those groups regarded as "electron releasing" promote migration of the ring to which they are attached, and those which are electron withdrawing groups retard it. The effect of the amino group is consistent when one recalls that the reactions were carried out in concentrated sulfuric acid, where the amino group would be entirely protonated and thus electron withdrawing.

Analogous results have been obtained with α-methylbenzhydryl azides[28] and from studies of the Schmidt reaction on 1,1-diarylethylenes[29–32] and on benzhydrols.[33] Only the phenyl groups migrated, and no products which correspond to migration of hydrogen or methyl were observed. The migration of phenyl groups was found to be in the order p-C$_2$H$_5$O = p-CH$_3$O > 3,4(CH$_3$)$_2$

[27] S. N. Ege and K. W. Sherk, J. Am. Chem. Soc., 75, 354 (1953).
[28] C. H. Gudmundsen and W. E. McEwen, J. Am. Chem. Soc., 79, 329 (1957).
[29] W. E. McEwen and N. Mehta, J. Am. Chem. Soc., 74, 526 (1952).
[30] W. E. McEwen, M. Gilliland, and B. I. Sparr, J. Am. Chem. Soc., 72, 3212 (1950).
[31] L. P. Kuhn and J. DiDomenico, J. Am. Chem. Soc., 72, 5777 (1950).
[32] D. R. Nielsen and W. E. McEwen, J. Am. Chem. Soc., 76, 4042 (1954).
[33] R. F. Tietz and W. E. McEwen, J. Am. Chem. Soc., 77, 4007 (1955).

$\sim p\text{-}CH_3 > p\text{-}C_2H_5 > m\text{-}CH_3 > p\text{-}C_6H_5 > p\text{-}F > H\cdot > p\text{-}Cl > m\text{-}Cl > p\text{-}NO_2$. The magnitude of these effects is shown by the fact that p-methoxy-α-methylbenzhydryl azide gives entirely acetophenone p-methoxy anil (eq. 25). A Hammett plot gives a regression constant, ρ, of about -2.

$$(2?)$$

The kinetics of the evolution of nitrogen from the rearrangement of 9-fluorenyl azide in solutions of sulfuric acid in acetic acid have been measured by Arcus and Evans.[34] They found the rate to be proportional to Hammett's h_0 acidity function [35] and to the concentration of the azide; an activation energy of 23.4 kcal./mole was calculated. They interpreted these results, in the light of all the foregoing observations, to mean that it is the conjugate acid of the azide that rearranges and that migration is synchronous with nitrogen release. Protonation of the azido group could reasonably occur at either end, but only that form protonated on the substituted nitrogen could reasonably lead to the rearrangements observed. In the Schmidt reaction

$$R\text{—}\overset{+}{N}\text{=}N\text{=}NH \rightleftharpoons R\text{—}N_3 \rightleftharpoons R\text{—}NH\text{—}\overset{+}{N}\text{≡}N$$

on olefins or alcohols, the acid catalyst has a dual function: to convert the olefin or alcohol to a carbonium ion which can combine with hydrogen azide and to maintain a high enough acidity to insure that the conjugate acid of the azide is present in sufficient concentration to result in rearrangement at a convenient rate.

Gudmundsen and McEwen [28] made similar kinetic studies on benzhydryl azide and found the same rate law as Arcus and Evans. In addition, however, they studied a series of meta- and para-substituted benzhydryl and α-methylbenzhydryl azides. They were able to fit their results to a Hammett plot,[35] log k/k_0 versus σ, with a regression constant, ρ, of -2.26; however, the p-methoxy compound deviated strongly. The use of σ^+ values,[36] which were not yet available when the work was reported, gives a more satisfactory straight line, with a somewhat smaller value for ρ. We will see, however, that the dependence of substituent constants should be compound.

As an approach to the problem of whether rearrangement of benzhydryl azides is synchronous with loss of nitrogen or occurs in two discrete steps

[34] C. L. Arcus and J. V. Evans, *J. Chem. Soc. (London)*, **1958**, 789.

[35] L. P. Hammett, *Physical Organic Chemistry*, McGraw-Hill, New York, 1940.

[36] (a) H. C. Brown and Y. Okamoto, *J. Am. Chem. Soc.*, **79**, 1913 (1957). (b) N. C. Deno and W. L. Evans, *J. Am. Chem. Soc.*, **79**, 5804 (1957).

(eq. 26), Gudmundsen and McEwen adapted the treatment that has been used in investigating the nature of the solvolysis of tertiary alkyl halides.[37]

$$R_3CN_3 \rightleftharpoons R_3C-NH-N_2{}^+ \rightarrow R_2C{=}\overset{+}{N}HR \quad \text{(concerted process)}$$

$$\downarrow$$

$$N_2 + R_3\overset{+}{C}-NH \qquad \text{(two-step process)}$$

(26)

They utilized the ratios of migration of aryl groups in the Schmidt reaction on substituted benzhydrols as determined by Tietz and McEwen.[33] These ratios are apparently identical with those obtained from separately prepared azides and must correspond to the relative rates of migration of substituted and unsubstituted phenyl groups

$$\frac{C_6H_5CH{=}N-C_6H_4A}{C_6H_5-N{=}CH-C_6H_4A} = \frac{k_A}{k_p}$$

where k_A and k_p are the specific rate constants for substituted and unsubstituted phenyl migration, respectively.

$$C_6H_5CHOHC_6H_4A \xrightarrow[H_2SO_4]{HN_3} H_2O + N_2 + \begin{array}{c} C_6H_5CH{=}N-C_6H_4A \\ and \\ C_6H_5-N{=}CH-C_6H_4A \end{array}$$

Kinetic measurements were made by observing the evolution of nitrogen from solutions of the azides and sulfuric acid in acetic acid. In view of the low basicity of hydrogen azide (pK$_a$ for $H_2N_3{}^+ = -6.21$),[38] one can expect that benzhydryl azides will be protonated to only a small extent in such solutions. If the azides had been present largely as their conjugate acids, simple dependence of the rates on acidity should not have been observed; if protonation is complete for all azides, there should be no dependence on acidity at all. Since the K_b's for the azides are therefore undoubtedly small, the approximation $K_b h_0 c$ can be used for the concentration $[Ar_2CHNHN_2{}^+]$, where c is the stoichiometric concentration of azide. Gudmundsen and McEwen's rate law can then be expressed as

$$d(N_2)/dt = k_N K_b h_0 c$$

where k_N is the specific rate constant for nitrogen evolution from the protonated azide. This constant would be expected to vary with substitution of one of the phenyl groups according to a Hammett equation, although if the migrating group does not participate in the nitrogen-losing step, the regression constant, ρ, for it might be small. K_b would also be expected to be a

[37] A. R. Olson and R. S. Halford, J. Am. Chem. Soc., 59, 2644 (1937); L. C. Bateman, E. D. Hughes, and C. K. Ingold, J. Chem. Soc. (London), 1938, 881.

[38] T. A. Bak and E. L. Praestgaerd, Acta Chem. Scand., 11, 901 (1957).

function of substitution, with a negative value for ρ of considerable magnitude, comparable to that for benzylamines, which is -0.723.[39]

If we assume that migration is synchronous with loss of nitrogen, then

$$k_N = k_A + k_p$$

Since the product ratio, PR, is necessarily k_A/k_p, we can write

$$k_N = k_p(PR) + k_p = k_p(1 + PR)$$

Dividing both sides by $k_N{}^\circ$ (for unsubstituted benzhydryl azide), we get

$$k_N/k_N{}^\circ = k_p/k_N{}^\circ(1 + PR)$$

or

$$\log k_N/k_N{}^\circ = \log k_p/k_N{}^\circ + \log (1 + PR)$$

However, since we have measurements for only h_0 and c and $d(N_2)/dt$, the actually calculated rate constant for nitrogen evolution is an apparent constant

$$k_2 = k_N K_b$$

Therefore, substituting k_2/K_b for k_N, we have

$$\log (k_2/k_2{}^\circ)/(K_b{}^\circ/K_b) = \log k_p K_b{}^\circ/k_2{}^\circ + \log (1 + PR)$$

which can also be expressed

$$\log k_2/k_2{}^\circ = \log K_b/K_b{}^\circ + \log k_p + \log (1 + PR) + \log K_b{}^\circ/k_2{}^\circ$$

Since k_p, the specific rate constant for phenyl migration, can be expected to have a small variation with substitution on the other phenyl, it is useful to add $\log k_p{}^\circ/k_p{}^\circ$ to the right-hand side, to get

$$\log k_2/k_2{}^\circ = \log K_b/K_b{}^\circ + \log k_p/k_p{}^\circ + \log (1 + PR) + \log K_b{}^\circ k_p{}^\circ/k_2{}^\circ$$

or

$$\log k_2 = \log K_b/K_b{}^\circ + \log k_p/k_p{}^\circ + \log (1 + PR) + \log K_b{}^\circ k_p{}^\circ$$

We have already seen that K_b should vary with substitution according to a Hammett relationship, $\rho_b\sigma$, with a value for ρ near that for benzylamines, approximately -0.75. On the other hand, k_p belongs to a reaction of the type where the σ^+ substituent constants,[36] associated with the generation of positive centers on or adjacent to an aromatic ring, would be more appropri-

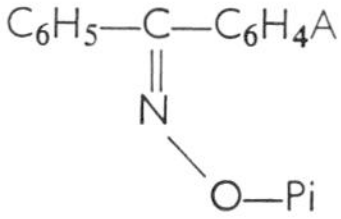

$$C_6H_5-\overset{\displaystyle\|}{\underset{\displaystyle N}{C}}-C_6H_4A$$
$$\overset{\diagdown}{}O-Pi$$

(5)

[39] H. H. Jaffé, *Chem. Revs.*, **53**, 191 (1953).

ate. The regression factor for k_p would, of course, be expected to be small, perhaps -0.25; some idea of its magnitude can be obtained by comparing the reaction to the Beckmann rearrangement of benzophenone oxime picryl $(Pi = C_6H_2(NO_2)_3)$ ethers (5) for which Chapman and Fidler[40] made direct measurements. We can thus express our equation as

$$\log k_2 = \rho_b\sigma + \rho_p\sigma^+ + \log (1 + PR) + \log K_b{}^\circ k_p{}^\circ$$

Since the last term is a constant, a plot of $\log k_2$ against the sum $\rho_b\sigma + \rho_p\sigma^+ + \log (1 + PR)$ should be of the form $X = y + a$; in other words, linear with a slope of $+1$. If we can obtain such a curve with reasonable estimated values for ρ_b and ρ_p, we will have strong support for a concerted reaction path. Figure 1 shows the points calculated from the published observations, using

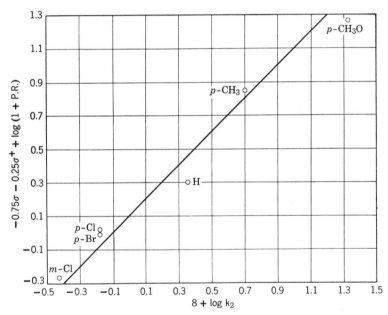

Figure 1. Rate constants for N_2 evolution from X—C_6H_4—CHN_3—C_6H_5 versus $-0.75\sigma - 0.25\sigma^+ + \log (1 + P. R.)$; the line is drawn with slope 1.00 (the points do not include indication of their uncertainty, which is considerable with some of them).

$\rho_b = -0.75$ and $\rho_p = -0.25$, compared to a line of slope $+1.0$. The discrepancies are not large and do not follow a trend, which suggests that they are due largely to experimental uncertainty. The recognition of dependence of the basic strength of the azide on substitution is essential to this treatment, for if it is ignored, an opposite conclusion results.[28]

[40] A. W. Chapman and F. A. Fidler, *J. Chem. Soc. (London)*, **1936**, 448.

Ferrocenylphenylcarbinyl azide shows an effect of acid on rearrangement in a different way. The ferrocenyl group does not migrate at all, apparently because it acquires a proton on the metal atom, greatly reducing its electron-releasing ability.[40a] Other metallocenyl groups are said to behave similarly.

The difference in behavior between acid-catalyzed and thermal decomposition of azides, referred to earlier, may reflect a difference in mechanism. Since thermal decompositions, to the limited extent that comparative observations have been made, are relatively insensitive to electronic influences, it seems likely that the loss of nitrogen from them is *not* concerted with migration, so the ability of a potential migrating group to assist in a concerted process would then not promote its competitive ability to migrate.

Tietz and McEwen [33] had earlier pointed out that a species of the type R—NH+, an electron-deficient nitrogen cation, should be of considerably higher energy and thus more difficult to form than its carbonium ion analog, R—CH$_2$+. A consequence of this characteristic would be a greater drive for rearrangements to be synchronous with reactions that could give rise to R—NH+. This is borne out by the considerable sensitivity of the migration ratios to substituents in the rearrangement of benzyhydryl azides, as compared to the isoelectronic carbon analog, the rearrangement of β,β-diarylethylamines to stilbenes on treatment with nitrous acid.[41] The relative insensitivity to substituents shown in the latter reaction is attributed to the absence of participation by the migrating aryl group in the loss of nitrogen from Ar$_2$CH—CH$_2$N$_2$+; in other words, the process is nonsynchronous. We have seen that in the acid-catalyzed rearrangement of benzyhydryl azides, migration concerted with nitrogen loss is probable. However, from one example to another, the transition state may vary considerably between the limits **6** and **7**, and a spectrum of mechanisms may actually be manifest.

$$\text{Ar—CH····NH}^+\text{····N}_2 \qquad\qquad \text{Ar—CH—NH}^+\text{····N}_2$$
$$\underset{\text{Ar}}{\overset{\cdots\cdots}{}} \qquad\qquad\qquad \overset{|}{\underset{\text{Ar}}{}}$$
$$\text{(6)} \qquad\qquad\qquad\qquad \text{(7)}$$

Purely aliphatic systems have not been so well investigated. Ethyl azide [42] when treated with fuming sulfuric acid produces some methylamine (about 14%) and formaldehyde, in addition to acetaldehyde and ammonia, indicating a significant amount of methyl migration, and butyl azide shows similar behavior in concentrated sulfuric acid,[43] but *n*-hexyl azide and higher homologs show only the aldehyde-forming reaction, corresponding to hydro-

[40a] A. Berger, W. E. McEwen, and J. Kleinberg, *J. Am. Chem. Soc.*, **83**, 2274 (1961).

[41] J. G. Burr and L. S. Ciereszko, *J. Am. Chem. Soc.*, **74**, 5426 (1952).

[42] K. W. Sherk, A. G. Houpt, and A. W. Browne, *J. Am. Chem. Soc.*, **63**, 329 (1940).

[43] (a) J. H. Boyer, F. C. Canter, J. Hamer, and R. K. Putney, *J. Am. Chem. Soc.*, **78**, 325 (1956). (b) J. H. Boyer and F. C. Canter, *J. Am. Chem. Soc.*, **77**, 3287 (1955).

gen migration. Increasing chain length appears to retard alkyl migration with respect to hydrogen.

Experiments with secondary or tertiary alkyl azides, in which two or three alkyl groups might be compared directly, are few. Pritzkow and Mahler[44] studied the four isomeric azidoheptanes both kinetically and with regard to products. They found second-order kinetics in solutions of perchloric acid in acetic acid, but the results showed a pronounced drift and could be called second-order only during the first 25% of reaction. Since these authors used concentration and not h_0 in their calculations, and quantities such that acidity changed appreciably during reaction, this deviation is understandable. They found little difference in the rate of nitrogen evolution or in the activation energies (24.9–27.4 kcal./mole) among the four isomers. The products of rearrangement were determined by paper chromatography of the amines obtained after hydrolysis. n-Heptyl azide gave 42% of basic product, of which 10–30% was hexylamine, and the rest ammonia. The three secondary heptyl azides each give a much higher proportion of alkyl migration; with 2-azidoheptane, n-amyl migrated to about twice the extent of methyl, and with the 3 isomer, n-butyl migrated appreciably more than ethyl. Pritzkow and Schuberth[45] also studied the Schmidt reaction on the isomeric heptanols with respect to products. They all produced complex mixtures consisting of methyl-, ethyl-, propyl-, butyl-, and amylamines, and 1-heptanol produced hexylamine as well. It appears that extensive carbonium ion rearrangements occurred before attachment of the azide; the concordance between the Schmidt reaction on alcohols and the rearrangement of separately prepared azides previously referred to depends on having structures that are not susceptible to carbonium ion rearrangement and obviously does not hold where hydrogen can shift readily.

The comparison of the isomeric heptanols also has some interest with respect to conditions required for the Schmidt reaction on alcohols. None of the heptanols would react appreciably at 0°, but 10° was high enough to bring about smooth reaction for all the secondary alcohols; 1-heptanol required 50–60°. These observations are consistent with the relative ease of carbonium ion formation in acid medium. They also demonstrate that the Schmidt reaction on aliphatic ketones can be carried out without affecting primary and secondary alcohols, since simple aliphatic ketones will usually react at 0° or even lower. Pritzkow and Schuberth made use of this differentiation in analyzing the mixtures of ketones and alcohols obtained from the oxidation of hydrocarbons.

Three secondary cyclic azides[43a]—cyclopentyl, cyclohexyl and cycloheptyl—have been found to undergo ring expansion (alkyl migration)

[44] W. Pritzkow and G. Mahler, *J. prakt. Chem.*, [4]8, 314 (1959).
[45] W. Pritzkow and A. Schuberth, *Chem. Ber.*, **93**, 1725 (1960).

predominantly; expansion of the five-membered ring appears to occur most readily. Parallel results [43b] were obtained by the Schmidt reaction on the corresponding alcohols. 2-Methylcyclohexanol gave products arising from prior carbonium ion isomerization to the 1-methylcyclohexyl structure (2-methyl-1-azacycloheptene-1 [30%] and cyclohexanone [trace]); menthol gave a mixture containing 2-isopropyl-5-methyl-1-azacycloheptene-1 (7%), 4-methylcyclohexylamine (14%), methyl 4-methylcyclohexyl ketone (23%) and acetone, indicating rearrangement to both possible tertiary carbonium ions before azide formation.[43b] Impure samples of 1-methyl- and 1-ethyl-cyclohexyl azides have been examined;[46] ring expansion predominates over methyl migration approximately four-fold (8). Two bicyclic olefins have been

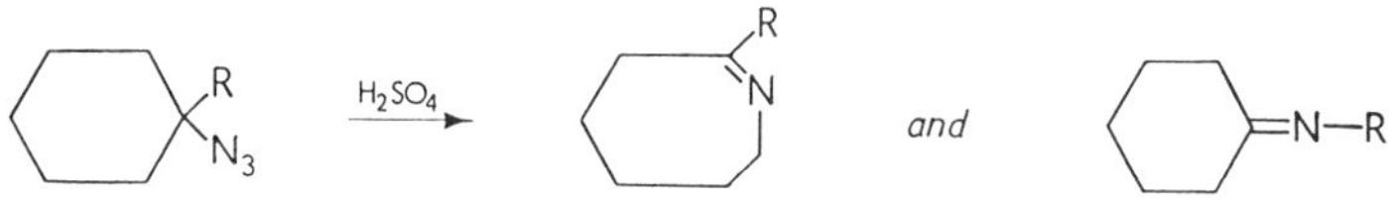

(8)   (4:1)

converted to heterocycles by the Schmidt reaction.[47] Norbornylene, like norborneol, gave a trimeric product, which was hydrogenated to 3-azabicyclo-[3.2.1]octane.[47a] 2,3-Decamethylenecyclopentene gave a mixture of piperideines arising from rearrangement of an azide formed at the bridgehead carbon; dehydrogenation gave a pair of decamethylenepyridines, in one of which there is a meta bridge (9).[47b]

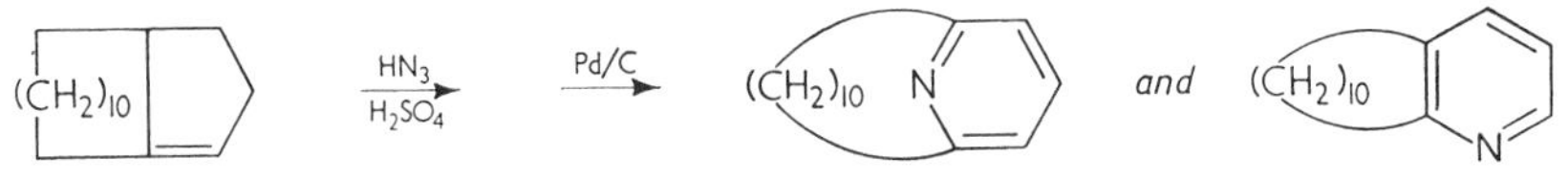

(17.6%)   (16%)
(9)

Competitive migration in the Schmidt reaction of tertiary alcohols has been studied by Yukawa and Tanaka [48a] in a group of α-alkyl-α-phenylethyl alcohols, $\phi CH_3 \cdot C(OH)R$. When R was isopropyl or cyclohexyl, it migrated

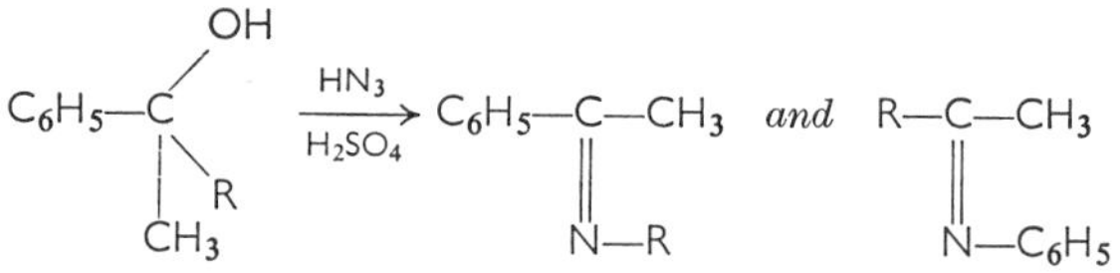

[46] P. A. S. Smith and J. Lakritz, unpublished results; J. Lakritz, doctoral dissertation, University of Michigan, 1960.

[47] (a) C. L. Arcus, R. E. Marks, and R. Vetterlein, *Chem. & Ind. (London)*, **1960**, 1193. (b) K. Biemann, G. Büchi, and B. H. Walker, *J. Am. Chem. Soc.*, **79**, 5558 (1957).

[48] (a) Y. Yukawa and K. Tanaka, *Mem. Inst. Sci. and Ind. Research Osaka Univ.*, **14**, 199, 205 (1957); *Chem. Abstr.*, **52**, 2795g, 4513g (1958). (b) Y. Yukawa and K. Tanaka, *Nippon Kagaku Zasshi*, **78**, 1049 (1957); *Chem. Abstr.*, **54**, 555 (1960).

(to form N-alkylacetophenoneimine) two to three times as much as did phenyl (to form a ketone anil); methyl migration did not appear to be significant. When R was methyl or ethyl, however, phenyl migration predominated. A series of 1-alkylcyclohexanols was also studied. The methyl, ethyl, and cyclohexyl members, and cyclohexanol itself, principally underwent ring expansion, just as has been found for the rearrangement of the isolated azides, but 1-phenylcyclohexanol gave principally cyclohexanone anil. The behavior of 1-isopropylcyclohexanol did not allow the isopropyl group to be compared with the other groups in this series, owing to the occurrence of a carbonium ion rearrangement before union with azide, and products derived from α-cyclohexylisopropyl azide were obtained instead. This further illustrates the inherent danger in using the Schmidt reaction of alcohols or olefins for structure proof or synthesis. It is not present [44] when the azide is prepared separately by a bimolecular displacement reaction, as usually can be done from primary and secondary alkyl halides.

An essentially complete compilation of Schmidt reactions on alcohols and olefins up to 1944 can be found in Volume III of *Organic Reactions*,[48b] but the number of examples is small. Since that review was prepared, in addition to the examples already cited here, triethylcarbinol has been found [49] to undergo the Schmidt reaction. The coverage of the decomposition of isolated azides involving carbon skeleton rearrangements given here is believed to be complete, but many more azides are of course known. Most of them have not been examined for acid-catalyzed rearrangement, but those that have show a complete preference for hydrogen shift when they are decomposed.[50a,51]

The various results cited in this Section show that a universally valid migration order for hydrogen, the various types of alkyl groups, and phenyl cannot be given. This is partly because the nonmigrating groups affect the mobility of the migrating group, and because steric as well as electronic factors are concerned. The behavior of benzyl azide and benzyhydryl azide, in each of which phenyl competes with hydrogen in migration, is illustrative (eq. 27). The first undergoes roughly equal extents of migration of phenyl and hydrogen and has an inherent statistical bias of 2:1 for hydrogen migration. In contrast, benzhydryl azide rearranges by migration of phenyl only and

48b H. Wolff, *Org. Reactions*, **3**, Chapt. 8.

49 C. Schuerch and E. H. Huntress, *J. Am. Chem. Soc.*, **71**, 2238 (1949).

50 C. L. Arcus and G. C. Barrett, *J. Chem. Soc. (London)*, **1960**, 2098.

50a Schmidt reactions on two heterologs of 9-fluorenol (in which one benzene ring has been replaced by either a thiazole ring or a thiophene ring, and on the benzylidene derivative of the thiazole heterolog) have been reported but only the first reacted, giving a compound presumed to be one of the corresponding isomeric heterologs of a phenanthridine.[50] Until the product has been properly identified, one cannot assess the significance of the observation.

51 T. Curtius, *Ber.*, **45**, 1057 (1912).

has a statistical bias of $2:1$ for phenyl migration. The statistical factor thus accounts qualitatively for less hydrogen migration in benzhydryl azide, but

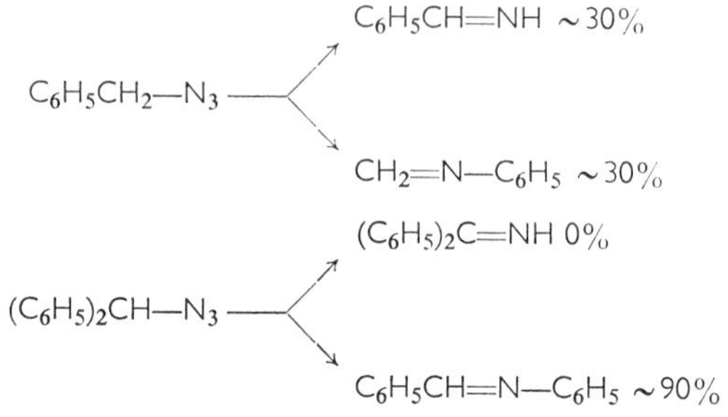

$$C_6H_5CH_2-N_3 \quad
\begin{cases}
C_6H_5CH=NH \sim 30\% \\
CH_2=N-C_6H_5 \sim 30\%
\end{cases}$$

$$(C_6H_5)_2CH-N_3 \quad
\begin{cases}
(C_6H_5)_2C=NH \ 0\% \\
C_6H_5CH=N-C_6H_5 \sim 90\%
\end{cases}$$

(27)

not for its complete suppression. A possible explanation of this and related cases can be found if we assume that rearrangement is a concerted process, resembling a nucleophilic displacement on nitrogen, and that rearrangement of the protonated azide is faster than rotation about the C—N bond. The latter assumption is questionable, although the C—N bond in alkyl azides is somewhat shorter (1.47 A.) than C—C bonds (1.54 A.).

The geometry of methyl azide [52] has been determined; the three nitrogens are linear, and the attached group forms an angle of $120°$ with the nitrogen axis (10).

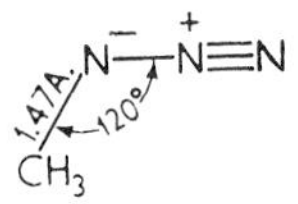

$$\underset{CH_3}{\overset{N\,\overset{-}{-}\,\overset{+}{N}\equiv N}{\Big\backslash}}$$

(10)

It is reasonable to assume that other azides are similarly disposed, and that protonated azides have a qualitatively similar geometry, with perhaps even a more acute C—N=N angle (11), similar to the C—C=N angle in aldimines

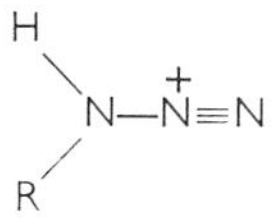

$$\underset{R}{\overset{H}{\diagdown}}N-\overset{+}{N}\equiv N \qquad \underset{R}{\overset{H}{\diagdown}}C=N-R'$$

(11) 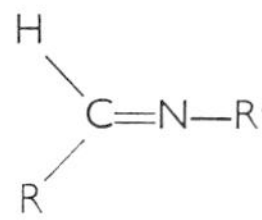   (12)

(12). The rotational conformation of such structures would encompass three positions in which the nitrogens and the substituents on the α carbon are not all the same; these positions would not be of equal energy, owing to differences in steric interference and possible field-effect repulsions. In a concerted rearrangement, the group on the side opposite from the departing pair of

---

[52] R. L. Livingston and C. N. R. Rao, *J. Phys. Chem.*, **64**, 756 (1960).

nitrogens would be expected to migrate, at an intrinsic rate largely characteristic of its structure but influenced somewhat by the other α substituents. The resultant extents of migration would be essentially determined by these intrinsic rate factors, if rotation among conformers is much faster than rearrangement, or by the relative populations of the three conformations, if rotation is appreciably slower; in situations where the rates of rotation and rearrangements are similar, both effects would be evident in the relative extents of migration.[53] That unassisted (but perhaps bimolecular) loss of nitrogen free of conformational influences is not rapid is shown by the fact that hydrogen azide does not decompose rapidly in solutions in which it is protonated to an appreciable extent;[38] assisted decomposition would be expected to be faster.

In benzyl azide, where R = phenyl and R′ = R″ = H, conformation **13c**, with the nitrogens as far from the bulky phenyl group as possible, would be of lowest energy, and the conformations **13a** and **13b** would be equivalent and slightly higher than **13c**. The statistical bias of 2:1 favoring hydrogen

R $\quad$ N_2^+ $\quad$ R′
N
H
R″
(13a)

R $\quad$ $\quad$ R′
NH
N_2^+
R″
(13b)

R $\quad$ $\quad$ R′
HN
N_2^+
R″
(13c)

migration would thus be partially counteracted by the lower energy of the form leading to phenyl migration. In benzhydryl azide, with R = R′ = phenyl and R″ = H, conformations **13b** and **13c** would be equivalent and subject to steric interference to an extent similar to conformations **13a** and **13b** of benzyl azide; however, they would now be of *lower* energy than the third conformation (**13a**) in which the nitrogens would lie between two phenyl groups instead of between a phenyl and hydrogen. Since hydrogen migration can take place only through this conformation, it could be depressed. The extent of depression might be large, since the potential energy of crowded structures generally goes up sharply as interference accumulates.[54]

Application of such an analysis to tertiary systems, such as those studied by Yukawa and Tanaka, leads to the expectation that the smallest groups will migrate the least, as has been generally observed. This follows not only from the conformational preferences but also from the relative rates of migration of primary, secondary, and tertiary alkyl groups that have been measured

[53] This general effect is discussed by D. Y. Curtin, *Record Chem. Progr.*, **15**, 111 (1954).
[54] For various examples see M. S. Newman, ed., *Steric Effects in Organic Chemistry*, Wiley, New York, 1956.

in the pinacol rearrangement.[55,56] When the possible expansion of an alicyclic ring is involved, relief of ring strain and conformational effects in the ring as well as in the C—N system must also be considered, of course.

The inertness of triphenylmethyl azide to acid-catalyzed rearrangement was mentioned at the beginning of this discussion. Gudmundsen and McEwen have suggested [56a] that this may be an entropy effect, for they observed a marked increase in negative entropy of activation in going from the secondary benzhydryl azides to the tertiary α-methylbenzhydryl series. Resistance to rearrangement would also result if electron withdrawal by each phenyl lowers the intrinsic mobility of the others. Such an explanation, however, runs counter to the observations of Arcus and Lucken [56b] on the qualitative comparison of the rates of the Schmidt reaction of a group of 9-substituted 9-fluorenols, in which the order was 9-phenyl > 9-ethyl > 9-isopropyl > 9-*tert*-butyl. This may not be a proper comparison, since the rate-determining step in the Schmidt reactions may not be the rearrangement.

Coombs [56c] has shown evidence that triarylmethyl azides dissociate reversibly in sulfuric acid to form the corresponding carbonium ion, which may then react with other nucleophiles, such as water, or may polymerize. The extent of such dissociation would be expected to be a function of the stability of the carbonium ion, and this has been demonstrated. 9-Phenyl-9-xanthyl azide, whose thermal rearrangement gives a mixture (eq. 22), is not re-

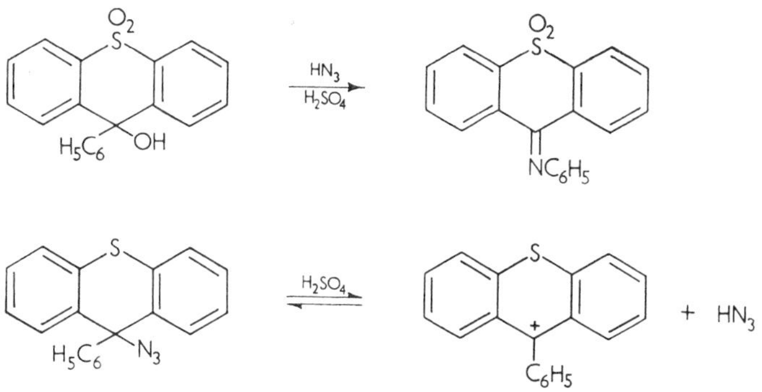

(28)

arranged at all by sulfuric acid, from which it can be recovered by dilution. However, its solution in sulfuric acid shows the color typical of the 9-xanthyl

[55] R. M. Stiles and R. P. Mayer, *J. Am. Chem. Soc.*, **81**, 1497 (1959).

[56] The relative mobilities of alkyl groups in these and related rearrangements are not unambiguous, however, and an opposite order has been observed in the reaction of diazomethane with ketones: H. O. House, E. J. Grubbs, and W. F. Gannon, *J. Am. Chem. Soc.*, **82**, 4099 (1960).

[56a] C. H. Gudmundsen and W. E. McEwen, *J. Am. Chem. Soc.*, **79**, 329 (1957).

[56b] C. L. Arcus and E. A. Lucken, *J. Chem. Soc.* (*London*), **1955**, 1634.

[56c] M. M. Coombs, *J. Chem. Soc.* (*London*), **1958**, 3454, 4200.

cation, and the presence of hydrogen azide can be demonstrated by achieving Schmidt reactions on ketones or more reactive carbinols when they are added. Although the sulfur analogue, 9-phenylthiaxanthyl azide, behaves similarly, its dioxide rearranges to thiaxanthone dioxide anil (eq. 28). The —SO$_2$— function destabilizes the xanthyl cation, but —O— and —S— do not.

Hydroxylamines. Rearrangements of tritylhydroxylamines to benzophenone anils was first observed by G. Reddick, working with Julius Stieglitz at the University of Chicago, and was reported in 1913.[57] Rearrangement was accomplished by warming with phosphorus pentachloride in ether, the same conditions as commonly used for the Beckmann rearrangement of oximes (see heading 2B), and was nearly quantitative. The behavior of the p-chloro compound, which was reported to give roughly 2/3 p-chlorobenzophenone anil and 1/3 benzophenone-p-chloroanil, suggests that the migration of groups is statistically determined in this reaction. The substance that actually rearranges is presumably a species of chlorophosphonate ester, from which the anion or phosphoryl chloride leaves; such intermediates have not been isolated, however. An alternative way to carry out the rearrangement is to treat the benzoyl derivative of the tritylhydroxylamine with soda lime (eq. 29). In

$$Ar_3C—NHOH \xrightarrow{PCl_5} [Ar_3C—NH—\overset{+}{O}PCl_3] \rightarrow Ar_2C{=}NAr + OPCl_3$$

$$Ar_3C—NHOCOC_6H_5 \xrightarrow{OH^-} Ar_3C—N^-—OCOC_6H_5 \rightarrow Ar_2C{=}N—Ar + C_6H_5COO^-$$

(29)

this case, an anion is presumably formed first, from which benzoate is lost during rearrangement. Rearrangement of tritylhydroxylamine has also been brought about by isopropyl methylphosphonochloridate,[58] i-Pr—O— CH$_3$PO—Cl, in the presence of triethylamine. O-Methyl- and O-benzyl-tritylhydroxylamine not unexpectedly are much more resistant and require strong heating with phosphorus pentachloride to bring about only partial rearrangement.[59] Dealkylation is probably a preceding or concurrent step.

The original work by Stieglitz and co-workers to answer the question of the influence of substituents on "migration aptitudes" in the rearrangement of trityl derivatives was severely limited by difficulties of synthesis, which confined their work to p-chloro and p-bromo substituents, and by the crudeness of the then available methods for determining the ratios of the products. The subject was taken up again by Newman and Hay[60] nearly forty years later. By using para substituents of more greatly differing electronic character,

[57] J. Stieglitz and P. N. Leech, *Ber.*, **46**, 2147 (1913); *J. Am. Chem. Soc.*, **36**, 272 (1914).

[58] R. E. Plapinger and O. O. Owens, *J. Org. Chem.*, **21**, 1186 (1956).

[59] W. S. Guthmann and J. Stieglitz, *J. Org. Chem.*, **1**, 31 (1936).

[60] M. S. Newman and P. M. Hay, *J. Am. Chem. Soc.*, **75**, 2322 (1953).

they were able to demonstrate that migration in the rearrangement of trityl-hydroxylamines was after all not merely statistically determined but that a moderate electronic effect exists. Compared to phenyl = 1, the tendency of p-methoxyphenyl to migrate was found to be over 9, that of p-chlorophenyl about 0.5, and that of p-nitrophenyl somewhat less. Unfortunately, their analytical methods were also imprecise, and they claimed qualitative significance only. However, these results make it clear that relative rates of migration in the Stieglitz rearrangement follow the same pattern observed in the rearrangement of benzhydryl azides, in the pinacol rearrangement, and other rearrangements that will be discussed: electron-releasing substituents promote migration, and electron-withdrawing substituents retard it.

Stieglitz rearrangement of alkyl or aralkyl hydroxylamines other than trityl compounds has not been reported. This can be attributed in part to the scarcity of such hydroxylamines, which are often inconvenient to synthesize. A difficulty can be foreseen in bringing about rearrangement, however, inasmuch as hydroxylamines are usually acylated on the nitrogen atom, and only when steric and/or electronic influences are strong enough to counteract the inherently greater nucleophilicity of nitrogen does O-acylation predominate. Because of this, direct treatment of alkylhydroxylamines with phosphorus pentachloride might not bring about rearrangement; on the other hand, the preparation of O-sulfonylhydroxylamines by one of the special methods recently developed [61] might lead to successful rearrangement.

A reaction which is probably a case of the Stieglitz rearrangement has been postulated [62] to occur in the reaction of phenolphthalein with hydroxylamine. The product, long called "phenolphthalein oxime," has been shown to be a benzophenone anil derivative (14). The rearrangement of an intermediate triarylmethylhydroxylamine derivative, perhaps 15, would be expected to

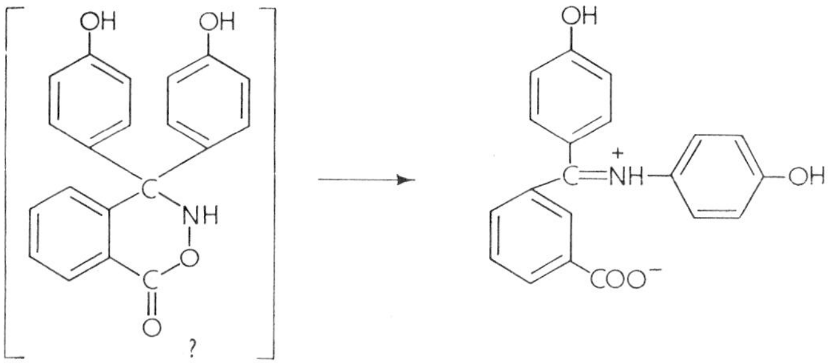

(15)   (14)

[61] (a) L. A. Carpino, J. Am. Chem. Soc., 82, 3133 (1960). (b) W. P. Jencks, J. Am. Chem. Soc., 80, 4581 (1958).

[62] H. Lund, Acta Chem. Scand., 14, 359 (1960).

occur particularly readily because of the strong activation by the p-hydroxy groups. A similar reaction was observed with N-methylhydroxylamine.

Haloamines. The rearrangement of trityl haloamines was reported by Stieglitz and Vosburgh[63] at about the same time as the report of the rearrangement of tritylhydroxylamines. They brought about the rearrangement of both chloro- and bromoamines by heating them with strong bases (soda lime or sodium methoxide); benzophenone anil was formed cleanly enough to be isolated. Examination of the hydrolysis products from the rearrangement of p-chloro- and p-bromotritylhaloamines[63a] showed that both phenyl and substituted phenyl groups had migrated, in ratios of about 2:1. Although this suggests only a simple statistical effect determining the migration ratios, it is probable in view of the work of Newman and Hay[60] with tritylhydroxylamines that these analyses were not sufficiently accurate to detect the small influences on migration to be expected of p-halogen substituents.

The choice of alkali as the agent for causing rearrangement was indicated by the parallel of the Hofmann rearrangement of haloamides; as in it, the N-attached hydrogen is presumably removed, and the resulting haloamine anion loses halide and rearranges (eq. 30). This view is supported by the failure of N-methyl-N-chlorotritylamine to rearrange.[63]

$$(C_6H_5)_3CNHCl \xrightarrow{OH^-} (C_6H_5)_3C\!-\!\bar{N}\!-\!Cl \rightarrow (C_6H_5)_2C\!=\!N\!-\!C_6H_5 + Cl^- \qquad (30)$$

Stieglitz and Vosburgh found that N,N-dichlorotritylamines would also rearrange when heated with soda lime; the second chlorine appeared in the products as hypochlorite (eq. 31). The initiating step in this rearrangement is probably analogous to that for the monochloro compounds, [Cl$^+$] being removed by base instead of [H$^+$].

$$(C_6H_5)_3C\!-\!NCl_2 \xrightarrow[132°]{soda\ lime} (C_6H_5)_2C\!=\!NC_6H_5 + Cl^- + ClO^- \qquad (31)$$

The only further development of the rearrangement of haloamines has been its application to the synthesis of 9-substituted phenanthridines (**17**) from 9-fluorenylhaloamines (**16**). Pinck and Hilbert[14] found it to occur in good

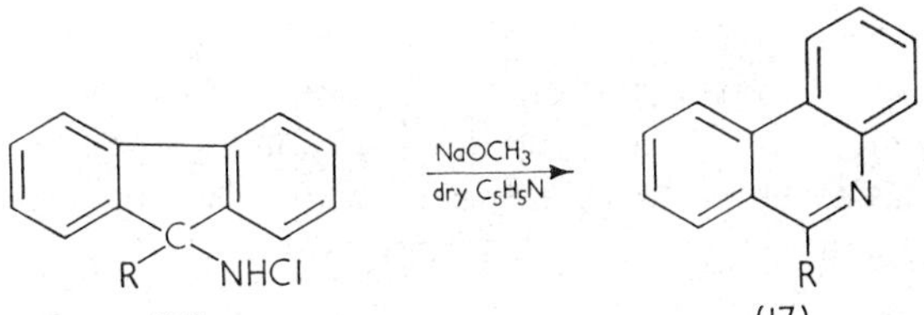

(16)   (17)

[63] J. Stieglitz and I. Vosburgh, *J. Am. Chem. Soc.*, **38**, 2081 (1916).
[63a] A. T. Morgan, *J. Am. Chem. Soc.*, **38**, 2095 (1916).

yields when the substituent was phenyl, α-naphthyl, or methyl; in all cases it was one of the fluorene rings that migrated, and not the substituent. The relief of strain in expanding the five-membered ring is presumably responsible for this preference.

No haloamines bearing primary or secondary alkyl or aralkyl groups have been observed to rearrange. Dehydrohalogenation,[64] giving ketimines or aldimines, occurs so readily that rearrangement apparently cannot compete. N,N-Dichloroamines bearing α hydrogens behave similarly,[65] the initially formed N-chloroimines undergoing a second dehydrohalogenation, giving ultimately α-amino ketones in a form of the Neber reaction (eq. 32).

$$R_2CH{-}NHCl \xrightarrow{\ OH^-\ } R_2C{=}NH$$

$$RCH_2CHRNCl_2 \xrightarrow{\ OH^-\ } [RCH_2CR{=}NCl] \rightarrow \left[R{-}CH{-}\underset{N}{\overset{}{C}}{-}R \right] \rightarrow R{-}\underset{NH_2}{CH}{-}\underset{O}{\overset{\parallel}{C}}{-}R \qquad (32)$$

A curious rearrangement which may belong to the broad group under discussion in this section has been described by White and Bergstrom.[66] Potassium amide and potassium nitrate in liquid ammonia between room temperature and 80° converted 9-phenyl-9-fluorenylamine to 9-amino-phenanthridine and triphenylmethylamine to benzamide. The authors believed that 9-phenyl-phenanthridine and benzophenone anil were formed first (eq. 33) and showed that potassium amide would indeed cleave these

compounds to the observed products under the conditions used. They postulated that rearrangement was initiated by oxidative attack on the amino group by nitrate.

The discussion of the rearrangements in this section has tacitly assumed that rearrangement is intramolecular. No direct evidence has yet been reported on this point, however, and the assumption is based on analogy with the rearrangements of oximes, acyl azides, N-haloamides, and hydroxamic acids, which have been shown to be intramolecular. The stereochemical events

---

[64] W. E. Bachmann, M. P. Cava, and A. S. Dreiding, *J. Am. Chem. Soc.*, **76**, 5554 (1954).

[65] (a) H. E. Baumgarten and F. A. Bower, *J. Am. Chem. Soc.*, **76**, 4561 (1954). (b) N. E. Baumgarten and J. M. Petersen, *J. Am. Chem. Soc.*, **82**, 459 (1960). (c) G. H. Alt and W. S. Knowles, *J. Org. Chem.*, **25**, 2047 (1960).

[66] H. C. White and F. W. Bergstrom, *J. Org. Chem.*, **7**, 497 (1942).

accompanying rearrangement of alkyl and aralkyl azides, hydroxylamines, and haloamines are also as yet uninvestigated, although it seems probable that migration occurs with retention of configuration, as has actually been demonstrated only for the acyl analogues.

B. Derivatives of Ketones and Aldehydes: Oximes, The Schmidt Reaction with Secondary and Related Reactions

Oximes. The classical C to N rearrangement of this group is the Beckmann rearrangement of oximes (eq. 34) which was first reported [67] in 1887. It has been much more extensively investigated than the Schmidt reaction on ketones and aldehydes, and so will be taken up first. The related rearrangement of *N*-haloimines will be discussed integrally with the Beckmann rearrangement.

The number of reported examples of the Beckmann rearrangement has become enormous because of sustained interest in its mechanism, its application to synthesis and degradation, and the industrial interest in it as a step in the manufacture of synthetic polyamides, such as Nylon 6. An encyclopedic review has only recently appeared,[67a] and it will therefore only be necessary in this section to review the mechanism in perspective and to include the most recent developments.

As the rearrangement was originally carried out, an oxime is treated with an equimolar quantity of phosphorus pentachloride in dry ether for a short time, with either warming or cooling, as may be necessary. The isolation of the product, usually an amide, is then accomplished by pouring the mixture on ice and evaporating the ether. Such a procedure remains a highly satisfactory laboratory method, but it does not lend itself to easy study of the mechanistic events occurring. Another widely used method, heating an oxime with sulfuric acid (in various concentrations, from moderate to fuming), also has practical advantages, but, we now know, involves a series of steps. Since the amides obtained by these procedures are isomers of original oximes, and since further mechanistic investigations were lacking, these reagents were regarded at first as catalysts that simply by their presence caused rearrangement to take place. Amides obtained by Beckmann rearrangements were often referred to as "isoximes" in the older literature. The phenomenon of geometri-

$$
\begin{array}{c}
R-\underset{\substack{\|\\N\\O\\H}}{C}-R' \xrightarrow[\text{H}_2\text{O}]{\text{H}_2\text{SO}_4 \text{ or PCl}_5} R-NH-COR' \text{ and/or} \\
R-CO-NH-R' \quad (34)
\end{array}
$$

cal isomerism of oximes was known at the time of Beckmann's work, and it did not take long to discover that different geometrical isomers sometimes

---

[67] E. Beckmann, *Ber.*, **20**, 1507 (1887).

[67a] W. Z. Heldt and L. G. Donaruma, *Org. Reactions*, **11**, Chapt. 1 (1960).

gave isomeric amides by the Beckmann rearrangement. Since the rearrangement was looked upon as a simple isomerization, it was assumed without much question that the groups closest to each other exchanged places, it being only necessary to postulate an enol-keto-like tautomerization (eq. 35).

$$R—C—R' \rightarrow R—C—OH \rightarrow R—C = O \qquad (35)$$
$$\underset{N—OH}{\overset{\|}{}} \quad \underset{N—R'}{\overset{\|}{}} \quad \underset{NH—R'}{\overset{|}{}}$$

This sort of "mechanism," which did not concern itself with how the exchange took place, was later referred to unkindly as "the flip-flop theory."[68] Although effectively disproved by Meisenheimer[69] in 1921, it kept adherents for as long as a decade afterward. Since the structure of oximes is basic to the understanding of the Beckmann rearrangement, this subject will be taken up first.

Oximes, which are generally made by the reaction of ketones or aldehydes with hydroxylamine, might in principle be formulated in any of the following ways (18, 19, 20) if the only evidence for their structure were their analysis and mode of formation. Of these, 18 is the structure accepted now, 19 is the

$$R_2C=NOH \qquad R_2C=\overset{+}{N}H \qquad R_2C——NH$$
$$\qquad\qquad\qquad \underset{O^-}{|} \qquad\qquad \underset{O}{\diagdown\diagup}$$
$$(18) \qquad\qquad (19) \qquad\qquad (20)$$

nitrone structure, well known as N-alkyl and N-aryl derivatives, and 20 is an oxazirane. In the absence of most of the physical methods for structure determination available today, the true structures could not be simply decided, and 18, 19, and 20 were actively debated. Many simple oximes were known in two isomeric forms, sometimes interconvertible. Although it soon became widely accepted that such isomers were the *cis* and *trans* forms of 18, this view was by no means unanimous. It is interesting that isomers of type 20 were eventually prepared by Emmons[70] and were found to be quite distinct from and not interconvertible with previously known oxime isomers. Much indirect evidence led most chemists to accept structure 18 a long time ago, and it has, of course, been adequately demonstrated by modern spectroscopic methods.

In the absence of any other method to establish the configuration of geometrically isomeric oximes, the Beckmann rearrangement was seized upon as a diagnostic tool, and oxime configurations were assigned on the basis of the assumed exchange of adjacent groups. The customary nomenclature for

[68] C. W. Porter, *Molecular Rearrangements*, Chemical Catalog Co., Inc., New York, 1928.

[69] J. Meisenheimer, *Ber.*, **54**, 3206 (1921).

[70] W. D. Emmons, *J. Am. Chem. Soc.*, **79**, 5739 (1957).

geometrical isomers, *cis* and *trans*, was not suitable for use with oximes, which did not bear pairs of similar groups, and the terms *syn* and *anti* were adopted. These prefixes are ambiguous about which group of an aldoxime or unsymmetrical ketoxime the hydroxyl is referred to, and authors have not always been clear in the matter. The usual convention is to refer the position of the hydroxyl group to the first-named portion of the ketone skeleton, or to the hydrogen of aldehydes, as in the following examples (**21**, **22** and **23**), and this will be used throughout this Section.

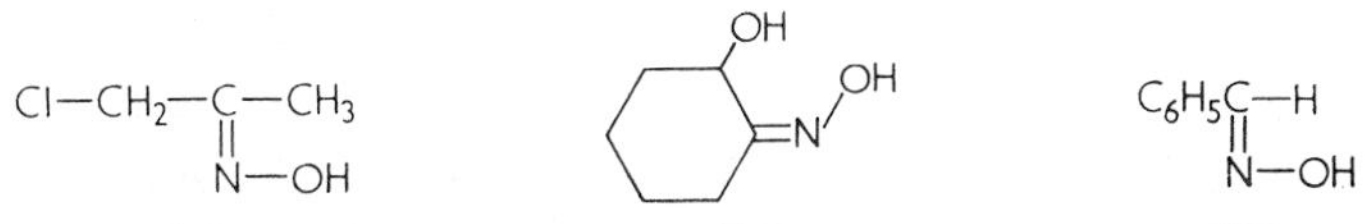

(21) (22) (23)

(*anti*–chloroacetoxime) (*syn*–2–hydroxycyclohexanone oxime) (*syn*–benzaldoxime)

In the many cases where evidence for configuration was totally lacking or especially ambiguous, the prefixes α and β, so dear to our scientific forebears, were applied. For aldoximes, these terms came to have the specific significance $\alpha = syn$-H and $\beta = anti$-H; for some ketoximes, particularly dioximes, where more than two geometrical isomers may exist, Greek letters are still widely used.

Direct evidence on the geometrical configuration of oximes finally appeared in the form of Meisenheimer's now classical paper,[69] in which β-benzil O-benzoylmonoxime (**25**) was prepared by opening an isoxazole ring (**24**) by ozonolysis, thus establishing a *syn*-carbonyl configuration. The oxime obtained from it was the isomer that undergoes phenyl migration in the Beckmann rearrangement to give phenylglyoxanilide (eq. 36), which therefore

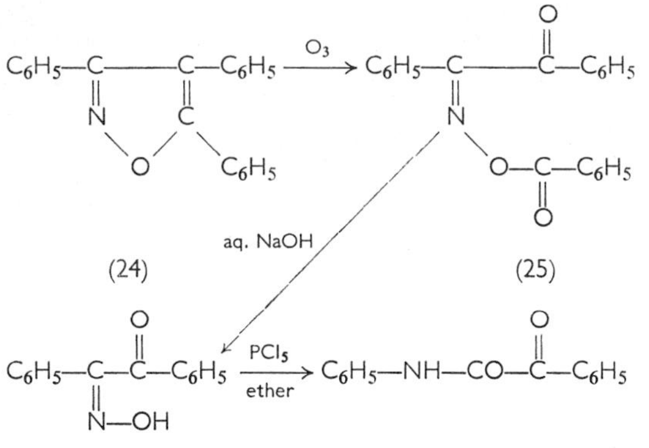

(24) (25) (36)

implies that rearrangement occurs by migration of the group *anti* to the oxime hydroxyl.

As accepting this conclusion would have necessitated reversing virtually all the configuration assignments for oximes made prior to that time, the chemists of that day were understandably cautious about generalizing from an isolated example to all of the Beckmann rearrangement. Additional examples of oximes soon appeared whose configuration could also be established by ring opening [71] or closing,[72] however; these, too, underwent rearrangement by migration of the *anti* group. Theoretical support for the concept of *trans* migration was found in the development of the theory of the Walden inversion on carbon atoms. In later years physical methods, such as dipole moment measurements,[73] infrared [74] and ultraviolet [75] spectroscopy, and nuclear magnetic resonance,[76] have also been used to establish configuration of oximes, and the mechanism of the Beckmann rearrangement involving *trans* migration has long been regarded as firmly established.

Although there is no longer any question that rearrangement involves *trans* migration, there is nevertheless much uncertainty about configurations of oximes determined by the products of the Beckmann rearrangement. Apart from the fact that there is a transition period in the 1920's when one must be very careful to discern for each paper whether the author has used the old or the new basis for assigning configurations, there is the fact of isomerization between configurations (eq. 37). This may be catalyzed by

$$R-\underset{\substack{\|\\N-OH}}{C}-R' \rightleftharpoons R-\underset{\substack{\|\\HO-N}}{C}-R' \tag{37}$$

acids [77] or by bases,[78] and since the conditions for rearranging oximes usually involve acidic or basic reagents, isomerization may take place while the Beckmann rearrangement is being carried out, giving rise to amides not derived from the original configuration. Aliphatic ketoximes isomerize so readily that nearly all of the reports of the isolation of pairs of geometrically isomeric oximes and observation of stereospecific rearrangement have been made for mono- or diaryl ketones. For most aliphatic ketoximes and those

[71] J. Meisenheimer and H. Lange, *Ber.*, **57**, 282 (1924); E. P. Kohler, *J. Am. Chem. Soc.*, **46**, 1733 (1924); E. P. Kohler and N. K. Richtmeyer, *J. Am. Chem. Soc.*, **50**, 3903 (1928).

[72] (a) J. Meisenheimer, P. Zimmermann, and U. von Kummer, *Ann.*, **446**, 205 (1926). (b) O. L. Brady and G. Bishop, *J. Chem. Soc.*, (*London*), **127**, 1357 (1925).

[73] (a) L. E. Sutton and T. W. J. Taylor, *J. Chem. Soc.* (*London*), **1931**, 2190. (b) T. W. J. Taylor and L. E. Sutton, *J. Chem. Soc.* (*London*), **1933**, 63.

[74] A. Palm and H. Werbin, *Can. J. Chem.*, (a) **31**, 1004 (1953), (b) **32**, 858 (1954).

[75] O. L. Brady and H. J. Grayson, *J. Chem. Soc.* (*London*), **1933**, 1037.

[76] W. D. Phillips, *Ann. N. Y. Acad. Sci.*, **70**, 817 (1958).

[77] A. Hantzsch and A. Lucas, *Ber.*, **28**, 744 (1895).

[78] E. Jordan and C. R. Hauser, *J. Am. Chem. Soc.*, **58**, 1304, 1419 (1936); C. R. Hauser and E. Jordan, *J. Am. Chem. Soc.*, **58**, 1772 (1936).

aryl ketoximes that isomerize especially readily, Beckmann rearrangement gives a mixture of isomeric amides regardless of whether a pure oxime isomer is used; this does not violate the principle of *trans* migration, for equilibration between isomers apparently takes place in the reaction medium faster than rearrangement. Under such circumstances, the composition of the mixture of amides produced would be influenced or even determined by the relative rates of migration of the two groups present; [79] in other words, "migration aptitudes" would be able to operate. This effect is well illustrated by *o*-methoxybenzophenone oxime; both isomers have been isolated, but in the Beckmann rearrangement each gives principally benz-*o*-anisidide (eq. 38).[80]

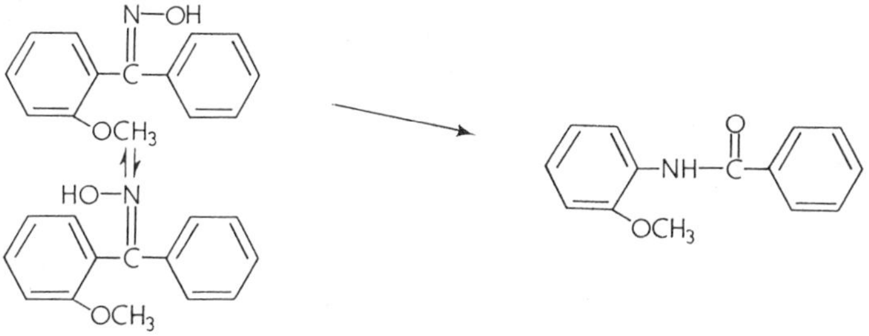

(38)

The occurrence of isomerization during a Beckmann rearrangement experiment depends to some extent on conditions as well as on the structure of the oxime. Phosphorus pentachloride in ether or benzene appears to be the reagent least prone to catalyze prior isomerization, whereas protonic acids, such as hydrogen chloride or sulfuric acid, in polar solvents, such as water or acetic acid, are particularly capable of isomerizing oximes. Pivalophenone oxime is a well-established example [81] where phosphorus pentachloride in ether brings about rearrangement without prior isomerization, but "Beckmann's mixture" (a solution of hydrogen chloride in acetic acid and acetic anhydride) gives products arising from isomerized oxime. The reliability of comparisons of the effects of different reagents on the occurrence of isomerization accompanying Beckmann rearrangements is reduced by the fact that the experiments to be compared have usually been carried out at different temperatures, often widely different. Not only the rate of equilibration but also the position of equilibrium and the intrinsic rate of migration of each group are temperature dependent.[79] Since the sensitivities of these properties to temperature changes are in general not the same, significant differences in

[79] P. A. S. Smith and E. P. Antoniades, *Tetrahedron*, **9**, 210 (1960).

[80] (a) P. Billon, *Ann. chim.*, [10]7, 341 (1927). (b) M. Martynoff, *Ann. chim.*, [11]7, 424 (1937).

[81] R. F. Brown, N. M. van Gulick, and G. H. Schmidt, *J. Am. Chem. Soc.*, **77**, 1094 (1955).

observed results may come about because of the temperature differences alone. Equilibration of oxime isomers at higher temperatures has been shown[79] to give a more nearly equal mixture of amides; the intrinsic migration rates would be expected to change in a similar way.

The nature of the fundamental intermediate steps in the Beckmann rearrangement was demonstrated by Kuhara[82] in a study never published in literature of wide circulation. He demonstrated that whereas oximes themselves do not rearrange without the aid of a catalyst, their benzenesulfonyl esters rearrange spontaneously at room temperature (eq. 39). The implication

$$(C_6H_5)_2C{=}NOH \rightarrow (C_6H_5)_2C{=}N{-}OSO_2C_6H_5 \xrightarrow{\text{spontaneous}}$$

$$\underset{\underset{OSO_2C_6H_5}{\mid}}{C_6H_5C{=}N{-}C_6H_5} \rightarrow \underset{\underset{O}{\overset{\|}{}} \underset{SO_2C_6H_5}{\mid}}{C_6H_5{-}C{-}N{-}C_5H_5} \tag{39}$$

(26)

of this is that the function of the so-called catalysts is to convert the oxime to a derivative capable of spontaneous rearrangement. Kuhara further showed that the initial product is not an amide, but an imidyl derivative (26), convertible to an amide only by an independent step. A claimed parallel observation on the rearrangement of an acetyl oxime[83] has been shown to be in error.[83a]

Although such specific stages cannot always be isolated, there is much indirect evidence that similar patterns are followed with each method of carrying out the rearrangement. The evidence takes the form of the appearance of products arising from interception of the imidyl intermediate before it can rearrange further. Various nucleophiles—alcohols, phenols, amines, and hydrogen azide—have been found to divert the Beckmann rearrangement so as to incorporate them, although they are incapable of reacting under the same conditions with amides already formed. For example, imido esters[84] are formed when oximes are rearranged in alcohol (eq. 40), and tetrazoles[85] when they are rearranged in the presence of hydrogen azide (eq. 41).

A further observation[86] of Kuhara's was that in a series of oxime esters (benzenesulfonyl, chloroacetyl, benzoyl, acetyl), the ease of rearrangement

[82] M. Kuhara, K. Matsumiya, and N. Matsunami, *Mem. Coll. Sci., Univ. Kyoto*, 1, 105 (1914); *Chem. Abstr.*, 9, 1613 (1915); M. Kuhara, *Beckmann Rearrangement*, Kyoto Univ., Kyoto, Japan, 1926.

[83] R. D. H. Heard, M. T. Ryan, and H. I. Bolker, *J. Org. Chem.*, 24, 172 (1959).

[83a] A. Hassner and I. H. Pomerantz, *J. Org. Chem.*, 27, 1760 (1962).

[84] P. Oxley and W. E. Short, *J. Chem. Soc. (London)*, 1948, 1514.

[85] R. L. Burke and R. M. Herbst, *J. Org. Chem.*, 20, 726 (1955).

[86] M. Kuhara and Y. Todo, *Mem. Coll. Sci., Kyoto Imp. Univ.*, 2, 387 (1910); M. Kuhara and H. Watanabe, *Mem. Coll. Sci., Kyoto Imp. Univ.*, 9, 349 (1916); *Chem. Abstr.*, 5, 1278 (1911), 11, 579 (1917).

was proportional to the strength of the esterifying acid. This was extended by Chapman and Fidler [86a] to include the picryl and 2,4,6-trinitro-m-tolyl groups. Chapman and his group [87] also contributed the first precise rate measurements of the Beckmann rearrangement, leading to the first unambiguous delineation of the separate roles of the structure of the migrating and nonmigrating carbon groups and of the nature of the solvent.

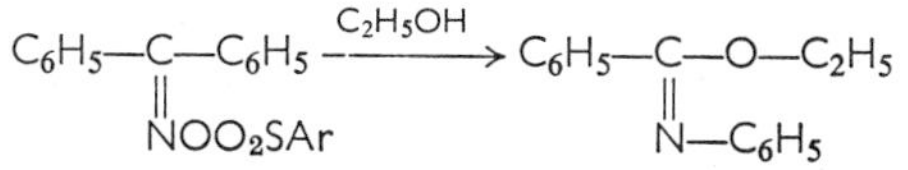

$$C_6H_5-\underset{\underset{NOO_2SAr}{\|}}{C}-C_6H_5 \xrightarrow{C_2H_5OH} C_6H_5-\underset{\underset{N-C_6H_5}{\|}}{C}-O-C_2H_5 \tag{40}$$

$$C_6H_5-\underset{\underset{NOH}{\|}}{C}-C_6H_5 \xrightarrow[H_2SO_4]{HN_3} \left[C_6H_5-\underset{\underset{N-C_6H_5}{\|}}{C}-N_3\right] \rightarrow \tag{41}$$

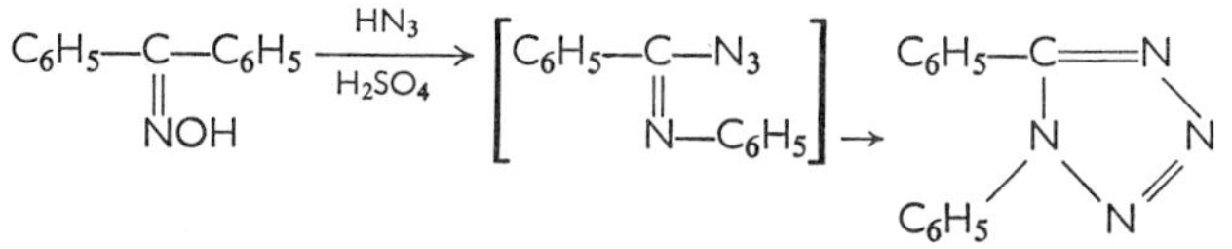

Chapman worked with the picryl and 3-methylpicryl (2,4,6-trinitro-m-tolyl) ethers of a group of para substituted benzophenone oximes, each in its separate geometrically isomeric forms (**27** and **28**). These substances re-

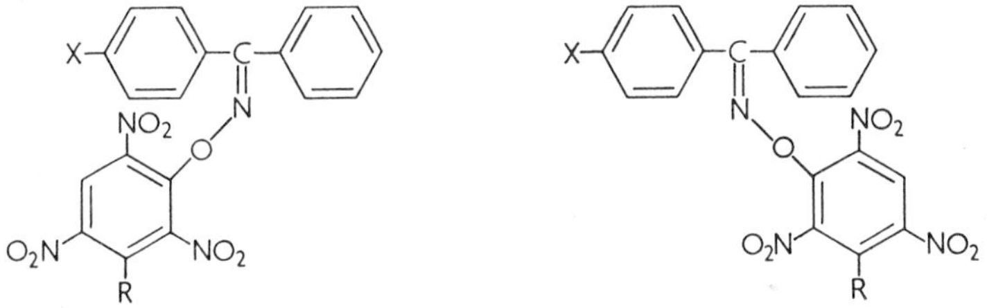

(27)   (28)
R = H or CH$_3$; X = H, CH$_3$,Cl, NO$_2$, or CH$_3$O

arranged to N-picryl- or 3-methylpicrylbenzanilides (eq. 42), which could be isolated quantitatively in crystalline form, and by whose formation the rates

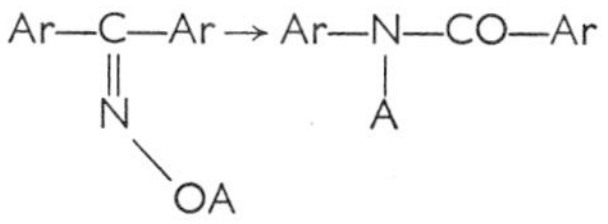

$$Ar-\underset{\underset{\underset{OA}{\diagdown}}{N}}{\overset{\|}{C}}-Ar \rightarrow Ar-\underset{\underset{A}{|}}{N}-CO-Ar \tag{42}$$

were followed. In every case the rate law was first order. Chapman had earlier studied [88] the rearrangement of imidyl esters to amides (eq. 43) and shown that it was intramolecular and, with O-picryl groups, much faster than the

[86a] A. W. Chapman and F. A. Fidler, *J. Chem. Soc.* (*London*), **1936**, 448.

[87] (a) A. W. Chapman, *J. Chem. Soc.* (*London*), **1935**, 1223; (b) A. W. Chapman and C. C. Howis, *J. Chem. Soc.* (*London*), **1933**, 806; (c) A. W. Chapman, *J. Chem. Soc.* (*London*), **1934**, 1550.

[88] A. W. Chapman, *J. Chem. Soc.* (*London*), **1927**, 1742.

rates observed for the Beckmann rearrangement when the group migrating was picryl, circumstances which allowed the rate-determining step in his experiments to be identified as the Beckmann rearrangement stage.

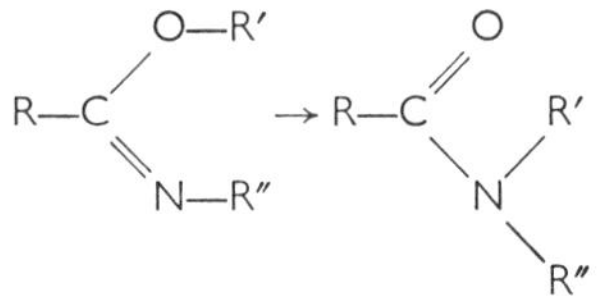

$$
R-C{\overset{O-R'}{\underset{N-R''}{\Big<}}} \rightarrow R-C{\overset{O}{\underset{\underset{R''}{N}}{\diagdown}}}R' \tag{43}
$$

Confirming evidence that the imidoyl ether structure is formed at an intermediate stage is found in the behavior of benzophenoxime picryl ether in aqueous acetone, in which the product is benzanilide itself (eq. 44), although

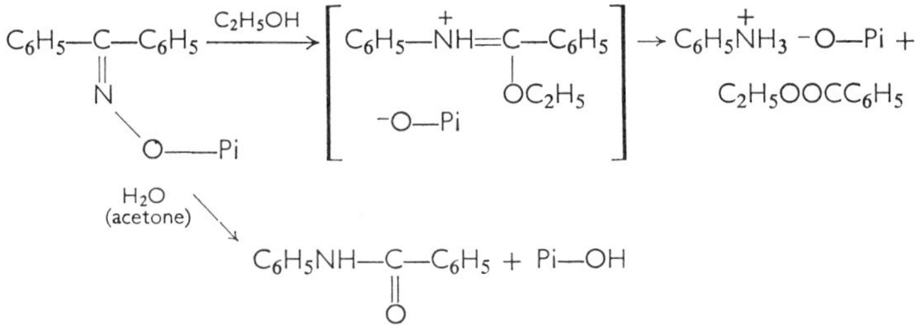

$$
C_6H_5-C-C_6H_5 \xrightarrow{C_2H_5OH} \left[C_6H_5-\overset{+}{N}H=C-C_6H_5 \atop {\underset{-O-Pi}{OC_2H_5}} \right] \rightarrow C_6H_5\overset{+}{N}H_3 {}^-O-Pi +
$$

$$
\text{(43)}
$$

with the left structure $C_6H_5-C-C_6H_5$ bearing N and $O——Pi$,

$$
\overset{H_2O}{\underset{(acetone)}{\searrow}}
$$

$$
C_6H_5NH-C-C_6H_5 + Pi-OH
$$

with carbonyl O,

$$
C_2H_5OOCC_6H_5 \tag{44}
$$

N-picrylbenzanilide is not hydrolyzed under such conditions.[89] Furthermore, Chapman reported that attempted rearrangement in alcohol solution resulted in deep-seated decomposition; the nature of this decomposition has been found [90] to be alcoholysis to aniline picrate and ethyl benzoate, a reaction characteristic of imidoyl ethers and not shown by amides.

Further experiments established that electron-withdrawing substituents (p-nitro and p-chloro) on the migrating group strongly retard rearrangement and electron-donating groups (p-methyl and p-methoxy) strongly accelerate it; the effect of para substituents can be described by a Hammett equation with a negative regression constant, ρ. The same substituents on the nonmigrating phenyl group have the same qualitative effect, but in a much smaller degree. Solvents exert a strong effect that can be correlated with their capability as ionizing media; rearrangement is nearly completely repressed in hydrocarbon solvents, but becomes very fast in acetonitrile, nitromethane, or alcohol.

The information thus far is sufficient to support the following picture of the rearrangement (eq. 45), which has been proposed by so many writers that it is perhaps not fruitful to attempt to find the originator; the earliest firm state-

[89] B. B. Lampert and F. G. Bordwell, *J. Am. Chem. Soc.*, **73**, 2369 (1951).

[90] P. A. S. Smith, unpublished observations.

ment in terms of a synchronous process seems to be that of Jones,[91a] although Hammett [91c] and Waters [91b] had earlier proposed the iminocarbonium ion

$$R-\underset{\underset{\overset{\displaystyle N}{\diagdown}}{\|}}{C}-R' \rightarrow R-N=\overset{+}{C}-R' \rightarrow R-N=C-R' \qquad (45)$$

$$\underset{\displaystyle OA}{} \qquad + ^-OA \qquad \underset{\displaystyle OA}{|}$$

(29)   (30)

(synchronous step)

$$\underset{\underset{\underset{\displaystyle OA}{\diagdown \cdot \cdot}}{\overset{\cdot \cdot}{N}}}{\overset{\displaystyle C-R'}{\underset{R}{\overset{\cdot \cdot}{\diagup} \|}}}$$

(31)

30 as an intermediate. The transition state for such a path would be a pseudo three-membered ring (**31**), and its structure might lie almost anywhere along the reaction coordinate between **29** and **30**. The process can be looked upon as an internal nucleophilic displacement of ¯OA by R:, and might be described as ionization by rearrangement.

A consequence of such a mechanism is that the group migrating from carbon to nitrogen should do so intramolecularly and with retention of configuration when the point of attachment is a center of optical asymmetry. Confirmation of this point had already been obtained by Kenyon, Campbell, and Young,[92] who showed that (+)-methyl-3-heptyl ketoxime is converted by rearrangement to 3-acetamidoheptane with retention of configuration.

$$(+)\text{-}C_4H_9-\overset{*}{\underset{\underset{\displaystyle C_2H_5}{|}}{C}}H-\underset{\underset{\displaystyle N-OH}{\|}}{C}-CH_3 \rightarrow C_4H_9-\overset{*}{\underset{\underset{\displaystyle C_2H_5}{|}}{C}}H-NH-COCH_3$$

(configuration retained)

A further consequence is that migration of the oxygen function should be intermolecular. Jones [91] quotes Chapman as communicating privately that the rearrangement of benzophenoxime picryl ether and p,p'-dimethylbenzophenoxime 3-methylpicryl ether simultaneously in the same solution produces "some" products of exchange of the picryl and 3-methylpicryl groups.

[91] (a) B. Jones, *Nature*, **157**, 519 (1946). (b) W. A. Waters, *Physical Aspects of Organic Chemistry*, Van Nostrand, New York, 1936, pp. 354 et seq. (c) L. P. Hammett, *Physical Organic Chemistry*, McGraw-Hill, New York, 1940.

[92] (a) A. Campbell and J. Kenyon, *J. Chem. Soc.* (*London*), **1946**, 25. (b) J. Kenyon and D. P. Young, *J. Chem. Soc.* (*London*), **1941**, 263. (c) But cf. R. K. Hill and O. T. Chortyk, *J. Am. Chem. Soc.* **84**, 1064 (1962).

This has since been confirmed [90] (eq. 46); in ethylene chloride solution, N-(3-methylpicryl)-benzanilide can be isolated to the extent of 17% from

$$
\left.\begin{array}{c}
\underset{\substack{\| \\ N \\ \diagdown \\ O-Pi}}{C_6H_5-C-C_6H_5} \\[2em]
and \\[1em]
\underset{\substack{\| \\ N \\ \diagdown \\ OPi-CH_3}}{p\text{-}CH_3C_6H_4-C-p\text{-}C_6H_4CH_3}
\end{array}\right\}
\rightarrow
\left.\begin{array}{c}
\underset{\substack{| \\ Pi}}{C_6H_5CON-C_6H_5} \\[1em]
\underset{\substack{| \\ CH_3-Pi}}{C_6H_5CON-C_6H_5} \\[1em]
\underset{\substack{| \\ Pi}}{p\text{-}CH_3C_6H_4CON-p\text{-}C_6H_4CH_3} \\[1em]
\underset{\substack{| \\ CH_3-Pi}}{p\text{-}CH_3C_6H_4CON-p\text{-}C_6H_4CH_3}
\end{array}\right\}
\begin{array}{c} \text{Exchange} \\ \text{products} \end{array}
\quad (46)
$$

simultaneous rearrangement of two equivalents of benzophenoxime picryl ether with one equivalent of its trimethyl analogue; this is close to the maximum theoretically possible when allowance is made for the difference in rates at the relative concentrations used. Furthermore, if benzophenoxime picryl ether is rearranged in ethylene chloride solution containing triethyl-ammonium 3-methylpicrate, exchange occurs to an even larger extent, although the N-picrylbenzanilides produced do not undergo such exchange themselves or with unrearranged oxime ethers.

Evidence for intermolecularity has also been obtained by carrying out rearrangement in the presence of limited amounts of water enriched with ^{18}O (eq. 47); the oxygen in the benzanilide formed from benzophenone oxime and

$$
(C_6H_5)_2C=NOH \xrightarrow[\text{H}_2{}^{18}\text{O}]{\text{PCl}_5} C_6H_5NHC^{18}OC_6H_5 \qquad (47)
$$

phosphorus pentachloride was found to have the same degree of enrichment as the water used, although benzanilide neither exchanged oxygen nor reacted with phosphorus pentachloride under the conditions of the experiment.[93]

Although none of these observations constitutes proof of intermolecularity, the only alternative is to postulate that the intermediate imidoyl ethers, which have been shown to have only a very short life, exchange with each other and with ionic substances with exceptional rapidity. Even then, the profound accelerating effect of polar solvents must be attributed to the development of a partially ionic condition in the transition state.

Before continuing this discussion in terms of the mechanism of equation 45, it might be well to consider briefly the more important older mechanistic proposals that can now be ruled out. Besides the primitive concept of a direct

[93] G. P. Miklukhin and A. I. Brodskii, *Acta Physicochim., U.R.S.S.*, **16**, 63 (1942).

exchange of groups, an early proposal, championed by Stieglitz, was that of dehydroxylation to produce a "univalent" nitrogen derivative,[93a]

$$R-\overset{\displaystyle R}{\underset{\displaystyle N+}{\overset{\displaystyle |}{\underset{\displaystyle ||}{C}}}}$$

Since such an intermediate has lost the source of geometrical isomerism, it cannot account for the observed stereospecificity without drastic modification. Suggestions that the departing hydroxyl group partially screens the nitrogen atom on one side long enough for the *anti* group to begin its migration are in essence the concept of synchronous rearrangement, more exactly expressed in later years. Another proposal was that the C=N moiety simply rotates through an angle of 90° while the three attached groups remain stationary;[94] for structure **29**, the rotation would be clockwise. This proposal, which ignored existing decisive evidence against it, has been adequately demolished.[91]

If a mechanism analogous to equation 45 is to be accepted for every reagent able to bring about the Beckmann rearrangement, we must consider how each reagent can accomplish the postulated steps. The driving force for the rearranging step is presumably the formation, by separation from nitrogen, of the conjugate base of a strong acid, a species of marked stability. Hydroxyl ion does not fulfill this requirement and must be converted to a suitable derivative. The simplest process would be protonation, which would give H_2O, the conjugate base of H_3O^+, as the leaving group. Monoacid salts of oximes, $R_2C=NOH \cdot HA$, do not rearrange readily, but there is much evidence that rearrangement can be catalyzed by strong acids,[95] although it is not clear whether this is due to protonation or acylation (*vide infra*).

The role of most acylating agents in bringing about rearrangement is clearly one of esterification, and the ease of rearrangement of the resulting derivatives would be expected to be proportional to the strength of the esterifying acid, as has been observed. For most acylating agents the oxime esters can be isolated,[96,97] although they are sometimes so labile that they rearrange explosively when brought to room temperature.[97] Phosphorus pentachloride, however, the acylating agent most widely used to effect rearrangement, has not yet yielded an isolable intermediate short of rearrangement. When used in a molar ratio, it leads to imidoyl chlorides, but with less than molar

[93a] C. W. Porter, *Molecular Rearrangements*, Chemical Catalog Co., Inc., New York, 1928.

[94] B. Higman, *Nature*, **156**, 242 (1945).

[95] (a) Y. Ogata, M. Okuno, and K. Matsumoto, *J. Am. Chem. Soc.*, **77**, 4643 (1955). (b) L. P. Hammett and A. I. Deyrup, *J. Am. Chem. Soc.*, **54**, 2721 (1932).

[96] P. Oxley and W. F. Short, *J. Chem. Soc.* (*London*), **1958**, 1514.

[97] E. Kühle and R. Wegler, *Ann.*, **616**, 183 (1958).

amounts, amide may become a significant or even major product.[98] It has been suggested by several authors [99] that a tetrachlorophosphonyl derivative (**32**) is first produced, followed by rearrangement with cleavage into phosphoryl chloride and chloride ion, which can unite with the iminocarbonium ion to form the observed imidoyl chloride (eq. 48). Since phosphoryl chloride

$$R-\underset{\underset{\underset{OPCl_4}{\diagdown}}{\overset{||}{N}}}{C}-R \quad \rightarrow R-N=\overset{+}{C}-R \rightarrow R-N=\underset{\underset{Cl}{|}}{C}-R \quad (48)$$
$$+ POCl_3 + Cl^-$$
$$(32)$$

is itself capable of effecting Beckmann rearrangement, although not as vigorously as phosphorus pentachloride, a molar ratio of pentachloride is not necessary.

Stephen and Staskun [98] have extensively investigated the activity of phosphorus pentachloride, thionyl chloride, and other acid chlorides in the Beckmann rearrangement. They showed that under suitable conditions as little as 6% (molar) of reagent is capable of bringing about nearly complete rearrangement; amide is, of course, the principal product, and only small amounts of imidoyl chloride are produced. They amplified Chapman's earlier observation [87] that imidoyl chlorides can themselves effect Beckmann rearrangement in the presence of hydrogen chloride, presumably according to equation 49. Such a process can be seen to be self-perpetuating. The unpro-

$$R_2C=NOH + R\underset{\underset{Cl}{|}}{N}=C-R \rightarrow R_2C=N-O-\underset{\underset{R}{|}}{C}=\overset{+}{\underset{\underset{Cl^-}{|}}{N}}-R \rightarrow R-NHCOR + R\underset{\underset{Cl}{|}}{N}=C-R \quad (49)$$

tonated imidoyl oxime would not be expected to rearrange, since the imidate ion is not the conjugate base of a strong enough acid.

Stephen and Staskun also proposed a path for Beckmann rearrangements in general. Noting that the effective reagents are all dehydrating agents in one way or another, they proposed that the common purpose of the reagents is to convert oximes into ether-like anhydrides (**33**), which would rearrange when protonated (eq. 50).

$$2R_2C=N-OH \rightarrow R_2C=N-O-N=CR_2 \rightarrow R_2C=N-O-\overset{+}{N}H=CR_2 \rightarrow$$
$$(33)$$

$$R-\underset{\underset{R}{|}}{\overset{+}{N}}H=C-O-N=CR_2 \rightarrow R-\underset{\underset{R}{|}}{\overset{+}{N}}H=C-O-\underset{\underset{R}{|}}{C}=N-R \overset{H_2O}{\longrightarrow} 2R-NHCOR \quad (50)$$

[98] A. Stephen and B. Staskun, *J. Chem. Soc. (London)*, **1956**, 980.

[99] E.g., M. J. S. Dewar, *The Electronic Theory of Organic Chemistry*, Clarendon Press, Oxford, 1949, p. 219.

While such a path does indeed correlate a great many observations, the suggestion has some fatal flaws. The rate of disappearance of oxime should be second order in oxime. The reported kinetics of the sulfuric acid–catalyzed rearrangement are first order in oxime,[95,100] so the above path cannot apply to this particular method of rearrangement. While no mechanism was suggested for the dehydration step, the only apparent ones are an S_N1 or an S_N2 process, analogous to the formation of ethers from alcohols. The first must necessarily involve the same "univalent nitrogen" cation, $R_2C=N^+$ proposed by Stieglitz, and would therefore result in a 50% loss in stereospecificity (and should lead to immediate rearrangement!). The S_N2 process, also occurring at the nitrogen atom, would result in at least 50% inversion of configuration, and thus a complete loss of stereospecificity. Since stereospecificity is often quite precise, especially with diaryl ketones (on which Stephen and Staskun's experiments were mostly performed), oxime anhydride formation must be rejected for all such oximes, and there seems to be no reason to compel acceptance of the mechanism for those oximes whose rearrangement is not stereospecific and whose kinetics have not yet been determined.

Sulfuric acid is particularly effective in accomplishing the Beckmann rearrangement, largely since it can be used in sufficient concentrations to produce high acidities and can be used over a wide temperature range. However, it appears to be more effective than perchloric acid at equivalent acidities.[95] Investigations [95,100,101] of the kinetics in sulfuric acid have shown that rearrangement is first order in oxime, and log k varies nearly linearly with the Hammett acidity function, H_0, and slightly more closely with the Gold-Hawes function, J_0 (i.e., $H_0 + \log a_{H_2O}$). At very high acidities, the rates level off. The interpretation of these observations has varied considerably. The existence of oxime-O-sulfonic acids has been demonstrated,[100,102] and they have been shown to be capable of rearrangement, but their role in the rearrangement of oximes by sulfuric acid is ambiguous. It has been proposed that both their rate of formation and their rearrangement are rate determining, and also that they are not significantly involved.

Simple monoprotonation of the oxime cannot account for the dependence of rate on acidity, as Ogata and co-workers [95] have pointed out, for oximes are reasonably basic and form well-defined salts; in the high acid concentrations used for rearrangement, oximes must be present entirely as their conjugate acids. The structure of the latter is probably tautomeric, with $R_2C=\overset{+}{N}HOH$

[100] (a) D. E. Pearson and F. Ball, *J. Org. Chem.*, **14**, 118 (1949). (b) D. E. Pearson and W. E. Cole, *J. Org. Chem.*, **20**, 488 (1955).

[101] (a) R. Huisgen, *Angew. Chem.*, **69**, 341 (1957). (b) O. Wichterle and J. Roček, *Chem. Listy*, **45**, 257, 379 (1951); *Chem. Abstr.*, **46**, 10809 (1952). (c) G. Roček and Z. Bergel, *Chem. Listy*, **47**, 472 (1953); *Chem. Abstr.*, **48**, 3279 (1954).

[102] P. A. S. Smith, *J. Am. Chem. Soc.*, **70**, 323 (1948).

predominating greatly over $R_2C{=}\overset{+}{N}OH_2$. The dependence of rate on acidity must thus depend on a second step involving acid; Ogata and co-workers have proposed that this step is sulfonation of $R_2C{=}\overset{+}{N}OH_2$ or, presumably, perchlorylation when $HClO_4$ is used, but it is hard to see how sulfonation could take place on an oxonium oxygen. If O-sulfonation is involved, it must take place on the N-protonated form. They interpret the rate data in terms of a rate-determining rearrangement of the oxime-O-sulfonic acid and derive an expression for the pseudo-first-order rate constant that includes the equilibrium constant for sulfonation and the activities of H_2SO_4 and H_2O, having the form

$$\log k = \log a_{H_2SO_4}/a_{H_2O} + H_0 + \text{constant}$$

They found that plots of $\log k$ against $\log a_{acid}/a_{H_2O} + H_0$ are indeed linear, with the required slope of 1.0, but at the highest acidities $\log k$ begins to level off to a constant value, an observation also made by others.[101] They show that this may be accounted for by assuming that the conversion to oxime-O-sulfonate becomes large, and eventually complete, in which case the observed rate should no longer depend on the equilibria preceding rearrangement. If sulfonation is involved, a more detailed understanding of the nature of the sulfonation process, and particularly of the nature of the active sulfonating species, will be required; at present, even sulfonation of benzene is incompletely understood.[103]

McNulty and Pearson [104] have proposed that a second proton is added to the oxygen, leading to a transition state which they represent as **34** for acetophenone oxime. However, if diprotonation is involved, it seems much more probable that one proton is added to nitrogen, as in **35**.

$$HSO_4^- {\cdots}\!\!\rightarrow C \overset{+\delta}{\cdots}\!\!\rightarrow N^{+\delta} \!\!\rightarrow O {\cdots} H^+$$

(34) $R_2C{=}\overset{+}{N}H - \overset{+}{O}H_2$

                                                  (35)

A less ambiguous case of acid catalysis is that of liquid hydrogen fluoride,[105] which cannot be considered an acylating agent in the ordinary sense. Kopple and Katz [105a] reported that it accomplishes slow rearrangement of benzo-

103 J. Hine, *Physical Organic Chemistry*, McGraw-Hill, New York, 1956.

104 P. J. McNulty and D. E. Pearson, *J. Am. Chem. Soc.*, **81**, 612 (1959).

105 (a) K. D. Kopple and J. J. Katz, *J. Org. Chem.*, **24**, 1975 (1959). (b) M. Hudlicky, Czechoslov. pat. 85, 971; *Chem. Abstr.*, **52**, 2894c (1958).

phenone oxime at room temperature, but does not affect cyclohexanone oxime, although Hudlicky [105b] claims yields of 30–74% of lactams from the rearrangement of cyclohexanone oxime and other cyclic ketoximes.

A most curious set of observations has been reported by Tokura, Tada, and Suzuki in connection with the use of liquid sulfur dioxide as a solvent in which to carry out the Beckmann rearrangement. With sulfur trioxide as catalyst, cyclodecan-1,6-dione dioxime underwent normal reaction, giving a cyclic diamide composed of two δ-aminovaleric acid moieties; with thionyl chloride as catalyst, however, δ-valerolactam was produced. Since the diamide could not be converted to the lactam under the reaction conditions, the authors proposed that the lactam arises from an unprecedented, transannular Beckmann rearrangement.[106]

Lewis acids, such as boron fluoride,[105] may also bring about rearrangement. With such reagents, coordination may occur at N or O, and it appears that the N-adduct, formed in the principal amount, must transform [106a] to the O-adduct in the rate-determining step (eq. 51). Similar behavior is observed in

$$R_2C{=}\overset{+}{N}\overset{OH}{\diagup}_{\diagdown BF_3{}^-} \;\longrightarrow\; R_2C{=}N{-}\overset{\overset{H}{|}}{\underset{|}{O}}{}^+ \quad or \quad R_2C{=}\overset{+}{N}H{-}OBF_3{}^- \qquad (51)$$
$$BF_3{}^-$$

the action of antimony pentachloride on O-methylbenzophenoxime.[107] Catalysis of rearrangement by certain metallic salts, such as cuprous chloride,[108] may be of this class. Other exceptional means of rearranging oximes, such as by pyrolysis alone [109] or over contact catalysts, such as copper,[110] are more difficult to interpret. They usually involve rather drastic conditions and give poor yields.

The kinetics of the Beckmann rearrangement have been studied from a number of aspects, some of which have already entered this discussion. Because several steps may be involved, especially in experiments in which the oxime itself is the starting material, the interpretation is sometimes ambiguous. The essential steps are (1) conversion of oxime to the rearranging species, (2) rearrangement, and (3) conversion of the initial rearrangement product to the isolated form. Other steps may intervene, however, and it is not usually possible to isolate all steps. The rate may be followed by disappearance [95,111]

[106] N. Tokura, R. Tada, and K. Suzuki, Bull. Chem. Soc. Japan, 32, 654 (1959).

[106a] C. R. Hauser and D. S. Hoffenburg, J. Org. Chem., 20, 1491 (1955).

[107] W. Theilacker, Angew. Chem., 51, 834 (1938).

[108] W. J. Comstock, Am. Chem., J., 19, 484 (1897).

[109] E. Wenkert and B. F. Barnett, J. Am. Chem. Soc., 82, 4671 (1960).

[110] S. Yamaguchi, Bull. Chem. Soc. Japan, 1, 35, 54 (1926); Chem. Abstr., 21, 75 (1927).

[111] R. Huisgen, I. Ugi, M. T. Assemi, and J. Witte, Ann., 602, 127 (1957).

of oxime or derivative, by appearance of an isolated end product,[111a] or by the appearance of an acidic solvolysis product.[112] The rate-determining step may be any one of the stages occurring, and studies to date have shown that a common rate-determining step cannot be found for all examples of Beckmann rearrangement.

Huisgen and co-workers [113] have determined the kinetics of rearrangement of a group of substituted acetophenone O-picryl oximes (eq. 52) by following

$$A-C_6H_4-\overset{\overset{\displaystyle O-Pi}{|} }{\underset{\displaystyle \|}{N}}{C}-CH_3 \rightarrow A-C_6H_4-\overset{\overset{\displaystyle Pi}{|}}{N}-COCH_3 \tag{52}$$

the diminution of their ultraviolet absorption. The results for meta and para substitution could be correlated by a Hammett plot with a regression factor of -4.1, which is of the order of magnitude of that for aromatic substitution. They interpreted this to mean that reaction proceeded through a bridged-cation intermediate (36), similar to the transition state representation 31, and occupying a shallow energy minimum. They represented the rate-determining step to be the formation of 36 (eq. 53), since the transition state lead-

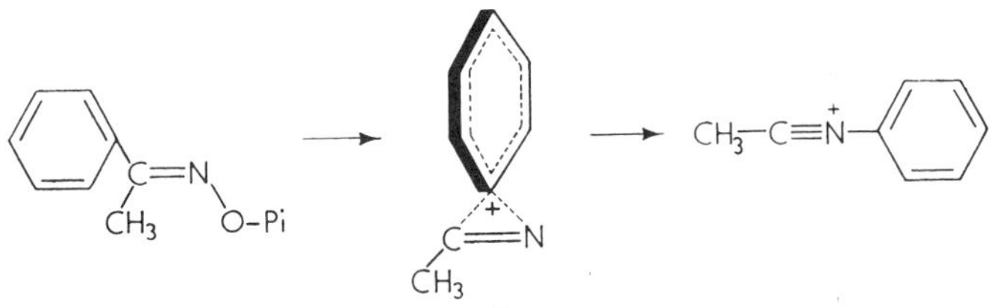

ing to it must resemble it closely to account for the large sensitivity to substituents. It is in principle possible, of course, in other compounds for the following step to be rate-determining. Ortho substituents had a large accelerating effect, which will be discussed later. The kinetics of acetophenone oximes have also been measured by Pearson and co-workers,[104,114] who used sulfuric acid on the oxime itself. They found a considerably smaller regression factor, -2.0, but its significance is not as clear since the rate-determining step may be sulfonation of the oxime, or an acid-base equilibrium prior to the rate-

[111a] (a) A. W. Chapman, J. Chem. Soc. (London), 1935, 1223; (b) A. W. Chapman and C. C. Howis, J. Chem. Soc. (London), 1933, 806; (c) A. W. Chapman, J. Chem. Soc. (London), 1934, 1550.

[112] W. Z. Heldt, J. Am. Chem. Soc., 80, 5972 (1958).

[113] R. Huisgen, J. Witte, H. Walz, and W. Jira, Ann., 604, 191 (1957).

[114] (a) D. E. Pearson, J. F. Baxter, and J. C. Martin, J. Org. Chem., 17, 1511 (1952). (b) D. E. Pearson and J. D. Bruton, J. Org. Chem., 19, 957 (1954). (c) W. Z. Heldt, J. Org. Chem., 26, 1695 (1961).

determining step may affect the rate expression, as has been pointed out for acid-catalyzed rearrangement of azides (see page 469).

A study of the rearrangement of arylsulfonyl oximes of cyclopentanone and cyclohexanone was made by Heldt [112] by titrating the strong acid that appeared—presumably

$$(CH_2)_n \underset{\diagdown}{\overset{\diagup}{}} \underset{C-OR}{\overset{NH^+}{\|}}$$

Such a procedure isolates the solvolysis phenomena that occur. He found that the rate-determining step precedes formation of imidoyl sulfonate and must thus be either the rearrangement itself or an additional intervening step. p-Bromobenzenesulfonyl ("brosyl") oximes rearrange markedly faster than p-toluenesulfonyl ("tosyl") oximes, as is to be expected from the difference in strength of the parent acids. By carrying out the rearrangement of the brosylate in acetic acid containing various salts, Heldt observed decreases in rate in the presence of added tosylate or increases in the presence of chloride or perchlorate; these indicated a certain amount of exchange of added anion for brosylate occurring before the rate-determining step. He interpreted this to mean that the rate-determining step is the solvolysis of the salt of a nonclassical cation, probably in the form of an ion pair (eq. 54).

$$-\overset{|}{\underset{\diagup}{C}} \underset{\diagdown}{\overset{|}{C}} = N-OBs \rightarrow -C \overset{-\overset{|}{C}-}{\equiv\!\equiv\!\equiv} N^+ \quad BsO^- \xrightarrow{AcOH} -\underset{\underset{OAc}{|}}{C} = NH^+ \qquad (54)$$

This proposal implies that the structure (31) suggested as a transition state earlier in this discussion is a true intermediate, separated from both acyl oxime and solvolysis products by distinct transition states, as proposed by Huisgen et al. for rearrangement of O-picryl acetophenoximes.[113] The possibility that exchange might have occurred before rearrangement was dismissed by Heldt on the basis of an experiment with acetophenone oxime. It was stated in a footnote [112] that the syn-methyl tosyloxime of acetophenone gave acetanilide as the only product when rearranged in the presence of brosylate; if exchange had occurred before rearrangement, it was argued, inversion of geometrical configuration would have resulted, through an S_N2 process on nitrogen, and a corresponding quantity of N-methylbenzamide should have been formed on rearrangement. This argument is not relevant, even if it is valid, for there was no evidence given, kinetic or other, that any anion exchange occurs during solvolytic rearrangement of acetophenone oxime esters. That exchange during rearrangement is not a general phenomenon is shown by the lack of kinetically demonstrable exchange when O-tosylcyclopentanone oxime rearranges in the presence of brosylate ion. In addition, there is no evidence that displacements on the nitrogen of oximes result in inversion, and there is reason to suspect the opposite, that displacement at an unsaturated nitrogen atom would result in equilibration to the most stable configuration, analogous to such processes at a vinyl carbon. The hypothesis of a nonclassical ion pair as a distinct intermediate may indeed be correct, but until it can be demonstrated less ambiguously, it can only be regarded as hypothetical.

The effect of different solvents on the rate of rearrangement of tosyl oximes has also been studied by Heldt,[114c] who was able to correlate the effects with solvent polarity functions. In general, the rates for a given tosyl oxime varied with solvent in the order $CH_3OH > CH_3COOH > CHCl_3$, and the rates for a given solvent were in the order cyclohexanone > benzophenone > other cycloalkanones $\simeq$ acetophenone > acetone; small effects, both positive and negative, were observed when strong acids were added.

Kinetic studies on oximes of cyclic ketones have provided information on the steric requirements of the transition state. The picryl ethers of the cyclanone oximes from C_5 to C_{15} rearrange at rates that vary within a twenty-fold range and show an irregular alternation; the activation enthalpies also alternate, in a somewhat better-defined way.[111] Huisgen and co-workers interpret these effects in terms of conformational effects related to the relative stabilities of endo- and exocyclic double bonds. A more striking effect is shown in the benzocycloalkenone series[115] (eq. 55), for which the transition state or

(55)

(From *anti* isomer)   (From *syn* isomer)

intermediate corresponding to **36** has three fused rings, as shown by **37**. For maximum stability the bridged cation structure should have the benzene ring at right angles to the C=N axis. This orientation can only be achieved at the expense of tremendous strain when the alicyclic ring is five-membered, but strain decreases as the ring size is increased. The rate constants ($k \times 10^6$ sec.$^{-1}$ at 70°) for rearrangement of the picryl ethers of the *anti* isomers show a pronounced effect corresponding to this interpretation; for ring size, $n = 5$,

[115] R. Huisgen, J. Witte, and I. Ugi, *Chem. Ber.*, **90**, 1844 (1957).

the rate was too slow to measure; for $n=6$, $k<0.02$; for $n=7$, $k=1865$, and for $n=8$, $k=42,900$.

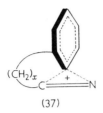

(37)

The *syn* isomers for $n=7$ and 8 do not show such an effect, the rate constants being 6.43 and 2.96, respectively. This is to be expected, for a migrating saturated group should not have such orientation requirements. It is noteworthy that the ratio of the rate constants for the *anti* and *syn* forms for $n=8$ is 14,000. Huisgen and co-workers propose that this is a truer picture of the relative intrinsic migration rates of aryl versus alkyl groups than are comparisons of acetophenone oxime with saturated ketoximes, where the ratios are less than 10. They point out that in acetophenone oxime, conjugation of the oxime double bond with the benzene ring probably retards rearrangement, but in benzocyclooctenone oxime, such conjugation is sterically reduced.

Ortho-substituted acetophenone oximes rearrange far more rapidly than their meta or para isomers.[100b, 113] This effect has been attributed to a steric influence which reduces conjugation of the benzene ring with the oxime double bond, thereby increasing the potential energy of the oxime.[116] The effect can be extremely strong and is believed to account for the fact that di-ortho-substituted acetophenone oximes have been found to rearrange during preparation from the ketone and hydroxylamine hydrochloride (eq. 56).[117]

$$\text{(ortho-R,R-C}_6\text{H}_3\text{)—COCH}_3 \; + \; NH_2OH \cdot HCl \longrightarrow \text{(ortho-R,R-C}_6\text{H}_3\text{)—NHCOCH}_3 \qquad (56)$$

A large number of examples have accumulated where an oxime fragments instead of rearranging to an amide or derivative. This reaction has been widely termed "the second-order Beckmann rearrangement," an abominable translation of the phrase [118] "Beckmannsche Umlagerung der zweiten Art"

[116] R. Huisgen, J. Witte, and W. Jira, *Chem. Ber.*, **90**, 1850 (1957).

[117] (a) R. G. Kadesch, *J. Am. Chem. Soc.*, **66**, 1207 (1944). (b) F. Greer and D. E. Pearson, *J. Am. Chem. Soc.*, **77**, 6649 (1955).

[118] A. Werner and A. Piguet, *Ber.*, **37**, 4295 (1904).

originally coined for it. In order not to perpetuate such a (kinetically) objectionable and confusing term, the name "Beckmann fission" will be used in this discussion. It is also sometimes called the "abnormal" Beckmann rearrangement.

A representative example is that of benzoin oxime,[118] whose *anti* isomer, when treated with benzenesulfonyl chloride and base, fragments to benzonitrile and benzaldehyde (eq. 57). The *syn* isomer gives phenyl isocyanide

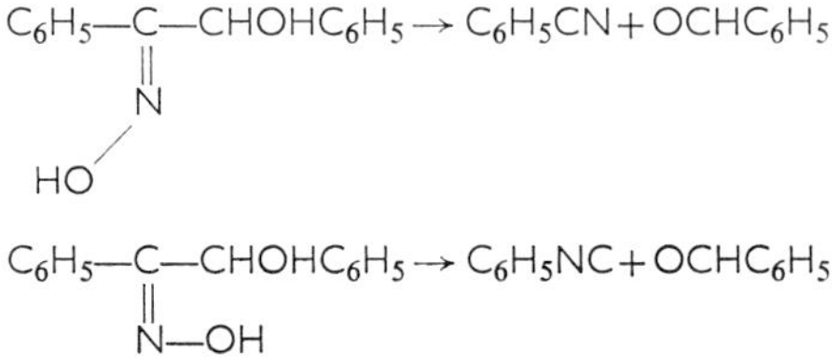

$$C_6H_5-\underset{\substack{\| \\ N \\ \diagup \\ HO}}{C}-CHOHC_6H_5 \rightarrow C_6H_5CN + OCHC_6H_5 \tag{57}$$

$$C_6H_5-\underset{\substack{\| \\ N-OH}}{C}-CHOHC_6H_5 \rightarrow C_6H_5NC + OCHC_6H_5$$

and benzaldehyde. The reaction is common with α-hydroxy and α-keto oximes and may be of much synthetic value, as in the preparation of the half-nitrile of diphenic acid from phenanthrene quinone monoxime (eq. 58).[118]

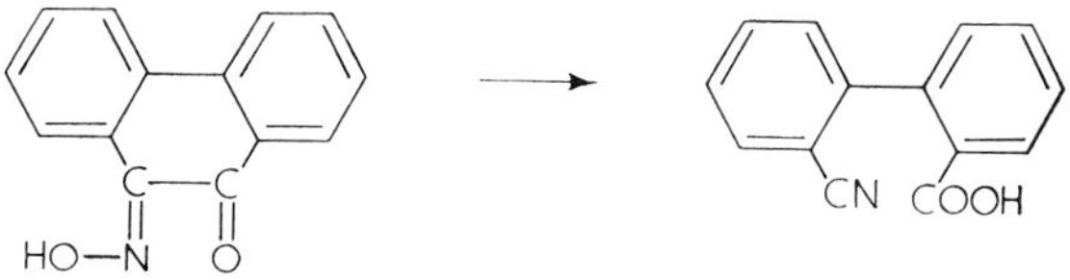

$$\tag{58}$$

The Beckmann fission appears to be possible when one of the groups attached to the oxime carbon is of a type that has greater than usual stability as a cation. In the examples above the cations would be $R-\overset{+}{C}HOH$ or $R-\overset{+}{C}O$; fragmentation also occurs readily when the separating group is a tertiary or even occasionally a secondary alkyl group.[119] Examples are 9,10-dihydro-9,10-(ketoethano)-anthracene,[120] whose oxime fragments to anthracene-9-acetonitrile with all common rearranging agents (eq. 59), and pivalophenone oxime, which loses a tertiary butyl group to form benzonitrile.[120a]

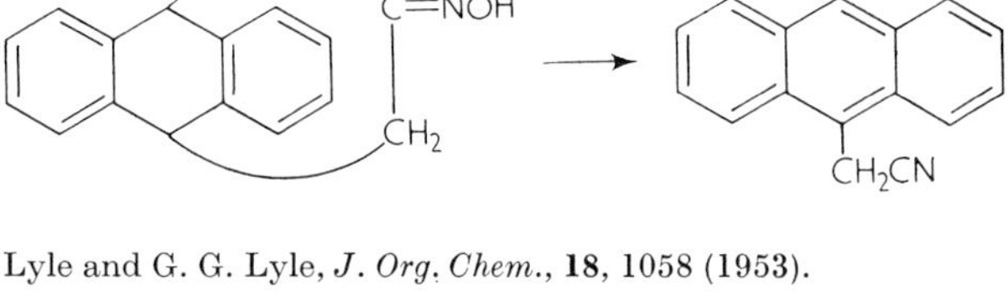

$$\tag{59}$$

[119] R. E. Lyle and G. G. Lyle, *J. Org. Chem.*, **18**, 1058 (1953).

[120] S. Wawzonek and J. V. Hallum, *J. Org. Chem.*, **24**, 364 (1959).

[120a] R. F. Brown, N. M. van Gulick, and G. H. Schmidt, *J. Am. Chem. Soc.*, **77**, 1094 (1955).

α-Oximino [121] and α-amino [127] oximes have also been observed to fragment.

In addition to the numerous isolated examples in the literature, there are several studies concerned specifically with the fission reaction. Blatt and Barnes [123] and later Ferris [124] have investigated and discussed the cleavage of α-keto oximes, and Conley and Mikulski [125] have investigated the occurrence of the reaction induced by polyphosphoric acid. Grob [122] studied a series of N-substituted α-amino oximes and found that the ease of fragmentation varied with the electron-releasing character of the α-amino group (eq. 60). Forcing reaction of α-benzamido oximes resulted substantially in normal Beckmann rearrangement. The *syn*-oximes fragmented less readily than the *anti* and underwent normal rearrangement as well.

$$-\overset{|}{\underset{\underset{R_2N}{|}}{C}}-\overset{\underset{\underset{NOH}{||}}{}}{C}-R \longrightarrow -\overset{|}{C}=\overset{+}{N}R_2 + N\equiv C-R \tag{60}$$

R_2N-:

Relative rate:	1	0.82	0.102	0.00051	0

Most authors have presented the reaction as an elimination competing with rearrangement. The parent ketones themselves can often be cleaved readily, and the oximes can usually be cleaved also by cyanide, which is not a catalyst for rearrangement.[123] Grob considered the fragmentation of *anti*-α-amino oximes to be a case of coplanar *trans* elimination (eq. 61) and has

$$R_2C-\overset{\overset{\underset{NOA}{||}}{}}{\underset{\underset{NR_2''}{|}}{C}}-R' \rightarrow R_2C=\overset{+}{N}R_2'' + N=C-R' + OA^- \tag{61}$$

related it to a variety of similar fragmentations not connected with the Beckmann rearrangement. However, it has been pointed out [123,124] that those fragmentations that produce isocyanides can occur only after ordinary Beckmann rearrangement has occurred, at least in part, and may perhaps be a separate type of phenomenon. However, the transition state (or nonclassical intermediate) of the ordinary Beckmann rearrangement can be considered to

[121] A. F. Ferris, G. S. Johnson, and F. E. Gould, *J. Org. Chem.*, **24**, 1812 (1960).

[122] C. A. Grob, *Bull. soc. chim. France* **1960**, 1360.

[123] A. H. Blatt and R. P. Barnes, *J. Am. Chem. Soc.*, **56**, 1148 (1934).

[124] A. F. Ferris, *J. Org. Chem.*, **25**, 12 (1960).

[125] R. T. Conley and F. A. Mikulski, *J. Org. Chem.*, **24**, 97 (1959).

account for both types of fragmentation as well (eq. 62), depending on its manner of cleavage.

$$
R\!-\!C\!\!=\!\!=\!\!N\cdots OA \left\langle
\begin{array}{l}
R\!-\!\overset{+}{C}\!\!=\!\!N\!-\!R' + OA^- \\
R\!-\!C\!\equiv\!N + R'^+ + OA^- \\
R^+ + CN\!-\!R' + OA^-
\end{array}
\right.
\qquad (62)
$$

Aldoximes and their derivatives usually undergo Beckmann fragmentation to nitriles so readily that examples [125a] of normal Beckmann rearrangement to give formamides are quite rare (eq. 63).[125b,126] In many cases, unsubstituted

$$
\begin{array}{c}
R\!-\!CH\!\!=\!\!NOH \\
\searrow \text{dehydrating} \\
\text{agent} \\
R\!-\!C\!\equiv\!N \\
\text{base} \nearrow \\
R\!-\!CH\!\!=\!\!NOA
\end{array}
\qquad (63)
$$

amides are formed instead of nitriles; it is probable that many of these result from hydrolysis of nitriles first formed, but evidence is incomplete. Experiments on N-chlorobenzaldimines [127] suggest that base-catalyzed nitrile formation is an elimination initiated by attack on the aldehyde hydrogen. Such a process would be expected to occur much more readily with the $anti$-H isomer. Indeed, there are a number of cases [126] where one isomer of an O-acetyl aldoxime undergoes elimination when treated with base, while the other (presumably the syn-H) is hydrolyzed back to the parent oxime.

An aspect of particular practical importance in using the Beckmann rearrangement is the prediction of which group of an unsymmetrical ketoxime will migrate predominantly. It has been pointed out earlier in this discussion that this may depend on the relative amounts of syn- and $anti$-oximes present or may be governed by relative migration aptitudes if the isomers are rapidly equilibrated. The position of equilibrium between oxime isomers is different for the anions, neutral oximes, or cations,[126] so the result may be determined by the method used in oximation and by subsequent handling. The circumstances are clearly complicated, and a simple statement cannot be given.[127a] There are a number of empirical rules, however, such as that benzo-

[125a] W. D. Phillips, *Ann. N. Y. Acad. Sci.*, **70**, 817 (1958).

[125b] W. Z. Heldt and L. G. Donaruma, *Org. Reactions*, **11**, Chapt. 1 (1960).

[126] J. Meisenheimer and W. Theilacker in K. Freudenberg, ed., *Stereochemie*, Vol. III; Franz Deuticke, Leipzig, 1932.

[127] C. R. Hauser, J. W. LeMaistre, and A. E. Rainsford, *J. Am. Chem. Soc.*, **57**, 1056 (1935).

[127a] P. A. S. Smith and E. P. Antoniades, *Tetrahedron*, **9**, 210 (1960).

phenones free of ortho substituents usually give equal amounts of each possible benzanilide,[128] and that with aliphatic and alicyclic ketones, the group with the greater bulk close to the carbonyl group will migrate to nitrogen preferentially. Acetophenone derivatives are converted, seemingly invariably, to acetanilides as the major products. For further details, other works [125b,126] (where this subject is discussed comprehensively) should be consulted.

Many side reactions are possible, particularly when other functional groups are present, with the acid catalysts commonly used. Such reactions may occur before or after rearrangement. It is sometimes possible to reduce side reactions by separately preparing a suitable oxime ester and rearranging it in the absence of acid; fuller details are available elsewhere.[125b] In the other extreme, it is also possible to telescope the oximation and rearrangement steps into one by treating a ketone with hydroxylamine and polyphosphoric acid (eq. 64).[129]

$$Ar\!-\!CO\!-\!Ar + 2NH_2OH \xrightarrow[\text{heat}]{(HPO_3)_x} 2ArNH_2 + CO_2 \qquad (64)$$

In this form the process operationally somewhat resembles the Schmidt reaction (discussed further on), where disubstituted ureas are sometimes produced as minor products, but it actually appears to be a Beckmann rearrangement followed by a Lossen rearrangement. The use of polyphosphoric acid as a reagent for the rearrangement of oximes has recently been reviewed.[130]

The Neber reaction[131] has been mentioned previously in connection with the Beckmann rearrangement. Neber and co-workers treated a variety of toluenesulfonyl oximes having α-hydrogens with base (usually alcoholic alkali), and obtained α-amino ketones or derivatives. An analogous reaction has been observed with N-chloroketimines.[65] In only one case, that of 2,4-dinitrobenzyl methyl ketoxime, were they able to isolate the postulated intermediate azirine (eq. 65). The formation of such azirines is of particular significance with respect to the possibility of the existence of a bridged cation intermediate (31) in the Beckmann rearrangement.

[128] W. E. Bachmann and M. X. Barton, $J.$ $Org.$ $Chem.$, **3**, 300 (1938).

[129] H. R. Snyder, C. T. Elston, and D. B. Kellom, $J.$ $Am.$ $Chem.$ $Soc.$, **74**, 2014 (1953).

[130] F. Popp and W. E. McEwen, $Chem.$ $Revs.$, **58**, 370 (1958).

[131] P. W. Neber, A. Burgard, and W. Thier, $Ann.$, **526**, 277 (1936); T. A. Geissmann and A. Armen, $J.$ $Am.$ $Chem.$ $Soc.$, **77**, 1623 (1955).

Cram and Hatch [132] have confirmed the isolation of the azirine and devoted much effort to establishing its structure firmly. They also studied [133] the reaction from the standpoint of mechanism and confirmed that the product is not determined by the configuration of the oxime. They were able to isolate an intermediate that could be reduced with lithium aluminum hydride to an ethylenimine in useful yield and formulated the intermediates as 2-alkoxy-aziranes (38) derived by addition of a mole of solvent alcohol. They proposed a mechanism involving simultaneous removal of an α-hydrogen and tosylate (eq. 66). However, the lack of stereospecificity could also reasonably be

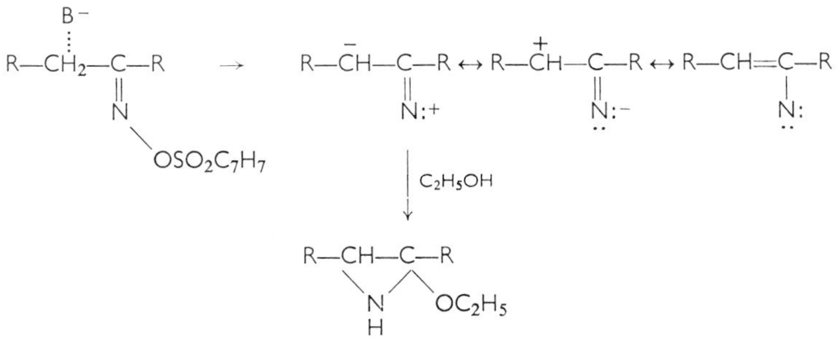

$$(66)$$

$$(38)$$

accounted for on the basis of base-catalyzed equilibration (eq. 67). The cyclization would then be a simple internal nucleophilic displacement, analogous to the formation of ethylene oxide from ethylenechlorohydrin.

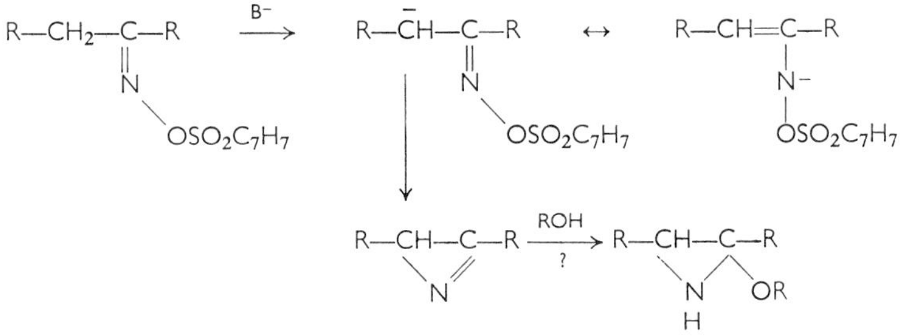

$$(67)$$

Occasional examples [134] of possibly base-catalyzed Beckmann rearrangement have been observed during reductions of oximes by lithium aluminum hydride (eq. 68); their actual nature is not clear at this time.

$$Ar-C-CH_3 \xrightarrow{\text{LiAlH}_4} (ArNHCOCH_3) \rightarrow Ar-NH-C_2H_5 \qquad (68)$$
$$\underset{\text{NOH}}{\|} \qquad\qquad\qquad ? \qquad\qquad 20\text{–}60\%$$

[132] D. J. Cram and M. J. Hatch, J. Am. Chem. Soc., **75**, 33 (1953).

[133] M. J. Hatch and D. J. Cram, J. Am. Chem. Soc., **75**, 38 (1953).

[134] (a) E. Larsson, Svensk Kem. Tidskr., **61**, 242 (1949); Chem. Abstr., **44**, 1898 (1950). (b) R. E. Lyle and H. J. Troscianiec, J. Org. Chem., **20**, 1757 (1955).

Nitrones (**39**), which are close relatives of oximes, also give amides on suitable treatment (eq. 69). The carbon skeleton is not rearranged, however, and

$$R—CH{=}N^+{—}R \rightarrow R—C—NH—R' \qquad (69)$$

$$\underset{O^-}{|} \qquad \underset{O}{\|}$$

(39)

the reaction appears to be a case of oxygen migration, unrelated to the Beckmann rearrangement.[135] The occasional case of ordinary Beckmann rearrangement of nitrones can be attributed to dealkylation or prior rearrangement to an oxime ether; derivatives of secondary amines are not formed.

N-Chloroketimines were at one time of interest as possible intermediates in the Beckmann rearrangement brought about by phosphorus pentachloride. They could not be prepared from oximes, but were eventually prepared in another way by Stieglitz,[136] who found that they would not rearrange under the conditions of the Beckmann rearrangement. Little attention has been paid to them since that time. It remained for Theilacker and Mohl[136a] to show that *N*-chloroketimines can after all be made to rearrange, but they required antimony pentachloride as catalyst. Presumably the catalyst functions by coordinating with the chlorine atom, converting it to a better leaving group (eq. 70). Phosphorus pentachloride is known to be a relatively poor

$$R_2C{=}N—Cl({+}SbCl_5) \rightarrow R—N{=}C—R \qquad (70)$$

$$\underset{Cl}{|}$$

coordinating group for a sixth chloride, owing to the crowding about the small phosphorus atom.

The question can still be asked why chloride ion should not function as a leaving group in the Beckmann rearrangement without a catalyst. It may be that there is simply a requirement for a sufficiently good solvating medium, for hydrogen chloride itself does not ionize in the absence of a suitable environment. At the time of Stieglitz's experiments, the powerful accelerating effect of polar solvents[136b] in the Beckmann rearrangement was not yet known, and only ether was used. Theilacker and Mohl were unable to achieve rearrangement of *N*-chloroketimines in refluxing chloroform.

The Schmidt Reaction. The acid-catalyzed reaction of hydrogen azide with ketones and aldehydes was discovered in 1923 by Karl Friedrich

[135] F. Kröhnke, *Ann.*, **604**, 203 (1957).

[136] J. Stieglitz and A. Stagner, *J. Am. Chem. Soc.*, **38**, 2056 (1916); J. Vosburgh, *J. Am. Chem. Soc.*, **38**, 2094 (1916).

[136a] W. Theilacker and H. Mohl, *Ann.*, **563**, 99 (1949).

[136b] (a) A. W. Chapman, *J. Chem. Soc. (London)*, **1935**, 1223; (b) A. W. Chapman and C. C. Howis, *J. Chem. Soc. (London)*, **1933**, 806; (c) A. W. Chapman, *J. Chem. Soc. (London)*, **1934**, 1550.

Schmidt [137] as a result of an investigation of the decomposition of HN_3. When he observed that aniline was produced when hydrogen azide was decomposed by sulfuric acid in the presence of benzene, he postulated that "imine radical," NH, was the species responsible. He introduced carbonyl compounds in an attempt to capture this intermediate; when he obtained amides (eq. 71),[138]

$$C_6H_5COC_6H_5 + HN_3 \xrightarrow{H_2SO_4} C_6H_5—NH—COC_6H_5 + N_2 \qquad (71)$$

he was convinced of the correctness of his hypothesis and apparently maintained this view throughout his career. Unfortunately, he chose not to publish more than his earliest discoveries, and most of his researches are recorded only in the patent literature.

Schmidt conceived of NH adding to a carbonyl group to form an intermediate that would either rearrange directly or would first isomerize to an oxime and undergo the Beckmann rearrangement.[139] It should have been obvious from Schmidt's own experiments that such a concept is untenable, for ketones were shown to react readily at $0°$, at which temperature hydrogen azide could be observed to be quite stable in sulfuric acid solution. It was also later pointed out [140,141] that oximes could not be intermediates, for the Beckmann rearrangement does not occur under the conditions where the Schmidt reaction takes place readily.

In 1925 Oliveri-Mandalá proposed [142] that the initial step was addition of hydrogen azide to the carbonyl group, producing an azidohydrin (or an oxatriazoline), which then rearranged to an amide with loss of nitrogen (eq. 72). With necessary modifications to account for the observed catalysis

$$R_2C{=}O + HN_3 \rightarrow R_2C\overset{\displaystyle OH}{\underset{\displaystyle N_3}{\diagup}} \rightarrow R—CO—NH—R + N_2 \qquad (72)$$

by acid and the formation of certain side products, this is essentially the path that is accepted today.

Although the principal products of the Schmidt reaction on ketones are amides, it is also possible to obtain nitriles from certain ketones and commonly from aldehydes (eq. 73). It is also possible to obtain tetrazoles and

$$R—CO—R' + HN_3 \xrightarrow{(H^+)} R'CN + (R^+) \qquad (73)$$

[137] K. F. Schmidt, *Z. angew. Chem.*, **36**, 511 (1923).

[138] K. F. Schmidt, *Ber.*, **57**, 704 (1924).

[139] K. F. Schmidt, *Ber.*, **58**, 2413 (1925).

[140] M. A. Spielman and F. L. Austin, *J. Am. Chem. Soc.*, **59**, 2658 (1937).

[141] L. H. Briggs and G. C. De Ath, *J. Chem. Soc. (London)*, **1937**, 456.

[142] E. Oliveri-Mandalá, *Gazz. chim. ital.*, **55 I**, 271 (1925).

ureas, both of which require two moles of hydrogen azide (eqs. 74 and 75).

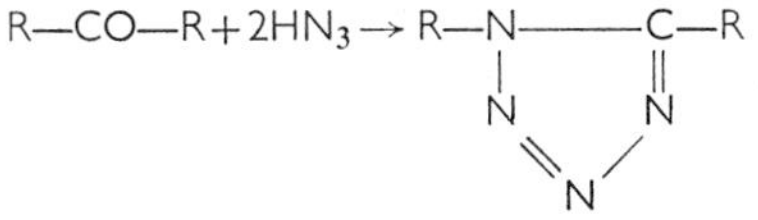

$$R\!-\!CO\!-\!R + 2HN_3 \rightarrow R\!-\!N\overline{}C\!-\!R \tag{74}$$

$$R\!-\!CO\!-\!R + 2HN_3 \rightarrow R\!-\!NH\!-\!CO\!-\!NH\!-\!R \tag{75}$$

When there is sufficient hydrogen azide, three moles may be consumed, producing aminotetrazoles (eq. 76). An important feature of these reactions is

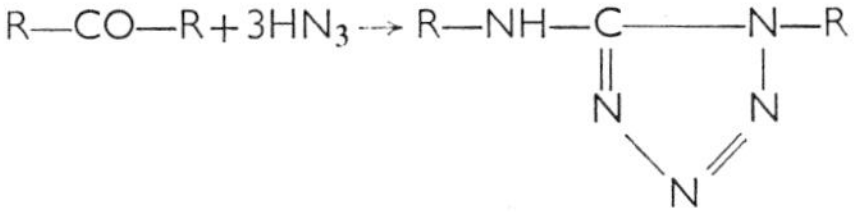

$$R\!-\!CO\!-\!R + 3HN_3 \rightarrow R\!-\!NH\!-\!C\overline{}N\!-\!R \tag{76}$$

that products derived from more than one mole of hydrogen azide cannot be obtained from those whose formation consumes less (with the exception of tetrazoles derived from nitriles). When the ketone is unsymmetrical, equations 72, 74, and 76 usually give rise to pairs of isomeric products, in proportions profoundly influenced by structure.

The Oliveri-Mandalá proposal has been successively elaborated [143–145] into a mechanism [146,147] in modern terms, which achieved expression in two

$$R_2C\!=\!O + HA \rightarrow R_2C\!=\!\overset{+}{O}H + A^-$$

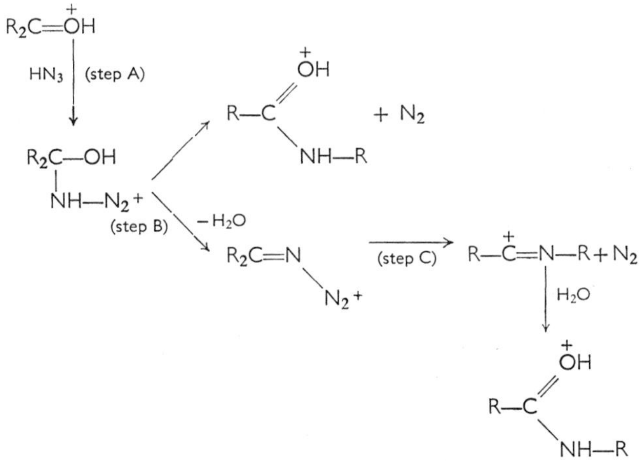

$$R\!-\!C\overset{\overset{+}{O}H}{\diagdown}_{NH\!-\!R} + N_2 \tag{77}$$

$$R_2C\!=\!N\underset{N_2^+}{\diagdown} \xrightarrow[\text{(step C)}]{} R\!-\!\overset{+}{C}\!=\!N\!-\!R + N_2 \tag{78}$$

$$R\!-\!C\overset{\overset{+}{O}H}{\diagdown}_{NH\!-\!R}$$

[143] C. D. Hurd in H. Gilman, ed., *Organic Chemistry*, Wiley, New York, 1938, Vol. I, 1st edition, p. 699.

[144] L. H. Briggs and J. W. Lyttleton, *J. Chem. Soc. (London)*, **1943**, 421.

[145] J. K. Sanford, F. T. Blair, J. Arroya, and K. W. Sherk, *J. Am. Chem. Soc.*, **67**, 1941 (1945).

slightly differing forms (eqs. 77 [146] and 78 [147]). Each assumes that the initial step is addition of hydrogen azide to the protonated carbonyl group.

The interposition of the dehydration step (B) in equation 78 was prompted by the necessity for an intermediate that could account for the formation of tetrazoles when hydrogen azide is used in excess, and to account for the parallel between the ratios of isomeric amides produced from unsymmetrical ketones by the Schmidt reaction and by oximation plus Beckmann rearrangement.

Amides, once formed, do not react with hydrogen azide, so the tetrazoles obtained must arise at an intermediate stage. The addition of a molecule of hydrogen azide to an iminocarbonium ion (eq. 79) would yield an imidyl

$$R-\overset{+}{C}=N-R + HN_3 \rightarrow R-\underset{\underset{\underset{N_2^+}{\diagdown}}{\overset{|}{HN}}}{C}=N-R \rightarrow R-\underset{\underset{\underset{N}{\diagdown\diagup}}{\overset{|}{N}}}{\overset{\|}{C}}\text{------}\underset{\overset{|}{N}}{N}-R + (H^+) \qquad (79)$$

azide, which should cyclize to a tetrazole according to the general experience that tetrazoles are formed when imidyl azides are prepared in other ways. [148] When other nucleophiles, such as alcohols, are present, they, too, may add to the iminocarbonium ion, forming imidyl esters (eq. 80), and such products are indeed formed when Schmidt reactions are carried out in alcohol solution. [149]

$$R_2C{=}O + HN_3 \xrightarrow{H_2SO_4} [R-\overset{+}{C}{=}N-R] \xrightarrow{ROH} R-\underset{\overset{|}{OR}}{\overset{+}{C}}{=}NH-R \qquad (80)$$

Equation 78 implies the possibility of geometrical isomerism of the intermediate iminodiazonium ion determining the products if *trans* migration applies in the Schmidt reaction as it does in the Beckmann rearrangement (eq. 81). The importance of geometrical isomerism as compared with elec-

$$R-\underset{\underset{N-N_2^+}{\overset{\|}{}}}{C}-R' \rightarrow R-N{=}\overset{+}{C}-R' \qquad\qquad R-\underset{\underset{^+N_2-N}{\overset{\|}{}}}{C}-R' \rightarrow R-\overset{+}{C}{=}N-R' \qquad (81)$$

tronically determined migration aptitudes was demonstrated by Smith and Horwitz. [150] From a group of para-substituted benzophenones, mixtures of isomeric benzanilides were obtained in which the ratios were very close to

[146] M. S. Newman and H. Gildenhorn, *J. Am. Chem. Soc.*, **70**, 317 (1948).

[147] P. A. S. Smith, *J. Am. Chem. Soc.*, **70**, 320 (1948).

[148] F. R. Benson, *Chem. Revs.*, **41**, 1 (1947); J. H. Boyer and F. C. Canter, *Chem. Revs.*, **54**, 1 (1954).

[149] K. F. Schmidt and P. Zutavern, U. S. Pat. 1,889,323; *Chem. Abstr.*, **27**, 1361 (1933).

[150] P. A. S. Smith and J. P. Horwitz, *J. Am. Chem. Soc.*, **72**, 3718 (1950).

1:1, regardless of whether the substituent was phenyl, methyl, chloro, or nitro (eq. 82); p-methoxybenzophenone showed a small preference for forming

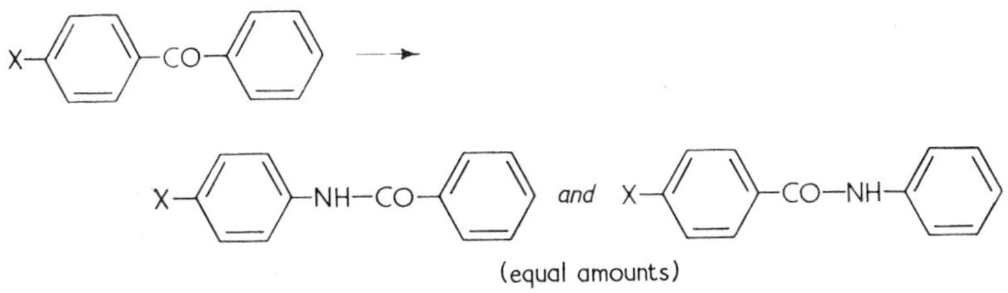

benzanisidide, but p-chloro-p'-methoxy- and p-nitro-p'-methoxybenzophenones gave 1:1 mixtures like the others.[151] These ratios are very much the same as those obtained by Bachmann and Barton[128] from the Beckmann rearrangement of the equilibrated oximes.

Effects attributable to steric influence on the relative stabilities of the geometrically isomeric iminodiazonium ions were observed[150] in the series of phenyl alkyl ketones with R = methyl, ethyl, isopropyl, and *tert*-butyl (eq. 83).

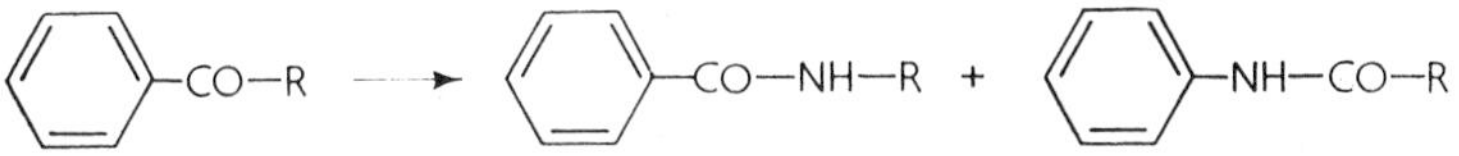

The first (R=CH$_3$) gives acetanilide and N-methylbenzamide in a ratio of 95:5; the second (R=C$_2$H$_5$) gives propionanilide and N-ethylbenzamide in a ratio of 85:15, and the third (R=(CH$_3$)$_2$CH) gives isobutyranilide and N-isopropylbenzamide in nearly equal amounts, 51:49. Pivalophenone (R=(CH$_3$)$_3$C) undergoes fragmentation analogous to the Beckmann fragmentation, a phenomenon that will be discussed separately; however, no products deriving from phenyl migration are formed. These ratios are consistent with the concept that the intermediate prefers a configuration in which steric interference with the diazo nitrogens is smallest, but, as we shall see presently, the same result might be obtained if migration aptitudes should determine the products.[151a] Many more unsymmetrical ketones have been subjected to the Schmidt reaction, but before attempting to correlate the results, we should examine the mechanism in more detail.

In equation 78, the rate-determining step for the release of nitrogen might reasonably be the addition of HN$_3$ (step A), the dehydration of the azidohydrin (step B), or the rearrangement step (C). With any of them, the position of equilibrium of the initial protonation of the carbonyl group could affect the rate, so that one might expect (HN$_3$), (R$_2$CO), and (H$^+$) or the

[151] P. A. S. Smith and B. Ashby, *J. Am. Chem. Soc.*, **72**, 2503 (1950).

[151a] P. A. S. Smith and E. P. Antoniades, *Tetrahedron*, **9**, 210 (1960).

acidity function, h_0, to appear in the rate expression. In addition, the nature of the dehydration step, which may be unimolecular as written or, more probably, may involve solvent and/or more of the acid catalyst, is uncertain.

There is a broad qualitative observation [147] that aliphatic ketones react more readily than alkyl aryl ketones, which in turn react more readily than benzophenones. This is in the same order as the basicity of the carbonyl groups [152] and is also the order of ease of oxime or hydrazone formation.[153] This effect is great enough that as a practical matter it is often convenient to carry out Schmidt reactions on aliphatic ketones in concentrated hydrochloric acid, in which aryl ketones are inert.[147] Molten trichloroacetic acid will usually catalyze the reaction of aryl alkyl ketones, but sulfuric acid is required for benzophenones.[147] It can be demonstrated in some cases that Schmidt reaction only becomes noticeable when the acidity reaches such a level as to produce a visible concentration of colored oxonium ions,[154] but this does not prove that they are involved. There is also the qualitative observation that sterically hindered ketones, such as tertiary alkyl ketones and ortho-substituted benzophenones, are sluggish compared to the analogous unhindered ketones and may be inert altogether. Although these observations point out factors important in determining the rate, they do not of themselves identify the rate-determining step.

The only step that can be assumed to be irreversible is step C, so we should write equation 78 as a series of equilibria. By analogy with oximation, which has been shown [155] to take place by similar steps of addition and dehydration, step B is probably slow and may be rate determining. The position of the

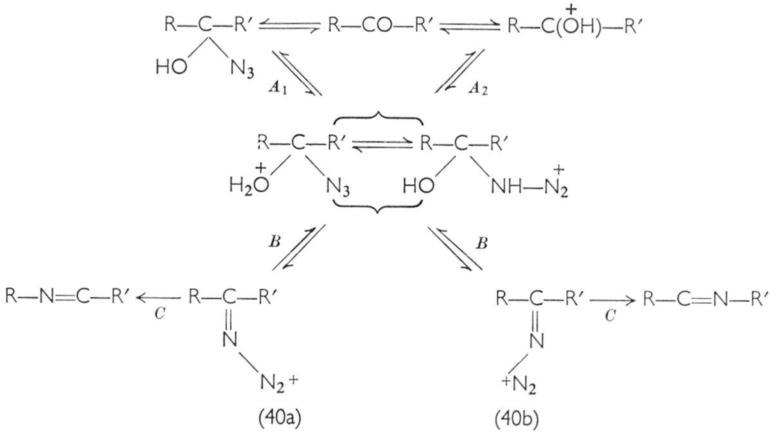

(40a)   (40b)

[152] W. Gordy and S. C. Sanford, *J. Chem. Phys.*, **8**, 170 (1940).

[153] F. P. Price, Jr., and L. P. Hammett, *J. Am. Chem. Soc.*, **63**, 2387 (1941).

[154] J. R. Dice and P. A. S. Smith, *J. Org. Chem.*, **14**, 179 (1949).

[155] W. P. Jencks, *J. Am. Chem. Soc.*, **81**, 475 (1959).

equilibria of protonation and azide addition (step A_1 or A_2) will vary with structure and with acidity; the concentrations of the species supplied by A_1 or A_2 will obviously affect the rate of step B if it is slower. The reversal of step B provides a path for equilibration between the geometrical isomers **40a** and **40b**. If rearrangement (step C) is faster than this equilibration, then the relative populations of **40a** and **40b** will determine the product ratios. The populations of **40a** and **40b** are determined by the relative rates of the two paths for step B, so correlations of product ratios with steric effects must be considered in terms of the transition state for step B. In other words, the ratio would be kinetically controlled. Since the product ratios from the Schmidt reaction have a strong resemblance to configuration ratios obtained by oximation under equilibrating conditions,[150a] which are thus thermodynamically controlled, it may not be unreasonable to assume that the transition states for step B sufficiently resemble the products, **40a** and **40b**, that we can approximate steric influences in the transition states by considering the effects in these products. Such an approximation may not always be valid, however, and occasional differences would be expected between Schmidt product ratios and oxime ratios.

On this basis, the independence of the nature of para substituents shown by the product ratios from benzophenones can be accounted for, since there is essentially no steric difference in the neighborhood of the reaction center. But let us consider the opposite possibility, that step C is slower than B, and thus rate determining. Equilibration between **40a** and **40b** would then be achieved continually while rearrangement is going on, so that the product ratios would be determined by the relative rates of rearrangement (step C); that is, migration aptitudes would govern the product ratios. Although the experiments with benzophenones show that this circumstance does not occur for the compounds studied, it may nevertheless be true for other ketones or other conditions. It is reasonable to expect that the relative intrinsic migration rates (migration aptitudes) measured in the Beckmann rearrangement should be paralleled in the Schmidt reaction. Since alkyl migration has been found to be slower than aryl,[155a] step C could be expected to be slower with aliphatic ketones, and effects traceable to migration aptitudes would be more likely to be found. The ratios in the products can be calculated to be dependent on the extent of reaction when the two paths for dehydration have different rates, and to have the limiting ratios k_{Ba}/k_{Bb} at $t = \infty$ and $k_{Ba}k_{Ca}/k_{Bb}k_{Cb}$ at $t = 0$, where the k's are the rate constants for steps B and C.[150a]

Evidence for such an effect has been obtained in the form of an isotope effect[156] in the Schmidt reaction of acetone-1-^{14}C. The ^{14}C-methyl group

[155a] R. Huisgen, J. Witte, and I. Ugi, *Chem. Ber.*, **90**, 1844 (1957).

[156] G. A. Ropp, W. A. Bonner, M. T. Clark, and V. F. Raaen, *J. Am. Chem. Soc.*, **76**, 1710 (1954).

migrates more slowly than the ^{12}C-methyl; not only is the ratio $^{14}CH_3NH_2/$ $^{14}CH_3COOH$ from the hydrolyzed products smaller than 1, but the unlabeled acetone present is converted to amide faster than the acetone-1-^{14}C. These results suggest that the product ratios from aliphatic ketones may be determined largely by migration aptitudes. Since the order of intrinsic rates of migration in the pinacol rearrangement,[156a] $CH_3 < C_2H_5 < (CH_3)_2CH < (CH_3)_3C$, is the same as the order of increasing bulk, the empirical rule applies that the group with the largest bulk in the neighborhood of the carbonyl group will migrate preferentially, regardless of the effect determining it, for saturated open chain alkyl groups. It also applies for many alicyclic ketones.

Some 2-substituted cyclohexanones and cyclopentanones were submitted to both the Schmidt reaction and oximation plus Beckmann rearrangement by Schechter and Kirk (eq. 84).[157] They found that the substituted side of the

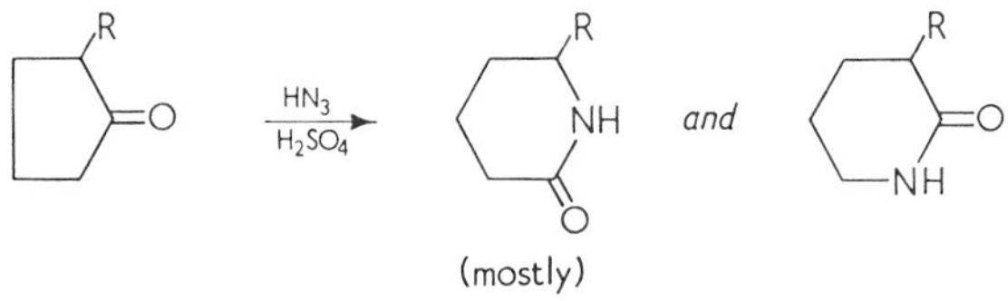

(mostly)

$$(84)$$

rings showed a strong preference for migration to nitrogen, although with 2-chlorocyclohexanone at least 23% of the product results from migration of the unsubstituted side. Similar observations have been made by others for both cyclic and open chain ketones.[158] However, norcamphor (eq. 85) and

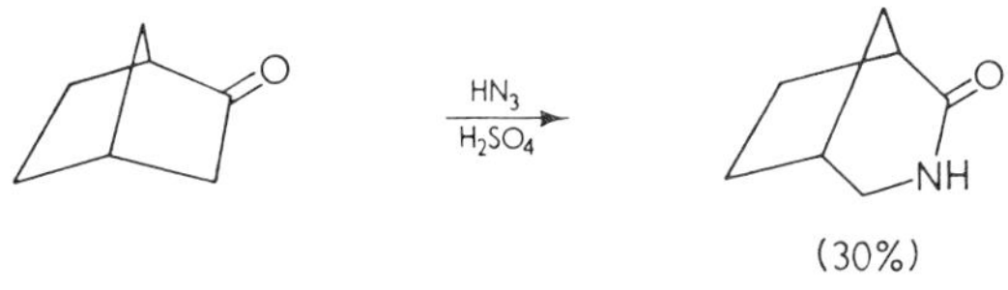

(30%)

$$(85)$$

cyclopentanonorcamphor[159] have given lactams resulting from migration of the unsubstituted side, although the significance of these results is limited by the low material balances.

A curious effect is found in the isomer ratios from a series of phenylalkyl methyl ketones, $C_6H_5(CH_2)_nCOCH_3$. The ratios show a damped alternation with increasing chain length. Acetophenone ($n=0$) gives a migration ratio $C_6H_5/CH_3 = 95:5$[147] phenylacetone[147] ($n=1$) gives a ratio $C_6H_5CH_2/CH_3 = 1:1$, benzylacetone[144] ($n=2$) gives a ratio $C_6H_5(CH_2)_2/CH_3 = 95:5$, and

[156a] R. M. Stiles and R. P. Mayer, *J. Am. Chem. Soc.*, **81**, 1497 (1959).

[157] H. Schechter and J. C. Kirk, *J. Am. Chem. Soc.*, **73**, 3087 (1951).

[158] R. Fusco and S. Rossi, *Gazz. chim. ital.*, **81**, 511 (1951); R. T. Conley, *Chem. & Ind.* (*London*), **1958**, 438.

[159] R. C. Elderfield and E. T. Losin, *J. Org. Chem.*, **26**, 1703 (1961).

5-phenyl-2-pentanone $(n=3)$ gives a ratio $C_6H_5(CH_2)_3/CH_3 = 80:20$; the members with $n=4$ and 5 appear to continue this behavior in decreasing magnitude.[159a] It is easier to account for these results on steric grounds than by electronic effects, but the cause is uncertain.

Although the methyl group migrates to a smaller extent than other alkyl groups, unsaturation may reverse this result, as shown by benzalacetone. It has been found [150,160] to give N-methylcinnamamide in 75% yield as the only product (eq. 86). The presence of a methyl group on the styryl group returns the behavior to the usual; the product presumed to be formed first, N-(1-methyl-2-phenylvinyl)acetamide, is apparently hydrolyzed to phenylacetone in the reaction mixture and is acted on further by hydrogen azide (eq. 87).

$$C_6H_5CH{=}CHCOCH_3 \rightarrow C_6H_5CH{=}CHCO{-}NH{-}CH_3 \tag{86}$$

$$\underset{\overset{|}{CH_3}}{C_6H_5CH{=}C}{-}COCH_3 \rightarrow \underset{\overset{|}{CH_3}}{C_6H_5CH{=}C}{-}NHCOCH_3 \xrightarrow{H_2O}$$

$$\underset{\overset{|}{CH_3}}{C_6H_5CH_2C}{=}O \rightarrow C_6H_5CH_2NHCOCH_3 + C_6H_5CH_2CONHCH_3 \tag{87}$$

It is still ambiguous which factors are operating to determine these results, but there is reason to suspect that the styryl group may have a low migration aptitude. Cyclopropyl groups, which have some similarity to vinyl groups, have also shown a depressed tendency to migrate in some ketones, and a low migration aptitude for cyclopropyl relative to n-butyl has been demonstrated in tertiary carbinyl azide rearrangement.[161]

It seems reasonable to conclude from the foregoing results that one may encounter the influence of both migration aptitudes and steric effects; in other words, the rate-determining step may be step B, or step C, or even step A, depending on the structure of the ketone and the reaction conditions. Some kinetic observations are available, but they do not unambiguously separate the possibilities and are consistent with a variable rate-determining step.

The rate expression $d(N_2)/dt = kh_0(HN_3)$ (ketone) has been obtained for both cyclohexanone in either sulfuric or hydrochloric acid and for acetophenone in sulfuric acid.[162] There appeared to be some acceleration in non-aqueous solvents relative to water.

[159a] P. A. S. Smith, unpublished observations.

[160] L. H. Briggs, G. C. De Ath, and S. R. Ellis, *J. Chem. Soc. (London)*, **1942**, 61.

[161] S. C. Bunce and J. B. Cloke, *J. Am. Chem. Soc.*, **76**, 2244 (1954); G. H. Potter and S. C. Bunce, Abstracts of Papers, Div. of Org. Chem., Am. Chem. Soc., Nat. Meeting, Chicago, Ill., Sept., 1958.

[162] D. M. Howell, doctoral thesis, University of Michigan, 1952.

Diisopropyl ketone showed almost the same rate constant as cyclohexanone, but that of acetophenone was lower by a factor of 20. This would be an expected consequence of the lower basicity of acetophenone (step A_2), or presumably, of its neutral azidohydrin (step A_1), as well as of a probably decreased rate of the addition reaction and a lower equilibrium concentration of neutral or protonated azidohydrin. Addition to the carbonyl group destroys conjugation with the benzene ring, whereas dehydration to the iminodiazonium ion restores it, and the situation is analogous to other carbonyl addition reactions [163,163a] and shares their complexities and ambiguities.

A rate law first order in ketone and in hydrogen azide at constant acidity has also been reported by Fishel, Newman, and Jensen,[163b] who worked with a series of substituted acetophenones. The relative rates of meta- and para-substituted derivatives did not correspond to simple migration aptitude affects, and some ortho substituents (—OH, —CH$_3$, —OCH$_3$) retarded the reaction, while others (—NO$_2$, —halogen) accelerated it. Activation enthalpies (8.26 to 25.0 kcal./mole) were mostly quite low compared to those that have been reported for azide decompositions and for other C—to—N rearrangements; activation entropies (-1.80 to -41.6) were mostly of large magnitude. The over-all kinetic picture indicates that some step other than the actual rearrangement is rate-determining.

The only other kinetic experiments so far reported are those of Bak.[164] They are concerned only with the diketones phenanthraquinone and retene quinone in sulfuric acid. These are more complex systems, since both mono- and diprotonated species may be reacting, and the eventual products, phenanthridones, are the result of several steps. Bak attempted to isolate the first stage by examining initial rates and found it to be first order in (HN$_3$) and (ketone), with a constant that *decreased* with increasing acidity in the range studied.

Secondary Reactions. The descriptive chemistry of the Schmidt reaction presented so far has been selected only to outline the major features of the mechanism. Before considering more of the many new applications since the publication of Wolff's comprehensive review,[164a] let us consider the major side reactions from the standpoint of mechanism.

Since a concurrent reaction, which may be the actual first step, is proto-

[163] C. K. Ingold, *Structure and Mechanism in Organic Chemistry*, Cornell Univ. Press, Ithaca, N. Y., 1953, pp. 676 *et seq.*

[163a] J. Hine, *Physical Organic Chemistry*, McGraw-Hill, New York, 1956.

[163b] D. L. Fishel, R. H. Newman, and N. Jensen, Abstracts of Papers, Div. of Org. Chem., Am. Chem. Soc. National Meeting, Chicago, September, 1961, p. 90 Q.

[164] T. A. Bak, *Acta Chem. Scand.*, 8, 1733 (1954).

[164a] H. Wolff, *Org. Reactions*, 3, Chapt. 8 (1946).

nation of the carbonyl group, certain side reactions can be looked for at this point. Some ketones containing tertiary alkyl groups undergo carbon-skeleton rearrangement under the usual conditions of the Schmidt reaction. Zook and Paviak [165] have found that such ketones recovered from incomplete Schmidt reactions are partially isomerized, although their Schmidt reaction products did not show appreciable contamination from this source. Another reaction to which protonated ketones are susceptible is condensation with aromatic rings. Self-condensation of simple benzophenones has not been observed under Schmidt reaction conditions, and would not be expected, owing to the deactivating effect of the carbonyl group on the rings. On the other hand, two o-(phenylthio)benzophenones have been found to cyclize to thiaxanthols, which only then react with hydrogen azide, forming acid-stable thiaxanthyl azides [165a] (eq. 88). In addition to these examples, tar formation, apparently

$$\text{(88)}$$

a result of aldol condensation, is sometimes encountered with aliphatic ketones. This may be minimized by using the weakest acidity that will still promote the Schmidt reaction; concentrated hydrochloric acid [165b] is often useful in such cases. Sulfonation can be avoided by using alkanesulfonic or trihaloacetic acids instead of sulfuric.

Side reactions directly attributable to the azidohydrin stage have not been unequivocally identified, but an important side reaction derives from the following stage, the iminodiazonium ion. This is fragmentation, producing a nitrile and another product arising from the ejected cation (eq. 73). Analogously to the Beckmann fragmentation, it appears to be possible whenever one of the groups attached to the carbonyl group has uncommon stability as a cation. It has been observed unequivocally with tert-butyl ketones such as pinacolone [165] and pivalophenone [150] and may occur with α-diketones,[164,166] although from the last only amides, not nitriles, have been isolated. When benzene or toluene is used as a solvent for Schmidt reactions on tert-alkyl

[165] H. D. Zook and S. C. Paviak, J. Am. Chem. Soc., 77, 2501 (1955).

[165a] R. H. B. Galt, J. D. Loudon, and A. D. B. Sloan, J. Chem. Soc. (London), 1958, 1588.

[165b] P. A. S. Smith, J. Am. Chem. Soc., 70, 320 (1948).

[166] G. M. Badger and J. H. Seidler, J. Chem. Soc. (London), 1954, 2329.

ketones, the ejected group alkylates the benzene ring (eq. 89).[165] Norcamphor appears to provide another example.[160]

$$CH_3\!\!-\!\!CO\!\!-\!\!C(CH_3)_3 \xrightarrow[H_2SO_4]{HN_3} CH_3\!\!-\!\!\underset{\underset{+N_2}{\overset{\|}{N}}}{C}\!\!-\!\!C(CH_3)_3 \longrightarrow CH_3\!\!-\!\!C\!\equiv\!N + \overset{+}{C}(CH_3)_3 + N_2$$

$$\xrightarrow{C_6H_6}$$

$$C_6H_5C(CH_3)_3 \quad and \quad (CH_3)_3C\!\!-\!\!\underset{}{\bigcirc}\!\!-\!\!C(CH_3)_3 \tag{89}$$

Aldehydes all undergo fragmentation to nitriles, although small to moderate amounts of formamides may be formed as well (eq. 90). The ratio of nitrile to

$$R\!\!-\!\!CHO + HN_3 \rightarrow \underset{(mostly)}{R\!\!-\!\!C\!\equiv\!N} \quad and \quad R\!\!-\!\!NH\!\!-\!\!CHO \tag{90}$$

formamide has been shown to vary with the acidity;[168] higher acidity favors formamide formation. This effect can be accounted for[168a] if the reasonable assumption is made that loss of the proton in the fragmentation step is sensitive to the availability of base. Under the conditions of the experiments, the effective base is bisulfate ion (from the reaction $NaN_3 + H_2SO_4 \rightarrow HN_3 + NaHSO_4$), and would be in much higher concentration at low ratios of acid to aldehyde (eq. 91). Fragmentation is very possibly a case of *cis* elimination

$$R\!\!-\!\!\overset{+}{N}\!\!=\!\!CH \leftarrow R\!\!-\!\!\underset{\underset{N_2^+}{\overset{\|}{N}}}{C}\!\!-\!\!H \xrightarrow{HSO_4^-} R\!\!-\!\!C\!\equiv\!N + N_2 + H_2SO_4 \tag{91}$$

$$\downarrow$$

$$R\!\!-\!\!NH\!\!-\!\!CHO$$

in these reactions, if the iminodiazonium ions show the same configuration preference (*syn*-H) as aldoximes and similar slowness of interconversion. *Cis* elimination would certainly be expected to be more difficult than *trans* elimination, but the combination of an excellent leaving group (N_2) and a positive charge to increase the acidity of the hydrogen could be expected to make *cis* elimination competitive with rearrangement at low acidities. However, anisaldehyde shows no more than traces of rearrangement even at high acidities. Since both the *syn*-H and *anti*-H isomers of anisaldoxime undergo Beckmann fragmentation to the exclusion of rearrangement, it is probable that interconversion of configuration is unusually rapid, and the faster process of *trans* elimination can thus compete in the Schmidt reaction of anisaldehyde.

[167] G. Caronna, *Gazz. chim. ital.*, **80**, 211 (1950).

[168] W. E. McEwen, W. E. Conrad, and C. A. VanderWerf, *J. Am. Chem. Soc.*, **74**, 1168 (1952).

[168a] P. A. S. Smith and E. P. Antoniades, *Tetrahedron*, **9**, 210 (1960).

Side reactions arising at the iminocarbonium stage ($R—N{=}\overset{+}{C}—R$) have been mentioned earlier. The most important is the reaction with more hydrogen azide, giving rise to tetrazoles (eq. 79). Since hydrogen azide must compete against water for the iminocarbonium ion, tetrazole formation is favored by excess hydrogen azide and low water (therefore high acid) concentrations. An illustrative example is that of benzosuberone; when reaction is carried out by adding sulfuric acid to a solution containing ketone and pre-formed hydrogen azide, mostly tetrazole and very little lactam are formed,[169] but when sodium azide is added in small portions to a mixture of ketone and trichloracetic acid, the lactam is formed in 82% yield[170] (eq. 92). When

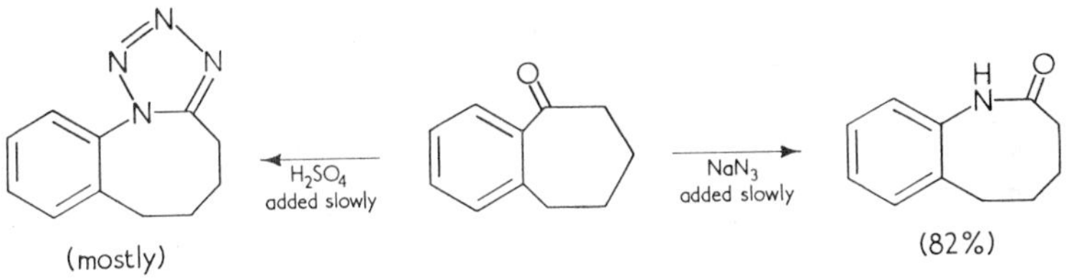

(mostly) $\xleftarrow{\substack{H_2SO_4 \\ \text{added slowly}}}$ $\xrightarrow{\substack{NaN_3 \\ \text{added slowly}}}$ (82%)   (92)

aqueous acid can be used, such as concentrated hydrochloric acid, tetrazole formation is easily avoided.[165b] On the other hand, tetrazole formation can be promoted so as to become the major reaction by use of excess hydrogen azide, appropriate order of addition of reagents, and concentrated sulfuric acid, although amide is still a significant product,[171] and by aprotic acids, such as anhydrous ferric,[172] aluminum,[173] and stannic[174] chlorides. This has been proposed as a convenient method for converting cyclohexanone to the heart stimulant metrazole (eq. 93).[172]

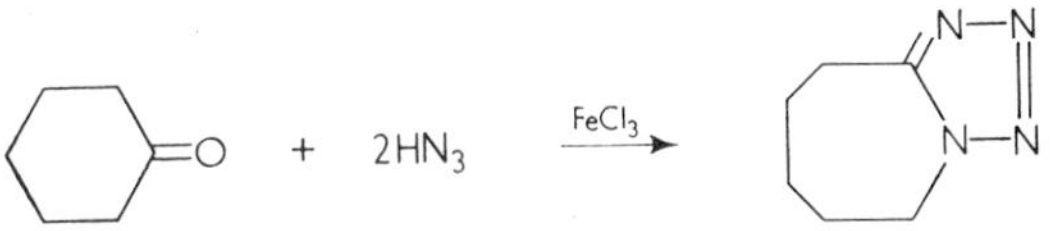

$$\text{(cyclohexanone)}{=}O \ + \ 2HN_3 \ \xrightarrow{FeCl_3} \ \text{(product)} \qquad (93)$$

Combination of the iminocarbonium ion with hydrogen azide may lead to ureas as the final products instead of tetrazoles. This is the result of rearrangement of the protonated imidyl azide before it cyclizes, thus leading through

[169] R. Huisgen, *Ann.*, **574**, 171 (1951).

[170] P. A. S. Smith and W. L. Berry, *J. Org. Chem.*, **26**, 27 (1961).

[171] E. K. Harvill, R. M. Herbst, E. C. Schreiner, and C. W. Roberts, *J. Org. Chem.*, **15**, 662 (1950).

[172] N. B. Chapman, H. McCombie, and B. C. Saunders, *J. Chem. Soc.* (*London*), **1945**, 929.

[173] P. A. S. Smith, *J. Am. Chem. Soc.*, **76**, 436 (1954).

[174] K. F. Schmidt, *Friedländer, Fortschr. in der Teerfarb. und Verwand. Ind.*, **21 I**, 675 (1937).

the stage of the conjugate acid of a carbodiimide (eq. 94).[173] Tetrazoles themselves do not give ureas under Schmidt reaction conditions, although

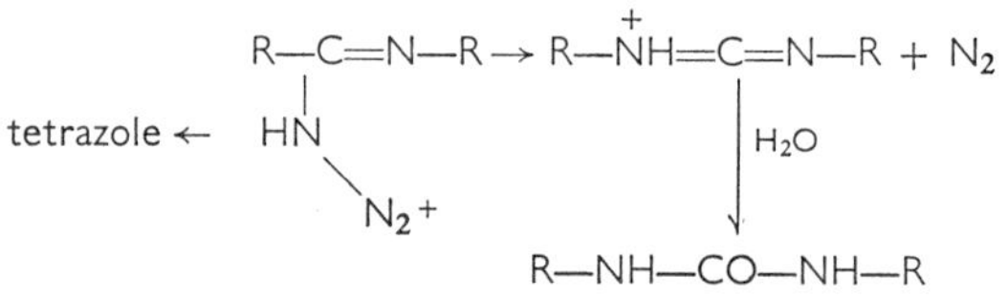

$$R-C{\equiv}N-R \rightarrow R-\overset{+}{N}H{=}C{=}N-R + N_2 \qquad (94)$$

$$\text{tetrazole} \leftarrow \quad HN \qquad\qquad \downarrow H_2O$$

$$\underset{N_2{}^+}{\diagdown}$$

$$R-NH-CO-NH-R$$

they can be made to follow such a path at much higher temperatures;[173] such reactions, which are related to the Curtius rearrangement and the Schmidt reaction with carboxylic acids, will be discussed under heading 2C. Formation of ureas during Schmidt reactions is not common, and has never been observed as more than a minor reaction. It has been encountered principally with ortho-substituted benzophenones.[173]

The formation of protonated carbodiimide species during a Schmidt reaction can lead to aminotetrazoles if they should react with still more hydrogen azide rather than water (eq. 95). Such a product has been reported only from benzophenone.[175]

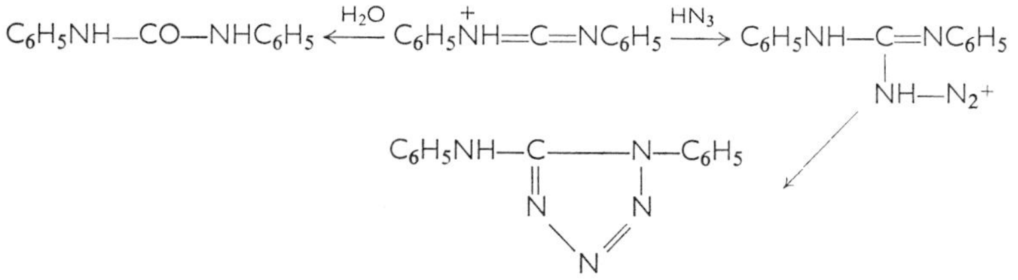

$$C_6H_5NH-CO-NHC_6H_5 \xleftarrow{\ H_2O\ } C_6H_5\overset{+}{N}H{=}C{=}NC_6H_5 \xrightarrow{\ HN_3\ } C_6H_5NH-C{=}NC_6H_5$$

$$\underset{NH-N_2{}^+}{\big|}$$

$$C_6H_5NH-\underset{\underset{N}{\diagup\diagdown}}{\overset{\overset{\displaystyle N}{\|}}{C}} \underset{N}{\diagup\diagup} N-C_6H_5 \qquad (95)$$

The iminocarbonium ion intermediate may combine with alcohol if that is used as the solvent, giving rise to salts of imido esters.[175a] Since these compounds are readily alcoholized in the presence of acid, the substances actually isolated are likely to be esters or ortho esters and amines (eq. 96).[175b]

$$R-N{\overset{+}{\equiv}}C-R \xrightarrow{\ C_2H_5OH\ } R-\overset{+}{N}H{=}C-R \xrightarrow{\ C_2H_5OH\ } R-\overset{+}{N}H_3 + (C_2H_5O)_3C-R \qquad (96)$$

$$\underset{OC_2H_5}{\big|}$$

The iminocarbonium ion should in principle be capable of electrophilic attack on suitably active benzene rings. Although no examples of an intermolecular reaction of this sort has yet been reported, an example of cycliza-

[175] K. F. Schmidt, *Friedländer, Fortschr. in der Teerfarb. und Verwand. Ind.*, **15**, 333 (1930).

[175a] K. F. Schmidt and P. Zutavern, U. S. Pat. 1,889,323; *Chem. Abstr.*, **27**, 1361 (1933).

[175b] P.A. S. Smith, unpublished observations.

tion is given by *o*-phenylbenzophenone, which is converted to 9-phenyl-phenanthridine in high yield[176] (eq. 97). As formulated here, this process

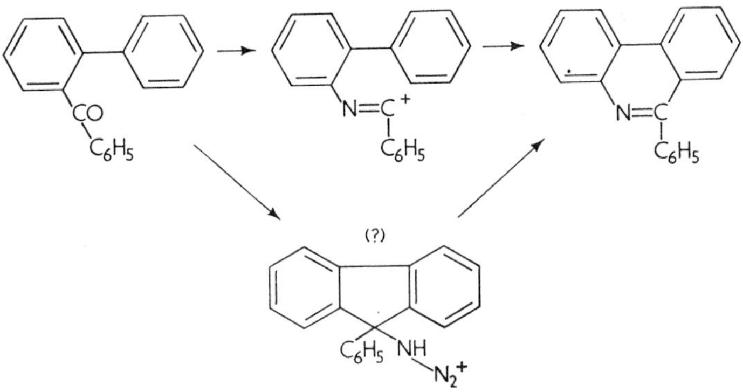

(97)

closely resembles the Bischler-Napieralsky isoquinoline synthesis,[177] but there is good reason to believe that it is actually a side reaction arising at the oxonium ion stage through conversion to 9-phenyl-9-fluorenyl azide (cf. discussion of ortho-substituted benzophenones later). β-Benzyllevulinic acid provides another example;[178] it has been reported to be converted to a quinoline derivative, although an isoquinoline would be more likely. Cyclization to enolic oxygen occurs in the Schmidt reaction with acetylacetone and benzoylacetone, which give oxazoles (eq. 98).[179]

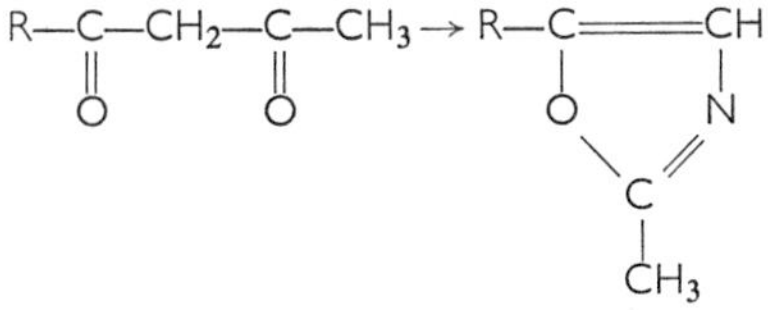

(98)

Aliphatic and Alicyclic Ketones. In general, aliphatic and alicyclic carbonyl groups react sufficiently more easily than those of alkyl aryl and diaryl ketones and carboxyl and ester groups that Schmidt reactions can be carried out selectively in the presence of less reactive carbonyl groups in the same molecule or in mixtures with other carbonyl compounds. Reactivity is also higher than most alcohols, and Pritzkow and Schuberth have shown that it is possible at 0° to achieve complete reaction of heptanones in the presence of mixtures of heptanols.[179] They also showed that it is possible to use acetic acid as the solvent for such reactions, with which it does not compete at

[176] P. A. S. Smith, *J. Am. Chem. Soc.*, **76**, 431 (1954).

[177] W. M. Whaley and T. R. Govindachari, *Org. Reactions*, **6**, Chapt. 2 (1951).

[178] L. Birkofer and I. Storch, *Ber.*, **86**, 749 (1953).

[179] W. Pritzkow and A. Schuberth, *Chem. Ber.*, **93**, 1725 (1960).

temperatures below 40°. They adapted such techniques for analysis of complex mixtures by hydrolyzing the amides produced to amines, which were then determined by paper chromatography.

Preference for reaction of a dialkyl rather than an aryl alkyl carbonyl group has been demonstrated with benzoylacetone.[179a] Reaction of aliphatic carbonyl groups in molecules containing carboxyl, ester, or lactone groups is not uncommon. The usual empirical rule applies regarding the direction of migration, and mixtures are produced; however, when the carbonyl bears a methyl group, the amount of methyl migration is usually small, and acetamide derivatives are the major products, making the reaction of preparative value. Ethyl pinonate, homoterpenyl methyl ketone,[180] and a series of ethyl x-ketocaproates[181] provide examples. When acetoacetic esters are used, α-amino acids are produced[182] (eq. 99), and β-alanines are formed from levulinic acids.[178]

$$CH_3CO—CHR—COOEt \rightarrow CH_3CO—NH—CHR—COOEt \rightarrow H_2N—CHR—COOH \quad (99)$$

Cyclic ketones of varying sizes are expanded readily to lactams.[183] When the cyclic ketone also holds a carboxyl group, as in the example of cyclopentanone-2-acetic acid,[178] amino dicarboxylic acids are produced (eq. 100). Selective reaction of an unhindered aliphatic carbonyl group has been accomplished in the cases of 8,11-dioxo-2-lanostanyl and 8,11-dioxo-9-lanosten-2-yl acetates.[184]

$$\text{(cyclopentanone ring with } CH_2COOH) \longrightarrow HOOC—(CH_2)_3CH—CH_2COOH \quad (100)$$
$$\underset{NH_2}{|}$$

Alkyl Aryl Ketones. It is a general rule that acetophenones always give nearly exclusive aryl migration to form acetanilides.[185] When this reaction is combined with Friedel-Crafts acetylation, a practical alternative to nitration and reduction is available for preparation of aromatic amines (eq. 101); it has

[179a] G. Caronna, *Gazz. chim. ital.*, **80**, 217 (1950).

[180] B. A. Perkin and G. W. Hedrick, *J. Am. Chem. Soc.*, **80**, 2899 (1958).

[181] W. Pritzkow and K. Dietzsch, *Chem. Ber.*, **93**, 1733 (1960).

[182] (a) K. F. Schmidt, *Friedländer, Fortschr. in der Teerfarb. und Verwand. Ind.*, **16**, 2862 (1931). (b) J. Dutta and R. Sengupta, *Sci. and Culture (India)*, **14**, 392 (1949).

[183] L. Ruzicka, M. W. Goldberg, M. Hürbin, and H. A. Boeckenoogen, *Helv. Chim. Acta*, **16**, 1323 (1933).

[184] C. S. Barnes, D. H. R. Barton, J. S. Fawcett, and B. R. Thomas, *J. Chem. Soc. (London)*, **1952**, 2339.

[185] (a) H. H. Szmant and J. S. McIntosh, *J. Am. Chem. Soc.*, **72**, 4835 (1950). (b) F. R. Benson, L. W. Harzel, and W. L. Savell, *J. Am. Chem. Soc.*, **71**, 11 (1949). (c) L. R. Dice and P. A. S. Smith, *J. Org. Chem.*, **14**, 179 (1949).

been demonstrated with several phenanthrene [185c] and fluoranthene [186] derivatives. Cyclic aryl alkyl ketones behave similarly when the α-methylene

$$Ar{-}H \xrightarrow[AlCl_3]{Ac_2O} Ar{-}CO{-}CH_3 \xrightarrow[Cl_3CCOOH]{HN_3} Ar{-}NHCOCH_3 \qquad (101)$$

$$\text{(almost exclusively)}$$

is unsubstituted, and various tetralones and benzosuberones have been converted to lactams in which the NH is attached to the benzene ring.[170,169] When the α-methylene is substituted, however, this orientation may be reversed, as in the 2-aminoalkylindanones, which give tetrahydroisoquinolones.[187] Selective reaction of an aryl alkyl carbonyl group in the presence of an amide function has been reported.[187a]

Diaryl Ketones. Benzophenones have received much attention because of the information they provide about mechanism; the behavior of some para-substituted benzophenones has already been mentioned. Reaction of benzophenones is likely to be sluggish, but in the absence of ortho substituents, sulfuric acid will usually bring about satisfactory results. Ortho-substituted benzophenones will react reasonably well unless the substituent is branched or there are two ortho substituents; o-nitrobenzophenone reacts with difficulty,[176] but o-tert-butylbenzophenone [168a] and phenyl mesityl ketone [176] are almost completely resistant.

The ratios of isomeric amides from ortho-substituted benzophenones (Table I) indicate predominant migration of the *unsubstituted* phenyl group,

TABLE I

Migration Ratios in Schmidt Reactions on Ortho-Substituted
Benzophenones [168a,176]

Ortho substituent	$C_6H_5NHCO{-}Ar,\%$	$ArNHCO{-}C_6H_5,\%$
CH_3	78	22
C_2H_5	78	22
$(CH_3)_2CH$	82	18
Cl	75	25
Br	82	18
CH_3O	50	50
NO_2	30	70
$COOH$	3	97
2,3-Benzo	70	30

[186] N. Campbell, W. K. Leadill, and J. F. K. Wilshire, *J. Chem. Soc. (London)*, **1951**, 1404.

[187] K. Hoffmann, H. J. Schmid, and A. Hunger, U. S. Pat. 2,785,159; *Chem. Abstr.*, **51**, 14828a (1957).

[187a] R. Fusco and S. Rossi, *Gazz. chim. ital.*, **81**, 511 (1951); R. T. Conley, *Chem. & Ind. (London)*, **1958**, 438.

when the substituent is methyl, ethyl, isopropyl, or halogen, and the ratios all lie in a small range [168a,176]—about 5–8 : 1. Similar behavior is shown when the ortho substituent is part of another aromatic ring, as in 1-benzoyl-naphthalene and 1-benzoylphenanthrene.[168a] o-Methoxybenzophenone gives nearly equal quantities of each isomeric amide, and o-nitro- and o-carboxy-benzophenones show predominant migration of the substituted phenyl group. These results, which do not show a simple correlation with either size or electronic character, have perplexed chemists for some time, particularly when it was found that ortho-substituted acetophenones are by contrast entirely normal, showing only aryl migration. Various hypotheses have been put forth in explanation.[176,188] The behavior of o-carboxybenzophenone has been satisfactorily accounted for by Arcus and Coombs,[189] who have provided good evidence that the products actually result from the azide derived from the lactol form of the reactant (eq. 102). The oxazine can actually be isolated

$$\text{(102)}$$

in good yield.[189,190] A similar explanation has been proposed to account for the behavior of o-nitro- and o-phenylbenzophenones [168a] (cf. eq. 97), and may also account for the behavior reported for o-acylamidobenzophenones, which give different types of products, depending on the nature of the acyl groups.[190a]

A clue to the effect of the other ortho substituents is provided by o-methoxy-benzophenone; the observed result, equal migration by phenyl and anisyl, could only be the result of two (or more) opposing factors. This led Smith and Antoniades [168a] to consider the effect of substituents on the conformation as well as the configuration of benzophenone derivatives. Because of the thickness of the benzene ring and the bond angles of the carbonyl group, only one phenyl group in benzophenone can be coplanar with the carbonyl group, and thus only that one can be effectively conjugated with it. A phenyl group bearing an ortho substituent has two possible conformations when not conjugated with the carbonyl group, but when fully conjugated, its conformation is essentially fixed as shown in 41, owing to strong interference with the phenyl group in the alternate rotational position. If the ortho substituent

[188] C. L. Arcus, M. M. Coombs, and J. V. Evans, J. Chem. Soc. (London), 1956, 1498.

[189] C. L. Arcus and M. M. Coombs, J. Chem. Soc. (London), 1953, 3698.

[190] G. M. Badger and R. T. Howard, Chem. & Ind. (London), 1950, 601.

[190a] S. Palazzo, Ann. Chim. (Rome), 49, 835 (1959); Chem. Abstr., 54, 24509-i (1960).

does not have an appreciable effect on the conjugating ability of the phenyl group to which it is attached, conformation **42** will be favored, and the

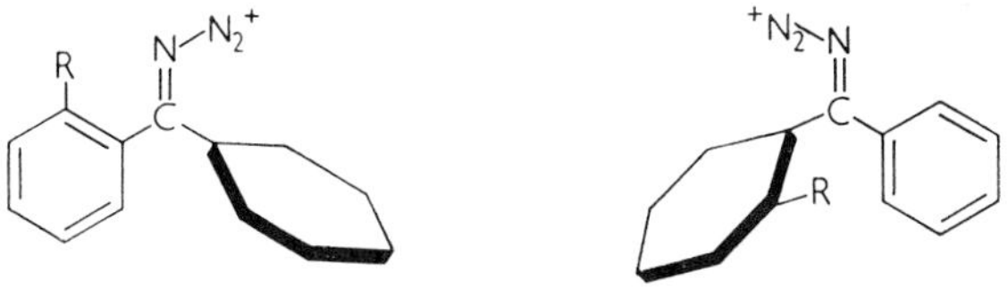

(41)   (42)

anti-phenyl configuration shown in **42** would be of lower energy; the *syn*-phenyl configuration would embody interference between the diazo nitrogens and an ortho-hydrogen. The result of all this would be favored migration of the unsubstituted phenyl (assuming migration to be faster than inter-conversion of isomers, as seems certain from the behavior of the analo-gous para-substituted benzophenones). On the other hand, the methoxyl group, unlike the sterically nearly equivalent ethyl group, should markedly enhance conjugation, thus favoring conformation **41** and the *syn*-phenyl con-figuration. The exact balance of the two effects in the Schmidt reaction is of course fortuitous. There is also some likelihood that interconversion of the configurations would be faster with methoxybenzophenones than with the others.

An implication of the foregoing treatment is that fluorenones, in which ring closure across a pair of ortho positions keeps both phenyl groups coplanar, should not show the special effect of ortho substituents just described. Instead, 1-substituted fluorenones should undergo ring expansion to phenanthridones with the nitrogen on the substituted side. Fluorenone itself readily undergoes conversion to phenanthridone. The only compound resembling a 1-substi-tuted fluorenone for which a Schmidt reaction has been reported is 1,3-dimethyl-2-azafluorenone, which follows this prediction[191] (eq. 103). 2-

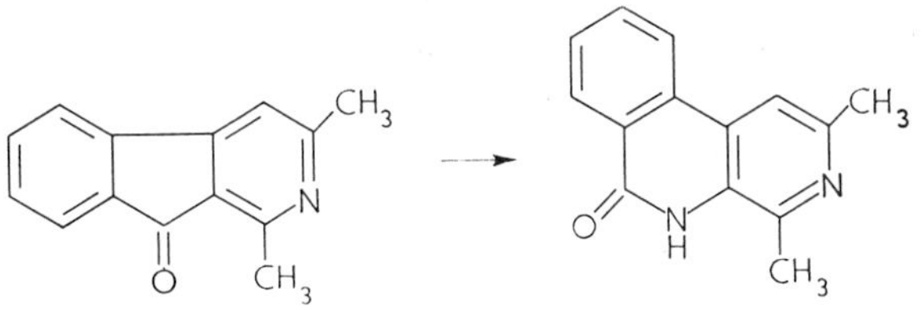

(103)

Nitro-, 3-nitro-, and 2-methoxyfluorenones have also been studied.[188] The first shows predominant migration of the nitrated ring, and the other two give approximately equal amounts of the two isomeric phenanthridones. The

[191] V. A. Petrow, *J. Chem. Soc. (London)*, **1946**, 200.

influence of the 2-nitro group could be considerable in determining the configuration of the iminodiazonium ion intermediate, owing to the buttressing effect,[168a,192] causing the result reported (eq. 104). The last word has

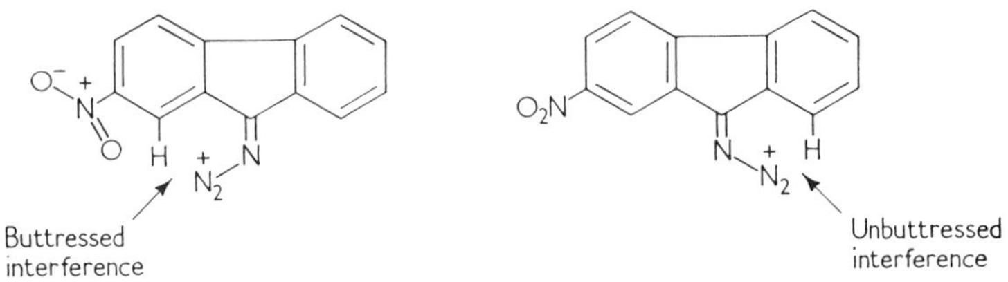

Buttressed
interference

Unbuttressed
interference

(104)

certainly not been said, however. Some quinones have been subjected to the Schmidt reaction. p-Xyloquinone and thymoquinone react with one mole of hydrogen azide to give products whose structures have not been fully established,[193] and anthraquinone and its 1- and 2-amino derivatives undergo reaction of one carbonyl group[194] (equation 105), but anthrone and dian-

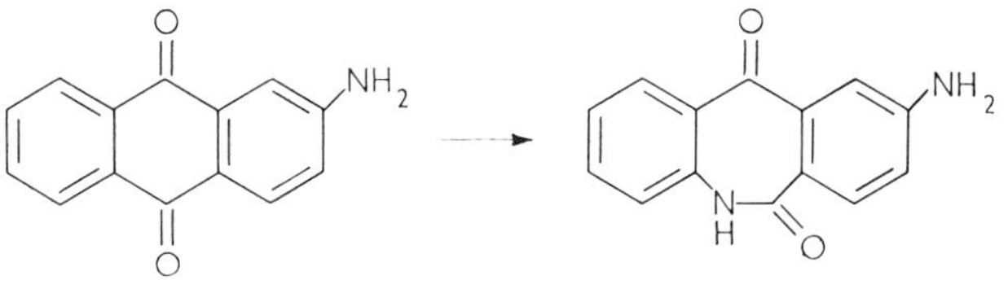

(105)

throne are inert. These observations are in accord with the generalization proposed by Coombs[194a] that carbonyl groups that show abnormally low infrared stretching frequencies are inert to the Schmidt reaction. Anthrone (1656 cm.$^{-1}$), xanthone (1660 cm.$^{-1}$), and thiaxanthone (1645 cm.$^{-1}$), which do not react, have low frequencies, but thiaxanthone dioxide (1684 cm.$^{-1}$) and anthraquinone (1684 cm.$^{-1}$), which do react, have normal frequencies.

Heterocyclic rings do not of themselves interfere with the success of the Schmidt reaction, as shown by tetrahydrothiapyrone,[195] thieno- and thiazoloindenones,[195a] 2-azafluorenones,[191] and isatins,[196] although some, such as benzisoxazoline, coumaranone, and oxindoles, are inert.[196]

[192] W. F. Forbes and W. A. Mueller, *J. Am. Chem. Soc.*, **79**, 6495 (1957).

[193] G. Caronna and S. Palazzo, *Gazz. chim. ital.*, **83**, 315 (1953).

[194] G. Caronna and S. Palazzo, *Gazz. chim. ital.*, **83**, 533 (1953).

[194a] M. M. Coombs, *J. Chem. Soc. (London)*, **1958**, 4200.

[195] I. L. Knunyants, M. A. Dmitriev, G. A. Sokol'skii, and P. A. Arteyev, U.S.S.R. Pat. 114,927; *Chem. Zentr.*, **131**, 10,065 (1960).

[195a] C. L. Arcus and G. C. Barrett, *J. Chem. Soc. (London)*, **1960**, 2098; **1961**, 1408.

[196] G. H. Edwards and V. Petrow, *J. Chem. Soc. (London)*, **1948**, 1713.

Related Reactions.   Benzhydrylidene diazide gives benzanilide in 98% yield when treated with sulfuric acid (eq. 106).[197] This is probably a case of

$$(C_6H_5)_2C(N_3)_2 \rightarrow (C_6H_5)_2C{=}N{-}N_2{}^+ \rightarrow C_6H_5{-}CO{-}NH{-}C_6H_5 \qquad (106)$$

conversion to the iminodiazonium ion common to the Schmidt reaction. Another route to such ions is through the nitrosation of hydrazones (equation 107) and semicarbazones. Its utility has been demonstrated by Pearson and

$$
\begin{array}{c}
\text{R--C--R} \xrightarrow[\text{H}_2\text{SO}_4]{\text{NOHSO}_4} \text{R--C--R} \rightarrow \text{R--NH--CO--R} \\
\;\;\;\|\qquad\qquad\qquad\quad\| \\
\;\;\;\text{N}\qquad\qquad\qquad\quad\text{N} \\
\quad\;\;\backslash\qquad\qquad\qquad\quad\backslash \\
\quad\quad\text{NH}_2\qquad\qquad\qquad\text{N}_2{}^+
\end{array}
\qquad (107)
$$

co-workers.[198] Another instance of the use of this route may exist in the patent claims[199] that cyclic ketones and hydrazine, or their hydrazones or semicarbazones, are converted to lactams by treatment with sodium nitrite and sulfuric acid; it is possible, however, that hydrogen azide is formed first from the inorganic reagents. Another variant[200] is the treatment of sodium salts of nitro alkanes with sulfuric acid and sodium azide, a process which presumably proceeds through formation of ketone by the Nef reaction.

There have been attempts to accomplish a Schmidt type of reaction using alkyl azides in place of hydrogen azide. With methyl azide and acetophenone, a trace of acetanilide is produced, but no N-methylacetanilide.[200a,200b] Since the methyl azide was strictly free of hydrogen azide, and it is not hydrolyzed by sulfuric acid, some demethylation apparently occurred at an intermediate stage. Benzaldehyde has also been found to be generally inert to reaction with alkyl azides,[200c] although a small amount of N-β-phenylethylbenzamide has been obtained with β-phenylethyl azide. However, 1,2- and 1,3-azidohydrins have been found to react with benzaldehyde under Schmidt reaction conditions to give oxazolines and dihydrooxazines, respectively (eq. 108).[200c,201]

$$
\text{HO--(CH}_2)_{\overline{n}}\text{N}_3 \;+\; \text{Ar--CHO} \longrightarrow \text{Ar--C} \overset{\displaystyle N}{\underset{\displaystyle O}{\diagup\hspace{-0.3em}\diagdown}} (\text{CH}_2)_n
\qquad (108)
$$

[197] S. Götzky, *Ber.*, **64**, 1555 (1931).

[198] (a) D. E. Pearson, K. N. Carter, and C. M. Greer, *J. Am. Chem. Soc.*, **75**, 5905 (1953). (b) D. E. Pearson and C. M. Greer, *J. Am. Chem. Soc.*, **71**, 1895 (1949).

[199] K. Ohashi, Jap. Pat. 125 (1952); *Chem. Abstr.*, **48**, 1430h (1954); L. G. Donaruma, U. S. Pats. 2,777,841, 2,763,644 (1956); *Chem. Abstr.*, **51**, 5822, 10565 (1957).

[200] L. G. Donaruma and M. L. Huber, *J. Org. Chem.*, **21**, 965 (1956).

[200a] P. A. S. Smith, *J. Am. Chem. Soc.*, **70**, 320 (1948).

[200b] L. H. Briggs, G. C. De Ath, and S. R. Ellis, *J. Chem. Soc.* (*London*), **1942**, 61.

[200c] J. H. Boyer, F. C. Canter, J. Hamer, and R. K. Putney, *J. Am. Chem. Soc.*, **78**, 325 (1956).

[201] J. H. Boyer and J. Hamer, *J. Am. Chem. Soc.*, **77**, 951 (1955).

C. Carboxyl Derivatives: The Curtius, Schmidt, Hofmann, Lossen, Wolff, and Related Rearrangements

Because their mechanisms are so closely related, the Curtius, Schmidt, Hofmann, Lossen, and Wolff rearrangements will be discussed concurrently with respect to mechanism, and then the individual characteristics and applications of each will be given. The Schmidt reaction of carboxylic acids has major features of mechanism not shared with the other rearrangements; these aspects will be discussed separately. The Tiemann and imidyl azide rearrangements, which have received much less attention, will then be considered.

Mechanism of the Curtius, Schmidt, Hofmann, Lossen, and Wolff Rearrangements. In each of these reactions, a species is lost from an atom adjacent to a carbonyl group, and the other carbonyl-attached group migrates to the site of loss. For the first four reactions this point is obvious, since a group originally attached to the carbonyl carbon atom is found attached to nitrogen in the products. For the Wolff rearrangement, where carbon-to-carbon migration occurs, this conclusion is not *per se* obvious. However, it has been demonstrated [202] conclusively by isotopic labeling that rearrangement is, indeed, a case of carbon-skeleton rearrangement that does not involve oxygen wandering (eq. 109).

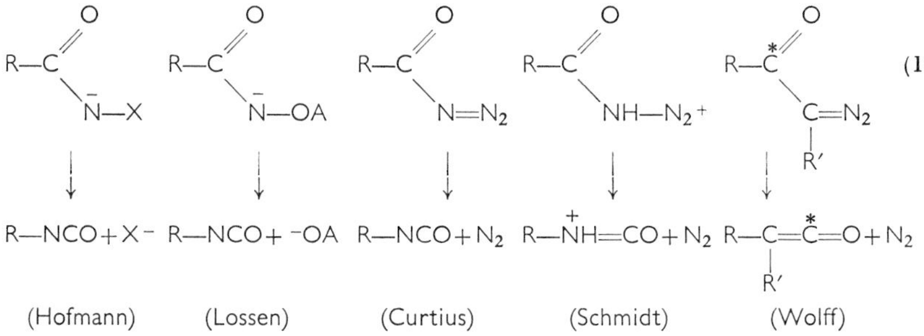

$$R-NCO+X^- \quad R-NCO+{}^-OA \quad R-NCO+N_2 \quad R-\overset{+}{N}H{=}CO+N_2 \quad R-\overset{*}{C}{=}\overset{}{C}{=}O+N_2 \tag{109}$$

      (Hofmann)   (Lossen)   (Curtius)   (Schmidt)   (Wolff)

It has been established for many examples of all of these reactions that isocyanates (or ketenes) are the initial products, although as usually carried out in practical syntheses, these substances undergo further reactions before

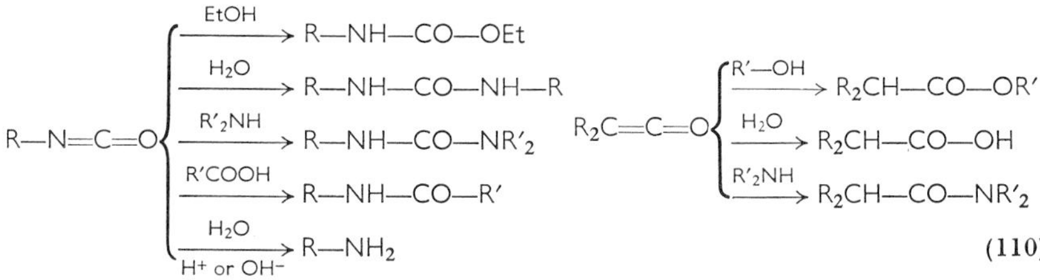

$$\tag{110}$$

202 C. Huggett, R. T. Arnold, and T. I. Taylor, *J. Am. Chem. Soc.*, **64**, 3043 (1942).

a product is isolated. Isocyanates and ketenes react readily with all types of compounds having —O—H or $\rangle$N—H functions, yielding urethans, ureas, esters, amides, etc., and isocyanates are hydrolyzable by acid or base (eq. 110).

The identification of the species that actually undergo rearrangement in each reaction is of varying certainty. For all of them there remains the question of whether loss of the ion or molecule from the migration terminus occurs before the act of rearrangement or simultaneously with it, a topic that will be treated separately. The isolation of hundreds of acyl azides, all of which rearrange spontaneously (and sometimes alarmingly) on warming establishes the rearranging species in the Curtius clearly. In the closely related Schmidt reaction, no intermediates have been isolated short of complete rearrangement, and the structure R—CO—NH—N$_2^+$ for the rearranging species is deduced from secondary evidence and by analogy. It has been shown that the rearrangement of acyl azides is subject to marked catalysis by strong acids,[202a] which must accomplish this by protonation. Acid-catalyzed hydration to R—C(OH)$_2$N$_3$ is the only reasonable alternative to simple formation of protonated acyl azide, R—CO—NH—N$_2^+$, but it is unlikely on two counts. Acid-catalyzed rearrangement occurs readily with nearly or quite anhydrous acids, including Lewis acids,[203] and in one case an isocyanate has been isolated from a Schmidt reaction,[204] a product that could not reasonably result from rearrangement of a hydrated azide.

As the Hofmann reaction is usually carried out, no intermediate is isolated between the stage of amide and that of amine. However, it is possible to isolate N-haloamides, which are appreciably acidic and form well-defined but unstable sodium salts.[205] Such salts rearrange spontaneously; the implication is strong, therefore, that it is the anions of such salts that rearrange in the strongly basic solutions used for Hofmann rearrangements.

In the Lossen rearrangement, O-acylhydroxamic acids are generally isolated, and rearrangement is carried out by treatment with base. Base is not necessary for the Lossen rearrangement, for heating, alone or in the presence of acids, can also cause rearrangement. When the nitrogen atom bears an alkyl or aryl group, however, Lossen rearrangement does not take place.[206] Salts of O-acylhydroxamic acids can be isolated; they rearrange spontaneously or on mild heating.[207]

In the Wolff rearrangement. α-diazo ketones are usually isolated, or at

[202a] M. S. Newman and H. Gildenhorn, J. Am. Chem. Soc., **70**, 317 (1948).

[203] R. A. Coleman, M. S. Newman, and A. B. Garrett, J. Am. Chem. Soc., **76**, 4534 (1954).

[204] K. G. Rutherford and M. S. Newman, J. Am. Chem. Soc., **79**, 213 (1957).

[205] C. Mauguin, Ann. chim., [8]**22**, 297 (1911).

[206] L. Horner and H. Steppan, Ann., **606**, 24 (1957).

[207] C. D. Hurd, C. M. Buess, and L. Bauer, J. Org. Chem., **17**, 865 (1952).

least prepared in solution in inert solvents from which they may be isolated if desired.[208] Although the usual procedure is to use a silver concoction, of which silver oxide is the simplest example, as a catalyst, it has been shown that a number of α-diazo ketones will rearrange simply when heated, by themselves or in an inert solvent, or when irradiated; α-diazodeoxybenzoin[209] is an example that is preparatively useful (eq. 111).

$$C_6H_5CO-\underset{\underset{N_2}{\|}}{C}-C_6H_5 \rightarrow (C_6H_5)_2C=C=O+N_2 \qquad (111)$$

Evidence is overwhelming that, for all five rearrangements, migration occurs with retention of optical and geometrical configuration, and the migrating group is thus never free. This fact was first demonstrated for the Curtius,[210] Hofmann,[211] and Lossen[212] rearrangements by Wallis and co-workers, using resolved α-benzylpropionic acid derivatives, and for the Schmidt reaction by von Braun and Friehmelt.[213] These experiments actually demonstrated only that optical activity was maintained in the product, but it was very soon deduced from the signs of rotation observed that configuration itself was retained.[214] Kenyon and co-workers[214a,215] subjected resolved α-phenylpropionic acid to the Curtius, Hofmann, Lossen, and Schmidt rearrangements (eq. 112), obtaining amines that showed better than 99% retention of activity

$$(+)C_6H_5-\underset{\underset{CH_3}{|}}{CH}-COOH \left\{ \begin{matrix} \text{Curtius} \\ \text{Hofmann} \\ \text{Lossen} \\ \text{Schmidt} \end{matrix} \right\} \rightarrow (-)C_6H_5-\underset{\underset{CH_3}{|}}{CH}-NH_2 \qquad (112)$$
$$\text{(95.8–99.6\% retention)}$$

in all except the Hofmann rearrangement, which had been accompanied by about 4% of racemization. Since strong alkali is used in the Hofmann, some racemization is to be expected from hydroxyl attack at the active α hydrogen.

Lane and Wallis[216] demonstrated retention of optical configuration in the Wolff rearrangement of α-butylhydratropyldiazomethane (eq. 113) which had been prepared from resolved α-butylhydratropic acid. The β-methyl-β-

[208] W. E. Bachmann and W. S. Struve, Org. Reactions, 1, Chapt. 2 (1942).

[209] L. I. Smith and H. N. Hoehn, Org. Syntheses, Coll. Vol. III, 356 (1955).

[210] L. W. Jones and E. S. Wallis, J. Am. Chem. Soc., 48, 169 (1926).

[211] E. S. Wallis and S. C. Nagel, J. Am. Chem. Soc., 53, 2787 (1931).

[212] E. S. Wallis and R. D. Dripps, J. Am. Chem. Soc., 55, 1701 (1933).

[213] J. von Braun and E. Friehmelt, Ber., 66, 684 (1933).

[214] J. Kenyon, H. Phillips, and V. P. Pittman, J. Chem. Soc. (London), 1935, 1072.

[214a] (a) A. Campbell and J. Kenyon, J. Chem. Soc. (London), 1946, 25; (b) J. Kenyon and D. P. Young, J. Chem. Soc. (London), 1941, 263.

[215] C. L. Arcus and J. Kenyon, J. Chem. Soc. (London), 1939, 916.

[216] J. F. Lane and E. S. Wallis, J. Am. Chem. Soc., 63, 1674 (1941).

phenylenanthic acid produced was degraded by the Barbier-Wieland method back to α-butylhydratropic acid having 99.5% of the original activity, of the same sign.

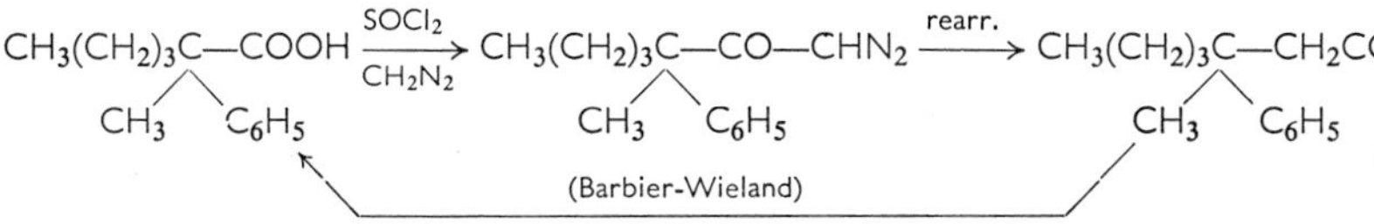

$$CH_3(CH_2)_3C-COOH \xrightarrow[CH_2N_2]{SOCl_2} CH_3(CH_2)_3C-CO-CHN_2 \xrightarrow{rearr.} CH_3(CH_2)_3C-CH_2COOH$$

(113)

(Barbier-Wieland)

While the foregoing experiments adequately demonstrate retention of optical configuration, they do not strictly prove that the migrating group never becomes fully separated from the remainder of the molecule. Experiments with optically active biphenyls, in which the activity is due to restricted rotation about the bond joining the two rings, have demonstrated that if full separation of the migrating group occurs, it does not last long enough for rotation in the biphenyl system to occur—presumably less than the average interval between molecular collisions. Such experiments have been reported for the Hofmann,[217,218] Curtius,[218] and Wolff[219] rearrangements (eqs. 114–116).

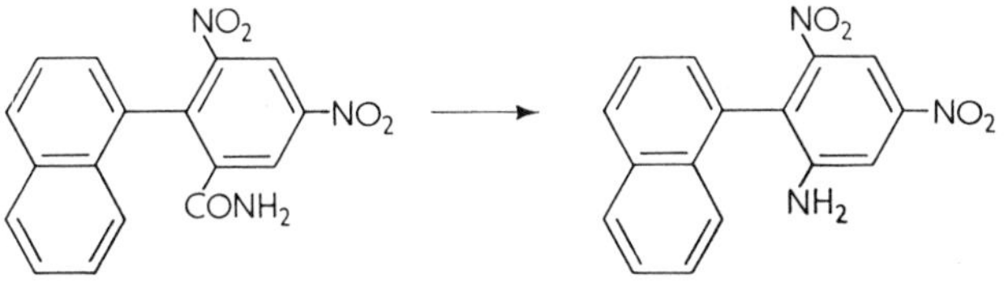

(114)

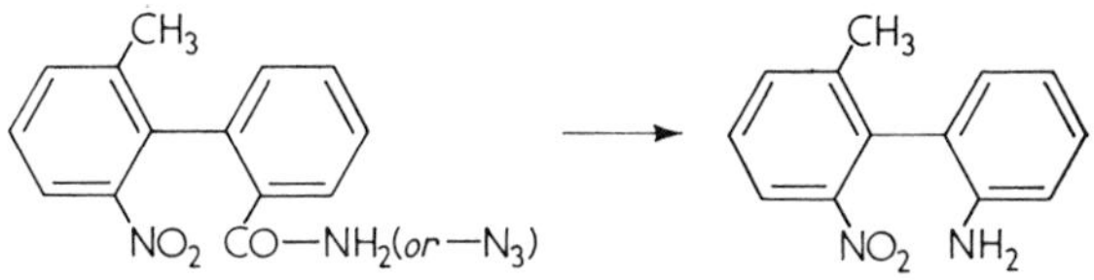

(115)

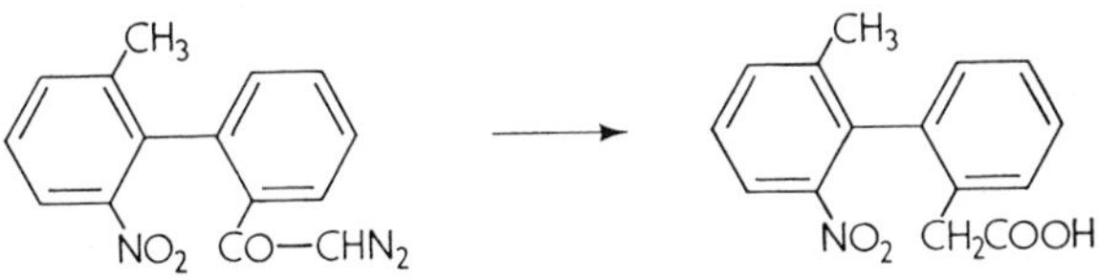

(116)

In addition to the foregoing observations, there have been many confirmatory pieces of evidence. Schrecker[220] showed that D-(−)-α-benzylacetic acid

[217] E. S. Wallis and W. W. Moyer, J. Am. Chem. Soc., 55, 2598 (1933).
[218] F. Bell, J. Chem. Soc. (London), 1934, 835.
[219] J. F. Lane and E. S. Wallis, J. Org. Chem., 6, 443 (1941).
[220] A. W. Schrecker, J. Org. Chem., 22, 33 (1957).

is converted to D-(−)-α-benzylethylamine in 90% yield by the Curtius reaction. Sax and Bergmann[221] converted D-(+)-α-methylbutyric acid into D-(+)-β-methylvaleric acid, whose configuration was confirmed by separate synthesis from D-2-methyl-1-chlorobutane via the Grignard reagent. They also converted 3β-acetoxybisnorchol-5-enyl chloride into the homologous acid with retention of configuration. It has also been pointed out[222] that evidence for retention of configuration in the Hofmann rearrangement had been available but unrecognized since 1914, when β-camphoramic acid was converted to an amino acid that readily formed a lactam (eq. 117). Since

$$ (cis) \qquad (cis) \tag{117} $$

lactam formation could only take place if the amine and carboxyl groups were cis, and β-camphoramic acid was known to have its carboxyl and carbonamide groups cis to each other owing to its derivation from camphor, configuration must have been preserved.

The extent to which optical configuration is retained was investigated by Wiberg and Hutton,[223] who were concerned about the source of the possible partial racemization that might have occurred in the earlier studies. Lane and Wallis had reported that their final product was obtained optically pure only after recrystallization, which might have removed small amounts of racemic material. In order to avoid this eventuality, Wiberg and Hutton chose (−)-α-methylbutyric acid as starting material because it would give rise only to liquid products in all steps. The diazo ketone was prepared by reaction of diazomethane with the acid chloride and was converted to (+)-β-methylvaleric acid by four different procedures: catalytically with $Ag(S_2O_3)_2^{3-}$ in aqueous dioxane, silver oxide in methanol, or silver benzoate and triethylamine in methanol, and by irradiation with ultraviolet light. Retention of configuration to the extent of 97% was established. When they applied these procedures to (+)-α-benzylpropionic acid, retention of configuration varied from 70 to 97%, with the best results being given with the silver benzoate–triethylamine catalyst. The possibility of racemization during preparation of the acid chloride or the diazo ketone was eliminated, leaving it uncertain whether the erratic partial racemization in the subsequent rearrangement step

[221] K. J. Sax and W. Bergmann, J. Am. Chem. Soc., 77, 1910 (1955).

[222] S. Archer, J. Am. Chem. Soc., 62, 1872 (1940).

[223] K. B. Wiberg and T. Hutton, J. Am. Chem. Soc., 78, 1640 (1956).

resulted from action of the reaction mixture on the diazo ketone prior to or concomitantly with rearrangement.

Intramolecularity of the Hofmann rearrangement has been demonstrated by the use of isotopes. Prosser and Eliel [224] prepared m-deuterobenzamide and benzamide-N^{15} and subjected a mixture of them to the Hofmann degradation. m-Deuteroaniline and aniline-N^{15} were the only products; no exchange had occurred, for it would have resulted in the formation of m-deuteroaniline-N^{15} and ordinary aniline.

When the fact of intramolecularity had not yet been established firmly, the possibility was considered that migration might take place through formation of a free radical or a carbonium ion. The free radical possibility was eliminated when the Curtius reaction was carried out in a solution containing triphenylmethyl radicals and found not to be interfered with.[225] Furthermore, the rearrangement of benzoyl azide in the presence of acrylonitrile was found to induce no more than 1% of polymerization,[226] providing additional evidence against free radical intermediates. These two experiments also indicate that if an azene intermediate, R—CO—N, occurs, it does not possess the properties of ordinary free radicals, or it has a lifetime less than the interval between molecular collisions. Carbonium ions were eliminated as intermediates in the Hofmann reaction when it was found that groups that are highly susceptible to Wagner-Meerwein rearrangement, such as neopentyl and 2,2,2-triphenylethyl, migrated to nitrogen with their structures undisturbed.[227]

The Schmidt reaction is potentially susceptible to effects not found in the other rearrangements, owing to the more drastic conditions—warm, concentrated sulfuric acid—required, and the possibility of carbon skeleton rearrangement can be more seriously entertained. It has been disproved in the case of β-phenylpropionic acid by degrading a sample in which the α carbon was isotopically labelled.[228] All the activity was found in the β-phenylethylamine produced, and the benzoic acid obtained by oxidizing the amine was free of excess activity, showing that the labeled carbon had not lost its position in the skeleton (eq. 118).

$$C_6H_5CH_2\overset{*}{C}H_2COOH \rightarrow C_6H_5CH_2\overset{*}{C}H_2NH_2 \rightarrow C_6H_5COOH + \overset{*}{C}O_2 \qquad (118)$$

Kinetic measurements have been made on all the C-to-N rearrangements

[224] T. J. Prosser and E. L. Eliel, *J. Am. Chem. Soc.*, **79**, 2544 (1957).

[225] G. Powell, *J. Am. Chem. Soc.*, **51**, 2436 (1929); E. S. Wallis, *J. Am. Chem. Soc.*, **51**, 2982 (1929).

[226] L. Horner, E. Spietschka, and A. Gross, *Ann.*, **573**, 17 (1951).

[227] (a) F. C. Whitmore and A. H. Homeyer, *J. Am. Chem. Soc.*, **54**, 3435 (1932). (b) L. Hellermann, *J. Am. Chem. Soc.*, **49**, 1735 (1927).

[228] C. C. Lee, G. P. Slater, and J. W. T. Spinks, *Can. J. Chem.*, **35**, 276 (1957).

of this group, but apparently not on the Wolff rearrangement; the Curtius, Hofmann, and Lossen rearrangements are first order. More extensive investigation of structural effects is possible in the Lossen rearrangement, since both the migrating and the leaving groups may be varied. Jones and Hurd [229] determined the relative rates of a series of O-benzoylhydroxamic acids, R—CO—NHO—COC$_6$H$_5$, to be in the order R = triphenylmethyl > benzhydryl > benzyl > methyl. Hauser and Renfrow [230] investigated a series of dibenzhydroxamic acids, Ar—CO—NH—O—CO—Ar, by preparing the potassium salts and measuring the rates of disappearance of reactant at 30° in 0.10N aqueous ammonia. The rates were first order and were accelerated by a m-nitro substituent on the leaving group and retarded by m-methoxy, giving a Hammett regression constant of 0.87. The effect of substituents on the migrating group was reversed, but conformity with the Hammett equation was only qualitative, giving a regression constant between -1.5 and -3. Bright and Hauser [231] extended these investigations to a group of thirty O-acylhydroxamic acids and determined enthalpies of activation as well. The rate constants vary directly as the acid strength of the leaving group, so that log k is linear with pK$_a$, even with ortho substituents. Hauser and Kantor [232] later determined that O-ethylbenzhydroxamic acid would not rearrange in base and proposed the generalization that the leaving group must be a weaker base than the parent ion, RCO—$\overline{\text{N}}$—OA. The change in rate constant with substitution on the migrating group is only roughly inversely proportional to the strength of the corresponding benzoic acids. All ortho substituents give faster rates than the corresponding meta or para compounds. A precise correlation appears to be a complicated matter, about which Bright and Hauser have contributed an extensive discussion.

The kinetics of the Hofmann reaction have been investigated by Hauser and Renfrow [233] with a group of benzamides. They isolated the bromoamides, dissolved them in 1.0N sodium hydroxide, and followed the disappearance of active bromine. The first-order rate constants varied with structure much as in the Lossen rearrangement; log k was approximately linear with the inverse of log K_a, except that o-chloro- and o-nitro-benzamides rearranged much faster than the dissociation constants of the benzoic acids would suggest. They concluded that the rate-determining step is release of halide ion, analogous to the rate-determining step of the Lossen rearrangement.

The kinetics of the Curtius rearrangement of benzoyl azide have been found

[229] L. W. Jones and C. D. Hurd, *J. Am. Chem. Soc.*, **43**, 2422 (1921).

[230] C. R. Hauser and W. B. Renfrow, Jr., *J. Am. Chem. Soc.*, **59**, 2308 (1937).

[231] R. D. Bright and C. R. Hauser, *J. Am. Chem. Soc.*, **61**, 618 (1939).

[232] C. R. Hauser and S. W. Kantor, *J. Am. Chem. Soc.*, **72**, 4284 (1950).

[233] C. R. Hauser and W. B. Renfrow, Jr., *J. Am. Chem. Soc.*, **59**, 121 (1937).

to be first order by Newman, Lee, and Garrett [234] and by Porter and Young.[235] Newman and co-workers studied solvent effects and observed a variation in rate constant over a fifteen-fold range from one solvent to another, the fastest rates occurring in the more polar solvents, such as aniline, acetic acid, and acetonitrile, and the slowest being in heptane. The rates were very sensitive to temperature, increasing three- to four-fold for a 10° rise; activation energies varied from 25.4 to 31.6 kcal./mole, depending on the solvent.

Yukawa and Tsuno [236] reported an extensive series of kinetic measurements on meta- and para-substituted benzoyl azides in toluene and found very little effect on the rate constants. Their rate constants could not be correlated by the Hammett equation, but were closely related to those reported for the decomposition of substituted benzenediazonium salts. They found activation energies in the range 26.2–29.2 kcal./mole. It is difficult to interpret their results, since they stated that no stirring was used in the reactions. The retention of nitrogen by solvents can be a considerable source of error if agitation is not vigorous, and the small differences among rate constants could be in part artifacts. However, their rate constant for benzoyl azide at 65.2°, 2.19×10^{-3} min.$^{-1}$, agrees reasonably well with that reported by Newman, Lee, and Garrett for the reaction in benzene at 65°, 2.58×10^{-3} min.$^{-1}$.

Yukawa and Tsuno also studied [237] o-hydroxy-, o-nitro, o-bromo-, o-chloro-, o-methyl-, and o-methoxybenzoyl azides. They found rates 50- to 100-fold greater than those for meta- or para-substituted compounds. There was a small variation in rate constants that appeared to be related to the bulk of the substituent.

Rearrangement of benzoyl azide is also accelerated by ultrasonic vibrations, to an extent proportional to the energy input.[238] It is also catalyzed by ultraviolet radiation.[226]

Catalysis in the Curtius rearrangement by aprotic Lewis acids is roughly proportional to the effectiveness of the catalyst in other reactions, such as Friedel-Crafts acylation, according to Coleman, Newman, and Garrett.[203] They found that $GaCl_3$, $AlCl_3$, $AlBr_3$, and $FeCl_3$ were effective catalysts that are not used up in the reaction; the reactions were first order in catalyst when azide was in excess, and first order in azide when catalyst was in excess. Their interpretation was that an acid-base adduct is formed rapidly, and the rate-determining step is its rearrangement with release of the catalyst (eq. 119). The weaker Lewis acids $SbCl_5$, $TiCl_4$, $SnCl_4$, and $TeCl_4$ were less effective, and $AsCl_3$, $AsBr_3$, PCl_3, and PCl_5 were inert.

[234] M. S. Newman, S. H. Lee, Jr., and A. B. Garrett, *J. Am. Chem. Soc.*, **69**, 113 (1947).

[235] C. W. Porter and L. Young, *J. Am. Chem. Soc.*, **60**, 1497 (1938).

[236] Y. Yukawa and Y. Tsuno, *J. Am. Chem. Soc.*, **79**, 5530 (1957).

[237] Y. Yukawa and Y. Tsuno, *J. Am. Chem. Soc.*, **80**, 6346 (1958).

[238] E. W. Barrett and C. W. Porter, *J. Am. Chem. Soc.*, **63**, 3434 (1941).

Catalysis by sulfuric acid in glacial acetic acid has been studied by Yukawa and Tsuno [239] with a group of substituted benzoyl azides. Acceleration was

$$RCON_3 + MX_3 \underset{\text{fast}}{\rightleftharpoons} RCON_3 \cdot MX_3 \xrightarrow{\text{slow}} RNCO + N_2 + MX_3 \qquad (119)$$

marked, and the rate constants could be correlated by a Hammett equation with a regression constant of -1.09. This result is to be expected if the rate constants for rearrangement of the protonated azides, $RCONHN_2^+$, vary little with substitution, for the concentrations of these species would depend on the base strengths of the azides. The sensitivity of the base strengths of benzoyl azides to substitution should be very similar to that of benzoic acids, for which the value -1.09 has recently been determined.[240] The results of Yukawa and Tsuno are thus consistent with a mechanism analogous to equation 119 (but without regeneration of the catalyst, which was used in large excess), in which the equilibrium for protonation is far to the left. They also found that glacial acetic acid alone as solvent gave rise to faster rates than toluene, but this is probably the polarity effect noted by Newman, Lee, and Garrett.

The kinetics of the Schmidt reaction for various benzoic acids have been investigated by Briggs and Lyttleton.[240a] They used a two-phase system of trichloroethylene and sulfuric acid, and followed the rate of nitrogen evolution. The half-lives were roughly inversely proportional to the strengths of the benzoic acids for meta substituents, and were later calculated [240b] to be correlatable by a Hammett equation with $\rho = -1.76$. o-Nitrobenzoic acid was much faster than any other, however. Similar acceleration by ortho substituents has been reported by Newman and Gildenhorn [240c] and by Schechter.[241] This phenomenon may have a special relation to the Schmidt reaction through the process of "acylization" ($RCOOH \rightarrow RCO^+$) and will be discussed more fully later.

A significant observation made by Briggs and Lyttleton was that nitrogen evolution is appreciable from hydrogen azide itself in sulfuric acid at $40°$, but its rate is *retarded* by the addition of m- or p-nitrobenzoic acid. This must mean that the hydrogen azide is largely converted to an adduct, presumably $RCON_3$, which loses nitrogen more slowly than HN_3 itself; furthermore, this adduct must be formed rapidly compared to the nitrogen-releasing process.

[239] Y. Yukawa and Y. Tsuno, *J. Am. Chem. Soc.*, **81**, 2007 (1959).

[240] R. Stewart and K. Yates, *J. Am. Chem. Soc.*, **82**, 4059 (1960).

[240a] L. H. Briggs and J. W. Lyttleton, *J. Chem. Soc. (London)*, **1943**, 421.

[240b] R. F. Tietz and W. E. McEwen, *J. Am. Chem. Soc.*, **77**, 4007 (1955).

[240c] M. S. Newman and H. Gildenhorn, *J. Am. Chem. Soc.*, **70**, 317 (1948).

[241] M. E. D. Hillman and H. Schechter, Abstracts of Papers, Div. of Org. Chem., Am. Chem. Soc. National Meeting, Chicago, September, 1958; H. Schechter, private communication.

This implies that in the Schmidt reaction we may be dealing with the acid-catalyzed Curtius rearrangement as the rate-determining step, preceded by a more rapid acid-catalyzed conversion of $RCOOH$ to $RCON_3$. This point will be elaborated later in connection with individual features of the Schmidt reaction.

It is difficult to draw clear conclusions about general features of mechanism from the kinetic studies of the four types of rearrangement of carboxyl derivatives, and further study is needed. The evidence is not conclusive for rearrangement concerted with loss of the N-attached species, nor for inter-mediate formation of a common azene species, RCO—N, and it may well be that the degree of assistance in the separation of the leaving group varies among the different reactions from considerable to negligible. A comparison of the rate constants reported for the Curtius reaction with those for the decomposition of aryl azides shows that benzoyl azides lose nitrogen very much faster. Since the decomposition of aryl azides is insensitive to polar substituents, one is tempted to consider that the higher rates for benzoyl azides result not from a polar influence of the carbonyl group but from a con-certed process. That, however, should cause a sensitivity to substituents not shown by the data of Yukawa and Tsuno. The one valid generalization seems to be that ortho substituents greatly accelerate all four rearrangements, just as they do the Beckmann rearrangement; presumably these effects are all attributable to the same cause, which is probably steric interference with conjugation between the benzene ring and the carbonyl group while promot-ing orientation of the phenyl group in the position of maximum effectiveness for overlap of its π orbital with that of the nitrogen atom to which it is migrating (see heading 2B).

The results of efforts to obtain evidence for the intermediacy of an acyla-zene by interception have so far been negative or inconclusive. The failure of benzoyl azide to react with triphenylmethyl radicals or to initiate vinyl polymerization during rearrangement has already been mentioned. It has also been suggested that an acylazene should react with water to form a hydroxamic acid. Hauser and Kantor [232] showed that no hydroxamic acid could be detected by the sensitive ferric chloride test when the Curtius re-arrangement was carried out in water, which only permits the conclusion that rearrangement of acylazenes must be a much faster reaction than their pos-sible hydration, if they are intermediates. The possibility that nitrile oxides,

R—$\overset{+}{C}$≡$\overset{-}{N}$—$\overset{-}{O}$, might be intermediates in the Lossen rearrangement has been discarded by Caronna,[242] who showed that rearrangement of benzohydrox-amic acid in the presence of quinone does not give rise to the benzisoxazole derivative that benzonitrile oxide is known to form.

242 G. Caronna, *Gazz. chim. ital.*, **83**, 527 (1953).

It is of interest to consider the behavior of the corresponding sulfonic acid derivatives, which do not rearrange. Benzenesulfonyl azide loses nitrogen on heating at a rate qualitatively slower, however, than benzoyl azide, but faster than aryl azides. The products obtained result from attack on the solvent and may easily be imagined as arising through the formation of a reactive sulfonylazene (eq. 120).[243] In support of this view, decomposing benzenesulfonyl

$$C_6H_5SO_2N_3 \xrightarrow[C_6H_6]{110°} C_6H_5SO_2NH_2 \ \ and \ \ C_6H_5SO_2NHC_6H_5 \tag{120}$$

azide initiates polymerization of vinyl monomers.[243] The analogous reaction may perhaps also occur in place of Lossen rearrangement with O-acyl-benzenesulfonhydroxamic acids, for it has been observed that O-acetyl-p-toluenesulfonhydroxamic acid, p-CH$_3$C$_6$H$_4$SO$_2$—NH—O—Ac, forms fairly stable salts, but some decomposition occurs to give p-toluenesulfonamide during their preparation.[244] Although N-halosulfonamides have in general not been found to rearrange, there is a single report of a reaction that may possibly involve a Hofmann rearrangement; o-hydroxybenzenesulfonamide when treated with aqueous bromine has been claimed to produce 2,4,6-tribromoaniline.[245]

Behavior analogous to that of sulfonic acid derivatives is shown by some carbamyl azides, which do not undergo the Curtius rearrangement, although the Hofmann reaction successfully converts ureas to hydrazine derivatives. Part of this difference in behavior is attributable to the fact that carbamyl azides are much more susceptible to solvolysis than are haloureas, and solvolysis may supplant rearrangement (eq. 121).[246] There is evidence, however,

$$H_2NCONH—X + B: \rightarrow H_2NCO—\bar{N}—X + B:H \qquad H_2NCO—N_3 + B: \rightarrow H_2NCO—B + N_3^- \tag{121}$$

that even when carbamyl azides are heated in an inert solvent until nitrogen is given off, rearrangement may be only a minor reaction. Curtius and co-workers have demonstrated reactions that are reasonably explained on the basis of a carbamylazene intermediate, R_2N—CO—N, which attacks the solvent to give urea derivatives,[247] in a manner analogous to sulfonyl azides. If this interpretation is correct, one must look for an explanation for why haloureas, which should also produce carbamylazenes (by loss of halide ion), rearrange well. One possibility is that rearrangement of the haloureide anion is more closely allied to the Neber type of reaction shown by O-acyl oximes

[243] O. C. Dermer and M. T. Edmison, *J. Am. Chem. Soc.*, **77**, 70 (1955).

[244] P. A. S. Smith and G. E. Hein, *J. Am. Chem. Soc.*, **82**, 5731 (1960).

[245] L. Raffa, *Il Farmaco, Ed. Sci.*, **11**, 62 (1956).

[246] F. L. Scott, *Chem. & Ind. (London)*, **1954**, 959.

[247] T. Curtius and F. Schmidt, *J. prakt. Chem.*, [2]**105**, 181 (1926).

and N-halo ketimines under alkaline conditions (see heading 2B). An intermediate diaziridone can be formulated (eq. 122), which, while undoubtedly of high

$$R\!-\!N\!-\!\overset{O}{\overset{\|}{C}}\!-\!\overset{-}{N}\!-\!X \leftrightarrow R_2N\!-\!\overset{O^-}{\underset{}{C}}\!\!=\!\!N\!-\!X \rightarrow R_2\overset{+}{N}\!\!\diagdown\!\!\overset{C=O}{\underset{N^-}{\diagup}} \leftrightarrow R_2\overset{+}{N}\!\!\diagdown\!\!\overset{C-O^-}{\underset{N}{\|}} \quad +X^- \qquad (122)$$

$$\downarrow (H_2O)$$

$$R_2NNH_2 + CO_2$$

energy, should exist as a discrete entity, occupying a small minimum on the potential energy profile. The formation of such an entity can also be conceived from carbamyl azide, of course. Such a reaction should be favored by a polar medium, such as the aqueous solution used for Hofmann rearrangements; in the case of carbamyl azides, the polar media that have been used are ones that would also be capable of effective solvolysis of the azide before rearrangement or cyclization. The behavior of carbamyl azides in highly polar solvents that are not capable of solvolysis appears not to have been studied. Diarylcarbamyl azides are less susceptible to solvolysis and rearrange normally in boiling ethanol, producing aminourethan derivatives.[248]

The subject of azides that do not rearrange when heated was reviewed by Bertho in 1929.[249]

Some α-diazo ketones resist Wolff rearrangement, although they lose nitrogen when heated or irradiated. The products obtained, in part analogous to those from azides that lose nitrogen without Curtius rearrangement, are the result of abstraction of hydrogen from the environment. Such behavior has been interpreted in terms of initial formation of a carbene, whose Wolff rearrangement is retarded by steric or electronic effects, allowing other reactions to intervene. Other products are also observed, corresponding to dimerization and to rearrangement of types other than Wolff. Examples are α-diazotrifluoroacetoacetic ester,[250] $CF_3COC(N_2)COOEt$; naphthalene-1,2-diazooxide,[250a] diazopinacolone,[251] $t\text{-Bu}\!-\!CO\!-\!CHN_2$; and α-diazoneopentyl $tert$-butyl ketone,[252] $t\text{-Bu}\!-\!CO\!-\!C(N_2)\!-\!t\text{-Bu}$. There is reason to believe that this behavior is at least partly a function of reaction conditions, for naphthalene-1,2-diazooxide will rearrange normally to give indenecarboxanilide when heated in analine, while in benzyl alcohol, which is a better source of

[248] F. L. Scott, *J. Am. Chem. Soc.*, **79**, 6077 (1957).

[249] A. Bertho, *J. prakt. Chem.*, [2]**120**, 94 (1929).

[250] F. Weygand, W. Schwenke, and H. J. Bestmann, *Angew. Chem.*, **70**, 506 (1958).

[250a] P. A. S. Smith and W. L. Berry, *J. Org. Chem.*, **26**, 27 (1961).

[251] K. B. Wiberg and T. Hutton, *J. Am. Chem. Soc.*, **76**, 5367 (1954).

[252] M. S. Newman and A. Arkell, *J. Org. Chem.*, **24**, 385 (1959).

hydrogen, it is converted to β-naphthol (eq. 123). Similarly, the rearrangement of tetrachlorobenzene-1,2-diazooxide can be arrested by phenylacetylene, which apparently intercepts a carbene intermediate by rapid addition.[252a] On the other hand, no matter how firm the establishment of carbene or azene intermediates might be in reactions of compounds that do not rearrange, it should not be taken as proof that they are a stage in the rearrangement process also.

$$(123)$$

The mechanism of the action of the various catalyst preparations used in the Wolff rearrangement has not been elucidated with certainty. Catalysis is effected by silver oxide or salts, but not by metallic silver, according to Wolff's original experiments.[253] However, Arndt and Eistert reopened the question,[254] noting that there is always some reduction to metallic silver, and suggesting that surface catalysis may be involved, requiring colloidal silver for effectiveness. Various other preparations have been used as catalysts, most of them being silver compounds. Newman and Beal[255] investigated the requirements of the catalysts and developed a particularly effective recipe in the form of a solution of silver benzoate and triethylamine in methanol. They showed that hydroquinone quenched rearrangement until enough silver reagent had been added to destroy the hydroquinone. The need for base was demonstrated with silver trifluoroacetate in benzene, which was impotent as a catalyst until triethylamine was added. They also found that their catalyst was not effective in rearranging α-diazopropiophenone, $C_6H_5CO-CN_2-CH_3$, which has no acidic hydrogen, although it worked very well on diazoacetophenone, which has.

The mechanism proposed for the catalyzed rearrangement is a free radical chain reaction, in which the function of the base is to generate a carbanion, which is oxidized to a radical by a silver salt (eq. 124). This reaction sequence does not appear to have been conclusively established or disproved. However, the suggestion by Huisgen[256] that catalysis involves silver ion functioning

[252a] R. Huishen, H. König, G. Binsch, and H. J. Sturm, *Angew. Chem.*, **73**, 368 (1961).

[253] L. Wolff, *Ann.*, **394**, 25 (1912).

[254] K. Arndt and B. Eistert, *Ber.*, **68**, 200 (1935).

[255] M. S. Newman and P. F. Beal III, *J. Am. Chem. Soc.*, **72**, 5162 (1950).

[256] R. Huisgen, *Angew. Chem.*, **67**, 439 (1955).

simply as a Lewis acid to coordinate with the diazo carbon atom is difficult to reconcile with Newman and Beal's observations.

$$RCO-CHN_2 + Et_3N \rightleftharpoons Et_3\overset{+}{N}H + RCO-\overset{-}{C}N_2 \xrightarrow{[Ag^+]} RCO-\overset{..}{C}N_2 \qquad (124)$$

$$RCO-\overset{..}{C}{=}N_2 + R-CH{=}C{=}O \xleftarrow{\quad RCOCHN_2 \quad} R-\overset{..}{C}{=}C{=}O$$

Copper compounds as catalysts have been investigated by Yates and Fugger,[257] who found that a solution of cuprous iodide in a mixture of acetonitrile and methanol is effective at room temperature in rearranging α-diazoacetophenone. Metallic copper, cuprous and cupric oxides, and cupric chloride, acetate, and benzoate were all poor or ineffective.

Catalysis is not essential for Wolff rearrangement. Heating alone succeeds with some diazo ketones, but even then it is seldom satisfactory. Wilds and Meader [258] have found that it is more successful in the presence of amines such as dimethylaniline or collidine, but relatively high temperatures (170–190°) are still required for rapid reaction. The energy required to bring about rearrangement may also be supplied by ultraviolet radiation, as was first reported by Süs,[259] who investigated the rearrangement of o-diazooxides by this method (eq. 125). Photolytic rearrangement was extended by Horner,

$$\text{(structure)} \xrightarrow{\;h\nu\;} \text{(structure)}{=}C{=}O \qquad (125)$$

Spietschka, and Gross,[259a] who showed that it can be accomplished in good yields at low temperatures with open chain diazo ketones, but is slow. For o-diazooxides, the quantum yield has been found [260] to be less than 1. Although diazo ketones absorb at both long and short wavelengths, the shorter wavelengths can bring about other, undesired, reactions; Roedig and Lunk [261] have obtained better results with ultraviolet light that has been filtered through copper sulfate solution.

Secondary Mechanistic Aspects and Side Reactions of the Curtius, Schmidt, Hofmann, and Lossen Rearrangements. Certain of the many individual features of the several methods for achieving C-to-N rearrangement of carboxyl derivatives are of particular interest from the standpoint of mechanism,

[257] P. Yates and J. Fugger, *Chem. & Ind. (London)*, **1957**, 1511.

[258] A. L. Wilds and A. L. Meader, Jr., *J. Org. Chem.*, **13**, 763 (1948).

[259] O. Süs, *Ann.*, **556**, 65 (1944).

[259a] L. Horner, E. Spietschka, and A. Gross, *Ann.*, **573**, 17 (1951).

[260] J. De Jonge, R. Dykstra, and G. L. Wiggerink, *Rec. trav. chim.*, **71**, 846 (1952).

[261] A. Roedig and H. Lunk, *Chem. Ber.*, **87**, 971 (1954).

and are of additional importance because they are associated with the formation of major side products. Such features do not lend themselves to a unified presentation and are therefore collected separately here.

Unlike the other rearrangements in this group, the Curtius rearrangement has the same kind of atom in the leaving group as at the migration terminus, and the question naturally arises whether migration actually proceeds to the nearest nitrogen of the linear azide group. Bothner-By and Friedman [262] have rearranged an azide in which the outermost nitrogen was isotopically labeled, and shown that the labeling is found entirely in the ejected nitrogen (eq. 126). There seems no reason to doubt that the inner nitrogen is the one retained.

$$ArCO-NHNH_2 + HN^*O_2 \rightarrow ArCO-\overset{-}{N}-\overset{+}{N}\equiv N^* \xrightarrow[\text{(2) H}_2\text{O}]{\text{(1) heat}} Ar-NH_2 + NN^* \quad (126)$$

The substances at one time thought [262a] to be thioacyl azides, formed from thioacyl hydrazides, such as thiosemicarbazides, and nitrous acid, have been shown conclusively to exist as thiatriazoles.[263] Heating causes loss of sulfur as well as nitrogen, and nitriles are formed without rearrangement [263,264]

$$\begin{array}{ccc} R-\underset{\overset{\|}{S}}{C}-NHNH_2 \rightarrow & \left[R-\underset{\overset{\|}{S}}{C}-N_3\right] \rightarrow & R-\underset{\underset{\diagdown_N\diagup}{S}\ \ \ \underset{}{N}}{C}\!\!=\!\!\!=\!\!\!=\!\!N \xrightarrow[\text{or acid}]{\Delta} R-CN + S + N_2 \end{array} \quad (127)$$

(eq. 127). If decomposition is effected with ultraviolet radiation, a small amount of rearrangement to isothiocyanate occurs (eq. 128).[264a]

$$Ar-\underset{\underset{\diagdown_N\diagup}{S}\ \ \ \underset{}{N}}{C}\!\!=\!\!\!=\!\!\!=\!\!N \xrightarrow{h\nu} ArNCS + N_2 \ (10\%) \quad (128)$$

The Schmidt reaction is distinguished from the other carbon-to-nitrogen rearrangements of carboxyl derivatives by the fact that conversion of the carboxyl group to a nitrogenous derivative and rearrangement take place as one laboratory step. This complicates the interpretation of the kinetics and makes the reaction susceptible to effects not encountered with the Curtius, Hofmann, and Lossen rearrangements.

Particular attention has been aroused by the fact that benzoic acids with

[262] A. A. Bothner-By and L. Friedman, J. Am. Chem. Soc., **73**, 5391 (1951).

[262a] P. A. S. Smith, Org. Reactions, **3**, Chapt. 9 (1946).

[263] E. Lieber, C. N. R. Rao, C. N. Pillai, J. Ramachandran, and R. D. Hites, Can. J. Chem., **36**, 801 (1958).

[264] P. A. S. Smith and D. H. Kenny, J. Org. Chem., **26**, 5221 (1961).

[264a] W. Kirmse, Chem. Ber., **93**, 2353 (1960).

ortho substituents undergo the Schmidt reaction faster or at lower temperatures than ordinary acids. This feature was first encountered by Newman and Gildenhorn [146] during an attempt to accomplish selective replacement of the unhindered carboxyl group of 2,6-dimethylterephthalic acid; instead, the hindered one was replaced (eq. 129). They then determined that mesitoic acid

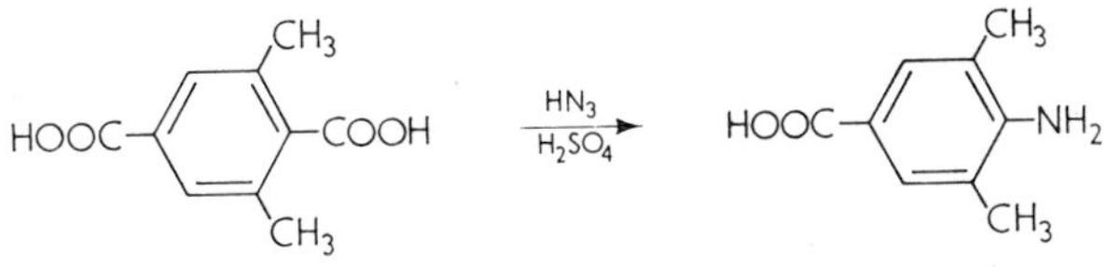

would undergo the Schmidt reaction at $0°$, although most carboxylic acids require warming; benzoic acid is intermediate in reactivity.[265] Since the same acids that so easily underwent the Schmidt reaction were known from freezing point depression studies to ionize with dehydration in concentrated sulfuric acid, it was natural to associate the two phenomena. The acylium ions, RCO^+, so formed are quite reactive and are converted to an ester simply by pouring their solutions into alcohol (eq. 130). Selected reactivity of hindered carboxyl groups has also been observed in aliphatic systems; the relative rates of carboxyl groups are in the order $tert > sec > prim.$[241]

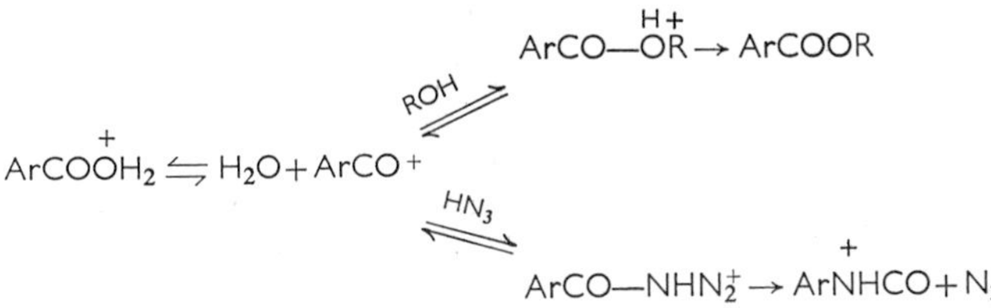

Kuhn and Corwin [265] used the phenomenon of rapid Schmidt reaction to study the formation of acylium ions from various esters and acids, a process they term "acylization." They found that p-anisic acid also undergoes Schmidt reaction at $0°$. Further studies have been made by Schechter and co-workers,[241] who found that all ortho substituents except fluoro, which is very small, accelerate the Schmidt reaction, and the degree of acceleration parallels the size of the group. The rates were second order overall at constant acidity, according to the expression

$$\text{Rate} = k(RCOOH)(HN_3)$$

However, meta and para substituents have been found to affect the rate according to a Hammett equation, the value of ρ being $-1.5.$[241]

Gould [266] has commented that any steric or electronic factors that would

[265] L. P. Kuhn and A. H. Corwin, *J. Am. Chem. Soc.*, **70**, 3370 (1948).

[266] E. S. Gould, *Mechanism and Structure in Organic Chemistry*, Holt, New York, 1959, p. 625.

favor dehydration of $\overset{+}{RCOOH_2}$ to RCO^+ should also favor the return of $RCO—NHN_2^+$ to RCO^+, and therefore the observed acceleration is consistent with attack of RCO^+ on HN_3, and not rearrangement, as the rate-determining step. That is, the acylium ion route cannot be expected to result in acceleration by providing a higher concentration of the rearranging species, but only by providing a faster route to it. This conclusion involves the unstated assumption that the rate of rearrangement of $RCO—NHN_2^+$ is not significantly affected by the factors that cause acylium ion formation and that the observed acceleration is due essentially to the route through the acylium ion. This assumption is almost certainly invalid, since the thermal and acid-catalyzed Curtius rearrangement, as well as the Hofmann and Lossen rearrangements, shows pronounced acceleration by ortho substituents, as has been mentioned earlier. Only if there were no such acceleration in these reactions, where the effects of events prior to the rearrangement step are eliminated, would it be necessary to invoke attack on hydrogen azide as the rate-determining step. As pointed out already (p. 536), Briggs and Lyttleton's observation that the self-decomposition of hydrogen azide is sharply reduced during Schmidt reaction on certain benzoic acids implies that in those cases, at least, rearrangement is the rate-determining step, and the initial attack of $\overset{+}{RCOOH_2}$ or RCO^+ on hydrogen azide must be fast enough to tie up substantial amounts of hydrogen azide. The published observations are consistent with the concept that either dehydration of

$$RCOOH_2 \quad \text{to} \quad \underset{NHN_2^+}{\overset{|}{RC—OH}} \rightleftharpoons \underset{NHN_2^+}{\overset{|}{RC=O}}$$

or rearrangement of one of these products, is rate determining, and that the steric acceleration is the result of faster rearrangement coupled with a rapid path for supplying the rearranging species. The acceleration observed with *p*-anisic acid can be assumed to be the normal electronic effect of the methoxyl group on the rate of migration, and not necessarily a result of acylization. Similar conclusions have been reached by Schechter and co-workers.[241]

An important side reaction occurs in the Schmidt reaction with tertiary alkyl carboxylic acids. Schuerch and Huntress obtained seven different alkyl amines from the Schmidt reaction on triethylacetic acid, plus triethylacetamide, mixtures of ketones, and carbon monoxide. They were able to obtain some of the normal product, *tert*-butylamine, from pivalic acid, but cleavage products were also formed in substantial quantities.[267] They observed that, although tertiary carboxylic acids are known to undergo decarbonylation in concentrated sulfuric acid, giving rise to products derived from the

[267] C. Schuerch and E. H. Huntress, *J. Am. Chem. Soc.*, **71**, 2223 (1949).

carbonium ion (eq. 131), such decomposition did not occur under their Schmidt reaction conditions in the absence of sodium azide. They therefore

$$R_3C\text{—}COOH \rightleftharpoons R_3C\text{—}CO\overset{+}{O}H_2 \rightleftharpoons R_3C^+ + CO + H_2O \qquad (131)$$

proposed that a nitrogen-containing intermediate, perhaps $RCONHN_2^+$, must be responsible for the production of carbon monoxide. It may be, however, that the effect of azide is to displace the equilibrium of equation 131 by reaction with the carbonium ion faster than with the carboxyl group; the existence of such an equilibrium has been demonstrated.[268] Schuerch and Huntress found that nitromethane is one of the few practical diluents for Schmidt reactions on carboxylic acids and that its use markedly retards cleavage reactions. With it as solvent, they were able to increase the yield of *tert*-butylamine from 33 to 55% and to obtain satisfactory yields of amines from ethyldimethylacetic acid and 1-methylcyclohexanecarboxylic acid.

The intermediacy of isocyanates or their conjugate acids in the Schmidt reaction is difficult to establish, since isocyanates are rapidly decomposed by concentrated sulfuric acid,[268a] which is virtually the only catalytic agent used with carboxylic acids. However, by using a mixture of trifluoroacetic acid and anhydride as the catalyst with phenanthrene-4-carboxylic acid, Rutherford and Newman [268b] were able to obtain the isocyanate in high yield (eq. 132).

$$(132)$$

There are several side reactions that can occur during the Hofmann rearrangement. The reaction of isocyanate with unrearranged amide to give an acyl urea (eq. 133) is particularly often encountered. It may be particularly

$$RNCO + R\text{—}CO\text{—}\overset{-}{N}\text{—}X \rightarrow RCO\text{—}\overset{-}{N}\text{—}CONR \xrightarrow{H_2O} RCO\text{—}NH\text{—}CONHR + OX^- \qquad (133)$$
$$\underset{X}{|}$$

prominent with large amides, where the solubilities of both reactants and products in aqueous solution are low and the hydrolysis of the isocyanate by hydroxide ion is thus retarded, but can be reduced by the use of a solvent other than water. The use of sodium methoxide in methanol, known as the Jeffreys' modification, is one of the most satisfactory alternatives. Recent

[268] A. Lundeen, *J. Am. Chem. Soc.*, **82**, 3228 (1960).
[268a] M. S. Newman and H. Gildenhorn, *J. Am. Chem. Soc.*, **70**, 317 (1948).
[268b] K. G. Rutherford and M. S. Newman, *J. Am. Chem. Soc.*, **79**, 213 (1957).

examples [269],[270] continue to demonstrate its value. Aqueous dioxane has also been used with marked success.[271]

Another side reaction in the Hofmann rearrangement is formation of nitriles. This is apparently not an example of fragmentation, but occurs by oxidation of the amine by halogen or hypohalite. Thus only when the attached group is primary are nitriles produced (eq. 134); when it is secondary,

$$R—CH_2NH_2 + 2X_2 \xrightarrow{OH^-} R—CN + 4H_2O + 4X^- \tag{134}$$

ketimines or derivatives are formed.[272] While this side reaction can be reduced by the obvious expedient of avoiding excess reagent, it is often not completely avoidable, owing to production of some amine before all the halogenating agent has reacted. If halogenation can be accomplished first at temperatures where rearrangement is slow, oxidation may be still further reduced. The effect of the order and rate of combination of the reactants may be of critical importance,[273],[274] but no generally valid recommendation can be made.

A reaction that may be related to the Hofmann rearrangement was reported in 1942 by White and Bergström [274a] but does not appear to have been further investigated. Treatment of 2-phenylcinchoninamide with potassium amide and potassium nitrate or mercury in liquid ammonia produced 2-phenyl-4-aminoquinoline in 90–98% yield; the carboxyl group appeared as cyanate (eq. 135). This reaction also occurred with two other cinchoninamide deriva-

tives, but failed with simpler amides such as benzamide and phenylacetamide. White and Bergström ruled out displacement of the carboxamido group by amide ion because that would have produced formamide instead of cyanate. Although they considered that rearrangement may have followed upon oxidation of the amide dianion, $Ar—CO—N^{2-}$, to an acylazene, $Ar—CO—N$, they gave evidence that the quinolyl isocyanate was not an intermediate. The isocyanate, prepared in another way, was found to react much more slowly

[269] J. A. Barltrop and R. F. Dodsworth, *J. Chem. Soc. (London)*, **1956**, 706.

[270] W. Treibs and S. Hauptmann, *Chem. Ber.*, **89**, 117 (1956).

[271] E. Magnien and R. Baltzly, *J. Org. Chem.*, **23**, 2029 (1958).

[272] A. Rahman and M. O. Farooq, *Rec. trav. chim.*, **76**, 423 (1954).

[273] N. Sperber and R. Fricano, *J. Am. Chem. Soc.*, **71**, 3352 (1949).

[274] B. L. Murr and C. T. Lester, *J. Am. Chem. Soc.*, **77**, 1684 (1955).

[274a] H. C. White and F. W. Bergström, *J. Org. Chem.*, **7**, 497 (1942).

with KNH_2 than the amide, and so could have been isolated had it been formed. On the other hand, it is possible that the acylazene could undergo displacement by amide ion to produce amine and cyanate

$$Ar—CO—\ddot{N}: + NH_2^- \rightarrow Ar—NH_2 + OCN^-$$

and rearrangement might not be involved at all.

An alternative haloamide rearrangement that competes successfully with the normal Hofmann rearrangement on α-haloamides has already been alluded to. The stoichiometric effect is replacement of the carboxamido group by halogen instead of an amino group (eq. 136). Stevens and co-workers[275]

$$R—CHX—CONH—X' \rightarrow R—CHXX' + NCO^- \tag{136}$$

demonstrated that α-halo isocyanates could not be intermediates, which indicated that Hofmann rearrangement could not have occurred. They also showed by use of isotopically labeled bromine that there is no exchange between N-bromoamide halogen and external bromide ion, which they interpreted to mean that the reaction is an internal displacement with a four-membered ring transition state (eq. 137). The reaction was found to proceed

$$R_2\underset{X}{C}—CO—\bar{N}—Br \longrightarrow \underset{X}{R_2C}\overset{O}{\underset{Br}{\overset{\parallel}{\diagdown}}}\overset{}{N} \longrightarrow R_2\underset{X}{C}—Br + NCO^- \tag{137}$$

best when hypobromite acted on α-chloroamides. Husted and Kohlhase[276] found other examples of this reaction among perfluoroamides, with yields as high as 92%; they were not able to achieve it with N-iodoamides, however. With trifluoroacetamide, only a small yield of trifluorobromomethane was obtained, and other workers[277] have reported obtaining hexafluoroethane. Replacement of carboxamide by bromine has also been encountered with nitrobromoacetamide, which gives no normal rearrangement;[278] nitroacetamide gives the same product, nitrodibromomethane, through first undergoing α bromination.

Another reaction of N-haloamides that accomplishes replacement of carboxyl by halogen is shown by N-bromosuccinimide. Johnson and Bublitz[279] have reported that it is converted to β-bromopropionyl isocyanate (eq. 138)

[275] C. L. Stevens, T. K. Mukherjee, and V. J. Traynelis, J. Am. Chem. Soc., 78, 2264 (1956).

[276] D. R. Husted and W. L. Kohlhase, J. Am. Chem. Soc., 76, 5141 (1954).

[277] E. Gryszkiewicz-Trochimowski, A. Sporszynski, and A. Wnuk, Rec. trav. chim., 66, 426 (1947).

[278] S. Brownstein, J. Org. Chem., 23, 113 (1958).

[279] H. W. Johnson and D. E. Bublitz, J. Am. Chem. Soc., 80, 3150 (1958).

when treated with benzoyl peroxide in the presence of allyl halides in chloroform or bromoform solution (but not in other solvents). This is evidently a free radical reaction and only superficially related to the Hofmann rearrangement.

$$
\underset{\substack{\text{(a succinimide-N-Br)}}}{}\quad \xrightarrow[\text{CH}_2\text{CHCH}_2\text{Cl}]{(\text{C}_6\text{H}_5\text{COO})_2}\quad \text{Br—CH}_2\text{CH}_2\text{CONCO}
\tag{138}
$$

In the Lossen rearrangement of O-acylhydroxamic acids, the O-acyl group may be sulfonyl or phosphoryl,[280] as well as the more usual carboxyl; the effectiveness in promoting rearrangement appears to be proportional to the anionic stability of the acylating acid. In many cases acylation under basic conditions is followed so rapidly by rearrangement that the O-acylhydroxamic acid cannot be isolated. A considerable amount of attention has been given to phosphorylation[281] in connection with the quest for anticholinesterase inhibitors. The rate-determining step for Lossen rearrangement carried out in this way is usually acylation.

Phosphorylation by polyphosphoric acid under acidic conditions is also effective; since this reagent is also capable of bringing about the conversion of carboxylic acids to hydroxamic acids by reaction with hydroxylamine salts, and since rearrangement follows rapidly upon phosphorylation, polyphosphoric acid can be used to bring about a one-step conversion of carboxylic acids to amines (eq. 139).[281(d)] This process is very much like the Schmidt

$$
\text{R—COOH} \xrightarrow[\text{NH}_2\text{OH},\Delta]{\text{PPA}} \text{R—NH}_2 + \text{CO}_2
\tag{139}
$$

reaction, but with hydroxylamine in place of hydrogen azide, and presumably follows a similar course. It gives good yields with benzoic acids, but moderate to poor with aliphatic acids.[282]

Thermal decomposition of O-acylhydroxamic acids has been reported to give ureas,[282a] but Walling and Naglieri[283] have shown that the initial products are an isocyanate and a carboxylic acid (eq. 140). They also investi-

[280] B. E. Hackley, Jr., R. Plapinger, M. Stolberg, and T. Wagner-Jauregg, *J. Am. Chem. Soc.*, **77**, 3651 (1955).

[281] (a) R. Swidler, R. E. Plapinger, and G. M. Steinberg, *J. Am. Chem. Soc.*, **81**, 3271 (1959). (b) R. Swidler and G. M. Steinberg, *J. Am. Chem. Soc.*, **78**, 3594 (1956). (c) A. L. Green, G. L. Sainsbury, B. Saville, and M. Stansfield, *J. Chem. Soc. (London)*, **1958**, 1583. (d) G. F. Endres and J. Epstein, *J. Org. Chem.*, **24**, 1497 (1959). (d) H. R. Snyder, C. T. Elston, and D. B. Kellom, *J. Am. Chem. Soc.*, **75**, 2014 (1953).

[282] H. R. Snyder and C. T. Elston, *J. Am. Chem. Soc.*, **76**, 3039 (1954).

[282a] G. Caronna, *Gazz. chim. ital.*, **83**, 527 (1953).

[283] C. Walling and A. N. Naglieri, *J. Am. Chem. Soc.*, **82**, 1820 (1960).

gated the kinetics with a group of para-substituted O-benzoylbenzohydrox-
amic acids. The rates were found to be first order, and the unsubstituted

$$C_6H_5CO-NH-O-COC_6H_5 \rightarrow C_6H_5-NCO+HOCOC_6H_5 \qquad (140)$$

compound had a half-life of about one hour at 114°; the activation energy
was about 33 kcal./mole. The initial products gave rise to ureas on further
heating. By extrapolation the ratio of the rate of thermal rearrangement of
acid to that of the potassium salt was estimated to be 1:3700. The strong
effect of substituents on the leaving group observed by Hauser and Renfrow with the rearrangement of the salts was absent from the behavior
of the free acids, and the effect of substituents on the migrating group, while
parallel to that on the rearrangement of the salts, was about 40% less.
Substitution of deuterium for hydrogen on the nitrogen, giving C_6H_5CO-
$ND-O-COC_6H_5$, reduced the rate by a factor of 1.29.

Walling and Naglieri concluded that there must be strong assistance by the
migrating group, and that there may be a rapid tautomeric equilibrium with
a zwitterionic form that does the rearranging (eq. 141). The effect of acid-

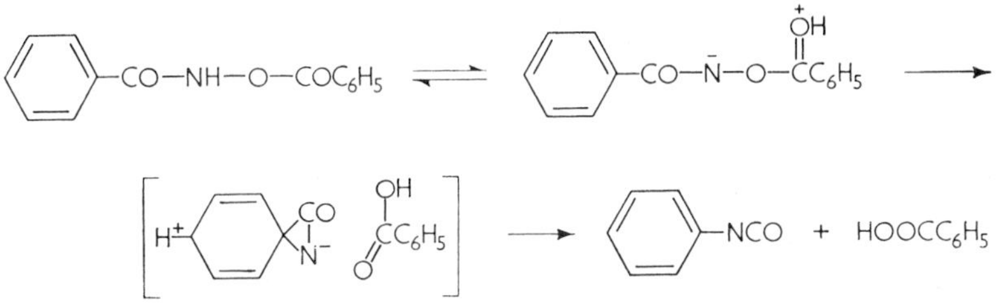

$$(141)$$

strengthening substituents on the leaving group would be to shift the equilibrium step to the left as well as to accelerate the rearrangement of the
zwitterion; the two effects, being opposed, would result in only a small over-
all influence. The suggestion of Leffler [284] that intramolecular hydrogen bonding between the —NH— and the carbonyl of the leaving group is involved in
thermal Lossen rearrangement can be looked upon as the path by which the
necessary proton transfer takes place. Leffler found no evidence for rearrangement in the opposite sense, involving C—to—O migration, even with O-p-
nitrobenzoylbenzohydroxamic acid. However, about 1% of a side reaction
capable of inducing polymerization of vinyl monomers was detected by
Walling and Naglieri; under photolytic conditions, this free radical reaction
becomes dominant.

Derivatives of the imido ester form of hydroxamic acids also rearrange.

[284] J. E. Leffler, *J. Am. Chem. Soc.*, **72**, 4294 (1950).

Kuhara and Ishikawa [285] prepared the benzenesulfonyl derivative of what was apparently ethyl N-hydroxybenzimidate and found that it rearranged to phenyl isocyanate and ethyl benzenesulfonate (eq. 142), a reaction that might

$$C_6H_5—C=N—OSO_2C_6H_5 \rightarrow C_6H_5—NCO + C_2H_5OSO_2C_6H_5 \qquad (142)$$
$$| \\ OC_2H_5$$

also be considered a Beckmann rearrangement. Another example is apparently at the same time the only example of rearrangement of a thiohydroxamic acid derivative. Ettlinger and Lundeen [286] synthesized glucotropaeolate from phenylacetothiohydroxamic acid and observed that it liberated benzyl isothiocyanate when exposed to the protein fraction of yellow mustard—an "enzymatic Lossen rearrangement" (eq. 143). A curious reaction whose rela-

$$R—S—C=N—OSO_3{}^- \rightarrow C_6H_5CH_2NCS \qquad (143)$$
$$| \\ CH_2C_6H_5$$
$$R = glucoside$$

tion to the Lossen rearrangement is not certain has recently been reported.[287] Trifluoroacetohydroxamic acid on heating alone to 160–200° gives trifluoronitrosomethane and formaldehyde (eq. 144). The authors assumed that nor-

$$CF_3CONHOH \xrightarrow{160-200°} CF_3NO + CH_2O \qquad (144)$$

mal rearrangement first took place, giving an isocyanate, which then underwent hydrolysis in an abnormal way. However, trifluoromethyl isocyanate has been prepared in other ways,[288] and its normal behavior toward alcohol and toward hydrogen halides does not support the above explanation.

Structural Effects, Scope, and Techniques of the Curtius, Schmidt, Hofmann, and Lossen Rearrangements. The purpose of this section is to give a brief survey of the principal developments in the use of these rearrangements since the last major reviews of them. For this reason, most of the references

[285] M. Kuhara and F. Ishikawa, *Mem. Coll. Sci., Kyoto Imp. Univ.*, **1**, 355 (1916); *Chem. Abstr.*, **11**, 580 (1917).

[286] M. G. Ettlinger and A. J. Lundeen, *J. Am. Chem. Soc.*, **79**, 1764 (1957), **78**, 4172 (1956).

[287] I. L. Knunyants and G. A. Sokol'skii, *Doklady Akad. Nauk S.S.S.R.*, **132**, 602 (1960).

[288] (a) D. A. Barr and R. N. Haszeldine, *J. Chem. Soc.* (*London*), **1956**, 3428. (b) A. H. Ahlbrecht and D. R. Husted, U. S. Pat. 2,617,817; *Chem. Abstr.*, **47**, 8775c (1953). (c) N. N. Yarovenko, S. P. Motornyi, L. I. Kirenskaya, and A. S. Vasil'eva, *Zhur. Obshchei Khim.*, **27**, 2243 (1957).

given are to publications since 1944; earlier references can be found in the reviews cited.[289]

Alkyl groups of all types—primary, secondary, and tertiary—migrate readily in all four rearrangements. A fragmentation side reaction in the Schmidt reaction, which has been discussed in the foregoing part, is not encountered with the other rearrangements. The migration of substituted amino groups to form hydrazines by the Curtius and Hofmann rearrangements has already been mentioned; an analogous Lossen rearrangement has not been observed.[291]

Multiple degradation of polycarboxylic acid derivatives is in general feasible by all methods, although complications may be expected with malonic and succinic derivatives. The Curtius rearrangement appears to be the only one generally successful with such compounds; double rearrangement gives *gem*-diisocyanates or 1,2-diisocyanates readily. Hydrolysis of *gem*-diisocyanates (or their urethane derivatives) does not give *gem*-diamines, of course, since these are unstable, but it does give rise to aldehydes or ketones in a preparatively useful manner.[292,293] In contrast, the Schmidt reaction converts only one carboxyl group of malonic and succinic acids to amines,[293a,294], and α- or β-amino acids are produced. It is apparently the electrostatic effect of the protonated amino group formed from one carboxyl group that protects the remaining carboxyl from reaction (which must proceed through protonation) when the groups are close. The Hofmann and Lossen rearrangements of malonic and succinic derivatives are complicated by cyclization, which occurs because both amide and hydroxamic functions are capable of reaction

[289] Over 500 examples of the Curtius rearrangement have been tabulated in *Organic Reactions*[289a] from work published up to 1944. The Schmidt reaction on carboxylic acids has also been reviewed up to 1944[289b]; it has seen much less application, partly because of its much later discovery and partly because the conditions required (warm concentrated sulfuric acid) may be undesirably severe. The Hofmann rearrangement[289c] is covered in the same volume of *Organic Reactions* as the foregoing rearrangements; about 200 examples reported up to 1942 are tabulated. The Lossen rearrangement is the oldest of the group, having been reported in 1872,[289d] but it has seen relatively little application; two good reviews exist.[290,290a]

[289a] P. A. S. Smith, *Org. Reactions*, **3**, Chapt. 9 (1946).

[289b] H. Wolff, *Org. Reactions*, **3**, Chapt. 8 (1946).

[289c] E. S. Wallis and J. F. Lane, *Org. Reactions*, **3**, Chapt. 7 (1946).

[289d] H. Lossen, *Ann.*, **161**, 347 (1872).

[290] H. L. Yale, *Chem. Revs.*, **33**, 209 (1943).

[290a] F. Mathis, *Bull. soc. chim. France*, **1953**, D9.

[291] C. D. Hurd, *J. Am. Chem. Soc.*, **45**, 1472 (1923).

[292] M. Mousseron and R. Jacquier, *Bull. soc. chim. France*, **1950**, 648.

[293] M. M. Fraser and R. Raphael, *J. Chem. Soc. (London)*, **1955**, 4280.

[293a] L. H. Briggs, G. C. De Ath, and S. R. Ellis, *J. Chem. Soc. (London)*, **1942**, 61.

[294] (a) D. W. Adamson, *J. Chem. Soc. (London)*, **1939**, 1564. (b) S. Rothschild and M. Fields, *J. Org. Chem.*, **16**, 1080 (1951).

with isocyanates at their —NH— sites. The result is formation of hydantoins or dihydrouracils,[295] which are derivatives of amino acids, although they are not easily hydrolyzed to them. Completion of double rearrangement may still be possible in the case of the Lossen, however, for it has been accomplished, albeit in an unusual manner, with succinhydroxamic acid.[295c] Treatment with benzenesulfonyl chloride produces N-benzenesulfonoxydihydrouracil, which is converted by lithium aluminum hydride into N,N'-dimethylethylene-diamine (eq. 145). The reducing agent apparently functions initially as a base

$$OCN-CH_2CH_2-NCO \xrightarrow{\text{LiAlH}_4} CH_3NH-CH_2CH_2-NHCH_3 \tag{145}$$

to bring about completion of the rearrangement. Attempts have been made to convert acrylic polymers to polyamines by the Curtius,[296] Hofmann,[297] and Lossen [296] rearrangements, but success was very limited, owing to cyclizations at an intermediate stage. There are many examples of successful preparation of diamines from 1,3- and more widely separated dicarboxylic acids by the Curtius,[298,299] Schmidt,[300,301] and Hofmann [302] rearrangements. Diphenic acids, however, give phenanthridones by the Schmidt reaction,[302a,b] although their amides can be converted to 2,2'-diaminobiphenyls readily by the Hofmann rearrangement.[303]

[295] (a) R. T. Jones, J. Org. Chem., 25, 956 (1960). (b) R. A. Baxter and F. S. Spring, J. Chem. Soc. (London), 1945, 229. (c) L. Bauer, J. Am. Chem. Soc., 78, 1945 (1956).

[296] (a) W. Kern, Angew. Chem., 64, 612 (1952). (b) M. Vrancken and G. Smets, J. Polymer Sci., 14, 521 (1954). (c) J. Kovács, V. Bruckner, and K. Kovács, J. Chem. Soc. (London), 1953, 145.

[297] M. Mullier and G. Smets, J. Polymer Sci., 23, 915 (1957); N. D. Zakharov and S. A. Pavlov, Zhur. Obshchei Khim., 26, 2290 (1956).

[298] P. A. S. Smith, Org. Syntheses, 36, 69 (1956).

[299] K. Hofmann, J. Am. Chem. Soc., 71, 164 (1949).

[300] D. E. Ames, R. E. Bowman, G. A. H. Buttle, and S. Squires, J. Chem. Soc. (London), 1952, 1057.

[301] (a) D. M. Hall, S. Mahboob, and E. E. Turner, J. Chem. Soc. (London), 1952, 149. (b) C. G. Overberger, A. Fischman, C. W. Roberts, L. H. Arond, and J. Lal, J. Am. Chem. Soc., 73, 2540 (1951).

[302] C. M. Samour and J. P. Mason, J. Am. Chem. Soc., 76, 441 (1954).

[302a] T. A. Bak, Acta Chem. Scand., 8, 1733 (1954).

[302b] G. M. Badger and J. H. Seidler, J. Chem. Soc. (London), 1954, 2329.

[303] N. Tokura and S. Anagawa, Sci. Repts. Research Insts. Tohoku Univ., Ser. A, 9, 239 (1957); Chem. Abstr., 52, 1964e (1958).

Stepwise degradation of di- and polycarboxylic acid derivatives is useful for the preparation of amino acids, and the limitations discussed in the fore-going paragraph applying to malonic and succinic derivatives become advantages. The rearrangement of diazides cannot be accomplished stepwise, however, and it is necessary to prepare monoazides if the Curtius rearrangement is to be used. A number of α-amino acids have been prepared [304] from cyanoacetic esters by the Curtius rearrangement, making use of the fact that only the ester function reacts readily with hydrazine, and can then be converted to an α-cyano acyl azide. Rearrangement of the monoazide of adipic acid in inert environment gives an apparently polymeric carboxylic-carbamic anhydride,[305] [—OOC—(CH$_2$)$_4$—NH—CO—]$_x$, which must be hydrolyzed to obtain an amino acid. The electrostatic protective effect of an adjacent amino group in the Schmidt reaction makes possible the conversion of malonic acids to α-amino acids.[293a,294,305a] This effect has been utilized in converting α- and β-aminodicarboxylic acids, such as the aminopimelic acids, to diamino acids;[305b,294] only the distant carboxyl is affected. Selective Hofmann degradation has been accomplished with ester amides,[270] such as EtOOC—(CH$_2$)$_{14}$—CONH$_2$, which give ω-amino acids, and with malonamic acids,[306] which give α-amino acids. An unusual case is the conversion of 4,5,6-tricarbethoxypicolinamide to an amino triester.[307] Amino acids (or the corresponding lactams) can also be obtained by the Hofmann rearrangement of cyclic imides [308,309] or the Lossen rearrangement of N-hydroxyimides; [310–312] hydrolysis to half amides or half hydroxamic acids apparently occurs first in a more or less predictable way.[288d] Lossen rearrangement of the benzoyl or benzenesulfonyl derivatives of half hydroxamic acids may be conducted so as to give polyamides, which result from loss of carbon dioxide from the carbamic-carboxylic anhydrides first formed; [313,314] the half hydroxamic

[304] (a) P. E. Gagnon, J. L. Boivin, and J. Giguére, *Can. J. Research*, **28B**, 352 (1950); P. E. Gagnon, J. L. Boivin, and P. A. Boivin, *Can. J. Research*, **28B**, 207 (1950).

[305] C. D. Hurd, C. M. Buess, and L. Bauer, *J. Org. Chem.*, **17**, 865 (1952).

[305a] S. Takagi and K. Hayashi, *Chem. and Pharm. Bull. (Tokyo)*, **7**, 183 (1959); K. Hayashi, *Chem. and Pharm. Bull. (Tokyo)*, **7**, 187 (1959); *Chem. Abstr.*, **54**, 22389 (1960).

[305b] L. Birkofer and I. Storch, *Ber.*, **86**, 749 (1953).

[306] W. Parker and R. A. Raphael, *J. Chem. Soc. (London)*, **1955**, 1723.

[307] R. G. Jones, *J. Am. Chem. Soc.*, **73**, 5610 (1951).

[308] A. N. Parshin, *Zhur. Obshchei Khim.*, **20**, 1826 (1950).

[309] Y. Yamazaki, T. Ishii, and S. Takeuchi, *Yûki Gôsei Kagaku Kyôkai Shi*, **15**, 35 (1957); *Chem. Abstr.*, **51**, 10454d (1957).

[310] L. Bauer and S. V. Miarka, *J. Org. Chem.*, **24**, 1293 (1959).

[311] C. M. Buess and L. Bauer, *J. Org. Chem.*, **20**, 33 (1955).

[312] E. Kühle and R. Wegler, *Ann.*, **616**, 183 (1958).

[313] C. D. Hurd and C. M. Buess, *J. Am. Chem. Soc.*, **73**, 2409 (1951).

[314] L. Bauer, *J. Org. Chem.*, **21**, 1182 (1956).

acids derived from succinic and phthalic acids form cyclic carbamic-carboxylic anhydrides (oxazolidiones),[314a] which do not lose carbon dioxide.

Unsaturation does not interfere with C—to—N migration, whether of vinyl, allyl, or other unsaturated structures. The intermediate vinyl isocyanates (and urethanes) are readily isolated in the Curtius rearrangement. However, the vinylamines which would be formed by hydrolysis are tautomeric with aldimines (or ketimines) and are rapidly hydrolyzed further to aldehydes or ketones (eq. 146). The preparation of a ketone by such a process has been

$$
\overset{|}{\underset{|}{C}}=\overset{|}{\underset{|}{C}}-COOH \rightarrow \overset{\diagdown}{}C=\overset{|}{\underset{\diagup}{C}}-NCO \rightarrow \left[\overset{\diagdown}{}C=\overset{|}{\underset{\diagup}{C}}-NH_2 \right] \rightarrow \overset{\diagdown}{}CH-\overset{|}{\underset{\diagup}{C}}=O \qquad (146)
$$

utilized in the synthesis of muscarone.[315] The same sort of conversion has been accomplished by the Schmidt reaction,[316] but since ketones are more susceptible to the Schmidt reaction than are carboxylic acids, the reaction of the carboxyl group must be completed before there has been time for hydrolysis of much vinyl isocyanate (or enamine).

Substitution by halogen does not prevent migration, although it may retard it; perfluoroalkyl groups have been found to migrate in the Curtius rearrangement,[317,288] but not in the Hofmann.[276] Although no special instability is associated with α-halo isocyanates, α-haloamines cannot be obtained from them; hydrolysis usually gives aldehydes or ketones instead. The Hofmann degradation of α-haloamides thus produces aldehydes directly,[318] unless the competing reaction leading to *gem*-dihalo compounds, discussed in the foregoing part, takes precedence. An alternative reaction observed with α-halo isocyanates is dehydrohalogenation to a vinyl isocyanate.[319]

Aldehydes or ketones also arise from α-hydroxy and α-amino acids. Rearrangement occurs normally by the Curtius,[320] Hofmann,[321] or Lossen[322] path, but α-hydroxy isocyanates spontaneously eliminate cyanic acid to form carbonyl compounds (eq. 147). When elimination is prevented, as in α-alkoxy acids, carbonyl compounds may still be produced, but only by hydrolysis of

[314a] C. Mauguin, *Ann. chim.*, [8]**22**, 297 (1911).

[315] C. H. Eugster, F. Häfliger, R. Denss, and E. Girod, *Helv. Chim. Acta*, **41**, 205 (1958).

[316] P. Bagchi and D. K. Banerjee, *J. Indian Chem. Soc.*, **23**, 397 (1946).

[317] (a) D. A. Barr and R. N. Haszeldine, *J. Chem. Soc.* (*London*), **1956**, 3428. (b) A. H. Ahlbrecht and D. R. Husted, U. S. Pat. 2,617,817; *Chem. Abstr.*, **47**, 8775c (1953). (c) N. N. Yarovenko, S. P. Motornyi, L. I. Kirenskaya, and A. S. Vasil'eva, *Zhur. Obshchei Khim.*, **27**, 2243 (1957).

[318] V. M. Rodionov, E. N. Alekseeva, and V. A. Vaver, *Zhur. Obshchei Khim.*, **23**, 1842 (1953).

[319] H. D. Zook, M. Ream, and E. W. Delchamps, *J. Am. Chem. Soc.*, **75**, 5590 (1953).

[320] T. Curtius, *J. prakt. Chem.*, [2]**94**, 273 (1916).

[321] C. L. Arcus and D. B. Greenwood, *J. Chem. Soc.* (*London*), **1953**, 1937.

[322] L. W. Jones and D. H. Powers, *J. Am. Chem. Soc.*, **46**, 2518 (1924).

the isocyanato group.[322] α-Amido groups, as found in peptides, lead to α-amido isocyanates, or ureas derived from them. Unlike the hydroxy analogues, they do not eliminate cyanic acid, but must be hydrolyzed to obtain conversion to aldehydes or ketones.[323] In this way the Lossen rearrangement has been applied to the stepwise degradation of peptides.[324]

$$\begin{array}{c}\diagdown \\ C-COOH \\ \diagup | \\ OH \end{array} \rightarrow \begin{array}{c}\diagdown \\ C-NCO \\ \diagup | \\ OH \end{array} \rightarrow \begin{array}{c}\diagdown \\ C=O + HNCO \\ \diagup \end{array} \qquad (147)$$

Hydroxyl groups at other sites have a different effect; normal rearrangement occurs, but urethane formation between the hydroxyl group and the isocyanato group occurs. When the hydroxyl group is β or γ, the products are cyclic.[321,325,326] A special case is represented by *trans*-2-hydroxycyclohexanecarbonyl azide, however, which has been reported to undergo ring contraction and elimination as well as Curtius rearrangement, giving cyclopentanecarboxaldehyde.[327] Normal Curtius rearrangement occurs in ethanol solution. A phenolic hydroxyl adjacent to an amide can interfere with the Hofmann rearrangement, however, for in such phenols the hydroxyl group is a stronger acid than the haloamido group. Rearrangement is retarded because the concentration of haloamide anion is low, and the competing reaction of ring halogenation occurs instead.[321] The use of unusually high alkalinity restores normal behavior. β-Amino or β-amido groups lead to cyclic ureas by reaction of the initially formed isocyanate with the —NH—structure if it is present; otherwise there is no effect.[328] The inhibiting effect of α- and β-amino groups in the Schmidt reaction has already been mentioned.

The ketonic carbonyl group does not interfere with rearrangement, as shown by the conversion of fluorenone-1-carboxamide [329] and tropolone-β-acetamide [330] to amines, although it may complicate the preparation of the required acid derivative. o-Benzoylbenzoic acid, for example, has been converted to an azide, but its structure is that of a lactol derivative, and its rearrangement [330a,331] (eq. 148) is more properly considered as that of a

[323] C. D. Hurd and J. W. Fan, *J. Am. Chem. Soc.*, **73**, 110 (1951).

[324] T. Wieland and H. Fritz, *Chem. Ber.*, **86**, 1186 (1953).

[325] (a) E. D. Bergmann and M. Sulzbacher, *J. Org. Chem.*, **16**, 84 (1951). (b) M. S. Newman and A. Kutner, *J. Am. Chem. Soc.*, **73**, 4199 (1951). (c) P. A. S. Smith and J. M. Sullivan, *J. Org. Chem.*, **26**, 1132 (1961).

[326] Z. Eckstein, *Roczniki Chem.*, **28**, 549 (1954); *Chem. Abstr.*, **50**, 305d (1956).

[327] M. Mousseron and R. Jacquier, *Bull. soc. chim. France*, **1950**, 238.

[328] S. I. Kanevskaya and D. S. Yaskina, *Zhur. Obshchei Khim.*, **27**, 65, 68 (1957).

[329] N. Kharasch and T. C. Bruice, *J. Am. Chem. Soc.*, **73**, 3240 (1951).

[330] R. A. Baxter, Brit. Pat. 771,484; *Chem. Abstr.*, **51**, 14819a (1957).

[330a] G. M. Badger and R. T. Howard, *Chem. & Ind.* (*London*), **1950**, 601.

[331] M. V. Bhatt, *Chem. & Ind.* (*London*), **1956**, 1390.

heterocyclic azide rather than as a Curtius rearrangement. α-Keto amides apparently undergo normal rearrangement, but the products are acids having

(148)

one less carbon atom,[332] along with cyanate. This cannot be the result of hydrolysis of an initially formed acyl isocyanate, since such compounds are known to hydrolyze instead to amides. The presumption is that it is actually the *gem*-diol hydrates of the α-keto amides, $RC(OH)_2CONH_2$, that react, and that the resulting α,α-dihydroxy isocyanate undergoes the customary elimination of cyanic acid (eq. 149); a path by formation of an *N*-bromoaziridone and its subsequent fragmentation is also consistent with the facts.

$$R-C(OH)_2NCO \rightarrow R-COOH + HNCO \qquad (149)$$

Carbocyclic rings of all sizes and complexity have been observed to migrate readily and without disruption in the Curtius [333-337] and Schmidt [316,338-340] rearrangements. The only reported abnormal occurrence is with benzonorcaradienecarbonyl azide, which when rearranged in benzyl alcohol gives a product in which the cyclopropane ring has been opened.[341] Normal rearrangement appears to take place first to give an isocyanate, since rearrangement in the absence of alcohol gave a product showing infrared absorption charac-

[332] C. L. Arcus and B. S. Prydal, *J. Chem. Soc. (London)*, **1954**, 4018.

[333] S. Wawzonek and J. V. Hallum, *J. Org. Chem.*, **18**, 288 (1953).

[334] P. D. Bartlett and F. D. Greene, *J. Am. Chem. Soc.*, **76**, 1088 (1954).

[335] (a) W. D. Crow, R. D. Haworth, and P. R. Jefferies, *J. Chem. Soc. (London)*, **1952**, 3705. (b) W. E. Parham, W. T. Hunter, and R. Hanson, *J. Am. Chem. Soc.*, **73**, 5068 (1951).

[336] D. N. Kursanov, M. E. Vol'pin, I. S. Akhrem, and I. Ya Kachkurova, *Izvest. Akad. Nauk S.S.S.R., Otdel. Khim. Nauk*, **1957**, 1371.

[337] (a) A. Burger and G. T. Fitchett, *J. Am. Chem. Soc.*, **74**, 3415 (1952). (b) H. A. Hoffman and A. Burger, *J. Am. Chem. Soc.*, **74**, 5485 (1952). (c) A. Burger and W. L. Yost, *J. Am. Chem. Soc.*, **70**, 2198 (1948).

[338] A. C. Cope and E. S. Graham, *J. Am. Chem. Soc.*, **73**, 4702 (1951).

[339] D. S. Noyce, *J. Am. Chem. Soc.*, **73**, 20 (1951).

[340] K. Sen and P. Bagchi, *Sci. and Culture (India)*, **21**, 545 (1956).

[341] W. E. Doering and M. J. Goldstein, *Tetrahedron*, **5**, 53 (1959).

teristic of that group. The closely related compound, norcaradienecarbonyl azide, is reported to give the isocyanate normally.[336]

Heterocyclic systems in great variety of ring size, degree of saturation, and composition have been found to migrate uneventfully in the Curtius [342-344] and Hofmann [344a,345] rearrangements. Since most heterocyclic systems are basic, the Schmidt reaction can be expected to be inhibited in a way similar to the effect of adjacent basic groups in open chain systems.

Some useful innovations in the application of these rearrangements to synthesis have appeared in recent years. When other functional groups must be protected from hydrolysis, the Curtius rearrangement can be conducted so as to lead to an amine by two nonhydrolytic paths. In one, rearrangement is carried out in benzyl alcohol, producing a benzyl urethane, which can be cleaved to an amine, carbon dioxide, and toluene by hydrogenolysis.[346] Alternatively, azides may be rearranged in a pyridine solution of phthalic anhydride, which converts them to phthalimides,[342] which may then be cleaved to amines with hydrazine. Secondary amines instead of primary can be obtained by reducing the intermediate isocyanates, obtainable in inert solvents, with lithium aluminum hydride.[347]

The Hofmann rearrangement has been conducted in a nonalkaline environment by the use of dry potassium fluoride suspended in benzene or cyclohexane; this reagent converts N-haloamides to acylureas.[348] Isocyanates, which are usually very difficult to isolate from Hofmann rearrangements, have been obtained in good yields from highly branched acids, in which the branching greatly retards the usually rapid hydrolysis of the isocyanate function.[348a,349] The Hofmann rearrangement has been adapted as an efficient method for preparing isotopically labeled amines.[350]

The Lossen rearrangement had until recently seen no true application to synthesis, principally because it seems to have no significant advantages over

[342] M. Aeberli and H. Erlenmeyer, *Helv. Chim. Acta*, **31**, 470 (1948).

[343] P. Gagnon, J. L. Boivin, and A. Chisholm, *Can. J. Chem.*, **30**, 904 (1952).

[344] B. R. Baker, R. E. Schaub, J. P. Joseph, F. J. McEvoy and J. H. Williams, *J. Org. Chem.*, **18**, 138 (1953).

[344a] (a) R. T. Jones, *J. Org. Chem.*, **25**, 956 (1960); (b) R. A. Baxter and F. S. Spring, *J. Chem. Soc. (London)*, **1945**, 229; (c) L. Bauer, *J. Am. Chem. Soc.*, **78**, 1945 (1956).

[345] H. Stenzl, *Helv. Chim. Acta*, **33**, 1183 (1950).

[346] M. Bergmann and L. Zervas, *J. Biol. Chem.*, **113**, 341 (1936).

[347] V. Boekelheide and G. K. Vick, *J. Am. Chem. Soc.*, **78**, 653 (1956).

[348] L. Rand and M. J. Albinak, *J. Org. Chem.*, **25**, 1837 (1960).

[348a] N. Sperber and R. Fricano, *J. Am. Chem. Soc.*, **71**, 3352 (1949).

[349] N. P. Buu-Hoï and L. Petit, *J. Org. Chem.*, **25**, 726 (1960).

[350] E. Sawicki, F. E. Ray, and V. Glocklin, *J. Org. Chem.*, **21**, 243 (1956).

the other rearrangements, but two examples [351,352] have now appeared. In addition, it has been used to generate phenyl isocyanate *in situ* for the phenylcarbamoylation of proteins.[353]

The Scope and Application of the Wolff Rearrangement. The rearrangement of α-diazo ketones was actually discovered in 1902 by Wolff and co-workers [354] when they treated several α-diazo-β-dicarbonyl compounds with boiling water (eq. 149a), although at the time it was thought that the diazo

$$CH_3CO—CN_2—COOEt \xrightarrow[H_2O]{\Delta} HOOC—CHCH_3—COOEt \qquad (149a)$$

compounds had an oxadiazole structure. Only much later did Wolff report [354a] the correct recognition of the rearrangement and the catalytic role of silver compounds. Little attention was paid to these discoveries until a general and convenient synthesis of α-diazo ketones from acid chlorides and diazoalkanes was reported by Arndt, Eistert, and Partale [355] in 1927 (eq. 150). This re-

$$R—CO—Cl + 2CH_2N_2 \rightarrow R—CO—CHN_2 + CH_3Cl + N_2 \qquad (150)$$

action is of great importance for the utilization of the rearrangement, for it allows an acid to be converted to its next higher homolog, taking advantage of the reactivity of ketenes toward addition of water, alcohols, and amines to give acids, esters, or amides, respectively. The over-all synthetic procedure has become known as the Arndt-Eistert synthesis and has been reviewed by Bachmann and Struve [355a] and by Eistert.[356] The reactions of diazoalkanes with acid chlorides as well as with numerous other reagents and functional groups have been reviewed by Huisgen.[356a] α-Diazo ketones can also be prepared by oxidation of the monohydrazones of α-diketones,[356b] by nitrosation of α-amino ketones,[354] by cleavage of N-nitroso-α-acetamido ketones with base,[357] by treatment of the N-toluenesulfonylmonohydrazones of α-diketones

[351] S. Kushner, L. M. Brancone, R. I. Hewitt, W. L. McEwen, Y. Subbarow, H. W. Stewart, R. J. Turner, and J. J. Denton, *J. Org. Chem.*, **13**, 144 (1948).

[352] E. K. Weisburger and J. H. Weisburger, *J. Org. Chem.*, **18**, 864 (1953).

[353] W. Andersen, *Compt. rend. trav. lab. Carlsberg, Sér. chim.*, **30**, 79 (1956); *Chem. Abstr.*, **51**, 10373i (1957).

[354] L. Wolff, P. Bock, G. Lorentz, and P. Trappe, *Ann.*, **325**, 134 (1902).

[354a] L. Wolff, *Ann.*, **394**, 25 (1912).

[355] K. Arndt, B. Eistert, and W. Partale, *Ber.*, **60**, 1364 (1927).

[355a] W. E. Bachmann and W. S. Struve, *Org. Reactions*, **1**, Chapt. 2 (1942).

[356] B. Eistert, *Neuere Methoden der präparativen organischen Chemie*, Vol. I, Verlag Chemie, Weinheim, 1944, p. 359.

[356a] R. Huisgen, *Angew. Chem.*, **67**, 439 (1955).

[356b] M. S. Newman and A. Arkell, *J. Org. Chem.*, **24**, 385 (1959).

[357] V. Franzen, *Ann.*, **614**, 31 (1958).

with base,[358] by reaction of monoximes of α-diketones with chloramine,[358-360] and by reaction of diazoalkanes with anhydrides.[361]

Although the initial products of rearrangement are ketenes, they have seldom been isolated, partly because aldoketenes (those having an α hydrogen, R—CH=C=O) are unstable and rapidly dimerize, and partly because the catalytic agent required usually entails a solvent with which ketenes react. Although water converts ketenes to carboxylic acids, it is not a convenient medium for rearrangement, since diazo ketones do not dissolve in it; aqueous dioxane is more satisfactory. It has frequently been noticed, however, that better yields are obtained when rearrangement is carried out in alcoholic solution. When the diazo ketone is one that rearranges slowly, excessive reduction of the catalyst to metallic silver may occur; for such cases, *tert*-butyl alcohol has been recommended.[361a] Amides are obtained by using alcoholic ammonia, and anilides by using neat aniline, at its boiling point for thermal rearrangement,[361b,361c] or at lower temperatures with a catalyst. Phenylhydrazine is not a satisfactory reagent with which to accompany rearrangement, for it produces osazones, and only poor yields of phenylhydrazides.[362]

Photolytic rearrangement can be carried out in the presence of substances that might not be compatible with the usual catalysts, and enables the ketenes to be utilized in reactions that would be unable to compete with acid, ester, or amide formation. β-Lactams have been prepared in this way, by generating the ketene in the presence of Schiffs bases[363] (eq. 150a). When azobenzenes are present, diazetidinones are formed[364] (eq. 151).

$$RCOCHN_2 \rightarrow [RCH=C=O] \xrightarrow{R_2C=NR} \begin{array}{c} R-CH-C=O \\ | \quad | \\ R_2C-N-R \end{array} \qquad (150a)$$

$$RCOCHN_2 \rightarrow [RCH=C=O] \xrightarrow{ArN=NAr} \begin{array}{c} R-CH-C=O \\ | \quad | \\ Ar-N-N-Ar \end{array} \qquad (151)$$

The scope of the Wolff rearrangement appears to be potentially nearly as broad as the C—to—N rearrangements, and additionally includes variation in substituents at the migration terminus. A substantial number of examples

[358] M. P. Cava, R. L. Litle, and D. R. Napier, *J. Am. Chem. Soc.*, **80**, 2257 (1958).

[359] L. Horner, K. Muth, and H. G. Schmelzer, *Chem. Ber.*, **92**, 2953 (1959).

[360] J. Meinwald, P. G. Gassman, and E. G. Miller, *J. Am. Chem. Soc.*, **81**, 4751 (1959).

[361] D. S. Tarbell and J. A. Price, *J. Org. Chem.*, **22**, 245 (1957).

[361a] M. S. Newman and P. F. Beal III, *J. Am. Chem. Soc.*, **72**, 5162 (1950).

[361b] P. A. S. Smith and W. L. Berry, *J. Org. Chem.*, **26**, 27 (1961).

[361c] L. Wolff, *Ann.*, **394**, 25 (1912).

[362] L. Canonica and A. M. Maderna, *Gazz. chim. ital.*, **80**, 412 (1950).

[363] W. Kirmse and L. Horner, *Chem. Ber.*, **89**, 2762 (1956).

[364] L. Horner and E. Spietschka, *Chem. Ber.*, **89**, 2765 (1956).

have been listed in reviews,[349,364a] the most recent of which appeared in 1960.[365] Variations in the migrating group will be taken up first.

Nearly all types of groups, aryl and alkyl, have been observed to migrate. Halogens appear to retard rearrangement when they are close to the α carbon, as shown by a series of experiments with perfluoroalkyl ketones.[366] Only when the perfluoroalkyl group was separated by at least one methylene group from the migrating carbon could significant rearrangement be obtained. However, trifluoromethyl and trichloromethyl diazoalkyl ketones have been successfully converted to trihalopropionic esters.[367] Pentachloroethyl diazomethyl ketone is unusually stable, being unaltered by silver oxide in boiling methanol, but has been rearranged thermally and photolytically.[367a] It underwent dehydrohalogenation, and only tetrachlorocrotonic acid derivatives could be obtained (eq. 152). Trichlorovinyl diazomethyl ketone is also unusually stable, but rearranges well photolytically. Single halogens at greater distances [368,369] do not appear to affect rearrangement.

$$C_2Cl_5COCHN_2 \xrightarrow[CH_3OH]{h\nu} CCl_3-CCl{=}CH-COOCH_3 \qquad (152)$$

Rearrangement is apparently retarded or interfered with by oxygen on the β carbon; Looker and Brown [370] obtained no rearranged product from β-phenoxyethyl diazomethyl ketone and only a low yield with the phenoxymethyl compound. α-Diazo-o-methoxyacetophenone also does not rearrange, but instead cyclizes with demethylation [371] (eq. 153). This appears to be a

$$ (153) $$

case of a favorably situated nucleophile competing for an intermediate carbene. An alkoxyl group will apparently not migrate, as shown by the behavior of ethyl diazoacetate and α-diazotrifluoropropionate, which attack the solvent instead.[371a,365]

[364a] W. E. Bachmann and W. S. Struve, *Org. Reactions*, **1**, Chapt. 2 (1942).

[365] F. Weygand and H. J. Bestmann, *Angew. Chem.*, **72**, 535 (1960).

[366] J. V. Parker, E. R. Larsen, H. v. Haller, and J. R. Lacher, *J. Org. Chem.*, **23**, 1166 (1958).

[367] F. Brown and W. K. R. Musgrave, *J. Chem. Soc. (London)*, **1953**, 2087.

[367a] A. Roedig and H. Lunk, *Chem. Ber.*, **87**, 971 (1954).

[368] J. Klein and E. D. Bergmann, *J. Org. Chem.*, **22**, 1019 (1957).

[369] (a) F. J. Buckle, F. L. M. Pattison, and B. C. Saunders, *J. Chem. Soc. (London)*, **1949**, 1471. (b) F. J. Buckle and B. C. Saunders, *J. Chem. Soc. (London)*, **1949**, 2774.

[370] J. H. Looker and L. L. Brown, *J. Org. Chem.*, **23**, 1062 (1958).

[371] P. Pfeiffer and E. Enders, *Chem. Ber.*, **84**, 247 (1951).

[371a] F. Weygand, W. Schwenke, and H. J. Bestmann, *Angew. Chem.*, **70**, 506 (1958).

Unsaturation does not appear to interfere with rearrangement or to alter the products, as shown with a group of ethylenic and acetylenic diazomethyl ketones by Wotiz and Buco,[372] except in the case of α,β-unsaturated compounds. The difficulty appears to be competing pyrazoline formation; this may occur during the preparation of the diazomethyl ketone, or, as perhaps in the case of styryl diazomethyl ketone, it may occur intermolecularly during attempted rearrangement. In one case, however, rearrangement has been carried out simultaneously with disruption of a pyrazoline ring. Grewe and Bokranz[373] treated triacetylshikimoyl chloride with excess diazomethane, converting it to both a pyrazoline and a diazomethyl ketone; heating at 180° in the presence of alcohol and base caused elimination of nitrogen and acetic acid as well as rearrangement, giving rise to a conjugated doubly unsaturated ester (eq. 154).

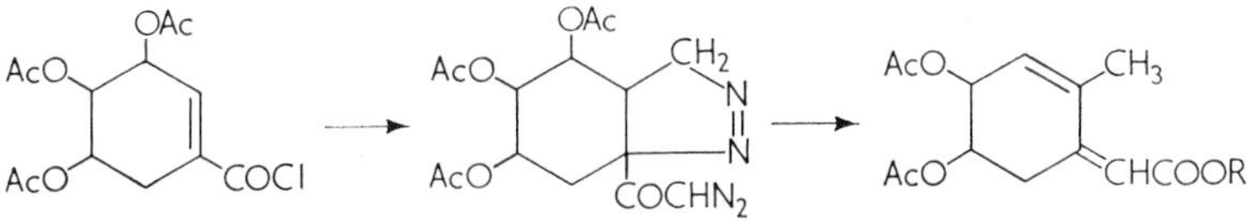

$$(154)$$

Amino groups in the α or β position do not interfere with rearrangement when they are protected by acylation. Balenović and co-workers[374] have explored the synthetic potentialities of homologation of α-phthalimido acids in great detail and have obtained many new optically active β-amino acids by this method. By carrying out rearrangement in the presence of α-amino esters, Fleš and Markovac-Prpić[375] have made use of the intermediate phthalimido ketene to form peptides of β-amino acids (eq. 155). Weygand and

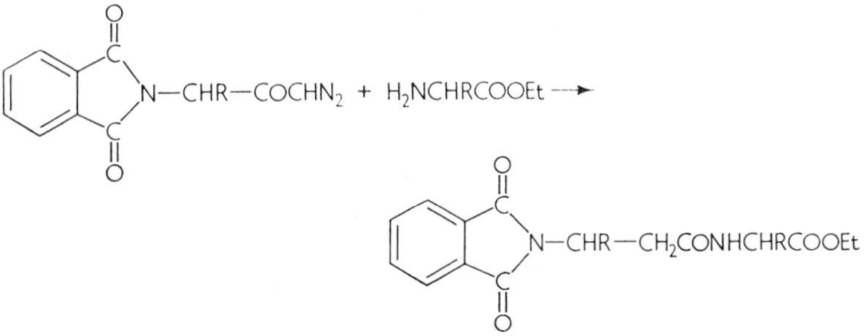

$$(155)$$

[372] J. W. Wotiz and S. N. Buco, *J. Org. Chem.*, **20**, 210 (1955).

[373] R. Grewe and A. Bokranz, *Chem. Ber.*, **88**, 49 (1955).

[374] (a) K. Balenović, J. J. Jambrešić, B. Gasperti, and D. Cerar, *Rec. trav. chim.*, **75**, 1252 (1956). (b) K. Balenović and J. Dvornik, *J. Chem. Soc. (London)*, **1954**, 2976. (c) K. Balenović, V. Thaller, and L. Filipović, *Helv. Chim. Acta*, **34**, 744 (1951). (d) K. Balenović, D. Cerar, and M. Tkalčić, *J. Org. Chem.*, **16**, 1308 (1951); K. Balenović and N. Štimac, *Croatica Chem. Acta*, **29**, 153 (1957).

[375] D. Fleš and M. Markovac-Prpić, *Croatica Chem. Acta*, **28**, 73 (1956), **29**, 79 (1957).

co-workers[376] have carried out homologation of amino acids by using trifluoroacetyl as the protective group, as illustrated by the preparation of the mono-ethyl ester of L-trifluoroacetylglutamic acid (eq. 156).

$$\underset{\underset{NHCOCF_3}{|}}{EtOOC-CH-CH_2COCHN_2} \xrightarrow[dioxane-H_2O]{h\nu} \underset{\underset{NHCOCF_3}{|}}{EtOOC-CH-CH_2CH_2COOH} \quad (156)$$

Many successful rearrangements have been carried out with α-diazo ketones bearing substituents at the migration terminus, but such substituents are not without effect. The usual synthesis of diazomethyl ketones from an acid chloride and diazomethane generally gives somewhat poorer results with larger diazoalkanes, although many examples of the successful use of diazo-ethane have been reported.[376c,377] Diazoacetic ester will react with acid chlorides to give α-diazo-α-carbethoxy ketones.[378] Rearrangement of diazo ketones having a methyl group at the migration terminus is generally more difficult than that of the unsubstituted compound, and may not be responsive to the usual silver catalysts.[376c,378a] Many such compounds have been successfully rearranged by one method or another, however, as illustrated by the homologation of α-phthalimido acids to α-methyl-β-amino acid derivatives (eq. 157).[379]

Increasingly bulky alkyl groups at the migration terminus hinder migration, and in one example a *tert*-butyl group almost completely prevented it.[379a] A carbethoxy group does not interfere, however, and substituted malonic acids have been prepared in this way (eq. 149a).[380] Dean and Robertson[381] have investigated diazo ketones with a variety of groups on the migration terminus. They generalized that the yield of rearrangement product varies

[376] (a) F. Weygand, H. J. Bestmann, and E. Klieger, *Chem. Ber.*, **91**, 1037 (1958). (b) F. Weygand, P. Klinke, and I. Eigen, *Chem. Ber.*, **90**, 1896 (1957). (c) A. L. Wilds and A. L. Meader, Jr., *J. Org. Chem.*, **13**, 763 (1948).

[377] K. Balenović, I. Jambrešić, and I. Ranogajec, *Croatica Chem. Acta*, **29**, 87 (1957); *Chem. Abstr.*, **53**, 11742h (1958).

[378] H. Staudinger, J. Becker and H. Hirzel, *Ber.*, **49**, 1978, 2522 (1916).

[378a] M. S. Newman and P. F. Beal III, *J. Am. Chem. Soc.*, **72**, 5162 (1950).

[379] K. Balenović and I. Jambrešić, *Chem. & Ind.* (*London*), **1955**, 1673.

[379a] M. S. Newman and A. Arkell, *J. Org. Chem.*, **24**, 385 (1959).

[380] T. Reichstein and H. J. Morsman, *Helv. Chim. Acta*, **17**, 1119 (1934).

[381] F. M. Dean and A. Robertson, *J. Chem. Soc.* (*London*), **1948**, 1674.

with substitution at the migration terminus in the order C_6H_5— > Ac— or —COOEt > H > alkyl, an order that suggests an electronic effect, although yield is not a reliable index. They reported complete failure only with α-diazo-p-nitropropiophenone, in which the electronic influence of the p-nitro group on the potential migrating group probably contributes heavily to the result.

Cyclic diazo ketones can rearrange, thereby undergoing ring contraction. Diazocamphor rearranges when irradiated,[382] but heating instead brings about cyclization without rearrangement [383] (eq. 158).

o-Diazooxides, sometimes distressingly called "o-quinone diazides," can be considered as unsaturated cyclic α-diazo ketones, and their rearrangement has already been mentioned (eq. 123). They are prepared by diazotization of o-aminophenols. Because they will undergo the usual diazo coupling reactions to give azo dyes, their destruction by photolytic rearrangement has attracted attention as a photographic technique. This same property puts difficulties in the way of their use for the preparation of cyclopentadienecarboxylic acid derivatives, however, since they couple readily with the active hydrogen of the product. Because of this, slow rearrangement usually gives largely coupling products,[383a,383b] and rapid rearrangement, which requires an intense ultraviolet light source, must be used to obtain good yields of nitrogen-free products. Photolytic rearrangement of o-diazooxides has been extensively investigated by Süs and co-workers [384,385a,385b] and by others,[385c,386] and extended to pyridine derivatives (eq. 159) as well. It is to be noted that

rearrangement destroys the benzene-o-quinone system, whose stabilization must be overcome in the rearrangement step. It is thus understandable that

[382] J. Meinwald, A. Lewis, and P. G. Gassman, J. Am. Chem. Soc., 82, 2649 (1960).

[383] J. Bredt and W. Holz, J. Prakt. Chem., 95, 133 (1917).

[383a] P. A. S. Smith and W. L. Berry, J. Org. Chem., 26, 27 (1961).

[383b] O. Süs, Ann., 556, 65 (1944).

[384] O. Süs, Ann., 556, 85 (1944), 579, 133 (1953).

[385] (a) O. Süs, M. Glos, K. Möller and H. D. Eberhardt, Ann., 583, 150 (1953). (b) O. Süs and K. Möller, Ann., 593, 91 (1955). (c) L. Horner, E. Spietschka, and A. Gross, Ann., 573, 17 (1951).

[386] J. De Jonge and R. Dykstra, Rec. trav. chim., 67, 328 (1947).

rearrangement should be more difficult than with simpler diazo ketones. In naphthalene diazooxides the stabilization is not so great, and it is significant that thermal rearrangement is practical with them [383a],[387] (eq. 123), but not with benzene diazooxides. The silver benzoate–triethylamine catalyst of Newman and Beal is ineffective.[383a]

With the diazooxides derived from α-aminotropolones, rearrangement produces a benzene ring and would be expected to be favored. Nozoe and collaborators[388] obtained p-isopropylsalicyclic acid from diazotized α'-amino-hinokitiol (eq. 160), for example, and similar observations have been made by Jefferies[389] and by Nicholls and Tarbell[390] on related systems.

$$\text{(160)}$$

Various side reactions can accompany the Wolff rearrangement, and a number of them have already been mentioned. Indoles may be formed from diazoacetophenones, in a reaction catalyzed by amine salts.[391] Dihydro-furanones have been obtained from both diazopinacolone and diazoaceto-phenone.[391a] Since the yields of rearrangement products are often far from quantitative, it is possible that a purposeful search would turn up many more examples of these and perhaps other side reactions. The many reactions that may occur with α-diazo ketones have been described by Weygand and Bestmann[391b] and by Huisgen and co-workers.[391c]

The Tiemann and Imidyl Azide Rearrangements. The rearrangement of amidoximes to ureas (eq. 161) by treatment with benzenesulfonyl chloride

$$C_6H_5-\underset{\underset{NH}{\|}}{C}-NHOH \xrightarrow[\text{base}]{C_6H_5SO_2Cl} C_6H_5-NHCONH_2 \qquad \text{(161)}$$

and base was reported simultaneously by Tiemann[392] and by Pinnow[393] in 1891. It has seen extremely little application.

[387] P. Yates and E. W. Robb, *J. Am. Chem. Soc.*, **79**, 5760 (1957).

[388] Y. Nozoe, Y. Kitihara, and R. Doi, *J. Am. Chem. Soc.*, **73**, 1895 (1951).

[389] R. D. Haworth and P. R. Jefferies, *J. Chem. Soc.* (*London*), **1951**, 2067.

[390] G. A. Nicholls and D. S. Tarbell, *J. Am. Chem. Soc.*, **75**, 1104 (1953).

[391] C. E. Blades and A. L. Wilds, *J. Org. Chem.*, **21**, 1013 (1956).

[391a] K. B. Wiberg and T. Hutton, *J. Am. Chem. Soc.*, **76**, 5367 (1954).

[391b] F. Weygand and H. J. Bestmann, *Angew. Chem.*, **72**, 535 (1960).

[391c] R. Huisgen, H. König, G. Binsch, and H. J. Sturm, *Angew. Chem.*, **73**, 368 (1961).

[392] F. Tiemann, *Ber.*, **24**, 4162 (1891).

[393] J. Pinnow, *Ber.*, **24**, 4167 (1891), **26**, 604 (1893).

The only serious investigation of the reaction was reported by Partridge and Turner [394] in 1953. They were able to isolate the benzenesulfonyl ester of phenylacetamidoxime and showed that when it is warmed in inert solvents, benzylcyanamid and benzenesulfonic acid are formed (eq. 162) and can be

$$C_6H_5CH_2-C-NHO-SO_2C_6H_5 \rightarrow C_6H_5CH_2-NH-CN+HO_3SC_6H_5 \qquad (162)$$
$$\underset{NH}{\overset{\|}{}}$$

isolated in good yields. The cyanamid may react further with the benzene-sulfonic acid to give a benzenesulfonylurea, R—NH—CO—NH—SO$_2$R. Benzamidoxime benzenesulfonyl ester was found to rearrange so easily that it could not be isolated; the phenylcyanamid produced was obtained as a tetramer. The Tiemann rearrangement was used to generate cyanamids in the presence of amines in order to prepare guanidines.

Unlike the Lossen rearrangement, which can be accomplished by heating unacylated hydroxamic acids strongly, the Tiemann rearrangement of benza-midoxime does not occur when it is heated.[395] Phosphorylated amidoximes have been prepared and found to rearrange to some extent.[396] Rearrangement of 3,4-dimethylbenzamidoxime has been brought about by treatment with p-acetamidobenzenesulfonyl chloride and sodium carbonate and also, sur-prisingly, upon attempted ethylation with ethyl iodide and calcium car-bonate.[397] There seems to be no reason why the Tiemann rearrangement should not be widely applicable as long as the requisite amidoximes can be prepared.

As a class, imidyl azides are usually unstable with respect to cyclization to form tetrazoles (eq. 163), and only a few examples have been isolated.[398]

$$R-C=N-R' \underset{\longleftarrow}{\longrightarrow} R-C-----N-R' \qquad (163)$$

However, tetrazoles appear to equilibrate with the imidyl azide structure at higher temperatures, and rearrangement may ensue.

The decomposition of 1,5-dimethyltetrazole to nitrogen, carbon dioxide, and two moles of methylamine when heated with fuming hydrochloric acid under pressure at 200° has been claimed in a patent,[399] and is probably an

[394] M. W. Partridge and H. A. Turner, *J. Pharm. and Pharmacol.*, **5**, 103 (1953).

[395] G. Leandri and P. Rebora, *Ann. chim. (Rome)*, **46**, 953 (1956).

[396] R. E. Plapinger and O. O. Owens, *J. Org. Chem.*, **21**, 1186 (1956).

[397] T. Kanazawa, E. Owada, M. Yoshida and T. Sato, *Nippon Kagaka Zasshi*, **76**, 654 (1955); *Chem. Abstr.*, **51**, 17814b (1957); T. Kanazawa and T. Sato, *Nippon Kagaku Zasshi*, **76**, 990 (1955); *Chem. Abstr.*, **51**, 17814g (1957).

[398] R. Huisgen, *Angew. Chem.*, **72**, 359 (1960).

[399] K. F. Schmidt, *Friedländer, Fortschr. in der Teerfarb, u. verwand. Ind.*, **15**, 333 (1930).

example of the rearrangement of a protonated imidyl azide. The formation of ureas as by-products in certain Schmidt reactions has been mentioned (heading 2B); it can best be accounted for by the hypothesis [399a] that an imidyl azide rearranges to a carbodiimide, which is converted by hydration to a urea (eq. 164). 1,5-Diaryltetrazoles have been found [399a] to undergo rearrangement

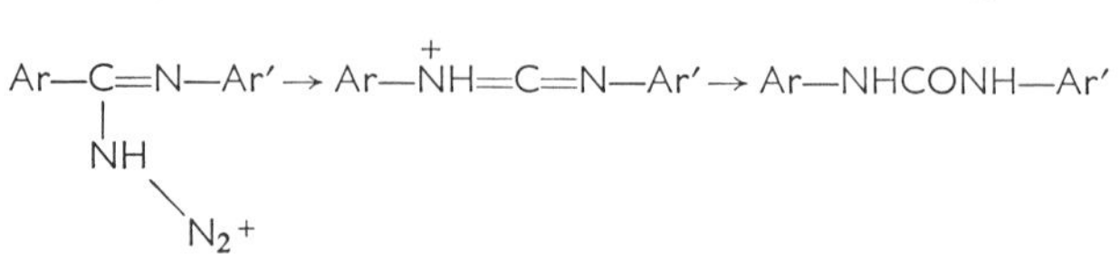

$$Ar-\underset{\underset{\underset{N_2^+}{\overset{|}{N}}}{\overset{|}{NH}}}{C}=N-Ar' \rightarrow Ar-\overset{+}{N}H=C=N-Ar' \rightarrow Ar-NHCONH-Ar' \qquad (164)$$

and hydrolysis in high yield when treated with orthophosphoric acid at 175°, conditions that convert carbodiimides and ureas alike to amines (eq. 165). Amino groups also migrate, giving rise to hydrazines; [400] the behavior of

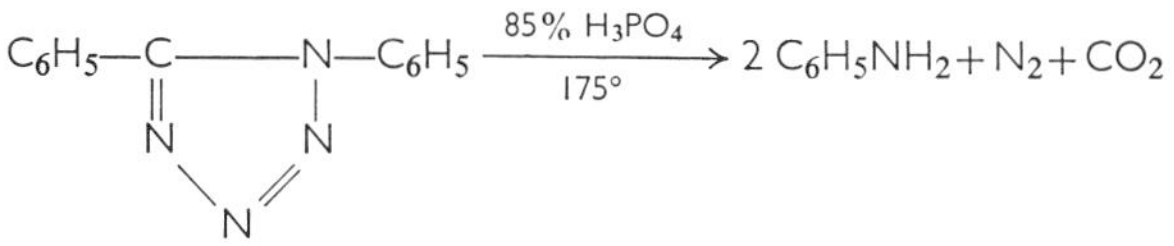

$$C_6H_5-\underset{\underset{N}{\overset{\|}{N}}}{\overset{}{C}}\underset{\underset{N}{\diagdown_N\diagup}}{-\!\!-\!\!-N}-C_6H_5 \xrightarrow[175°]{85\% \ H_3PO_4} 2 \ C_6H_5NH_2+N_2+CO_2 \qquad (165)$$

5-anilinotetrazole shows that the unsubstituted amino group migrates more readily than anilino (eq. 166). An attempt to utilize this reaction to prepare

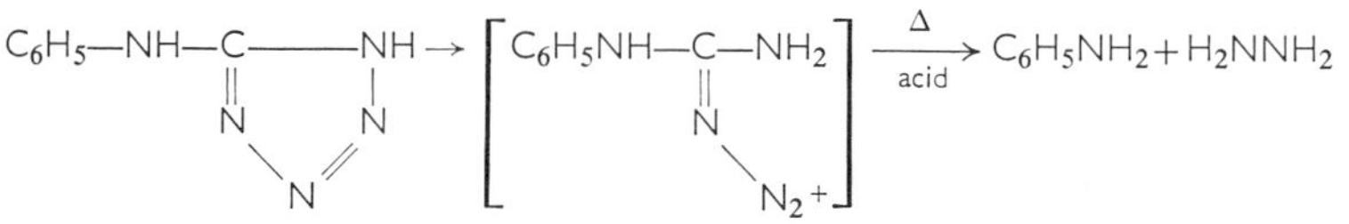

$$C_6H_5-NH-\underset{\underset{N}{\overset{\|}{N}}}{\overset{}{C}}\underset{\underset{N}{\diagdown_N\diagup}}{-\!\!-\!\!-NH} \rightarrow \left[C_6H_5NH-\underset{\underset{N_2^+}{\overset{\|}{N}}}{\overset{}{C}}-NH_2\right] \xrightarrow[acid]{\Delta} C_6H_5NH_2+H_2NNH_2 \quad (166)$$

tert-butylhydrazine from 1-*tert*-butyl-5-*tert*-butylaminotetrazole failed; elimination occurred, and unsubstituted hydrazine was produced. [401] The reaction

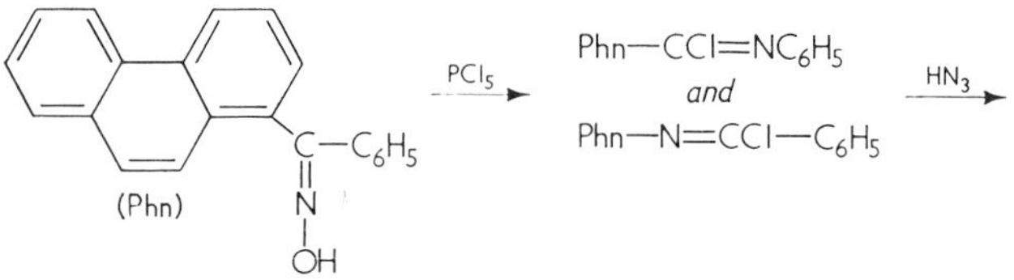

$$(167)$$

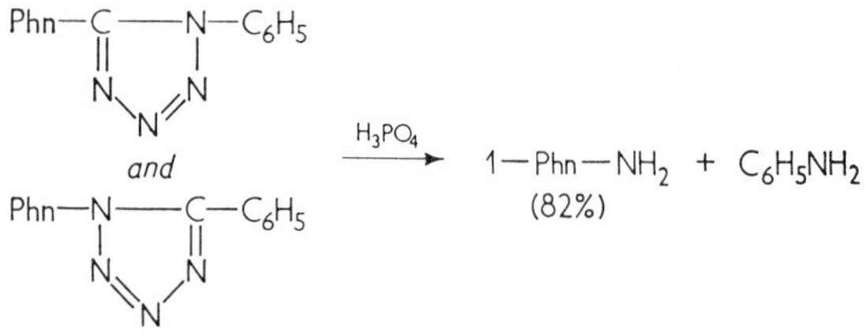

has potential synthetic value for obtaining amines from unsymmetrical ketones whose oximes rearrange with predominant migration of the undesired group. Such a situation is shown by 1-benzoylphenanthrene, which by the Beckmann rearrangement gives mostly 1-phenanthranilide. If the intermediate imidyl chloride is treated with hydrogen azide to give tetrazole by the von Braun–Rudolf procedure, and then decomposed with hot phosphoric acid (eq. 167), an 82% conversion to 1-aminophenanthrene can be achieved.[399a]

Imidyl azides are also presumably intermediates in the von Braun–Rudolf tetrazole synthesis[402] (eq. 168). Usually the conversion occurs without side

$$R-N{=}CCl-R + HN_3 \rightarrow R-N{=}C-R \rightarrow R-N\underset{N{\diagdown}N{\diagup}N}{\overset{}{\longrightarrow}}C-R + HCl \qquad (168)$$

reactions, but some examples are accompanied by rearrangement to produce carbodiimides. N-Phenyl-1-phenanthrimidyl chloride is such a case,[399a] and several other examples have been encountered[403] (eq. 169). This reaction is

$$Ar-N{=}CCl-Ar + HN_3 \rightarrow Ar-N{=}C{=}N-Ar + HCl + N_2 \qquad (169)$$

favored by ortho substituents on the group that must migrate,[404] as would be expected from the effect of ortho substituents in the Curtius, Hofmann, Lossen, Schmidt, and Beckmann rearrangements. It is also promoted by an acidic environment and is prevented when the von Braun–Rudolf synthesis is carried out in the presence of tertiary amines.[404]

Rearrangement of tetrazoles may also be accomplished pyrolytically, presumably through equilibration with the imidyl azide structure. Temperatures just above 200° are required. Distillation of 1,5-diphenyltetrazole gives good yields of diphenylcarbodiimide, accompanied by 12–14% of 2-phenylbenzimidazole (eq. 170).[403] This presumably indicates initial formation of an imidyl azene, after which there is competition between migration and attack on the ortho position of a benzene ring. As would be expected, a p-methyl substituent on the 1-phenyl group decreases benzimidazole formation by accelerating migration, and a p-chloro group has the opposite effect.[405]

[399a] P. A. S. Smith, *J. Am. Chem. Soc.*, **76**, 436 (1954).

[400] E. Lieber, R. A. Henry, and W. G. Finnegan, *J. Am. Chem. Soc.*, **75**, 2023 (1953).

[401] P. A. S. Smith and J. Lakritz, unpublished results; J. Lakritz, doctoral thesis, University of Michigan, 1960.

[402] J. von Braun and J. Rudolf, *Ber.*, **74**, 264 (1941).

[403] P. A. S. Smith and E. Leon, *J. Am. Chem. Soc.*, **80**, 4647 (1958).

[404] P. A. S. Smith and R. D. Westland, unpublished results; R. D. Westland, doctoral thesis, University of Michigan, 1959.

[405] J. Vaughan and P. A. S. Smith, *J. Org. Chem.*, **23**, 1909 (1958).

$$C_6H_5-C\underset{\underset{N\diagdown_N\diagup^N}{|}}{\overset{|}{\rule{0pt}{0pt}}}N-C_6H_5 \longrightarrow \left[C_6H_5-\underset{\overset{||}{N}}{\overset{|}{C}}=N-C_6H_5 \right] \tag{170}$$

(with products: $C_6H_5-N{=}C{=}N-C_6H_5$ (mostly), and C_6H_5-C benzimidazole)

3. CARBON TO OXYGEN REARRANGEMENTS

The rearrangements in this group parallel the C—to—N rearrangements discussed in Part 2, with the limitation that the leaving group in all cases is an oxy anion (or the conjugate acid), formed by heterolytic cleavage of the O—O bond in peroxides. It is possible that hypohalites might rearrange analogously, but treatment of silver salts of carboxylic acids with halogens causes instead replacement of carboxyl by halogen, the well-known Hunsdiecker reaction.[406] Tertiary alkyl hypochlorites decompose to ketones and alkyl halides,[407] but the fact that this is induced by sunlight is evidence that it is really a free radical reaction. The production of benzophenone from triphenylcarbinol when it is treated with bromine at 130° has been reported,[408] but there is no reason to believe that it involves an ionic rearrangement. Trinitrotriphenylmethyl nitrate, in which an N—O bond might cleave heterolytically, gives no evidence of rearrangement when dissolved in concentrated sulfuric acid.[409] An attempt to obtain C—to—O rearrangement with N_2 as the leaving group has been made by treating O-benzoylhydroxylamine, $C_6H_5COONH_2$, with nitrous acid, but no phenolic products could be detected.[410] Attempts to obtain a reaction between ketones and nitrous oxide analogous to the Schmidt reaction have also failed.[410]

Peroxides are well known for their propensity for homolytic cleavage of the O—O bond, which may give rise to free radical rearrangements (see Section 7), but only the heterolytic rearrangements are considered here.

A. Alkyl and Aralkyl Derivatives: Hydroperoxide Esters, Hydroperoxide Ethers and Hydroperoxides

The earliest report of the rearrangement of an alkyl or aralkyl peroxide by a process that may involve heterolytic cleavage of an O—O bond is that of

[406] C. V. Wilson, *Org. Reactions*, **9**. Chapt. 5 (1957).

[407] F. D. Chattaway and O. G. Backeberg, *J. Chem. Soc. (London)*, **123**, 2999 (1923); F. D. Greene, *J. Am. Chem. Soc.*, **81**, 2688 (1959).

[408] E. A. Flood and L. Horvitz, *J. Am. Chem. Soc.*, **55**, 2534 (1933).

[409] M. F. Hawthorne, *J. Am. Chem. Soc.*, **77**, 5523 (1955).

[410] P. A. S. Smith, R. L. Baumgarten, and L. C. Mitchell, unpublished results.

Gomberg and Cone [411] in 1904, who observed the conversion of triphenyl-methyl peroxide to benzhydrylidene dichloride and triphenylmethyl chloride in high yield when heated with phosphorus pentachloride (eq. 171). No

$$(C_6H_5)_3C—O—O—C(C_6H_5)_3 + PCl_5 \rightarrow (C_6H_5)_2CCl_2 + Cl—C(C_6H_5)_3 \qquad (171)$$

immediate notice appears to have been taken of this reaction, and it was not until 27 years later that Wieland and Maier [412] reported another example, the acid-catalyzed rearrangement of triphenylmethyl hydroperoxide (eq. 172), which has since been firmly established as an ionic process.

$$(C_6H_5)_3C—O—OH \xrightarrow{H_2SO_4} (C_6H_5)_2C{=}O + C_6H_5OH \qquad (172)$$

In the ensuing development of the field, not only hydroperoxides but also their esters have been found to rearrange. Although the rearrangements are very similar, there are sufficient differences to make it convenient to discuss them separately.

Hydroperoxide Esters. The rearrangement of hydroperoxide esters was first reported by Criegee [413] in 1944 for the acetate and benzoate of *trans*-9-decalyl hydroperoxide; the products are 1,6-epoxycyclodecyl esters, which on hydrolysis give 6-hydroxycyclodecanone (eq. 173). 8-Hydrindanylperoxy esters behave similarly.[414]

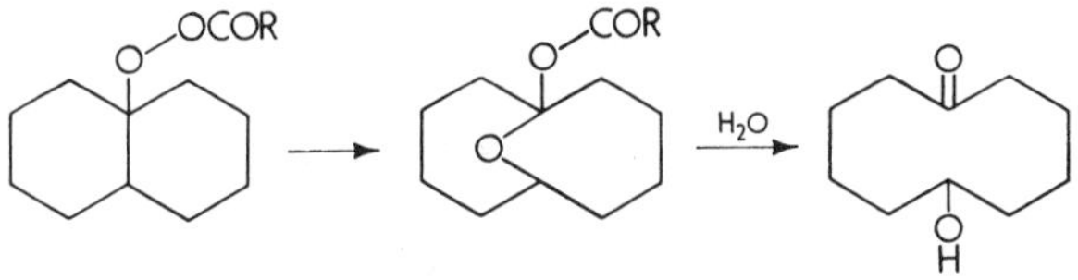

$$(173)$$

Criegee and Kaspar [415] studied the rate of rearrangement as a function of both the esterifying acid and the solvent. The rate was proportional to the anionic stability of the parent acid, in the order $Cl_3CCO— > p\text{-}O_2NC_6H_4CO— > C_6H_5CO— > CH_3CO—$, and increased with increasing polarity of the solvent, in the order $AcOH > CH_3OH > CH_3NO_2 > CH_3CN > CHCl_3 > C_6H_6 > CCl_4$. In view of these effects, they proposed that the reaction involved hetero-lytic rather than homolytic cleavage of the O—O bond, according to equation 174, and explained that they considered that the intermediate dissociation was not sufficiently complete to remove the anion from the field of the cation. In other words, they proposed that rearrangement occurred through the

[411] M. Gomberg and L. H. Cone, *Ber.*, **37**, 3538 (1904).

[412] H. Wieland and J. Maier, *Ber.*, **64**, 1205 (1931).

[413] R. Criegee, *Ber.*, **77**, 722 (1944).

[414] R. Criegee and H. Zogel, *Chem. Ber.*, **84**, 215 (1951).

[415] R. Criegee and R. Kaspar, *Ann.*, **560**, 127 (1948).

"intimate ion-pair" type of intermediate conceptualized by Winstein and collaborators [416] for other processes of a similar nature.

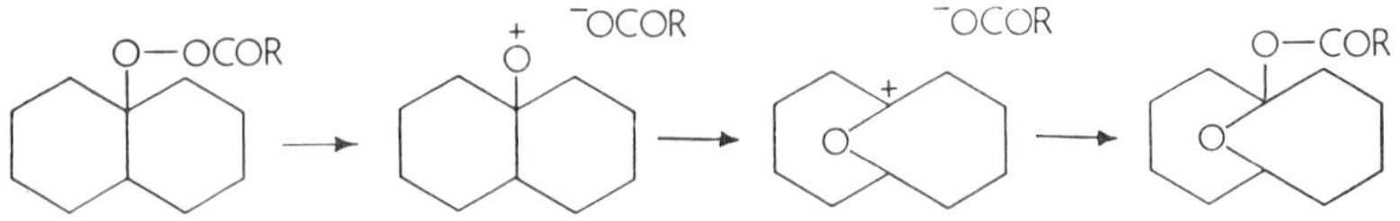

$$(174)$$

The rearrangement of 9-decalyl peroxy esters has been studied intensively by several investigators since Criegee's initial reports. The kinetics are first order.[417,418] The rate is increased by electron-attracting substituents on the phenyl group of the benzoate, and retarded by electron-donating ones, and follows the Hammett equation with $\rho = +1.34$.[417] There is no exchange during rearrangement in the presence of salts of other acids, such as lithium p-nitrobenzoate or sodium p-bromobenzoate, confirming Criegee's postulate of only partial dissociation in the intermediate stage.[417,418] Goering and Olson [418] also studied the kinetics of the solvolysis that accompanies rearrangement in aqueous methanol solution and deduced from the results that there exists an intermediate which has the choice of conversion to the epoxycyclodecyl ester or of complete dissociation to give hydroxycyclodecanone. This intermediate corresponds to Criegee's ion pair, and it can be formulated as in equation 174, or as the mesomeric oxonium ion, $-\overset{+}{O}=C\langle$, or as a bridged cationic structure that still retains some C—C bonding at the central bridge.

Further information on the structure of the intermediate was obtained by Denney and Denney,[419] who prepared 9-decalyl perbenzoate in which the carbonyl oxygen was isotopically labeled. Rearrangement produced epoxycyclodecyl benzoate in which the labeled oxygen was retained entirely in the carbonyl group (eq. 175), demonstrating that the benzoate oxygen atoms

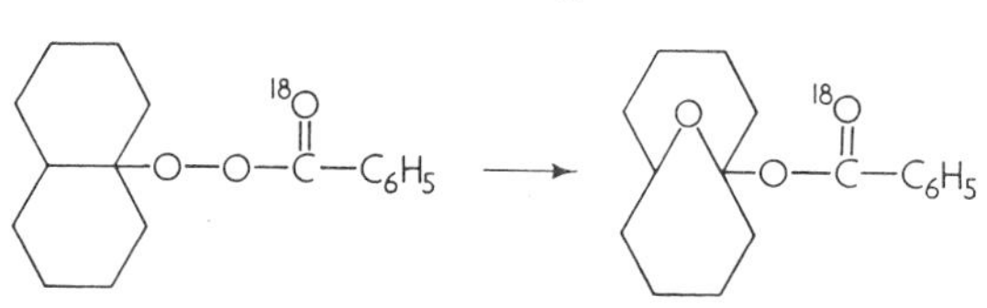

$$(175)$$

cannot become equivalent at any intermediate stage. In order to reconcile these observations with the general characteristics of a polar process shown by the rearrangement, it is necessary to postulate an ion pair in which not only the anionoid group as a whole, but also its originally peroxy oxygen, is inti-

[416] S. Winstein, E. Clippinger, A. H. Fainberg, R. Heck, and G. G. Robinson, *J. Am. Chem. Soc.*, **78**, 328 (1956).

[417] P. D. Bartlett and J. L. Kice, *J. Am. Chem. Soc.*, **75**, 5591 (1953).

[418] H. L. Goering and A. C. Olson, *J. Am. Chem. Soc.*, **75**, 5853 (1953).

[419] D. B. Denney and D. G. Denney, *J. Am. Chem. Soc.*, **79**, 4806 (1957).

mately bound to the site of rearrangement. Rearrangement through a five-membered ring transition state (**43**) is specifically ruled out. Denney and Denney represented the intermediate as **44** (the notational device used to

(43)   (44)

represent the required type of intermediate can be expected to change with the evolution of our understanding of the nature of bonding forces in transition states in general; the dotted lines only represent bonds in the process of either forming or breaking and thus of order between zero and one).

The rearrangement of *tert*-butyl peroxy esters has also been studied; heterolytic rearrangement is somewhat more difficult, and the decomposition of the acetate and benzoate is a free radical process.[420] The trifluoroacetate, however, decomposes heterolytically, as shown by the dependence of the rate on the polarity of the solvent;[420] the products isolated—acetone, methyl trifluoroacetate, etc.—result from secondary changes of the presumed ketal intermediate (eq. 176).

$$(CH_3)_3C-O-O-COCF_3 \rightarrow \left[\begin{matrix} (CH_3)_2C-O-COCF_3 \\ | \\ OCH_3 \end{matrix} \right] \rightarrow (CH_3)_2C{=}O, CH_3OOCCF_3, \text{ etc.} \quad (176)$$

The benzenesulfonyl peroxy esters undergo heterolytic rearrangement readily, as is to be expected from the great stability of the sulfonate anions whose partial development is presumed to be a feature of the transition state, and acetone is produced nearly quantitatively at 20–25° in methanol solution.[421] Bartlett and Storey [421] studied the effect of para substituents on the rate constants and found that it followed the Hammett equation with a value for the regression constant, $+1.36$, almost identical with that determined for the decalyl perbenzoates. This is in significant contrast to the value, -0.9, that was found for the free radical decomposition of *tert*-butyl perbenzoates. Further evidence that the rearrangement of *tert*-butyl tosylate is not a free radical process is found in the observation that its decomposition in benzene does not catalyze the polymerization of styrene. Bartlett and Storey also studied the rates of rearrangement of *tert*-butyl tosylate and 9-decalyl perbenzoate as a function of solvent composition in the water–methanol system.

[420] P. D. Bartlett and R. R. Hiatt, *J. Am. Chem. Soc.*, **80**, 1398 (1958).
[421] P. D. Bartlett and B. T. Storey, *J. Am. Chem. Soc.*, **80**, 4954 (1958).

The rates were linear with the Grunwald-Winstein [422] solvating factor, Y, except that the rate for the tosylate showed a sharp drop at solvent compositions below $0.05M$ H_2O. This effect was tentatively attributed to the appearance of a substantial degree of "internal return," without rearrangement of the intermediate ion pair, at low solvating power of the medium.

The decomposition of tert-butyl trichloroperacetate can be brought about in solvents of low polarity by a free radical path, but the high anionic stability of trichloroacetate is conducive to a heterolytic process. Bartlett and Simons[423] found that the heterolytic process is autocatalytic, owing to the liberation of some trichloroacetic acid, and if it once begins, the free radical path is bypassed. The manner of the apparent acid catalysis has not been elucidated, but in view of the extreme inertness of trichloroacetic acid to protonation even by concentrated sulfuric and perchloric acids,[424] it is most unlikely that it takes place through protonation of either of the carboxyl oxygens. On the other hand, protonation of the alkoxyl oxygen should not facilitate separation of the trichloroacetate anion. It therefore seems that catalysis must either involve the entire acid molecule, in a manner other than simple protonation, or operate through a cyclic transition state derived from the alkoxyl-protonated form, with resulting generation of molecular trichloroacetic acid. The acid-catalyzed rearrangement of esters of weaker acids, such as peracetates, can reasonably proceed by protonation at any of the oxygens.

The relative mobilities (migration aptitudes) of different groups in the rearrangement of peroxy esters has not been specifically studied. There is little reason to believe that these should be qualitatively different from those observed in the acid-catalyzed rearrangement of hydroperoxides, to be discussed next, except for expansion or contraction of the scale with changes in substitution on the oxygen (and thus on the stability of the pseudo-leaving group). Evidence for such a parallel is provided by α-cumyl perbenzoate, which rearranges exclusively by phenyl migration,[425] (eq. 177), as does

$$C_6H_5CMe_2-O-O-COC_6H_5 \rightarrow C_6H_5-O-CMe_2-O-COC_6H_5 \qquad (177)$$

α-cumyl hydroperoxide. Similarly, 1-phenylcyclohexyl p-nitroperbenzoate gives the same products—cyclohexanone and phenol—as does the hydroperoxide.[426] The relative reluctance of alkyl groups to migrate is qualitatively evident from the sluggishness of tertiary alkyl peroxy esters compared to benzyl peroxy esters. Further demonstration is provided by the behavior

[422] E. Grunwald and S. Winstein, J. Am. Chem. Soc., **70**, 846 (1948).

[423] P. D. Bartlett and D. M. Simons, J. Am. Chem. Soc., **82**, 1753 (1960).

[424] L. P. Hammett and A. J. Deyrup, J. Am. Chem. Soc., **55**, 1900 (1933); M. Ussanovich and V. Tartakovskaya, Zhur. Obshchei Khim., **16**, 1987 (1946); T. Sumarokova and Z. Grishkun, Zhur. Obshchei Khim., **16**, 1991 (1946).

[425] H. Hock and H. Knopf, Chem. Ber., **88**, 1544 (1955).

[426] H. Kwart and R. T. Keen, J. Am. Chem. Soc., **81**, 943 (1959).

of the *p*-nitrobenzene-sulfonate of 1,3,3-trimethylcyclohexyl hydroperoxide, in which cyclization by electrophilic attack on a methyl group competes with rearrangement [427] (eq. 178).

$$ \text{(178)} $$

$$ (5-10\%) $$

The rearrangement of peroxy esters has not yet seen much application to synthesis, but that of 9-decalyl perbenzoate has been utilized as a route to cyclodecane derivatives.[428]

Hydroperoxide Ethers. Base-catalyzed decomposition of α-phenylethyl *tert*-butyl peroxide (eq. 179) has been reported by Kornblum and De La Mare.[429] This is, strictly speaking, a fragmentation rather than a rearrange-

$$ C_6H_5CH-O-O-t\text{-}Bu \xrightarrow{\text{B:}} \left[C_6H_5-C^{\ominus}-O-O-t\text{-}Bu \right] \rightarrow C_6H_5-C{=}O + {}^{-}O-t\text{-}Bu $$
$$ \underset{CH_3}{|} \qquad\qquad \underset{CH_3}{|} \qquad\qquad \underset{CH_3}{|} \qquad\qquad \text{(179)} $$

ment. A parallel reaction occurs with benzyl *tert*-butyl peroxide.[430] The rearrangement of triphenylmethyl peroxide brought about by phosphorus pentachloride was mentioned at the beginning of part 3A.

Hydroperoxides. The acid-catalyzed rearrangement of triarylmethyl hydroperoxides was extended considerably from Wieland and Maier's original example by Dilthey, Quint, and Dierichs.[431] They showed that it is not necessary to prepare the hydroperoxides separately, but triarylcarbinols or their salts can be treated directly with hydrogen peroxide in the presence of strong acids, thereby achieving a one-step conversion of carbinol to ketone and phenol (eq. 180). This is exactly analogous to the case of alkyl and aralkyl

$$ Ar_3C-OH \xrightarrow[\;HClO_4\;]{H_2O_2} Ar_2CO + ArOH \qquad \text{(180)} $$
$$ \quad\longrightarrow Ar_3C-O-OH \xrightarrow{HClO_4} $$

azides (see heading 2A). In this manner, triphenylmethane dyes, such as malachite green and crystal violet, were successfully degraded. The products of the few unsymmetrically substituted compounds showed that electron-releasing substituents, such as *p*-methoxy, conferred increased mobility on

[427] E. J. Corey and R. W. White, *J. Am. Chem. Soc.*, **80**, 6686 (1958).

[428] A. C. Cope and G. Holzmann, *J. Am. Chem. Soc.*, **72**, 3062 (1950).

[429] N. Kornblum and H. E. De La Mare, *J. Am. Chem. Soc.*, **73**, 880 (1951).

[430] R. P. Bell and A. O. McDougall, *J. Chem. Soc. (London)*, **1958**, 1697.

[431] W. Dilthey, F. Quint, and H. Dierichs, *J. prakt. Chem.*, **151**, 25 (1938).

the phenyl group, but even tris(p-nitrophenyl)carbinol underwent rearrangement. p-Nitrotriphenylmethyl hydroperoxide showed essentially no p-nitrophenyl migration, however, and gave p-nitrobenzophenone in 94% yield,[432] in contrast to its rearrangement by a free radical path.

Kharasch and collaborators[433–435] have studied a wide variety of hydroperoxide rearrangements. Rearrangement was found to be catalyzed by strong protonic acids, such as sulfuric and perchloric, and also by Lewis acids, such as anhydrous ferric chloride, boron fluoride, and aluminum chloride.[433] Reaction is highly exothermic and can be accomplished at quite low temperatures: for example, at $-80°$ with α-cumyl hydroperoxide. In addition to the separately prepared hydroperoxide and the carbinol, *tert*-alkyl chlorides and olefins can be used.[434] The products obtained fit the generalization[435] that migration of aryl groups occurs to the almost total exclusion of alkyl migration in mixed aryl alkyl carbinols and competes significantly with hydrogen migration in primary and secondary benzylic alcohols. Thus α-cumyl hydroperoxide gives acetone and phenol quantitatively (eq. 181); 1,1-diphenylethylene gives acetophenone and phenol (eq. 182); and p-methylbenzyl

$$C_6H_5\!-\!\overset{\overset{\displaystyle CH_3}{|}}{\underset{\underset{\displaystyle CH_3}{|}}{C}}\!-\!O\!-\!OH \xrightarrow[\text{AcOH}]{\text{HClO}_4} C_6H_5OH + CH_3COCH_3 \qquad (181)$$

$$(C_6H_5)_2C\!\!=\!\!CH_2 \xrightarrow[\text{H}^+]{\text{H}_2\text{O}_2} C_6H_5COCH_3 + C_6H_5OH \qquad (182)$$

hydroperoxide gives 61% of p-tolualdehyde and 38% of p-cresol (eq. 183). The mobility of vinyl groups is apparently similar to that of phenyl, for

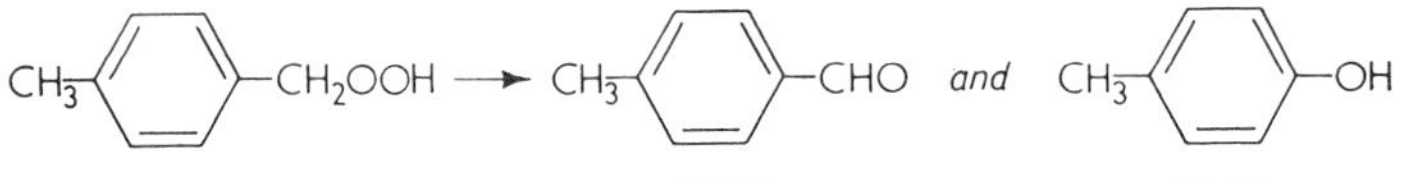

$$(61\%) \qquad\qquad (38\%) \qquad (183)$$

3-hydroperoxycyclohexene gives 39% of cyclopentene-1-carboxaldehyde (a self-condensation product of adipaldehyde) as well as 6% of adipaldehyde itself (eq. 184). As also shown by Dilthey's more limited observations, the

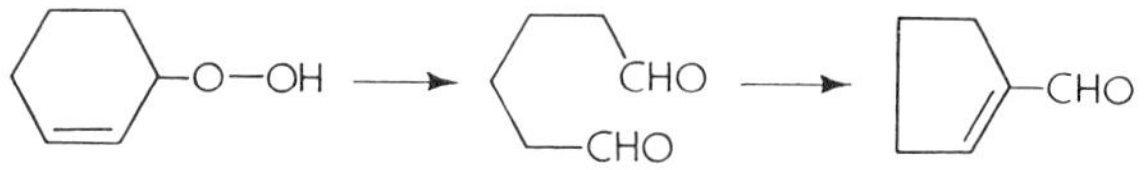

$$(184)$$

[432] P. D. Bartlett and J. D. Cotman, *J. Am. Chem. Soc.*, **72**, 3095 (1950).

[433] M. S. Kharasch, A. Fono, and W. Nudenberg, *J. Org. Chem.*, **15**, 748 (1950).

[434] M. S. Kharasch, A. Fono, W. Nudenberg, and A. C. Poshkus, *J. Org. Chem.*, **15**, 775 (1950).

[435] M. S. Kharasch and J. G. Burt, *J. Org. Chem.*, **16**, 150 (1951).

mobility of aryl groups was found to be qualitatively a function of their ability to sustain a positive charge, in the expected order p-CH_3O—> p-$CH_3 > H > p$-NO_2 for substituted phenyl groups (for quantitative information on this subject, see the discussion on kinetics, ahead). Ortho substituents showed qualitatively similar influences. The very low mobility of alkyl groups permitted the use of *tert*-butyl hydroperoxide as a source of peroxide for reaction with other carbinols, peroxide exchange presumably taking place under the strongly acidic conditions.

A comparison of the relative mobilities of alkyl groups can only be made from isolated examples and by inference, but the order $H >$ tertiary $>$ secondary $>$ primary $>$ methyl is suggested. Primary and secondary alkyl hydroperoxides thus decompose without carbon skeleton changes, giving aldehydes and ketones, respectively [436] (eq. 185); and 1-methylcyclohexyl

$$R_2CH-O-OH \rightarrow R_2C{=}O + H_2O \qquad (185)$$

hydroperoxide rearranges by ring methylene migration to give 6-keto-1-heptanol (eq. 186).

$$\qquad (186)$$

Kinetic studies by three groups of investigators [437-440] on α-cumyl hydroperoxide and derivatives conform to an over-all second-order rate equation of the form

$$\text{Rate} = k(ROOH)(acid)$$

The most appropriate acidity function seems to be Hammett's h_0, but most of the experiments were conducted under such conditions that h_0 and (H_3O^+) were proportional. Seubold and Vaughan [437] observed that there is no catalysis by acetic acid in solutions of toluenesulfonic acid in 50% aqueous acetic acid, which indicates specific rather than general acid catalysis. Activation energies fall in the range 21.1–23.1 kcal./mole.[440]

The studies of de Ruyter van Steveninck and Kooyman [440] permit a quantitative comparison of the effects of substituents on aryl migration. The results fit the Hammett equation in σ^+ rather than σ, with a reaction constant of -4.57. This large value is similar to that for aromatic substitution reactions

[436] W. Pritzkow and K. A. Müller, *Chem. Ber.*, **89**, 2321 (1956).

[437] F. H. Seubold and W. E. Vaughan, *J. Am. Chem. Soc.*, **75**, 3790 (1953).

[438] O. Wichterle and P. Cefelin, *Collection Czechoslov. Chem. Communs.*, **22**, 1083 (1957).

[439] A. W. de Ruyter van Steveninck, *J. Chem. Soc. (London)*, **1958**, 2066.

[440] A. W. de Ruyter van Steveninck and E. C. Kooyman, *Rec. trav. chim.*, **79**, 413 (1960).

and is strong evidence for a concerted rearrangement of the protonated hydroperoxide (eq. 187). The rearrangement must be the rate-determining

$$Ar\!-\!CR_2\!-\!O\!-\!OH \rightleftharpoons Ar\!-\!CR_2\!-\!O\!-\!\overset{+}{O}H_2 \rightarrow \left[\begin{array}{c} CR_2 \\ Ar \vdots \\ \underset{\delta+}{O}\!\cdots\!\underset{\delta+}{OH_2} \end{array} \right] \rightarrow Ar\!-\!\overset{+}{O}\!=\!CR_2 + H_2O$$

$$\downarrow (187)$$

$$ArOH + R_2CO + H^+$$

step, and the acidity appears in the rate equation because of the prior acid-base equilibrium. The position of this equilibrium undoubtedly varies somewhat with substitution, and the observed reaction constant must be the combined result of effects on the position of the acid-base equilibrium and the rate of rearrangement of the protonated species. The reaction constant for protonation can be estimated from those measured in other cases of protonation at a site separated from the ring by one saturated atom: negative and less than 1. The composite value of -4.57 is thus largely a result of the rearrangement step. (Protonation at the alkylated oxygen, $R\!-\!\overset{+}{O}H\!-\!OH$, presumably occurs as well, but this would not be likely to lead to rearrangement.)

Ortho substituents, whose effects are not correlated by the Hammett equation owing to the occurrence of steric influences, give rates only one-fourth to one-fifth as fast as the same substituents on the para position.[440] This is presumably the result of interference with the orientation of the benzene ring in the position most favorable for concerted migration: at right angles to the C—O bond.

An effect on rate by structural changes in the nonmigrating, alkyl groups is shown by the rate constants for rearrangement of the peroxides of

$$C_6H_5\!-\!\underset{|}{C}HCH_3 \quad C_6H_5\!-\!C(CH_3)_2\!-\!, \quad C_6H_5\!-\!\!\!\triangleleft \boxed{} \;, \; and \; C_6H_5\!-\!\!\!\triangleleft \bigcirc$$

whose relative values are $0.19:1:2:4.4$. This range, though small, indicates an electronic effect as well as a steric one. There is also a noticeable effect on the rates by dissolved electrolytes.[439,440]

Further evidence for the concerted nature of the rearrangement step has come out of experiments whose primary purpose was to elucidate the path by which alcohols are converted to hydroperoxides by reaction with hydrogen peroxide and strong acids.[441] This process might in principle take place with cleavage of either the original O—O bond or the original C—O bond. It has

---

[441] M. Bassey, C. A. Bunton, A. G. Davies, T. A. Lewis, and D. R. Llewellyn, *J. Chem. Soc. (London)*, **1955**, 2471.

been found, however, that alcohol labeled with ^{18}O is converted to hydroperoxide free of isotope, showing that the reaction is a displacement on carbon (eq. 188). When α-phenylethyl hydroperoxide is prepared in this manner,

$$R{-}^{18}OH + H_2O_2 \rightarrow R{-}O{-}OH + H_2{}^{18}O \tag{188}$$

some of it undergoes rearrangement, which must therefore have occurred in an environment containing $H_2{}^{18}O$. Since the unrearranged hydroperoxide contained no ^{18}O, it must never have taken part in an equilibrium with $R{-}O^+$ (eq. 189), and rearrangement must either occur immediately upon

$$C_6H_5CHCH_3{-}O{-}OH + H^+ \rightleftharpoons\!\!\!/ \;\; C_6H_5CHCH_3{-}O^+ + H_2O \tag{189}$$

formation of $R{-}O^+$ or go by a concerted path (eq. 187) in which $R{-}O^+$ plays no discrete part.[441]

The nature of the displacement reaction by hydrogen peroxide on the carbon of an alcohol can be expected to vary with the structure of the alcohol; evidence has been presented that under suitable circumstances it can be an S_N1, S_N2, or S_Ni process.[442]

Synthetic applications of hydroperoxide rearrangements have been quite limited, although the production of phenol from cumene by this route has become an important commercial process. A synthesis of neopentyl alcohol by the reaction of hydrogen peroxide with diisobutylene in 65% sulfuric acid has been reported.[443]

Rearrangements of hydroperoxides have been treated in several reviews.[444-446]

B. Carbonyl Derivatives: The Baeyer-Villiger Oxidation

The oxidation of ketones to esters by means of peroxy acids (eq. 190) was discovered in 1899 by Baeyer and Villiger.[447] They used Caro's acid (peroxy-

$$R{-}CO{-}R \xrightarrow{H_2SO_5} R{-}CO{-}O{-}R \tag{190}$$

sulfuric acid) in their experiments, but in subsequent years several other peroxy acids have also come into use, of which the principal ones are peroxyacetic, trifluoroperoxyacetic, peroxybenzoic, and monoperoxyphthalic acids.

[442] A. G. Davies and R. Feld, *J. Chem. Soc. (London)*, **1958**, 4637.

[443] (a) J. Hoffman and C. E. Boord, *J. Am. Chem. Soc.*, **77**, 3139 (1955). (b) M. S. Newman and T. Fukunaga, *J. Am. Chem. Soc.*, **77**, 6073 (1955).

[444] P. D. Bartlett, *Record Chem. Progr.*, **11**, 47 (1950).

[445] J. E. Leffler, *Chem. Revs.*, **45**, 385 (1949).

[446] E. Testa, *Oxydationen durch Wasserstoffperoxyd und Persäuren die zur Spaltung von C—C-Bindungen führen*, Juris Verlag, Zurich, 1950.

[447] A. v. Baeyer and V. Villiger, *Ber.*, **32**, 3625 (1899).

The reaction can also be brought about by hydrogen peroxide in weakly basic solution. The early work has been reviewed in several places, and a treatment of applications and experimental techniques is available in *Organic Reactions*.[447a,445,446]

Baeyer and Villiger were the first to suggest a path for the reaction, involving a dioxirane (oxoxide) intermediate (eq. 191). Later, various other mecha-

$$R_2C=O \rightarrow R_2C\overset{O}{\underset{O}{\diagup\!\diagdown}} \rightarrow R-CO-O-R \tag{191}$$

nisms were suggested, such as attack by peroxide or by OH^+ to form **45** or **46** and the addition of peroxy acid to form **47**; an alternative path by which **45** might be produced is loss of AO^- from **47**. Furthermore, **47** might rearrange directly or first be converted to **48** by loss of hydroxyl.

$$\underset{(45)}{R_2C\overset{OH}{\underset{O^+}{\diagup\!\diagdown}}} \qquad \underset{(46)}{R_2C=\overset{+}{O}-OH} \qquad \underset{(47)}{R_2C\overset{OH}{\underset{O-OA}{\diagup\!\diagdown}}} \qquad \underset{(48)}{R_2C=\overset{+}{O}-OA}$$

Most of the ambiguity was dispelled by an experiment by Doering and Dorfman[448] using benzophenone containing isotopically labeled oxygen. The phenyl benzoate obtained had the same isotope content in the carbonyl group as had the starting material (eq. 182), a result which at once eliminated

$$C_6H_5-\overset{^{18}O}{\overset{\|}{C}}-C_6H_5 \xrightarrow{C_6H_5CO_3H} C_6H_5-\overset{^{18}O}{\overset{\|}{C}}-O-C_6H_5 \tag{192}$$

equation 191 as the mechanism. The dioxirane intermediate, having two equivalent oxygens, would lead to a nearly equal distribution of isotope between the two oxygens of the ester. The species **46** is also ruled out if one considers that the only reasonable way in which it could be expected to rearrange would be by a shift of a phenyl group to the adjacent oxygen atom, the original carbonyl oxygen; this would give ester with none of the isotope in the carbonyl group. The species **48** cannot so simply be ruled out, although its formation from **47** would entail loss of all the isotopic oxygen to the solvent as $H_2^{18}O$, for it could be picked up again in a subsequent step (eq. 193).

$$R_2C\overset{^{18}OH}{\underset{O-OA}{\diagup\!\diagdown}} \xrightarrow{H^+} R_2C=\overset{+}{O}-OA \rightarrow R-\overset{+}{\underset{-OA}{C}}=\overset{+}{O}-R \xrightarrow{H_2^{18}O} R-\overset{^{18}O}{\overset{\|}{C}}-O-R \tag{193}$$

[447a] C. H. Hassall, *Org. Reactions*, **9**, Chapt. 3 (1957).

[448] W. E. Doering and E. Dorfman, *J. Am. Chem. Soc.*, **75**, 5595 (1953).

The solvent was benzene, so isotope dilution should not occur. There is nevertheless much reason to doubt that **48** is a significant intermediate, for its rearrangement would involve separating an anion from an already positively charged species. We are thus left with **47**, often called the Criegee intermediate after its originator,[448a] and **45**, which might be formed from **47**, before rearrangement (eq. 194). A decision between them must be made on other

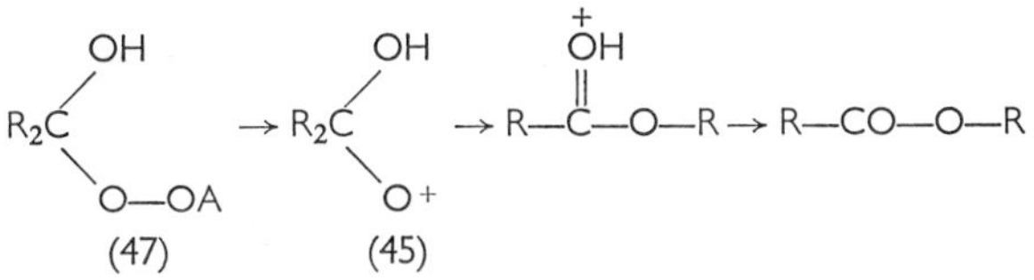

$$
\begin{array}{c}
\text{OH} \\
R_2C \\
\diagdown \\
\text{O—OA} \\
(47)
\end{array}
\rightarrow
\begin{array}{c}
\text{OH} \\
R_2C \\
\diagdown \\
\text{O +} \\
(45)
\end{array}
\rightarrow
R—\overset{+}{\underset{\|}{\overset{\text{OH}}{C}}}—O—R
\rightarrow R—CO—O—R
\qquad (194)
$$

evidence. It must also be considered that one of the three isomeric conjugate acids of **47**, resulting from protonation at any of the three oxygen atoms, may be an intermediate.

The nature of the actual migration, regardless of the precise intermediate, is clearly defined as an internal process by experiments that show there is complete retention of configuration by the migrating carbon atom. This was first done independently by Turner,[449] who worked with the *cis* and *trans* isomers of 1-acetyl-2-methylcyclopentane and 1-acetyl-2-methylcyclohexane (eq. 195), and by Gallagher and Kristschevsky,[450] who worked with 3α-ace-

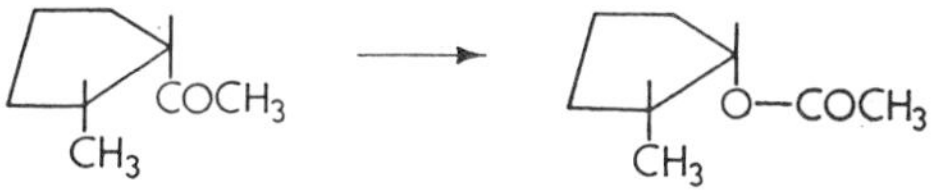

$$ (195) $$

toxy-17β-pregnan-20-one. All the foregoing compounds have more than one asymmetric center, and it was therefore desirable to confirm the behavior with a ketone in which the migrating carbon atom is the only asymmetric center. This was done by Mislow and Brenner,[451] who used α-phenylethyl methyl ketone (eq. 196). The stereochemistry of the Baeyer-Villiger oxidation

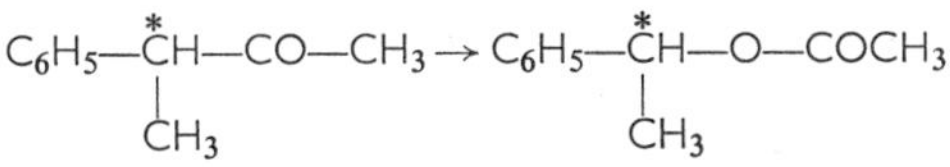

$$
C_6H_5—\overset{*}{C}H—CO—CH_3 \rightarrow C_6H_5—\overset{*}{C}H—O—COCH_3 \qquad (196)
$$
$$
\underset{\displaystyle CH_3}{|} \qquad\qquad\qquad \underset{\displaystyle CH_3}{|}
$$

(complete retention)

is thus the same as that of carbon-to-nitrogen rearrangements, discussed under heading 2.

[448a] R. Criegee and R. Kaspar, *Ann.*, **560**, 127 (1948).

[449] R. B. Turner, *J. Am. Chem. Soc.*, **72**, 879 (1950).

[450] T. F. Gallagher and T. H. Kristschevsky, *J. Am. Chem. Soc.*, **72**, 882 (1950).

[451] K. Mislow and J. Brenner, *J. Am. Chem. Soc.*, **75**, 2319 (1953).

The kinetics of the reaction have been measured by Friess and co-workers,[452–456] by Yukawa and co-workers,[457,458] and by Hawthorne and Emmons.[459] The earlier measurements were made on reactions with peroxybenzoic or peroxyacetic acids, with which there is only a small change in acidity during reaction. A distinct acid catalysis was nevertheless observed, suggesting that it is general acid catalysis. Catalysis by strong acids, such as sulfuric, can be very pronounced.[460] Friess' results showed second-order kinetics, apart from the acid catalysis, for most ketones. Changes to more polar solvents accelerated the reaction. The introduction [461] of trifluoroperoxyacetic acid as a reagent for the Baeyer-Villiger reaction made it possible to make more varied and meaningful measurements, since it is a more reproducible reagent and reacts quickly and nearly quantitatively; the earlier results, obtained with more difficult systems, though still of significance, are perhaps now of less importance than the newer results [459] obtained with trifluoroperoxyacetic acid.

Hawthorne and Emmons established that a third-order rate expression

$$\text{Rate} = k(\text{ketone})(\text{peroxide})(\text{acid})$$

is generally applicable, but under certain circumstances it may degenerate to pseudo-first or second order. Such an expression demands that the transition state be derived from all three reagents, most reasonably by a pair of second-order steps leading to the species that actually rearranges, the rearrangement step itself being a first-order process. We must therefore consider how the rearranging species, presumably the Criegee intermediate **47** or its conjugate acid, might arise. Either addition of peroxy acid to the protonated ketone (eq. 197) or protonation of a ketone–peroxy acid adduct would be a reason-

$$R_2CO + A\text{—COOH} \rightleftharpoons R_2C\overset{+}{=}OH \underset{\longleftarrow}{\overset{ACO\text{-}O\text{-}OH}{\longrightarrow}} R_2C\overset{\displaystyle OH}{\underset{\displaystyle \underset{H}{\overset{|}{O^{\pm}}}\text{—O—COA}}{\Big<}} \tag{197}$$

[452] S. L. Friess, *J. Am. Chem. Soc.*, **71**, 2571 (1949).

[453] S. L. Friess and N. Farnham, *J. Am. Chem. Soc.*, **72**, 5518 (1950).

[454] S. L. Friess and A. H. Soloway, *J. Am. Chem. Soc.*, **73**, 3968 (1951).

[455] S. L. Friess and R. Pinson, Jr., *J. Am. Chem. Soc.*, **74**, 1302 (1952).

[456] S. L. Friess and P. E. Frankenburg, *J. Am. Chem. Soc.*, **74**, 2679 (1952).

[457] Y. Yukawa and T. Yokoyama, *Mem. Inst. Sci. Ind. Research, Osaka Univ.*, **9**, 180 (1952); *Chem. Abstr.*, **49**, 5370g (1955).

[458] Y. Yukawa and T. Yokoyama, *J. Chem. Soc. Japan*, **73**, 371 (1952).

[459] M. F. Hawthorne and W. D. Emmons, *J. Am. Chem. Soc.*, **80**, 6398 (1959).

[460] W. E. Doering and L. Speers, *J. Am. Chem. Soc.*, **72**, 5515 (1950).

[461] W. D. Emmons and G. B. Lucas, *J. Am. Chem. Soc.*, **77**, 2287 (1955); W. F. Sager and A. Duckworth, *J. Am. Chem. Soc.*, **77**, 188 (1955).

able process and would fulfill the kinetic requirement. Since ketones are known to be readily protonated, and a reaction between ketones and trifluoroacetic acid has been verified,[459] the order given in equation 197 seems to be the most likely one.

Rearrangement of the tautomer produced by equation 197 with simultaneous heterolytic cleavage of the O—O bond (eq. 198) would involve sepa-

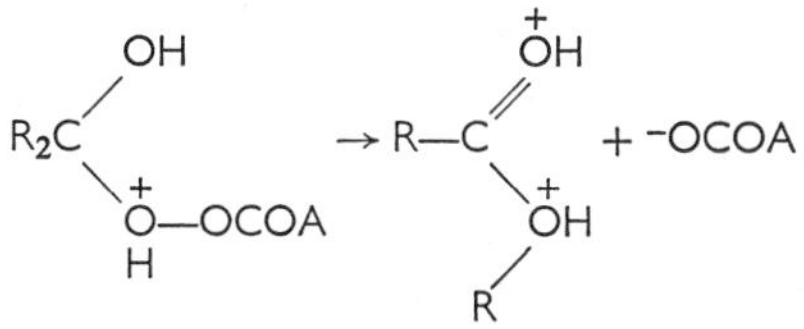

$$R_2C\overset{OH}{\underset{\overset{+}{O}—OCOA}{\diagup}} \rightarrow R—C\overset{\overset{+}{OH}}{\underset{\overset{+}{OH}}{\diagup}} + {}^-OCOA \qquad (198)$$

ration of an anion from an already positively charged site, and would therefore be unlikely. On the other hand, there are three additional tautomeric conjugate acids, **49**, **50** and **51**, that could be quickly formed in a suitable

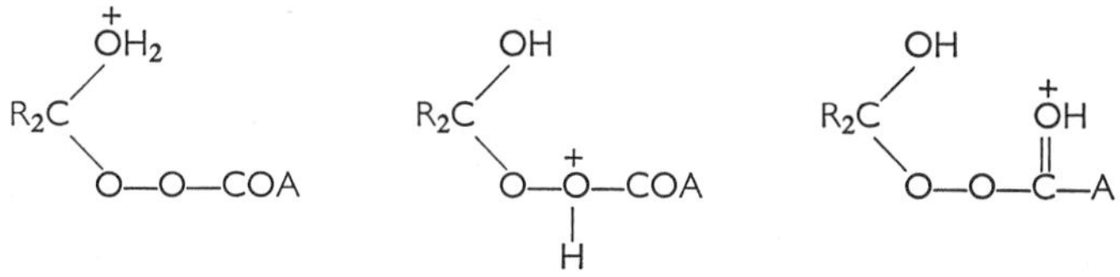

$$R_2C\overset{\overset{+}{OH_2}}{\underset{O—O—COA}{\diagup}} \qquad R_2C\overset{OH}{\underset{O—\overset{+}{O}—COA}{\diagup}} \qquad R_2C\overset{OH}{\underset{O—O—\overset{\|}{C}—A}{\diagup}}$$

(49)   (50)   (51)

medium. One of them, **49**, would also involve separation of an anion from a positively charged species. The other two involve no such objection, and rearrangement would produce a neutral molecule of acid and the protonated ester. However, if A is trifluoromethyl, protonation of either of the carboxyl oxygens would be expected to be extremely difficult, considering the great acid strength of trifluoroacetic acid and the known inertness of the analogous trichloroacetic acid to protonation,[424] and it does not seem reasonable to assign to such a species the role of key intermediate. A cyclic transition state derived from either **49** or the product of equation 197 would enable separation of a neutral molecule of acid, however (eq. 199). While the con-

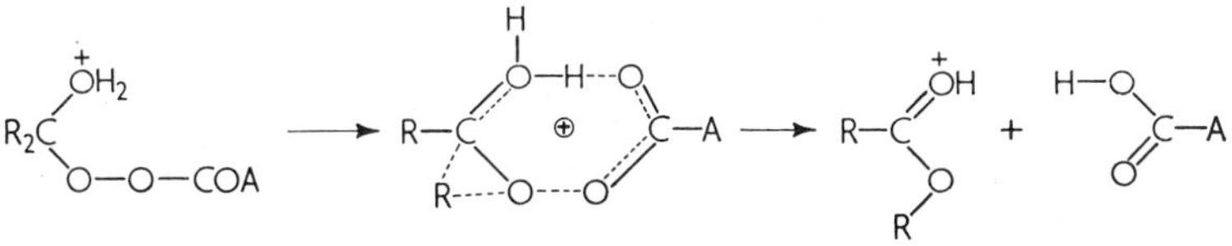

$$R_2C\overset{\overset{+}{OH_2}}{\underset{O—O—COA}{\diagup}} \longrightarrow R—C\overset{O—H\cdots O}{\underset{R\cdots\cdots O\cdots\cdots O}{\oplus}}C—A \longrightarrow R—C\overset{\overset{+}{OH}}{\underset{O}{\diagup}} + \overset{H—O}{\underset{O}{}}C—A \qquad (199)$$

certed process as written satisfies the requirements, we must look further for evidence that migration from C to O contributes significantly to the transition state, for cleavage might equally well give rise to the cationic oxygen intermediate **45** before rearrangement.

It would be consistent with the kinetics for the rate-determining step to be either the rearrangement or the formation of one of the protonated adducts. If it is the formation, there should be a correlation of the rate constants for different ketones with the rate constants for other carbonyl addition reactions, and if it is rearrangement, there should be a correlation with the relative mobilities of groups in this and related reactions. Hawthorne and Emmons [459] determined the rate constants for a group of substituted acetophenones and showed that they could be correlated by the Hammett equation, with reaction constants of -1.10 for reactions in ethylene chloride solution and -1.45 for those in acetonitrile. Since addition reactions to the carbonyl group show small, positive reaction constants, they concluded that migration contributes significantly to the energy of activation, which could only be true if rearrangement were rate determining. The observed values are, however, a composite of the effects on all the steps and thus include the equilibrium constants for protonation and for addition to the carbonyl group, both of which must vary with substitution. The protonation of acetophenones has been studied by Stewart and Yates,[462] who found a reaction constant of -2.17. Simple additions to the carbonyl group of acetophenones destroy the conjugation with the benzene ring and are therefore influenced by substitution in an opposite manner. We cannot be sure from these data alone, then, that rearrangement is rate determining or that it is a concerted process.

Additional evidence is provided by a comparison of the rate constants for the reactions of cyclohexanone with peroxyacetic acid and with trifluoroperoxyacetic acid under catalysis by the same acid, trifluoroacetic. The rate constant with peroxyacetic acid is only 1/200 that with trifluoroperoxyacetic acid. If addition to the carbonyl group were rate determining, one would expect the weaker peroxy acid, being more nucleophilic, to add faster; if rearrangement were rate determining, one would expect the stronger acid to give the faster reaction, for it could more readily sustain the negative charge developing from heterolysis of the O—O bond. It is difficult to reconcile the observed difference with any rate-determining step other than rearrangement, for the particular ketone under the conditions used. It is entirely conceivable, however, that the rate-determining step should shift to the carbonyl addition step under other conditions or with other ketones.

It may be significant that cyclohexanone was the fastest of all ketones investigated by Hawthorne and Emmons, having a rate constant over ten times that for acetophenone. It also has an exceptionally high equilibrium constant for formation of a cyanohydrin by addition of HCN.[463] If the rate-

[462] R. Stewart and K. Yates, *J. Am. Chem. Soc.*, **80**, 6355 (1958).

[463] V. Prelog and M. Kobelt, *Helv. Chim. Acta*, **32**, 1187 (1949).

determining step is in all cases the rearrangement, then we must attribute the greater rate of cyclohexanone to a much greater concentration of peroxide adduct with it than with acetophenone in the prerearrangement equilibrium, for the relative mobilities of phenyl and primary alkyl are in the opposite order. It is, however, possible that the reactive aliphatic ketones show rate-determining rearrangement because addition reactions are fast with them, and other ketones less reactive toward addition may show a transition to rates determined by the addition reaction.

Baeyer-Villiger oxidation may proceed without acid catalysis, or at least with only very weak acidity, as shown by the many successful reactions carried out with peroxyacetic and peroxybenzoic acids in the absence of any stronger acid. It is possible that the neutral intermediate **47** may rearrange at a significant rate, as well as its conjugate acid. The base-catalyzed reaction with hydrogen peroxide probably involves the addition of HO_2^- to form **52** and **53**, which may rearrange as they are or first acquire a proton to form a neutral peroxyhydrin, **54**. There is as yet insufficient evidence to decide such matters, but equation 200 is a reasonable process.[464]

$$R_2C \underset{O-OH}{\overset{O^-}{<}} \quad (52) \qquad R_2C \underset{O-O^-}{\overset{OH}{<}} \quad (53) \qquad R_2C \underset{O-OH}{\overset{OH}{<}} \quad (54)$$

$$R_2C \underset{O-OH}{\overset{O^-}{<}} \;\rightarrow\; R-C \underset{O-R'}{\overset{O}{<}} \;+OH^- \qquad (200)$$

There are several studies in which comparisons are possible of the rates of reaction as a function of ketone structure, but they cannot all be compared because of differences in conditions, which, as pointed out above, may lead to different reaction paths. Nevertheless, useful information can be drawn from the results of individual groups of investigators. Perhaps the most striking feature is that rates do not vary widely, most of the constants lying within a range of two powers of ten. Hawthorne and Emmons' work showed a drop in rate of only about two-thirds between methyl ethyl ketone and pinacolone, but acetone reacted only 1/25 as fast (it has even been recommended as a solvent for the oxidation of other ketones).[465] Phenyl alkyl ketones showed only a three-fold range with wide variations in the alkyl group. Cyclohexanone was the fastest of all, having a rate constant about twenty times that of

[464] H. O. House and R. L. Wasson, *J. Org. Chem.*, **22**, 1157 (1957).
[465] P. S. Starcher and B. Phillips, *J. Am. Chem. Soc.*, **80**, 4079 (1958).

acetone or cyclopentanone. A comparison of cyclanones [456] of ring size four to eight showed that cyclohexanone occupies a sharp maximum, with only minor differences among the other members. Methyl cycloalkyl ketones show alternating rate constants with damped amplitude, cyclopropyl being the slowest and cyclobutyl the fastest.[455] The effect of substituents on the rate constants of acetophenones as determined by Hawthorne and Emmons has already been mentioned; additional members of this group were compared by Friess and Soloway,[454] who also observed a correlation to the Hammett equation, (with the exception of m-methoxyacetophenone). Their fit was rough, however, owing to inconstancy of the order of the rate expression; ketones with electron-attracting substituents showed first-order kinetics, those with electron-donating substituents showed second-order kinetics, and acetophenone itself showed mixed order. These differences are presumably due to differing extents of conversion of the ketones to peroxide adducts and possibly to a change in rate-determining step. Yukawa and Yokayama [458] observed an inverse correlation with rates of oximation, except for cyclic ketones. The significance of correlations, or lack of them, with rates of oxime or semicarbazone formation is questionable, since it now appears that the rate-determining step in these processes is usually the dehydration step, not the addition.[465a]

The question of relative migration aptitudes (mobilities) has been investigated with many types of unsymmetrical ketones. Hawthorne, Emmons, and McCallum [466] demonstrated that the peroxy acid used may have a large effect on the results obtained; phenyl cyclohexyl ketone gave a phenyl/cyclohexyl migration ratio of 1:9 with peroxyacetic acid, but 1:4 with trifluoroperoxyacetic acid. In view of this, comparisons of results by investigators using different reagents cannot be made with any precision. It is clear from all reports,[455,466,467] however, that the order of preference for migration among alkyl groups is tertiary > secondary > primary > methyl. It is interesting that the apocamphyl group, which is tertiary at a bridgehead position, migrates as well as $tert$-butyl. Phenyl appears to be near isopropyl and cyclopentyl. As a result, it can be generalized that all methyl ketones will give mostly if not entirely acetate ester. This behavior is parallel to that observed in the C—to—N rearrangements of headings 1A and 1B. Cycloalkyl groups vary considerably in mobility, cyclopropyl being about as low as primary alkyl, and cyclohexyl being the fastest, above isopropyl.

The effect of para substitution on phenyl migration was studied by Doering

[465a] W. P. Jencks, *J. Am. Chem. Soc.*, **81**, 475 (1959).

[466] M. F. Hawthorne, W. D. Emmons, and K. S. McCallum, *J. Am. Chem. Soc.*, **80**, 6393 (1958).

[467] Y. Yukawa and T. Yokoyama, *Mem. Inst. Sci. Ind. Research, Osaka Univ.*, **13**, 171 (1956); *Chem. Abstr.*, **51**, 2633h (1957).

and Speers [460] with benzophenones. The order of preference for migration—$CH_3O > CH_3 > H > Cl > NO_2$—is that expected for a reaction in which rearrangement is a concerted process. It shows the same relative mobilities as have been observed in other migrations to an electron-deficient atom and demonstrates that there is no steric control of the type found in the Beckmann rearrangement and the Schmidt reaction (heading 1). Ortho-substituted phenyl groups migrate less readily than their para-substituted counterparts, but may be above or below phenyl, depending on their electronic effect.[468]

It can be said of most of the results that the group that migrates preferentially is the one best able to sustain a positive charge in the transition state. There are, however, apparent deviations, as well as the phenomenon of variation as a function of reagent, which require further comment.

Camphor is the most significant exception and has occasioned much comment. Baeyer and Villiger [447] originally obtained α-campholide in 30% yield by the use of Caro's acid (eq. 201). This is a case of apparent preference for

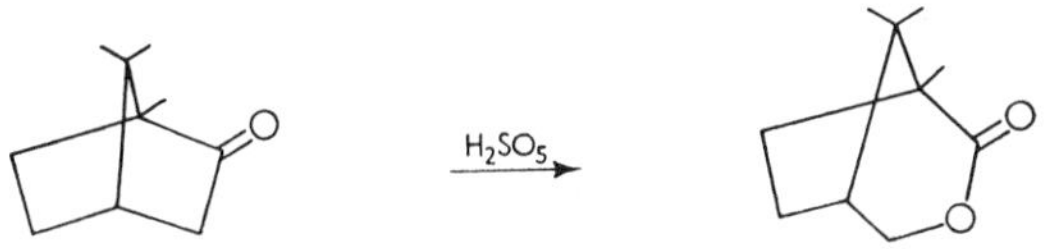

$$(201)$$

migration of a primary group over a tertiary. An early suggestion that the location of the tertiary carbon at a bridgehead position might have lowered its mobility has been made improbable by the later observation [469] that norcamphor, which lacks the methyl groups, gives the lactone from bridgehead migration. Murray, Johnson, Pederson, and Ott [470] attributed the result to the steric effect of the methyl groups, which is known to hinder approach to the carbonyl group from the side bearing them. Addition of peroxy acid from the less hindered side would give the adduct of configuration 55.

Migration of the bridgehead position would pass through a transition state having a boat conformation (56), which would be of higher energy, owing to nonbonded interactions, than the transition state for methylene migration, which would have a chair conformation (57). This argument would only be

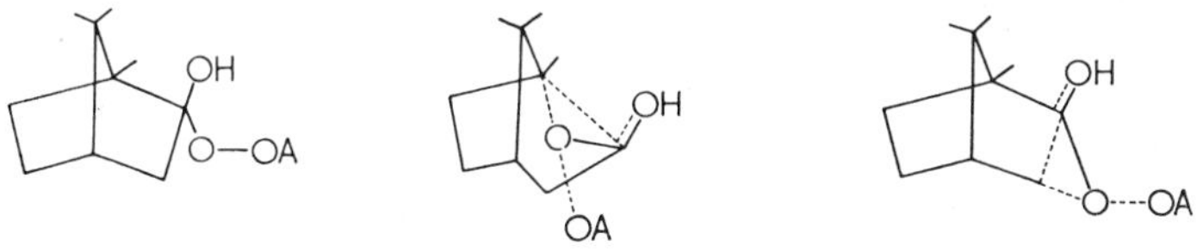

(55)   (56)   (57)

[468] W. H. Saunders, Jr., J. Am. Chem. Soc., 77, 4679 (1955).

[469] J. Meinwald and E. Frauenglass, J. Am. Chem. Soc., 82, 5235 (1960).

[470] M. F. Murray, B. A. Johnson, R. L. Pederson, and A. C. Ott, J. Am. Chem. Soc., 78, 981 (1956).

valid if equilibration between epimers **55** and **58** were slower than rearrangement; that is, if addition were the rate-determining step. Epimer **58** is undoubtedly of higher energy than **55**, owing to steric compression between the acyl group and the methyl groups, and would therefore be present in a lower concentration than **55** at equilibrium, but these facts would not be relevant as long as equilibration between **55** and **58** is rapid. The thermodynamically most stable transition state for rearrangement, whether derived from **55** or **58**, would determine the major product.[470a] Meinwald and Frauenglass [469] have pointed out that with epimer **58**, the electronically favored migration of the bridgehead carbon can proceed by a sterically favored chair configuration in the transition state.

Sauers [471a] reinvestigated and confirmed the original report of Baeyer and Villiger and added the observation that the isomeric lactone (**59**), resulting

(58)   (59)

from bridgehead migration, is unstable under the conditions used by Baeyer and Villiger and would not have been found even if it had been the major initial product. The products, recently examined and elucidated by Conolly and Overton,[471b] that are obtained from the Baeyer-Villiger reaction after separation of the α-campholide closely resembled the decomposition products of the missing lactone. Sauers also oxidized camphor with peroxyacetic acid in sodium acetate–acetic acid buffer; the product under these conditions was the other lactone, **59**, in 72% yield, and no α-campholide was obtained. It thus appears that the major question is really how one set of conditions can promote the electronically unfavored migration of the methylene group to the extent of 30%.

The possibilities seem to be either (*a*) that the product from Caro's acid is determined by a rate-limiting *addition* reaction and the product from peroxyacetic acid is determined by a rate-limiting *rearrangement* or (*b*) that rearrangement is rate-determining with both reagents, but the relative energies of the transition states vary appreciably with the reagent. There is reason in support of both explanations. With Caro's acid, the rearrangement step should be much faster, because of the greater anionic stability of the leaving group, sulfate, than with peroxyacetic acid, where the leaving group is acetate; the

[470a] This general effect is discussed by D. Y. Curtin, *Record Chem. Progr.*, **15**, 111 (1954).

[471a] R. R. Sauers, *J. Am. Chem. Soc.*, **81**, 925 (1959).

[471b] J. D. Conolly and K. H. Overton, *Proc. Chem. Soc.* (*London*), **1959**, 188.

faster the rearrangement step, the more likely is a preceding step to be rate limiting. Of the four possible transition states for rearrangement, the two derived from **58** would be of higher energy than those from **55**, owing to steric compression. The extent of this difference should be a function both of the size of the acyl group and of the degree to which the O—O bond is stretched in the transition state. Sulfate is larger than acetate, and the O—O bond should be stretched less in the transition state since sulfate is a better leaving group. Both these effects would act to raise the energy of both transition states derived from **58** with respect to **56** and **57**, and the course of rearrangement could be channeled more through **57**, which gives α-campholide. With peroxyacetic acid, where the smaller size of the acetate group and the greater extent of stretching of the O—O bond necessary in the transition state would reduce steric compression, the chair configuration transition state derived from **58**, by which the electronically favored migration of the bridgehead occurs, would be more likely to determine the major product. Another consequence to be expected of a change to a better leaving group is contraction of the scale of the energy effects for migration of different groups, resulting in less discriminate product ratios.[469,471] Although we cannot measure all the variables, the resultant effects do not seem unreasonable.

Strong additional support for the view that steric effects can compete with (and even dominate) electronic ones in determining the products of Baeyer-Villiger oxidations has recently been provided by the work of Sauers and Ahearn [471c] with epicamphor, which shows methylene migration exclusively, 1-methylnorcamphor, which shows only bridgehead migration, and fenchone and camphor, from which both isomeric products appear. A bridgehead methyl group, alpha to the carbonyl group, appears to exert an unusually large steric effect, and greatly retards the over-all rate.

Rassat and Ourisson [472] have suggested that differences observed between the results of oxidations in acidic and in buffered media may be due to the possibility of rapid interconversion of epimers through the anion of the adduct, according to equation 201a.

$$(201a)$$

Where the steric influence due to the methyl groups in camphor is lacking, there is no reason to expect other than bridgehead migration. Meinwald and Frauenglass [469] observed just this not only with norcamphor, but also with a ring homolog, bicyclo[2.2.2]octanone, and its unsaturated counterpart,

[471c] R. R. Sauers and G. P. Ahearn, *J. Am. Chem. Soc.*, **83**, 2759 (1961).
[472] A. Rassat and G. Ourisson, *Bull. soc. chim. France*, **1959**, 1133.

bicyclo[2.2.2]oct-5-en-2-one. The latter substance also undergoes isomerization as well as oxidation, and the isolated product is a phthalide derivative (eq. 202). Similar behavior is shown by dehydronorcamphor,[473] which gives

$$(202)$$

some of the unrearranged lactone as well, and by carvone camphor.[474] It is significant that in the two unsaturated ketones, oxidation occurs exclusively at the carbonyl group. Another example of this effect is found in the oxidation of Δ^5-cholestenone, where a lactone is formed instead of the epoxide.[475] Benzylidenecyclopentanones (eq. 203) and -cyclohexanones also show this effect; here the vinyl side migrates in preference to the saturated side.[476]

$$(203)$$

Neopentyl and neophyl methyl ketones, in which groups very susceptible to rearrangement migrate, are converted to normal acetate esters,[477] as is *exo*-2-acetylnorbornane,[477a] in which the migrating group is even more sensitive to rearrangement (i.e., racemization in this case). It is clear that even though the migrating group may acquire some cationic character in the transition state, the alpha carbon is so tightly bound that common rearrangements are excluded, and beta carbons, even when oriented very favorably, do not take part.

β-Diketones capable of enolization react with monoperoxyphthalic acid by initial oxidation of the enolizable hydrogen, resulting in mixtures of cleavage products, and apparently no normal Baeyer-Villiger reaction occurs.[478] House and Gannon could not confirm an earlier claim[479] that an unexplained carbon skeleton rearrangement takes place.

The oxidation of ketones by alkaline hydrogen peroxide has received much less attention than the peroxy acid reactions, presumably because it is much slower. House and Wasson[480] have determined the products from a group of

[473] J. Meinwald, M. C. Seidel, and B. C. Cadoff, *J. Am. Chem. Soc.*, **80**, 6303 (1958).

[474] G. Büchi and I. M. Goldman, *J. Am. Chem. Soc.*, **79**, 4741 (1957).

[475] S. Mori and F. Mukawa, *Bull. Chem. Soc. Japan*, **27**, 479 (1954).

[476] H. M. Walton, *J. Org. Chem.*, **22**, 1161 (1957).

[477] J. W. Wilt and A. Danielzadeh, *J. Org. Chem.*, **23**, 920 (1958).

[477a] J. A. Berson and S. Suzuki, *J. Am. Chem. Soc.*, **81**, 4088 (1959).

[478] H. O. House and W. F. Gannon, *J. Org. Chem.*, **23**, 879 (1958).

[479] J. Boeseken and J. Jacobs, *Rec. trav. chim.*, **55**, 804 (1936).

[480] H. O. House and R. L. Wasson, *J. Org. Chem.*, **22**, 1157 (1957).

simple aliphatic ketones, but the conversions were mostly well under 10%, and the results therefore of limited significance. The order of preference for migration appeared to be primary > secondary > methyl and phenyl, which is not the same as the order obtaining with peroxy acids. 2-Methyl-3-phenyl-2-cyclopentenone was converted to β-hydroxypropiophenone, which suggests that the saturated side of the carbonyl migrates in preference to the vinyl side, followed by a C=C double-bond cleavage (eq. 204).

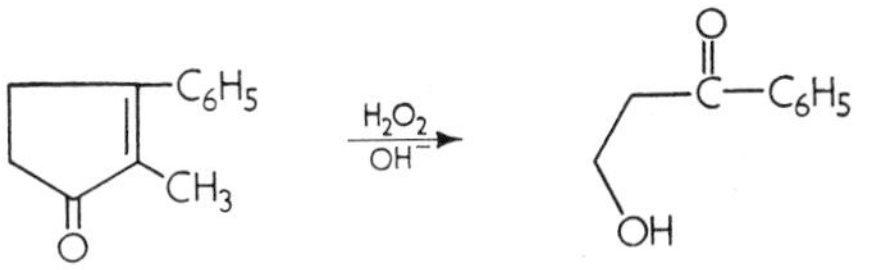

$$(204)$$

Aldehydes also undergo the Baeyer-Villiger oxidation;[481a] carboxylic acids usually result, either from fragmentation of the intermediate or by hydrogen migration. When the mobility of an aryl group is strongly increased by electron-releasing substituents, formate esters may be formed as well.[481]

The cleavage of benzils by hydroperoxide, tert-butylperoxide, or peroxyacetate, which gives carboxylic acids or their esters, shows kinetic and substituent effects that indicate it does not involve migration from C to O of the Baeyer-Villiger type, but is, instead, a fission process.[481a]

The applications of the Baeyer-Villiger oxidation to synthesis and degradation have been summarized recently by Hassall,[481b] and such a survey will not be given here. In addition to the more recent work already discussed here, however, there are two applications that are new. Geiseler, Asinger, and Wien [482] have adapted the Baeyer-Villiger oxidation for analysis of mixtures of ketones derived from oxidation of hydrocarbons; the esters obtained from them were saponified and the alcohols separated by paper chromatography. The quantitative reaction of trifluoroperoxyacetic acid with ketones has been used for functional group determination.[483] Boyer and Morgan [484] have made use of the Baeyer-Villiger oxidation of aminoquinones in a process for converting a benzene to a pyridine ring (eq. 205).

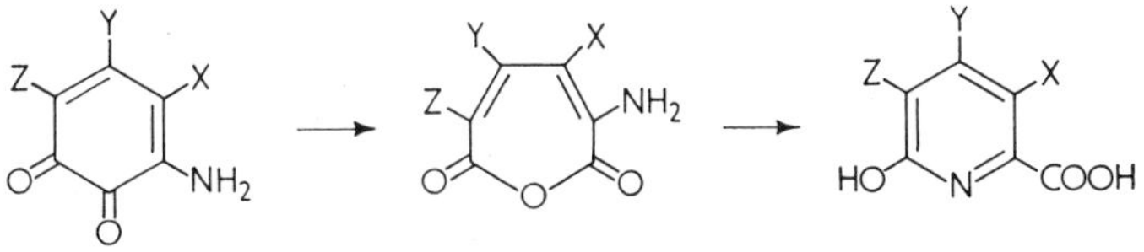

$$(205)$$

[481] E. Bamberger, *Ber.*, **36**, 2042 (1903).

[481a] H. Kwart and N. J. Wegemer, *J. Am. Chem. Soc.*, **83**, 2746 (1961).

[481b] C. H. Hassall, *Org. Reactions*, **9**, Chapt. 3 (1957).

[482] G. Geiseler, F. Asinger, and H. Wien, *Chem. Ber.*, **92**, 958 (1959).

[483] M. F. Hawthorne, *Anal. Chem.*, **28**, 540 (1956).

[484] J. H. Boyer and L. R. Morgan, Jr., *J. Am. Chem. Soc.*, **82**, 4748 (1960).

C. Carboxyl Derivatives: Diacyl Peroxides

The susceptibility of diacyl peroxides to homolytic cleavage of the O—O bond is well known. This cleavage occurs so readily that it has been only rarely that heterolytic cleavage has been observed.

Bartlett and Leffler [485] observed that benzoyl peroxide is weakly susceptible to acid-catalyzed decomposition, but phenylacetyl peroxide undergoes such a reaction readily. The products—benzyl alcohol, carbon dioxide, and phenylacetic acid—suggest a carbon-to-oxygen rearrangement, although they can equally well be accounted for by a fragmentation process (eq. 206). The

$$C_6H_5CH_2CO—O \atop \underset{\underset{H}{|}}{C_6H_5CH_2CO—O^+} \rightarrow \begin{array}{l} C_6H_5CH_2{}^+ + CO_2 \xrightarrow{H_2O} C_6H_5CH_2OH \quad (206) \\ + \ C_6H_5CH_2COOH \end{array}$$

reaction is first order, and the effectiveness of catalysis is proportional to acid strength.

A clearer case of C—to—O rearrangement is encountered with the unsymmetrical p-anisoyl p-nitrobenzoyl peroxide, which rearranges to p-methoxyphenyl p-nitrobenzoyl carbonate (eq. 207) in nitrobenzene or

$$CH_3OC_6H_4COO—OCO—C_6H_4NO_2 \rightarrow CH_3OC_6H_4OCO—O—COC_6H_4NO_2 \quad (207)$$

thionyl chloride.[486] In contrast, it gives no carbonate or other phenol derivative by free radical decomposition. Denney [487] investigated the rearrangement of the same peroxide in which the anisoyl carbonyl group was labeled with oxygen-18. The p-methoxyphenol obtained by hydrolysis of the initial product was free of ^{18}O (eq. 208), which shows that a species such as

$$Ar—C{\overset{\displaystyle O}{\diagdown}}\!\!\!\!\diagup \atop O^+$$

in which the oxygen atoms could become equivalent, could not be an intermediate.

$$CH_3OC_6H_4{\underset{\underset{18O}{\|}}{—C}}—O—O—{\underset{\underset{O}{\|}}{CC_6H_4NO_2}} \rightarrow CH_3OC_6H_4—O—{\underset{\underset{O}{\|}}{C}}—O—{\underset{\underset{O}{\|}}{CC_6H_4NO_2}} \rightarrow$$

$$CH_3OC_6H_4OH \quad (208)$$
$$\text{(free of } ^{18}O\text{)}$$

Denney and Denney [487a] also investigated this peroxide with the p-nitro-

[485] P. D. Bartlett and J. E. Leffler, *J. Am. Chem. Soc.*, **72**, 3030 (1950).

[486] J. E. Leffler, *J. Am. Chem. Soc.*, **72**, 67 (1950).

[487] D. B. Denney, *J. Am. Chem. Soc.*, **78**, 590 (1956).

[487a] D. B. Denney and D. G. Denney, *J. Am. Chem. Soc.*, **79**, 4806 (1957).

benzoyl carbonyl group isotopically labeled. Only 66% of the isotope remained in the carbonyl group after rearrangement, and the remainder appeared between the carbonyl groups (eq. 209). This shows that the p-nitro-

$$CH_3C_6H_4CO-O-O-\underset{\underset{18O}{\|}}{C}-C_6H_4NO_2 \rightarrow CH_3OC_6H_4-O-CO-^{18}O-\underset{\underset{18O}{\|}}{C}-C_6H_4NO_2 \quad (209)$$

34% 66%

benzoate oxygens do not become equivalent during the reaction; the ion pair through which the rearrangement presumably proceeds must either have a structure about the carboxyl group such that it can collapse to product by two paths to unequal extents, or such an ion pair may equilibrate partially before collapse to product. The behavior is reminiscent of that of 9-decalyl peroxybenzoate, in which the oxygens remain completely nonequivalent.

Acid-catalyzed decomposition of peroxy acids gives only carboxylic acids and oxygen, and no rearrangement is detectable.[488]

[488] W. E. Parker, L. P. Witnauer, and D. Swern, *J. Am. Chem. Soc.*, **80**, 323 (1958).

TRANSANNULAR HYDRIDE SHIFTS

9

V. PRELOG
Eidgenössische Technische Hochschule, Zürich,
Switzerland

JAMES G. TRAYNHAM[1]
Louisiana State University,
Baton Rouge, Louisiana

I. INTRODUCTION

It is now well established that medium-sized ring compounds (number of ring members $n = 8-12$) exhibit features which set them apart from compounds of other ring sizes.[1a] At first these compounds were notable by their relative unavailability, which prevented extensive studies; methods of ring closure that are quite satisfactory for common ($n = 5-7$) and even large (n over 12) rings often fail to give analogous compounds in the medium ring range or give extremely small yields. After synthetic methods had been developed, it was soon realized that medium ring compounds have also unusual physical and chemical properties. Although organic chemists have rationalized these by assuming that unusual nonclassical strains are present in medium rings, it is only recently that data which confirm unambiguously the validity of such assumptions have become available.

In extension of earlier studies [2] van Kamp and Coops [3] have determined

[1] Acknowledgment is made to the donors of the Petroleum Research Fund administered by the American Chemical Society for an international award to one of us (J. G. T.).

[1a] For a summary of older evidence for medium-ring effects see V. Prelog, *J. Chem. Soc.* (*London*), **1950**, 420.

[2] S. Kaarsemaker and J. Coops, *Rec. trav. chim.*, **71**, 261 (1952).

[3] H. van Kamp, Thesis, Vrije Universiteit, Amsterdam, Netherlands, 1957; *cf.* J. Coops, H. van Kamp, W. A. Lambregts, B. J. Visser, and H. Dekker, *Rec. trav. chim.*, **79**, 1226 (1960).

the heats of combustion in the gas phase of carefully purified samples of cycloalkanes with $n = 5$–17. Their measurements show that the medium-sized cycloalkanes, compared with normal paraffins and cyclohexane, possess considerable thermochemical strain, which reaches a maximum of approximately 12 kcal./mole in cyclononane and cyclodecane.

The main factors determining the strain in medium ring compounds are the deviation of the valence angle of ring atoms from the optimal value (*Baeyer strain*) and the strong intramolecular nonbonding interactions which are enforced by the geometry of the ring. The well-known lateral repulsion between atoms (or orbitals) attached to ring members in the vicinal 1,2 position is an example of the latter type of interaction (deviation from minimum is called *Pitzer strain*). A second example is the end-on interaction of atoms (or orbitals) in more remote positions (e.g., 3, 4, 5), which cause the *transannular strain* typical of medium rings.

The relative importance of these three factors follows from recent X-ray studies of Dunitz et al.[4-6] which furnish the first direct information about the conformation of medium ring compounds with $n = 8$–10. In accordance with thermochemical measurements, which indicate the absence of strain, there is no appreciable deviation from tetrahedral valence angles and from optimal torsion angles in cyclododecane. On the other hand, the investigated compounds with strained eight-, nine-, and ten-membered rings exhibit valence angles which are significantly larger than tetrahedral. The torsion angles in eight- and nine-membered ring compounds are partially eclipsed. Pitzer strain seems to be important in these compounds. Surprisingly enough, the investigated ten-membered ring compound exhibits a conformation free of Pitzer strain. Because the exact positions of the hydrogen atoms could not be determined by X-ray analysis, there is no direct proof of transannular strain, but calculations based on reasonable assumptions show that in nine- and ten-membered rings certain hydrogen atoms (called intraannular) on ring members in 1,3, 1,4, and 1,5 positions must be very close to each other, thus indicating strong transannular interactions and strain.

Only a larger number of X-ray analyses will reveal whether different compounds of the same ring size have the same conformation or whether conformations vary from compound to compound. It is also not proved that the conformations in the solid state are the same as those in the liquid state and in solution, which are of greatest interest to the organic chemist in the discussion of reaction mechanisms. The reasons that allow one to conclude with some

[4] R. F. Bryan and J. D. Dunitz, *Helv. Chim. Acta*, **43**, 3 (1960).

[5] E. Huber-Buser and J. D. Dunitz, *Helv. Chim. Acta*, **43**, 760 (1960).

[6] J. D. Dunitz and H. M. M. Shearer, *Proc. Chem. Soc. (London)*, **1958**, 348, **1959**, 268; *Helv. Chim. Acta*, **43**, 18 (1960).

confidence that the conformations found by X-ray analysis are indeed of general validity are discussed by Dunitz and Prelog,[7] and we shall assume that the conformations found in crystals are applicable to the discussion of the reactions with which we shall deal in this section. A schematic representation of the conformations of nine-, ten-, and twelve-membered rings as determined by X-rays is given in Figure 1. The positions of intraannular hydrogens in nine- and ten-membered rings are indicated by small circles (black = up, white = down).

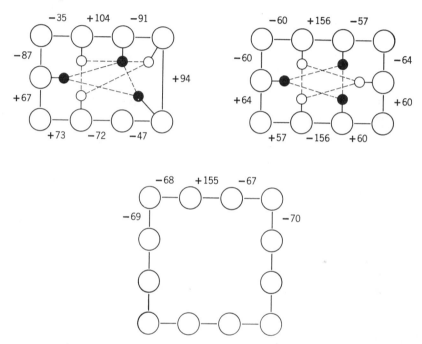

Figure 1. Schematic representation of conformations of 9-, 10-, and 12-membered rings. The numbers refer to torsion angles around the ring about the corresponding bond. Small circles represent intraannular hydrogens—black, up; white, down.

The same proximity of atoms across the ring that is assumed to be responsible for the transannular strain in medium rings can also lead to previously unexpected transannular reactions involving sites which would be inert in other aliphatic or alicyclic compounds. If a transannular reaction also involves migration of an atom or a group across the ring, it may be classified as a *transannular rearrangement*. Although transannular rearrangements of other atoms or groups have been postulated in some special cases, the most important type concerns hydride shifts. Unambiguous experimental

[7] J. D. Dunitz and V. Prelog, *Angew. Chem.*, **72**, 896 (1960).

demonstration of migration has been limited to this type of rearrangement. This section deals therefore primarily with the *evidence* and *conditions* for *transannular hydride shifts* in *medium ring compounds*.

This type of hydride shift rearrangement was first reported for hydroxylation of olefins with performic acid and was inferred from substantial or exclusive formation of nonvicinal diols as products.[8,9] Considerable data have since been accumulated for the solvolysis of cycloalkyl tosylates by using reactants labeled with ^{14}C and deuterium.[10] Because of its simplicity and well-understood reaction mechanism, the latter reaction will be discussed first in this section. Studies with labeled reactants have been extended to include deamination of cycloalkylamines with nitrous acid[11] and also other reactions for which electron-deficient intermediates are postulated, but the investigations are still very incomplete.[10]

2. INVESTIGATED REACTIONS

A. Solvolysis of Cycloalkyl Tosylates

The most thorough experimental inquiry about transannular hydride shifts has been associated with the tosylates.

Solvolyses of alkyl tosylates give mixtures of products which are formed by both substitution and elimination. Rearrangements during reactions of unsubstituted cycloalkyl tosylates can be detected only by use of isotopic labeling. Tosylates of cycloalkanols (ring sizes 7 and 9–12) labeled with ^{14}C have been prepared and subjected to solvolysis.[12–16] Cycloheptyl tosylate, synthesized from cyano-labeled suberonitrile by the Ziegler procedure (Scheme 1), was labeled only in the position α to the tosyl group; the others, prepared from carboxyl-labeled dicarboxylic acid esters by the acyloin condensation (Scheme 2), had ^{14}C in the α and β positions. Solvolyses of these tosylates in water-free acetic acid gave mixtures of olefin and acetate (isolated as alcohol). Degradation of the products by successive oxidations and Schmidt reactions (Scheme 3) removed two carbons at a time, and radioassay on the fragments revealed the distribution of the ^{14}C label. Completely classical reactions would give products in which the ^{14}C distribution was the

[8] V. Prelog and K. Schenker, *Helv. Chim. Acta*, **35**, 2044 (1952).

[9] A. C. Cope, S. W. Fenton, and C. F. Spencer, *J. Am. Chem. Soc.*, **74**, 5884 (1952).

[10] V. Prelog, *Record Chem. Progr.*, **18**, 247 (1957); *Angew. Chem.*, **70**, 145 (1958).

[11] V. Prelog, H. J. Urech, A. A. Bothner-By, and J. Würsch, *Helv. Chim. Acta*, **38**, 1095 (1955).

[12] S. J. Rhoads, unpublished; cf. footnote 10.

[13] V. Prelog, H. Kägi, and E. H. White, *Helv. Chim. Acta*, **45**, 1658 (1962).

[14] V. Prelog, W. Küng, and T. Tomljenović, *Helv. Chim. Acta*, **45**, 1352 (1962).

[15] L. O. Moore, unpublished.

[16] W. Küng and V. Prelog, *Croatica Chem. Acta*, **29**, 357 (1957).

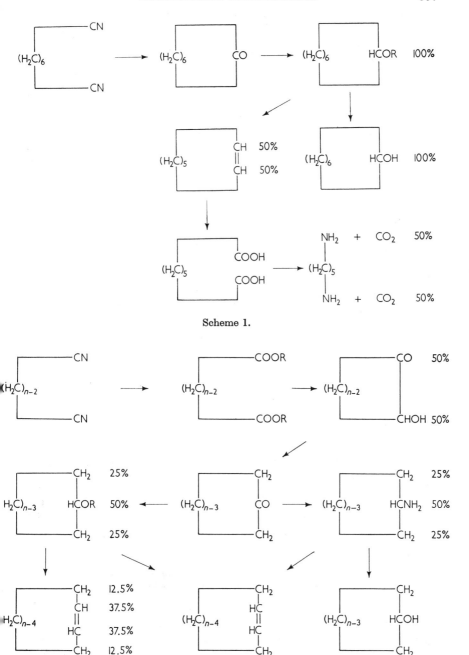

Scheme 1.

Scheme 2.

same as in the reactants. That is, in the case of the seven-membered ring, all radioactivity would be found in the first pair of carbon atoms removed in the

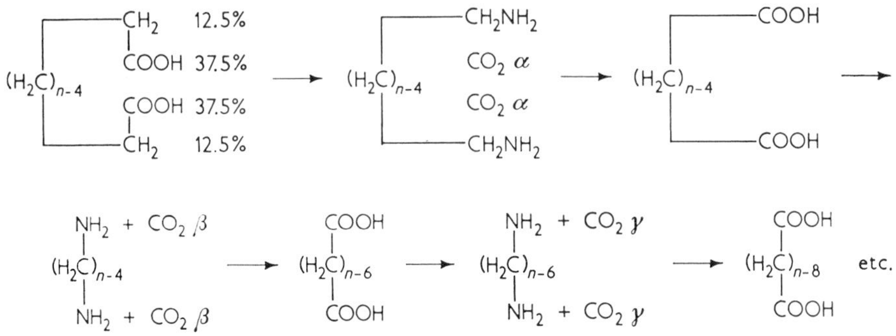

Scheme 3.

degradation scheme; for all the others, with labeling in β as well as in the α positions, 75% of the radioactivity would be found in the first pair and 25% in the second pair of carbon atoms. Only in the case of cyclododecyl tosylate is such a result obtained. Less than 5% radioactivity was found in the products from cycloheptyl p-tosylate after the first degradation. With

TABLE I

^{14}C Distribution in Products from Solvolyses of Cycloalkyl Tosylates
(Radioactivity of Reactants = 100)

Pair of carbon atoms	C_7 ene[12]	C_7 ol[12]	C_9 cis-ene[13]	C_9 trans-ene[13]	C_9 ol[13]	C_{10} cis-ene[14]	C_{10} trans-ene[14]	C_{11} trans-ene[15]	C_{12} ene[16]
1st (α)	96.5	95.5	55	54	53	52	62	68	75
2nd (β)			19	25	24	19	26	21	25
3rd (γ)	3.5	4.5	5	4	6		1.5		
4th (δ)			13	10	17	29	4	11	less than 0.2
All others			8	7			6.5		
Total beyond β carbons			26	21	23	29	12	11	<0.2

the nine-, ten-, and eleven-membered rings, varying but substantial amounts of ^{14}C are found beyond the first two stages in the degradation. The actual distribution data are summarized in Table I. Wherever braces appear in the table, the distribution of ^{14}C is not subdivided because either the amount of sample at this stage was too small for further degradation (C_9 ol) or the subsequent stages of the degradation scheme employed were later shown to be unreliable.[13]

The data in Table I are different from those published originally for cyclodecyl tosylate.[17] The early experimental work was plagued with irreproducible ratios of *cis*- and *trans*-cyclodecenes, a trouble finally traced to the spontaneous decomposition of cyclodecyl tosylate in the solid state.[14] By this decomposition, cyclodecenes, with ^{14}C extensively distributed in all positions, are produced along with small amounts of decalins. The main product is *cis*-cyclodecene, the exact proportion depending on the reaction conditions. By contrast, when very pure tosylate is used in the acetolysis experiments, the olefin mixture contains about 83% *trans*-cyclodecene.[14]

The nearly random distribution of ^{14}C and the formation of the thermodynamically favored *cis*-cyclodecene by the spontaneous decomposition may well indicate that the intermediate carbonium ion formed and trapped in the crystal reacts differently from the one in solution. On the other hand, repeated reaction of the *trans*-cyclodecene with *p*-toluenesulfonic acid could also lead to the same result, for *trans*-cyclodecene does indeed react with p-CH_3-$C_6H_4SO_3D$ in CH_3CO_2D; at $100°$ deuterium is rapidly incorporated into the olefin and is almost evenly distributed throughout the ring. At the same time, but at a slower rate, the *trans* olefin is isomerized to the *cis* isomer.[18]

Comparison of the distribution data for cyclononyl and cyclodecyl tosylates with the distributions calculated for the various types of hydride shifts (in the calculations the eliminations on both sides of the carbonium ion were assumed to be energetically equivalent) reveals that 1,5 and higher shifts certainly have occurred, for only then can a minimum of ^{14}C in the third (γ) pair of carbon atoms be achieved. No such minimum can occur by any combination of single 1,2, 1,3, and 1,4 shifts (Fig. 2). Since a second 1,5 or 1,2 shift will make the minimum of radioactivity on the third carbon atom pair less pronounced, the nonclassical distribution data represent minimum extents of transannular hydride shifts. Although a small amount of transannular reaction may take place in the case of cycloheptyl tosylate (the ^{14}C found beyond the α carbons includes 1,2 shifts), the greater importance of this type of process among the medium ring compounds with 8–11 ring members is readily apparent in Table I.

The relative extents of the two competing processes—substitution and elimination—differ among the various rings. Alcohol and olefin are formed in about equal amounts from cycloheptyl tosylate and in a 1 : 2 ratio from cyclononyl tosylate, but cyclodecyl and cycloundecyl tosylate give olefin almost exclusively. A particularly striking difference among the three medium ring compounds is found in the compositions of the olefin mixtures. *trans*-Cyclene

[17] H. J. Urech and V. Prelog, *Helv. Chim. Acta*, **40**, 477 (1957).
[18] E. Wunderlich and S. Smolinski, unpublished.

(thermodynamically less stable) is formed predominantly from cyclodecyl and cycloundecyl tosylates ($trans/cis \simeq 5:1$ and $13:1$, respectively). However, the *cis* olefin is the main product from cyclononyl tosylate ($cis/trans \simeq 2:1$). These differences, particularly the opposite behavior of C_9 and C_{10} rings,

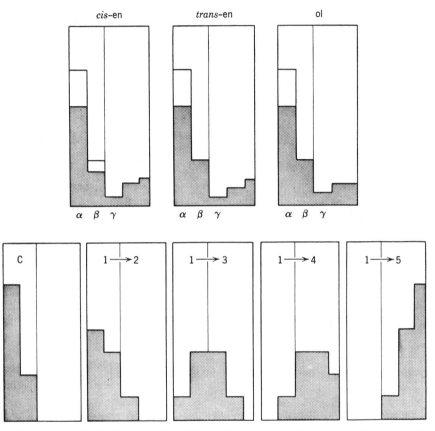

Figure 2. Distribution of radioactivity in the products of acetolysis of cyclononyl-[$^{14}C_2$]p-tosylate. Top: Distribution found in products (calculated classical distribution shown in outline). Bottom: Distribution calculated for different single hydride shifts; C, classical, i.e., no shift.

emphasize the conformational individuality of the medium ring compounds discussed in the Introduction (see Fig. 1, page 595) and in the article of Dunitz and Prelog.[7]

The course of the solvolysis of cyclodecyl tosylate has also been followed by labeling the reactant with deuterium.[19] Cyclodecanol-1-d was prepared easily

[19] V. Prelog and S. Borčić, *Helv. Chim. Acta*, **41**, 199 (1958).

by the reduction of cyclodecanone with $LiAlD_4$. Acetolysis of the tosylate (Scheme 4) gives a mixture of cyclodecenes without loss of deuterium, and

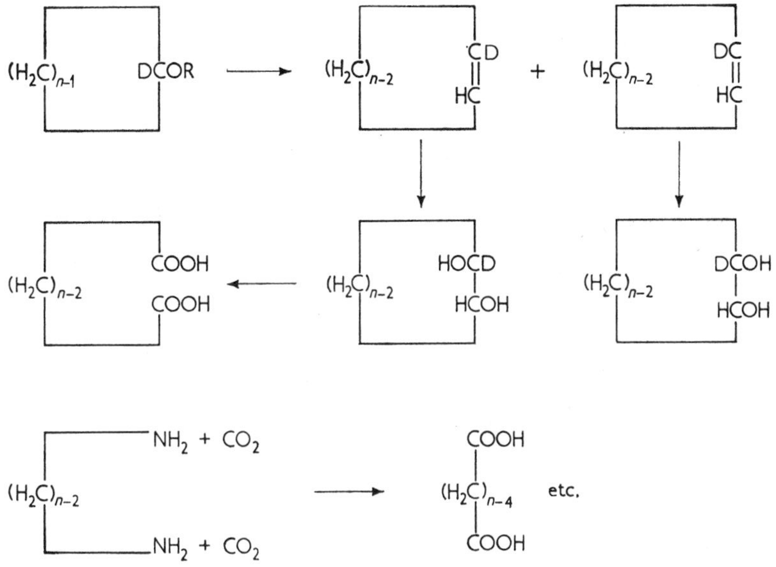

$(H_2C)_{n-1}$ DCOR $\longrightarrow$ $(H_2C)_{n-2}$ $\overset{CD}{\underset{HC}{\|}}$ + $(H_2C)_{n-2}$ $\overset{DC}{\underset{HC}{\|}}$

$(H_2C)_{n-2}$ $\overset{COOH}{\underset{COOH}{}}$ $\longleftarrow$ $(H_2C)_{n-2}$ $\overset{HOCD}{\underset{HCOH}{}}$ $(H_2C)_{n-2}$ $\overset{DCOH}{\underset{HCOH}{}}$

$(H_2C)_{n-2}$ $\overset{NH_2 + CO_2}{\underset{NH_2 + CO_2}{}}$ $\longrightarrow$ $(H_2C)_{n-4}$ $\overset{COOH}{\underset{COOH}{}}$ etc.

Scheme 4.

the ratio of *trans-* to *cis-*cyclodecene is virtually the same as that obtained from acetolysis of ^{14}C-labeled tosylate (*trans/cis* $\simeq$ 5:1). Systematic degradation of the *trans* olefin demonstrated that considerable rearrangement occurs during acetolysis. Only 81% of the deuterium was on the olefinic carbons (α); 3% was found on the β pair of carbons (probably from 1,2 shift of hydride from C—2 followed by proton loss from C—3); and 16% was found on the δ and ϵ transannular pairs. The slight differences in apparent extents of transannular migration between [14]C- and D-labeled compounds may not be significant—that is, they may be reflections of experimental errors only—or they may be a manifestation of an isotope effect.

Although the transannular hydride shift plays a relatively minor role in the solvolysis of simple cycloalkyl tosylates as far as product proportions are concerned, this course for reaction apparently can be promoted by appropriate substitution. When the ditosylates of *cis-* and *trans-*1,2-cyclooctanediols are solvolyzed in acetic acid, mixtures of several different products are obtained (Scheme 5).[20] These mixtures include bicyclic olefins and alcohols, unsaturated alcohols, dienes, and a bicyclic ether. By the use of gas chromatography and absorption spectra, the structures and proportions of the

[20] A. C. Cope, S. Moon, and P. E. Peterson, *J. Am. Chem. Soc.*, **81**, 1650 (1959).

components of these complex mixtures have been determined. The products indicate that a carbonium ion adjacent to a tosylate group in the C_8 ring undergoes reaction exclusively by a 1,5 hydride shift. The destabilization

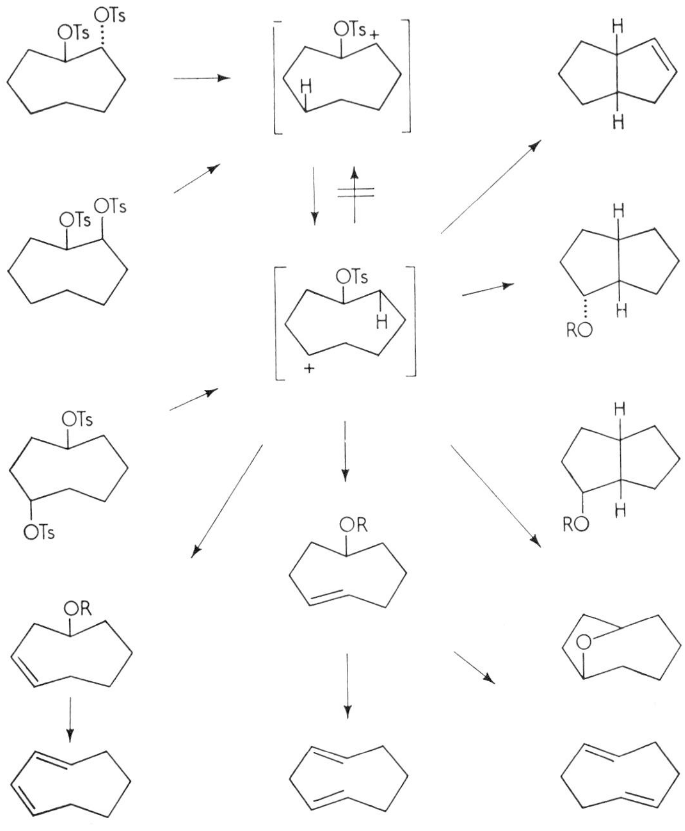

Scheme 5.

of a carbonium ion by a neighboring arenesulfonate group, through its strong electron-withdrawing effect, has been reported previously [21] and is indicated in these studies by the much slower rate of reaction of the 1,2-ditosylate compared with cyclooctyl tosylate (rate factor of 720 at 73°). Rearrangement of the initial carbonium ion by transannular hydride shift leads to a more stable ion. By contrast, the mixture obtained by solvolysis of the ditosylate of cis-1,4-cyclooctanediol contains no products which indicate any course other than normal reaction.[20] Since 1,5 hydride shift in the initial carbonium ion derived from the 1,4-ditosylate would lead to the less stable ion with neigh-

[21] S. Winstein, E. Grunwald, and L. L. Ingraham, J. Am. Chem. Soc., **70**, 821 (1948).

boring tosylate, transannular reaction has been excluded in this case. In the absence of this type of energy barrier, however, even the presence of a participating neighboring group such as acetate does not circumvent the transannular type of reaction. The solvolysis of trans-2-acetoxycyclooctyl tosylate does give substantial amounts of cis-1,2-cyclooctanediol, probably by hydrolysis of an intermediate cyclic acetoxonium ion,[22] but the major proportion of the product mixture still is formed by way of a 1,5 hydride shift.[20]

B. Hydroxylation of Olefins and Hydrolysis of Epoxides

Transannular substitution was first reported for the oxidation of cyclooctenes [9] and cyclodecenes [8] with peroxyformic acid, and further examples of transannular reactions have been found with related reactants.[23-32]

Peroxyformic acid oxidation of olefins and the closely related acid-catalyzed hydrolysis of epoxides normally lead to 1,2-diols as major products. However, with medium ring cycloalkenes and cycloalkene oxides, 1,2-diols are formed only as minor products or not at all; 1,4-, 1,5-, or 1,6-diols become the major or only simple substitution products (Scheme 6). Substantial amounts of bicyclic and olefinic compounds may be formed also.

The limits of ring size for transannular reactions are revealed by the data on reactions of cycloalkenes with peroxyformic acid and acid hydrolysis of cycloalkene oxides. A trace (0.03%) of trans-1,4-cyclohexanediol is obtained, along with a good yield (85%) of the normal trans-1,2-diol, in the peroxyformic acid oxidation of cyclohexene.[26] A small amout (2.4%) of cis-1,4-cycloheptanediol is formed in the hydrolysis of cycloheptene oxide with dilute hydrochloric acid.[27] With cyclooctene and cyclooctene oxide, the transannular diol becomes the major product formed. cis-Cyclooctene and its oxide give 25–30% of cis-1,4-diol and about 20% of trans-1,2-diol; [9,28] trans-cyclooctene oxide gives 33% of trans-1,4-diol, 1% of trans-1,3-diol, and no

[22] S. Winstein, C. Hanson, and E. Grunwald, J. Am. Chem. Soc., 70, 812 (1948).

[23] V. Prelog, K. Schenker, and W. Küng, Helv. Chim. Acta, 36, 471 (1953).

[24] V. Prelog and V. Boarland, Helv. Chim. Acta, 38, 1776 (1955).

[25] V. Prelog and M. Speck, Helv. Chim. Acta, 38, 1786 (1955).

[26] A. C. Cope, H. E. Johnson, and J. S. Stephenson, J. Am. Chem. Soc., 78, 5599 (1956).

[27] A. C. Cope, T. A. Liss, and G. W. Wood, Chem. & Ind. (London), 1956, 823; J. Am. Chem. Soc., 79, 6287 (1957).

[28] A. C. Cope, A. H. Keough, P. E. Peterson, H. E. Simmons, Jr., and G. W. Wood, J. Am. Chem. Soc., 79, 3900 (1957).

[29] A. C. Cope, A. Fournier, Jr., and H. E. Simmons, Jr., J. Am. Chem. Soc., 79, 3905 (1957).

[30] A. C. Cope, J. M. Grisar, and P. E. Peterson, J. Am. Chem. Soc., 81, 1640 (1959); A. C. Cope and P. E. Peterson, J. Am. Chem. Soc., 81, 1643 (1959).

[31] A. C. Cope and W. N. Baxter, J. Am. Chem. Soc., 76, 279 (1954).

[32] A. C. Cope, G. A. Berchtold, P. E. Peterson, and S. H. Sharman, J. Am. Chem. Soc., 82, 6366 (1960)

1,2-diol.[29] Neither *cis-* nor *trans*-cyclononene gives any 1,2-diol, but each yields both stereomeric 1,5-diols.[23] With cyclodecenes, again no 1,2-diols are formed, but *cis*-cyclodecene gives only one, and *trans*-cyclodecene gives the other, stereoisomeric 1,6-diol.[8] From *cis-* and *trans*-cycloundecenes, only non-vicinal diols of undetermined structure and configuration are obtained.[24] In contrast, cyclododecenes yield only the normal 1,2-diols.[25]

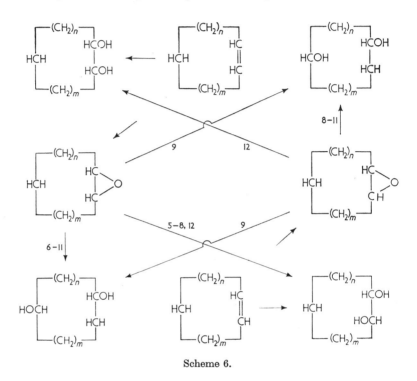

Scheme 6.

In addition to the nonvicinal diols, other products obtained in substantial amounts provide evidence for the transannular nature of these reactions. *cis*-Cyclooctene oxide also gives 15% of a mixture of unsaturated alcohols (3- and 4-cycloocten-1-ols) and small amounts of 1,4- and 1,5-epoxycyclo-octanes.[28] The formation of unsaturated alcohols can be accounted for only by hydride shifts. The exclusive formation of 1,4-diol as the only nonvicinal substitution product simplifies the mechanism requirements of the reaction. The same ion (4-hydroxycyclooctyl carbonium ion), formed by a 1,5 hydride shift, which leads to formation of the 1,4-diol could, by proton loss, give both 3- and 4-cycloocten-1-ols (Scheme 7). The trace amounts of 1,5-epoxycyclo-octane which are found among the products may indicate that a slight amount of 1,2 shift occurs subsequent to the 1,5 shift and prior to intramolecular attack by hydroxyl on the carbonium ion, or that the epoxide is formed by intramolecular attack on the olefinic bond. The other products from *trans-*

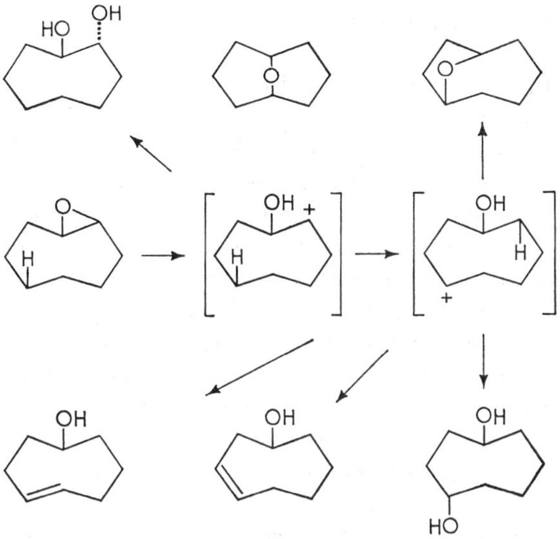

Scheme 7.

cyclooctene oxide include 4-cycloocten-1-ol (12%) and ring contraction products such as β-methylcyclohexanecarboxaldehyde (1) (25%).[29] Recent investigations with deuterium-labeled *cis*-cyclooctene oxide provide further information about the type of hydride shifts in eight-membered ring series.[32]

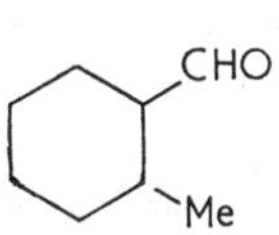

(1)

cis-Cyclooctene oxide, labeled with deuterium in positions 5 and 6, was solvolyzed with 90% formic acid, and the transannular products, *cis*-1,4-cyclooctanediol and 3-cycloocten-1-ol, were oxidized with potassium permanganate to adipic acid. The deuterium in α position to the carboxyl groups of the adipic acid was removed by equilibration of the dimethyl ester with sodium methoxide in methanol. The remaining deuterium corresponds to the products formed by 1,3 hydride shift. It was found by this method that *cis*-1,4-cyclooctanediol was formed to the extent of 61% and 3-cycloocten-1-ol to the-extent of 94% by the 1,5 hydride shift.

The relative importance of the normal and transannular reactions depends on the reaction medium.[30] When *cis*-cyclooctene oxide is solvolyzed in tri-fluoroacetic acid, the transannular reaction occurs exclusively: only *cis*-1,4-diol and 3- and 4-cyclooctenols are obtained. With trichloroacetic acid and formic acid as solvents, the normal products are also formed in small yield. In acetic acid the transannular and normal processes are almost equally important, and in acetic acid with added sodium acetate the normal course accounts for about 3/4 of the products. No reaction at all was obtained in trimethylacetic acid. There is no correlation between the extent of trans-annular reaction and either the size of the solvent molecules or the dielectric constant of the medium; there is, however, a good correlation with the relative strengths of the acids in water (although the undiluted acids were used in the experiments described). These results are related to the medium effects in neighboring group participation;[30] as the solvent becomes relatively less nucleophilic (trifluoroacetic acid less nucleophilic than acetic acid), the nucleophilic properties of the migrating hydride become more important. The gross difference in the proportions of normal and transannular reactions in acetic acid and formic acid[30] suggests that the relative nucleophilicity of the solvent is not the only factor determining the reaction course; relative ioniz-ing power may also play a part.

The importance of solvent is revealed also in the investigation of cyclo-heptene and its oxide. Early reports stated that no transannular products were found in the reaction of cycloheptene[23] or its oxide[31] with peroxyformic acid or formic acid, respectively. Later, solvolysis of the epoxide with 2% hydrochloric acid gave a small amount (2.4%) of *cis*-1,4-cycloheptanediol in addition to normal 1,2 products.[27]

In the experiments with cycloalkenes and cycloalkene oxides, the difference in stereospecificity of the transannular reaction is noteworthy. Only the nine- and eleven-membered olefins, both *cis* and *trans*, give mixtures of stereoiso-meric nonvicinal diols[23,24] A single transannular diol is obtained, in each case, from the six-, the seven-, both of the eight-, and both of the ten-membered ring olefins.[8,9,26-29]

cis-1,4-Diol is formed from *cis*-cyclooctene, *trans*-1,4-diol from *trans*-cyclooctene.[9,28,29] Similar stereospecificity is found with *cis*- and *trans*-cyclodecenes.[8] From cyclohexene (a *cis*-cycloalkene), only the *trans*-1,4-diol is obtained, in contrast to the *cis*-diol formation from the other *cis*-cyclo-alkenes. These results can be accounted for by assuming that carbonium ions which are probably the intermediates of the reaction have different confor-mational stability.

In eight- and ten-membered ring series the ring geometry is essentially unchanged in passing from epoxide to carbonium ion to rearranged carbonium ion.[7] One lobe of the *p* orbital of the carbonium ion protrudes into the ring in proximity to intraannular hydrogens where it is protected from attack of nucleophilic reagent; thus the transannular reaction is stereospecific. In the C_6 ring, however, the situation is different. Cyclohexene oxide undergoes ionization probably with breaking of the equatorial C—O bond. Most of the resulting ions react normally, but 1,3 shift of axial hydride occurs to a small extent. Either before or after hydride shift, the ring undergoes rapid conformational change to place the axial hydroxyl in the more favorable equatorial position. Subsequent combination of ion with solvent approaching equatorially gives *trans*-1,4-cyclohexanediol. A third type of "floppy" carbonium ion, in which conformation is neither completely retained nor inverted, can also be imagined and may account for the formation of both stereoisomeric diols from the nine- and eleven-membered cyclenes.

C. Deamination of Cycloalkylamines

Investigations of the nitrous acid deamination of medium ring cycloalkylamines have been much less extensive than studies of tosylate solvolysis and epoxide hydrolysis.

The reaction of primary aliphatic amines with nitrous acid generates a diazonium cation which may form substitution and elimination products by several competing paths: (*a*) bimolecular displacement by solvent, (*b*) concerted elimination by simultaneous loss of the nitrogen and a hydrogen, or (*c*) formation of a carbonium ion by elimination of nitrogen.[32a] Since bimolecular substitution reactions with medium ring reactants are slow compared with carbonium ion reactions,[33] little substitution product is to be expected from direct reaction between solvent and the diazonium cation derived from a medium ring cycloalkylamine. Similarly, little or no olefin comes from concerted elimination since the only hydrogens in favorable trans coplanar steric position to leaving nitrogen are intraannular ones, which are protected from attack by base. Therefore virtually all products are probably formed from the carbonium ions as intermediates.

The deamination with nitrous acid was only investigated with cyclononyl- and cyclodecylamines, which give mixtures of the corresponding cycloalkanols and cycloalkenes as products.[11,34] Comparison of these mixtures with those obtained from the corresponding cycloalkyl tosylates reveals similarities in behavior between the two types of compounds but also significant differences. Just as with the tosylates, more alcohol is derived from the cyclononyl reactant than from the cyclodecyl one, yet both amines yield more alcohol than do the tosylates. This may be at least partially attributable to differences in the nucleophilic properties of the solvents used (water versus acetic acid).

[32a] A. Streitwieser, *J. Org. Chem.*, **22**, 861 (1957).

[33] J. Sicher, unpublished; cf. J. Sicher in Vol. III of Progress in Stereochemistry, Butterworth, London, 1962.

[34] F. Mathys, unpublished.

The ratio of alcohol (substitution) to olefin (elimination) is about $1:4$ for cyclodecylamine, but substitution is the major course for the reaction of cyclononylamine (alcohol/olefin $\simeq 4:1$).

A very important difference between the deamination and solvolysis is that the olefin obtained from cyclodecyl tosylate is largely *trans*-cyclodecene, while that from cyclodecylamine is *cis*-cyclodecene.

Transannular hydride shifts during the reactions of cycloalkylamines with nitrous acid have been traced with ^{14}C labeling. The amines were obtained by reduction of the oximes of ^{14}C-labeled cycloalkanones, which had been prepared by acyloin condensation of carboxyl-labeled dicarboxylic acid esters (cf. Scheme 2). Half of the radioactivity was again at the α position, the remainder was equally distributed between the two β positions. The already described systematic degradation of the obtained alcohol and olefin, two carbons at a time, demonstrated that a substantial amount of transannular hydride shift must have occurred during the deamination. Reaction without any hydride shifts would have led to 75% of the total radioactivity in the first pair of carbons removed and 25% in the second pair. The actual distribution data are summarized in Table II.

TABLE II

[14]C Distribution in Products from Cycloalkylamine Deaminations
(Radioactivity of Reactants = 100)

Pair of carbon atoms	C_9 ol[34]	C_9 ene[34]	C_{10} ol[11]	C_{10} ene[11]
1st (α)	42	73	51	59
2nd (β)	20	17	24	24.5
All others	38	10	25	16.5[a]

[a] 3.5% on γ pair of carbons, 13% on $\delta + \epsilon$ pairs.

The characteristic minimum of activity on the γ pair of carbons in the *cis*-cyclodecene is a clear manifestation of 1,5 and/or 1,6 hydride shifts in the intermediates leading to this product. Such shifts probably occur also in the case of the other products where the experimental data are not available or not reliable.

In contrast with the near uniformity in the extents of rearrangements in the olefin and alcohol from the acetolyses, the olefins from the amine reactions are formed with less rearrangement than are the corresponding alcohols. The difference between cyclodecene and cyclodecanol is relatively small, but there is a large difference between cyclononene and cyclononanol. The reason for the differences between deamination and solvolysis probably lies in the exothermicity of the deamination reaction and in the existence of conformational isomers in cyclononyl derivatives. Such isomers were detected by X-rays in solid state of cyclononylammonium bromide.[4]

3. GENERAL MECHANISTIC FEATURES

The evidence for substantial carbonium ion character in the intermediate is compelling. Although the acid-catalyzed hydrolysis of cyclooctene oxide leads to transannular reactions, the same oxide reacts with anhydrous hydrogen bromide in a nonionizing solvent (CCl_4) to give the normal bromohydrin.[35] The reaction of *trans*-1,2-dibromocyclooctane with silver acetate in anhydrous acetic acid gives transannular products (diacetates and unsaturated acetates) almost exclusively,[36] but the reaction of this dibromide with tetraethylammonium acetate in acetone (typical S_N2 conditions) yields only normal substitution and elimination products.[35]

The bromonium ion intermediates formed in the addition of bromine to olefins are formally analogous to the oxonium ion intermediates involved in the acid-catalyzed hydrolysis of epoxides. The predominant or exclusive formation of the normal *trans*-1,2-dibromide from cyclooctene and bromine probably indicates that less bond breaking has occurred (less carbonium ion character developed) in the transition state between intermediate and product in the case of bromine addition than in the case of epoxide hydrolysis. A similar conclusion has been drawn from other studies.[37]

Differences in the extent of transannular rearrangement accompanying hydrolysis of epoxides, solvolysis of tosylates and bromides, and deamination of amines probably reflect *inter alia* differences in degree of development of the positive charge or in the type of the carbonium ion intermediates in these reactions.

Although 1,2 shifts of alkyl and phenyl groups are well known, these substituents do not migrate in a transannular manner even under apparently favorable circumstances. For example, phosphoric acid causes 1-methyl-1,6-cyclodecanediol (2) to rearrange by a 1,6 hydride shift to 6-methylcyclo-

(2)

[35] A. C. Cope and H. E. Johnson, *J. Am. Chem. Soc.*, **79**, 3889 (1957).

[36] A. C. Cope and G. W. Wood, *J. Am. Chem. Soc.*, **79**, 3885 (1957).

[37] J. G. Traynham and O. S. Pascual, *Tetrahedron*, **7**, 165 (1959). J. Závada and J. Sicher, *Proc. Chem. Soc.* (*London*), **1961**, 199, have shown that addition of bromine to clylodecenes gives rise, in a stereospecific reaction, to 1,6 dibromocyclodecanes.

decanone, but only bicyclic hydrocarbon is obtained when the same treatment is applied to the two stereoisomeric 1,6-dimethyl-1,6-cyclodecanediols (3). [38] If a methyl group were to undergo a 1,6 shift, 6,6-dimethylcyclodecanone (4)

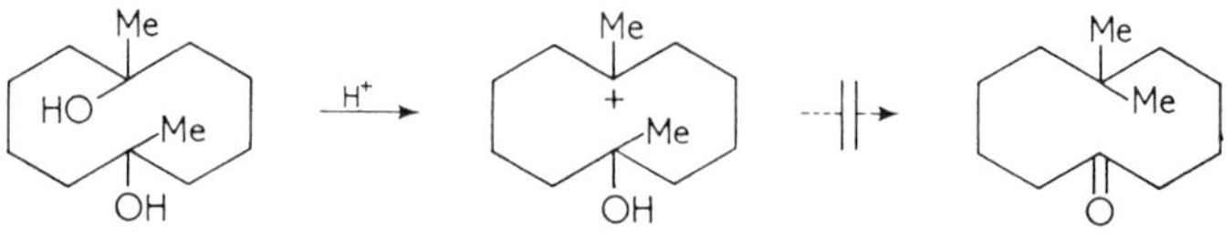

(3)   (4)

would be produced from the dimethyl diol. The complete absence of ketonic product therefore indicates that a methyl group shows no tendency toward transannular migration. The fact that a 1,6 hydride shift occurs in the monomethyl diol was demonstrated by the use of a deuterium label. Reduction of 6-hydroxy-6-methylcyclodecanone (5) with $LiAlD_4$ gives 6-methyl-1,6-cyclodecanediol (6), which rearranges to 6-methylcyclodecanone (7). Both the ketone and its oxidation product, γ-methylsebacic acid (8), contain one atom of deuterium per molecule. Reaction by way of a 1,5 hydride shift, followed by elimination to enol, would have given deuterium-free ketone and sebacic acid.

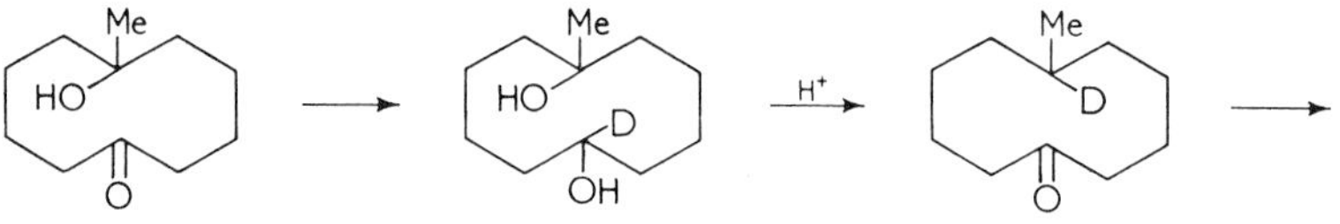

(5)   (6)   (7)

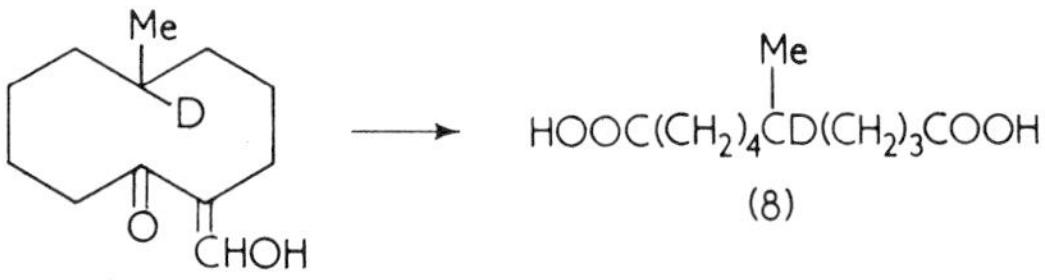

$$HOOC(CH_2)_4CD(CH_2)_3COOH$$

(8)

Acetolyses of 5,5-dimethyl- and 5,5-diphenylcyclononyl tosylates demonstrate further the specificity of hydride transfer in transannular reactions.[39] Not only is there no kinetic assistance by the substituents (there is actually some rate retardation), but the products obtained show clearly that no methyl or phenyl migration has occurred. This specificity for hydrogen migration undoubtedly arises from the physical requirements for the transannular shifts. At least two features are likely to be of importance.

[38] V. Prelog and W. Küng, Helv. Chim. Acta, 39, 1394 (1956).

[39] A. T. Blomquist and Y. C. Meinwald, J. Am. Chem. Soc., 80, 630 (1958); A. T. Blomquist and B. F. Hallam, J. Am. Chem. Soc., 81, 676 (1959).

The medium-sized cycloalkanes are flexible and can undergo conformational changes which place a given hydrogen atom in a number of different environments.[40] A larger substituent, however, may induce energy barriers which are sufficiently large to restrict these changes. In nine- and ten-membered rings (the only ones which have been studied in this connection), intraannular hydrogens cannot be replaced by larger substituents. It follows that the positions available for a geminal pair of substituents are restricted to just those which are unfavorable for proximity effects and transannular shifts, and this restriction may in itself account for the different course of the diol reaction in the case of 1,6-dimethyl-1,6-cyclodecanediol[38] and for the diminished rates in the case of solvolysis of 5,5-disubstituted-cyclononyl tosylates.[39] In the latter case, even 1,5 hydride migration may be sterically prohibited. Moreover, proximity may be a necessary but not a sufficient condition for transannular migration. The geometrical relationship of the system must also be favorable for bond breaking and bond formation. Whereas shift of hydrogen requires little more than a shift in electron density, shift of methyl would require inversion of the configuration of the migrating carbon, a process which probably has prohibitive energy requirements because of nonbonded interactions with the ring. A transfer of hydrogen from methyl is also energetically unfavorable because it involves formation of a primary carbonium ion.

Even with the same ring system, the kind of transannular hydride shift may vary. The 1,6-diol obtained from cyclodecene and peroxyformic acid, for example, clearly indicates that a 1,5 shift must have occurred (although other products could have been formed by 1,6 shifts).[40a] Acid-catalyzed rearrangement of 6-methyl-1,6-cyclodecanediol leads probably to a 1,6-hydride shift.[38] During acetolysis of cyclodecyl tosylate[40b,40c] and deamination of cyclodecylamine[40d] both 1,5 and 1,6 hydride shifts probably occur. Similar examples could be drawn from data on other rings. These differences may arise from electronic control and conformational restrictions by the different substituents. The unsubstituted rings can utilize more conformational possibilities than substituted rings, and mixtures of the possible hydride shifts occur. Conformation restrictions as well as electronic effects of the various substituents may therefore often simplify the reaction course.

We now consider whether a bridged ion is formed as an intermediate. The

[40] The NMR spectrum of cyclodecane exhibits a single peak, indicating an average environment for all hydrogens in the molecule; H. H. Günthard, private communication.

[40a] V. Prelog and K. Schenker, *Helv. Chim. Acta*, **35**, 2044 (1952).

[40b] V. Prelog, W. Küng, and T. Tomljenovic, *Helv. Chim. Acta*, **45**. 1352 (1962).

[40c] H. J. Urech and V. Prelog, *Helv. Chim. Acta*. **40**, 477 (1957).

[40d] V. Prelog, H. J. Urech, A. A. Bothner-By, and J. Würsch, *Helv. Chim. Acta*, **38**, 1095 (1955).

investigation of this point illustrates the necessity of utilizing every possible experimental approach in the elucidation of the nature of transient intermediates in organic reactions. A high degree of stereospecificity has been observed in some, but not in all, transannular reactions. To explain this stereospecificity, it was assumed first that development of the carbonium ion center, migration of hydride, and bond formation at the new transannular reaction site occur in a concerted manner. At first sight, kinetic data appeared to support such a view. If the reaction were a concerted process, or if C—H bond breaking were involved in the rate-determining step, as in the formation of the intermediate bridged ion, the reaction rate should be reduced when deuterium is substituted for migrating hydrogen. Since the transannular course accounts for only about 10% of the acetolysis of cyclodecyl tosylate, the net kinetic isotope effects would be small in this case. A small but definite isotope effect was indeed found when the rates of acetolysis of cyclodecyl tosylate and its 5,5,6,6-tetradeuterio analog were compared: $k_H/k_D = 1.08$.[41] By contrast, not even a slight isotope effect could be detected by comparing the rates of acetolysis of cyclopentyl tosylate and its 3,3,4,4-tetradeuterio derivative.[41]

If the observed isotope effect were really due to involvement of transannular C—H (or C—D) bond breaking in the rate-determining step, there would be a significant change not only in the rate of reaction but also in the ratio of normal and transannular products. The results obtained with cyclopentyl tosylate indicate that the normal reaction rate is unchanged by deuterium substitution in the 3 and 4 positions. To account for the observed isotope effect in the acetolysis of cyclodecyl tosylate, the transannular course would have to be reduced from 11 to 3% of the total reaction when the cyclodecyl-5,5,6,6-d_4 tosylate is used. However, degradation of the main deuterated reaction product, *trans*-cyclodecene, to sebacic and suberic acids shows that the ratio of transannular to normal reaction course is not reduced and thus demonstrates that the slower rate for the deuterium-substituted tosylate does not arise from differences in rates of C—H and C—D bond breaking. Therefore it seems unlikely that a hydrogen-bridged ion is involved in the rate-determining step.

The small isotope effect may arise as yet another manifestation of the rather unusual geometrical relationships which occur in the crowded ten-membered ring. The intraannular hydrogens introduce strain in the ground state of the cyclodecane derivative by transannular interference. Because of the smaller vibration amplitude of bound deuterium, its effective van der Waals radius is approximately 0.015 A. smaller than that of hydrogen.[42] The ground state of the cyclodecyl-5,5,6,6-d_4 tosylate should therefore be less

---

[41] V. Prelog and S. Borčić, unpublished.

[42] A. R. Ubbelohde, *Trans. Faraday Soc.*, **32**, 525 (1936).

strained than that of the deuterium-free compound. The corresponding transition states, which are approached with relief of strain and diminished transannular hydrogen-hydrogen interactions, should be less different from each other in energy. The consequent net difference in activation energies could account for the observed small kinetic isotope effect.

The observed acceleration of acetolysis among medium ring tosylates could thus arise from the change of nonclassical strain in these systems rather than from anchimeric assistance by the migrating hydride. But just as the extents of transannular reactions with other systems differ from that with tosylate solvolysis, so the nature of the intermediate in the transannular hydride shift may differ among different reactions.

Although transannular hydride shifts have been reported most frequently for medium ring systems, they can occur also in other compounds where the steric and energetic requirements are fulfilled. For instance, bridged polycyclic systems can provide the steric proximity, and two examples will illustrate the kind of reactants which lead to such shifts. Under the influence of BF$_3$, endrin (9) is isomerized to the half-cage ketone 10.[43] The acid catalyst pro-

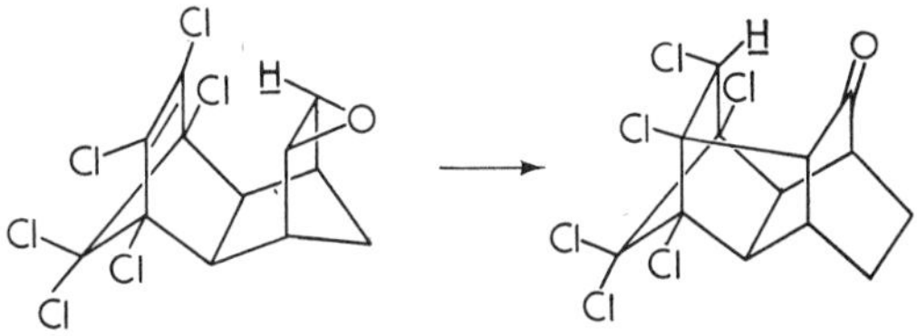

(9)   (10)

motes displacement of the epoxide by the olefinic electrons, and a 1,5 hydride shift completes the reaction. A second and more straightforward example of such a hydride shift during a solvolysis is represented by the formation of 11 and 12.[44] In certain suitably constituted nonbridged systems, a 1,5 hydride

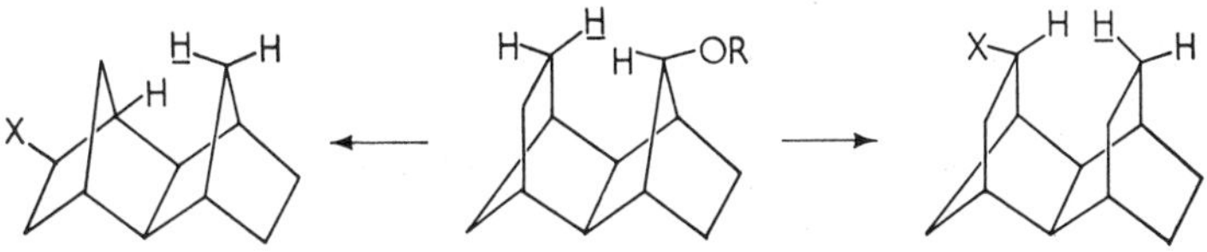

(11)   (12)

shift can sometimes also take place with surprising ease. Chromatography on alumina causes complete isomerization of 1-hydroxy-8-methyl-cis-5-hydrin-danone (13) to 5-hydroxy-8-methyl-cis-1-hydrindanone (14).[45] This strictly

[43] R. C. Cookson and E. Crundwell, Chem. & Ind. (London), 1959, 703.
[44] S. Winstein and R. L. Hansen, J. Am. Chem. Soc., 82, 6206 (1960).
[45] W. Acklin and V. Prelog, Helv. Chim. Acta, 42, 1239 (1959).

stereospecific isomerization probably proceeds by an intramolecular 1,5 hydride shift promoted by the alumina. The relative stabilities of five- and six-membered cycloalkanones and cycloalkanols provide the driving force for the rearrangement.[45a]

(13)   (14)

4. SOME RELATED REACTIONS OF MEDIUM RINGS

Evidence has been presented that transannular rearrangements occur as a result of the development of an electron-deficient center which accepts a hydrogen with its electrons from the opposite side of the ring. Provided that the necessary geometrical and possibly other relationships can be maintained, other electron-donating groups may supply electrons to the electron-deficient center. The formation of bicyclic ethers in the reactions of epoxides [40a,45b] and 1,2-ditosylates [45c] has already been mentioned. In these cases, an oxygen (in hydroxyl or acetate) saturates the electron deficiency of the carbonium ion, with consequent ether formation. Since the original carbon-oxygen bond is not broken, although a new one is formed, the reaction is only formally related to the hydride shifts.

Although complete experimental evidence for intramolecular migration is lacking, the products obtained in several investigations imply that transannular shifts of stable anions may also occur. The formation of some cis, trans-1-decalyl tosylate in the solvolysis of cis-5-cyclodecenyl tosylate is readily accounted for by the proposal that tosylate moves from C-1 to C-5, with a change in the position of the double bond, by internal return from an ion pair intermediate.[46] Such shifts are not confined to medium rings; acetolysis of trans-4-methoxycyclohexyl tosylate labeled at C-1 with tritium leads to, among other products, trans-4-methoxycyclohexyl acetate, about half of which is labeled at the 4 position.[47] That is, methoxide ion has migrated across the ring in a stereospecific manner. In contrast to transannular hydride shifts, however, the methoxy group assists solvolysis kinetically, most likely through a bridged ion intermediate.

[45a] H. C. Brown, J. H. Brewster, and H. Shechter, J. Am. Chem. Soc., 76, 467 (1954).

[45b] A. C. Cope, A. H. Keough, P. E. Peterson, H. E. Simmons, Jr., and G. W. Wood, J. Am. Chem. Soc., 79, 3900 (1957).

[45c] A. C. Cope, S. Moon, and P. E. Peterson, J. Am. Chem. Soc., 81, 1650 (1959).

[46] H. L. Goering, H. H. Espy, and W. D. Closson, J. Am. Chem. Soc., 81, 329 (1959).

[47] D. S. Noyce and B. N. Bastian, J. Am. Chem. Soc., 82, 1246 (1960).

Some experimental results suggest that hydrogen may undergo transannular shift also as a hydrogen atom. Such a shift from one ring carbon to
another is assumed to be a reaction step in the pyrolysis of the cyclononenes.
Both *cis*- and *trans*-cyclononenes (**15**) give at 500° 1,8-nonadiene (**16**), the

(15)   (16)

trans isomer with better yield than the *cis*. In the mechanism proposed,
hydrogen atom is shifted from C-5 to C-1 with accompanying shifts of electrons to give the acyclic diene.[48]

[48] A. T. Blomquist and P. R. Taussig, *J. Am. Chem. Soc.*, **79**, 3505 (1957).

10

MOLECULAR REARRANGEMENTS IN SOME HETEROCYCLIC COMPOUNDS

G. M. BADGER and J. W. CLARK-LEWIS
University of Adelaide,
South Australia

CONTENTS

The formation of an unexpected reaction product may mean that a molecular rearrangement has occurred. In nearly every case, however, the mechanism of the rearrangement is not at first known and the consequent element of mystery in such reactions is one of the chief attractions of their study. Very few of the reactions discussed in this section have been studied in sufficient detail to establish the mechanisms of the rearrangements.

I. RING CONTRACTIONS

A. Pyridine and Quinoline Derivatives to Pyrroles and Indoles

When pyridine is boiled under reflux with a degassed Raney nickel catalyst the main product is 2,2'-bipyridyl, and this is accompanied by a small quantity of 2,2',2''-terpyridyl and an organo-nickel complex. The reaction proceeds very smoothly and large amounts of pure 2,2'-bipyridyl, free from other bipyridyl isomers, can be obtained without difficulty by this method.[1] The present interest in this reaction lies in the nickel complex which has been shown to be a metal chelate containing 1 molecule of 2,2'-bipyridyl and 2 molecules of 2,2'-pyrrolylpyridine,[2] thus indicating that part of the pyridine had been converted to pyrrole. This has since been confirmed.[3] Moreover, the formation of small quantities of pyrroles from pyridines during hydrogenations over nickel catalysts has also been reported.[4]

This ring contraction over a nickel catalyst seems to be general for six-membered aromatic N-heterocyclic compounds, and the products obtained by boiling quinoline over a degassed nickel catalyst have been investigated recently in great detail.[5] Quinoline yields small amounts of indole, 3-methylindole, carbazole, aniline, o-toluidine, 1,2,3,4-tetrahydroquinoline, 2-methylquinoline, 2,2'-biquinolyl and an aliphatic hydrocarbon.[5] The reactions with methylquinolines were found to be similarly complex. Carbon-nitrogen and carbon-carbon bond fission must clearly occur under the reaction conditions, and formation of o-toluidine (1), aniline (2), and carbazole (3) can be thus rationalized.

The ring contraction is less easily explained and awaits further study. It is noteworthy, however, that quinoline, 2-methyl-, 3-methyl- and 4-methylquinoline all gave mixtures of indole and 3-methylindole, but no 2-methylindole could be detected.[5] Moreover, 2,2'-biquinolyl suffered slow decomposition over degassed nickel with formation of small quantities of indole, 3-methylindole, and quinoline.

[1] G. M. Badger and W. H. F. Sasse, J. Chem. Soc. (London), **1956**, 616; G. M. Badger, Australian J. Sci., **21**, P45 (1958).

[2] A. M. Sargeson and W. H. F. Sasse, Proc. Chem. Soc. (London), **1958**, 150.

[3] W. H. F. Sasse, J. Chem. Soc. (London), **1959**, 3046.

[4] M. Padoa, Gazz. chim. ital., **38**, 228 (1908); through Chem. Abstr., **2**, 1716 (1908); C. Granelli, Farm. ital., **5**, 708 (1937); through Chem. Abstr., **33**, 4245 (1939), J. I. Jones, J. Chem. Soc. (London), **1950**, 1392. J. I. Jones and A. S. Lindsey, J. Chem. Soc. (London), **1952**, 3261.

[5] W. H. F. Sasse, J. Chem. Soc. (London), **1960**, 526.

Pyrroles have also been obtained following irradiation of the diazo-anhydrides obtained from 3-aminopyridones. 3-Diazo-2(3H)-pyridone, for

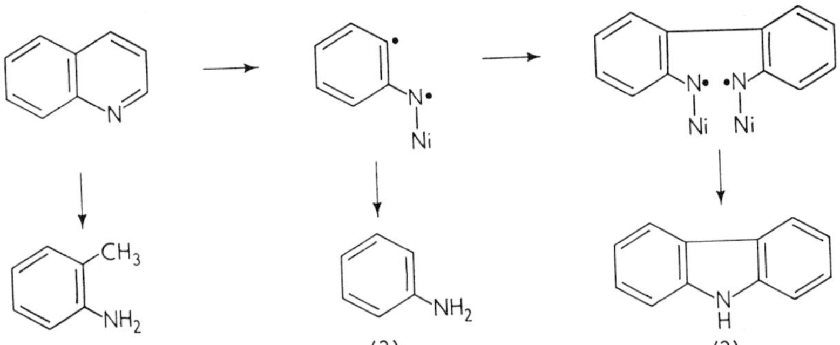

(1)   (2)   (3)

example, gives pyrrole-2-carboxylic acid; 3-diazo-4(3H)-quinolone (**4**) gives indole-3-carboxylic acid (**5**); and many substituted derivatives have been shown to behave similarly.[6] This reaction proceeds through the related ketene; it is discussed in more detail elsewhere in Part One (Section 8).

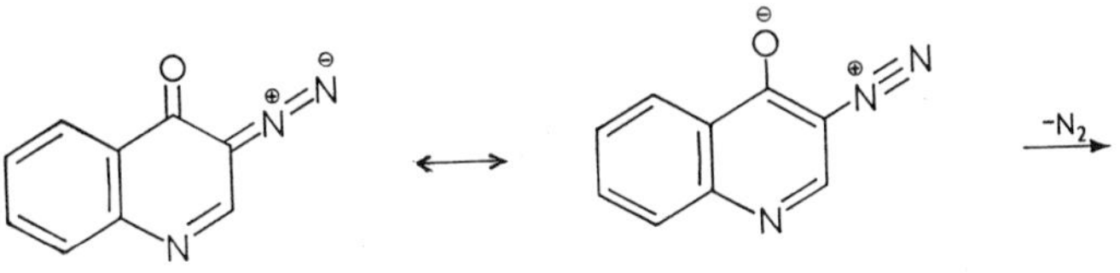

(4)

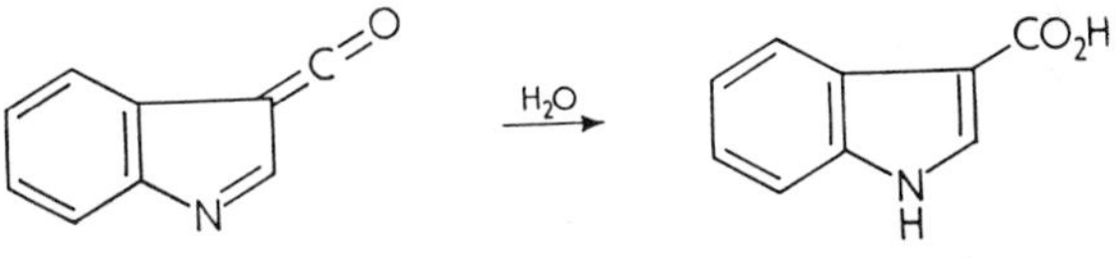

(5)

B. Benzodiazepines to Quinoxalines and Benzimidazoles

It has long been known that o-phenylenediamines react with β-diketones to give derivatives of the seven-membered ring system, 2,3-benzo-1,4-diazepine,[7] and it has recently been shown by Finar[8] that certain 1,2,4-tricarbonyl compounds yield benzodiazepines instead of the alternatively possible quinoxalines. Benzodiazepines with a carbonyl group (or hydroxyimino group) in

[6] O. Süs, _Ann._, **556**, 65 (1944); O. Süs, M. Glos, K. Möller, and H-D. Eberhardt, _Ann._, **583**, 150 (1953); O. Süs and K. Möller, _Ann._, **593**, 91 (1955); O. Süs and K. Möller, _Ann._, **599**, 233 (1956).

[7] J. Thiele and G. Steimmig, _Ber._, **40**, 955 (1907).

[8] I. L. Finar, _J. Chem. Soc. (London)_, **1958**, 4094.

the 6 position apparently are unstable, and suffer acid-catalyzed ring-contraction to 2-acylquinoxalines. Thus, oxidation of 5,7-dimethyl-2,3-benzo-1,4-diazepine (6) with monopersulfuric acid or with peracetic acid gave 2-acetyl-3-methylquinoxaline (7) (12%), and the methylphenyldiazepine (8) gave a

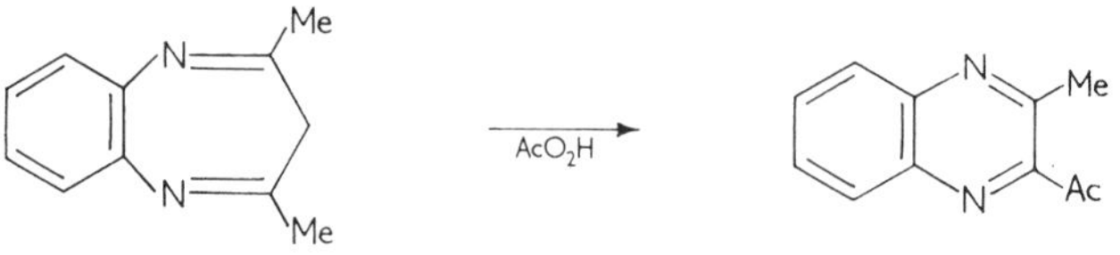

(6)   (7)

higher yield of 2-acetyl-3-phenylquinoxaline (9).[9] Reaction is thought to proceed through the 6-oxo intermediate (10), and this view is strengthened by

(8)   (9)

the observation that the oxime of 10 undergoes acid-catalyzed ring contraction to 2-acetyl-3-methylquinoxaline (11) and its oxime.[9] The benzodiazepine oxime suffers more complex decomposition under alkaline conditions to products which include 2-methylbenzimidazole and 2-hydroxy-3-methylquinoxaline.

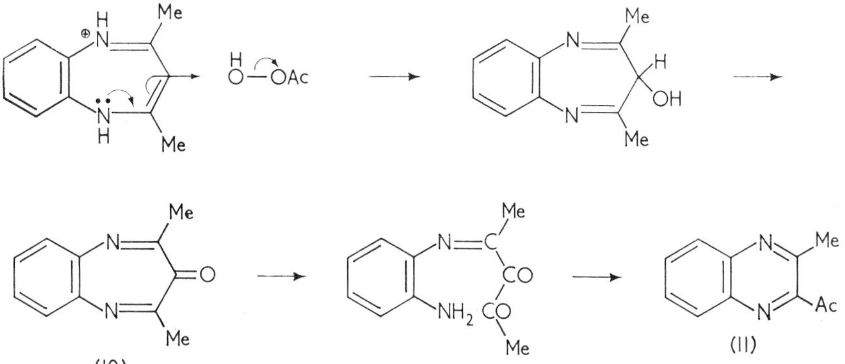

(10)   (11)

Ring contractions of the above type apparently depend upon the presence of the 6-oxo (or oximino) group in the molecule, and a more general reaction

[9] J. A. Barltrop, C. G. Richards, D. M. Russell, and G. Ryback, *J. Chem. Soc.* (*London*), **1959**, 1132.

of the benzodiazepines is their conversion into benzimidazoles, which occurs readily in hot dilute mineral acid.[7] The dimethylbenzodiazepine (6) thus gives 2-methylbenzimidazole and acetone, and the phenyl anolog (8) gives a mixture of 2-phenylbenzimidazole, acetone, 2-methylbenzimidazole and acetophenone. In these reactions the benzodiazepines behave as double Schiff's bases, and the 5,7-dimethyl compound (6) with diacetyl under acid conditions yields 2,3-dimethylquinoxaline, and with phenylhydrazine it gives 1-phenyl-3,5-dimethylpyrazole.[9] Benzimidazoles could arise by similar hydrolysis of the benzodiazepines followed by recombination of the components, or they may arise as shown in equation 1.[9] Acid-catalyzed ring contractions to benzi-

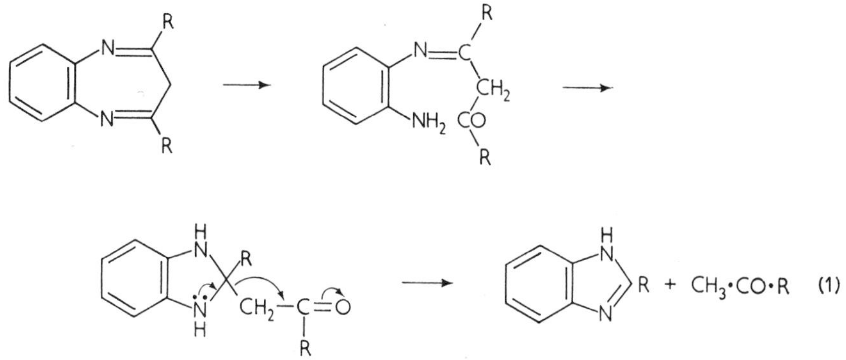

midazoles occur also in benzodiazepines which contain amide carbonyl groups. Thus the methylbenzodiazepine (12) gave 2-methylbenzimidazole (13) (11.5%) and acetone when boiled with dilute sulfuric acid, and the 7-phenylbenzodiazepine analog gave 2-phenylbenzimidazole (13%) and acetophenone.[10] With stronger acid (20% sulfuric acid) the methyl compound (12) gave benzimidazolone and acetone, and 1-isopropenyl-2-benzimidazolone (14) was formed in

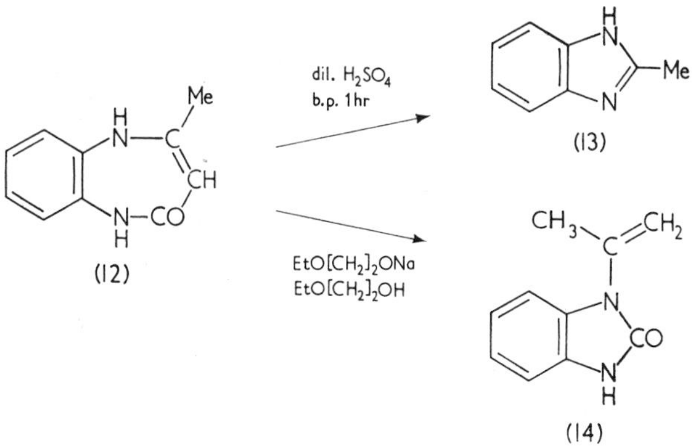

[10] J. Davoll, *J. Chem. Soc.* (*London*), **1960**, 308.

79% yield by boiling the methyldiazepine (**12**) with sodium 2-ethoxyethanol in 2-ethoxyethanol under conditions which left the 7-phenyl analog unaffected.

o-Phenylenemalonamide (**15**) is converted into 2,2'-methylenebisbenzimidazole (**16**) when heated with *o*-phenylenediamine hydrochloride in ethylene

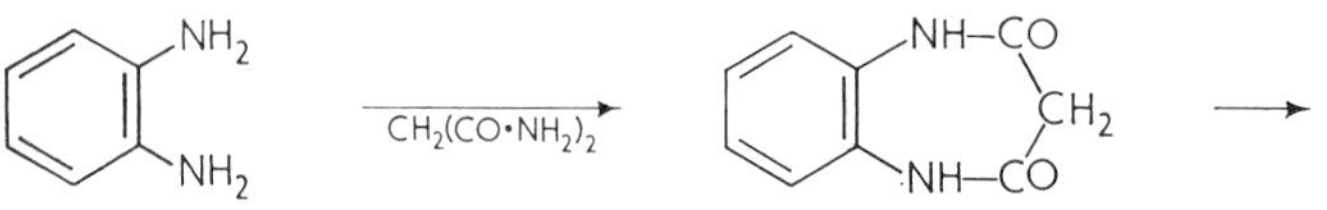

(15)

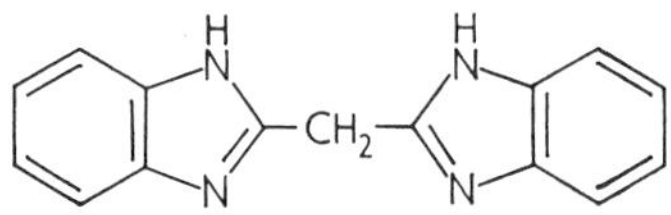

(16)

glycol, and it has been recognized as an intermediate in the synthesis of bisbenzimidazoles from malondiamide and *o*-phenylenediamine.[11] Methylation of *o*-phenylenemalonamide (**15**) gave the NN'-dimethyl derivative (**17**) which when boiled with 20% sulfuric acid gave a product originally formulated as a dihydrobenzimidazole pseudobase (**18**),[12] but now recognized as monoacetyl NN'-dimethyl-*o*-phenylenediamine (**19**).[13]

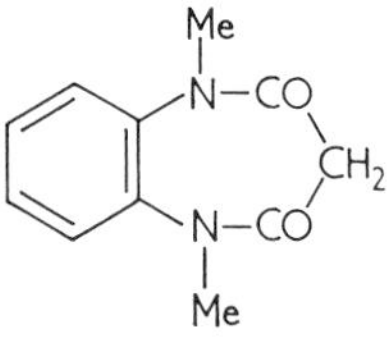

(17) 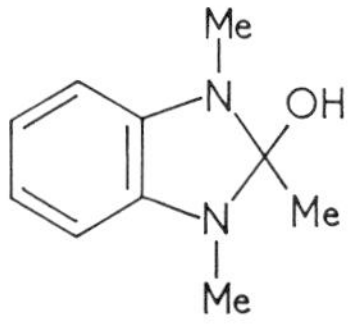   (18) 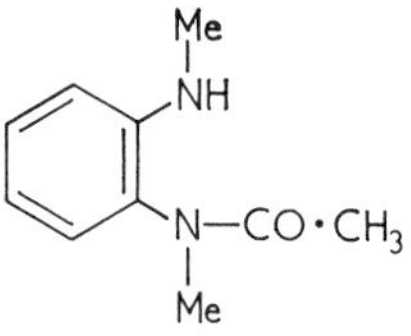   (19)

Compounds formed by cyclization of 2-acylaminobenzophenone oximes (and analogous benzaldoximes) (**20**) have now been identified as quinazoline 3-oxides (**21**)[14] and are not 4,5-benzocyclohepta-1,2,6-oxadiazines (**22**) as previously supposed. The formation of dihydroquinazolines (**23**) by catalytic hydrogenation of these compounds does not therefore involve ring contraction as supposed by Ried and Stahlhofen,[15] but is a normal reduction of an

[11] E. S. Lane, *J. Chem. Soc. (London)*, **1955**, 1079.

[12] R. L. Shriner and P. G. Boermans, *J. Am. Chem. Soc.*, **66**, 1810 (1944).

[13] C. W. Smith, R. S. Rasmussen, and S. A. Ballard, *J. Am. Chem. Soc.*, **71**, 1082 (1949); J. B. Wright, *Chem. Revs.*, **48**, 397 (1951).

[14] H. L. Sternbach, S. Kaiser, and E. Reeder, *J. Am. Chem. Soc.*, **82**, 475 (1960).

[15] W. Ried and P. Stahlhofen, *Chem. Ber.*, **90**, 828 (1957).

N-oxide. Oxidation of the dihydroquinazoline with potassium ferricyanide gives the corresponding quinazoline (**24**).[15]

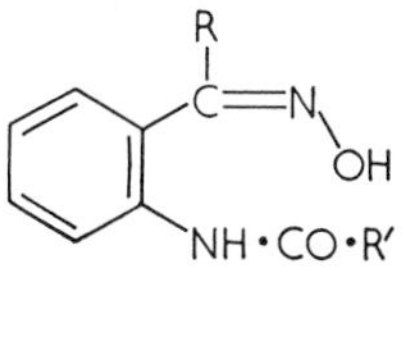

(20) 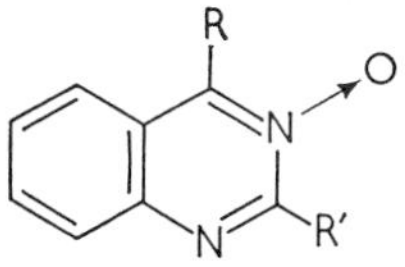   (21) 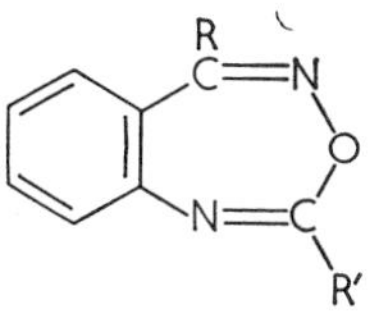   (22)

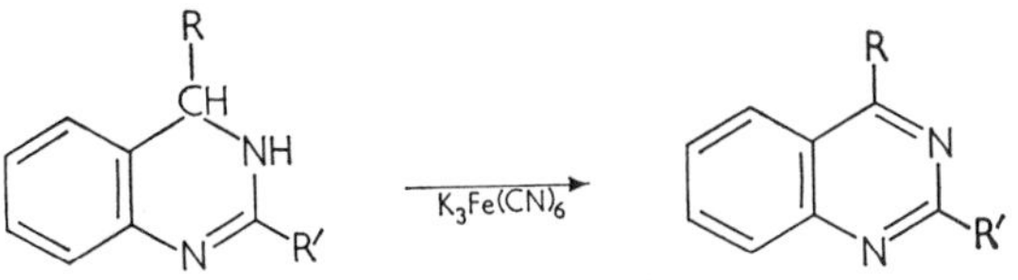

(23)   (24)

C. Quinoxalines to Benzimidazoles

Very few ring contractions of quinoxalines to benzimidazoles have been reported. Condensation of 2-amino-4-nitrodiphenylamine with benzil leads to an anil (**25**) which in the presence of hydrochloric acid is in equilibrium with the quaternary chloride (**26**). When the acidity is reduced under care-

(25)   (26)

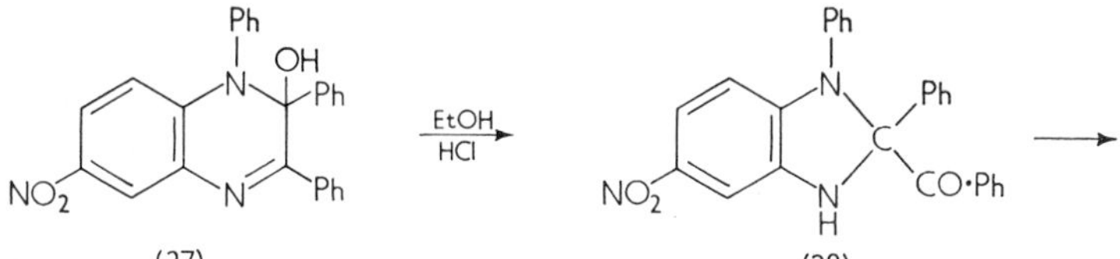

(27)   (28)

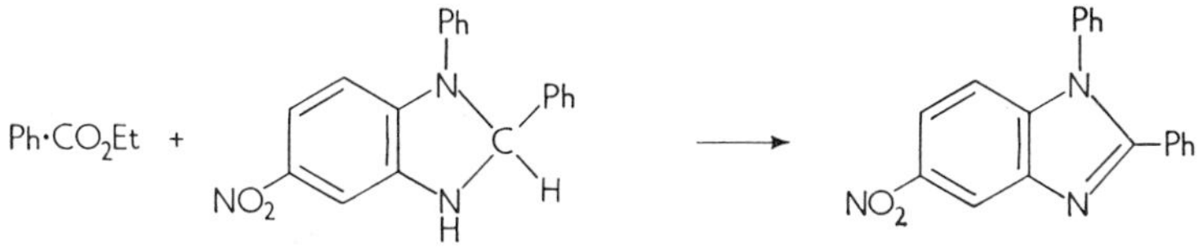

(29)   (30)

fully defined conditions, the pseudobase (27) may be obtained, and this yields 5-nitro-1,2-diphenylbenzimidazole (30).[16]

It seems clear that this reaction is essentially a reaction of the anil (25) which may cyclize to the dihydrobenzimidazole (28). Ethyl benzoate was identified among the products, and the last stage was formulated as oxidation of the dihydrobenzimidazole (29) to 5-nitro-1,2-diphenylbenzimidazole (30) by the nitro compounds present.[16] This reaction is by no means a general reaction of quinoxalines, and both the 1-phenyl and 6-nitro groups appear to be essential for the ring contraction. 2-Amino-4-nitro-N-methylaniline condenses with benzil under acid conditions to give a mixture of 6-nitro-2,3-diphenylquinoxaline (with demethylation) and the carbinolamine (31), which does not yield a benzimidazole.

2,3-Dihydroxyquinoxaline (32) has been recognized as an intermediate [11] in the conversion of o-phenylenediamine and oxamide into 2,2'-bisbenzimidazole (33).[17] Condensation of equimolecular proportions of o-phenylenediamine and oxamide gave the intermediate quinoxaline (32), which with a second molecule of o-phenylenediamine in boiling ethylene glycol gave the bisbenzimidazole (33). The quinoxaline was reported, however, not to react with 3,4-diaminotoluene or with 4-nitro-o-phenylenediamine.[11]

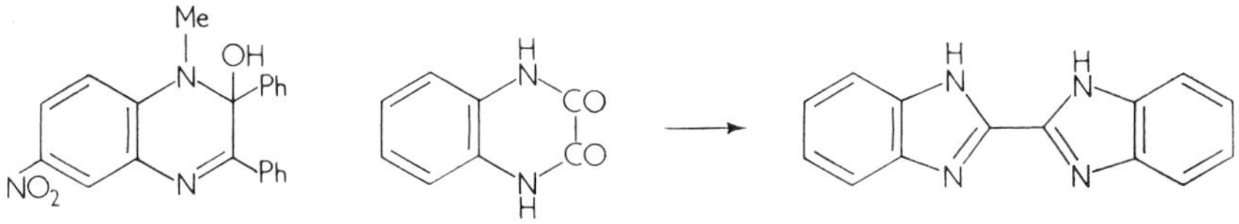

(31)   (32)   (33)

D. Phthalazines and Cinnolines to Isoindoles and Indoles

Heterocyclic derivatives of hydrazine undergo a number of ring contractions which are frequently accompanied by N—N bond fission. Thus, reduction of phthalazines (34) with zinc or tin and hydrochloric acid gives dihydroisoindoles (35),[18] and reduction of phthalazones (36) yields isoindolones (37)

(34)   (35)

[16] K. Brand and E. Wild, Ber., 56, 105 (1923); J. C. E. Simpson, Condensed Pyridazine and Pyrazine Rings, Interscience, New York, 1953, 288.

[17] E. S. Lane, J. Chem. Soc. (London), 1953, 2238.

[18] S. Gabriel and G. Eschenbach, Ber., 30, 3022 (1897); S. Gabriel and A. Neumann, Ber., 26, 521, 705 (1893).

or gives *N*-aminophthalimidine derivatives.[19] Reduction of 4-arylcinnolines with sodium and ethanol similarly gives 3-arylindoles.[20]

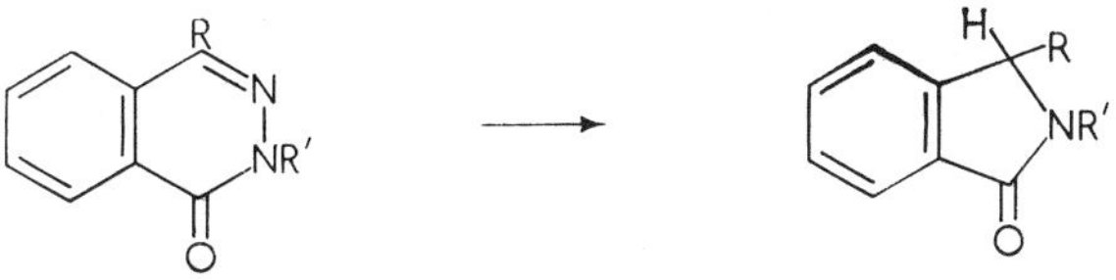

(36)   (37)

Another ring contraction to *N*-aminodihydroisoindole derivatives occurs when phthalhydrazide (**38**) is condensed with aromatic aldehydes to give the arylidene derivatives (**39**).[21]

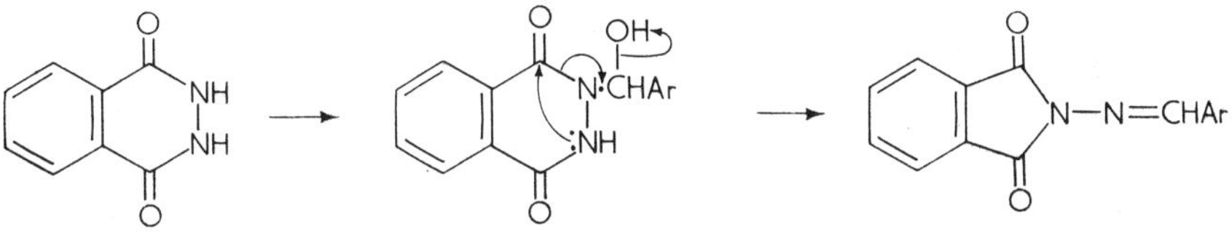

(38)   (39)

E. Dihydroflavonols to Benzyl- and Benzylidene-coumaranones

This ring contraction of dihydroflavonols was observed and correctly interpreted by Oyamada[22] during his work which established fustin as 7,3',4'-trihydroxydihydroflavonol, the first representative of the dihydroflavonols.[23] Fustin trimethyl ether (**40**), when treated with alkali, gives a diketone which then undergoes a benzilic acid rearrangement and loss of water to yield the 3-benzylidenecoumaran-2-one (**41**),[22,24] and this and similar rearrangements have caused considerable confusion in dihydroflavonol chemistry.

Ampelopsin pentamethyl ether (**42**) is similarly converted by alkali into an isomer, apoampelopsin pentamethyl ether, shown by Kubota to be the

[19] A. Daube, *Ber.*, **38**, 206 (1905); W. R. Vaughan, *Chem. Revs.*, **43**, 447 (1948).

[20] J. C. E. Simpson, *Condensed Pyridazine and Pyrazine Rings*, Interscience, New York, **1953**, 10.

[21] H. D. K. Drew and H. H. Hatt, *J. Chem. Soc. (London)*, **1937**, 16; H. D. K. Drew and F. H. Pearman, *J. Chem. Soc. (London)*, **1937**, 26; H. D. K. Drew, H. H. Hatt, and F. A. Hobart, *J. Chem. Soc. (London)*, **1937**, 33.

[22] T. Oyamada, *J. Chem. Soc. Japan*, **55**, 755 (1934); through *Chem. Abstr.*, **29**, 762 (1935); *J. Chem. Soc. Japan*, **56**, 980 (1935); through *Chem. Abstr.*, **30**, 459 (1936); *Ann.*, **538**, 44 (1939).

[23] J. E. Gowan, E. M. Philbin, and T. S. Wheeler, *Chemistry of Vegetable Tannins*, Society of Leather Trades' Chemists, Croydon, **1956**, p. 133.

[24] M. Chadenson, L. Molho-Lacroix, D. Molho, and C. Mentzer, *Compt. rend.*, **240**, 1362 (1955).

hemiketal hydroxybenzylcoumaranone (**43**).[25] Whether the intermediate
diketone suffers the benzilic acid rearrangement or not depends upon the

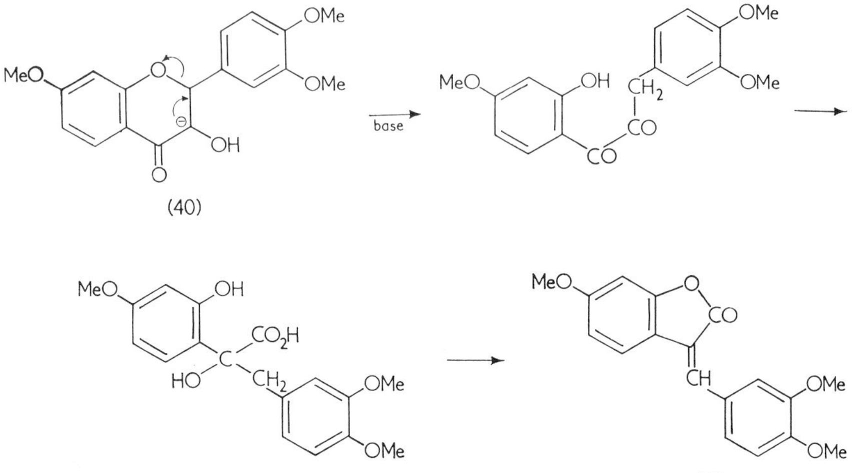

(40)

(4l)

strength of the alkali and duration of the action, and under mild conditions
2-hydroxy-2-benzylcoumaran-3-ones result. The same product (**43**) was obtained by treating the methoxychalcone (**44**) with acid in the expectation
that it would yield the dihydroflavonol (**42**).

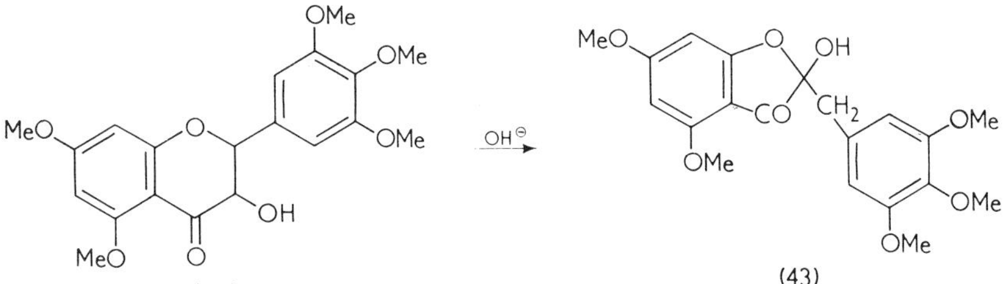

(42)   (43)

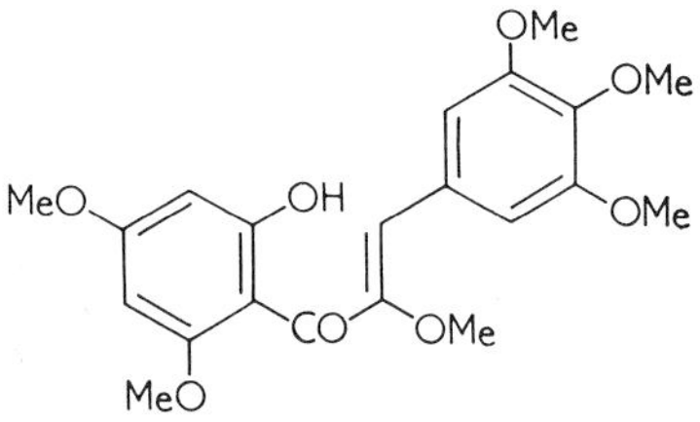

(44)

[25] T. Kubota, *J. Chem. Soc. Japan*, **73**, 571 (1952); through *Chem. Abstr.*, **48**, 2058
(1954).

Methylation of dihydroquercetin (**45**) in methanol by alternate addition of dimethyl sulfate and aqueous potassium hydroxide gave a mixture of penta-

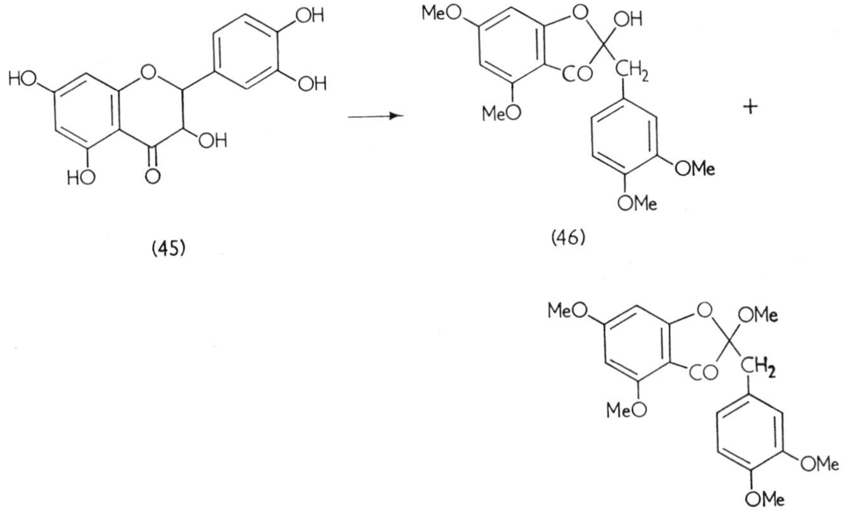

(45)   (46)

(47)

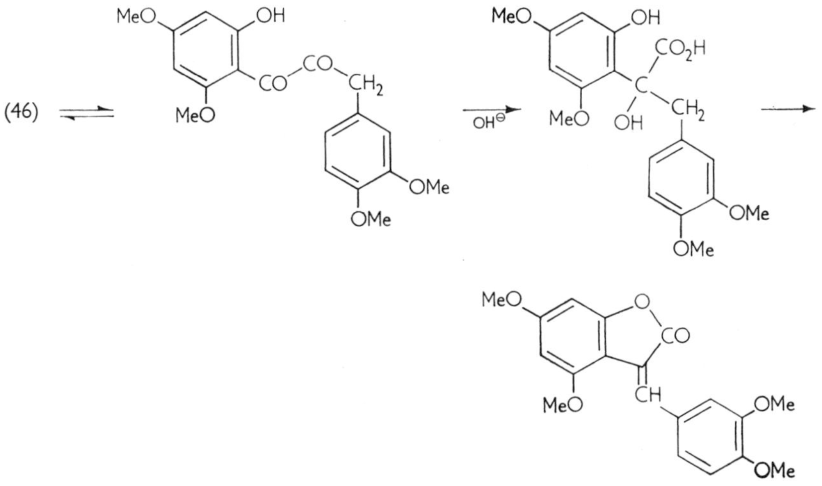

(48)

and tetramethyl ethers originally thought to have retained the dihydroquer-cetin structure, but later recognized as coumaranones **46** and **47**.[26] Enebäck

[26] H. L. Hergert, P. Coad, and A. V. Logan, *J. Org. Chem.*, **21**, 304 (1956).

and Gripenberg [27] then showed that **46** undergoes a benzilic acid rearrangement when boiled with aqueous methanolic potassium hydroxide, and yields the 3-benzylidenecoumaran-2-one (**48**) as the final product.

Pew's reduction [28] of quercetin (**49**) to dihydroquercetin with alkaline sodium hydrosulfite was shown by Geissman and Lischner [29] to lead also to the 2-benzylcoumaran-3-one (**50**). This reaction may involve the epoxide

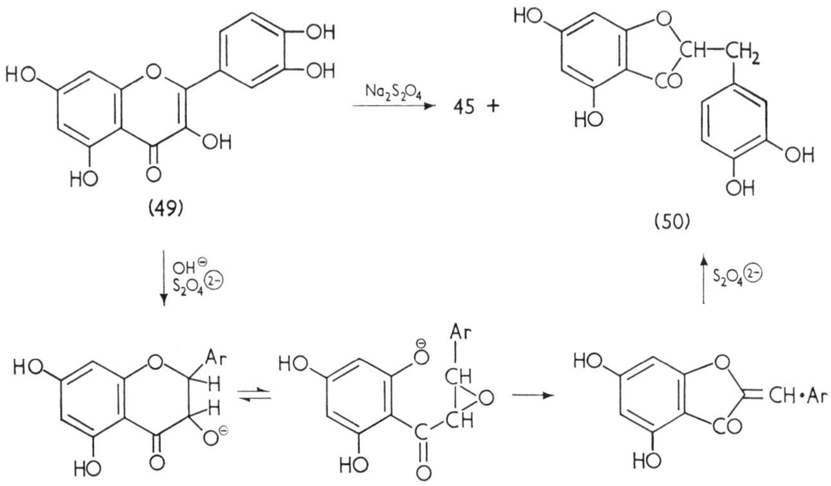

(49)　　　　　　　　　　　　　　　　　　　　　(50)

intermediate and the 2-benzylidenecoumaran-3-one,[29] or the product **50** may perhaps arise through reduction of the 2-hydroxy-2-benzylcoumaran-3-one **51**.[23]

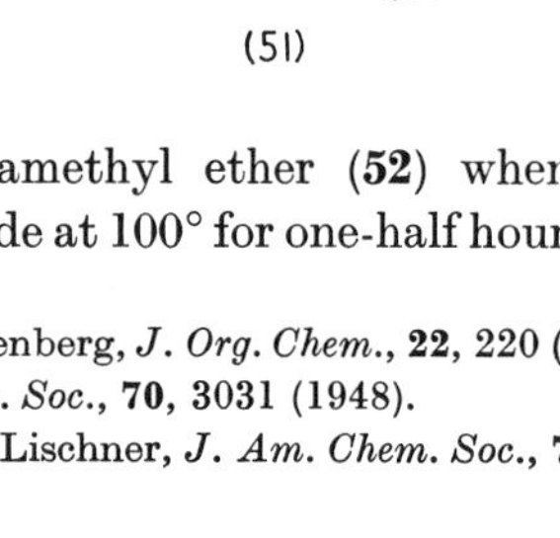

(51)

Dihydrorobinetin tetramethyl ether (**52**) when warmed with aqueous alcoholic sodium hydroxide at 100° for one-half hour is partly dehydrogenated

[27] C. Enebäck and J. Gripenberg, *J. Org. Chem.*, **22**, 220 (1957).

[28] J. C. Pew, *J. Am. Chem. Soc.*, **70**, 3031 (1948).

[29] T. A. Geissman and H. Lischner, *J. Am. Chem. Soc.*, **74**, 3001 (1952).

to the flavonol [a general reaction of the natural (*trans*) dihydroflavonols]; the remainder undergoes rearrangement analogous to that discussed above for dihydroquercetin (45) tetramethyl ether and yields the 3-benzylidene-coumaran-2-one (53), the structure of which was confirmed by synthesis.[30]

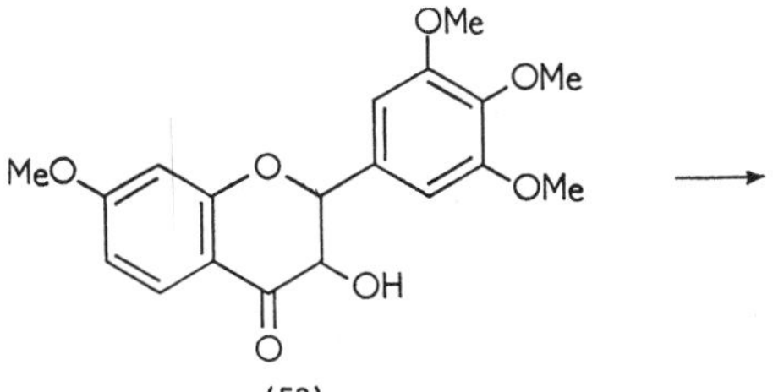

(52)

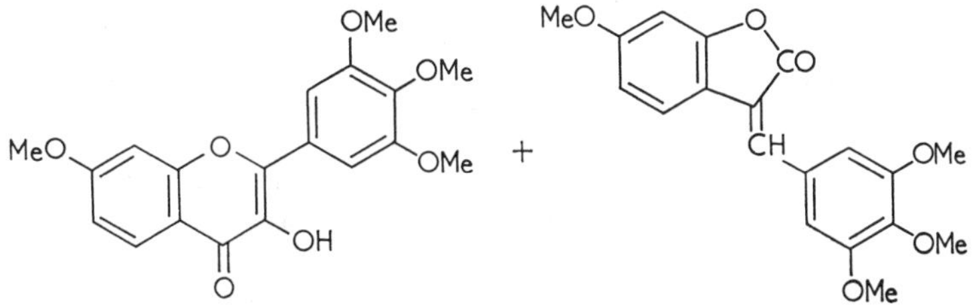

(53)

Pinobanksin dimethyl ether (54) yields the 2-hydroxy-2-benzylcoumaran-3-one (55),[31] and under more vigorous conditions might yield the product from benzilic acid rearrangement.

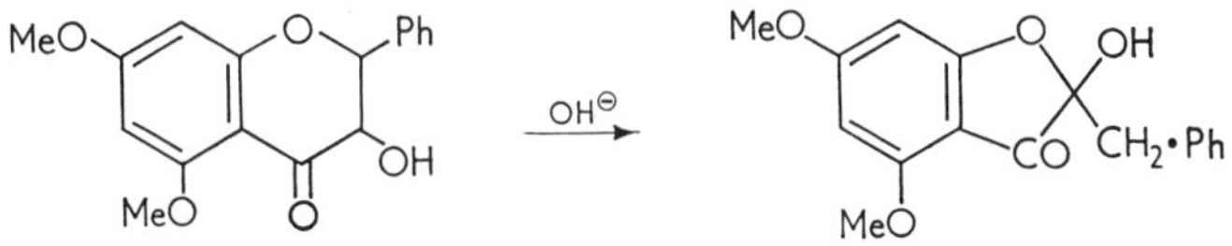

(54)   (55)

F. Flavan-3,4-diol Derivative to a Coumarone

Periodate oxidation of melacacidin tetramethyl ether (56) was found to give the coumarone (benzofuran) (57), and the reaction was formulated as shown.[31]

[30] D. Molho and M. Chadenson, *Bull. soc. chim. France*, **1959**, 453.
[31] W. Bottomley, *Chem. & Ind.* (*London*), **1956**, 170.

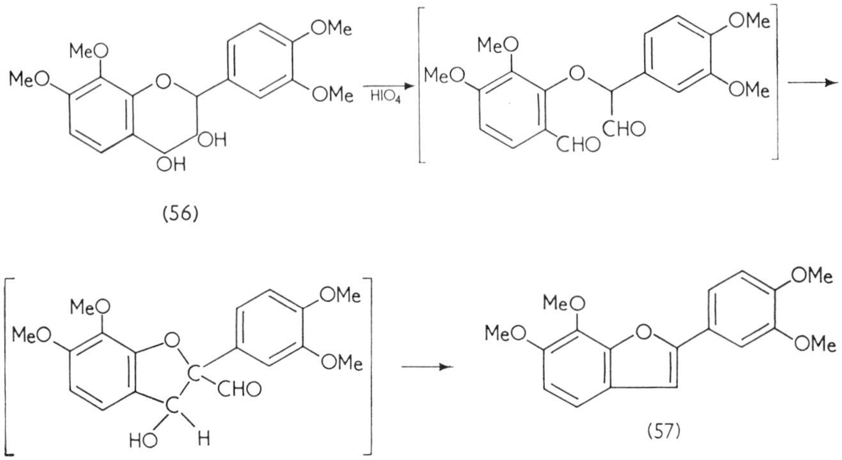

(56)

(57)

G. Ring Contractions of Cyclic Amides

This group of ring contractions appears to result from the greater stability of a five-membered cyclic anion compared with its six-membered counterpart and the acyclic ion which this yields by ring fission. Such ring contractions include the formation of oxazolidine-2,4-diones from dialuric acids, hydantoins from 5-bromo- and 5-aminobarbituric acids, and alloxanic acid and its amides from alloxan.

Dialuric acids. Dialuric acids (58) are converted by the action of 2–3 equivalents of aqueous alkali at 100° for 20–30 minutes into 2,4-oxazolidinediones (59), and this transformation has been reviewed.[32] The ring contraction was discovered by Pellizzari[33] in 1887, but the products were formulated as tartronimides (60) and, although a number of other representatives were

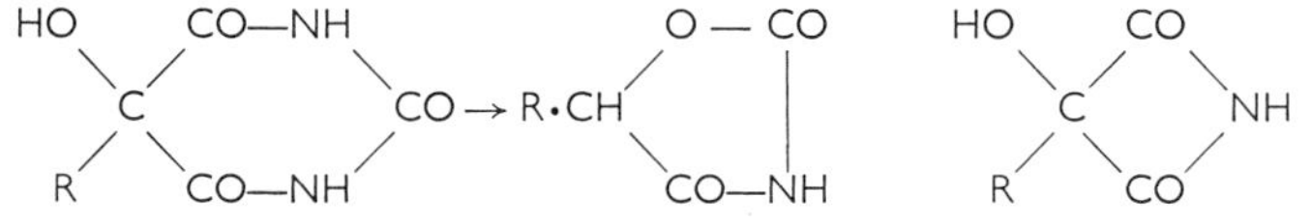

(58)   (59)   (60)

prepared industrially,[34] their oxazolidinedione structure was not recognized until much later.[35] N-Monosubstituted dialuric acids similarly give oxazolidinediones[36] which in earlier papers had been regarded as 1,3-di(α-hydroxy-

[32] J. W. Clark-Lewis, *Chem. Revs.*, **58**, 63 (1958).

[33] G. Pellizzari, *Gazz. chim. ital.*, **17**, 409 (1887); **18**, 340 (1888); *Ann.*, **255**, 230 (1889).

[34] Chemische Fabrik Boehringer & Söhne, Ger. Pat. 108,026 (October 30, 1899); *Frdl.*, **5**, 117 (1901).

[35] F. E. King and J. W. Clark-Lewis, *J. Chem. Soc.* (*London*), **1951**, 3077.

[36] H. Aspelund, *Acta Acad. Aboensis, Math. et Phys.*, **10**, No. 14, p. 42 (1937).

acyl)ureas. N-Alkyloxazolidine-2,4-diones are unstable toward alkali, and this suggests one reason why the yield of 5-benzyl-3-methyl-2,4-oxazolidinedione is higher when 5-benzyl-1,3-dimethyldialuric acid is merely boiled with water instead of with alkali.[36] 5-Benzyl-1-methyl-3-phenyldialuric acid (61) similarly undergoes ring contraction in boiling water to give 5-benzyl-5-methyl-carbamoyl-3-phenyl-2,4-oxazolidinedione (62), so that ring fission in this case

involves the 1,2 bond of dialuric acid.[37] Recently it was found that the methylamine salt of 1,3,5-trimethylbarbituric acid was slowly converted during crystallization into 5-methyl-5-methylcarbamoyl-3-methyl-2,4-oxazo-lidinedione (64).[38] This transformation was accelerated by aeration of a boiling ethanolic solution of the methylamine salt, and the reaction was presumed to occur by oxidation of the barbituric acid anion to the dialuric acid (63) followed by ring contraction to the oxazolidinedione (64).[38]

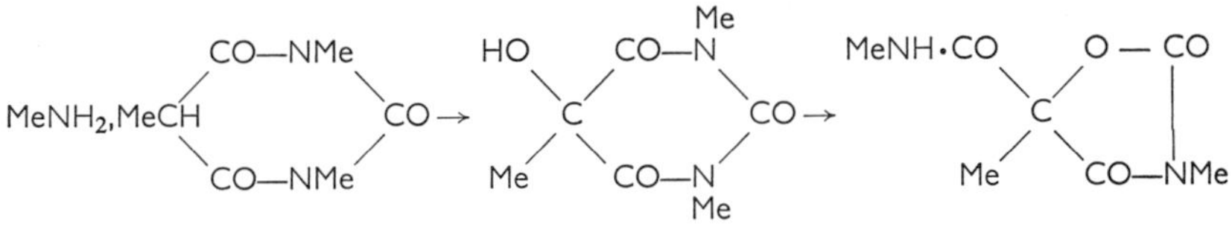

5-Bromobarbituric acids. Most 5-bromobarbituric acids are converted by boiling aqueous or alcoholic alkali into mixtures of 2-imino-oxazolid-4-ones (pseudohydantoins) and hydantoins, in which the former predominate,[39] and the preferential cyclization to an oxazolidinedione derivative accounts for the very poor yields of hydantoins obtained by this method.[40] 5-Bromo-1,5-diphenylbarbituric acid (65) is converted into a mixture of 5-phenyl-2-phenylimino-oxazolidine-4-one (66) (45%) and 1,5-diphenylhydantoin (67) ($\sim 21\%$).[41] α-Bromo-acylureas have been isolated as intermediates in the reaction.[32] NN'-Disubstituted 5-bromobarbituric acids yield only hydantoins or mixtures of two hydantoins if the N-substituents are different,[39] although

[37] H. Aspelund, *Acta Acad. Aboensis, Math. et Phys.*, **13**, No. 1, p. 22 (1942); *Chem. Abstr.*, **39**, 2053 (1945).
[38] J. W. Clark-Lewis and M. J. Thompson, *J. Chem. Soc.* (*London*), **1959**, 2401.
[39] H. Aspelund, *Acta Acad. Aboensis, Math. et Phys.*, **12**, No. 5, p. 33 (1939).
[40] E. Ware, *Chem. Revs.*, **46**, 422 (1950).
[41] F. E. King and J. W. Clark-Lewis, *J. Chem. Soc.* (*London*), **1951**, 3080.

the absence of 3-alkyl(or aryl)-2-alkyl(or aryl)imino-oxazolid-4-ones may be due to their lability (ring fission) under alkaline conditions.

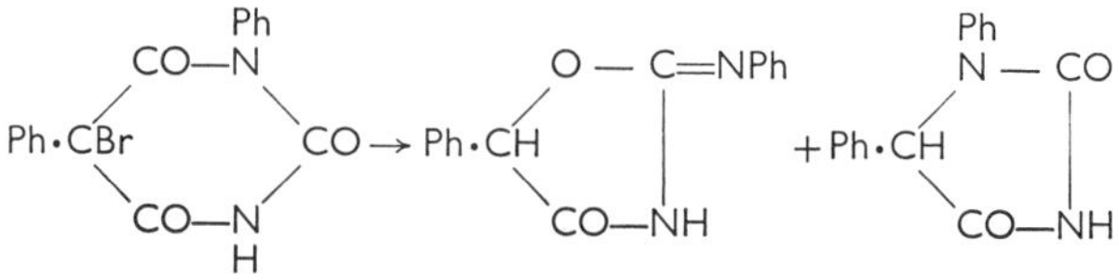

(65)　　　　　　　　　(66)　　　　　　　　(67)

5-Aminobarbituric acids. 5-Aminobarbituric acids may be expected to undergo ring contraction to hydantoins under alkaline conditions, a reaction formally analogous to the conversion of dialuric acids into oxazolidinediones discussed above (page 630). Few aminobarbituric acids are known, but the formation of the quinoxalinohydantoin (69) from the spirobarbituric acid (68) exemplifies the reaction and provides important evidence for the *spiro* structure of the product (68) obtained from *o*-dimethylaminoaniline and

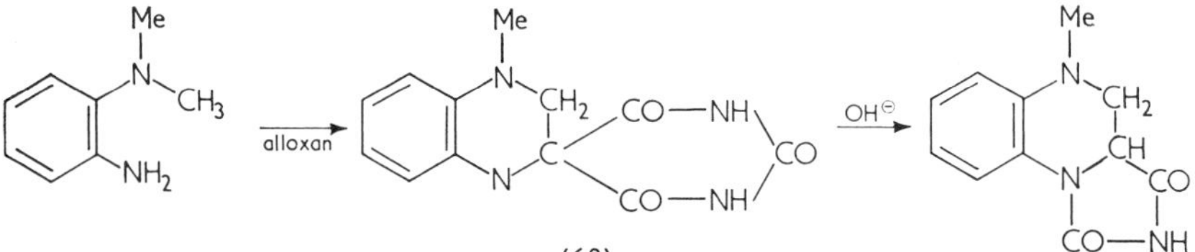

(68)

(69)

alloxan.[41] The structure of the hydantoin (69) was established by synthesis of its *N*-methyl derivative. A few close analogs of the spiran (68) are known, and the 6,7-dimethyl compound is similarly converted by boiling aqueous sodium hydroxide into the 6,7-dimethyl analog of the hydantoin (69).[41]

Alloxan. Alloxan hydrate (70) is converted rapidly into alloxanic acid (71) by alkalis, and the conversion is conveniently effected with aqueous

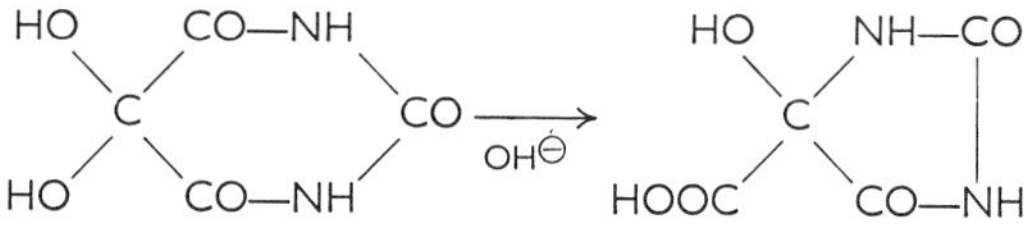

(70)　　　　　　　　　(71)

barium hydroxide.[42] The cyclic structure of alloxanic acid was established by Biltz, Heyn, and Bergius.[42] This ring contraction occurs sufficiently rapidly in the blood stream to prevent intravenously injected alloxan from reaching the pancreas and causing the damage associated with alloxan-induced experi-

---

[42] H. Biltz, M. Heyn, and M. Bergius, *Ann.*, **413**, 68 (1916); H. Biltz and M. Kobel, *Ber.*, **54**, 1802 (1921).

mental diabetes.[43] The reaction may be interpreted as a hydrolytic ring fission and recyclisation (eq. 2) or as a benzilic acid type of rearrangement (eq. 3). On the first view, reaction can be considered to follow attack on the 4-carbon atom by OH$^-$, and subsequent rearrangement need not involve formation of the acyclic hydrolysis product (eq. 2). The alternative benzilic acid rearrange-

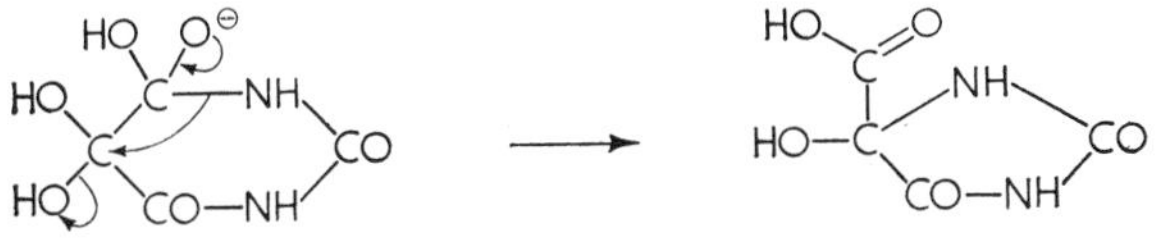

$$(2)$$

ment can be regarded as an attack by OH$^-$ on the 5 position with removal of a proton from a hydroxyl group followed by 1,2 rearrangement (eq. 3). Recent

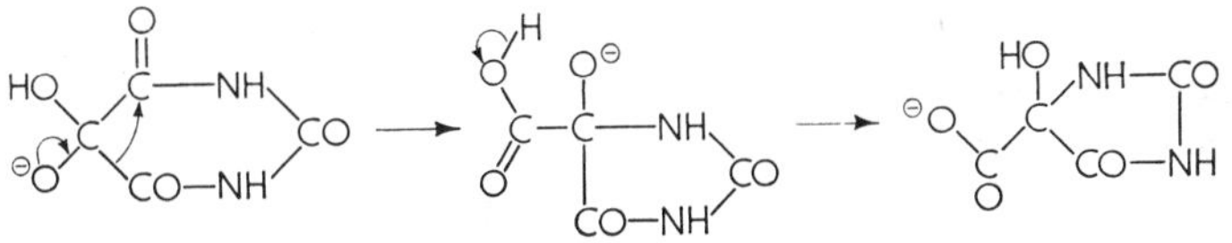

$$(3)$$

tracer studies, however, are compatible only with the former mechanism.[43a]

Ethyl alloxanate (72) is formed when anhydrous alloxan is treated with ethanolic sodium ethoxide and then with hydrochloric acid,[43] and this may be held to favor the second mechanism for the rearrangement (eq. 4).

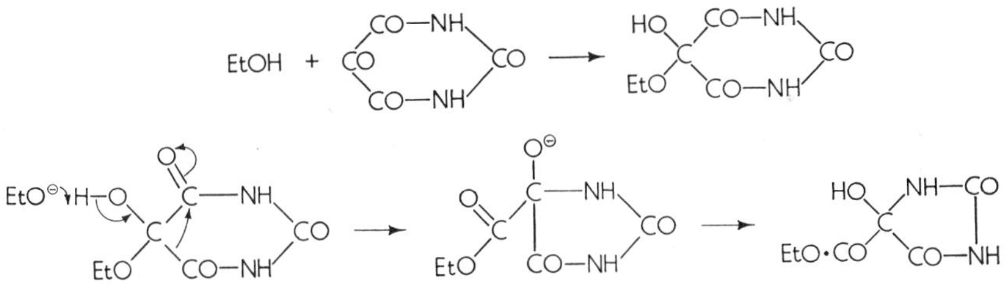

$$(4)$$

$$(72)$$

Secondary amines (morpholine, piperidine, pyrrolidine, and dimethylamine) also react with alloxan hydrate to give products formulated as alloxanic acid amides (73) by Fisher and Day[43] who proposed the mechanism shown in equation 5. A plausible alternative mechanism (eq. 6) involves attack

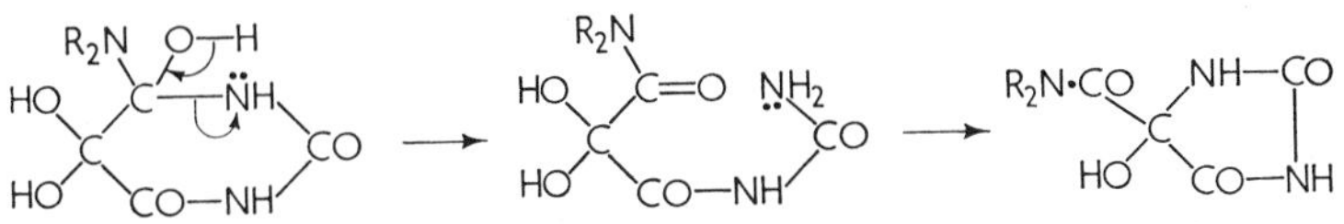

$$(5)$$

$$(73)$$

[43] F. R. Fisher and A. R. Day, *J. Am. Chem. Soc.*, **77**, 4894 (1955).
[43a] H. Kwart, R. W. Spayd, and J. C. Collins, *J. Am. Chem. Soc.*, **83**, 2579 (1961).

by the secondary amine on the carbinolamine (74) present in equilibrium with alloxan hydrate (70). The mechanism shown in equation 6 could operate with

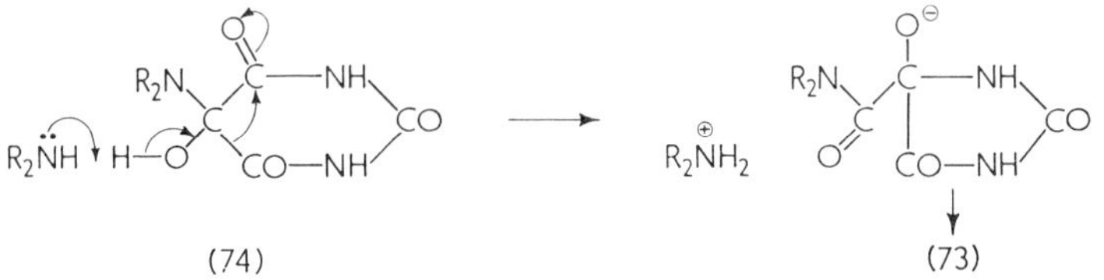

$$(6)$$

(74)   (73)

equal plausibility on alloxan hydrate (70) and thus yield secondary amine salts of alloxanic acid by a process similar to that shown in equation 3. It is therefore possibly significant that the products* formulated as amides all contain a molecule of water which cannot be removed except by decomposition of the molecules, and that their general properties are compatible with their formulation as salts. The same products were obtained [43] from ethyl alloxanate and aqueous alcoholic solutions of the secondary amines by the method used by Biltz and Lachmann [44] for preparing monoalkylamides of alloxanic acid. Some of the products obtained by Biltz and Lachmann also contained a molecule of water.

H. Dihydrofurans to Cyclopropyl Ketones

When 2,3-dihydrofuran itself was passed through a tube at 375°, a small amount of cyclopropane aldehyde was formed, together with crotonaldehyde, propylene, and carbon monoxide. The reaction appears to be reversible, for a little 2,3-dihydrofuran was detected after pyrolysis of cyclopropane aldehyde.[45] In the same way, 2-methyl-4,5-dihydrofuran was isomerized to methyl cyclopropyl ketone (eq. 7). Since no methylcyclopropane aldehyde was formed, it seems that ring fission occurs at the 1,5 bond and not at the 1,2 bond [46] (see also Section 4).

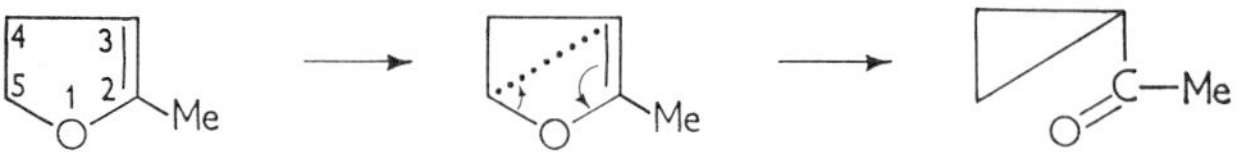

$$(7)$$

2. RING EXPANSIONS

A. Pyrrole Derivatives to Pyridines

When pyrrole is treated with chloroform or bromoform in the presence of alkali (Reimer-Tiemann reaction) the expected pyrrole aldehyde is accom-

---

* The products have now been shown to be salts (J. W. Clark-Lewis and J. A. Edgar, J. Chem. Soc. (London), **1962**, in press).

[44] H. Biltz and F. Lachmann, J. prakt. Chem., **113**, 309 (1926).

[45] C. L. Wilson, J. Am. Chem. Soc., **69**, 3002 (1947).

[46] N. I. Shuikin, I. F. Bel'skii, and R. A. Karakhanov, Doklady Akad. Nauk S. S. S. R., **125**, 1051 (1959).

panied by some 3-chloro(or bromo)pyridine. This interesting ring expansion was first observed by Ciamician and Dennstedt,[47] who obtained 3-bromopyridine in 10% yield from pyrrylpotassium and bromoform. Pyridine itself was obtained in very poor yield from pyrrole and methylene iodide,[48] and 3-phenylpyridine[49] was formed similarly from benzal chloride, pyrrole, and sodium ethoxide. There can therefore be no doubt that the additional carbon atom occupies the 3 position in the pyridine ring. Attempts to improve the yields, e.g. by the use of pyrryl-lithium,[50] have met with only limited success. The reaction is a general one for substituted pyrroles,[51] and indoles[52] also undergo ring expansion under similar conditions.

When treated with chloroform in the presence of alcoholic potassium hydroxide, 2,5-dimethylpyrrole (75) gave the 3-aldehyde (76), 3-chloro-2,6-dimethylpyridine (77) and 2(or 3)-dichloromethyl-2,5-dimethyl-2H-pyrrole (78).[51] The latter was found to rearrange to the pyridine derivative (77) when treated with sodium ethoxide.

Ring expansion occurs also with indenes, and the formation of a stable anion seems to facilitate the reaction.[53,54] There is some evidence for the existence of dichlorocarbene in the basic hydrolysis of chloroform,[55] and a rational mechanism (eq. 8) can be postulated for the ring expansion if it be assumed that dichlorocarbene is an intermediate.[53]

$$(8)$$

[47] G. L. Ciamician and M. Dennstedt, *Ber.*, **14**, 1153 (1881); **15**, 1172 (1882); see also H. Wynberg, *Chem. Revs.*, **60**, 169 (1960).

[48] M. Dennstedt and J. Zimmermann, *Ber.*, **18**, 3316 (1885).

[49] G. L. Ciamician and P. Silber, *Ber.*, **20**, 191 (1887).

[50] E. R. Alexander, A. B. Herrick, and T. M. Roder, *J. Am. Chem. Soc.*, **72**, 2760 (1950).

[51] G. Plancher and V. Ponti, *Chem. Abstr.*, **4**, 2452 (1910); O. Boechi, *Gazz. chim. ital.*, **30**, 89 (1900); through *Chem. Soc. (London) Abstr.*, **78**, 357 (1900).

[52] G. Plancher and O. Carrasco, *Atti reale accad. Lincei*, **14**, I, 162, 704 (1905); through *Chem. Soc. (London) Abstr.*, **88**, 298, 666, (1905); G. Magnanini, *Gazz. chim. ital.*, **17**, 246 (1887); through *Chem. Soc. (London) Abstr.*, **52**, 1113 (1887).

[53] W. E. Parham and H. E. Reiff, *J. Am. Chem. Soc.*, **77**, 1177 (1955).

[54] W. E. Parham, H. E. Reiff, and P. Swartzentruber, *J. Am. Chem. Soc.*, **78**, 1437 (1956); W. E. Parham and R. R. Twelves, *J. Org. Chem.*, **22**, 730 (1957).

[55] J. Hine, *J. Am. Chem. Soc.*, **72**, 2438 (1950).

An alternative mechanism (eq. 9) involving the formation of a 2H-pyrrole derivative must also be considered, but here again an intermediate cyclopropane must be postulated.

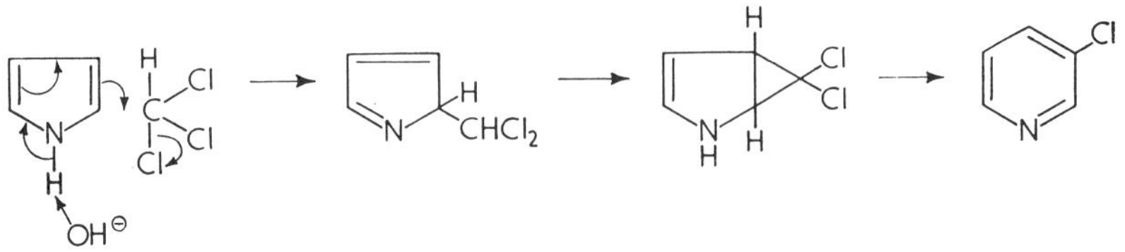

$$(9)$$

On the other hand, it may be noted that chloroform has been found to react only slowly with sodium phenoxide and rapidly if sodium hydroxide is also present. This has been interpreted [56] as proof that the Reimer-Tiemann reaction is not initiated by nucleophilic attack of phenoxide ion on chloroform, and the same argument may be valid with the ring-expansion reaction.

Ring enlargement of pyrrole can also be brought about under neutral conditions in the vapor phase: the passing of pyrrole and chloroform through a glass tube at 550°, for example, gave 3-chloropyridine (33%) and 2-chloropyridine (2–5%).[57]

Two related reactions involving the conversion of pyrroles into pyridines also deserve mention. When ethyl N-pyrrylacetate is heated, it gives pyridine, carbon dioxide, ethylene, and hydrogen;[58] the first step presumably involves N to C migration, and ring expansion is then accompanied by decarboxylation (eq. 10).

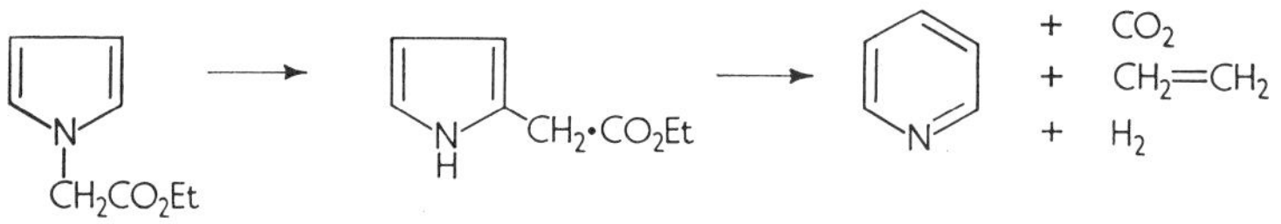

$$(10)$$

The second analogous reaction involves ring expansion when 2-aminomethylpyrrole is treated with nitrous acid, and leads with loss of water to pyridine,[59] in a reaction reminiscent of the Demjanov rearrangement (eq. 11).

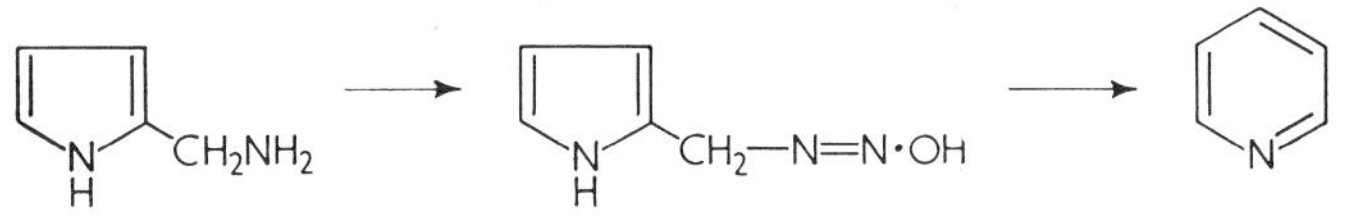

$$(11)$$

[56] J. Hine and J. M. van der Veen, *J. Am. Chem. Soc.*, **81**, 6446 (1959).

[57] H. L. Rice and T. E. Londergan, *J. Am. Chem. Soc.*, **77**, 4678 (1955).

[58] W. E. Sohl and R. L. Shriner, *J. Am. Chem. Soc.*, **53**, 4168 (1931).

[59] N. Putochin, *J. Russ. Phys. Chem. Soc.*, **62**, 2226 (1930); through *Chem. Abstr.*, **25**, 3996 (1931).

B. Furan Derivatives to Pyridines

Furfural is reported to yield 3-hydroxypyridine and 2,5-dihydroxypyridine when heated with hydrazine in an autoclave,[60] and 2,5-dihydroxypyridine when similarly heated with hydroxylamine hydrochloride. 5-Methyl-2-furfural gave 5-hydroxy-2-methylpyridine when heated at 160° under pressure with ammonium sulfate,[60] and 2,5-dihydrofuran-2,5-dicarboxylic acid was converted with ammonium bromide and ammonia into 6-hydroxypicolinic acid.[61]

C. Benzylidenecoumaranones (Aurones) into Flavones and Flavonols

2-Arylidenecoumaran-3-ones are known as aurones and, in some cases, can be converted with ethanolic potassium cyanide into flavones (eq. 12); others

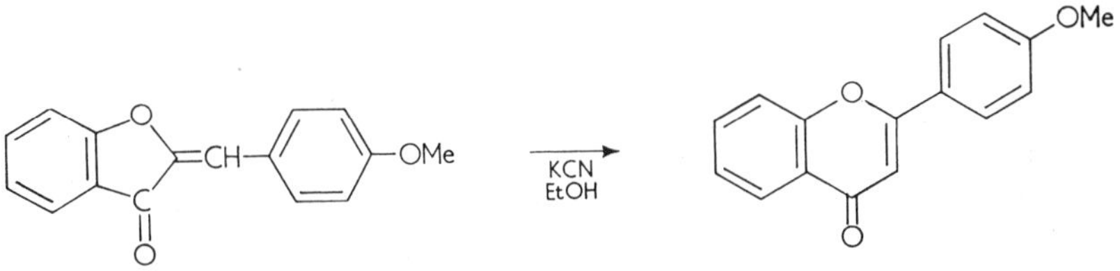

$$(12)$$

can be converted into flavonols with alkaline hydrogen peroxide (eq. 13). These ring expansions have been summarized by Gowan, Philbin, and Wheeler,[62] and in any particular case the reaction (if any) depends upon the position of methoxyl and hydroxyl substituents.

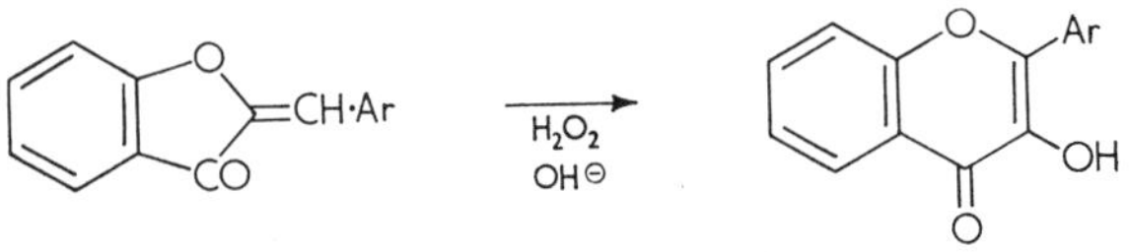

$$(13)$$

The ring expansion of aurones (and chalcone dibromides) with alcoholic potassium cyanide was found to occur with compounds containing a 6-methoxyl group, but not with those with the 4,6-dimethoxy (phloroglucinol) pattern, and the mechanism shown in equation 14 was proposed.[63]

Ring expansion of aurones to flavonols with alkaline hydrogen peroxide is accompanied by the formation of aurone epoxides, which are possible intermediates in formation of the flavonols (eq. 15).[62,64]

[60] K. Aso, *Bull. Inst. Phys. Chem. Research (Tokyo)*, **18**, 177, 180, 182 (1939); through *Chem. Abstr.*, **34**, 3273 (1940).

[61] E. Fischer, K. Hess, and A. Stahlschmidt, *Ber.*, **45**, 2456 (1912).

[62] J. E. Gowan, E. M. Philbin, and T. S. Wheeler, *Sci. Proc. Roy. Dublin Soc.*, **27**, 185 (1956).

[63] D. M. Fitzgerald, J. F. O'Sullivan, E. M. Philbin, and T. S. Wheeler, *J. Chem. Soc. (London)*, **1955**, 860.

[64] W. E. Fitzmaurice, W. I. O'Sullivan, E. M. Philbin, T. S. Wheeler, and T. A. Geissman, *Chem. & Ind. (London)*, **1955**, 652.

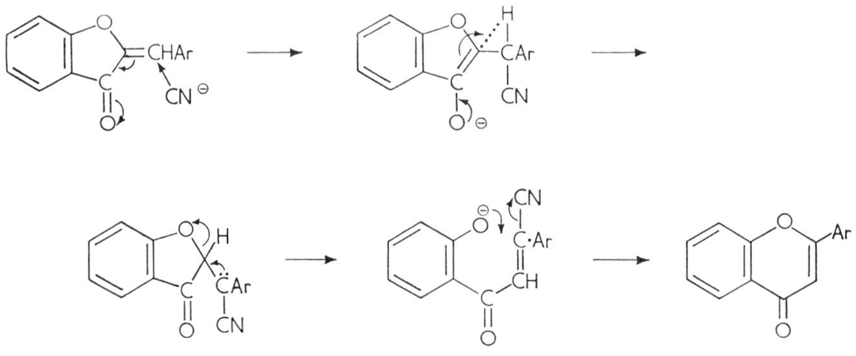

(14)

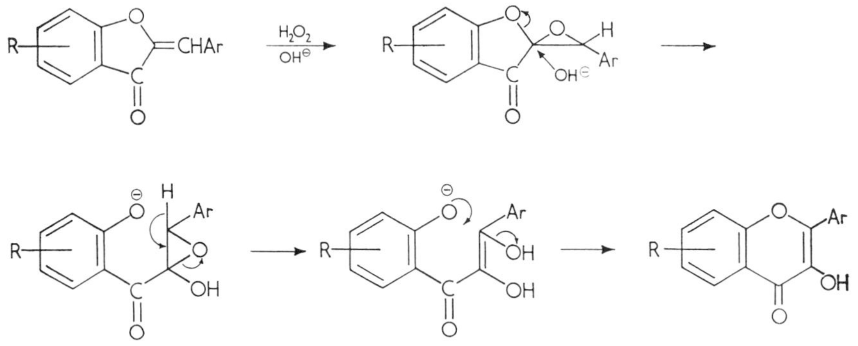

$\dfrac{H_2O_2}{OH^\ominus}$

(15)

D. Tetrahydrofurfuryl Alcohol to Dihydropyran

When tetrahydrofurfuryl alcohol is dehydrated over alumina or a similar catalyst at 300–340°, it gives dihydropyran in good yield. This transformation, which is of commercial importance, was first studied by Paul[65] but the rearrangement has been carried out under a variety of conditions and many different catalysts have been recommended.[66] At higher temperatures the product decomposes to acrolein and ethylene. It seems likely that a carbonium ion is first formed (eq. 16) and that this subsequently undergoes ring

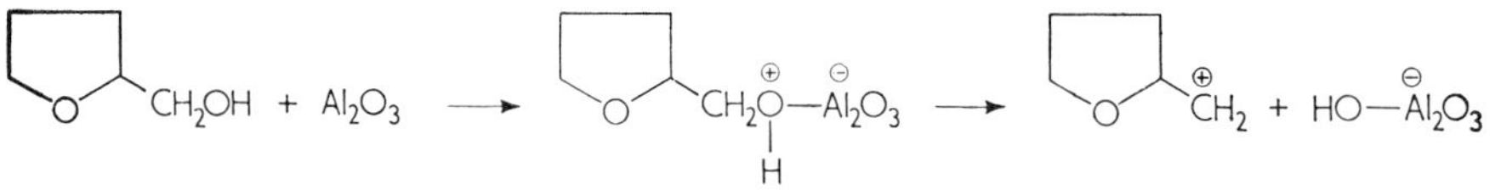

(16)

[65] R. Paul, *Bull. soc. chim. France*, **53**, 1489 (1933).

[66] J. G. M. Bremner, D. McNeil, and Imperial Chemical Industries Ltd., Brit. Pat. 547,334 (1942); through *Chem. Abstr.*, **37**, 5988 (1943); Revertex Ltd. and C. L. Wilson, Brit. Pat. 569,625 (1945); through *Chem. Abstr.*, **41**, 6275 (1947); C. H. Kline and J. Turkevich, *J. Am. Chem. Soc.*, **67**, 498 (1945); C. L. Wilson, *J. Am. Chem. Soc.*, **69**, 3004 (1947); R. L. Sawyer and D. W. Andrews, *Org. Syntheses*, Coll. Vol. III, 276.

enlargement by a process analogous to the Wagner-Meerwein rearrangement (eq. 17).

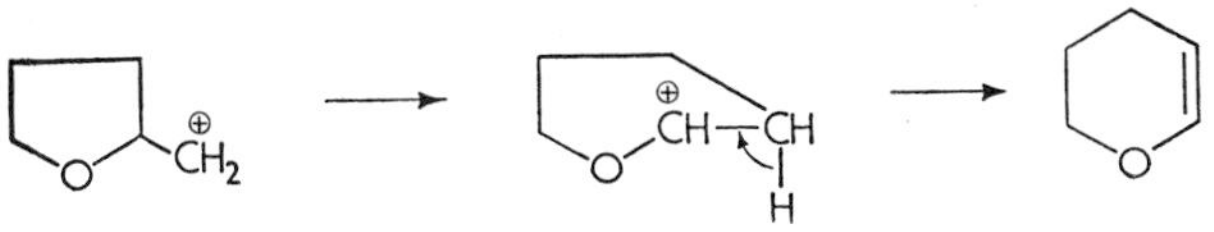

(17)

3. N-OXIDE REARRANGEMENTS

A. Pyridine N-Oxides and Related N-Oxides

When pyridine N-oxide was boiled with acetic anhydride, the product, after hydrolysis, was found to be 2-pyridone.[67] The N-oxides of quinine, dihydroquinine, benzo[h]quinoline, and 3-methylpyridine behave similarly,[68,69] and isoquinoline-N-oxide gives a mixture of isocarbostyril and 4-hydroxyisoquinoline.[70] There seems little doubt that in these reactions the first step is the formation of a salt between the N-oxide and the acetic anhydride (eq. 18).

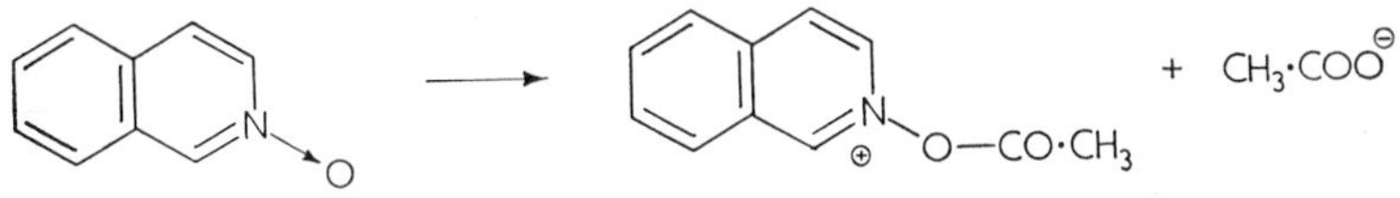

$+ \ CH_3 \cdot COO^{\ominus}$ (18)

Subsequent steps can be formulated as a series of additions and eliminations which, in the case of isoquinoline N-oxide,[70] can be summarized as shown in equation 19, and hydrolysis would yield the observed products.

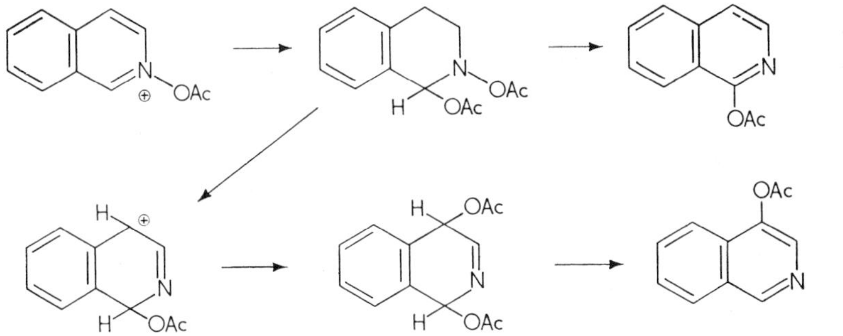

(19)

A rearrangement of a somewhat different type has been observed when the N-oxides of 2- and 4-alkylpyridines are boiled with acetic anhydride.[69,71]

[67] M. Katada, *J. Pharm. Soc. Japan*, **67**, 51 (1947); through *Chem. Abstr.*, **45**, 9536 (1951).

[68] E. Ochiai, *J. Org. Chem.*, **18**, 534 (1953).

[69] V. Boekelheide and W. J. Linn, *J. Am. Chem. Soc.*, **76**, 1286 (1954).

[70] M. M. Robison and B. L. Robison, *J. Org. Chem.*, **21**, 1337 (1956).

The reaction of 2-picoline *N*-oxide (**79**) with acetic anhydride, for example, gives 2-pyridylmethyl acetate (**80**) in 78% yield, and this when converted into the *N*-oxide and subjected to a second rearrangement gives 2-pyridine-aldehyde diacetate (**81**) in 46% yield. Similarly, 2,6-lutidine *N*-oxide gives

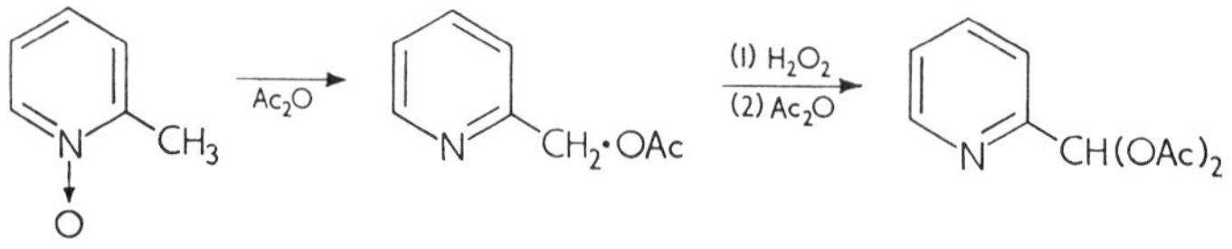

(79)   (80)   (81)

6-methyl-2-pyridylmethyl acetate and, on a second treatment, 2,6-di(acetoxy-methyl)-pyridine; 4-methylpyridine *N*-oxide gives a mixture of 4-pyridyl-methyl acetate and 3-hydroxy-4-methylpyridine.[72]

With many of the compounds studied there was an induction period followed by an exothermic reaction,[69] and the demonstration that added styrene was rapidly polymerized suggested a free-radical mechanism for the rearrangement.[73] A plausible reaction mechanism of this type may be summarized as shown in equations 20–22.

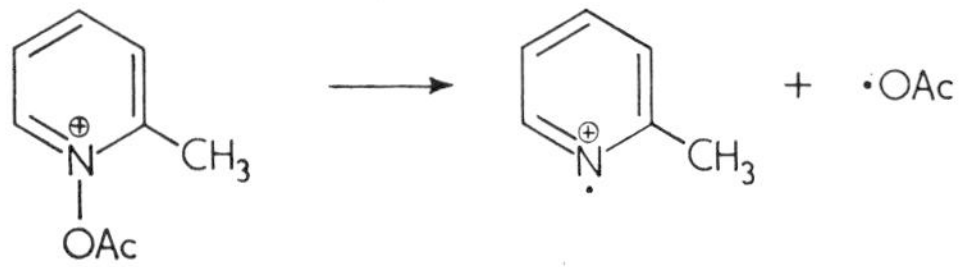

(20)

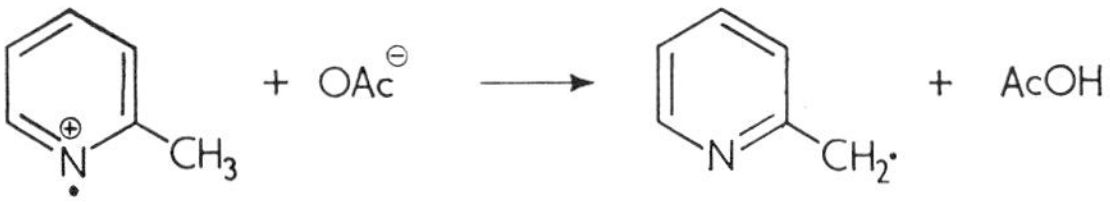

(21)

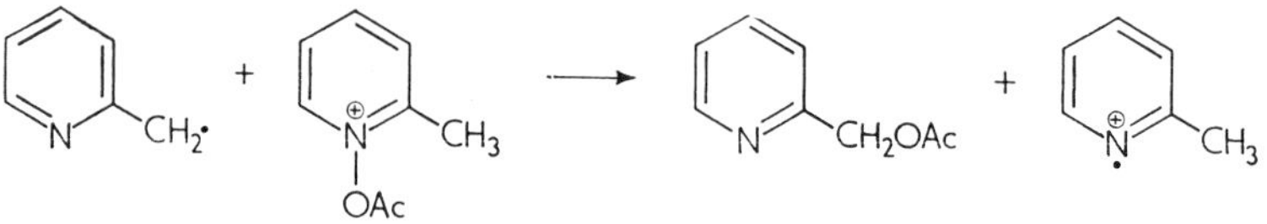

(22)

On the other hand, the yield of rearranged product was hardly affected by addition of free-radical scavengers to the reaction mixture, although the polymerization of styrene was thereby effectively inhibited.[74] It therefore

[71] O. H. Bullitt and J. T. Maynard, *J. Am. Chem. Soc.*, **76**, 1370 (1954).

[72] J. A. Berson and T. Cohen, *J. Am. Chem. Soc.*, **77**, 1281 (1955).

[73] V. Boekelheide and D. L. Harrington, *Chem. & Ind. (London)*, **1955**, 1423.

[74] V. J. Traynelis and R. F. Martello, *J. Am. Chem. Soc.*, **80**, 6590 (1958).

seems that although free radicals are present during the reaction, free-radical intermediates are not involved to any important extent in this rearrangement, and this leads us back to the alternative ionic mechanism proposed by Boekelheide and Harrington (eq. 23).[73] The reaction is formally similar to the

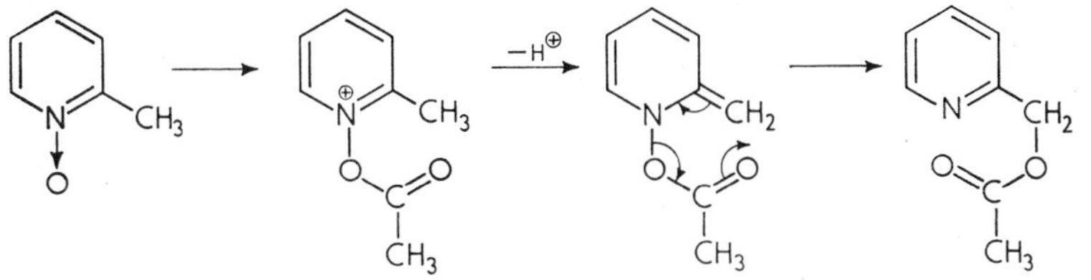

$$(23)$$

rearrangement which occurs when quinaldine N-oxide is treated with benzoyl chloride and sodium hydroxide to give 2-hydroxymethylquinoline, and for which an intramolecular ionic mechanism was suggested.[75] In this connection it is of interest that 3-methylisoquinoline N-oxide gives mainly 3-methylisocarbostyril and 4-hydroxy-3-methylisoquinoline when treated with acetic anhydride,[70] which is in agreement with the inability of 3-methylisoquinoline to form an o-quinonoid structure. By the same token, one would expect formation of 1-acetoxymethylisoquinoline from 1-methylisoquinoline N-oxide.

An intramolecular mechanism is not feasible for the formation of 4-acetoxymethylpyridine from 4-methylpyridine N-oxide, but the following modified mechanism (eq. 24) seems to account for the known facts. A reaction similar

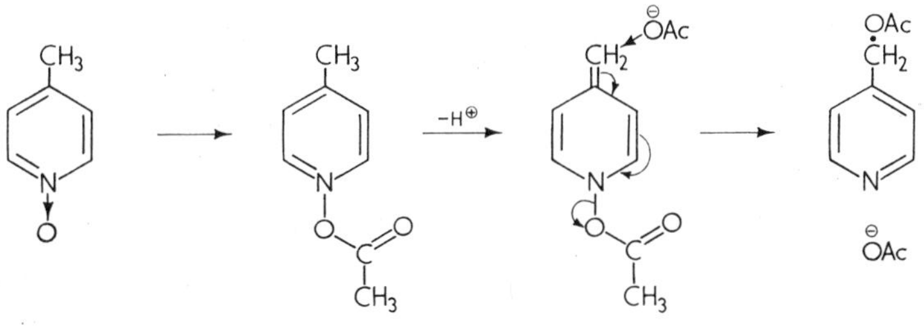

$$(24)$$

to that with acetic anhydride occurs when 2-picoline N-oxide is heated with toluene-p-sulfonyl chloride,[76] which gave 2-chloromethylpyridine (eq. 25). The reported formation of 5-toluene-p-sulfonoxy-3-methylpyridine[77] from

[75] I. J. Pachter, J. Am. Chem. Soc., **75**, 3026 (1953).

[76] E. Matsumara, J. Chem. Soc. Japan, **74**, 363 (1953); through Chem. Abstr., **48**, 6442 (1954).

[77] E. Matsumara, J. Chem. Soc. Japan, **74**, 446 (1953); through Chem. Abstr., **48**, 6442 (1954).

3-methylpyridine N-oxide may perhaps be explained in the same way as the formation of 4-acetoxyisoquinoline (see eq. 19, p. 639).

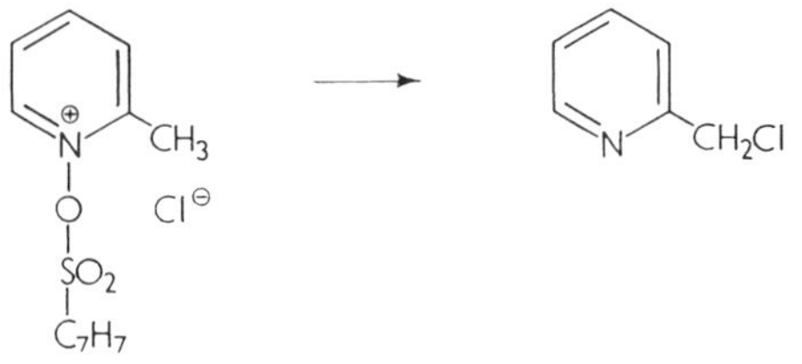

(25)

B. N-Oxides of Quinoxaline- and of Pyrazine-2-carboxyanilides

Carbon dioxide is rapidly eliminated when 3,4-dihydro-4-methyl-3-oxo-quinoxaline-2-carboxy-N-methylanilide 1-oxide (**82**) is added to cold sulfuric acid, and 3,4-dihydro-4-methyl-2-o-methylaminophenyl-3-oxoquinoxaline (**83**) is formed in 75% yield.[78]

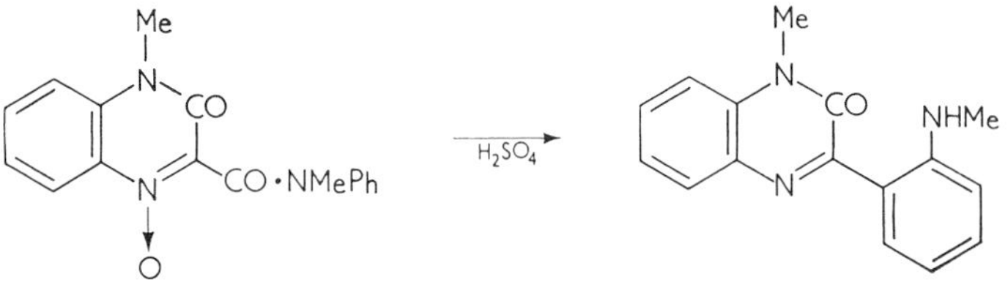

The reaction is considered to proceed by protonation of the N-oxide group (**84**) followed by electrophilic substitution by the quinoxaline 2-carbon atom at the o-position of the anilide to give the N-hydroxy-spiro intermediate (**85**).[79,80] This then suffers hydrolysis, decarboxylation, and dehydration to

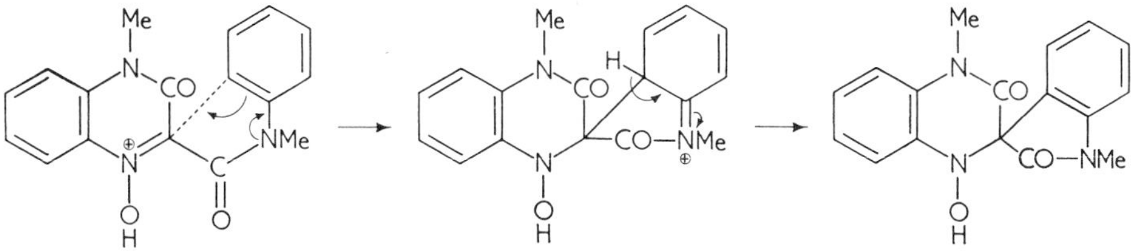

give the final product (**83**). This view of the mechanism was strengthened by study of the structural features necessary for the rearrangement, and the

[78] J. W. Clark-Lewis, *J. Chem. Soc.* (*London*), **1957**, 439.

[79] J. W. Clark-Lewis and G. F. Katekar, *J. Chem. Soc.* (*London*), **1959**, 2825.

[80] M. S. Habib and C. W. Rees, *Chem. & Ind.* (*London*), **1959**, 367; *J. Chem. Soc.* (*London*), **1960**, 3371.

electronic influence of substituents on the speed of the reaction,[80] which is greatly reduced by the nitro group in the p-nitro-anilide (82, with p-nitro-phenyl in place of phenyl). The rearrangement occurs more slowly with any decrease in the electrophilic character of the 2C atom, and pyrazine analogs rearrange more slowly than the quinoxaline derivatives (82).[80] The intra-molecular nature of the reaction was established by rearrangement of a mixture of the pyrazines 86 and 87, which gave the expected products without interchange of groups,[80] and by rearrangement of the N-oxide (82) in the presence of aromatic amines, again without exchange.[79]

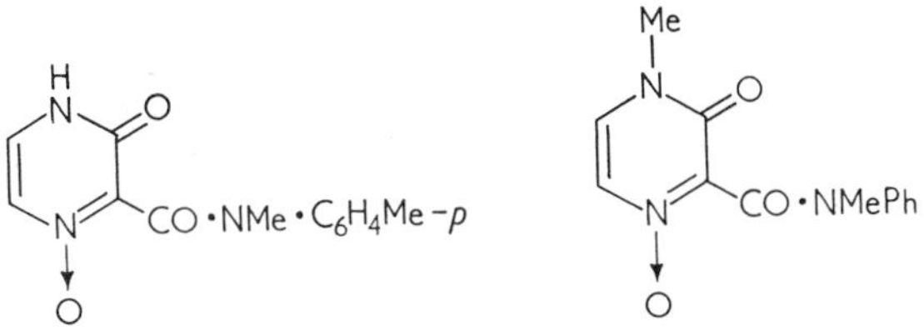

(86)   (87)

An interesting series of reactions occurs when the N-oxide (79) is boiled with ethanolic hydrogen chloride, and with acetyl chloride.[79,81] The former reagent yields the 6-chloroquinoxaline-2-spiro-3'-indole (88; R=H), which is converted by acetyl chloride into the 1-acetyl derivative (88; R=Ac), which is also formed directly from the N-oxide and acetyl chloride.[79] The 1-hydroxy-spiro-indole (85) is again thought to be an intermediate in these reactions, and with hydrogen chloride, for example, it yields the 6-chloro compound (88; R=H) by nucleophilic substitution in the para position as occurs with other N-phenylhydroxylamines. Hydrolysis of the 1-acetyl derivative (88; R=Ac) with a mixture of hydrochloric acid and ethanol gave 6-chloro-3,4-dihydro-4-methyl-3-oxo-2-o-methylaminophenylquinoxaline (89), the 6-chloro analog of the quinoxaline (83).[79]

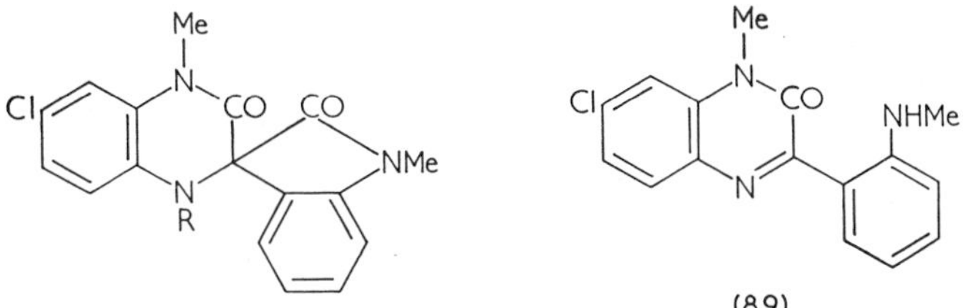

(88)   (89)

C. 2-Phenylisatogen to 3-Benzoylanthranil

A rearrangement of somewhat different type occurs with 2-phenylisatogen (90), which is converted by methanolic sulfuric acid into an isomer recently

[81] E. H. Usherwood and M. A. Whiteley, J. Chem. Soc. (London), 123, 1069 (1923).

shown to be 3-benzoylanthranil (**91**).[82] This may proceed though the steps indicated in **90** and **91**.

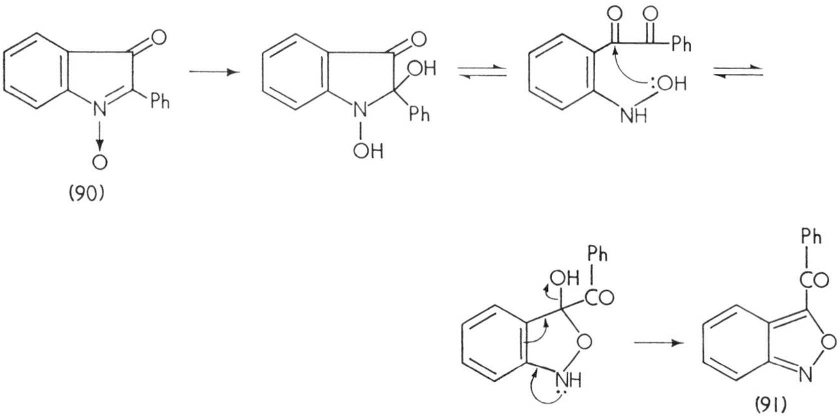

(90)

(91)

4. 1,2 REARRANGEMENTS IN HETEROCYCLIC SYSTEMS

A. *1,2 Rearrangements of Catechin Derivatives*

Structural investigations of catechin and epicatechin by Freudenberg and his co-workers during the 1920s [83,84] were greatly complicated by the 1,2-molecular rearrangements which occurred with the catechin compounds. Epicatechins did not suffer these 1,2 rearrangements and this difference in behavior was later helpful in assigning to catechin the 2,3-*trans* arrangement and to epicatechin the 2,3-*cis* arrangement of substituents.[84-87] (+)-Catechin tetramethyl ether (**92**) reacts rapidly with phosphorus pentachloride at room temperature to give the reactive 2-chloroisoflavan (**93**), which with alcohols readily exchanges the halogen for alkoxyl to yield optically active 2-alkoxyisoflavans such as the 2-ethoxyisoflavan (**94**).[88-90] The

[82] J. Pinkus, T. Cohen, M. Sundaralingam, and G. A. Jeffrey, *Proc. Chem. Soc.* (*London*), **1960**, 70.

[83] F. A. Mason, *J. Soc. Chem. Ind.* (*London*), **47**, 269 (1928).

[84] S. Wawzonek, in R. C. Elderfield's *Heterocyclic Compounds*, Vol. II, Wiley, New York, 1951, p. 358.

[85] F. E. King, J. W. Clark-Lewis, and W. F. Forbes, *J. Chem. Soc.* (*London*), **1955**, 2948.

[86] J. W. Clark-Lewis, *Chem. & Ind.* (*London*), **1955**, 1218.

[87] W. B. Whalley, *Chemistry of Vegetable Tannins*, Society of Leather Trades' Chemists, Croydon, 1956, p. 151.

[88] J. J. Drumm, *Proc. Roy. Irish Acad.*, **36B**, 41 (1923–1924); J. J. Drumm, R. J. P. Carolan, and H. Ryan, *Proc. Roy. Irish Acad.*, **39B**, 114 (1929).

[89] W. Baker, *J. Chem. Soc.* (*London*), **1929**, 1593.

[90] K. Freudenberg, G. Carrara, and E. Cohn, *Ann.*, **446**, 87 (1925).

2-ethoxyisoflavan (**94**) was also obtained recently by heating (+)-catechin tetramethyl ether 3-toluene-*p*-sulfonate with ethanolic potassium acetate in an attempt to replace the toluene-*p*-sulfonoxy group by an acetoxy group.[91]

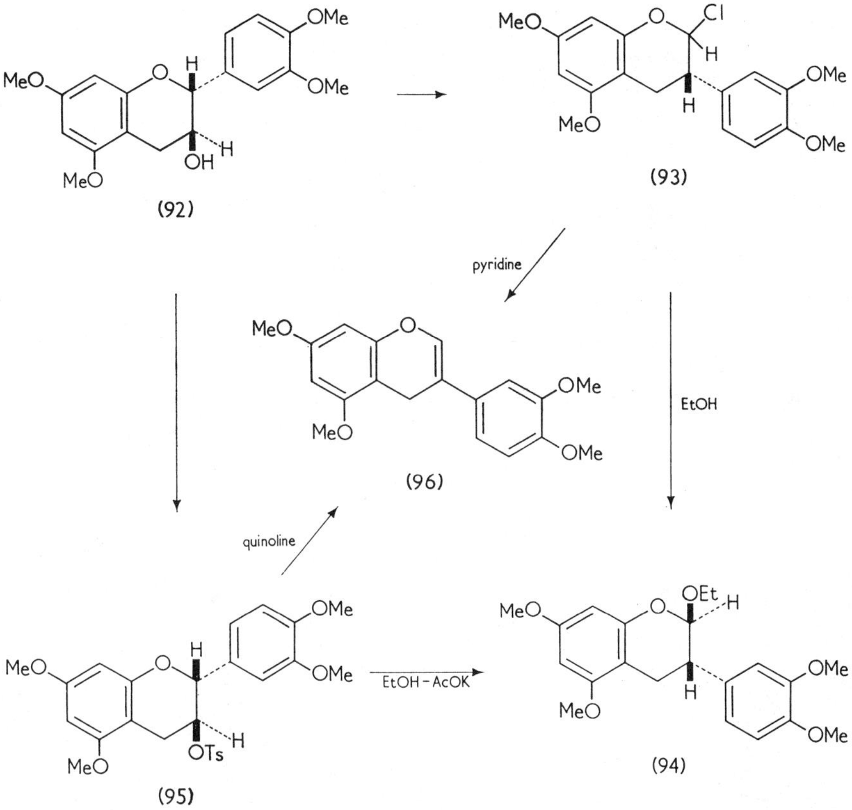

Heating the 2-chloroisoflavan (**93**) with pyridine gives the isoflavene (**96**) which was also obtained by heating the toluene-*p*-sulfonate (**95**) in boiling quinoline.[90] (−)-Epicatechin tetramethyl ether (**97**) is the *cis* analog of (+)-catechin tetramethyl ether and does not undergo these rearrangements; but its 3-toluene-*p*-sulfonate when heated with anhydrous hydrazine undergoes a smooth elimination reaction to give the flav-2-ene (**98**). This reaction has the characteristics of an E2 elimination and is compatible with the *trans* elimination of coplanar diaxial groups from the *cis* compound, epicatechin.[88] Molecular rearrangement of (+)-catechin tetramethyl ether with phosphorus pentachloride probably proceeds by a concerted process in which heterolysis of the C₃—O bond is accompanied by migration of the aryl group. If it be

[91] J. W. Clark-Lewis and W. Korytnyk, *J. Chem. Soc. (London)*, **1958**, 2367.

assumed that the final product (93) results from reaction of the bridged carbonium ion with a chloride ion (or its equivalent) the chloro compound will
possess the configuration opposite to that of the 2-aryl group before migration, and the reaction will have proceeded with double inversion. A similar
double inversion was postulated[91] for the rearrangement of the 3-toluene-*p*-
sulfonate of (+)-catechin tetramethyl ether to 2-ethoxy-5,7,3',4'-tetra-
methoxyisoflavan (94), and if these rearrangements are correctly formulated
it follows that conversion of the 2-chloroisoflavan (93) into the ethoxy compound (94) proceeds with retention of configuration at the 2 position.

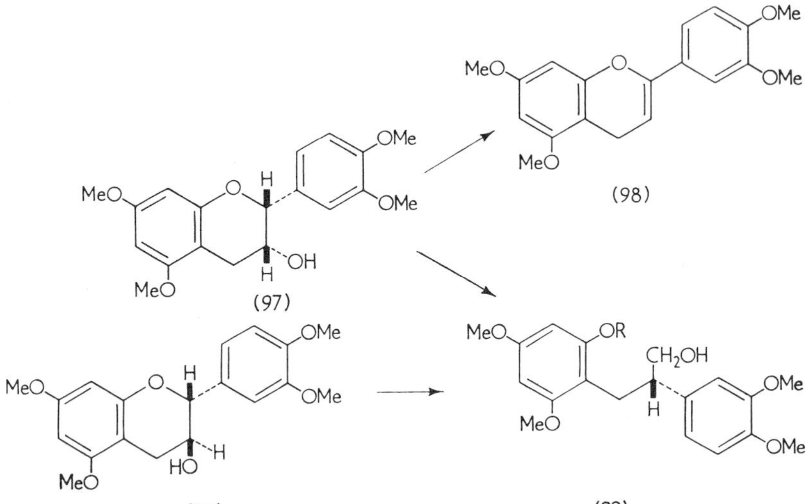

In view of the preceding examples it was surprising to find that both (+)-
catechin (92) and (−)-epicatechin tetramethyl ether (97) suffered molecular
rearrangement when reduced with a mixture of lithium aluminum hydride
and aluminum chloride in boiling tetrahydrofuran. The phenolic product
(99; R = H) was converted into the methyl ether (99; R = Me) and this was at
first thought [92] to be the isomeric 1,3-diarylpropan-2-ol which had previously
been obtained by reduction of the diastereoisomers (92 and 97) with sodium
and liquid ammonia.[93] However, (+)-catechin and (−)-epicatechin differ in
the configuration of the 3-hydroxyl group and, as they both gave the same
levorotatory propanol in the metal hydride reduction, it was clear that the
product was not the 1,3-diarylpropan-2-ol. This was confirmed by comparison

[92] B. R. Brown and G. A. Somerfield, *Proc. Chem. Soc.* (*London*), 1958, 236.

[93] A. J. Birch, J. W. Clark-Lewis, and A. V. Robertson, *J. Chem. Soc.* (*London*), 1957,
3586.

of the infrared spectra, and it was shown by synthesis of the racemate that the alcohol is the 2,3-diarylpropan-1-ol (**99**, R=Me, or enantiomorph)[94] formed by 1,2 rearrangement. This is not unusual with catechin compounds, but had not previously been encountered in the epicatechin series. It was thought at first that rearrangement of the (+)-catechin compound would occur by aryl-group migration as in the rearrangements already discussed, which would lead to the 2S-propanol (**99**; R=Me).[94,95] Further work, however, established that the levorotatory propan-1-ol formed from (+)-catechin and (−)-epicatechin tetramethyl ethers has the 2R-configuration.[96] This precludes interpretation by aryl-group migration and indicates that rearrangement occurs instead by migration of the benzyl group, as shown for (+)-catechin tetramethyl ether (**100**), and reduction of the resulting aldehyde would

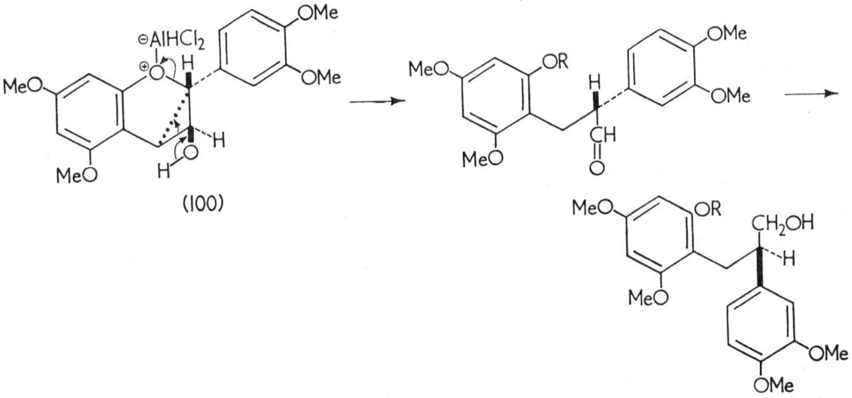

(100)

then give the 2R-propan-1-ol.[96] The configuration of the propanol is thus determined by the configuration of the 2-aryl group and, as this is the same in (+)-catechin and (−)-epicatechin, the diastereoisomers give the same propan-1-ol.

B. 1,2 Rearrangements of Indole Derivatives

Another type of acid-catalyzed 1,2 rearrangement is exemplified by the smooth conversion of 11b-methyl-5,6-dihydro-11b-benzo[c]carbazole (**101**) into 6-methyl-5,6-dihydro-6a-benzo[a]carbazole (**102**) when heated with polyphosphoric acid.[97]

[94] J. W. Clark-Lewis, *Proc. Chem. Soc.* (*London*), **1959**, 388.

[95] R. S. Cahn, C. K. Ingold, and V. Prelog, *Experientia*, **12**, 81 (1956).

[96] J. W. Clark-Lewis and G. C. Ramsay, *Proc. Chem. Soc.* (*London*), **1960**, 359.

[97] M. Nakazaki, Y. Yamamoto, and K. Yamagami, *Bull. Chem. Soc. Japan*, **33**, 466 (1960); see also S. Isoe and M. Nakazaki, *Chem. & Ind.* (*London*), **1959**, 1574.

In the same way, 2'-phenylcyclopentane-1-spiro-3'-indole has been converted into 11-phenyltetrahydrocarbazolenine.

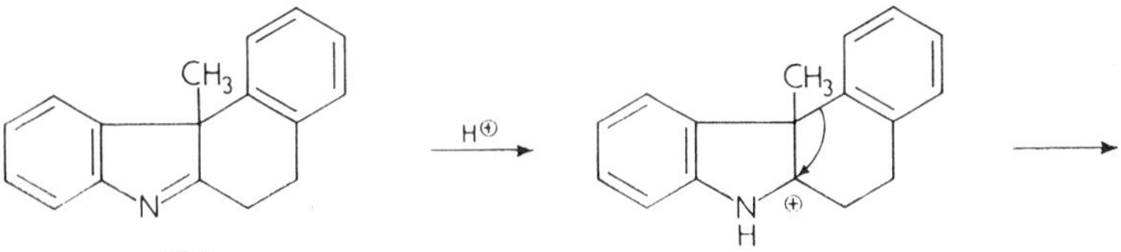

(101)

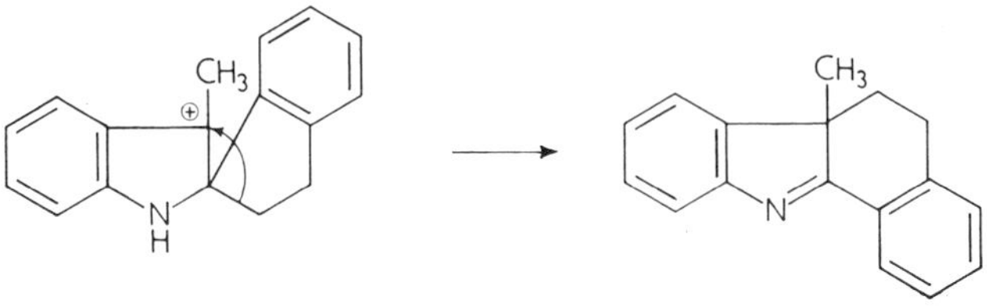

(102)

Rearrangement with ring enlargement also occurs when leucoisoindigo
(**103**) is boiled with 4N-hydrochloric acid, which leads to the quinolino-
quinoline (**104**).[98]

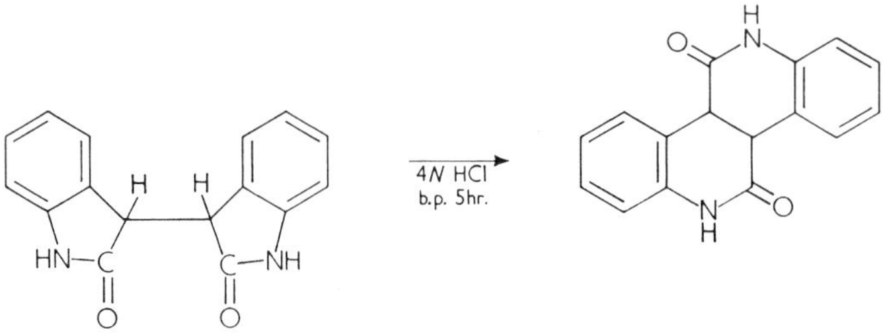

(103)   (104)

C. 1,2 Rearrangements During Clemmensen Reductions

Wolff-Kishner reduction of 1-oxoquinolizidine (**106**) yields the expected
product (**105**), but reduction by the Clemmensen method[99] gives an isomeric
compound,[100] which has been identified as 1-azabicyclo[5.3.0]decane (**107**).[101]

[98] R. B. Woodward, N. C. Yang, T. J. Katz, V. M. Clark, J. Harley-Mason, R. F.
Ingleby, and N. Sheppard, *Proc. Chem. Soc. (London)*, **1960**, 76.

[99] E. L. Martin, *Organic Reactions*, Wiley, New York, 1942, Vol. I, p. 155; J. H. Brewster, *J. Am. Chem. Soc.*, **76**, 6364 (1954).

[100] G. R. Clemo and G. R. Ramage, *J. Chem. Soc. (London)*, **1931**, 437; G. R. Clemo,
T. P. Metcalfe, and R. Raper, *J. Chem. Soc. (London)*, **1936**, 1429.

[101] V. Prelog and R. Seiwerth, *Ber.*, **72**, 1638 (1939).

The rearrangement proceeds by contraction of the ketone ring, for although 8-methyl-1-oxoquinolizidine and 2-methyl-1-oxoquinolizidine both gave

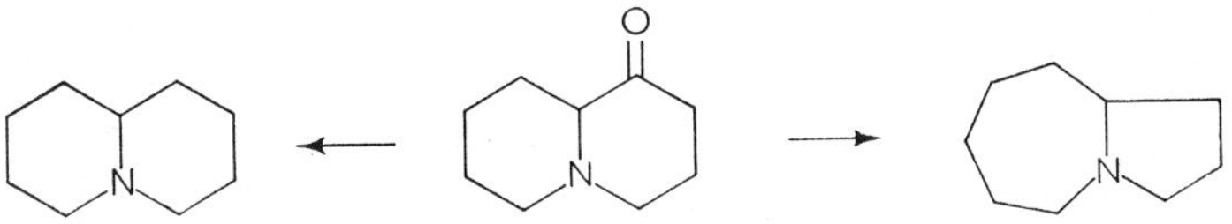

(105)   (106)   (107)

2-methylquinolizidine when reduced by the Wolff-Kishner method, Clemmensen reduction gave two different products (**108** and **109**).[102]

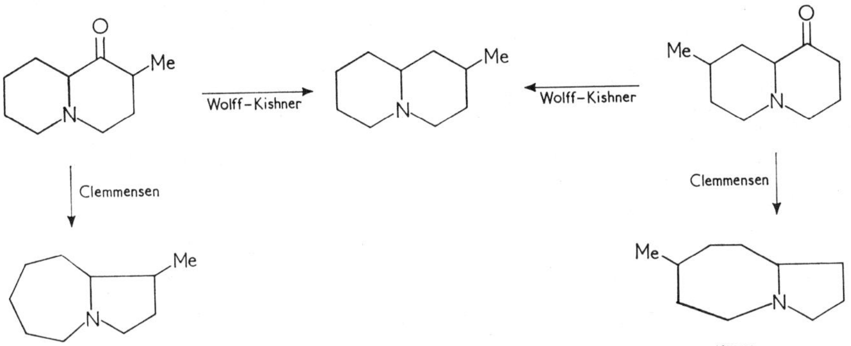

(108)   (109)

Many other α-amino-ketones have been shown to undergo similar rearrangements under the conditions of the Clemmensen reduction, and 6-oxo-1-azabicyclo[5.3.0]decane (**110**) is thus converted into quinolizidine (**105**).[103] 1-Methyl-2-ethyl-1-azacycloheptan-3-one (**111**) undergoes reduction and ring contraction to 1-methyl-2-*n*-propylpiperidine (**112**),[104] and many substituted

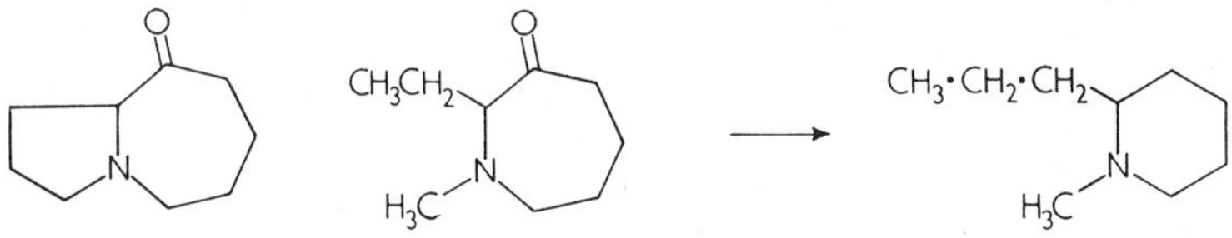

(110)   (111)   (112)

3-piperidones have been shown to yield the corresponding pyrrolidines by similar ring contraction and reduction.[105] 1,2,2-Trimethyl-3-piperidone (**113**),

[102] N. J. Leonard and W. C. Wildman, *J. Am. Chem. Soc.*, **71**, 3089 (1949).

[103] N. J. Leonard and W. C. Wildman, *J. Am. Chem. Soc.*, **71**, 3100 (1949).

[104] N. J. Leonard and E. Barthel, *J. Am. Chem. Soc.*, **71**, 3098 (1949).

[105] N. J. Leonard and W. V. Ruyle, *J. Am. Chem. Soc.*, **71**, 3094 (1949); N. J. Leonard and E. Barthel, *J. Am. Chem. Soc.*, **72**, 3632 (1950); N. J. Leonard, G. Fuller and H. L. Dryden, *J. Am. Chem. Soc.*, **75**, 3727 (1953).

for example, gives 1-methyl-2-isopropylpyrrolidine (**114**). It is also of interest that Clemmensen reduction of 3-oxoquinolizidine (**115**) gave two racemates of

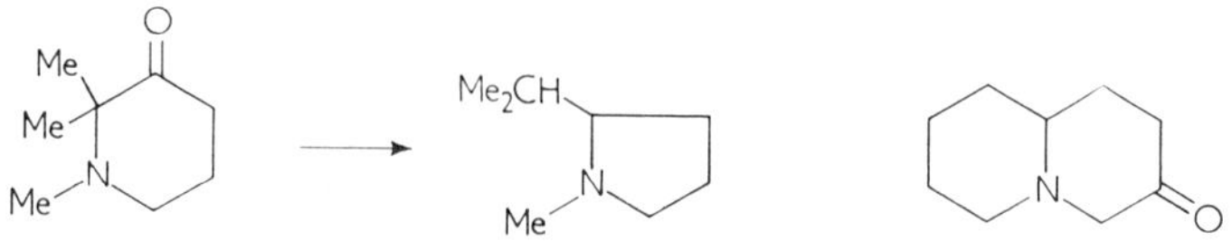

(113)   (114)   (115)

3-methyloctahydropyrrocoline (**116**),[106] and reduction of 3-oxo-1-azabicyclo-[5.4.0]hendecane (**117**) gave 4-methylquinolizidine (**118**).[107]

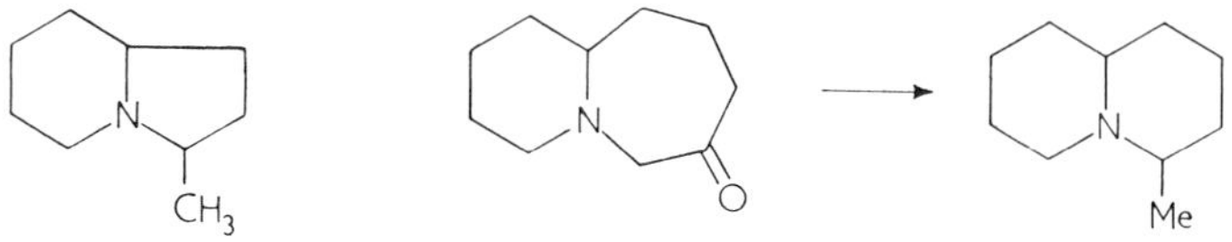

(116)   (117)   (118)

A clue to the mechanism of this rearrangement reaction was provided by Clemmensen reduction of 1-methyl-2-acetylpiperidine (**119**) which gave 7-methylaminoheptan-2-one (**120**) and N-methylheptylamine (**121**).[108] Isola-

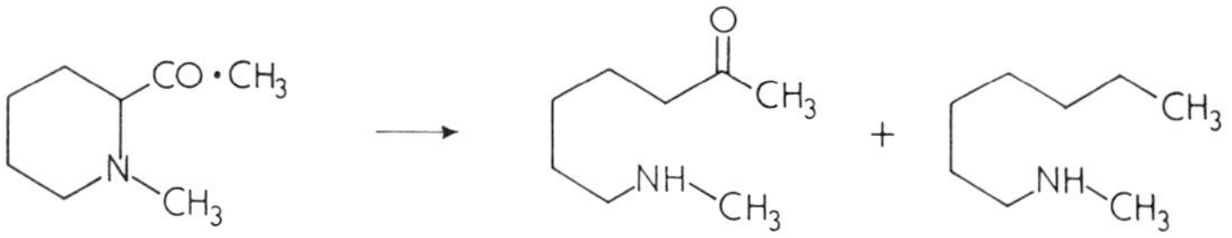

(119)   (120)   (121)

tion of 7-methylaminoheptan-2-one suggests that the N—C bond in these α-aminoketones undergoes preferential hydrogenolysis. Normal reduction of this ketone would then give the observed N-methylheptylamine. In certain circumstances (formation of 5- or 6-membered rings), however, intramolecular elimination of water could occur, and a feasible mechanism for the reductive rearrangement of 1-oxoquinolizidine (**122**) can be formulated as shown.[108]

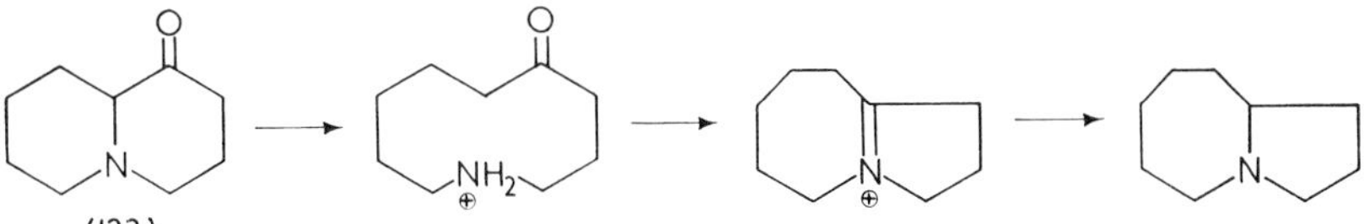

(122)

[106] N. J. Leonard and S. H. Pines, *J. Am. Chem. Soc.*, **72**, 4931 (1950).
[107] N. J. Leonard and E. D. Nicolaides, *J. Am. Chem. Soc.*, **73**. 5210 (1951).
[108] G. R. Clemo, R. Raper, and H. J. Vipond, *J. Chem. Soc. (London)*, **1949**, 2095.

The reduction and rearrangement of 2-acetyl-1-methylpyrrolidine (**123**) to 1,2-dimethylpiperidine can be similarly explained by assuming C—N hydrogenolysis to 6-methylaminohexan-2-one, cyclization by elimination of water, and reduction.[108] The intermediate 6-methylaminohexan-2-one (**124**) is known to cyclize spontaneously to 1,2-dimethyl-1,4,5,6-tetrahydropyridine (**125**) which, in turn, is known to undergo ready reduction (with tin and hydrochloric acid) to 1,2-dimethylpiperidine.

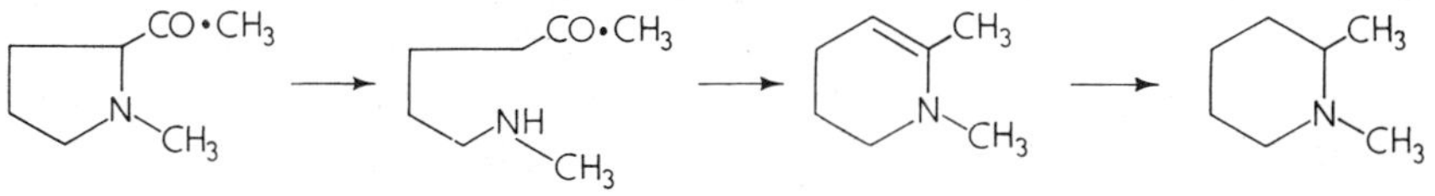

(123)   (124)   (125)

Further evidence that scission of the C—N bond is the initial step during Clemmensen reduction of α-aminoketones was provided by a study of optically active 1,2-dimethyl-2-ethyl-3-piperidone. The 1-methyl-2-*sec*butylpyrrolidine (**126**) produced was devoid of optical activity, as expected on the above

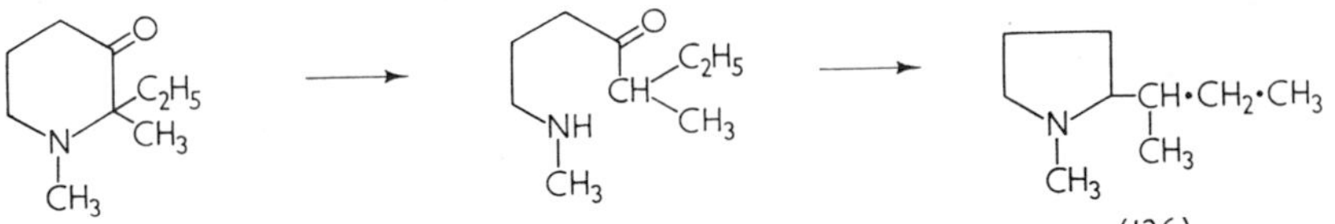

(126)

mechanism through racemization of the intermediate ketone.[109] The preferential scission of the C_α—N bond in α-aminoketones is evidently due to the ability of the nitrogen atom to accept the electrons of the C—N bond, and this ability will be increased by protonation of the nitrogen atom. Coordination to the metal used in the Clemmensen reduction would have a similar electronic effect and 2-thiaketones might thus be expected to react similarly. It is therefore of some interest that 4-oxoisothiachroman (**127**) has been shown to undergo reduction and rearrangement under Clemmensen conditions to 1-methyl-1,3-dihydroisothianaphthene (**128**).[110]

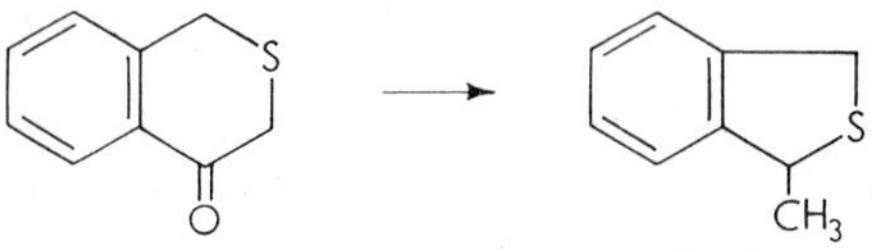

(127)   (128)

[109] N. J. Leonard, R. C. Sentz, and W. J. Middleton, *J. Am. Chem. Soc.*, **75**, 1674 (1953).
[110] J. von Braun and K. Weissbach, *Ber.*, **62**, 2416 (1929).

5. REARRANGEMENTS INVOLVING RING FISSION AND RECYCLIZATION

A. The Wessely-Moser Rearrangement

Flavones and flavanones possessing a 5-hydroxyl group are prone to rearrangement through fission of the heterocyclic ring and ring closure in the alternative direction, i.e., to the 5-hydroxyl group of the starting material. Most of the changes studied have concerned ring A, but rearrangement can involve ring B (the 2-aryl group) if this contains a 2'-hydroxyl, as in the conversion of 2',5'-dimethoxyflavone (131) into 6,2'-dihydroxyflavone (132).

The rearrangement is usually known as the Wessely-Moser rearrangement, as it was described by them in the preparation of scutellarein (130) from the flavone (129).[111] The reaction has been comprehensively reviewed by

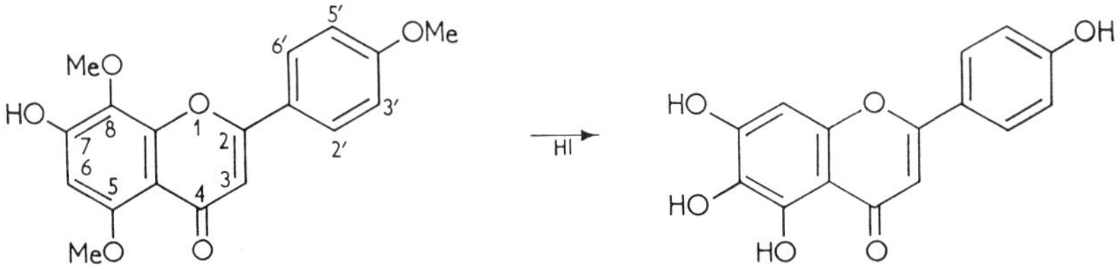

(129)　　　　(130)

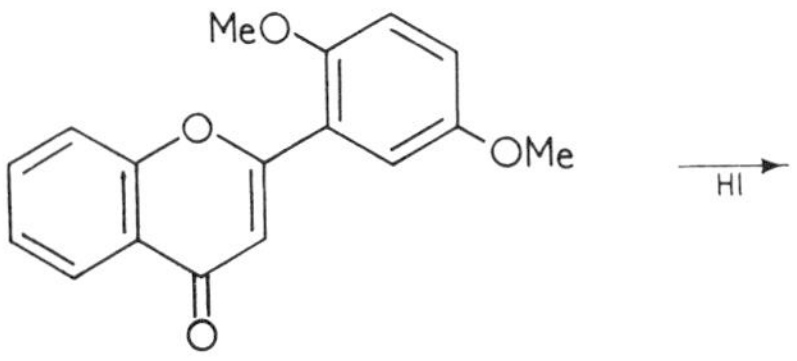

(131)

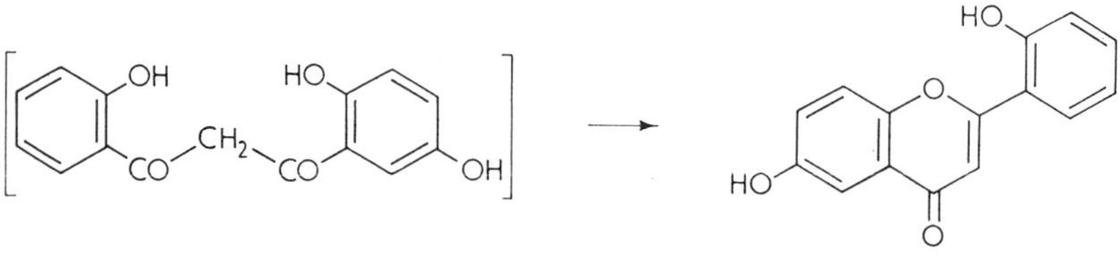

(132)

Wheeler,[112] and also by others.[113] The rearrangement is characteristic of flavones, and 5,7,8-substituted compounds yield 5,6,7 derivatives and 5,8-

[111] F. Wessely and G. H. Moser, *Monatsh.*, **56**, 97 (1930).

[112] T. S. Wheeler, *Record Chem. Progr.* (*Kresge-Hooker Sci. Lib.*), **18**, 133 (1957).

[113] S. K. Mukerjee and T. R. Seshadri, *Chem. & Ind.* (*London*), **1955**, 271; T. R. Seshadri, *Tetrahedron*, **6**, 169 (1959).

disubstituted compounds yield the 5,6 isomers in the rearrangement, which occurs under the conditions usually employed for demethylating ethers in this series. Flavonols are less prone to rearrangement but may undergo the transformation under more vigorous conditions, and 5,8 dimethoxyflavonol (**133**) gave 5,6-dihydroxy-flavonol (**134**) when heated in a sealed tube with hydrogen iodide at 180–190°.

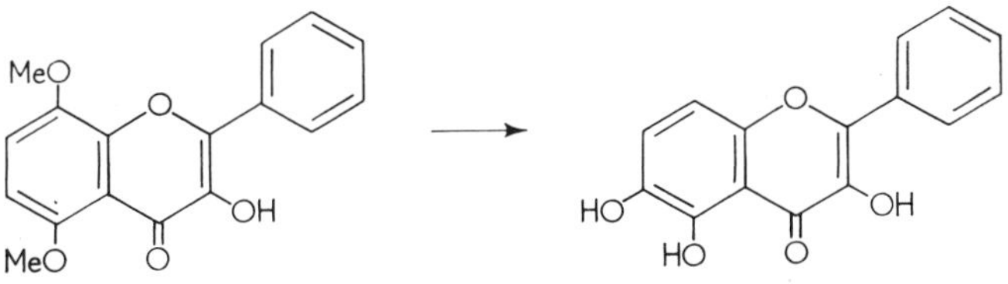

(133)   (134)

Although the Wessely-Moser rearrangement is particularly well known with flavones, it has also been observed with chromones, isoflavones, flavonols, xanthones, flavylium salts, and furanochromones.[112]

The dihydroflavones (flavanones) (**135**) are usually considered to be tautomeric with the chalcones (**136**), and alkaline conditions disturb the equilibrium

(135)   (136)

in favor of the chalcones. If the flavanone contains a 5-hydroxyl group, ring closure may yield a different flavanone, and isomerization under mildly acidic and mildly basic conditions has been observed. The relative stability of the two possible structures is not necessarily the same as with the flavones.[114–116] Thus, 5,8-dihydroxy-7-methoxyflavanone, 5,8-dihydroxy-7,4'-dimethoxy-flavanone, and 5,8-dihydroxyflavanone were found to be stable in aqueous alkali and acid, whereas 5-hydroxy-7,8-dimethoxy- and 5-hydroxy-8-methoxy-flavanone isomerize very easily, even under methylation conditions with acetone and potassium carbonate.[115]

B. Miscellaneous Examples of Rearrangement with Ring Fission

When fused with aluminum chloride, chromanone (**137**) is converted into 7-hydroxyindanone (**138**) in good yield, and dihydrocoumarin undergoes simi-

[114] J. Chopin, D. Molho, H. Pachéco, and C. Mentzer, *Compt. rend.*, **243**, 712 (1956).
[115] H. G. Krishnamurty and T. R. Seshadri, *J. Sci. Ind. Research (India)*, **18B**, 151 (1959).
[116] J. Chopin and M. Chadenson, *Bull. soc. chim. France*, **1959**, 1585.

lar rearrangement to 4-hydroxyindanone.[117] An analogous ring fission occurs with 2,3-dihydro-4-methyl-3-oxobenz-1,4-oxazine which gives 7-hydroxy-1-methyloxindole.[118] These rearrangements can be rationalized if it is assumed

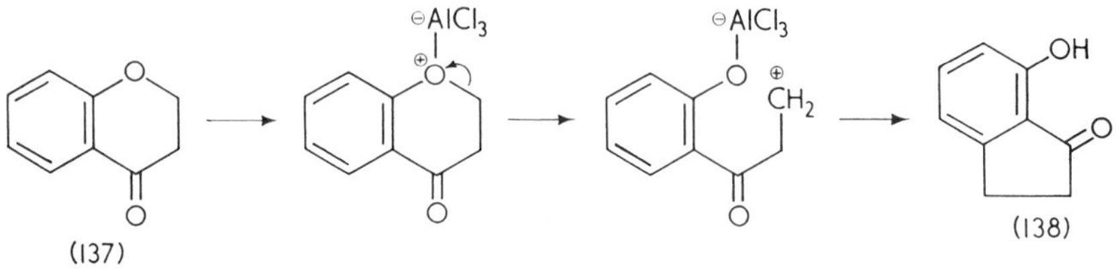

(137)   (138)

that the initial step involves coordination of the aluminum chloride to the hetero-oxygen atom, followed by ring fission and cyclization.

An interesting rearrangement accompanied by considerable change in ultraviolet light absorption was observed during the investigations of the actinomycins (**139**, R·CO = peptide side chain). Hydrolysis with aqueous barium hydroxide removes the peptide side chains and gives actinomycinol (**140**) by rearrangement which apparently takes place in stages tentatively formulated by Johnson in the following way.[119]

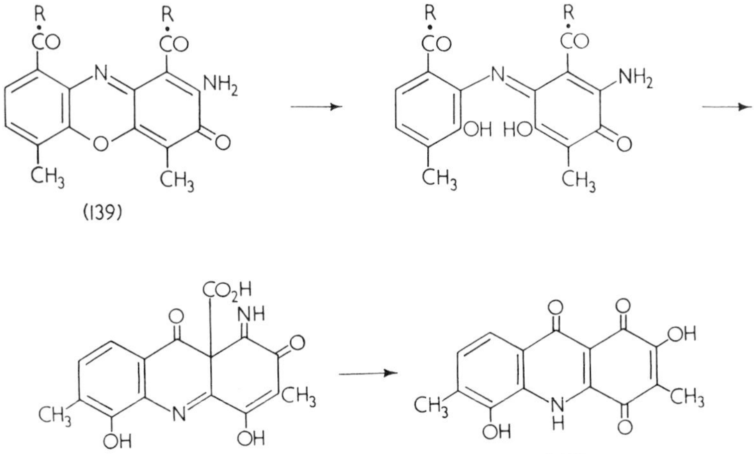

(139)

(140)

[117] J. D. Loudon and R. K. Razdan, *J. Chem. Soc. (London)*, **1954**, 4299.

[118] J. W. Cook, J. D. Loudon, and P. McCloskey, *J. Chem. Soc. (London)*, **1952**, 3904.

[119] A. W. Johnson, *Symposium on Antibiotics and Mould Metabolites*, Chem. Soc. (London) Special Publication No. 5, 1956, 94; cf. W. G. Hanger, W. C. Howell, and A. W. Johnson, *J. Chem. Soc. (London)*, **1958**, 496.

11

REARRANGEMENTS PROCEEDING THROUGH "NO MECHANISM" PATHWAYS: THE CLAISEN, COPE, AND RELATED REARRANGEMENTS[1]

SARA JANE RHOADS

University of Wyoming, Laramie, Wyoming

I. INTRODUCTION

The application of the various mechanistic criteria now at the disposal of the organic chemist has enjoyed considerable success in establishing and describing, with some degree of precision, two major and distinct classes of organic reaction mechanisms, the "ionic" and the "radical" processes. The characteristics of reactions in each of these classes are well known, and the

[1] The writer is indebted to her many colleagues who graciously furnished material for this chapter in advance of publication and who, by their suggestions and constructive criticism, are responsible in large measure for whatever merit the manuscript possesses. Special thanks go to Prof. Rebecca Raulins for invaluable assistance in the preparation of the chapter and to Prof. William von E. Doering for his unflagging interest in the writing and for the benefit of his incisive analysis of many questions which arose in the course of the work.

methods of detecting charged or polar intermediates in the first case and reactive particles with unpaired electrons in the second need no review here,[cf. 1a,1b] and are covered elsewhere in this volume.

There is, however, a third class of organic reactions, long recognized but little discussed, which has thus far eluded the chemist's efforts at precise description. Reactions which fall into this category are "neither fish nor fowl" in the sense that they cannot be shown to involve either heterolytic or homolytic bonding processes by the usual diagnostic tests, although they may, in certain instances, show trends reminiscent of polar or nonpolar reactions. In general, they are relatively insensitive to external catalytic influence (including solvent) and often are insensitive to internal structural variation, the very effects which are the most telling criteria for radical and ion processes. In short, these reactions of the "twilight zone" exhibit a degree of self-sufficiency which makes them independent of their extramolecular environment and, because of this, difficultly accessible to mechanistic study.

Formal recognition of this category of reaction type has been made in recent times, and some of the problems inherent in the study of such systems have been pointed out.[1b,2-6] The reactions have been variously designated as "four-centered" reactions,[1b] "cyclic" or "circular" processes,[2,4] "molecular" reactions,[1a,5] and "no mechanism" reactions.[7] Regardless of the name one prefers to give to this type of reaction,[8] the central problem is one of describing a transition state (or, perhaps, several transition states with intervening intermediates) which is achieved solely through the electronic resources of the molecular system or molecular aggregate itself. A precise description of such systems is difficult, if not impossible, with methods presently at hand.

[1a] P. D. Bartlett in H. Gilman, ed., *Organic Chemistry, An Advanced Treatise*, Vol. III, Wiley, New York, 1953, p. 1.

[1b] J. Hine, *Physical Organic Chemistry*, McGraw-Hill, New York, 1956, p. 86.

[2] C. K. Ingold, *Structure and Mechanism in Organic Chemistry*, Cornell University Press, Ithaca, N. Y., 1953, pp. 598, 619, 718.

[3] J. E. Leffler, *The Reactive Intermediates of Organic Chemistry*, Interscience, New York, 1956, p. 234.

[4] J. Mathieu and J. Valls, *Bull. soc. chim. France*, **1957**, 1509.

[5] Ya. K. Syrkin, *Bull. acad. sci., U.S.S.R., Div. Chem. Sci. S.S.R. (English translation)*, **1959**, 238.

[6] R. B. Woodward and T. J. Katz, *Tetrahedron*, **5**, 70 (1959).

[7] A term originated by Prof. W. von E. Doering as "a humorous way of calling attention to the serious predicament organic chemists are in when the classical criteria of mechanism aren't fulfilled."

[8] The term "no mechanism" reaction will be used in this chapter since it seems to convey the distinctive character of these reactions. It hardly need be pointed out that the term is not to be taken literally since any reaction has a mechanism in the sense that there is at least one transition state to be considered. The term "no mechanism" reaction simply reflects a serious limitation of the experimental approach to mechanism study.

Although this problem will be illustrated in the rearrangements to be discussed, it is not irrelevant at this time to point to the corresponding difficulty with the Diels-Alder reaction, a bimolecular process of the "no mechanism" variety. A detailed mechanistic description of this reaction has challenged the efforts of many eminent chemists since the gross details of structure and stereochemistry were elucidated by the German workers some twenty years ago, and still, today, there is no unanimity of opinion.[9-12]

The relative inaccessibility of "no mechanism" or "molecular" reactions to mechanistic study can further be illustrated by considering two contrasting examples from the field of gas phase kinetics, namely, the hydrogen-iodine reaction and the hydrogen-chlorine reaction. The hydrogen-iodine reaction (as well as the reverse hydrogen iodide decomposition) is an elementary bimolecular process proceeding homogeneously in the gas phase by a "molecular" process which involves simply the interaction of hydrogen and iodine molecules welded into a "four-centered" activated complex usually represented as $\begin{smallmatrix} H\cdots H \\ \vdots \quad \vdots \\ I\cdots I \end{smallmatrix}$. It is noteworthy that this reaction has received very little experimental attention, except of a confirmatory nature, since its kinetic study was first reported by Bodenstein at the turn of the century. On the other hand, the large volume of investigative work reported for the hydrogen-chlorine reaction must be attributed to the fact that this reaction is a complex, radical-chain process, consisting of a number of elementary steps and, as such, is very responsive to environmental variation.[13]

Although the definition of a "no mechanism" reaction is a rather nebulous matter, reflecting the lack of precision in the description of the transition state, the characteristics whereby the reactions of this category may be recognized are fairly clear cut. The reactions are thermally induced, show no response to free radical initiators or inhibitors, and are relatively insensitive to acid-base catalysis, structural changes, and solvation effects. The electron

[9] For a historical review of the principal ideas concerning the mechanism of the Diels-Alder reaction as well as the postulation of a new theory, see Woodward and Katz.[6]

[10] M. J. S. Dewar, *Tetrahedron Letters*, No. **4**, 16 (1959).

[11] M. G. Ettlinger and E. S. Lewis, 138th Meeting, ACS, New York, September, 1960, *Abstracts*, p. 95P.

[12] J. A. Berson, A. Remanick, and W. A. Mueller, *J. Am. Chem. Soc.*, **82**, 5501 (1960); J. A. Berson and A. Remanick, *J. Am. Chem. Soc.*, **83**, 4947 (1961); and J. A. Berson and W. A. Mueller, *J. Am. Chem. Soc.*, **83**, 4940 (1961).

[13] The reader is referred to K. J. Laidler, *Chemical Kinetics*, McGraw-Hill, New York, 1950, pp. 90 ff., 208 ff., for discussion and references. The difference in these two reaction processes, of course, has been accounted for in terms of the energetics of the "molecular" versus "atomic" pathways available to the two halogens. The point emphasized here is that the "molecular" process, involving a single activated complex of self-contained electronic nature, is simply not vulnerable to external diversion.

reorganizations which constitute the bond-making and -breaking processes must be closely synchronized so that such processes are spoken of as "concerted, or nearly concerted," "cyclic" reactions. In the special cases of rearrangements proceeding through this pathway, the reactions invariably are unimolecular and intramolecular and exhibit definite stereochemical characteristics.

The scope of the "no mechanism" category of reactions is a very broad one, bordering on homolytic dissociation processes at one extreme and "tight ion pair" processes at the other. Clearly, the position of a given reaction within this mechanistic spectrum will be conditioned by the special structural features of the molecular system.

A pertinent example of the first extreme is the thermal *cis-trans* isomerization of 1,2-dideuterocyclopropane reported by Rabinovitch, Schlag, and Wiberg.[14] Their findings are accommodated by a process of ring rupture and reversible recyclization, $trans\text{-}\nabla\text{-}d_2 \rightleftharpoons C\text{—}C\text{—}C \rightleftharpoons cis\text{-}\nabla\text{-}d_2$, in which the activated complex is conceived as an expanded ring model with highly hindered internal rotation. The much higher rate of intramolecular recyclization of trimethylene over that of ring rupture of cyclopropane renders the diradical undetectable by intermolecular collision processes. Closely related to this reaction are the thermal isomerizations of cyclopropane and methylcyclopropane to propylene [14,15] and a mixture of butenes,[16] respectively, and the decomposition of cyclobutane to ethylene.[17] A suggestion that the Diels-Alder reaction may involve a "diradical" transition state has been made by Walling.[18]

The "quasi-heterolytic" gas phase reactions discussed by Maccoll [19] may be taken as representative of the other extreme of the "no mechanism" category. The thermal eliminations from alkyl halides and, to a lesser extent, from esters to form olefins show rather pronounced response to structural variation near the reaction site, behavior which is interpreted to mean that the transition state has a high degree of polar character. Such reactions have

[14] B. S. Rabinovitch, E. W. Schlag, and K. B. Wiberg, *J. Chem. Phys.*, **28**, 504 (1958); E. W. Schlag and B. S. Rabinovitch, *J. Am. Chem. Soc.*, **82**, 5966 (1960). See also F. T. Smith, *J. Chem. Phys.*, **29**, 235 (1959).

[15] H. O. Pritchard, R. G. Sowden, and A. F. Trotman-Dickenson, *Proc. Roy. Soc. (London)*, **A217**, 563 (1953).

[16] J. P. Chesick, *J. Am. Chem. Soc.*, **82**, 3277 (1960).

[17] C. T. Genaux, F. Kern, and W. D. Walters, *J. Am. Chem. Soc.*, **75**, 6196 (1953).

[18] C. Walling, *Free Radicals in Solution*, Wiley, New York, 1957, p. 184.

[19] A. Maccoll in *Theoretical Organic Chemistry, Proceedings and Discussions of the Kekulé Symposium, London, 1958*, Butterworth Scientific Publications, London, 1959, p. 230. However, cf. C. H. DePuy and R. W. King, *Chem. Revs.*, **60**, 431 (1960), and C. H. DePuy, C. A. Bishop, and C. N. Goeders, *J. Am. Chem. Soc.*, **83**, 2151 (1961).

been spoken of as "gas phase ion pair" processes.[20] Another borderline case is encountered in the uncatalyzed isomeric rearrangement of allylic esters which has been interpreted both as a synchronized process involving concerted electron reorganization [21] and as a "tight ion pair" process.[22]

In the following pages a somewhat arbitrary selection of such reactions has been made. In the main, those rearrangements to be discussed will involve six atomic centers and may be generalized as diallylic systems (**A**) which rearrange to isomeric diallylic systems (**C**) through a closed, activated complex (**B**). In

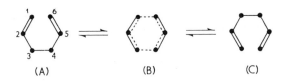

A, B, and C the six atomic centers may be varied somewhat. Thus, when an all-carbon system is involved, the rearrangement is the familiar Cope rearrangement; when atom 3 is oxygen and atoms 1 and 2 are part of an aromatic system, the first step of the Claisen rearrangements is depicted. Other variations in the six atomic centers will be pointed out as they arise. It will be noted that the process involves a simple electron reorganization with accompanying small bond angle and distance adjustments so that **A** and **C** are related to each other as valence tautomers.

While the diallylic systems represent the most thoroughly studied and clearly recognized examples of "no mechanism" rearrangements, it should be pointed out that rearrangements of this sort need not involve six atomic centers. A number of rearrangements involving four centers are known which appear to belong in this category. Among these may be mentioned the thermal conversion of vinylcyclopropane to cyclopentene,[23] the corresponding interconversion of cyclopropanecarboxaldehyde and dihydrofuran [24] and the heat-induced rearrangement of cyclobutene derivatives to butadiene derivatives.[25] Less frequently, processes involving eight atomic centers have been

---

[20] E. S. Gould, *Mechanism and Structure in Organic Chemistry*, Holt, New York, 1959, p. 504.

[21] E. A. Braude, D. W. Turner, and E. S. Waight, *Nature*, **173**, 863 (1954); E. A. Braude and D. W. Turner, *Chem. & Ind. (London)*, **1955**, 1223.

[22] H. L. Goering and M. M. Pombo, *J. Am. Chem. Soc.*, **82**, 2515 (1960); S. Winstein and G. C. Robinson, *J. Am. Chem. Soc.*, **80**, 169 (1958).

[23] C. G. Overberger and A. E. Borchert, *J. Am. Chem. Soc.*, **82**, 4896 (1960); M. C. Flowers and H. M. Frey, *J. Chem. Soc. (London)*, **1961**, 3547.

[24] C. L. Wilson, *J. Am. Chem. Soc.*, **69**, 3002 (1947).

[25] E. Vogel, *Ann.*, **615**, 14 (1958). See also E. Vogel, *Angew. Chem.*, **72**, 4 (1960), for other examples.

postulated.[26-28] At least one of these, the previtamin D_2–vitamin D_2 equilibration, has been studied sufficiently to establish that the process does indeed meet the requirements of a "no mechanism" reaction. This rearrangement is considered in some detail in Part 5.

2. THE CLAISEN REARRANGEMENTS

A. Structural Features

In his pioneering work in this area of thermal rearrangements, Claisen elucidated the structural requirements for the group of rearrangements which bears his name. First detected in the O-allyl derivative of acetoacetic ester,[29] the rearrangement was extended to allylic ethers of phenols.[30,31] Formally, the structural requirement is a "diallylic" system of a vinyl (or phenyl) allyl ether (1) which rearranges to the isomeric γ,δ-unsaturated carbonyl system (2). In principle, this fundamental process may be followed by other rearrangements and a final enolization step according to the demands of the system involved.

(1)   (2)

The term "Claisen rearrangement" as it is generally used today implies the above process (including the enolization step) in allylic aryl ethers.[31a] Two over-all conversions are recognized: the ortho rearrangement in which the migrating group remains attached to the carbon ortho to the oxygen (eq. 1a) and the para rearrangement, best observed when both ortho positions are blocked, in which the allylic group migrates to the para position (eq. 1b).

Of special significance are the structural features in the migrating allylic

[26] K. Schmid, P. Fahrni, and H. Schmid, *Helv. Chim. Acta*, **39**, 708 (1956).

[27] K. B. Wiberg, T. M. Shryne, and R. R. Kintner, *J. Am. Chem. Soc.*, **79**, 3160 (1957).

[28] A. Verloop, A. L. Koevoet, and E. Havinga, *Rec. trav. chim.*, **76**, 689 (1957).

[29] L. Claisen, *Ber.*, **45**, 3157 (1912).

[30] L. Claisen and O. Eisleb, *Ann.*, **401**, 21 (1913).

[31] See D. S. Tarbell in *Organic Reactions*, Vol. II, Wiley, New York, 1944, p. 1, for a survey of early investigations of the Claisen rearrangements.

[31a] Although they are not included in the present discussion, the corresponding rearrangements of sulfur and nitrogen analogs deserve recognition. Tarbell[31] has summarized the information available for the rearrangements of allyl aryl sulfides, while the recently announced ortho rearrangement of N-allyl-1-naphthylamine[31b] represents the first successful Claisen rearrangement of N-substituted aryl amines.

[31b] S. Marcinkiewicz, J. Green, and P. Mamalis, *Chem. & Ind.* (*London*), **1961**, 438; *Tetrahedron*, **14**, 208 (1961).

system. It is now well established that in the ortho rearrangement the allylic group appears in the product with an "inverted" structure, i.e., the original

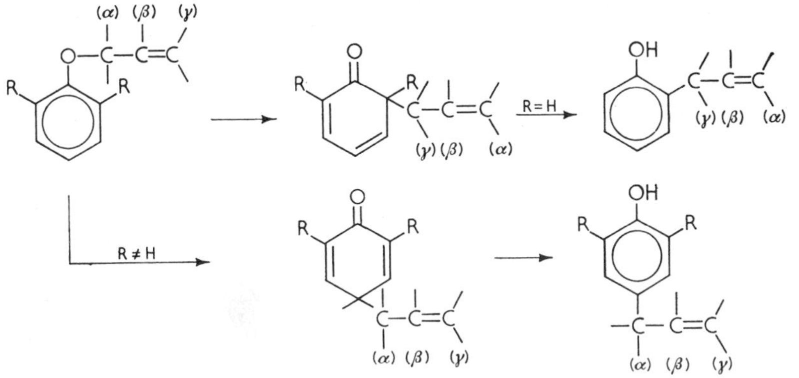

γ carbon of the ether side chain becomes attached to the ring carbon, while in the para rearrangement the reverse is true. In the latter case, the original structure of the allylic system is retained as indicated in the equation 1b above. These conclusions are based on rearrangement studies in which the allylic group was unsymmetrically marked, either by alkyl groups in the α or γ positions [31,32,33] or by the more elegant method of tagging these positions with ^{14}C.[34,35]

B. Evidence for the Cyclic Process

The gross mechanistic picture of the ortho rearrangement as a cyclic process involving simultaneous bond-breaking and -making processes, accompanied by the relocation of the double bond in the allylic system, and leading to the o-dienone as the immediate precursor of the phenolic product was specifically described by Claisen in 1925.[36] Since that time evidence has accumulated which verifies this picture in all details. The invariable inversion of the allylic structure mentioned above, the intramolecular nature of the rearrangement demonstrated by the absence of mixed products in "crossing" experiments,[35,37] the first-order kinetics and the negative entropy of

[32] (a) S. J. Rhoads, R. Raulins, and R. D. Reynolds, *J. Am. Chem. Soc.*, **75**, 2531 (1953), **76**, 3456 (1954). (b) S. J. Rhoads and R. L. Crecelius, *J. Am. Chem. Soc.*, **77**, 5183 (1955).

[33] E. N. Marvell, A. V. Logan, L. Friedman, and R. W. Ledeen, *J. Am. Chem. Soc.*, **76**, 1922 (1954).

[34] J. P. Ryan and P. R. O'Connor, *J. Am. Chem. Soc.*, **74**, 5866 (1952).

[35] (a) H. Schmid and K. Schmid, *Helv. Chim. Acta*, **35**, 1879 (1952), (b) **36**, 489 (1953).

[36] L. Claisen and E. Tietze, *Ber.*, **58**, 275 (1925).

[37] C. D. Hurd and L. Schmerling, *J. Am. Chem. Soc.*, **59**, 107 (1937).

activation,[38] all serve to support the general correctness of the concerted one-step process leading to the o-dienone.

The course of the para rearrangement, although in doubt for some time,[39] is now accepted as involving the same first step as the ortho rearrangement. In this case, since the rapid and irreversible enolization step cannot occur, the o-dienone (3) may undergo a second rearrangement of the Cope type to a p-dienone intermediate, (4), which, by enolization, gives rise to the observed

(3)   (4)

product. This process, first proposed by Hurd and Pollack,[4-] requires two inverting rearrangements and is supported by the facts that over-all retention of structure in the migrating allylic system is observed [32-34,35b] and that the reaction is strictly intramolecular [35b,41] and displays first-order kinetic behavior with rates and activation parameters which are similar to those of the ortho rearrangement.[42,43]

The past decade has witnessed a strong revival of interest in the Claisen rearrangements, and the problems posed by these systems have been attacked with vigor and ingenuity. With the gross details of structure and intramolecularity of the rearrangements now settled, recent interest has focused on the finer details of the processes. In particular, much detailed information concerning the individual steps of the para rearrangement has become available through the isolation and direct study of the o-dienone intermediate [44,45] and the kinetic analysis of the rearrangement with the help of ^{14}C tracers.[46] The stereochemistry of the cyclic process has also proved an intriguing subject since the first report [47] that the rearrangement of optically active ethers pro-

[38] J. F. Kincaid and D. S. Tarbell, J. Am. Chem. Soc., 61, 3085 (1939).

[39] For a discussion of this problem and its resolution, see Rhoads et al.[32a]

[40] C. D. Hurd and M. A. Pollack, J. Org. Chem., 3, 550 (1939).

[41] S. J. Rhoads and R. L. Crecelius, J. Am. Chem. Soc., 77, 5060 (1955).

[42] D. S. Tarbell and J. F. Kincaid, J. Am. Chem. Soc., 62, 728 (1940).

[43] S. J. Rhoads and R. L. Crecelius, J. Am. Chem. Soc., 77, 5057 (1955).

[44] H. Conroy and R. A. Firestone, J. Am. Chem. Soc., 75, 2530 (1953), 78, 2290 (1956).

[45] D. Y. Curtin and R. J. Crawford, Chem. & Ind. (London), 1956, 313; J. Am. Chem. Soc., 79, 3156 (1957).

[46] (a) F. Kalberer and H. Schmid, Helv. Chim. Acta, 40, 13, 225 (1957). (b) W. Haegele and H. Schmid, Helv. Chim. Acta., 41, 657 (1958). (c) P. Fahrni and H. Schmid, Helv. Chim. Acta, 42, 1102 (1959).

[47] E. R. Alexander and R. W. Kluiber, J. Am. Chem. Soc., 73, 4304 (1951).

ceeded with some over-all retention of activity.[48-50] Finally, efforts have been made to delineate more closely the electrical nature of the rearrangements by a systematic study of the effects of substituents on the rates of rearrangement.[51,52] Some of these more recent studies are discussed in the following sections.

C. The Dienone Intermediate

The first evidence for the existence of the o-dienone intermediate, postulated for both the ortho and the para rearrangements, was obtained by Conroy and Firestone[44] who carried out the rearrangement of allyl 2,6-dimethylphenyl ether (5) in a solution of maleic anhydride and obtained a small amount of a Diels-Alder adduct of 6-allyl-2,6-dimethylcyclohexa-2,4-dienone (6). When heated, the adduct gave rise to the rearrangement product, 2,6-dimethyl-4-allylphenol (7). This result, while suggestive, does not require

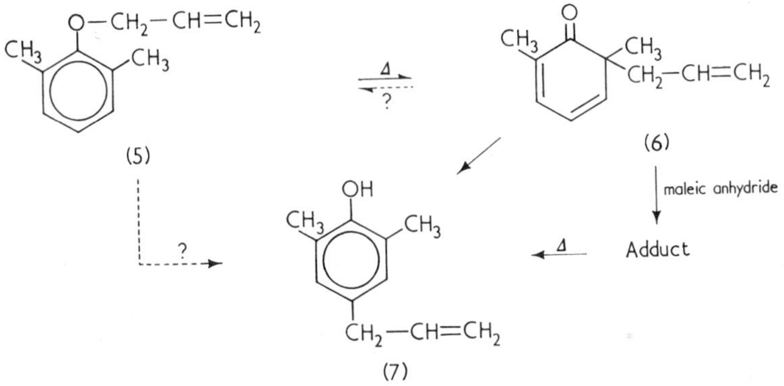

that the rearrangement pathway involve 6 since conceivably 6 could be formed reversibly from 5. Regeneration of 6 from the adduct, then, could lead to 5, which, in turn, could rearrange by some other pathway to yield 7 directly.

More compelling evidence that the 2,6,6-trisubstituted cyclohexadienone is indeed an intermediate in the para rearrangement was obtained by experiments carried out with systems which permit exchange of allylic groups at the

[48] E. N. Marvell and J. L. Stephenson, *J. Org. Chem.*, **25**, 676 (1960).

[49] A. W. Burgstahler, *J. Am. Chem. Soc.*, **82**, 4681 (1960).

[50] (a) W. N. White and B. E. Norcross, *J. Am. Chem. Soc.*, **83**, 1968 (1961). (b) W. N. White and B. E. Norcross, *J. Am. Chem. Soc.*, **83**, 3265 (1961).

[51] H. L. Goering and R. R. Jacobson, *J. Am. Chem. Soc.*, **80**, 3277 (1958).

[52] (a) W. N. White, D. Gwynn, R. Schlitt, C. Girard, and W. K. Fife, *J. Am. Chem. Soc.*, **80**, 3271 (1958). (b) W. N. White, C. D. Slater, and W. K. Fife, *J. Org. Chem.*, **26**, 627 (1961). (c) W. N. White and W. K. Fife, *J. Am. Chem. Soc.*, **83**, 3846 (1961). (d) W. N. White and C. D. Slater, *J. Org. Chem.*, **27**, 2908 (1962).

ortho carbon.[53-55] In their study of the rearrangement of two so-constituted ethers, allyl 2,6-dimethallylphenyl ether (**8**) and methallyl 2-allyl-6-methallyl-phenyl ether (**9**), Curtin and Johnson [53] not only found evidence for the intervention of the dienones **10** and **11** in the rearrangement pathways but also were able to demonstrate the reversibility of the ether–o-dienone rearrangements, i.e., **8** ⇌ **10**, **9** ⇌ **10**, and **9** ⇌ **11**.

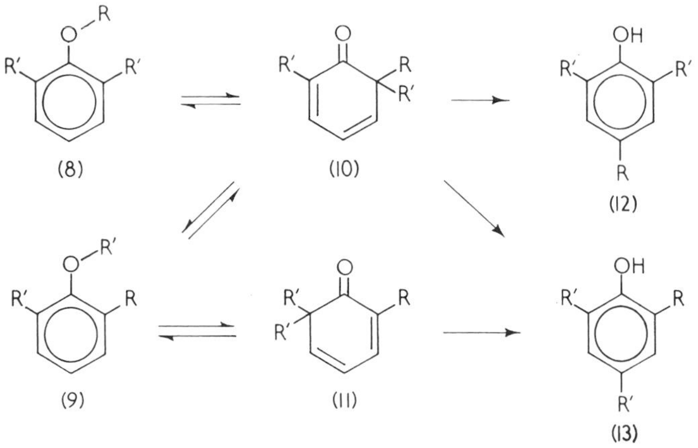

$$(R = -CH_2-CH=CH_2; \quad R' = -CH_2-C(CH_3)=CH_2)$$

It was reasoned that if the dienones (**10** and **11**) were necessarily involved in the rearrangements, then ethers (**8** and **9**) should give rise to mixtures of phenols (**12** and **13**), since in the dienone intermediates the two allylic groups at one ortho carbon become equivalent in the sense that either can undergo further migration. On the other hand, if the dienone formation were not a necessary step in the rearrangement, and if the two ethers (**8** and **9**) were not rapidly interconverted by way of their common dienone (**10**), then **8** should give only **12** and **9** should give only **13**. In fact, both ethers underwent rearrangement to yield mixtures of the phenols (**12** and **13**).

In order to eliminate the possibility that the phenols formed directly and independently from the ethers after equilibration through the dienone (**10**), Curtin and Johnson compared the relative rates of ether interconversion (**8** ⇌ **9**) and over-all rearrangement (**8** → **12** + **13** and **9** → **13** + **12**) by product analysis of the ether and phenol fractions at intervals throughout the heating period. It was found that the rate of ether interconversion was slow relative

[53] D. Y. Curtin and H. W. Johnson, Jr., *J. Am. Chem. Soc.*, **76**, 2276 (1954), **78**, 2611 (1956).

[54] K. Schmid, W. Haegele, and H. Schmid, *Experientia*, **9**, 414 (1953); *Helv. Chim. Acta*, **37**, 1080 (1954).

[55] E. N. Marvell and R. Teranishi, *J. Am. Chem. Soc.*, **76**, 6165 (1954).

to the formation of phenolic products but that the composition of the phenolic mixture was essentially constant throughout. These facts argue against an independent, direct pathway for the ether-phenol rearrangement and support the notion of the o-dienone as a true intermediate.

The reversibility of dienone formation in the para rearrangement was also demonstrated by Schmid and his students by means of a radioactive tracing technique.[56] Thus, allyl 2,6-dimethyl-4-allyl-γ-^{14}C phenyl ether (14), equilibrated at 170°, yielded ethereal material in which the radioactivity was uniformly distributed in the γ carbons of the O- and C-allyl groups (15).

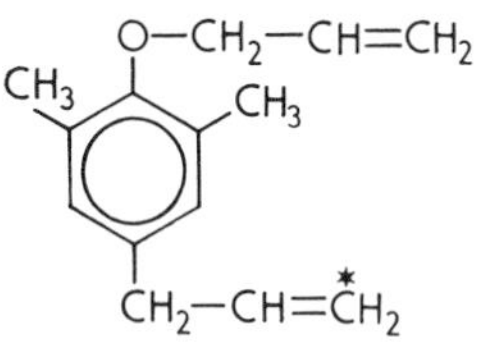

(14) 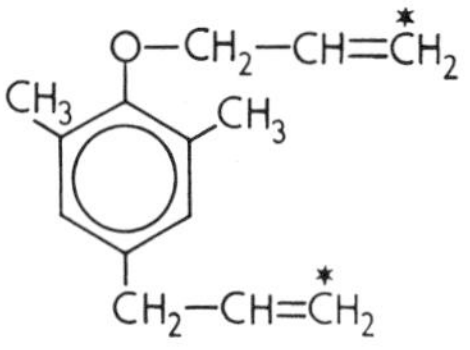   (15)

A direct study of the o-dienone intermediate was made possible by the observation of Curtin and Crawford [45] that under special conditions of solvent and temperature, the trisubstituted dienone (6) could be prepared in good yield by direct ring allylation of the sodium salt of 2,6-dimethylphenol. The heat-sensitive dienone could be isolated in yields amounting to 60% over-all conversion from the starting phenol.

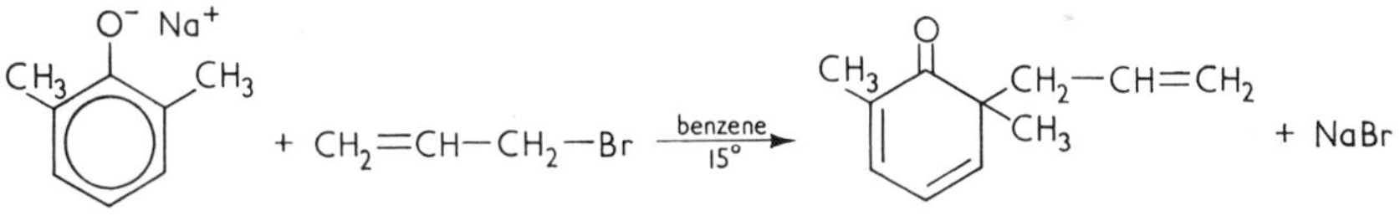

(6)

With the dienone (6) in hand, Curtin and Crawford were able to study its conversion to the ether (5) and the phenol (7) in the temperature range 75–100°. At these temperatures the rearrangement of the ether (5) to the dienone (6) and the side reaction of dimerization of 6 are negligible ($k_1 \cong 0$, $k_{dimer} \cong 0$).

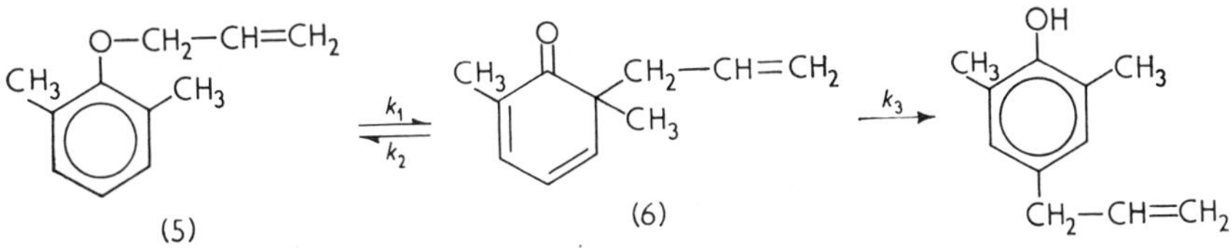

(5)   (6)   (7)

[56] F. Kalberer, K. Schmid, and H. Schmid, Helv. Chim. Acta, 39, 555 (1956).

The rate of disappearance of **6**, then, is the sum of the rates of its conversion to ether (k_2) and its conversion to phenol (k_3). From the observed rate constant ($k_{obs} = k_2 + k_3$) and by product analysis of the rearrangement mixture, the individual rate constants k_2 and k_3 could be evaluated. In the temperature range studied, the rate ratio k_3/k_2 remained essentially constant with a value of 2.7–2.8.

D. Kinetics

Early work on the kinetics of the ortho and para rearrangements served to establish that the rates followed the first-order rate expression, were insensitive to added acid or base, were little affected by the presence of or change in solvent, and showed similar activation energies and entropies.[38,42] The similarity of the activation parameters in the two rearrangements was commented on at the time, and the suggestion was put forward that the close agreement of these parameters pointed to a similar rate-determining step.[42]

With the intervention of the dienone intermediates now established, the observed rate constants for the rearrangements are recognized to be composites of the rate constants of the individual steps summarized in equation 2.

$$\text{Allyl aryl ether} \underset{k_2}{\overset{k_1}{\rightleftharpoons}} o\text{-Dienone} \xrightarrow{k_3} p\text{-Dienone} \xrightarrow{k_\text{H}} p\text{-Allylphenol} \qquad (2)$$

$$\downarrow k_\text{H}$$

$$o\text{-Allylphenol}$$

Since the rate of rearrangement is unaffected by added base, the enolization step (k_H) must be very rapid compared with the other steps and does not contribute to the over-all rate. For the ortho rearrangement, the observed rate constant, k_o, is equal to $2k_1$ since there are two ortho positions open to the allylic group. When the two ortho positions are blocked with identical groups, the allyl group will proceed to the para position with an observed rate constant which is a composite of k_1, k_2, and k_3. By the application of the steady state approximation, it is found that $k_p = 2k_1k_3/(k_2 + k_3)$. In order to evaluate k_1 for the slow ether-dienone conversion a knowledge of the value of the quotient $k_3/(k_2 + k_3)$ is required. If the dienone is available, this value may be obtained by direct measurement of k_2 and k_3 at temperatures below the rearrangement temperature as demonstrated by Curtin and Crawford. Otherwise, it must be obtained indirectly.

Schmid and his co-workers, exploiting the advantages of radioactive tracers in rate studies, have presented a detailed kinetic analysis of the para rearrangement.[46b] By incorporating ^{14}C into one of the allylic groups of allyl 2,6-diallylphenyl ether and following the rates of isotope distribution in the various components of the reaction mixture, the Swiss group was able to evaluate rate constants for the individual steps. The reaction is shown in Scheme 1.

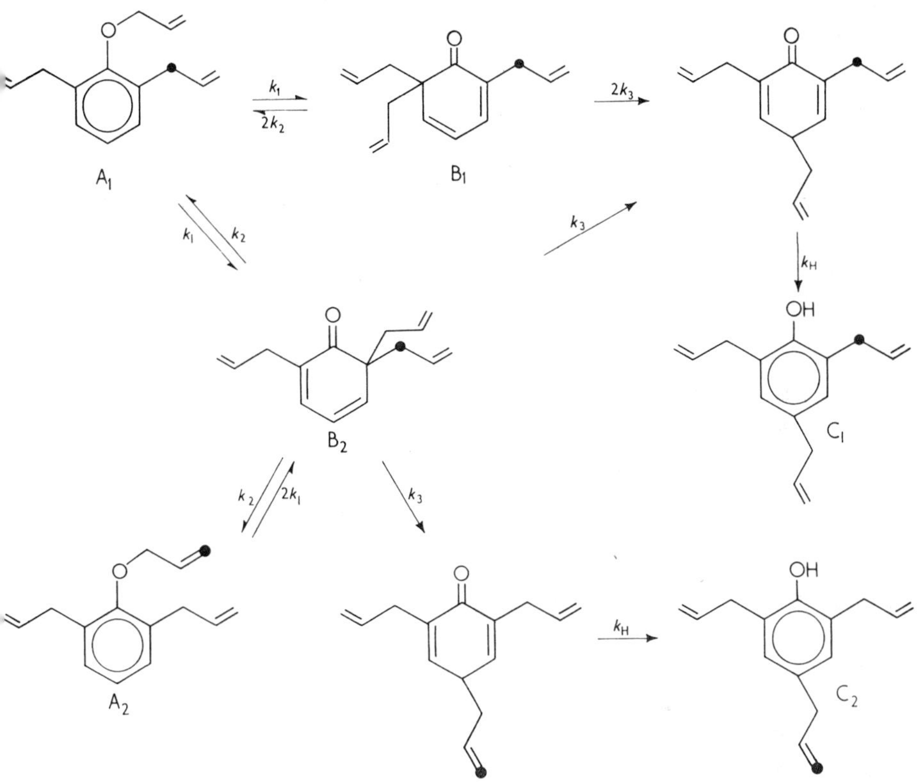

Scheme 1.   Rearrangement of allyl 2,6-diallylphenyl ether marked with [14]C. The position of the radioactive carbon is indicated by the solid circle.

By progressive analysis of the ethereal fraction $(A_1 + A_2)$ for the ^{14}C distribution in the O- and C-allyl groups, the isomerization $A_1 \rightleftharpoons A_2$ could be measured. The rate constant, k_i, with which this equilibrium is established is related to the individual rate constants by

$$k_i = \tfrac{3}{2}k_1k_2/(k_2+k_3)$$

Since $k_p = 2k_1k_3/(k_2+k_3)$, a knowledge of k_p and k_i permits the evaluation of k_3/k_2 and of k_1.

Of further interest in the Schmid study is the ^{14}C distribution in the products, C_1 and C_2, as a function of time. It can be shown that the fraction of the total radioactivity of the phenolic products present in the product C_2 (on a terminal methylene group) is a complex function of the rate constants

k_p and k_i and time. A plot of the experimentally determined values gave a curve which agreed very closely with that calculated from the measured rate constants k_p and k_i. This internal consistency of the experimental data is a good indication of the mechanistic uniformity of the para rearrangement. The only important reaction steps are those characterized by the rate constants k_1, k_2, k_3 (and k_H). The rate constant of any other internal rearrangement pathway for allyl 2,6-disubstituted phenyl ethers must be small compared with k_2 and k_3.

Table I shows the data for the individual steps of the para rearrangement obtained from the Curtin and Crawford study of the dienone intermediate in

TABLE I

Kinetic Data for Individual Steps of the Claisen Rearrangements of Allyl 2,6-Dimethyl-phenyl Ether, Allyl 2,6-Diallylphenyl Ether, and Allyl p-Tolyl Ether at 170° [46a,46b]

Rate constants	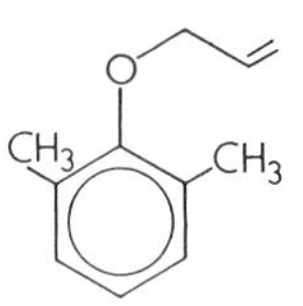 5	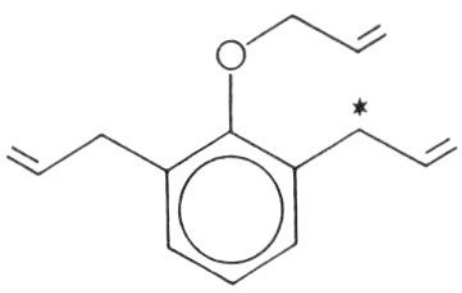 16	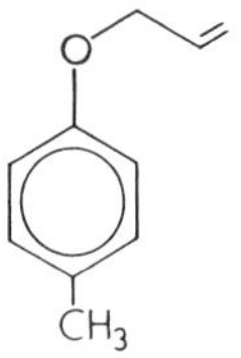 17
$k \times 10^5$/sec.	6.5[a]	7.0[d]	0.76[a]
k_3/k_2	2.7[b]	3.0	×
k_2/k_1	330[c]	—	×
$k_1 \times 10^5$/sec.	4.4[c]	4.7	0.38[e]
$k_2 \times 10^5$/sec.	1.5×10^{3c}	—	×
$k_3 \times 10^5$/sec.	4×10^{3c}	—	×

Activation quantities	k_1	k_2	k_3	k_1	k_1
$E_a^{\ddagger}$[f]	31.0	26.8	26.8	30.5	33.1
$\Delta H^{\ddagger}_{170}$[f]	30.1	25.9	25.9	29.6	32.2
$\Delta S^{\ddagger}_{170}$[g]	−11.3	−9.3	−7.3	−12.2	−11.5

[a] Data from refs. 38 and 42. Solvent was diphenyl ether.

[b] Data from ref. 45. Solvent was cyclohexane.

[c] Calculated for 170° assuming constancy of k_3/k_2 measured in temperature range 75–100°.

[d] Solvent was diethylaniline.

[e] Since $k_o = 2k_1$ for ortho rearrangement.

[f] In kcal./mole.

[g] In e.u.

the rearrangement of allyl 2,6-dimethylphenyl ether (5) and from Schmid's ^{14}C analysis of the rearrangement of allyl 2,6-diallylphenyl ether (16) together with corresponding data on the ortho rearrangement of allyl p-tolyl ether

(17). The very close agreement of the individual rate constants and the activation parameters in the two para rearrangements is noteworthy. Apparently, the differences in polar and steric effects of methyl and allyl groups in the ortho position are negligible for these rearrangements. The insignificant effect of the solvent change is also illustrated.

The close correspondence of the activation quantities for the para and ortho rearrangements is also of interest and constitutes the kinetic evidence for the mechanistic identity of the first step in the two rearrangements. The some ten-fold difference in rate for the para and ortho rearrangements must be attributed to the o-alkyl substituents and their effect on the activation energy. It is to be noted that the entropies of activation for the first step (k_1) in the para rearrangement of **5** and the ortho rearrangement of **17** are identical, a fact which suggests that steric interactions of ortho substituents with the γ carbon of the ether side chain are of little importance in the transition states adopted by these compounds.

While the kinetic studies of the para rearrangement have not been extensive, a few other data are available which offer interesting comparisons with the data in Table I. Rhoads and Crecelius [43] recorded the kinetic behavior of the allyl ether of methyl o-cresotinate (**18**) ($k_{170} = 3.31 \times 10^{-5}/\text{sec.}$; $E_a = 31.3$ kcal./mole; $\Delta H^{\ddagger}_{170} = 30.2$ kcal./mole; $\Delta S^{\ddagger}_{170} = -11.7$ e.u.). Its rate of rearrangement at $170°$ is about one-half that of allyl 2,6-dimethylphenyl ether (**5**), and its activation quantities are almost identical with those found for the step of rearrangement to one ortho carbon (k_1) in **5**. This relationship suggested to Kalberer and Schmid [46a] that in **18** the allyl group migrates down

(18)

one side of the ring only, i.e., over the carbon bearing the methyl group rather than over the carbomethoxy-bearing carbon. If this is true, then for **18**, $k = k_1 k_3/(k_2 + k_3)$. With the assumption that k_1, k_2, and k_3 for this process in **18** have the same values as the corresponding steps in **5**, then k_{18} should be just half of k_5 as observed.

Another interesting case is that of allyl 2,4-dimethylphenyl ether (**19**) ($k_{170} = 1.58 \times 10^{-5}/\text{sec.}$; $E_a = 32.2$ kcal./mole; $\Delta H^{\ddagger}_{170} = 31.3$ kcal./mole; $\Delta S^{\ddagger}_{170} = -10.7$ e.u.), also reported by Kalberer and Schmid.[46a] Superficially, this ether appears to undergo an ortho rearrangement leading to 2,4-dimethyl-6-allylphenol. However, its rate constant, which lies between those of allyl p-tolyl ether (**17**) and allyl 2,6-dimethylphenyl ether (**5**), implies either that the 2-methyl group, in some way, is activating the 6 position rather strongly or that more than a simple, direct rearrangement to the unoccupied ortho position is involved. A possible explanation, due to Schmid,[46a] is that, to an appreciable extent, the allyl group migrates to the 6 position by going "around" the ring over the 2 and 4 positions, i.e., by a

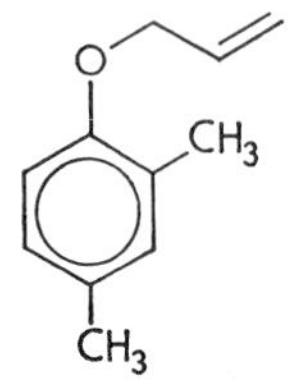

(19)

para rearrangement pathway. The same arguments obtain in cases of allyl aryl ethers which are substituted at one ortho carbon only (**20**). Such ethers may, and usually do, give rise to mixtures of rearrangement products by the competitive ortho and para rearrangement processes. Since the magnitude of k_p may often be comparable with that of k_o, this is a serious problem that generally has been overlooked in synthetic work.

Using the sensitive ^{14}C probe, Schmid and his students have carried out several other significant kinetic studies, among which is the investigation of

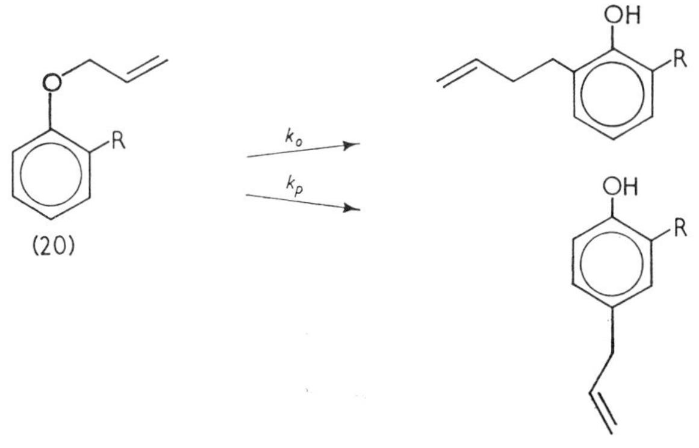

the thermal behavior of allyl-γ-^{14}C mesityl ether (**21**).[46c] When **21** was recovered after being heated 96 hours at 170° in diethylaniline, the radioactivity was almost uniformly distributed in the α and γ carbons of the allyl ether. Such a result, of course, is inexplicable by the rearrangement routes thus far discussed and points to another rearrangement pathway, available but ordinarily untraversed in the irreversible Claisen rearrangements (those in which a final enolization step is possible). With detailed supporting evidence and closely reasoned argument, Schmid excluded the possible explanation that this distribution resulted from homolytic or heterolytic dissociation followed by recombination of the fragments and concluded that the observed isomerization occurs by still another intramolecular rearrangement which has its origin in one of the dienone intermediates. A possible alternate pathway (eq. 3)

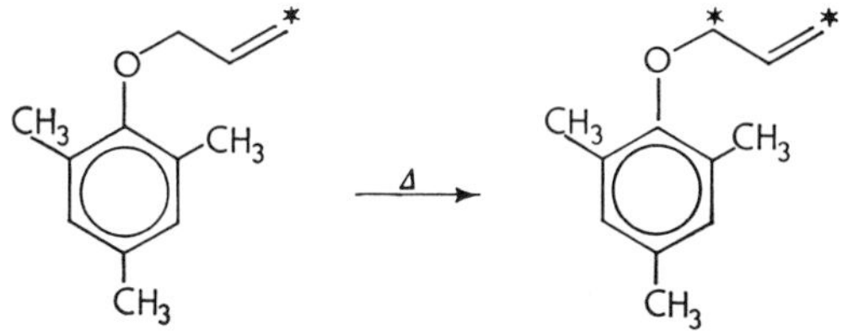

(21)

which could account for the result and still preserve the intramolecular character and origin in the o-dienone is an ortho-ortho' rearrangement, in which the molecule passes through a transition state summarized as **22**. Presumably the rate constant for the ortho-ortho' rearrangement is small

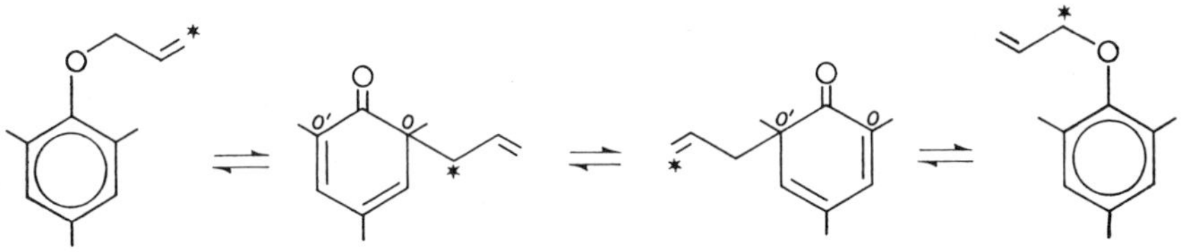

(3)

relative to k_3 in the para rearrangement (and to k_H of the ortho rearrangement) so that this intramolecular rearrangement remains latent in the irreversible ortho and para rearrangements. The intervention of such a rearrangement may also explain the small discrepancies in isotope distribution found in the equilibration of allyl 2,6-dimethyl-4-allyl-γ-^{14}C-phenyl

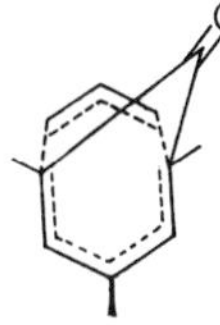

(22)

ether (**14**) [56] and the quite appreciable discrepancy found in the rearrangement of allyl-γ-^{14}C 2-propenyl 4,6-disubstituted phenyl ethers (**23**) to 2-(β-methyl-penta-α,δ-dienyl)-4,6-disubstituted phenols (**24**) in which 16% of the total activity appears in the γ carbon of the pentadienyl side chain.[56a] Here the bulk of the rearrangement product can be accommodated by a para-type

[56a] K. Schmid, P. Fahrni, and H. Schmid, *Helv. Chim. Acta*, **39**, 708 (1956).

rearrangement in which the propenyl side chain takes over the role of the "second" allylic system in the Cope rearrangement step. This process would lead to over-all retention of structure in the migrating allyl group. The occurrence of a concurrent inverting process to the extent of 16% requires some other explanation, such as the ortho-ortho' rearrangement.

No systematic study of the effect of nuclear substituents on the rate of the

(23)   (24)

para rearrangement is available. A few observations have been reported on the effect of substitution in the side chain. Alkyl substituents in the α position enhance the rearrangement rate appreciably as is evident from the fact that the α-alkylallyl ethers of methyl o-cresotinate may be preferentially rearranged in a mixture of isomeric α- and γ-alkylallyl ethers.[56b] The effect of γ-alkyl substituents in the allyl side chain is less predictable. A γ-methyl group slightly enhances the rate when compared with the simple allyl system, but a γ-ethyl group has essentially no effect relative to the unsubstituted allyl system. These results have been rationalized in terms of steric interactions of the ortho substituents and the γ-alkyl group in the transition state.[56c]

As pointed out in the introduction, the electrical nature of the "no mechanism" reactions is subject to wide variation depending on the structural characteristics of the system in which the transformation is occurring. Moreover, it was anticipated that the specific nature of the electronic changes involved in the reactions should be difficult to assess because of the closed, self-contained character of the electron reorganization process. Recent studies of the effects of substituents of widely different electronic capacities on the rate of the ortho rearrangement illustrate this problem rather graphically and serve to point up the "no mechanism" character of these rearrangements.

Two groups have reported on systematic kinetic investigations of the ortho rearrangement.[51,52] In both studies, a series of para-substituted allyl phenyl ethers was studied in which the substituents ranged from powerful electron donors such as —NH$_2$ to strong electron-withdrawing groups such as —CN and —NO$_2$. In the study by Goering and Jacobson [51] the rates were measured

[56b] S. J. Rhoads, R. Raulins, and R. D. Reynolds, J. Am. Chem. Soc., **75**, 2531 (1953), **76**, 3456 (1954); S. J. Rhoads and R. L. Crecelius, J. Am. Chem. Soc., **77**, 5183 (1955).

[56c] S. J. Rhoads and R. L. Crecelius, J. Am. Chem. Soc., **77**, 5057 (1955).

in diphenyl ether, while the White group [52a] employed Carbitol as a solvent. Qualitatively, the results are very similar in the two solvents. The electron-donating groups produce an accelerating effect, while the electron-withdrawing groups retard the rate somewhat. However, these effects are small, the spread in rates from p-NH_2 to p-NO_2 being only 20-fold in Carbitol and 10-fold in diphenyl ether in the temperature range of 180–185°. The kinetic data collected by Goering and Jacobson are shown in Table II. Included are two examples of meta-substituted ethers studied under the same conditions.

Examination of the data reveals some interesting qualitative facts. The electron-withdrawing groups are practically without effect on the rearrangement rate; the largest change in rate among the ethers substituted

TABLE II

Kinetic Data for the Ortho Rearrangement of X—$\langle$◯$\rangle$—$O-CH_2-CH{=}CH_2$

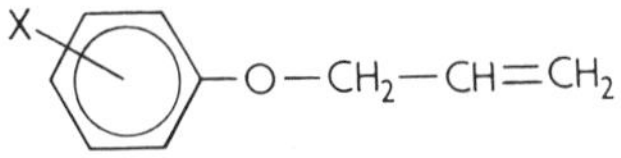

in Diphenyl Ether at 184.85° [51]

X	$k_o \times 10^5$/sec.[a]	E_a(kcal./mole)[b]	$\Delta S^{\ddagger}$(e.u.)[c]
p-$N(CH_3)_2$	14.3	34.3	-2
p-NH_2	10.0	34.7	-2
p-OC_2H_5	4.77	33.1	-7
p-OCH_3	4.58	33.6	-6
p-CH_3	2.08	34.0	-7
p-C_2H_5	2.00	34.8	-5
p-Cl	1.70	31.2	-13
p-Br	1.58	31.2	-13
p-H	1.52	31.6	-12
p-$CO_2C_2H_5$	1.115	31.5	-13
p-CHO	1.07	32.2	-12
p-$COCH_3$	0.994	32.2	-12
p-CN	0.903	32.0	-13
p-NO_2	0.892	31.9	-13
m-OCH_3	4.92	30.4	-13
m-$CO_2C_2H_5$	1.48	29.8	-16

[a] Rates were generally reproducible to $\pm 1\%$.

[b] Estimated reliability, ± 1 kcal.

[c] Estimated reliability, ± 2–3 e.u.

with such groups is less than two, and the activation parameters show essential constancy within the reliability of the data. The more marked changes in rate are observed when the para substituent is an electron-releasing group, and, with these, the net effect of the substituent is a manifestation of a change in the entropy of activation; the activation energies actually increase with increasing electron-releasing power of the substituent.[57] These observations concerning the activation parameters are not duplicated in the rearrangements of the same compounds when the rates are measured in Carbitol.[52a] Insofar as the thermodynamic quantities of activation were determined in this solvent, the trend appears to lie in the opposite direction. The increase in rate observed with electron-releasing substituents is roughly paralleled by a decrease in activation energy (Table III). Whatever the explanation for these

TABLE III

Kinetic Data for the Rearrangement of Allyl p-X-Phenyl Ethers in Carbitol at 181° [52a]

X	$k \times 10^5$/sec.	E_a(kcal./mole)	$\Delta S^{\ddagger}$(e.u.)
p-OCH$_3$	8.66 ± 0.09	30.8	− 12.1
p-CH$_3$	4.71 ± 0.04	31.2	− 12.6
p-H	2.59 ± 0.06	32.2	− 11.5
p-Br	2.48 ± 0.06	30.7	− 14.8
p-COC$_6$H$_5$	1.57 ± 0.05	34.5	− 7.3

differences may be, it is clear that the solvent is implicated in some important way.[58]

Another interesting aspect of the substituent effects appears in the Goering and Jacobson data for the meta-substituted ethers. The rate of rearrangement of the allyl m-carbethoxyphenyl ether is identical with that of the unsubstituted compound through compensating changes in the energy and entropy of activation. When the ether is substituted in the meta position with the methoxy group, however, a relatively large change in rate is observed ($k_{m-OCH_3}/k_H = 4.92/1.52$), comparable in magnitude with that observed when the methoxy group is in the para position ($k_{p-OCH_3}/k_H = 4.58/1.52$). In fact, the effect is even greater than the measured rates suggest, since the rate of rearrangement in the case of the m-OCH$_3$ compound is essentially the rate of

---

[57] This unusual inverse relationship between k and E_a may be due to a very low isokinetic temperature for these rearrangements in diphenyl ether. This condition would place the rearrangements carried out at 185° in the entropy-controlled category. An attempt to determine the isokinetic temperature from a plot of $\Delta H^{\ddagger}$ against $\Delta S^{\ddagger}$ was rather unsatisfactory, the linear correlation of these quantities being poor. If the isokinetic temperature is 50°, as the data crudely suggest, then the sign of ρ obtained in the Hammett $\rho\sigma^+$ correlation is opposite that which would be characteristic of the rearrangement at temperatures below the isokinetic temperature. Since most $\rho\sigma$ correlations have been derived from rate data gathered at temperatures below the isokinetic temperature the significance of the sign of ρ might be questioned in this case. Cf. J. E. Leffler, J. Org. Chem., **20**, 1202 (1955).

[58] A somewhat similar effect of solvent on the activation parameters in the Diels-Alder reaction has been reported by M. Gillois and P. Rumpf, Bull. soc. chim. France, **1959**, 1823.

rearrangement to *one* ortho position (k_1),[59] while the observed rate for the p-OCH_3 derivative is the rate of rearrangement to *two* ortho positions $(2k_1)$. Corrected for this statistical factor, the relative rates are m-OCH_3:p-OCH_3: H::9.84:4.58:1.52. The m-OCH_3 group, then, is roughly as effective as the p-NH_2 group in accelerating the rearrangement.[59a]

The data for the para-substituted ethers from both teams of investigators failed to show satisfactory correlations in the Hammett equation using either σ_p or σ_m constants. However, in both cases, good correlations were obtained when the σ_p^+ constants for electrophilic substitution were used. In each case ρ was negative and rather small ($\rho = -0.609$;[52a] $\rho = -0.510$[51]). The theoretical significance of these correlations is not clear. The sign and value of ρ imply that the reactions are electron demanding and insensitive to substituent effects, implications which were already clear from the rate data. If the σ_p^+ correlation is interpreted literally, it means that electron deficiency develops para to the substituent (i.e., at the ring carbon of the ether link) before or during the transition state. This situation is difficult to visualize and even more difficult to rationalize when the relatively great effect of the m-OCH_3 group is recalled.

(25)   (26)

Very recently, White and his students have extended the kinetic study to substituted cinnamyl p-tolyl ethers of type **25**[52c] and to meta-substituted allyl phenyl ethers of structure **26**.[52b,59b] With these systems, also, the rate data were correlated better by σ^+ constants than by σ constants, and the values of ρ were small and negative ($\rho_{25} = -0.40$; $\rho_{26} = -0.66$). Of special interest is the fact that the σ^+ correlation for the meta-substituted ethers (**26**) was made with σ_p^+ not σ_m^+, constants.

To devise a single mechanistic scheme which accommodates all these

[59] It has been reported that rearrangement of the ether gives rise to only one phenolic product, that one in which the allyl group migrates to the less hindered ortho position, i.e., para to the —OCH_3 group.[51]

[59a] According to a recent report,[59b] isotope dilution analysis shows that, in fact, both possible isomers are formed in the rearrangement of the m-methoxy compound, contrary to the original report by Mauthner quoted in ref. 51. In Carbitol, the isomer product ratio is ~ 2:1 in favor of the 2-allyl-5-methoxyphenol. The order of reactivities given above, however, is not changed by this correction.

[59b] W. N. White and C. D. Slater, *J. Org. Chem.*, **26**, 3631 (1961), **27**, 2908 (1962).

correlations poses a difficult problem.[60] The results seem to imply that it is of little consequence where the activating group is in the molecule since it is capable of interacting in some manner with the electron reorganizations which constitute the bond-making and -breaking processes in the transition state. In this connection, the activating effect of the o-methyl group will be recalled from the rate data for the para Claisen rearrangement (Table I, page 668). The fact that the rates of the Claisen rearrangements are practically unaffected by electron-withdrawing groups and only slightly responsive to electron-releasing groups, regardless of their position, is illustrative of the self-sufficient nature of these reactions.

A priori, there is no compelling reason to expect a characteristic reaction constant ρ for these reactions. As Swain [61] and Jaffé [62] have pointed out, some of the reactions which characteristically fail to give good correlations with σ constants are those involving concerted bond-making and -breaking processes for which a delicate balance between these processes in the transition state may be visualized. The relative importance of these two processes and their degree of concertedness would reasonably be expected to depend on the substituents present. In such cases, ρ would not be a constant but a function of σ, and curvilinear dependence of log k on σ would result. It is of more than passing interest that plots of both White's and Goering's data for the para-substituted allyl phenyl ethers against σ_m give two intersecting straight lines, one accommodating the compounds substituted with electron-withdrawing groups and the unsubstituted compound with $\rho = -0.3$ to -0.4 and another accommodating the compounds substituted with the electron-releasing groups and the halogens with $\rho = -1.4$ to -1.6. To the extent that the transition state has some ion pair character of the type implied in the formulation **27** the

(27)

results could be accommodated by a concept of gradually changing mechanism wherein the bond-making process at the ortho carbon is always of major importance, energetically (hence, the negative ρ), but assumes an even greater role in the determination of the transition state energy when electron-releasing groups are present in the reacting system, even though they be meta disposed and must exert their influence inductively. When such substituents are present in the meta position on the ring, but para to the carbon where bond

[60] For the formulation of the transition state in terms of quasi-radical structures, see White et al.[52b,52c,59b].

[61] C. G. Swain and W. P. Langsdorf, Jr., J. Am. Chem. Soc., **73**, 2813 (1951).

[62] H. H. Jaffé, Chem. Revs., **53**, 236 (1953).

formation occurs, their importance would be enhanced by the resonance interaction possible. Finally, it should be noted that if ionic forces are at work in these rearrangements, the over-all effect of a substituent in the aryl portion of the ether should be small since it must necessarily affect the ease of bond-making and bond-breaking processes in opposite ways.

The over-all effect of a solvent change on the rate of the ortho rearrangement has been reported on briefly by Goering and Jacobson [51] and by White and his group.[52a] Here, the effect of change in dielectric constant of the medium is small. The largest effects are shown by the hydroxylic solvents and especially by the phenolic ones. Goering and Jacobson report a rate enhancement of some 40-fold for the rearrangement of allyl *p*-tolyl ether in phenol as compared with that in decalin.[51] Recently, White has undertaken a more elaborate study of solvent effects and has found a 100-fold difference in rates of rearrangement of allyl *p*-tolyl ether in chlorophenol versus tetradecane.[63]

E. Stereochemistry

From considerations of the geometry of allylic aryl ethers and the intra-molecular nature of the Claisen rearrangements it appears that the most

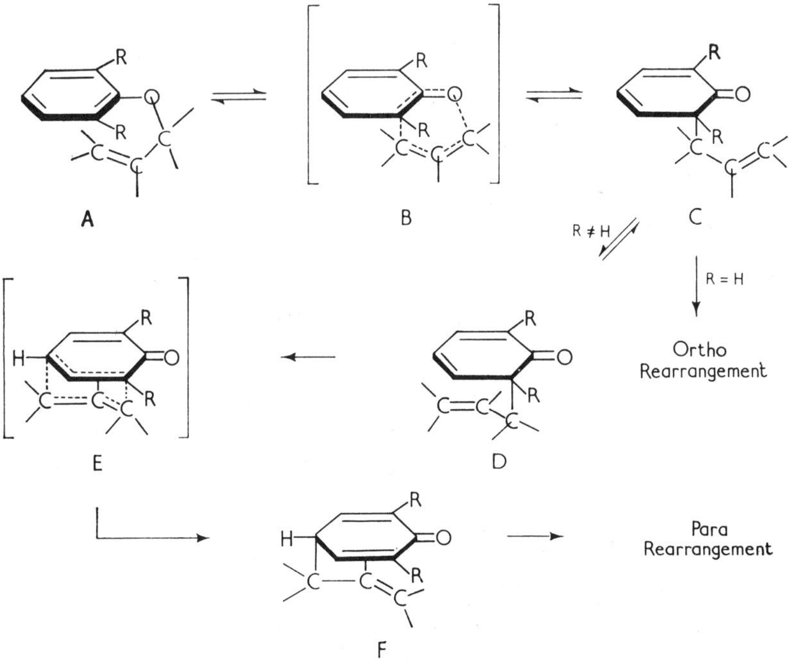

Scheme 2.   Stereopath of the Claisen rearrangements.

[63] W. N. White and E. F. Wolfarth, 140th Meeting, ACS, Chicago, September, 1961, *Abstracts*, p. 52Q.

reasonable stereopath for the conversion is one in which the allylic side chain of the molecule assumes a position in a plane which is almost parallel with that of the aromatic ring, the γ carbon of the allylic side chain positioning directly below (or above) the ortho carbon of the ring.[63a] (Scheme 2,A). Bond formation at the ortho carbon and bond cleavage of the α carbon–oxygen linkage, then, may occur in a highly synchronized fashion through a transition state which resembles a somewhat strained six-membered ring, (B). Re-arrangement to the para position may be accomplished through a similar orientation and cyclic process involving the o-allylic side chain and a three-carbon allylic portion of the ring of the o-cyclohexadienone intermediate (D, E, and F).

The orientation of the allylic and ring portions of the molecule specified in this description may be achieved in two ways depending on the relative position of the β carbon of the side chain. If the three carbons of the side chain allylic system line up directly with the three atom allylic system of the ring ($-O-\overset{1}{C}=\overset{2}{C}-$), then the β carbon would lie directly over (or under) C_1 of the ring (G), and this orientation has the conformational character of a boat form of cyclohexane. The transition state derived therefrom has been referred to as possessing a "quasi-boat" or "elbowed-in" [50,63b] arrangement. On the other hand, if only the α and γ carbons of the side chain lie directly above their counterparts of the allylic portion of the ring (H), then this orientation re-

G   H

sembles the chair form of cyclohexane, and the corresponding transition state possesses a "quasi-chair" or "elbowed-out" arrangement. (In the representations, G and H, the allylic side chain is pictured as lying above the ring and is emphasized by the heavy line.[50])

Regardless of the conformational character of the cyclic transition state, it may be anticipated that as substituents are introduced into the side chain and into the close-lying ring positions, steric interactions will be introduced which may lead to a preference for one of several possible transition states.

The first indication of a preferred transition state geometry for the Claisen

[63a] S. J. Rhoads, R. Raulins, and R. D. Reynolds, *J. Am. Chem. Soc.*, **75**, 2531 (1953), **76**, 3456 (1954); S. J. Rhoads and R. L. Crecelius, *J. Am. Chem. Soc.*, **77**, 5183 (1955).

[63b] The two orientations have also been described as "six-centered" and "four-centered." W. von E. Doering and W. Roth, *Tetrahedron*, **18**, 67 (1962).

rearrangements was provided by Alexander and Kluiber[63c] who studied the rearrangement of optically active *trans*-α,γ-dimethylallyl phenyl ether (**28**) and found that it yielded active 2-(α,γ-dimethylallyl)-phenol (**29**). The over-

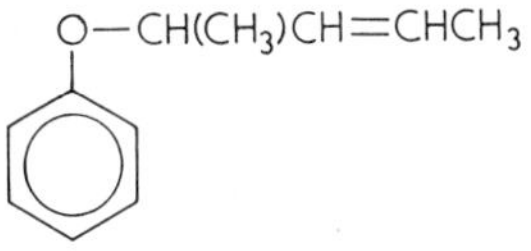

(−) (**28**) 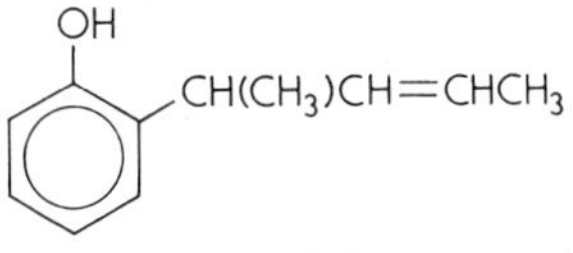   (+) (**29**)

all retention of activity in the rearrangement points to asymmetric induction through stereoselection among possible transition states, but since the relative configurations and optical purities of starting material and product were not established, the direction and degree of the stereoselective process could not be estimated. Subsequently, Hart,[64] basing his arguments on a presumption of configurational retention in the conversion of **28** to **29**, reasserted the proposal of Alexander and Kluiber that the rearrangement proceeded preferentially through a transition state arising from an orientation of geometry (**30**) which minimizes the interaction of the α-methyl group and the

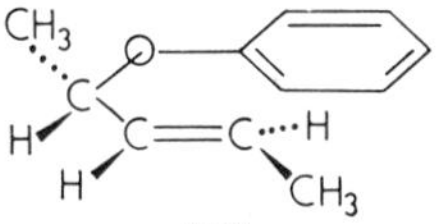

(30)

β hydrogen of the side chain. Such an orientation of the reacting centers would lead to retention of configuration at the new asymmetric center in the phenolic product. However, it will be noted that such a geometry in the transition state would also require the formation of a *cis*-substituted double bond in the product.

The stereochemical problems posed by the Claisen rearrangements have been reapproached in recent years by several groups of investigators.[64a-64d] As intimated above, in rearrangements of the Claisen type, there is an invariable relationship between the geometry change about the double bond and the configurational change at the asymmetric centers. Therefore, the stereochemistry of the rearrangements may be studied equally well by optical methods or by the determination of the double bond geometry of the starting

[63c] E. R. Alexander and R. W. Kluiber, *J. Am. Chem. Soc.*, **73**, 4304 (1951).

[64] H. Hart, *J. Am. Chem. Soc.*, **76**, 4033 (1954).

[64a] E. N. Marvell and J. L. Stephenson, *J. Org. Chem.*, **25**, 676 (1960).

[64b] A. W. Burgstahler. *J. Am. Chem. Soc.*, **82**, 4681 (1960).

[64c] W. N. White and B. E. Norcross, *J. Am. Chem. Soc.*, **83**, 1968 (1961).

[64d] W. N. White and B. E. Norcross, *J. Am. Chem. Soc.*, **83**, 3265 (1961).

ether and its rearrangement product. Utilizing the latter approach, Marvell and Stephenson [64a] have examined the rearrangements of *cis*- and *trans*-α,γ-dimethylallyl phenyl ethers and have provided evidence against the transition state geometry proposed by Alexander and Hart.

The possible relationships between the double bond geometry of starting material and final product and the resulting configuration at the new asymmetric center are summarized in Table IV. The correspondence indicated in the tabulation holds for the 16 possible transition states involving all combi-

TABLE IV

Relationship Between Configurational Change and Double Bond
Geometry in the Ortho Claisen Rearrangement [64a]

Geometry		
Initial double bond	Final double bond	Configurational change
trans	*trans*	Inversion
trans	*cis*	Retention
cis	*trans*	Retention
cis	*cis*	Inversion

nations of initial *cis* or *trans* and final *cis* or *trans* double bonds, quasi-boat or chair arrangements and R or S configurations, providing only that the bond-making and -breaking processes occur on the same side of the aromatic ring. This correspondence of configurational change and double bond geometry may be illustrated by considering the four possible orientations for the *trans*-R-α,γ-dimethylallyl phenyl ether molecule (**28a–28d**) which would lead to four different transition states for the rearrangement.[64e] It is clear that from the orientations **28a–28d** the following geometries and configurations are predictable for the phenolic products: **28a** → *trans* S (inv.); **28b** → *cis* R (ret.); **28c** → *cis* R (ret.); **28d** → *trans* S (inv.). Regardless of the "elbowed-out" or "elbowed-in" orientation adopted by the rearranging molecule,

---

[64e] Strictly speaking, there are four paths (each with two extreme conformations) by which a transition state leading to the ortho rearrangement may be achieved; i.e., the γ carbon of the allylic group may approach either C_2 or C_6 of the ring from either side of the ring. However, the transition state achieved by approach of the γ carbon to the 2 position on one side of the ring is identical with that achieved by its approach to the 6 position on the other side of the ring, so that only two of the four possible approaches need be considered. In the Newman projection formulas (**28a–28d**) the allylic side chain of the molecule is pictured as lying directly above the aromatic ring and is emphasized by the heavy lines. Unsaturated linkages are omitted for clarity.

then, it follows that a given relationship of double bond geometry between starting material and product implies a corresponding configurational change as summarized in Table IV.

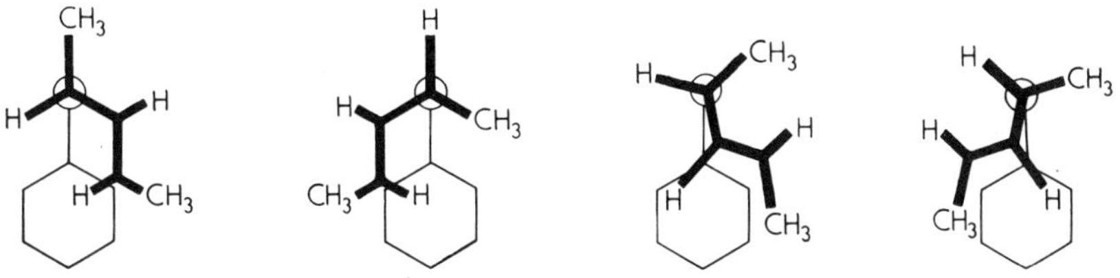

(28a)   (28b)   (28c)   (28d)

Marvell and Stephenson carried out the rearrangements of the *trans-* and *cis-α,γ*-dimethylallyl phenyl ethers (**28** and **31**) and found that, in both cases, the phenolic product was at least 90% the *trans* isomer (**32**). A small amount of the *cis* phenolic product (**33**) was also found in each case, and it was notably

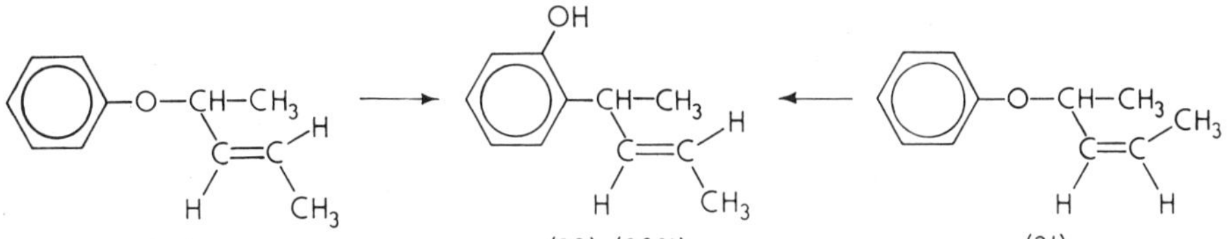

(28)   (32) (90%)   (31)

+

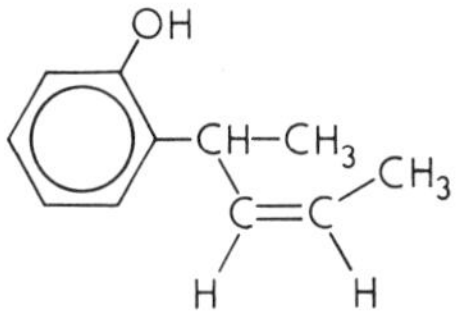

(33) (small amount)

greater in the rearrangement product from the *trans* ether. The stability of the product mixture obtained in both cases was established by the fact that prolonged heating of the phenolic mixtures produced no change in composition that could be detected in their infrared spectra.

These results, as well as similar findings by Burgstahler who studied the rearrangements of *cis-* and *trans-α,γ*-dimethylallyl vinyl ethers,[64b] suggest that the stereoselective nature of the ortho Claisen rearrangement is conditioned largely by factors related to product stability, that transition state (or states) being preferred which gives rise to the thermodynamically more stable *trans* isomer. The possibility that the results can be explained by *cis-trans* isomerization of the ethers prior to rearrangement or by *cis-trans* isomerization of the phenolic products after rearrangement appears to be slight. Burgstahler [64b] found that the unrearranged *cis* vinyl ethers could be recovered unchanged, and Marvell and Stephenson showed that the *cis* ether (**31**), only slowly isomerized to the *trans* ether (**28**), presumably at a rate much slower than the rate of rearrangement of **31** to **32**. The demonstrated stability of the product mixture of **32** and **33** under rearranging conditions seems to safeguard against an isomerization subsequent to rearrangement.

An alternative way of treating the stereoselectivity of the rearrangement has been suggested by Marvell and Stephenson [64a] who proposed that their results can consistently be interpreted by assuming that the transition state adopts a quasi-chair or "elbowed-out" arrangement (cf. orientations **28a** and **28b**) and applying the principles of conformational analysis. Thus orientation **28a** would lead to a transition state **34**[64f] in which the two methyl

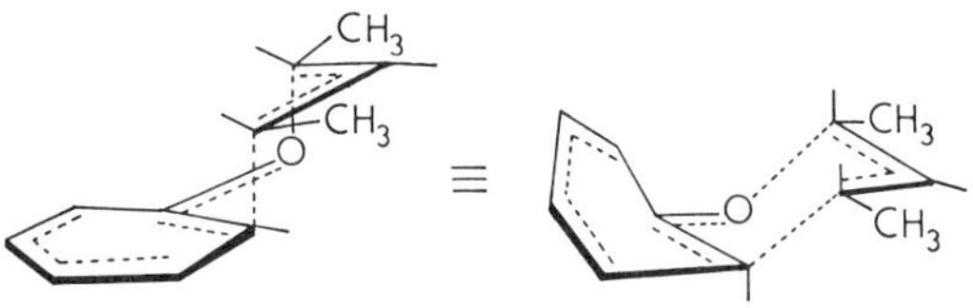

(34)

groups are equatorially disposed in the quasi-chair conformation. On the other hand, orientation **28b** leads to a transition state **35** [64f] in which the methyl groups assume an "ea" relationship. Other things being equal, the

(35)

greater stability of **34** should cause it to be preferred in the rearrangement pathway, and the preponderance of the *trans* isomer (**32**) in the phenolic product can be explained. A similar analysis of the two possible "elbowed-out" transition states for the rearranging *cis* ether (**31**) reveals that the transition state which gives rise to the *cis* phenolic product is badly crowded with the two methyls occupying "aa" positions while that transition state leading to the *trans* product is sterically more favorable, the two methyls possessing

[64f] These transition state representations have been constructed assuming that some progress has been made toward the geometry of the *o*-dienone intermediate; i.e., C_2, in developing some sp^3 character is buckling up out of the original plane of the aromatic ring and the developing carbonyl group is correspondingly displaced downward.

an "ea" relationship. It is also possible that the apparently slightly greater stereoselectivity of the rearrangement of the *cis* ether, as well as its slower rate,[64c] may be traced to these differences in the degree of steric crowding in the transition states available to the two ethers.

It may be pointed out that the results of the experiments described above do not, of themselves, furnish a basis for choosing between the two conformational possibilities for the transition state, it being entirely possible that the quasi-boat arrangement represents an atomic array of lower energy than the quasi-chair arrangement because of more effective orbital overlap between the two allylic systems involved. Quite recently, White and Norcross have reported two series of experiments designed to resolve this ambiguity.[64c,64d] In the first, *cis-trans* isomeric pairs of ethers were prepared and their rates of rearrangement studied. It was anticipated that if the "elbowed-out" or quasi-chair arrangement, J, best describes the transition state, then,

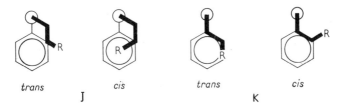

| *trans* | *cis* | *trans* | *cis* |
| J | | K | |

other factors being negligible, the *trans* isomer should rearrange faster than the *cis* since the R group would be free of steric interaction with the ring in the former. If, however, the "elbowed-in" arrangement, K, obtains, then the *cis* isomer should rearrange more rapidly than the *trans*. In fact, the *trans* isomer of each *cis-trans* pair examined rearranged somewhat faster than the *cis*.[65] Representative data for crotyl and cinnamyl *p*-methoxyphenyl ethers are shown in Table V.

In the second series of experiments, White and Norcross[64d] studied the rates of rearrangement of some β substituted allylic ethers of phenol and *p*-methoxyphenol, expecting that if the "elbowed-out" orientation were the correct one the rates would be relatively insensitive to a change in bulk of the β substituent while in the "elbowed-in" orientation steric interactions of the β substituent with the ring would lead to a decrease in rearrangement rate as the size of the group increased. Since the variation of the β substituent through the series H, CH_3, $C_4H_9{}^t$ produced no significant change in the rates, it was concluded that the "elbowed-out" arrangement represented the preferred transition state.

[65] L. D. Huestis and L. J. Andrews, *J. Am. Chem. Soc.*, **83**, 1963 (1961), have reported similar results in a parallel study of the effect of *cis-trans* geometry of the allyl group on the rates of the Claisen rearrangements.

While the results described above can be interpreted most simply and consistently in terms of a chairlike transition state, the evidence is less compelling than one would wish. As White [64c] has pointed out, the small differences in the rates of rearrangement of the *cis* and *trans* isomers could also be accommodated by the view that the *trans* isomer rearranges by the "elbowed-out" arrangement while the *cis* isomer chooses the "elbowed-in" arrangement

TABLE V

Kinetic Data for the Rearrangement of *cis* and *trans* γ-Substituted Allyl *p*-Methoxyphenyl Ethers in Diphenyl Ether[a]

Side chain substituent	Temp., °C.	$k \times 10^5$/sec.
trans-γ-CH_3	208.5	6.20
cis-γ-CH_3	208.5	3.78
trans-γ-C_6H_5	184.5	6.88
cis-γ-C_6H_5	183.5	3.44

[a] The data reproduced here are incomplete. Rates were determined at three or more temperatures in each case, and other isomeric pairs of ethers were examined.[64c]

as a compromise dictated by opposing energy-determining factors. The question of the transition-state geometry in diallylic rearrangements is encountered again in connection with the Cope rearrangement (heading 3D). There, the structural features of the systems examined permit a more decisive answer.

3. THE COPE AND RELATED REARRANGEMENTS

A. Structural Features

The all-carbon analog of the ortho Claisen rearrangement was first recognized by Cope and Hardy [66] in their study of the diallylic system ethyl

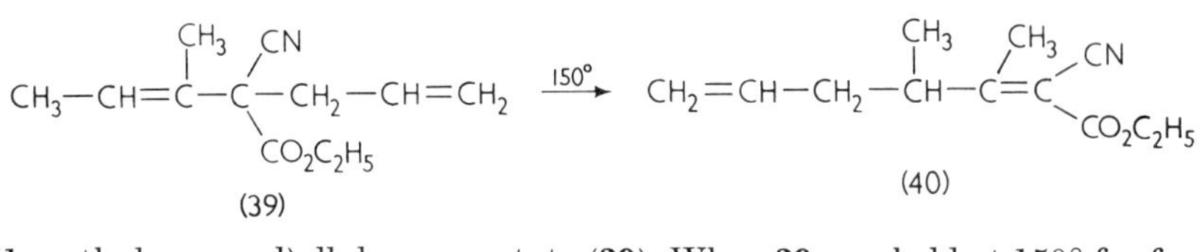

(39)   (40)

(1-methylpropenyl)allylcyanoacetate (**39**). When **39** was held at 150° for four hours, it rearranged to the unsaturated cyano ester (**40**). Further study of

[66] A. C. Cope and E. M. Hardy, *J. Am. Chem. Soc.*, **62**, 441 (1940).

such systems established that the minimum structural requirement for the rearrangement is the simple diallylic system

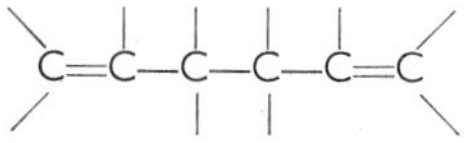

$$\diagdown C=C-C-C-C=C\diagup$$

Although the rearrangement is facilitated by the presence of groups such as —CN, —CO$_2$R, and —C$_6$H$_5$ on one or both of the central methylene carbons,[67-69] such activation is not essential. Even the simple molecule 3-methyl-1,5-hexadiene (**41**) rearranges, albeit slowly and reversibly, at 300°.[70]

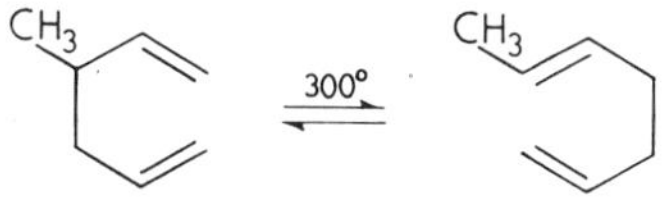

(41)

The vinyl group of the vinylallylcyanoacetic esters, vinylallylmalonic esters, and similarly constituted systems may be incorporated in a ring as in **42**.[69] However, the reaction fails if the vinyl group is part of an aromatic

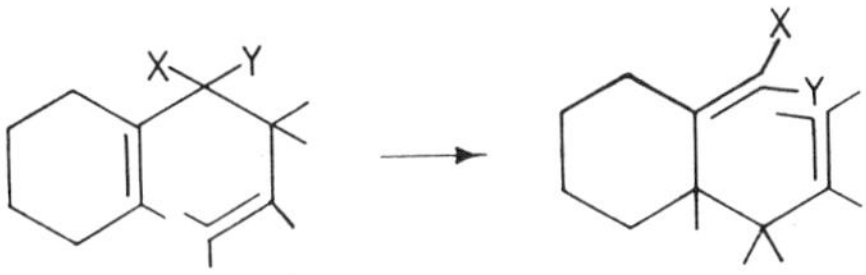

(42)

X = CN, CO$_2$C$_2$H$_5$
Y = H, allyl, C$_6$H$_5$, CO$_2$C$_2$H$_5$, CN

system. Thus Cope and co-workers [71,72] were unable to realize the rearrangement of **43**.

Substitution at the double bonds with alkyl groups of varying size does not seem to inhibit the rearrangement appreciably.[67,68]

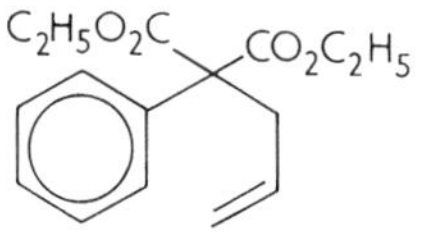

(43)

[67] A. C. Cope, C. M. Hofmann, and E. M. Hardy, *J. Am. Chem. Soc.*, **63**, 1852 (1941).
[68] A. C. Cope, K. E. Hoyle, and D. Heyl, *J. Am. Chem. Soc.*, **63**, 1843 (1941).
[69] D. E. Whyte and A. C. Cope, *J. Am. Chem. Soc.*, **65**, 1999 (1943).
[70] H. Levy and A. C. Cope, *J. Am. Chem. Soc.*, **66**, 1684 (1944).
[71] A. C. Cope, L. Field, D. W. H. MacDowell, and M. E. Wright, *J. Am. Chem. Soc.*, **78**, 2547 (1956).
[72] A. C. Cope, J. E. Meili, and D. W. H. MacDowell, *J. Am. Chem. Soc.*, **78**, 2551 (1956).

B. Evidence for the Cyclic Process

In ways completely paralleling the early work on the ortho Claisen rearrangement, the Cope rearrangement was shown to proceed with inversion of the structure of the migrating allylic group,[67] to be intramolecular,[67] and to follow the first-order rate expression.[68] Activation energies and entropies for the rearrangements bear a strong resemblance to those found for the Claisen rearrangements.[73,74] Although the Cope rearrangement has not been so thoroughly scrutinized as the Claisen, it appears that all of the information available today is consistent with a single-step, concerted process of the "no mechanism" type and may be summarized by the general equation for diallylic systems (eq. 4).

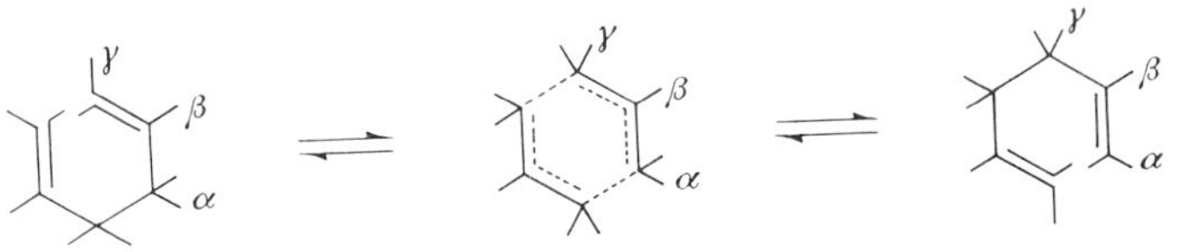

$$\text{(4)}$$

The activating effect noted for groups such as —CN, —CO$_2$R, and —C$_6$H$_5$ may be attributed to their ability to stabilize the transition state by conjugative interaction with the allylic systems.

C. Rearrangements of 1,5-Hexadiene Systems

The Cope rearrangement of hydrocarbons was examined by Levy and Cope[70] for a limited series of substituted 1,5-hexadienes. Since that time a few other such rearrangements have been reported.[74a–79] These rearrangements are summarized in Table VI. In the absence of rate data, the rearrangement temperature and yield data may be used as a rough guide to the relative reactivities of the hydrocarbons.

The effect of phenyl substitution on the ease of rearrangement and the point of equilibrium is apparent from a comparison of reactions (a), (b), and (c) in Table VI. The rearrangement of 3,4-diphenyl-1,5-hexadiene (**44**) represents an especially interesting example since two products were obser-

[73] E. G. Foster, A. C. Cope, and F. Daniels, *J. Am. Chem. Soc.*, **69**, 1893 (1947).

[74] G. R. Aldridge and G. W. Murphy, *J. Am. Chem. Soc.*, **73**, 1158 (1951).

[74a] R. B. Woodward and T. J. Katz, *Tetrahedron*, **5**, 70 (1959).

[75] H. P. Koch, *J. Chem. Soc.* (*London*), **1948**, 1111.

[76] E. Vogel, *Angew. Chem.*, **72**, 21 (1960); E. Vogel, K. H. Ott, and K. Gajek, *Ann.*, **644**, 172 (1961).

[77] E. Vogel, *Ann.*, **615**, 1 (1958).

[78] C. A. Grob and P. Schiess, *Angew. Chem.*, **70**, 502 (1958).

[79] W. von E. Doering and M. J. Goldstein, *Tetrahedron*, **5**, 53 (1959).

ved, *trans*-dicinnamyl (**45**) and "isodicinnamyl" (**47**) in a ratio of 3:2. Koch[75] suggested that the co-formation of **45** and **47** could be explained in terms of two competing processes, (*1*) the intramolecular, nondissociative Cope rearrangement and (*2*) a homolytic cleavage of **44** to the mesomeric radicals (**46**) which could recombine to form **47** (as well as **45**). Although the

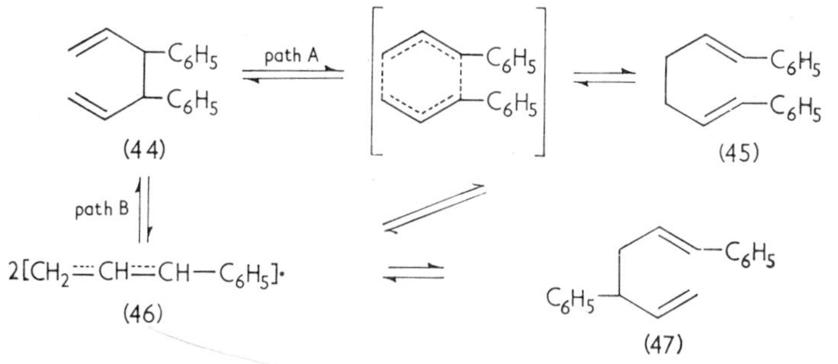

formation of both products could be accommodated by the operation of the single process (path B), the observed product ratio seems to require the concurrence of the intramolecular process (path A), since if path B alone were used, "isodicinnamyl" (**47**) would be expected to predominate in the product mixture.[75,79a] In any event, there can be no doubt that the homolytic dissociation process (path B) is contributing in some measure in the rearrangement of **44**, and the point of interest here is that this rearrangement appears to be a "limiting" case of the "no mechanism" category—i.e., the free energies of activation for paths A and B lie very close together.

Woodward and Katz[74a] have provided an excellent example of a Cope rearrangement in which the diallyl system is contained in a bicyclic structure. When α-1-hydroxydicyclopentadiene (**48**) is heated at 140°, it is smoothly converted, in part, to the isomeric alcohol, *syn*-8-hydroxydicyclopentadiene (**49**). That the isomerization is, in fact, an equilibration was established by the observation that **49** gave the same equilibrium mixture under the conditions cited. The interconversion of **48** and **49** at 140° is a very smooth, essentially homogeneous reaction. No other product or evidence of extensive decomposition was found. In the same way, the β isomer (**50**) was found to rearrange homogeneously to give the single product, *anti*-8-hydroxydicyclopentadiene (**51**). In this case, the equilibrium lies strongly on the side of the 8-hydroxy derivative. The stereochemical specificity implied by these findings was further substantiated by the demonstration that optical activity in the

[79a] It was established that the products **45** and **47** were stable up to temperatures of 200°. The rearrangement, then, though reversible in principle, is irreversible under the conditions employed.

TABLE VI

Cope Rearrangements in 1,5-Hexadiene Systems

1,5-Hexadiene	Temp., °C.	Yield, %	Rearrangement product(s)	Ref.
(a) 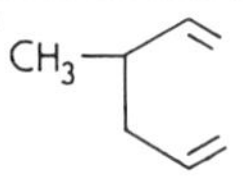	300	~ 30[a]	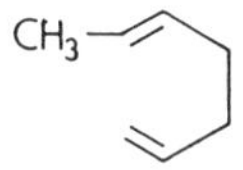	70
(b) 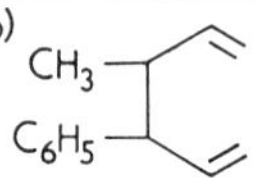	185	90	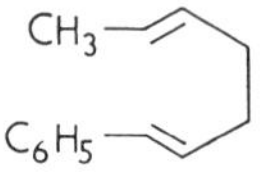	70
(c) 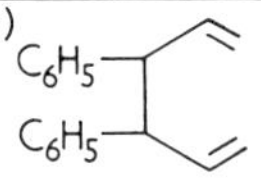 meso	150	quant.	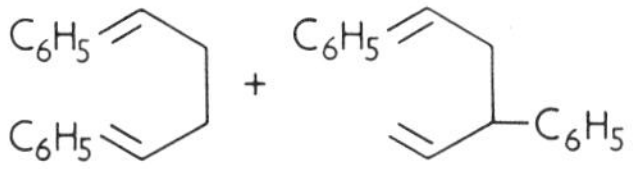 trans–trans	75
(d) 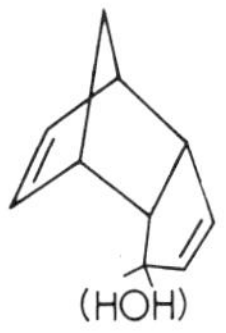 (HOH) (α- and β-)	140	(α) 50[b] (β) 90	 (syn and anti)	74a
(e) 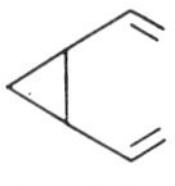 cis and trans	(cis) ?[c] (trans) 200	— —	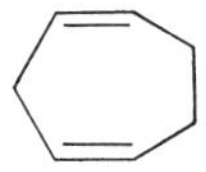	76
(f) 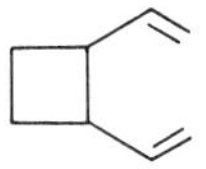 cis	120	91	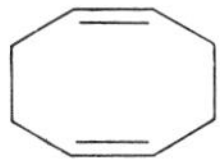	77
(g) 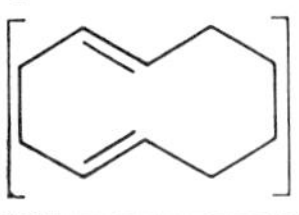	120–150[c]	—	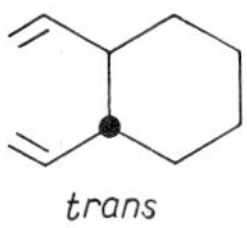 trans	78

[a] This isomerization is reversible under the reaction conditions. Since some concurrent polymerization was observed, the yield is only roughly indicative of K_{eq}.

[b] The isomerizations are reversible with $K_{eq} \sim 1$ for the α isomer. For the β isomer, the point of the equilibrium lies far to the right in favor of the anti-8-hydroxydicyclopentadiene.

[c] The starting material was not isolated. The rearrangement occurred under conditions of its preparation.

α and β isomers was retained in the products. Clearly, the observed isomerizations are brought about through a Cope rearrangement of a 1,5-hexadiene system in these molecules. Thus, in **48**, C_2, C_3, C_{10}, C_4, C_5, and C_6 of the di-

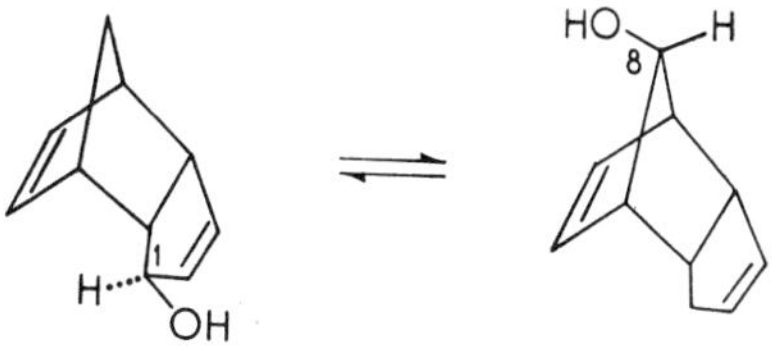

(48)   (49)

cyclopentadiene skeleton constitute the diallylic system. The facility with which these Cope rearrangements occur, even without benefit of activating

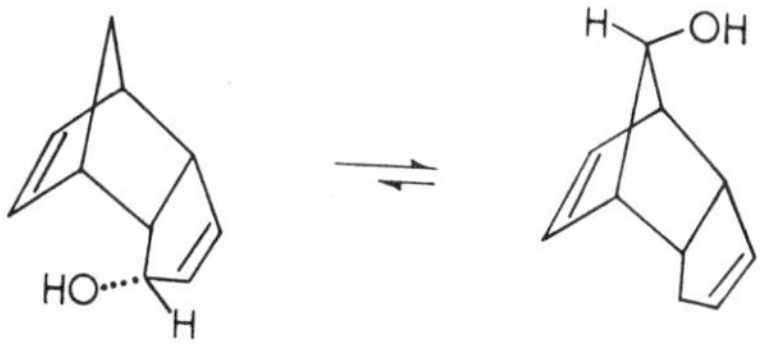

(50)   (51)

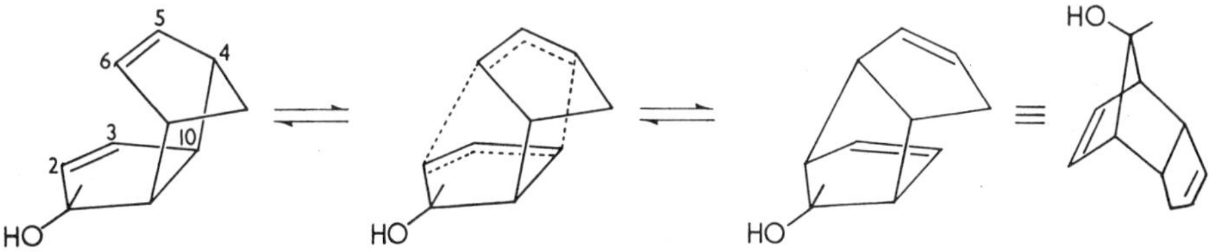

(48)   (49)

groups, must be a result of the favorable preorientation of the diallylic system imposed by the fixed geometry of the bicyclic structure.[80]

[80] In a recent communication, R. P. Lutz and J. D. Roberts, *J. Am. Chem. Soc.*, **83**, 2198 (1961), have reported a similar rearrangement of optically active methacrolein dimer, labeled with deuterium at the aldehyde group (A). The rearrangement product (B), identical with A except for the position of the deuterium label, was formed with 99.5% retention of configuration at the optically active site, a result which requires a rearrangement process of the type formulated by Woodward. In this example, two atoms of the rearranging diallylic system are oxygen.

A   B

Whatever bearing these results have on the Diels-Alder reaction [74a,80a–80c] their significance for the Cope rearrangement is clear. Inspection of the transition state geometry required by the bicyclic system (52) shows that the orientation assumed by the two allylic systems must possess the quality of the quasi-boat conformation discussed for the Claisen rearrangements. The ease of these isomerizations implies, at the very least, that the quasi-boat arrangement is not of prohibitively high energy and can be adopted by rearranging molecules in certain cases (see heading 2E).

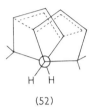

(52)

The isomerizations of the divinylcycloalkanes, *cis*- and *trans*-divinylcyclopropane and *cis*-divinylcyclobutane, recently announced by Vogel [76,77] are interesting examples of Cope rearrangements of hydrocarbons which derive their driving force from the ring strain of the small cycles. They also represent systems which must rearrange through transition states with quasi-boat orientations. Vogel reported that *cis*-divinylcyclopropane (53) was so labile

(53)   (54)   (55)

that it isomerized to 1,4-*cis,cis*-cycloheptadiene (54) under the conditions of its formation. The more stable *trans*-divinylcyclopropane (55), on the other hand, underwent rearrangement to the same cyclic diene only when heated to 200°. Consideration of the molecular geometries involved in these rearrangements leads to the conclusion that the only transition state arrangement available to these cyclopropane derivatives is that of a quasi-boat in which

[80a] M. J. S. Dewar, *Tetrahedron Letters*, No. **4**, 16 (1959).

[80b] M. G. Ettlinger and E. S. Lewis, 138th Meeting, ACS, New York, September, 1960, *Abstracts*, p. 95P.

[80c] J. A. Berson, A. Remanick, and W. A. Mueller, *J. Am. Chem. Soc.*, **82**, 5501 (1960); J. A. Berson and A. Remanick, *J. Am. Chem. Soc.*, **83**, 4947 (1961); and J. A. Berson and W. A. Mueller, *J. Am. Chem. Soc.*, **83**, 4940 (1961).

the vinyl groups are folded back over the three-membered ring (**56**). Alternative orientations of the two vinyl groups with respect to the cyclopropane ring in quasi-boat or quasi-chair arrangements would lead to *trans,trans*- or *cis,trans*-cycloheptadienes, molecules incapable of existence. Since only small changes in the relative positions of the vinyl groups in the *cis* isomer (**53**) are necessary to achieve the required orientation (**56**), it is clear that the rearrangement, with attendant relief of ring strain, should proceed very easily. In the *trans* isomer (**55**), however, the vinyl groups are unable to approach each other for bonding purposes without rupture of the ring (**57**) and/or

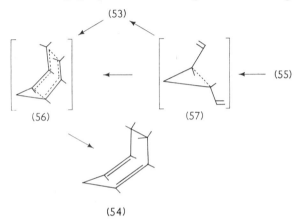

(53)

(56)   (57)   (55)

(54)

isomerization to the *cis* isomer. The energy required for such a *trans-cis* isomerization does not seem prohibitively high for the conditions employed. Rabinovitch, Schlag, and Wiberg [80d] found an activation energy of 64 kcal./mole for the *cis-trans* isomerization of cyclopropane-1,2-d_2. This value may be taken as an upper limit for the dissociation energy of the C—C bond in cyclopropane and represents $\sim 80\%$ of the dissociation energy for the C—C bond of ethane.[81] The dissociation energy of diallyl, $CH_2 = CHCH_2CH_2CH = CH_2$, has been estimated at 38 kcal./mole.[81] Assuming that the effect of the cyclopropane ring is the same in the parallel cases, one may crudely estimate that the *cis-trans* isomerization of the divinylcyclopropanes would have an activation energy of ~ 30 kcal./mole. This seems a reasonable value for the temperature range required.

In connection with the rearrangements of *cis*- and *trans*-divinylcyclopropanes mention should be made of a corresponding rearrangement encountered by Doering and Goldstein [79] in the benzonorcaradiene series.

[80d] B. S. Rabinovitch, E. W. Schlag, and K. B. Wiberg, *J. Chem. Phys.*, **28**, 504 (1958); E. W. Schlag and B. S. Rabinovitch, *J. Am. Chem. Soc.*, **82**, 5996 (1960). See also F. T. Smith, *J. Chem. Phys.*, **29**, 235 (1959).

[81] E. W. R. Steacie, *Atomic and Free Radical Reactions*, Reinhold, New York, 1954, p. 98.

Benzonorcaradiene carbonyl azide (**58**) was observed to undergo an unusual rearrangement in the presence of benzyl alcohol to yield a compound of structure **59** instead of the normal product of a Curtius rearrangement (**60**). With

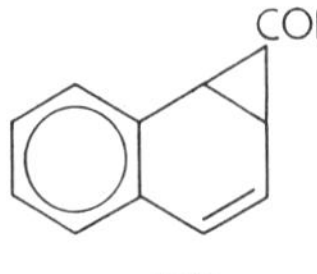

(58) 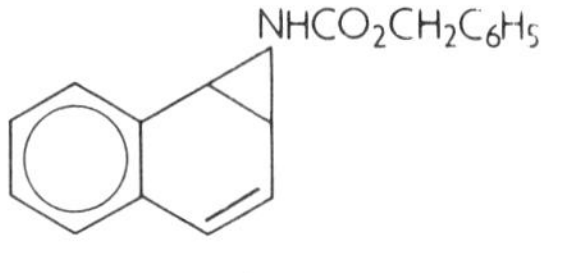   (60) 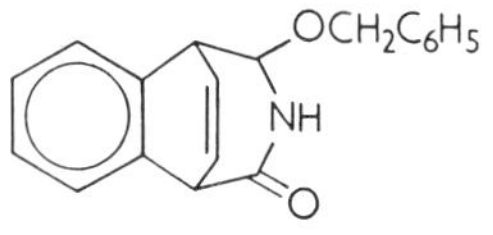   (59)

the reasonable assumption that the azide (**58**) rearranges normally to the isocyanate (**61**), the subsequent transformation may be visualized as a rearrangement of a "divinyl"cyclopropane in which the role of one of the vinyl groups is taken by the nitrogen-carbon double bond of the isocyanate group. The

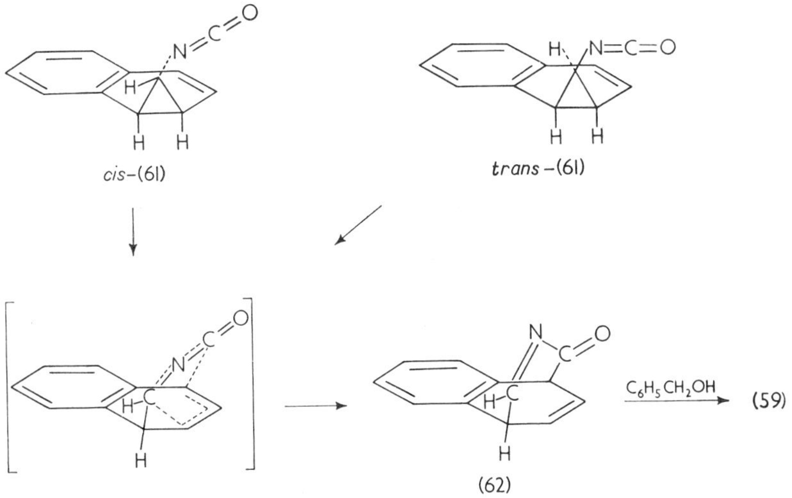

cis–(61)   trans –(61)

(62)

Cope rearrangement of **61** leads to the imino ketone (**62**) which by addition of the elements of benzyl alcohol accounts for the product observed. If the isocyanate (**61**) has the *trans* structure, as suggested by the literature, then cleavage of the three-membered ring and relocation of the isocyanate group must precede the achievement of the transition state just as in the *trans*-divinylcyclopropane case. If the isocyanate has the *cis* geometry, however, the rearrangement can proceed directly. The question of the stereochemistry of **61** is as yet unanswered.[79,81a]

The rearrangement of *cis*-divinylcyclobutane (**63**), while not so facile as

[81a] This same rearrangement has recently been reported for the simple cyclopropane derivative. In this case, the *trans* isomer (*trans*-2-vinylcyclopropyl isocyanate) was stable up to 200°. E. Vogel and R. Erb, *Angew. Chem.*, **74**, 76 (1962).

that of the cyclopropane derivative, still proceeds with remarkable ease at 120° to give a quantitative yield of 1,5-*cis,cis*-cyclooctadiene (**64**) in ten minutes.[77] Again, the geometries of the starting material and the product

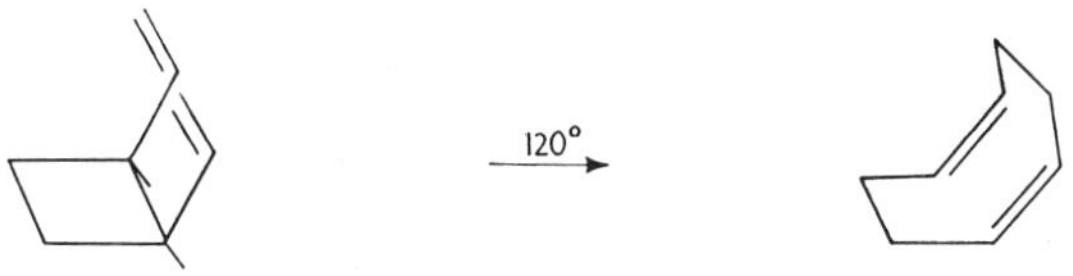

(63)   (64)

appear to demand that the transition state possess the quasi-boat arrangement in which the vinyl groups are folded over the four-membered ring. The *trans* isomer (**65**), on the other hand, reportedly decomposes at 240° to yield two moles of butadiene,[76] a reaction which is not surprising in view of the known decomposition pattern of cyclobutane.[81b]

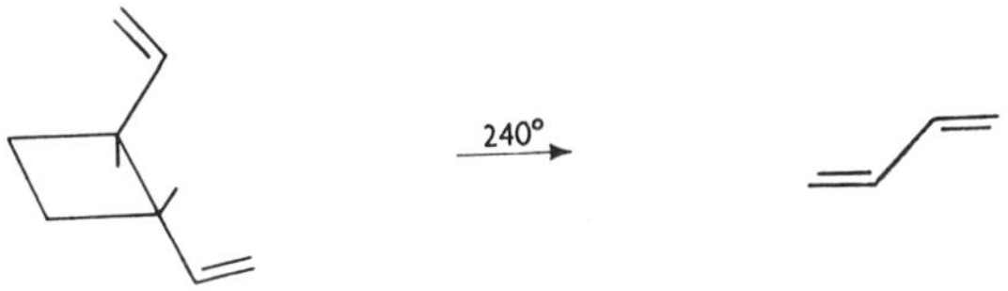

(65)   (2 mols.)

Grob and Schiess[78] observed that when the bis(*N*-oxide) of either the *cis*- or the *trans*-diamine (**66**) was pyrolyzed, the reaction product contained over 40% *trans*-1,2-divinylcyclohexane (**68**). In addition to **68**, a mixture of 1,6-cyclodecadienes was formed. Similar results were obtained when the bis-quaternary salts of **66** were subjected to the Hofmann degradation. The formation of **68** may be accommodated by a Cope rearrangement of the first-formed 1,5-cyclodecadiene (**67**) which isomerizes under the reaction conditions (120–150°) to the stable, strain-free cyclohexane derivative. If the 1,5-cyclo-

(66)   (67)   (68)

decadiene (**67**) has the *trans,trans* geometry assumed, then the rearrangement to *trans*-divinylcyclohexane (**68**) is easily rationalized since the diallylic system of **67** can readily assume a quasi-chair orientation which leads to the *trans*-divinylcyclohexane product.

[81b] C. T. Genaux, F. Kern, and W. D. Walters, *J. Am. Chem. Soc.*, **75**, 6196 (1953).

D. Stereochemistry

The stereochemical problems discussed for the Claisen rearrangements are duplicated in systems undergoing the Cope transformation. Accepting the basic premise that the two allylic systems must adopt positions in roughly parallel planes with the α and γ carbons of each system directly aligned, one is still faced with the question of quasi-boat and quasi-chair arrangements in the transition state. It has been pointed out that in certain cases, the quasi-boat arrangement is required by the special geometry of the rearranging molecules (cf. page 690), while for other systems, not so constrained, the evidence is less compelling, but has been interpreted in favor of the quasi-chair arrangement (heading 2E).

For the final resolution of this question the diallylic systems containing only carbon, i.e., the 1,5-hexadiene systems, offer a very definite advantage over the diallylic systems of allyl vinyl ethers. With properly constituted all-carbon systems, the geometric outcome of the rearrangement can be observed at *two* double bonds, while in the Claisen rearrangements such observations are restricted to the *one* double bond of the allylic side chain (cf. page 680).

In the first completely definitive test of the conformation question, Doering and Roth [81c] have examined the Cope rearrangement in such hexadienes. The systems they employed were the *meso-* and *rac-*3,4-dimethyl-1,5-hexadienes (**68a**). It may be seen at once that the geometric outcome of the Cope rearrangements of this pair of hydrocarbons provides an unambiguous answer to the question of the transition-state geometry. In Table VII are shown the possible orientations for the two isomers and the product derived from each orientation. To the extent that the quasi-boat arrangement is preferred for the transition state, it follows that the racemic isomer could give *only* the *cis,trans* product (orientation "a"), while the meso isomer could give *trans,trans* and *cis,cis* products (orientations "d" and "e"). In view of the greater thermodynamic stability of the *trans,trans* product over that of the *cis,cis* product and the higher energy of orientation "e" over that of "d," it further might be anticipated that the *trans,trans* product would predominate in this instance. On the other hand, if the quasi-chair arrangement is preferred for the transition state in these rearrangements, then the racemic isomer could give only *cis,cis* and *trans,trans* products (orientations "b" and "c") with the *trans,trans* expected to predominate, while the meso isomer could give only *cis,trans* product (orientation "f").

The rearrangements of both *rac-* and *meso-* **68a** were found to proceed with a high degree of stereoselectivity. The results are summarized in Table VIII and establish beyond any doubt that the quasi-chair arrangement represents the preferred transition state orientation for those molecules which are struc-

[81c] W. von E. Doering and W. Roth, *Tetrahedron*, **18**, 67 (1962).

TABLE VII

Relationship between Transition-State Conformation and Double-Bond Geometry in the Cope Rearrangement of *meso*- and *rac*-3,4-Dimethyl-1,5-hexadiene (**68a**)

$$CH_2{=}CH{-}CH(CH_3)CH(CH_3){-}CH{=}CH_2 \longrightarrow CH_3{-}CH{=}CH{-}CH_2CH_2{-}CH{=}CH{-}CH_3$$

(68a)   (68b)

68a Isomer	Transition-state conformation	Orientation[a]	Double-bond geometry in 68b
rac	*quasi*-boat	(a) 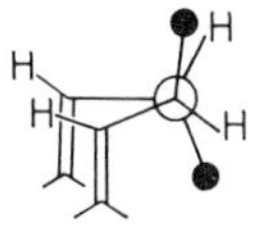	*cis – trans*
rac	*quasi*-chair ("aā")	(b) 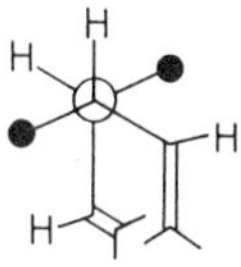	*cis – cis*
rac	*quasi*-chair ("ee")	(c) 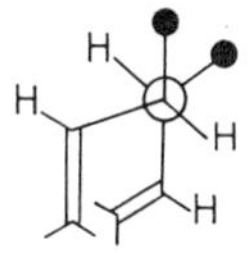	*trans – trans*
meso	*quasi*-boat	(d) 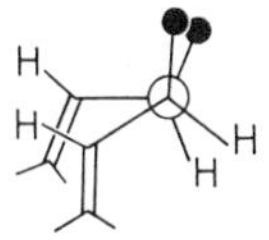	*trans – trans*
meso	*quasi*-boat	(e) 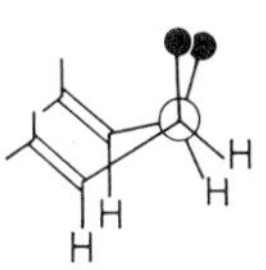	*cis – cis*
meso	*quasi*-chair ("eā")	(f) 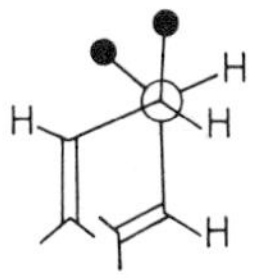	*cis – trans*

[a] In the Newman formulas, the solid circles represent the methyl groups.

TABLE VIII

Cope Rearrangement of *rac*- and *meso*-3,4-Dimethyl-1,5-
Hexadienes (**68a**) to 2,6-Octadiene (**68b**)[81c]

	Geometry of 2,6-octadiene (**68b**)		
68a Isomer	*cis-trans*	*cis-cis*	*trans-trans*
rac[a]	<1%	9%	90%
meso[b]	99.7%	—	0.3%

[a] T = 180°C.
[b] T = 225°C.

turally capable of assuming either arrangement. From the rate differences implied by the product composition in the rearrangement of the *meso* isomer (**68a**), it may be estimated that the chairlike and boatlike transition states differ in free energy by at least 5.7 kcal./mole for this system at 225°C.[81c] That the quasi-boat transition state may be used in special cases, however, has been pointed out earlier. Certainly, there is no other possibility for the rearrangement of the 1-hydroxy-dicyclopentadienes and the divinylcyclo-alkanes of three and four ring members (cf. page 690ff).

4. REARRANGEMENTS IN CONJUGATED TRIENE SYSTEMS. VALENCE TAUTOMERISM

It was pointed out in the introduction that the structures A and C immediately involved in rearrangements of the diallylic variety are formally related to each other as valence tautomers. This type of tautomerism is a subtle one and refers to those isomers which differ from each other only by small variations in interatomic distances and bond angles accompanied by appropriate changes in the localization of the binding electrons. Moreover, if the term

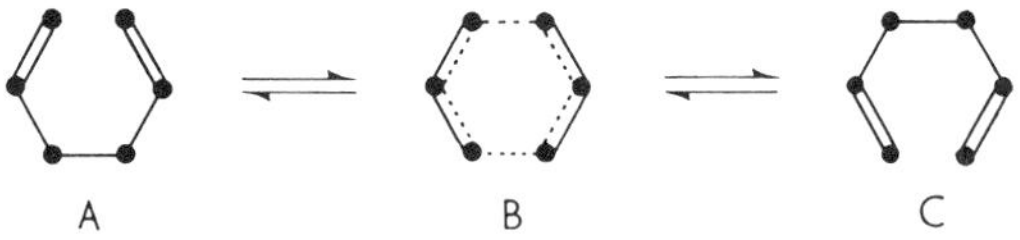

"tautomerism" is properly to apply, the isomers should be interconvertible under normal working conditions by the surmounting of a relatively small energy barrier from either side. If the latter condition is not met, compounds so related are better called "valence isomers."[78] The concept of valence tautomerism must be carefully distinguished from that of resonance to which it bears an only superficial resemblance. In valence tautomers, the differences in the positions of corresponding atomic nuclei, although small, are real, and the structures of the atomic assemblies, being separated by small energy barriers, are capable of finite existence. Although the detection of such tautomerism often presents experimental difficulties, the phenomenon remains conceptually distinct.

The most common examples of valence isomers and/or tautomers are encountered in the cyclic polyenes, doubtlessly as a result of their favorable electronic and steric constitution. Rings containing a conjugated triene system are especially labile in this respect. Alder and Dortmann [82] encountered a case of this sort when they sought to prepare 1,3,5-cyclononatriene (70) by the stepwise degradation of homopseudopelletierine. Only traces of the triene (70) could be detected in the reaction mixture from the final Hofmann degradation of the amine (69). The major product of the reaction was the valence isomer, *trans*-bicyclo-[4.3.0]nona-2,4-diene (71). Although Alder

assigned the *cis,cis,trans* structure to the intermediate triene (70), models suggest that it probably was largely the *trans,cis,trans* isomer, as shown in the formulation. In this isomer, the closeness of C_1 and C_6 introduces a steric interaction of their opposing hydrogen atoms. Effectively this interference of the 1 and 6 hydrogen atoms forces the two ends of the triene system into roughly parallel planes, and the entire triene system assumes a distorted "chair" arrangement. Very small adjustments of angles, bond distances, and electron distribution lead directly to the *trans* bicyclic isomer (71).

Very similar results were reported by Grob and Schiess [78] in the degradation of 1,6-bis(dimethylamino)-3,8-cyclodecadiene (72). In both the N-oxide elimination procedure and the Hofmann degradation of 72, the olefinic products isolated consisted in large measure of the bicyclic isomers, *cis*- and *trans*-bicyclo[4.4.0]deca-2,4,8-trienes (74 and 75). Their formation can be accommodated by valence isomerization of the initially formed tetraene (73). Although the complete geometry of the intermediate cyclic tetraene (or tetraenes) is not known, inspection of models of possible intermediates shows that the formation of both *cis* (74) and *trans* (75) bicyclic products, can reasonably be accounted for by the cyclic process.

[82] K. Alder and H. A. Dortmann, *Chem. Ber.*, **87**, 1905 (1954); K. Alder and F. H. Flock, *Chem. Ber.*, **87**, 1916 (1954).

Recently Marvell[83] has examined an acyclic triene system analogous to the cyclic trienes **70** and **73**. When *cis*-1,2-di-(1'-cyclohexenyl)ethene **(76)** is

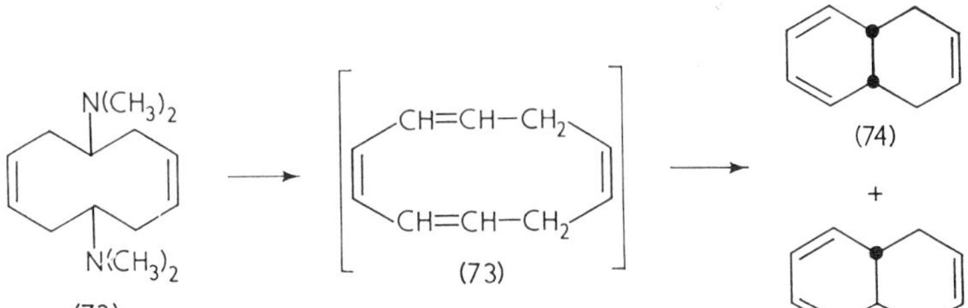

heated briefly at 180°, it smoothly isomerizes to a decahydrophenanthrene **(77)** in over 70% conversion.

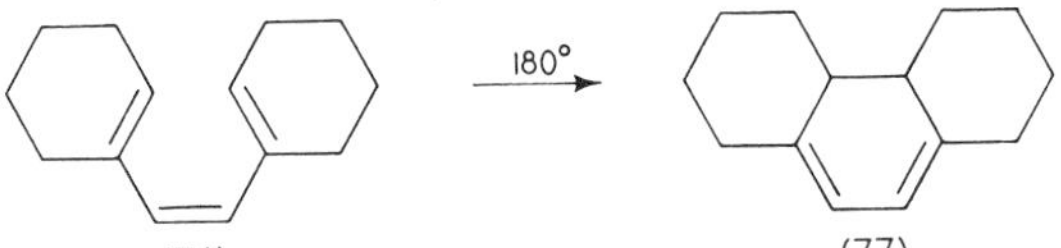

A clear-cut example of a true valence tautomerism is furnished by the 1,3,5-*cis,cis,cis*-cyclooctatriene **(78)**–bicyclo[4.2.0]octa-2,4-diene **(79)** pair discovered by Cope and co-workers.[84] When either **78** or **79** is heated to 80–100° a rapid interconversion occurs with the formation of an equilibrium mixture consisting of 85% of the monocyclic tautomer **(78)** and 15% of the bicyclic tautomer **(79)**. Since the tautomers proved to be relatively stable at temperatures below 30°, each could be isolated in pure form and separately

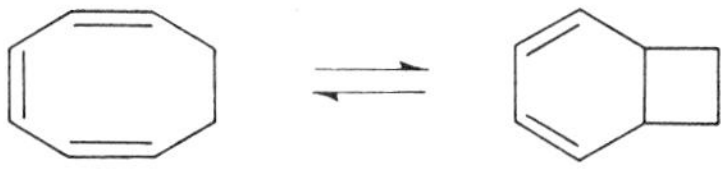

studied. Of the many differences reported for the two hydrocarbons perhaps the most dramatic is their behavior in the Diels-Alder reaction. The bicyclic isomer **(79)** reacts quantitatively with maleic anhydride in benzene solution at 10° to form the adduct **(80)** in 98% yield. Under the same conditions, the triene **(78)** fails completely to react. However, when a benzene solution of **78** and maleic anhydride is heated under reflux—conditions which permit

[83] E. N. Marvell, private communication (1960).
[84] A. C. Cope, A. C. Haven, Jr., F. L. Ramp, and E. R. Trumbull, *J. Am. Chem. Soc.*, **74**, 4867 (1952).

equilibration of the tautomers—a good yield of the same adduct (80) is obtained.

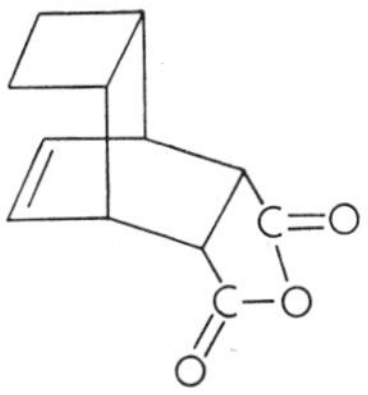

(80)

The question of a similar valence tautomerism in cyclooctatetraene (81) has often been raised.[85-87] In many of its reactions, cyclooctatetraene behaves as if it had the structure of its bicyclic isomer (82). For example, it reacts with

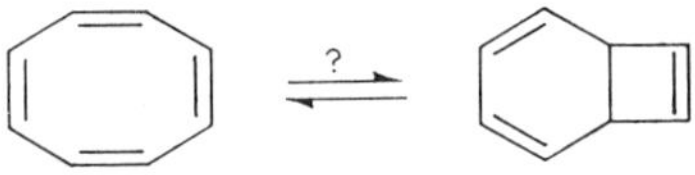

(81)   (82)

halogens forming dihalo derivatives of the bicyclic system (83) and with a variety of dienophiles giving adducts with the basic structure 84.[87] Nevertheless, there is no physical evidence for a detectable amount of the bicyclic isomer (82) in equilibrium with the monocyclic tetraene (81), at least under ordinary conditions.

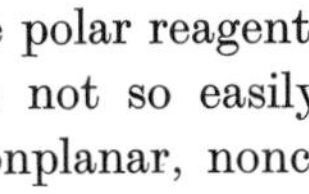

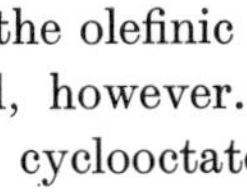

(83)   (84)

Reactions such as the halogenation above can easily be rationalized in terms of the single structure 81 by assuming that a rearrangement is initiated by the attack of the polar reagent at one of the olefinic bonds.[88] The Diels-Alder reactions are not so easily dismissed, however. Indeed, when the geometry of the nonplanar, nonconjugated, cyclooctatetraene molecule is

[85] O. Hecht and H. Kröper in K. Zeigler, ed., *FIAT Review*, **36I**, 75 (1948).

[86] K. Ziegler and H. Wilms, *Ann.*, **567**, 1 (1950).

[87] W. Reppe, O. Schlichting, K. Klager, and T. Toepel, *Ann.*, **560**, 1 (1948). For recent studies on the configurations of the adducts of cyclooctatetraene with maleic anhydride and acetylenic dicarboxylic esters, see M. Avram, G. Mateescu, and C. D. Nenitzescu, *Ann.*, **636**, 174 (1960).

[88] S. L. Friess and V. Boekelheide, *J. Am. Chem. Soc.*, **71**, 4145 (1949).

considered,[89] it appears that a substantial distortion of the ring would be required to achieve a diene system capable of participating in the Diels-Alder reaction. Further, in order to account for the rearranged structure in the product, some "bridging" process would have to occur during, or closely following, adduct formation. It seems just as reasonable, and considerably more simple, to assume that under the conditions required for the Diels-Alder reactions of cyclooctatetraene (ca. 150°), the valence tautomerism phenomenon becomes active and that it is, in fact, the bicyclic isomer (82), which accounts for the observed products just as in the cyclooctatriene case, i.e.,

The best illustration of the ofttimes delicate problems associated with the valence tautomer phenomenon is afforded by the triply unsaturated, seven-membered ring hydrocarbon, variously called "tropilidene," "cycloheptatriene" (85), and "norcaradiene" (86). The latter two names reflect classical valence tautomeric possibilities analogous to those demonstrated for the eight- and nine-membered ring homologs. Doering [90] has proposed, however, that in the case of the seven-membered tropilidene molecule, there exists a third valence tautomer possibility (87), which is characterized as "pseudoaromatic". The orbital overlap across the 1 and 6 positions implied in the formulation (87) would produce a closed, aromatic-like, system of six π

(85)   (86)   (87)

electrons and is entirely analogous to the homoconjugation postulated in recent years for homoallylic and homoaromatic systems.[91] Effective interaction of the π electrons in this way carries with it the requirement that the

[89] D. P. Craig in D. Ginsburg, ed., *Non-Benzenoid Aromatic Compounds*, Interscience, New York, 1959, p. 23.

[90] W. von E. Doering, G. Laber, R. Vonderwahl, N. F. Chamberlain, and R. B. Williams, *J. Am. Chem. Soc.*, **78**, 5448 (1956).

[91] See S. Winstein, *J. Am. Chem. Soc.*, **81**, 6254 (1959), and S. Winstein and J. Sonnenberg, *J. Am. Chem. Soc.*, **83**, 3244 (1961), for a discussion of homoaromatic systems and references to earlier work. Prof. Winstein has suggested the term "monohomobenzene" for **87**.

seven-membered ring in **87** be planar. Structures **85** and **86**, on the other hand, represent nonplanar molecules. The three formulations **85–87**, then, correspond to three possible valence tautomeric systems, distinguishable from one another by subtle, but none the less real, differences.[92]

As in the cyclooctatetraene case, chemical evidence bearing on the question of the structure of tropilidene and the possibility of its existing in valence tautomeric forms is conflicting and often misleading. Many tropilidene derivatives are prone to react as if they possessed the norcaradiene structure (**86**).[93,94] Tropilidene itself reacts with maleic anhydride in boiling xylene,[94] but not at 5°,[95] to yield an adduct of structure **88**. On the other hand, oxidative degradation of tropilidene reportedly gives no evidence for the presence of a cyclopropane ring.[96] Meerwein and co-workers[97] have inferred from hydrogenation data that mixtures of cycloheptatriene (**85**) and norcaradiene (**86**) are obtained from the photo-induced reaction of benzene and diazomethane and that the unstable norcaradiene tautomer is easily transformed to the monocyclic triene by heat or further irradiation.

[92] Another possible valence tautomeric system which at times has been considered and rejected as the structure of tropilidene (for a review see Evans and Lord[92a]) is bicyclo[3.2.0]hepta-2,6-diene (**87a**). A compound of this structure has been synthesized,

(87a)

and its spectral and chemical properties are quite different from those of tropilidene itself.[92a] Quite recently, Dauben and Cargill[92b] have shown that this same bicyclic isomer may be prepared by the photoisomerization of tropilidene. The photoisomer is reconverted to tropilidene by pyrolysis at 400°. Similar results were obtained for the 1,3-cycloheptadiene (**87b**)–bicyclo[3.2.0]heptene-6 (**87c**) pair. Analogous photochemical

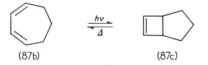

(87b)   (87c)

transformations have been observed in the tropolone, eucarvone, and pyrocalciferol systems (for discussion and references see Dauben and Cargill[92b]).

[92a] M. V. Evans and R. C. Lord, *J. Am. Chem. Soc.*, **82**, 1876 (1960).

[92b] W. G. Dauben and R. L. Cargill, *Tetrahedron*, **12**, 186 (1961).

[93] (a) E. J. Corey and H. J. Burke, *J. Am. Chem. Soc.*, **76**, 5257 (1954), **78**, 174 (1956); (b) E. J. Corey, H. J. Burke, and W. A. Remers, *J. Am. Chem. Soc.*, **78**, 180 (1956).

[94] K. Alder and G. Jacobs, *Chem. Ber.*, **86**, 1528 (1953).

[95] H. L. Dryden, Jr., and B. E. Burgert, *J. Am. Chem. Soc.*, **77**, 5633 (1955).

[96] R. Willstätter, *Ann.*, **317**, 204 (1901).

[97] H. Meerwein, H. Disselnkötter, F. Rappen, H. von Rintelen, and H. van de Vloed, *Ann.*, **604**, 151 (1957).

All efforts directed toward an unequivocal demonstration of the coexistence of valence tautomers related to the basic monocyclic and bicyclic structures **85** and **86** have failed. Thus, in a reinvestigation of the Buchner acids, Doering and his co-workers [90] were able to show that the so-called "δ-cycloheptatriene

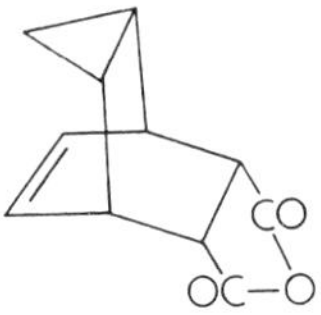

(88)

carboxylic acid," which had been assigned structure **89** by Buchner and Einhorn, was, in fact, nonexistent. There are but four tropilidenecarboxylic acids and these are related as position isomers with the carboxy group occupying positions 1, 2, 3, and 7 of the tropilidene ring. The valence tautomeric relationship originally ascribed to "δ-cycloheptatrienecarboxylic acid" (**89**) and "norcaradienecarboxylic acid" (**90**) is, therefore, without foundation. There is only *one* isomeric acid with the carboxy group in the 7 position. Similarly, an attempt to prepare tautomeric amides corresponding to the acids **89** and **90** was without success.[98]

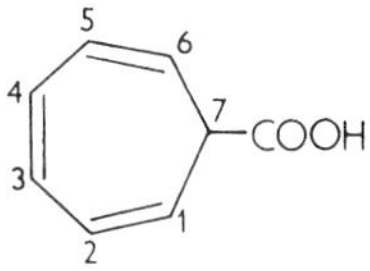

(89) 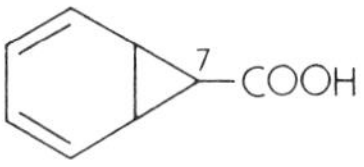   (90)

It must be concluded that for these derivatives, at least, one of the valence tautomeric structures corresponding to **85**, **86**, or **87** must represent a system of considerably greater stability than the others. In their study of the Buchner acids, Doering and co-workers found that the NMR (nuclear magnetic resonance) spectra of the methyl esters of the four isomeric acids were very similar to each other and to the spectrum of tropilidene itself.[90] Moreover, it was noted that all the spectra were unusually complex in the vinyl C—H region in sharp contrast to the simple pattern expected for the nonplanar cycloheptatriene structure (**85**). The norcaradiene structure (**86**) also was found untenable for tropilidene from evidence adduced by Corey, Burke, and Remers.[99] The Yale group concluded that tropilidene and the Buchner acids

[98] W. von E. Doering and L. H. Knox, *J. Am. Chem. Soc.*, **79**, 352 (1957).

[99] E. J. Corey, H. J. Burke, and W. A. Remers, *J. Am. Chem. Soc.*, **77**, 4941 (1955).

were adequately represented by neither of the classical structures **85** and **86**, possessing, rather, the planar, pseudoaromatic structure **87**.

In a parallel investigation of the valence tautomer problem in tropilidene systems, Corey, Burke, and Remers [99] examined the NMR spectra for a series of enol esters of eucarvone (**91**). The absence of absorption in the region expected for two tertiary bridge hydrogens of the caradiene structure (**92**) and the general agreement of the spectrum with that predicted for the mono-cyclic structure (**91**) permitted elimination of the bicyclic structure (**92**) for

(91)   (92)

these derivatives. It is of further interest to note that low temperature ozono-lysis of the eucarvone enol esters produced large amounts of *cis*-caronic acid, despite the fact that the presence of any appreciable amount of the valence tautomer **92** was unambiguously denied by the NMR results.

While the question of the structure of tropilidene and its derivatives and the problem of valence tautomerism in these systems cannot be regarded as finally answered,[100] it may be pointed out that the Raman and infrared spectra of tropilidene,[101] its resonance energy of 9–10 kcal./mole,[102] its characteristic-ally complicated NMR spectrum,[90] and its reactions have all been interpreted to be consistent with its formulation as a pseudo aromatic structure.[102a]

---

[100] Evidence is presently accumulating which points up the important role that substituents may play in determining the intimate structure of the molecular systems found in the tropilidene and the 1,3,5-cyclooctatriene-bicyclo[4.2.0]octa-2,4-diene series. For examples and discussion, see J. Schreiber, W. Leimgruber, M. Pesaro, P. Schudel, T. Threllfall, and A. Eschenmoser, *Helv. Chim. Acta*, **44**, 540 (1961); E. Vogel, O. Roos and K-H. Disch, *Angew. Chem.*, **73**, 342 (1961); E. Vogel, 141st Meeting, ACS, Washington, D.C., March, 1962, Abstracts, p. 2–0; and K. Conrow and M. E. H. Howden, *J. Am. Chem. Soc.*, (in press).

[101] M. V. Evans and R. C. Lord, *J. Am. Chem. Soc.*, **82**, 1876 (1960).

[102] R. B. Turner, W. R. Meador, W. von E. Doering, L. H. Knox, J. R. Mayer, and D. W. Wiley, *J. Am. Chem. Soc.*, **79**, 4127 (1957).

[102a] See, however, J. D. Dunitz and P. Pauling, *Helv. Chim. Acta*, **43**, 2188 (1960), for X-ray diffraction evidence opposing this view and K. Conrow, *J. Am. Chem. Soc.*, **83**, 2958 (1961), and K. Conrow and M. E. H. Howden, *J. Am. Chem. Soc.*, (in press), for additional arguments against the psuedoaromatic structure, at least as it applies to heavily substituted tropilidene derivatives.

5. REARRANGEMENTS INVOLVING EIGHT ATOMIC CENTERS

Cyclic "no mechanism" pathways involving eight atomic centers have been invoked occasionally to provide a rationale for certain rearrangements and decompositions.[103] An example is found in an early suggestion of Schmid [103a] that the formation of some product with "inverted" structure (24) in the Claisen rearrangement of allyl-γ-^{14}C-2-propenyl 4,6-disubstituted phenyl

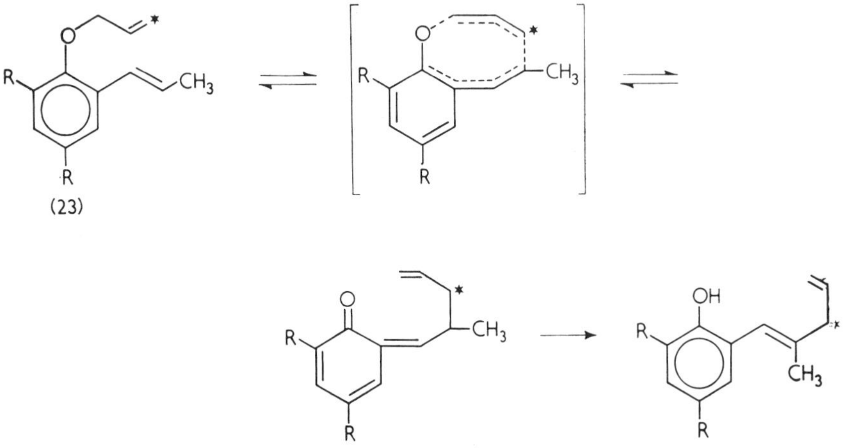

(23)

(24)

ethers (23) could be accounted for by such a rearrangement process. As discussed earlier, however, these results are probably better accommodated by an ortho-ortho′ rearrangement (heading 2D).

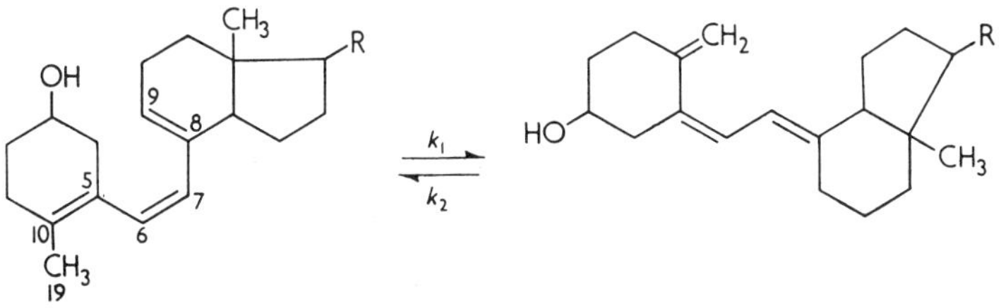

(94a) $R = C_9H_{17}$ (95a)

An example of a rearrangement which appears to demand an eight-centered transition state is the reversible, thermal isomerization of previtamin D_2 (94a) to vitamin D_2 (95a).

First detected by Velluz and Amiard [104a] as a concurrent rearrangement in the photo-induced transformations of ergosterol, the previtamin D_2–vitamin

[103] For discussion and illustrative cases, see J. Mathieu and J. Valls, *Bull. soc. chim. France*, **1957**, 1509.

[103a] K. Schmid, P. Fahrni, and H. Schmid, *Helv. Chim. Acta*, **39**, 708 (1956).

D_2 interconversion was shown by these investigators to proceed independently of the photoisomerizations.[105] Benzene solutions of previtamin D_2 (**94a**) and of vitamin D_2 (**95a**) were found to equilibrate rapidly at 40–60° in the dark. Moreover, this very facile interconversion was unaffected by radical inhibitors or promoters and was insensitive to catalytic amounts of acid or base.[104] The rate at which equilibrium was established was found to be independent of the reaction medium and K_{eq} for the isomerization previtamin $D_2 \rightleftharpoons$ vitamin D_2 was found to be ~ 3 at 60°.[106] More recently, Legrand and Mathieu [107] have carried out a kinetic study of the isomerizations in the temperature range 40–70° and have reported the following data for the forward and reverse processes at 60°: $k_1 = 12.2 \times 10^{-5}$/sec., $E_a = 19.6$ kcal./mole, $\Delta S^{\ddagger} = -3.4$ e.u.; $k_2 = 3.4 \times 10^{-5}$/sec., $E_a = 25.0$ kcal./mole, $\Delta S^{\ddagger} = -1$ e.u.

The characteristics of the reaction are strongly suggestive of an intramolecular "no mechanism" process which must involve the trienoic system and the 10-methyl group of **94a** and in which the cycle is closed by the bridging of C_9 and C_{19} by a hydrogen atom of the methyl group. Models of the molecular systems **94a** and **95a** further suggest that the course and the facility of the isomerizations may be traced to the exceptional geometries of these systems.[106]

(94a)   (95a)

(94b)   (96)   (95b)

[104] (a) L. Velluz and G. Amiard, *Compt. rend.*, **228**, 692, 853 (1949). (b) L. Velluz, G. Amiard, and A. Petit, *Bull. soc. chim. France*, **1949**, 501. (c) L. Velluz, G. Amiard, and B. Goffinet, *Bull. soc. chim. France*, **1955**, 1341.

[105] Previtamin D_2 arises from ergosterol by the photochemical fission of the 9,10 bond. Its conversion to vitamin D_2, however, is purely thermal.

[106] A. Verloop, A. L. Koevoet, and E. Havinga, *Rec. trav. chim.*, **76**, 689 (1957); E. Havinga and K. L. M. A. Schlatmann, *Tetrahedron*, **16**, 146 (1961).

[107] H. Legrand and J. Mathieu, *Compt. rend.*, **245**, 2502 (1957).

In order for the forward reaction to occur, the previtamin which exists largely in the more stable conformation (94a) with a *trans*oid 5,6 bond must take up the *cis*oid arrangement (94b) by rotation about the 5,6 bond. In this form, however, the tendency of the double bond system to assume a planar arrangement will be seriously opposed by the steric interactions of the methyl group at C_{10} and the hydrogen atom at C_9. The methyl group of 94b, then, is effectively held above the terminal C_9 of the trienoic system, but one of its hydrogen atoms may approach to within bonding distance of C_9 to achieve an eight-centered, cyclic, nonplanar transition state (96). A similar situation exists for the reverse process which must involve the less stable conformation of vitamin D_2 (95b) with the *cis*oid 6,7 bond.